P9-BBO-052

Financial Aid for African Americans 2014-2016

RSP FINANCIAL AID DIRECTORIES OF INTEREST TO MINORITIES

Financial Aid for African Americans 2014-2016

Gail Ann Schlachter
R. David Weber

A Listing of Scholarships, Fellowships, Grants, Awards, and Other Sources of Free Money Available Primarily or Exclusively to African Americans, Plus a Set of Six Indexes (Program Title, Sponsoring Organization, Residency, Tenability, Subject, and Deadline Date)

Reference Service Press
El Dorado Hills, California

ISBN 10: 1588412423
ISBN 13: 9781588412423

10 9 8 7 6 5 4 3 2 1

Reference Service Press (RSP) began in 1977 with a single financial aid publication *(The Directory of Financial Aids for Women)* and now specializes in the development of financial aid resources in multiple formats, including books, large print books, print-on-demand reports, eBooks, and online sources. Long recognized as a leader in the field, RSP has been called by the *Simba Report on Directory Publishing* "a true success in the world of independent directory publishers." Both Kaplan Educational Centers and Military.com have hailed RSP as "the leading authority on scholarships."

Reference Service Press
El Dorado Hills Business Park
5000 Windplay Drive, Suite 4
El Dorado Hills, CA 95762-9319
(916) 939-9620
Fax: (916) 939-9626
E-mail: info@rspfunding.com
Visit our web site: www.rspfunding.com

Manufactured in the United States of America
Price: $45, plus $7 shipping.

Contents

Introduction

WHY THIS DIRECTORY IS NEEDED

Despite our country's ongoing economic problems and increased college costs, the financial aid picture for minorities has never looked brighter. Currently, billions of dollars are set aside each year specifically for African Americans, Asian Americans, Hispanic Americans, and Native Americans. This funding is open to minorities at any level (high school through postdoctoral and professional) for a variety of activities, including study, research, travel, training, career development, and creative projects.

While numerous print and online listings have been prepared to identify and describe general financial aid opportunities (those open to all segments of society), those resources have never covered more than a small portion of the programs designed primarily or exclusively for minorities. As a result, many advisors, librarians, scholars, researchers, and students often have been unaware of the extensive funding available to African Americans and other minorities. But, with the ongoing publication of *Financial Aid for African Americans,* that has all changed. Here, in just one place, African American students, professionals, and postdoctorates now have current and detailed information about the special resources set aside specifically for them.

Financial Aid for African Americans is prepared biennially as part of Reference Service Press' four-volume *Minority Funding Set* (the other volumes in the set cover funding for Asian Americans, Hispanic Americans, and Native Americans). Each of the volumes in this set is sold separately, or the complete set can be purchased at a discounted price. For more information, e-mail Reference Service Press's marketing department (info@rspfunding.com) or visit www.rspfunding.com/prod_prodalpha.html.

No other source, in print or online, comes anywhere close to matching the extensive coverage of funding for minorities provided by these titles. That's why the Grantsmanship Center labeled the set "a must for every organization serving minorities," *Reference Sources for Small and Medium-Sized Libraries* called the titles "the absolute best guides for finding funding," and *Reference Books Bulletin* selected each of the volumes in the *Minority Funding Set* as their "Editor's Choice." *Financial Aid for African Americans,* itself, has also received rave reviews. *Off to College* rated it as "the top of all books of this sort," About.com selected it as one of the seven "Top Financial Aid and Scholarship Guides," and *EMIE Bulletin* called it "the only comprehensive and current listing of programs for this group." Perhaps *Multicultural Review* sums up the critical reaction best: "nothing short of superb."

WHAT'S UPDATED?

The preparation of each new edition of *Financial Aid for African Americans* involves extensive updating and revision. To make sure that the information included here is both reliable and current, the editors at Reference Service Press 1) reviewed and updated all relevant programs covered in the previous edition of the directory, 2) collected information on all programs open to African Americans that were added to Reference Service Press' funding database since the last edition of the directory, and then 3) searched extensively for new program leads in a variety of sources, including printed directories, news reports, journals, newsletters, house organs, annual reports, and sites on the Internet. We only include program descriptions that are written directly from information supplied by the sponsoring organization in print or online (no information is ever taken from secondary sources). When that information could not be found, we sent up to four data collection letters (followed by up to three telephone or e-mail inquiries, if necessary) to those sponsors. Despite our best efforts, however, some sponsoring organizations still failed to respond and, as a result, their programs are not included in this edition of the directory.

The 2014-2016 edition of *Financial Aid for African Americans* completely revises and updates the previous (seventh) edition. Programs that have ceased operations have been dropped from the listing. Similarly, programs that have broadened their scope and no longer focus on African Americans have also been removed from the directory. Profiles of continuing programs have been rewritten to reflect current requirements; nearly 80 percent of the continuing programs reported substantive changes in their locations, requirements (particularly application deadline), benefits, or eligibility requirements since the 2012-2014 edition. In addition, hundreds of new entries have been added to the program section of the directory. The resulting listing describes the more than 1,330 biggest and best sources of free money available to African Americans, including scholarships, fellowships, grants, awards, and other funding opportunities.

WHAT MAKES THIS DIRECTORY UNIQUE?

The 2014-2016 edition of *Financial Aid for African Americans* identifies billions of dollars available for study, research, creative activities, past accomplishments, future projects, professional development, and many other activities. The listings cover every major subject area, are sponsored by more than 900 different private and public agencies and organizations, and are open to African Americans at any level, from college-bound high school students through professionals and postdoctorates.

Not only does *Financial Aid for African Americans* provide the most comprehensive coverage of available funding (1,334 entries), but it also displays the most informative program descriptions (on the average, more than twice the detail found in any other listing). In addition to this extensive and focused coverage, *Financial Aid for African Americans* also offers several other unique features. First of all, hundreds of funding opportunities listed here have never been covered in any other source. So, even if you have checked elsewhere, you will want to look at *Financial Aid for African Americans* for additional leads. And, here's another plus: all of the funding programs in this edition of the directory offer "free" money; not one of the programs will ever require you to pay anything back (provided, of course, that you meet the program requirements).

Further, unlike other funding directories, which generally follow a straight alphabetical arrangement, *Financial Aid for African Americans* groups entries by intended recipients (undergraduates, graduate students, or professionals/postdoctorates), to make it easy for you to search for appropriate programs. This same convenience is offered in the indexes, where title, sponsoring organization, geographic, subject, and deadline date entries are each subdivided by recipient group.

Finally, we have tried to anticipate all the ways you might wish to search for funding. The volume is organized so you can identify programs not only by intended recipient, but by subject focus, sponsoring organization, program title, residency requirements, where the money can be spent, and even deadline date. Plus, we've included all the information you'll need to decide if a program is right for you: purpose, eligibility requirements, financial data, duration, special features, limitations, number awarded, and application date. You even get fax numbers, toll-free numbers, e-mail addresses, and web sites (when available), along with complete contact information.

WHAT'S EXCLUDED?

While this book is intended to be the most comprehensive source of information on funding available to African Americans, there are some programs we've specifically excluded from the directory:

- *Programs that do not accept applications from U.S. citizens or residents.* If a program is open only to foreign nationals or excludes Americans from applying, it is not covered.
- *Programs that are open equally to all segments of the population.* Only funding opportunities set aside primarily or exclusively for African Americans are included here.

SAMPLE ENTRY

(1) **[490]**

(2) **RON BROWN SCHOLAR PROGRAM**

(3) CAP Charitable Foundation
Attn: Ron Brown Scholar Program
1160 Pepsi Place, Suite 206
Charlottesville, VA 22901
(434) 964-1588
E-mail: info@ronbrown.org
Web: www.ronbrown.org

(4) **Summary** To provide financial assistance for college to African American high school seniors.

(5) **Eligibility** This program is open to academically-talented African American high school seniors who have demonstrated social commitment and leadership potential. They must be interested in attending a 4-year college or university as a full-time student. U.S. citizenship or permanent resident status is required. Finalists are invited to participate in a weekend selection program in Washington, D.C.; their expenses are reimbursed. Final selection is based on academic excellence, leadership, skills, school and community involvement, and financial need.

(6) **Financial data** The stipend is $10,000 per year. Funds may be used to cover tuition, fees, books, room, board, and other college-related expenses. Payment is made directly to the recipient's school.

(7) **Duration** 4 years.

(8) **Additional Information** Established in 1996, this program honors a former Secretary of Commerce who served during the Clinton administration. During college, recipients are required to pursue 1 or more summer internships devoted to community service (e.g., in education, health, government, or politics) and at least 1 pre-professional internship.

(9) **Number awarded** 10 to 20 each year.

(10) **Deadline** January of each year.

DEFINITION

(1) **Entry number:** The consecutive number that is given to each entry and used to identify the entry in the index.

(2) **Program title:** Title of scholarship, fellowship, grant, award, or other source of free money described in the directory.

(3) **Sponsoring organization:** Name, address, and telephone number, toll-free number, fax number, e-mail address, and/or web site (when information was available) for organization sponsoring the program.

(4) **Summary:** Identifies the major program requirements; read the rest of the entry for additional detail.

(5) **Eligibility:** Qualifications required of applicants, plus information on application procedure and selection process.

(6) **Financial data:** Financial details of the program, including fixed sum, average amount, or range of funds offered, expenses for which funds may and may not be applied, and cash-related benefits supplied (e.g., room and board).

(7) **Duration:** Period for which support is provided; renewal prospects.

(8) **Additional information:** Any unusual (generally nonmonetary) benefits, features, restrictions, or limitations associated with the program.

(9) **Number awarded:** Total number of recipients each year or other specified period.

(10) **Deadline:** The month by which applications must be submitted.

- *Money for study or research outside the United States.* Since there are comprehensive and up-to-date directories that describe the available funding for study, research, and other activities abroad (see the list of Reference Service Press titles opposite the directory's title page), only programs that fund activities in the United States are covered here.
- *Very restrictive programs.* In general, programs are excluded if they are open only to a limited geographic area (less than a state) or offer limited financial support (less than $1,000). Note, however, that the vast majority of programs included here go way beyond that, paying up to full tuition or stipends that exceed $25,000 a year!
- *Programs administered by individual academic institutions solely for their own students.* The directory identifies "portable" programs—ones that can be used at any number of schools. Financial aid administered by individual schools specifically for their own students is not covered. Write directly to the schools you are considering to get information on their offerings.
- *Money that must be repaid.* Only "free money" is identified here. If a program requires repayment or charges interest, it's not listed. Now you can find out about billions of dollars in aid and know (if you meet the program requirements) that not one dollar of that will ever need to be repaid.

HOW THE DIRECTORY IS ORGANIZED

Financial Aid for African Americans is divided into two sections: 1) a detailed list of funding opportunities open to African Americans and 2) a set of six indexes to help you pinpoint appropriate funding programs.

Financial Aid Programs Open to African Americans. The first section of the directory describes 1,334 sources of free money available to African Americans. The focus is on financial aid aimed at American citizens or residents to support study, research, or other activities in the United States. The programs listed here are sponsored by more than 900 different government agencies, professional organizations, corporations, sororities and fraternities, foundations, religious groups, educational associations, and military/veterans organizations. All areas of the sciences, social sciences, and humanities are covered.

To help you focus your search, the entries in this section are grouped into the following three chapters:

- **Undergraduates:** Included here are more than 600 scholarships, grants, awards, and other sources of free money that support undergraduate study, research, or creative activities. These programs are open to high school seniors, high school graduates, currently-enrolled college students, and students returning to college after an absence. Money is available to support these students in any type of public or private postsecondary institution, ranging from technical schools and community colleges to major universities in the United States.
- **Graduate Students:** Described here are nearly 500 fellowships, grants, awards, and other sources of free money that support post-baccalaureate study, training, research, and creative activities. These programs are open to students applying to, currently enrolled in, or returning to a master's, doctoral, professional, or specialist program in public or private graduate schools in the United States.
- **Professionals/Postdoctorates:** Included here are more than 250 funding programs for U.S. citizens or residents who 1) are in professional positions (e.g., artists, writers), whether or not they have an advanced degree; 2) are master's or professional degree recipients; 3) have earned a doctoral degree or its equivalent (e.g., Ph.D., Ed.D., M.D.); or 4) have recognized stature as established scientists, scholars, academicians, or researchers.

Within each of these three chapters, entries appear alphabetically by program title. Since some of the programs supply assistance to more than one specific group, those are listed in all relevant chapters. For example, the Agnes Jones Jackson Scholarships support both undergraduate or graduate study, so the program is described in both the Undergraduates *and* Graduate Students chapters.

Each program entry has been designed to give you a concise profile that, as the sample on page 7 illustrates, includes information (when available) on organization address and telephone numbers (including toll-free and fax numbers), e-mail address and web site, purpose, eligibility, money awarded, duration, special features, limitations, number of awards, and application deadline.

The information reported for each of the programs in this section was gathered from research conducted through the beginning of 2014. While the listing is intended to cover as comprehensively as possible the biggest and best sources of free money available to African Americans, some sponsoring organizations did not post information online or respond to our research inquiries and, consequently, are not included in this edition of the directory.

Indexes. To help you find the aid you need, we have constructed six indexes; these will let you access the listings by program title, sponsoring organization, residency, tenability, subject focus, and deadline date. These indexes use a word-by-word alphabetical arrangement. Note: numbers in the index refer to entry numbers, not to page numbers in the book.

Program Title Index. If you know the name of a particular funding program and want to find out where it is covered in the directory, use the Program Title Index. To assist you in your search, every program is listed by all its known names, former names, and abbreviations. Since one program can be included in more than one place (e.g., a program providing assistance to both undergraduate and graduate students is described in both the first and second chapters), each entry number in the index has been coded to indicate the intended recipient group (for example, "U" = Undergraduates; "G" = Graduate Students). By using this coding system, you can avoid duplicate entries and turn directly to the programs that match your eligibility characteristics.

Sponsoring Organization Index. This index makes it easy to identify agencies that offer funding primarily or exclusively to African Americans. More than 900 organizations are indexed here. As in the Program Title Index, we've used a code to help you determine which organizations sponsor programs that match your educational level.

Residency Index. Some programs listed in this book are restricted to African Americans in a particular state or region. Others are open to African Americans wherever they live. This index helps you identify programs available only to residents in your area as well as programs that have no residency requirements. Further, to assist you in your search, we've also indicated the recipient level for the funding offered to residents in each of the areas listed in the index.

Tenability Index. This index identifies the geographic locations where the funding described in *Financial Aid for African Americans* may be used. Index entries (city, county, state, region) are arranged alphabetically (word by word) and subdivided by recipient group. Use this index when you are looking for money to support your activities in a particular geographic area.

Subject Index. This index allows you to identify the subject focus of each of the financial aid opportunities described in *Financial Aid for African Americans.* More than 250 different subject terms are listed. Extensive "see" and "see also" references, as well as recipient group subdivisions, will help you locate appropriate funding opportunities.

Calendar Index. Since most financial aid programs have specific deadline dates, some may have closed by the time you begin to look for funding. You can use the Calendar Index to determine which programs are still open. This index is arranged by recipient group (Undergraduates, Graduate Students, and Professionals/Postdoctorates) and subdivided by the month during which the deadline falls. Filing dates can and quite often do vary from year to year; consequently, this index should be used only as a guide for deadlines beyond 2016.

HOW TO USE THE DIRECTORY

Here are some tips to help you get the most out of the funding opportunities listed in *Financial Aid for African Americans.*

To Locate Funding by Recipient Group. To bring together programs with a similar educational focus, this directory is divided into three chapters: Undergraduates, Graduate Students, and Professionals/Postdoctorates. If you want to get an overall picture of the sources of free money available to African Americans in any of these categories, turn to the appropriate chapter and then review the entries there. Since each of these chapters functions as a self-contained entity, you can browse through any of them without having to first consulting an index.

To Find Information on a Particular Financial Aid Program. If you know the name of a particular financial aid program, and the group eligible for that award, then go directly to the appropriate chapter in the directory (e.g., Undergraduates, Graduate Students), where you will find the program profiles arranged alphabetically by title. To save time, though, you should always check the Program Title Index first if you know the name of a specific award but are not sure in which chapter it has been listed. Plus, since we index each program by all its known names and abbreviations, you'll also be able to track down a program there when you may not know its exact official title.

To Locate Programs Sponsored by a Particular Organization. The Sponsoring Organization Index makes it easy to identify agencies that provide financial assistance to African Americans or to identify specific financial aid programs offered by a particular organization. Each entry number in the index is coded to identify recipient group (Undergraduates, Graduate Students, Professionals/Postdoctorates), so that you can quickly target appropriate entries.

To Browse Quickly Through the Listings. Look at the listings in the chapter that covers the educational level of interest to you (Undergraduates, Graduate Students, or Professionals/Postdoctorates) and read the "Summary" paragraph in each entry. In seconds, you'll know if this is an opportunity that you might want to pursue. If it is, be sure to read the rest of the information in the entry, to make sure you meet all of the program requirements before writing or going online for an application form. Please, save your time and energy. Don't apply if you don't qualify!

To Locate Funding Available to African Americans from or Tenable in a Particular City, County, or State. The Residency Index identifies financial aid programs open to African Americans in a specific state, region, etc. The Tenability Index shows where the money can be spent. In both indexes, "see" and "see also" references are used liberally, and index entries for a particular geographic area are subdivided by recipient group (Undergraduates, Graduate Students, and Professional/Postdoctorates) to help you identify the funding that's right for you. When using these indexes, always check the listings under the term "United States," since the programs indexed there have no geographic restrictions and can be used in any area.

To Locate Financial Aid Programs Open to African Americans in a Particular Subject Area. Turn to the Subject Index first if you are interested in identifying funding programs for African Americans that are focused on a particular subject area. To make your search easier, the intended recipient groups (Undergraduates, Graduate Students, Professionals/Postdoctorates) are clearly labeled in the more than 250 subject listings. Extensive cross-references are also provided. Since a large number of programs are not restricted by subject, be sure to check the references listed under the "General programs" heading in the index, in addition to the specific terms that directly relate to your interest areas. The listings under "General programs" can be used to fund activities in any subject area (although the programs may be restricted in other ways).

To Locate Financial Aid Programs for African Americans by Deadline Date. If you are working with specific time constraints and want to weed out the financial aid programs whose filing dates you won't be able to meet, turn first to the Calendar Index and check the program references listed under the appropriate recipient group and month. Note: not all sponsoring organizations supplied deadline information; those programs are listed under the "Deadline not specified" entries in the index. To identify every relevant financial aid program, regardless of filing date, go the appropriate chapter and read through all the entries there that match your educational level.

To Locate Financial Aid Programs Open to All Segments of the Population. Only programs available to African Americans are listed in this publication. However, there are thousands of other programs that are open equally to all segments of the population. To identify these programs, talk to your local librarian, check with your financial aid office on campus, look at the list of RSP print resources on the page opposite the title page in this directory, or see if your library subscribes to Reference Service Press' interactive online funding database: *RSP FundingFinder.* For more information on that award-winning resource, go online to: www.rspfunding.com/esubscriptions.html.

PLANS TO UPDATE THE DIRECTORY

This volume, covering 2014-2016, is the eighth edition of *Financial Aid for African Americans.* The next biennial edition will cover the years 2016-2018 and will be issued by the beginning of 2016.

OTHER RELATED PUBLICATIONS

In addition to *Financial Aid for African Americans,* Reference Service Press publishes several other titles dealing with fundseeking, including the award-winning *Directory of Financial Aids for Women; Financial Aid for the Disabled and Their Families;* and *Financial Aid for Veterans, Military Personnel, and Their Families.* Since each of these titles focuses on a separate population group, there is very little duplication in the listings. For more information on Reference Service Press' award-winning publications, write to the company at 5000 Windplay Drive, Suite 4, El Dorado Hills, CA 95762, give us a call at (916) 939-9620, fax us at (916) 939-9626, send us an e-mail at info@rspfunding.com, or visit our expanded web site: www.rspfunding.com.

ACKNOWLEDGEMENTS

A debt of gratitude is owed all the organizations that contributed information to the 2014-2016 edition of *Financial Aid for African Americans.* Their generous cooperation has helped to make this publication a current and comprehensive survey of awards.

ABOUT THE AUTHORS

Dr. Gail Ann Schlachter has worked for more than three decades as a library manager, a library educator, and an administrator of library-related publishing companies. Among the reference books to her credit are the biennially-issued *Directory of Financial Aids for Women* and two award-winning bibliographic guides: *Minorities and Women: A Guide to Reference Literature in the Social Sciences* (which was chosen as an "outstanding reference book of the year" by *Choice)* and *Reference Sources in Library and Information Services* (which won the first Knowledge Industry Publications "Award for Library Literature"). She was the reference book review editor for *RQ* (now *Reference and User Services Quarterly)* for 10 years, is a past president of the American Library Association's Reference and User Services Association, is the former editor-in-chief of the *Reference and User Services Association Quarterly,* and is currently serving her sixth term on the American Library Association's governing council. In recognition of her outstanding contributions to reference service, Dr. Schlachter has been named the University of Wisconsin School of Library and Information Studies "Alumna of the Year" and has been awarded both the Isadore Gilbert Mudge Citation and the Louis Shores/Oryx Press Award.

Dr. R. David Weber taught history and economics at Los Angeles Harbor College (in Wilmington, California) for many years and continues to teach history there as an emeritus professor. During his years at Harbor College, and earlier at East Los College, he directed the Honors Program and was frequently chosen the "Teacher of the Year." He has written a number of critically-acclaimed reference works, including *Dissertations in Urban History* and the three-volume *Energy Information Guide.* With Gail Schlachter, he is the author of Reference Service Press' *Financial Aid for the Disabled and Their Families,* which was selected by *Library Journal* as one of the "best reference books of the year," and a number of other financial aid titles, including the *College Student's Guide to Merit and Other No-Need Funding,* which was chosen as one of the "outstanding reference books of the year" by *Choice.*

Financial Aid Programs Open to African Americans

- *Undergraduates*
- *Graduate Students*
- *Professionals/Postdoctorates*

Undergraduates

Listed alphabetically by program title and described in detail here are 604 scholarships, forgivable loans, grants, awards, and other sources of "free money" set aside for African Americans who are college-bound high school seniors or continuing and returning undergraduate students. This funding is available to support study, training, research, and/or creative activities in the United States.

[1]
ACA/MARTIN LUTHER KING JR. SCHOLARSHIP AWARDS

American Correctional Association
Attn: Scholarship Award Committee
206 North Washington Street, Suite 200
Alexandria, VA 22314
(703) 224-0000 Toll Free: (800) ACA-JOIN
Fax: (703) 224-0179 E-mail: jenniferb@aca.org
Web: www.aca.org/pastpresentfuture/awards.asp

Summary To provide financial assistance for undergraduate or graduate study to African Americans and other minorities interested in a career in the criminal justice field.

Eligibility Members of the American Correctional Association (ACA) may nominate a minority person for these awards. Nominees do not need to be ACA members, but they must have been accepted to or be enrolled in an undergraduate or graduate program in criminal justice at a 4-year college or university. Along with the nomination package, they must submit a 250-word essay describing their reflections on the ideals and philosophies of Dr. Martin Luther King and how they have attempted to emulate those qualities in their lives. They must provide documentation of financial need, academic achievement, and commitment to the principles of Dr. King.

Financial data A stipend is awarded (amount not specified). Funds are paid directly to the recipient's college or university.

Number awarded 1 each year.

Deadline May of each year.

[2]
ACCENTURE NSBE CORPORATE SCHOLARSHIP PROGRAM

National Society of Black Engineers
Attn: Programs Department
205 Daingerfield Road
Alexandria, VA 22314
(703) 549-2207 Fax: (703) 683-5312
E-mail: scholarships@nsbe.org
Web: www.nsbe.org/Programs/Scholarships.aspx

Summary To provide financial assistance to members of the National Society of Black Engineers (NSBE) who are majoring in engineering or applied sciences.

Eligibility This program is open to members of the society who are entering their sophomore, junior, or senior year at a 4-year college or university and majoring in engineering or applied sciences. Applicants must have a GPA of 3.2 or higher and be authorized to work in the United States. Along with their application, they must submit an essay on 1) how they will use this scholarship opportunity to advance their career goals; and 2) which of the financing sponsor's values best aligns with their personal core values. Financial need is not considered in the selection process.

Financial data The stipend is $2,000.

Duration 1 year.

Additional information This program is sponsored by Accenture.

Number awarded 5 each year.

Deadline May of each year.

[3]
ACT SIX SCHOLARSHIPS

Act Six
c/o Degrees of Change
1109 A Street, Suite 101
P.O. Box 1573
Tacoma, WA 98401
(253) 642-6712 E-mail: tim.herron@actsix.org
Web: www.actsix.org

Summary To provide financial assistance to African Americans and other residents of Washington and Oregon who come from diverse backgrounds and are interested in attending designated private faith-based universities in those states.

Eligibility This program is open to high school seniors or recent graduates and planning to enter college as freshmen who come from diverse, multicultural backgrounds. Applicants must be residents of the following regions and interested in attending designated colleges for that region: Portland: George Fox University or Warner Pacific College; Spokane: Gonzaga University or Whitworth University; Tacoma-Seattle: Gonzaga University, Northwest University, Pacific Lutheran University, Trinity Lutheran College, or Whitworth University; or Yakima Valley: Heritage University. Students are not required to make a faith commitment, but they must be willing to explore Christian spirituality as it relates to service and leadership. Ethnicity and family income are considered as factors in selecting an intentionally diverse group of scholars, but there are no income restrictions and students from all ethnic backgrounds are encouraged to apply.

Financial data The program makes up the difference between any other assistance the student receives and full tuition. For recipients who demonstrate financial need in excess of tuition, awards cover some or all of the cost of room and board, books, travel, and personal expenses.

Duration 1 year; may be renewed.

Number awarded Varies each year; recently, 65 of these scholarships were awarded.

Deadline October of each year.

[4]
ACT-SO (AFRO-ACADEMIC, CULTURAL, TECHNOLOGICAL AND SCIENTIFIC OLYMPICS)

National Association for the Advancement of Colored People
Attn: ACT-SO Director
4805 Mt. Hope Drive
Baltimore, MD 21215
(410) 580-5650 Toll Free: (877) NAACP-98
E-mail: ACTSO@naacpnet.org
Web: www.naacp.org/programs/entry/act-so

Summary To recognize and reward (with college scholarships) outstanding African American high school students who distinguish themselves in the Afro-Academic, Cultural, Technological and Scientific Olympics (ACT-SO) program.

Eligibility This competition is open to high school students (grades 9-12) of African descent who are U.S. citizens and amateurs in the category in which they wish to participate. Competitions are held in 26 categories in 5 general areas: humanities (music composition, original essay, playwriting, and poetry), sciences (biology and microbiology, chemistry and biochemistry, computer science, earth and space science, engineering, mathematics, medicine and health, and physics), performing arts (dance, dramatics, music instrumental/classical, music instrumental/contemporary, music vocal/classical, music vocal/contemporary, and oratory), visual arts (architecture, drawing, filmmaking, painting, photography, and sculpture), and business (entrepreneurship). Competition is first conducted by local chapters of the NAACP; winners in each event at the local level then compete at the national level.

Financial data In each category, the first-prize winner receives a gold medal and a $1,000 scholarship, the second-prize winner receives a silver medal and a $750 scholarship, and the third-prize winner receives a bronze medal and a $500 scholarship.

Duration The competition is held annually.

Additional information This competition began in 1977.

Number awarded 78 each year: 3 in each of 26 categories.

Deadline Local competitions usually take place between February and April. The national finals are held each year in July.

[5]
ACTUARIAL DIVERSITY SCHOLARSHIPS

Actuarial Foundation
Attn: Actuarial Education and Research Fund Committee
475 North Martingale Road, Suite 600
Schaumburg, IL 60173-2226
(847) 706-3535 Fax: (847) 706-3599
E-mail: scholarships@actfnd.org
Web: www.actuarialfoundation.org

Summary To provide financial assistance to African American and other minority undergraduate students who are preparing for a career in actuarial science.

Eligibility This program is open to members of minority groups, defined as having at least 1 birth parent who is Black/African American, Hispanic, Native North American, or Pacific Islander. Applicants must be graduating high school seniors or current full-time undergraduate students working on or planning to work on a degree at an accredited 2- or 4-year college or university that may lead to a career in the actuarial profession. They must have a GPA of 3.0 or higher; high school seniors must also have a minimum score of 28 on the ACT mathematics examination or 600 on the SAT mathematics examination. Along with their application, they must submit a 1- or 2-page personal statement that covers why they are interested in becoming an actuary, the steps they are taking to enter the actuarial profession, participation in actuarial internships, and participation in extracurricular activities. Financial need is not considered in the selection process.

Financial data Annual stipends are $1,000 for high school seniors applying for freshman year, $2,000 for college freshmen applying for sophomore year and for college sophomores applying for junior year, $3,000 for college juniors applying for senior year, or $3,000 for college seniors applying for graduate school or continuing graduate students.

Duration 1 year; may be renewed, provided the recipient remains enrolled full time, in good academic standing, in a course of study that may lead to a career in the actuarial profession, and (for college juniors and higher) passes actuarial examinations.

Additional information This program began in 1977 by the Casualty Actuarial Society and the Society of Actuaries. In 2008, it was transferred to the Actuarial Foundation.

Number awarded Varies each year; recently, 32 of these scholarships were awarded.

Deadline May of each year.

[6]
A.D. OSHERMAN SCHOLARSHIP FUND

Greater Houston Community Foundation
Attn: Scholarship Coordinator
5120 Woodway Drive, Suite 6000
Houston, TX 77056
(713) 333-2205 Fax: (713) 333-2220
E-mail: lgardner@ghcf.org
Web: www.ghcf.org/Recieve/Scholarships

Summary To provide financial assistance to African Americans and members of other designated groups who are residents of Texas and attending or planning to attend college in any state.

Eligibility This program is open to Texas residents who are graduating high school seniors or full-time freshmen, sophomores, or juniors at an accredited public 2- or 4-year college or university in any state. Applicants must qualify as a member of a recognized minority group, the first in their family to attend college, or a veteran with active service, particularly service in Iraq or Afghanistan. They must have a GPA of 2.75 or higher and a history of community service. Financial need is considered in the selection process.

Financial data The stipend is $2,500 per year for students at 4-year universities or $1,500 per year for students at 2-year colleges.

Duration 1 year; recipients may reapply.

Number awarded 2 each year.

Deadline March of each year.

[7]
ADDIE B. MORRIS SCHOLARSHIP

American Association of Railroad Superintendents
P.O. Box 200
La Fox, IL 60147
(630) 762-0754 E-mail: aars@supt.org
Web: www.railroadsuperintendents.org/Scholarships

Summary To provide financial assistance to undergraduate and graduate students, with preference given to African Americans and other minorities working on a degree in transportation.

Eligibility This program is open to full-time undergraduate and graduate students enrolled at accredited colleges and universities in Canada or the United States. Applicants must have completed enough credits to have standing as a sophomore and must have a GPA of 2.75 or higher. Preference is given to minority students enrolled in the transportation field who can demonstrate financial need.

Financial data The stipend is $1,000. Funds are sent directly to the recipient's institution.

Duration 1 year.

Number awarded 1 or more each year.

Deadline May of each year.

[8]
AFPD MINORITY SCHOLARSHIPS

Associated Food and Petroleum Dealers
Attn: AFPD Foundation
5779 West Maple Road
West Bloomfield, MI 48322
(248) 671-9600 Toll Free: (800) 666-6233
Fax: (866) 601-9610 E-mail: info@afpdonline.org
Web: www.afpdonline.org/michigan-scholarship.php

Summary To provide financial assistance to African American and other minority high school seniors and current college students from Michigan who are enrolled or planning to enroll at a college in any state.

Eligibility This program is open to Michigan residents who are high school seniors or college freshmen, sophomores, or juniors. Applicants must be members of 1 of the following minority groups: African American, Hispanic, Asian, Native American, or Arab/Chaldean. They must be enrolled or planning to enroll full time at a college or university in any state. Preferential consideration is given to applicants with a membership affiliation in the Associated Food and Petroleum Dealers (AFPD), although membership is not required. Selection is based on academic performance, leadership, and participation in school and community activities; college grades are considered if the applicant is already enrolled in college.

Financial data The stipend is $1,500.

Duration 1 year; nonrenewable.

Additional information This program is administered by International Scholarship and Tuition Services, Inc. The AFPD was formed in 2006 by a merger of the Associated Food Dealers of Michigan and the Great Lakes Petroleum Retailers and Allied Trades Association.

Number awarded At least 10 each year, of which at least 3 must be awarded to member customers.

Deadline March of each year.

[9]
AFRICAN AMERICAN FUTURE ACHIEVERS SCHOLARSHIP PROGRAM

Ronald McDonald House Charities
Attn: U.S. Scholarship Program
One Kroc Drive
Oak Brook, IL 60523
(630) 623-7048 Fax: (630) 623-7488
E-mail: info@rmhc.org
Web: rmhc.org/what-we-do/rmhc-u-s-scholarships

Summary To provide financial assistance for college to African American high school seniors in specified geographic areas.

Eligibility This program is open to high school seniors in designated McDonald's market areas who are legal residents of the United States and have at least 1 parent of African American or Black Caribbean heritage. Applicants must be planning to enroll full time at an accredited 2- or 4-year college, university, or vocational/technical school. They must have a GPA of 2.7 or higher. Along with their application, they must submit a personal statement, up to 2 pages in length, on their African American or Black Caribbean background, career goals, and desire to contribute to their community; information about unique, personal, or financial circumstances may be added. Selection is based on that statement, high school transcripts, a letter of recommendation, and financial need.

Financial data Most awards are $1,000 per year. Funds are paid directly to the recipient's school.

Duration 1 year; nonrenewable.

Additional information This program is a component of the Ronald McDonald House Charities U.S. Scholarship Program, which began in 1985. It is administered by International Scholarship and Tuition Services, Inc., 200 Crutchfield Avenue, Nashville, TN 37210, (615) 320-3149, Fax: (615) 320-3151, E-mail: info@applyists.com. For a list of participating McDonald's market areas, contact Ronald McDonald House Charities (RMHC).

Number awarded Varies each year; since RMHC began this program, it has awarded more than $44 million in scholarships.

Deadline January of each year.

[10]
AFRICAN AMERICAN MONUMENTAL LIFE SETTLEMENT SCHOLARSHIPS

Kansas Insurance Department
Attn: Scholarship Fund
420 S.W. Ninth Street
Topeka, KS 66612-1678
(785) 296-3071 Toll Free: (800) 432-2484 (within KS)
Fax: (785) 296-7805 E-mail: bhanson@ksinsurance.org
Web: www.ksinsurance.org/gpa/scholarship.htm

Summary To provide financial assistance to African American students from any state who are majoring in business, computer science, or mathematics at a college or university in Kansas.

Eligibility This program is open to African American students from any state enrolled at accredited institutions of higher education in Kansas. Applicants must be majoring in business (with an emphasis in accounting, economics, finance, or investments), computer science, or mathematics. They must have a GPA of 3.0 or higher. Along with their application, they must submit a 1-page essay describing their career goals and how this scholarship would help them achieve those goals. An interview is required.

Financial data The stipend is $1,000.

Duration 1 year.

Additional information This program began in 2005 with funds received in a settlement with Monumental Life as a result of the firm's race-based pricing of life insurance policies.

Number awarded 12 each year.

Deadline April of each year for fall semester; September of each year for spring semester.

[11]
AFRICAN AMERICAN NETWORK-CAROLINAS SCHOLARSHIP FUND

Foundation for the Carolinas
Attn: Vice President, Scholarships
220 South Tryon Street
Charlotte, NC 28202
(704) 973-4537 Toll Free: (800) 973-7244
Fax: (704) 973-4935 E-mail: tcapers@fftc.org
Web: www.fftc.org/page.aspx?pid=729

Summary To provide financial assistance to African American and other high school seniors from North and South Carolina who are interested in studying designated fields in college.

Eligibility This program is open to seniors graduating from high schools in North and South Carolina. Applicants must be planning to attend a 4-year college or university in those states to major in accounting, business administration, computer science, engineering, finance, mathematics, or the sciences. Selection is based on GPA, residence, leadership skills, and financial need.

Financial data A stipend is awarded (amount not specified).

Duration 1 year; recipients may reapply, provided they remain enrolled full time and meet all qualifying requirements.

Additional information This program is sponsored by the African American Network, a resource group of African American employees of Duke Energy. Recipients are selected by colleges, universities, and community service organizations according to criteria established by the Network. Interested students must contact their college, university, or community service organization to apply for this scholarship.

Number awarded 3 each year: 2 selected by colleges and universities and 1 selected by a community service organization.

Deadline February of each year.

[12]
AFRICAN HERITAGE CAUCUS SCHOLARSHIPS

African Heritage Caucus
c/o Stephanie Haiba Collier, Scholarship Chair
3100 Sasparilla Cove
Austin, TX 78748
E-mail: swcollier@swmail.sw.org
Web: www.africanheritagecaucus.org

Summary To provide financial assistance to members of the African Heritage Caucus within the American Academy of Physician Assistants (AAPA).

Eligibility This program is open to physician assistant students entering their clinical phase of training and members of both the AAPA and its African Heritage Caucus. Applicants must submit an essay of 500 to 750 words on 1 of the following topics: 1) their opinion on the impact of universal health care in addressing the issues of racial health care disparities in our country; or 2) the major health care disparities facing the African American community and how they will address those as a practicing physician assistant. Selection is based on academic progress, financial need, community and/or professional activities, and knowledge of health care issues and the physician assistant's role.

Financial data Stipends range from $500 to $1,000.

Duration 1 year.

Number awarded Up to 2 each year.

Deadline April of each year.

[13]
AGA INVESTING IN THE FUTURE STUDENT RESEARCH FELLOWSHIPS

American Gastroenterological Association
Attn: AGA Research Foundation
Research Awards Manager
4930 Del Ray Avenue
Bethesda, MD 20814-2512
(301) 222-4012 Fax: (301) 654-5920
E-mail: awards@gastro.org
Web: www.gastro.org/aga-foundation/grants

Summary To provide funding for research on digestive diseases or nutrition to undergraduate and medical students who are African Americans or from other underrepresented minority groups.

Eligibility This program is open to undergraduate and medical students at accredited U.S. institutions who are African Americans, Hispanic/Latino Americans, Alaska Natives, American Indians, or Natives of the U.S. Pacific Islands. Applicants must be interested in conducting research on digestive diseases or nutrition. They may not hold similar salary support awards from other agencies (e.g., American Liver Foundation, Crohn's and Colitis Foundation). Research must be conducted under the supervision of a preceptor who is a full-time faculty member at an institution in a state other than the student's, directing a research project in a gastroenterology-related area, and a member of the American Gastroenterological Association (AGA).

Financial data Fellowships provide payment of housing, travel, and a stipend of $5,000.

Duration 8 to 10 weeks. The work may take place at any time during the year.

Number awarded 10 each year.

Deadline February of each year.

[14]
AGNES JONES JACKSON SCHOLARSHIPS

National Association for the Advancement of Colored People
Attn: Education Department
4805 Mt. Hope Drive
Baltimore, MD 21215-3297
(410) 580-5760 Toll Free: (877) NAACP-98
E-mail: youth@naacpnet.org
Web: www.naacp.org/pages/naacp-scholarships

Summary To provide financial assistance to members of the National Association for the Advancement of Colored People (NAACP) who are attending or planning to attend college or graduate school.

Eligibility This program is open to members of the NAACP who are younger than 25 years of age and full-time undergraduates or full- or part-time graduate students. The minimum GPA is 2.5 for graduating high school seniors and undergraduate students or 3.0 for graduate students. All applicants must be able to demonstrate financial need (family income must be less than $16,245 for a family of 1, ranging up to $49,905 for a family of 7) and U.S. citizenship. Along with their application, they must submit a 1-page essay on their interest in their major and a career, their life's ambition, what they hope to accomplish in their lifetime, and what position they hope to attain.

Financial data The stipend is $1,500 per year for undergraduate students or $2,500 per year for graduate students.

Duration 1 year; recipients may apply for renewal.

Number awarded Varies each year; recently, 5 of these scholarships were awarded.

Deadline March of each year.

[15]
AHLEF/HYATT HOTELS FUND FOR MINORITY LODGING MANAGEMENT STUDENTS

American Hotel & Lodging Educational Foundation
Attn: Manager of Foundation Programs
1201 New York Avenue, N.W., Suite 600
Washington, DC 20005-3931
(202) 289-3100 Fax: (202) 289-3199
E-mail: scholarships@ahlef.org
Web: www.ahlef.org/content.aspx?id=19468

Summary To provide financial assistance to African American and other minority college students working on a degree in hotel management.

Eligibility This program is open to students majoring in hospitality management at a 4-year college or university as at least a junior. Applicants must be members of a minority group (African American, Hispanic, American Indian, Alaskan Native, Asian, or Pacific Islander). They must be enrolled full time. Along with their application, they must submit a 500-word essay on their personal background, including when they became interested in the hospitality field, the traits they possess or will need to succeed in the industry, and their plans as related to their educational and career objectives and future goals. Selection is based on industry-related work experience; financial need; academic record and educational qualifications; professional, community, and extracurricular activities; personal attributes, including career goals; the essay; and neatness and completeness of the application. U.S. citizenship or permanent resident status is required.

Financial data The stipend is $2,000.

Duration 1 year.

Additional information Funding for this program, established in 1988, is provided by Hyatt Hotels & Resorts.

Number awarded Varies each year; recently, 18 of these scholarships were awarded. Since this program was established, it has awarded scholarships worth $588,000 to 294 minority students.

Deadline April of each year.

[16]
AKA/EAF ENDOWMENT AWARDS

Alpha Kappa Alpha Sorority, Inc.
Attn: Educational Advancement Foundation
5656 South Stony Island Avenue
Chicago, IL 60637
(773) 947-0026 Toll Free: (800) 653-6528
Fax: (773) 947-0277 E-mail: akaeaf@akaeaf.net
Web: www.akaeaf.org/fellowships_endowments.htm

Summary To provide financial assistance to undergraduate and graduate students (especially African American women) who meet designated requirements.

Eligibility This program is open to undergraduate and graduate students who are enrolled full time as sophomores or higher in an accredited degree-granting institution and are planning to continue their program of education. Applicants may apply for scholarships that include specific requirements established by the donor of the endowment that supports it. Along with their application, they must submit 1) a list of honors, awards, and scholarships received; 2) a list of organizations in which they have memberships, especially minority organizations; and 3) a statement of their personal and career goals, including how this scholarship will enhance their ability to attain those goals. The sponsor is a traditionally African American women's sorority.

Financial data Award amounts are determined by the availability of funds from the particular endowment. Recently, stipends averaged more than $1,700 per year.

Duration 1 year or longer.

Additional information Each endowment establishes its own requirements. Examples of requirements include residence of the applicant, major field of study, minimum GPA, attendance at an Historically Black College or University (HBCU) or member institution of the United Negro College Fund (UNCF), or other personal feature. For further information on all endowments, contact the sponsor.

Number awarded Varies each year; recently, 32 of these scholarships, with a total value of nearly $76,00, were awarded.

Deadline April of each year.

[17]
AKA/EAF UNDERGRADUATE SCHOLARSHIPS

Alpha Kappa Alpha Sorority, Inc.
Attn: Educational Advancement Foundation
5656 South Stony Island Avenue
Chicago, IL 60637
(773) 947-0026 Toll Free: (800) 653-6528
Fax: (773) 947-0277 E-mail: akaeaf@akaeaf.net
Web: www.akaeaf.org/undergraduate_scholarships.htm

Summary To provide financial assistance to students (especially African American women) who are working on an undergraduate degree in any field.

Eligibility This program is open to undergraduate students who are enrolled full time as sophomores or higher in an accredited degree-granting institution and are planning to continue their program of education. Applicants may apply either for a scholarship based on merit (requires a GPA of 3.0 or higher) or on financial need (requires a GPA of 2.5 or higher). Along with their application, they must submit 1) a list of honors, awards, and scholarships received; 2) a list of organizations in which they have memberships, especially minority organizations; and 3) a statement of their personal and career goals, including how this scholarship will enhance their ability to attain those goals. The sponsor is a traditionally African American women's sorority.

Financial data Stipends range up to $2,500.

Duration 1 year; nonrenewable.

Number awarded Varies each year; recently, 133 of these scholarships, with a total value of $69,950 were awarded.

Deadline April of each year.

[18]
ALAN COMPTON AND BOB STANLEY MINORITY AND INTERNATIONAL SCHOLARSHIP

Baptist Communicators Association
Attn: Scholarship Committee
1519 Menlo Drive
Kennesaw, GA 30152
(770) 425-3728 E-mail: mmdempsey@bellsouth.net
Web: www.baptistcommunicators.org/about/scholarship.cfm

Summary To provide financial assistance to African American, other minority, and international students who are working on an undergraduate degree to prepare for a career in Baptist communications.

Eligibility This program is open to undergraduate students of minority or international origin. Applicants must be majoring in communications, English, journalism, or public relations and have a GPA of 2.5 or higher. Their vocational objective must be in Baptist communications. Along with their application, they must submit a statement explaining why they want to receive this scholarship.

Financial data The stipend is $1,000.

Duration 1 year; recipients may reapply.

Additional information This program began in 1996.

Number awarded 1 each year.

Deadline March of each year.

[19]
ALASKA AIRLINES MAINTENANCE AND ENGINEERING SCHOLARSHIP

Organization of Black Aerospace Professionals, Inc.
Attn: Scholarship Coordinator
1 Westbrook Corporate Center, Suite 300
Westchester, IL 60154
(708) 449-7755 Toll Free: (800) JET-OBAP
Fax: (708) 449-7754 E-mail: obapscholarship@obap.org
Web: www.obap.org/scholarships/scholarship-opportunities

Summary To provide financial assistance to members of the Organization of Black Aerospace Professionals (OBAP) who are interested in further training as a mechanic to advance their career in the aviation industry.

Eligibility This program is open to OBAP members who are enrolled in or accepted at an aviation mechanic's training school. Applicants must have a GPA of 2.7 or higher. Along with their application, they must submit a 500-word essay on how this award will help advance their aviation career.

Financial data The stipend is $2,500. Funds are paid directly to the training facility.

Duration 1 year.

Additional information The OBAP was originally established in 1976 as the Organization of Black Airline Pilots to make certain Blacks and other minorities had a group that would keep them informed about opportunities for advancement within commercial aviation. This program is sponsored by Alaska Airlines.

Number awarded 1 each year.

Deadline May of each year.

[20]
ALASKA AIRLINES PILOT SCHOLARSHIP

Organization of Black Aerospace Professionals, Inc.
Attn: Scholarship Coordinator
1 Westbrook Corporate Center, Suite 300
Westchester, IL 60154
(708) 449-7755 Toll Free: (800) JET-OBAP
Fax: (708) 449-7754 E-mail: obapscholarship@obap.org
Web: www.obap.org/scholarships/scholarship-opportunities

Summary To provide financial assistance to members of the Organization of Black Aerospace Professionals (OBAP) who are interested in further training as a pilot to advance their career in the aviation industry.

Eligibility This program is open to OBAP members who have a private pilot's license and are enrolled in an aviation program. Applicants must have a GPA of 3.0 or higher. Along with their application, they must submit a 500-word essay on how this award will help advance their aviation career and a copy of their second class medical certificate.

Financial data The stipend is $2,500. Funds are paid directly to the training facility.

Duration 1 year.

Additional information The OBAP was originally established in 1976 as the Organization of Black Airline Pilots to make certain Blacks and other minorities had a group that would keep them informed about opportunities for advancement within commercial aviation. This program is sponsored by Alaska Airlines.

Number awarded 1 each year.

Deadline May of each year.

[21]
ALICE S. MARRIOTT SCHOLARSHIP FUND

Alpha Kappa Alpha Sorority, Inc.
Attn: Educational Advancement Foundation
5656 South Stony Island Avenue
Chicago, IL 60637
(773) 947-0026 Toll Free: (800) 653-6528
Fax: (773) 947-0277 E-mail: akaeaf@akaeaf.net
Web: www.akaeaf.org/alice_s_marriott.htm

Summary To provide financial assistance to African Americans and members of other underrepresented groups who are attending college to prepare for a career in the hospitality industry.

Eligibility This program is open to members of groups traditionally underrepresented in the hospitality industry who are working on a bachelor's degree in the field. Applicants must submit an essay explaining their understanding of what the hospitality industry entails, the specific careers that interest them in the industry, and their career goals upon graduation. Financial need is not considered in the selection process.

Financial data The stipend is $1,000.

Duration 1 year.

Additional information Marriott International established this program in 2012 in partnership with the Educational Advancement Foundation of Alpha Kappa Alpha, a traditionally African American sorority.

Number awarded 2 each year.

Deadline April of each year.

[22]
ALLISON E. FISHER SCHOLARSHIP

National Association of Black Journalists
Attn: Communications Coordinator and Program Manager
University of Maryland
1100 Knight Hall, Suite 3100
College Park, MD 20742
(301) 405-2573 Fax: (301) 314-1714
E-mail: tjohnson@nabj.org
Web: www.nabj.org/?page=SEEDScholarships

Summary To provide financial assistance to undergraduate or graduate student members of the National Association of Black Journalists (NABJ) who are working on a degree in journalism.

Eligibility This program is open to African American undergraduate or graduate student members of NABJ who are currently enrolled full time at an accredited 4-year college or university. Applicants must be majoring in journalism or another communications-related discipline and have a GPA of 3.0 or higher. They must be able to demonstrate financial need. Along with their application, they must submit 5 samples of their work, an official college transcript, 3 letters of recommendation, a resume, and an essay of 1,000 to 2,000 words on the reasons why they are preparing for a career in journalism and what they hope their legacy as a journalist will be.

Financial data The stipend is $2,500. Funds are paid directly to the recipient's college or university.

Duration 1 year; nonrenewable.

Number awarded 1 each year.

Deadline March of each year.

[23]
ALMA EXLEY SCHOLARSHIP

Community Foundation of Greater New Britain
Attn: Scholarship Manager
74A Vine Street
New Britain, CT 06052-1431
(860) 229-6018, ext. 305 Fax: (860) 225-2666
E-mail: cfarmer@cfgnb.org
Web: www.cfgnb.org

Summary To provide financial assistance to African American and other minority college students in Connecticut who are interested in preparing for a teaching career.

Eligibility This program is open to students of color (African Americans, Asian Americans, Hispanic Americans, and Native Americans) enrolled in a teacher preparation program in Connecticut. Applicant must 1) have been admitted to a traditional teacher preparation program at an accredited 4-year college or university in the state; or 2) be participating in the Alternate Route to Certification (ARC) program sponsored by the Connecticut Department of Higher Education.

Financial data The stipend is $1,500 per year for students at a 4-year college or university or $500 for a student in the ARC program.

Duration 2 years for students at 4-year colleges or universities; 1 year for students in the ARC program.

Number awarded 2 each year: 1 to a 4-year student and 1 to an ARC student.

Deadline October of each year.

[24]
ALPHA PHI ALPHA FRATERNITY SCHOLARSHIPS

Alpha Phi Alpha Fraternity, Inc.
Attn: Education Foundation
2313 St. Paul Street
Baltimore, MD 21218-5211
(410) 554-0040 Fax: (410) 554-0054
E-mail: apaef@apa1906.net
Web: www.alpha-phi-alpha.com/Page.php?id=102

Summary To provide financial assistance for college or graduate school to brothers of Alpha Phi Alpha Fraternity.

Eligibility This program is open to brothers of the fraternity who either 1) are working full time on an undergraduate degree; or 2) have been admitted to a graduate or professional program. Applicants must have a GPA of 3.5 or higher. Along with their application, they must submit a resume, a list of their involvement in the fraternity's national programs and special projects, an official transcript, 3 letters of recommendation, and an essay on their career ambitions, goals, and why they should be awarded the scholarship.

Financial data The stipend is $1,500.

Duration 1 year.

Additional information Alpha Phi Alpha is the first collegiate fraternity established primarily for African American men.

Number awarded 15 each year: 3 in each of the fraternity's 5 geographic regions.

Deadline April of each year.

[25]
ALPHONSO DEAL SCHOLARSHIP AWARD

National Black Police Association
3100 Main Street, Suite 256
Dallas, TX 75226
Toll Free: (855) 879-6272 Fax: (855) 879-6272
E-mail: nationaloffice@blackpolice.org
Web: www.blackpolice.org

Summary To provide financial assistance to African American high school seniors interested in preparing for a career in criminal justice.

Eligibility This program is open to African American high school seniors who are planning to attend an accredited 2- or 4-year college or university to prepare for a career in criminal justice. Applicants must be U.S. citizens and of good character. Along with their application, they must submit a brief statement describing the course of study they plan to pursue and their general outlook as to future endeavors. Selection is based on academic record, extracurricular activities, and recommendations; financial need is not considered.

Financial data A stipend is awarded (amount not specified).

Duration 1 year.

Number awarded Varies each year; recently, 10 of these scholarships were awarded.

Deadline May of each year.

[26]
ALTRIA SCHOLARS

Virginia Foundation for Independent Colleges
Attn: Director of Development
8010 Ridge Road, Suite B
Richmond, VA 23229-7288
(804) 288-6609 Toll Free: (800) 230-6757
Fax: (804) 282-4635 E-mail: info@vfic.org
Web: www.vfic.org/scholarships/scholarships_vfic.html

Summary To provide financial assistance to students (especially African Americans and other underrepresented minorities) who are majoring in designated fields at a college or university that is a member of the Virginia Foundation for Independent Colleges (VFIC).

Eligibility This program is open to sophomores who are enrolled as full-time second-semester sophomores at 1 of the 15 VFIC member institutions. Applicants must be nominated by their institution. They must have a GPA of 3.0 or higher and a declared major in accounting, biology, business management, business, chemistry, computer science, economics, engineering, finance, marketing, or physics. Selection is based on merit and financial need. Special consideration is given to underserved populations. U.S. citizenship is required.

Financial data The stipend is $5,000 per year.

Duration 1 year (the junior year). May be renewed for the senior year, provided the recipient maintains a GPA of 3.0 or higher and a record of good citizenship and conduct.

Additional information Funding for this program, established in 2001, is provided by Altria Group (parent company of Philip Morris USA). Recipients also have an opportunity to apply for paid internships with Altria. The 15 member institutions are Bridgewater College, Emory and Henry College, Hampden-Sydney College, Hollins University, Lynchburg College, Mary Baldwin College, Marymount University, Randolph College, Randolph-Macon College, Roanoke College, Shenandoah University, Sweet Briar College, University of Richmond, Virginia Wesleyan College, and Washington and Lee University.

Number awarded 10 each year.

Deadline October of each year.

[27]
ALTRIA SCHOLARSHIPS OF THE THURGOOD MARSHALL COLLEGE FUND

Thurgood Marshall College Fund
Attn: Campus Relations Associate
901 F Street, N.W., Suite 300
Washington, DC 20004
(202) 507-4851 Fax: (202) 652-2934
E-mail: info@tmcfund.org
Web: www.thurgoodmarshallfund.net

Summary To provide financial assistance to African American upper-division students working on a degree in designated fields at public Historically Black Colleges and Universities (HBCUs) that are members of the Thurgood Marshall College Fund (TMCF).

Eligibility This program is open to students currently enrolled as juniors at any of the 47 TMCF member institutions. Some awards are designated for students at Florida A&M University, North Carolina A&T State University, or Winston-Salem State University. Applicants must be majoring in accounting, business, economics, engineering, finance, mathematics, science, or technology. They must have a GPA of 3.5 or higher and be able to demonstrate financial need. Along with their application, they must submit a 500-word essay on 1 of the following topics: 1) a significant setback, challenge, or opportunity in their life and the impact it has had on them; 2) what inspired them to pursue a degree in their current field of study and the impact it will have on our society; or 3) what it means to be the first person in their family to receive a college degree. U.S. citizenship or permanent resident status is required.

Financial data The stipend is $3,100 per semester ($6,200 per year).

Duration 1 year; nonrenewable.

Additional information This program is sponsored by Altria Group (parent company of Philip Morris USA). Recipients also have an opportunity to apply for paid summer internships at the company between their junior and senior year.

Number awarded 17 each year.

Deadline April of each year.

[28]
ALVAN T.-VIOLA D. FULLER JUNIOR RESEARCH FELLOWSHIP

American Cancer Society-New England Division
30 Speen Street
Framingham, MA 01701
(508) 270-3109 Toll Free: (800) 952-7664, ext. 3109
Fax: (508) 270-4607 E-mail: koconnor@cancer.org
Web: www.cancer.org

Summary To provide funding for cancer research during the summer to undergraduate students (particularly African American and other minority students) in New England.

Eligibility This program is open to residents of New England currently enrolled as juniors or seniors at a college or university in any state. Applicants must be interested in working on a summer research project at a teaching hospital, university, or medical school in New England. They must be interested in working under the supervision of an accomplished cancer investigator. Preference is given to students with advanced science course work, laboratory skills, and an interest in research. Minority students and those with American Cancer Society volunteer experience are especially encouraged to apply.

Financial data The grant is $4,500.

Duration 10 weeks during the summer.

Number awarded 1 or more each year.

Deadline January of each year.

[29]
AMELIA KEMP MEMORIAL SCHOLARSHIP

Women of the Evangelical Lutheran Church in America
Attn: Scholarships
8765 West Higgins Road
Chicago, IL 60631-4101
(773) 380-2741 Toll Free: (800) 638-3522, ext. 2741
Fax: (773) 380-2419 E-mail: valora.starr@elca.org
Web: www.womenoftheelca.org

Summary To provide financial assistance to African American and other lay women of color who are members of Evangelical Lutheran Church of America (ELCA) congregations and who wish to study on the undergraduate, graduate, professional, or vocational school level.

Eligibility This program is open to ELCA lay women of color who are at least 21 years of age and have experienced an interruption of at least 2 years in their education since high school. Applicants must have been admitted to an educational institution to prepare for a career in other than ordained ministry. U.S. citizenship is required.

Financial data The maximum stipend is $1,000.

Duration Up to 2 years.

Number awarded 1 or more each year.

Deadline February of each year.

[30] AMERICAN ASSOCIATION OF BLACKS IN ENERGY NATIONAL SCHOLARSHIPS

American Association of Blacks in Energy
Attn: Scholarship Committee
1625 K Street, N.W., Suite 405
Washington, DC 20006
(202) 371-9530 Fax: (202) 371-9218
E-mail: info@aabe.org
Web: www.aabe.org/index.php?component=pages&id=4

Summary To provide financial assistance to African American and other underrepresented minority high school seniors who are interested in preparing for a career in a field related to energy in college.

Eligibility This program is open to members of minority groups underrepresented in energy-related fields (African Americans, Hispanics, and Native Americans) who are graduating high school seniors. Applicants must have a GPA of 3.0 or higher overall and in mathematics and science courses. They must be planning to attend an accredited college or university to major in business, engineering, mathematics, technology, or the physical sciences. Along with their application, they must submit a 350-word essay that includes why they should receive this scholarship and how their professional career objectives relate to the energy field. Financial need is considered in the selection process. All applications must be submitted to the local office of the sponsoring organization in the student's state. For a list of local offices, contact the scholarship committee at the national office. The highest-ranked applicant receives the Premier Award.

Financial data The stipends are $3,000. The Premier Award is $5,000. All funds are paid directly to the students upon proof of enrollment at an accredited college or university.

Duration 1 year; nonrenewable.

Number awarded 6 each year (1 in each of the organization's regions); of those 6 winners, 1 is chosen to receive the Premier Award.

Deadline February of each year.

[31] AMERICAN ASSOCIATION OF UNIVERSITY WOMEN CAREER DEVELOPMENT GRANTS

American Association of University Women
Attn: AAUW Educational Foundation
301 ACT Drive, Department 60
P.O. Box 4030
Iowa City, IA 52243-4030
(319) 337-1716, ext. 60 Fax: (319) 337-1204
E-mail: aauw@act.org
Web: www.aauw.org

Summary To provide financial assistance to African American and other women who are seeking career advancement, career change, or reentry into the workforce.

Eligibility This program is open to women who are U.S. citizens or permanent residents, have earned a bachelor's degree, received their most recent degree more than 4 years ago, and are making career changes, seeking to advance in current careers, or reentering the workforce. Applicants must be interested in working toward a master's degree, second bachelor's or associate degree, professional degree (e.g., M.D., J.D.), certification program, or technical school certificate. They must be planning to undertake course work at an accredited 2- or 4-year college or university (or a technical school that is licensed, accredited, or approved by the U.S. Department of Education). Primary consideration is given to women of color and women pursuing their first advanced degree or credentials in nontraditional fields. Support is not provided for prerequisite course work or for Ph.D. course work or dissertations. Selection is based on demonstrated commitment to education and equity for women and girls, reason for seeking higher education or technical training, degree to which study plan is consistent with career objectives, potential for success in chosen field, documentation of opportunities in chosen field, feasibility of study plans and proposed time schedule, validity of proposed budget and budget narrative (including sufficient outside support), and quality of written proposal.

Financial data Grants range from $2,000 to $12,000. Funds may be used for tuition, fees, books, supplies, local transportation, dependent child care, or purchase of a computer required for the study program.

Duration 1 year, beginning in July; nonrenewable.

Additional information The filing fee is $35.

Number awarded Varies each year; recently, 63 of these grants, with a value of $670,000, were awarded.

Deadline December of each year.

[32] AMERICAN BAPTIST CHURCHES OF OHIO/FAYE AND ROBERT LETT SCHOLARSHIP

American Baptist Churches of Ohio
Attn: Ohio Baptist Education Society
647 South Diamond Street
Mansfield, OH 44907
(419) 524-4761 E-mail: pastorchris@neo.rr.com
Web: www.abc-ohio.org/index.php/menu-obes

Summary To provide funding to African American upper-division and graduate students from Ohio who are interested in preparing for the Baptist ministry at a college or seminary in any state.

Eligibility This program is open to African American residents of Ohio who have completed at least 2 years of study at an accredited college or university in any state and are interested in continuing their education as an upper-division or seminary student. Applicants must 1) hold active membership in a church affiliated with the American Baptist Churches of Ohio or a church dually-aligned with the American Baptist Churches of Ohio; 2) be in the process of preparing for a professional career in Christian ministry (such as a local church pastor, church education, youth or young adult ministries, church music, specialized ministry, chaplaincy, ministry in higher education, or missionary service); 3) be committed to working professionally within the framework of the American Baptist Churches USA; and 4) acknowledge a personal commitment to the Gospel of Jesus Christ, an understanding of the Christian faith, and a definite call to professional Christian ministry as a life work. Financial need must be demonstrated.

Financial data Stipends generally range from $1,000 to $1,500 a year.

Duration 1 year.

Additional information This program began in 1990.

Number awarded 1 or more each year.

Deadline March of each year.

[33] AMERICAN CHEMICAL SOCIETY SCHOLARS PROGRAM

American Chemical Society
Attn: Scholars Program
1155 16th Street, N.W.
Washington, DC 20036
(202) 872-6250 Toll Free: (800) 227-5558, ext. 6250
Fax: (202) 872-4361 E-mail: scholars@acs.org
Web: portal.acs.org

Summary To provide financial assistance to African American and other underrepresented minority students who have a strong interest in chemistry and a desire to prepare for a career in a chemically-related science.

Eligibility This program is open to 1) college-bound high school seniors; 2) freshmen, sophomores, and juniors enrolled full time at an accredited college or university; 3) community college students planning to transfer to a 4-year school; and 4) community college students working on a 2-year degree. Applicants must be African American, Hispanic/Latino, or Native American. They must be majoring or planning to major in chemistry, biochemistry, chemical engineering, or other chemically-related fields, such as environmental science, materials science, or toxicology, in preparation for a career in the chemical sciences or chemical technology. Students planning careers in medicine or pharmacy are not eligible. U.S. citizenship or permanent resident status is required. Selection is based on academic record (GPA of 3.0 or higher), career objective, leadership ability, participation in school activities, community service, and financial need.

Financial data Annual stipends are $2,500 for freshmen, $3,000 for sophomores, or $5,000 for seniors. Funds are sent directly to the recipient's college or university.

Duration 1 year; may be renewed.

Additional information This program began in 1994.

Number awarded Approximately 135 new awards are granted each year.

Deadline February of each year.

[34] AMERICAN HEALTH INFORMATION MANAGEMENT ASSOCIATION FOUNDATION DIVERSITY SCHOLARSHIPS

American Health Information Management Association
Attn: AHIMA Foundation
233 North Michigan Avenue, 21st Floor
Chicago, IL 60601-5809
(312) 233-1175 Fax: (312) 233-1475
E-mail: info@ahimafoundation.org
Web: www.ahimafoundation.org

Summary To provide financial assistance to African American and other members of the American Health Information Management Association (AHIMA) who are interested in working on an undergraduate or graduate degree in health information management (HIM) or health information technology (HIT) and will contribute to diversity in the profession.

Eligibility This program is open to AHIMA members who are enrolled at least half time in a program accredited by the Commission on Accreditation for Health Informatics and Information Management Education (CAHIM). Applicants must be working on a degree in HIM or HIT at the associate, bachelor's, post-baccalaureate, master's, or doctoral level. They must have a GPA of 3.5 or higher and at least 1 full semester remaining after the date of the award. To qualify for this support, applicants must demonstrate how they will contribute to diversity in the health information management profession; diversity is defined as differences in race, ethnicity, nationality, gender, sexual orientation, socioeconomic status, age, physical capabilities, and religious beliefs. Selection is based on GPA and academic achievement, volunteer and work experience, commitment to the HIM profession, quality and relevance of references, and completeness and clarity of thought.

Financial data Stipends are $1,000 for associate degree students, $1,500 for bachelor's degree or post-baccalaureate certificate students, $2,000 for master's degree students, or $2,500 for doctoral degree students.

Duration 1 year.

Number awarded Varies each year; recently, 9 of these scholarships were awarded: 6 to undergraduates and 3 to graduate students.

Deadline September of each year.

[35] AMERICAN INSTITUTE OF ARCHITECTS MINORITY/DISADVANTAGED SCHOLARSHIP PROGRAM

American Institute of Architects
Attn: American Architectural Foundation
1799 New York Avenue, N.W.
Washington, DC 20006-5292
(202) 626-7511 Fax: (202) 626-7420
E-mail: scholarships@aia.org
Web: www.aia.org/education/aiab081881

Summary To provide financial assistance to African American and other high school and college students from minority and/or disadvantaged backgrounds who are interested in studying architecture in college.

Eligibility This program is open to students from minority and/or disadvantaged backgrounds who are high school seniors, students in a community college or technical school transferring to an accredited architectural program, or college freshmen entering a professional degree program at an accredited program of architecture. Students who have completed 1 or more years of a 4-year college curriculum are not eligible. Initially, candidates must be nominated by 1 of the following organizations or persons: an individual architect or firm, a chapter of the American Institute of Architects (AIA), a community design center, a guidance counselor or teacher, the dean or professor at an accredited school of architecture, or the director of a community or civic organization. Nominees are reviewed and eligible candidates are invited to complete an application form in which they write an essay describing the reasons they are interested in becoming an architect and provide documentation of academic excellence and financial need. Selection is based primarily on financial need.

Financial data Stipends range from $3,000 to $4,000 per year, depending upon individual need. Students must apply for supplementary funds from other sources.

Duration 9 months; may be renewed for up to 2 additional years.

Additional information This program, established in 1970, is offered jointly by the American Architectural Foundation (AAF) and the AIA.

Number awarded Up to 5 each year.

Deadline April of each year.

[36]
AMERICAN METEOROLOGICAL SOCIETY INDUSTRY MINORITY SCHOLARSHIPS

American Meteorological Society
Attn: Development and Student Program Manager
45 Beacon Street
Boston, MA 02108-3693
(617) 227-2426, ext. 3907 Fax: (617) 742-8718
E-mail: dFernandez@ametsoc.org
Web: www.ametsoc.org

Summary To provide financial assistance to African Americans and other underrepresented minority students entering college and planning to major in meteorology or an aspect of atmospheric sciences.

Eligibility This program is open to members of minority groups traditionally underrepresented in the sciences (especially Hispanics, Native Americans, and Blacks/African Americans) who are entering their freshman year at a college or university and planning to work on a degree in the atmospheric or related oceanic and hydrologic sciences. Applicants must submit an official high school transcript showing grades from the past 3 years, a letter of recommendation from a high school teacher or guidance counselor, a copy of scores from an SAT or similar national entrance exam, and a 500-word essay on a topic that changes annually; recently, applicants were invited to write on global change and how they would use their college education in atmospheric science (or a closely-related field) to make their community a better place in which to live. Selection is based on the essay and academic performance in high school.

Financial data The stipend is $3,000 per year.

Duration 1 year; may be renewed for the second year of college study.

Additional information This program is funded by grants from industry and by donations to the American Meteorological Society (AMS) 21st Century Campaign. Requests for an application must be accompanied by a self-addressed stamped envelope.

Number awarded Varies each year; recently, 5 of these scholarships were awarded.

Deadline February of each year.

[37]
AMERICAN METEOROLOGICAL SOCIETY NAMED SCHOLARSHIPS

American Meteorological Society
Attn: Development and Student Program Manager
45 Beacon Street
Boston, MA 02108-3693
(617) 227-2426, ext. 3907 Fax: (617) 742-8718
E-mail: dFernandez@ametsoc.org
Web: www.ametsoc.org

Summary To provide financial assistance to undergraduates (particularly African Americans, other minorities, women, and students with disabilities) who are majoring in meteorology or an aspect of atmospheric sciences.

Eligibility This program is open to full-time students entering their final year of undergraduate study and majoring in meteorology or an aspect of the atmospheric or related oceanic and hydrologic sciences. Applicants must intend to make atmospheric or related sciences their career. They must be U.S. citizens or permanent residents enrolled at a U.S. institution and have a cumulative GPA of 3.25 or higher. Along with their application, they must submit 200-word essays on 1) their most important attributes and achievements that qualify them for this scholarship; and 2) their career goals in the atmospheric or related sciences. Financial need is considered in the selection process. The sponsor specifically encourages applications from women, minorities, and students with disabilities who are traditionally underrepresented in the atmospheric and related sciences.

Financial data Stipend amounts vary each year.

Duration 1 year.

Additional information All scholarships awarded through this program are named after individuals who have assisted the sponsor in various ways.

Number awarded Varies each year; recently, 20 of these scholarships were awarded.

Deadline February of each year.

[38]
AMERICAN PLANNING ASSOCIATION/JUDITH MCMANUS PRICE SCHOLARSHIPS

American Planning Association
Attn: Leadership Affairs Associate
205 North Michigan Avenue, Suite 1200
Chicago, IL 60601
(312) 431-9100 Fax: (312) 786-6700
E-mail: fellowship@planning.org
Web: www.planning.org/scholarships/apa

Summary To provide financial assistance to African Americans, other underrepresented minority students, and women enrolled in undergraduate or graduate degree programs at recognized planning schools.

Eligibility This program is open to undergraduate and graduate students in urban and regional planning who are women or members of the following minority groups: African American, Hispanic American, or Native American. Applicants must be citizens of the United States and able to document financial need. They must intend to work as practicing planners in the public sector. Along with their application, they must submit a 2-page personal and background statement describing how their education will be applied to career goals and why they chose planning as a career path. Selection is based (in order of importance), on: 1) commitment to planning as reflected in their personal statement and on their resume; 2) academic achievement and/or improvement during the past 2 years; 3) letters of recommendation; 4) financial need; and 5) professional presentation.

Financial data Stipends range from $2,000 to $4,000 per year. The money may be applied to tuition and living expenses only. Payment is made to the recipient's university and divided by terms in the school year.

Duration 1 year; recipients may reapply.

Additional information This program began in 2002.

Number awarded Varies each year; recently, 3 of these scholarships were awarded.

Deadline April of each year.

[39]
AMERICAN SOCIETY OF SAFETY ENGINEERS/ BLACKS IN SAFETY ENGINEERING SCHOLARSHIP

American Society of Safety Engineers
Attn: ASSE Foundation
Scholarship Award Program
1800 East Oakton Street
Des Plaines, IL 60018
(847) 699-2929 Fax: (847) 768-3434
E-mail: bzylstra@asse.org
Web: www.asse.org

Summary To provide financial assistance to upper-division students, especially Blacks, who are working on a degree related to occupational safety.

Eligibility This program is open to students who are majoring in occupational safety, health, environment, industrial hygiene, occupational health nursing, or a closely-related field (e.g., industrial or environmental engineering). Priority is given to students who are Black. Applicants must be full-time students who have completed at least 60 semester hours with a GPA of 3.0 or higher. U.S. citizenship is not required. Membership in the American Society of Safety Engineers (ASSE) is not required, but preference is given to members.

Financial data The stipend is $1,000 per year.

Duration 1 year; recipients may reapply.

Number awarded 1 each year.

Deadline November of each year.

[40]
AMERICAN SYSTEMS HBCU SCHOLARSHIPS

Armed Forces Communications and Electronics Association
Attn: AFCEA Educational Foundation
4400 Fair Lakes Court
Fairfax, VA 22033-3899
(703) 631-6138 Toll Free: (800) 336-4583, ext. 6138
Fax: (703) 631-4693 E-mail: scholarshipsinfo@afcea.org
Web: www.afcea.org

Summary To provide funding to students majoring in fields of science, technology, engineering, or mathematics (STEM) at an Historically Black College or University (HBCU).

Eligibility This program is open to sophomores and juniors enrolled full time at an accredited 2- or 4-year HBCU or in a distance learning or online degree program affiliated with those institutions. They must be working toward a bachelor's degree in such STEM fields as engineering (aerospace, computer, electrical, or systems), computer science, computer engineering technology, computer information systems, mathematics, physics, information systems management, or other field directly related to the support of U.S. intelligence or homeland security enterprises. Special consideration is given to military enlisted personnel and veterans.

Financial data The stipend is $5,000.

Duration 1 year; may be renewed.

Additional information This program began in 2010 with support from American Systems.

Number awarded At least 2 each year.

Deadline April of each year.

[41]
AMS FRESHMAN UNDERGRADUATE SCHOLARSHIPS

American Meteorological Society
Attn: Development and Student Program Manager
45 Beacon Street
Boston, MA 02108-3693
(617) 227-2426, ext. 3907 Fax: (617) 742-8718
E-mail: dFernandez@ametsoc.org
Web: www.ametsoc.org

Summary To provide financial assistance to high school seniors (particularly African Americans, other minorities, women, and individuals with disabilities) who are planning to attend college to prepare for a career in the atmospheric or related oceanic or hydrologic sciences.

Eligibility This program is open to high school seniors entering their freshman year of college to work on a bachelor's degree in the atmospheric or related oceanic or hydrologic sciences. Applicants must be U.S. citizens or permanent residents planning to enroll full time. Along with their application, they must submit a 500-word essay on how they believe their college education, and what they learn in the atmospheric and related sciences, will help them to serve society during their professional career. Selection is based on performance in high school, including academic records, recommendations, scores from a national examination, and the essay. Financial need is not considered. The sponsor specifically encourages applications from women, minorities, and students with disabilities who are traditionally underrepresented in the atmospheric and related oceanic sciences.

Financial data The stipend is $2,500 per academic year.

Duration 1 year; may be renewed for the second year of college study.

Number awarded Varies each year; recently, 14 of these scholarships were awarded.

Deadline February of each year.

[42]
ANA MULTICULTURAL EXCELLENCE FUND

American Association of Advertising Agencies
Attn: AAAA Foundation
1065 Avenue of the Americas, 16th Floor
New York, NY 10018
(212) 262-2500 E-mail: ameadows@aaaa.org
Web: www.aaaa.org

Summary To provide financial assistance to African American and other multicultural students who are working on an undergraduate degree in advertising.

Eligibility This program is open to undergraduate students who are U.S. citizens of proven multicultural heritage and have at least 1 grandparent of multicultural heritage. Applicants must be participating in the Multicultural Advertising Intern Program (MAIP). They must be entering their senior year at an accredited college or university in the United States and have a GPA of 3.0 or higher. Selection is based on academic ability.

Financial data The stipend is $2,500.

Duration 1 year.

Additional information This program was established by the Association of National Advertisers (ANA) in 2001. The American Association of Advertising Agencies (AAAA) assumed administration in 2003.

Number awarded 2 each year.

Deadline Deadline not specified.

[43]
ANGELA DUCKER-RICHARDSON MEMORIAL SCHOLARSHIP IN HEALTH AND SCIENCE

Alpha Kappa Alpha Sorority, Inc.-Rho Mu Omega Chapter
Attn: DC Pearls III Foundation
Program Chair
P.O. Box 91436
Washington, DC 20090-1436
E-mail: programs@rhomuomega.org
Web: www.whomuomega.org/scholarship

Summary To provide financial assistance to high school seniors in Washington, D.C. who plan to attend an Historically Black College or University (HBCU) and major in health or science.

Eligibility This program is open to seniors graduating from high schools in Washington, D.C. and planning to attend an HBCU. Applicants must be majoring in health or science.

Financial data The stipend is $1,000.

Duration 1 year.

Number awarded 1 each year.

Deadline March of each year.

[44]
ANN MCALLISTER HUGHES FOUNDATION FELLOWSHIP

Alpha Kappa Alpha Sorority, Inc.
Attn: Educational Advancement Foundation
5656 South Stony Island Avenue
Chicago, IL 60637
(773) 947-0026 Toll Free: (800) 653-6528
Fax: (773) 947-0277 E-mail: akaeaf@akaeaf.net
Web: www.akaeaf.org/fellowships_endowments.htm

Summary To provide financial assistance to undergraduates (especially African American women) who are working on a degree in art.

Eligibility This program is open to undergraduate students who are enrolled full time as sophomores or higher in an accredited degree-granting institution in any state. Applicants must be majoring in art. Along with their application, they must submit 1) a list of honors, awards, and scholarships received; 2) a list of organizations in which they have memberships, especially minority organizations; and 3) a statement of their personal and career goals, including how this scholarship will enhance their ability to attain those goals. The sponsor is a traditionally African American women's sorority.

Financial data A stipend is awarded (amount not specified).

Duration 1 year.

Number awarded 1 or more each even-numbered year.

Deadline April of each even-numbered year.

[45]
ANNA M. WINSTON AWARD

National Association of Black Accountants
Attn: National Scholarship Program
7474 Greenway Center Drive, Suite 1120
Greenbelt, MD 20770
(301) 474-NABA Fax: (301) 474-3114
E-mail: scholarships@nabainc.org
Web: www.nabainc.org

Summary To provide financial assistance to student members of the National Association of Black Accountants (NABA) who are attending an Historically Black College or University (HBCU) to work on an undergraduate or graduate degree in a field related to accounting.

Eligibility This program is open to minorities who are NABA members and enrolled full time as 1) an undergraduate freshman, sophomore, junior, or first-semester senior majoring in accounting, business, or finance at an HBCU; or 2) a graduate student working on a master's degree in accounting at an HBCU. High school seniors are not eligible. Applicants must have a GPA of 2.0 or higher in their major and 2.5 or higher overall. Along with their application, they must submit a 500-word personal statement on their involvement in NABA, career objectives, leadership abilities, and community activities. Financial need is not considered in the selection process.

Financial data The stipend ranges from $500 to $1,000.

Duration 1 year.

Additional information Applicants for this scholarship are required to sign a pledge form with a promise to fund it within 5 years of graduation from college.

Number awarded 1 each year.

Deadline January of each year.

[46]
ANS/ACCELERATOR APPLICATIONS DIVISION SCHOLARSHIP

American Nuclear Society
Attn: Scholarship Coordinator
555 North Kensington Avenue
La Grange Park, IL 60526-5535
(708) 352-6611 Toll Free: (800) 323-3044
Fax: (708) 352-0499 E-mail: outreach@ans.org
Web: www.new.ans.org/honors/scholarships

Summary To provide financial assistance to undergraduate students (particularly African Americans or other minorities and women) who are interested in preparing for a career dealing with accelerator applications aspects of nuclear science or nuclear engineering.

Eligibility This program is open to students entering their junior year in physics, engineering, or materials science at an accredited institution in the United States. Applicants must submit a description of their long- and short-term professional objectives, including their research interests related to accelerator aspects of nuclear science and engineering. Selection is based on that statement, faculty recommendations, and academic performance. Special consideration is given to members of underrepresented groups (women and minorities), students who can demonstrate financial need, and applicants who have a record of service to the American Nuclear Society (ANS).

Financial data The stipend is $1,000 per year.

Duration 1 year (the junior year); may be renewed for the senior year.

Additional information This program is offered by the Accelerator Applications Division (AAD) of the ANS.

Number awarded 1 each year.

Deadline January of each year.

[47]
AP-GOOGLE JOURNALISM AND TECHNOLOGY SCHOLARSHIP PROGRAM

Online News Association
Attn: Scholarship Manager
P.O. Box 65741
Washington, DC 20035
(646) 290-7900 E-mail: irving@journalists.org
Web: journalists.org/next-gen/ap-google-scholarship

Summary To recognize and reward undergraduate and graduate students (especially African Americans and those from other diverse backgrounds) who propose outstanding projects "at the intersection of journalism and technology."

Eligibility This program is open to full-time undergraduates (at least sophomores) and graduate students at U.S. institutions who have at least 1 year of study remaining and a GPA of 3.0 or higher. Students from diverse backgrounds (defined as ethnic and racial minorities, members of the lesbian, gay, bisexual, and transgender (LGBT) community, and students with disabilities) and those attending rural area institutions are strongly encouraged to apply. Some scholarships are reserved for students who can demonstrate financial need. Applicants must develop original journalistic content with computer science elements; they should explain how their strategy moves digital journalism forward or provides valuable lessons or outcomes. Examples include data visualization, data mining, mobile devices and applications, 3-D storytelling, digital ethics, or microcomputers. In the selection process, emphasis is placed on innovation and creativity. U.S. citizenship is required.

Financial data The award is a $20,000 scholarship, of which half is paid to the winner's institution at the beginning of the first semester and half at the beginning of the second semester, provided the recipient earns a GPA of 3.0 or higher for the first semester.

Duration The competition is held annually.

Additional information This competition is supported by Google.

Number awarded 6 each year.

Deadline February of each year.

[48]
APPLE PROGRAM

American Psychological Association
Attn: Division 41 (American Psychology-Law Society)
c/o Jennifer Hunt, Minority Affairs Committee Chair
Buffalo State University of New York, Psychology Department
Classroom Building C308
1300 Elmwood Avenue
Buffalo, NY 14222
(716) 878-3421 E-mail: huntjs@buffalostate.edu
Web: www.ap-ls.org/grantsfunding/APPLEprogram.php?t=4

Summary To provide an opportunity for undergraduate students (particularly African Americans and members of other underrepresented groups) to gain research and other experience to prepare them for graduate work in psychology and law.

Eligibility This program is open to undergraduate students who are members of underrepresented groups, including, but are not limited to, racial and ethnic minorities; first-generation college students; lesbian, gay, bisexual, and transgender students; and physically disabled students. Applicants must be interested in participating in a program in which they work on research for approximately 10 hours per week; participate in GRE classes and/or other development opportunities; attend a conference of the American Psychology-Law Society (AP-LS); submit a proposal to present their research at an AP-LS conference or in the Division 41 program of an American Psychological Association (APA) conference; submit a summary of their research experience to the AP-LS Minority Affairs Committee chair within 1 month of its completion; and correspond with a secondary mentor from the Minority Affairs Committee to participate in the ongoing assessment of this program. Selection is based on the quality of the proposed research and mentoring experience and the potential for the student to become a successful graduate student.

Financial data Grants range up to $3,000, including a stipend of $1,200 per semester or $800 per quarter or summer, $100 for research expenses, and up to $500 to attend the AP-LS conference.

Duration Up to 1 year.

Additional information The abbreviation APPLE in the program title stands for Access Path to Psychology and Law Experience.

Number awarded 5 each year.

Deadline November of each year.

[49]
APPRAISAL INSTITUTE MINORITIES AND WOMEN EDUCATIONAL SCHOLARSHIP PROGRAM

Appraisal Institute
Attn: Appraisal Institute Education Trust
200 West Madison Street, Suite 1500
Chicago, IL 60606
(312) 335-4133 Fax: (312) 335-4134
E-mail: educationtrust@appraisalinstitute.org
Web: www.appraisalinstitute.org

Summary To provide financial assistance to African American, other minority, and women undergraduate students majoring in real estate or allied fields.

Eligibility This program is open to members of groups underrepresented in the real estate appraisal profession. Those groups include women, American Indians, Alaska Natives, Asians and Pacific Islanders, Blacks or African Americans, and Hispanics. Applicants must be full- or part-time students enrolled in real estate courses within a degree-granting college, university, or junior college. They must have a GPA of 2.5 or higher and be able to demonstrate financial need. U.S. citizenship is required.

Financial data The stipend is $1,000. Funds are paid directly to the recipient's institution to be used for tuition and fees.

Duration 1 year.

Number awarded At least 1 each year.

Deadline April of each year.

[50]
APS SCHOLARSHIPS FOR MINORITY UNDERGRADUATE PHYSICS MAJORS

American Physical Society
Attn: Committee on Minorities
One Physics Ellipse
College Park, MD 20740-3844
(301) 209-3232 Fax: (301) 209-0865
Web: www.aps.org

Summary To provide financial assistance to African American and other underrepresented minority students interested in studying physics on the undergraduate level.

Eligibility Any African American, Hispanic American, or Native American who plans to major in physics and who is a high school senior or college freshman or sophomore may apply. U.S. citizenship or permanent resident status is required. The selection committee especially encourages applications from students who are attending or planning to attend institutions with historically or predominantly Black, Hispanic, or Native American enrollment. Selection is based on commitment to the study of physics and plans to work on a physics baccalaureate degree.

Financial data Stipends are $2,000 per year in the first year or $3,000 in the second year; funds must be used for tuition, room, and board. In addition, $500 is awarded to the host department.

Duration 1 year; renewable for 1 additional year with the approval of the APS selection committee.

Additional information APS conducts this program, which began in 1980 as the Corporate-Sponsored Scholarships for Minority Undergraduate Students Who Major in Physics, in conjunction with the Corporate Associates of the American Institute of Physics. Each scholarship is sponsored by a corporation, which is normally designated as the sponsor. A corporation generally sponsors from 1 to 10 scholarships, depending upon its size and utilization of physics in the business.

Number awarded Varies each year; recently, 39 of these scholarships were awarded.

Deadline January of each year.

[51]
ARKANSAS SPACE GRANT CONSORTIUM STEM MAJORS UNDERREPRESENTED MINORITY STUDENT SCHOLARSHIPS

Arkansas Space Grant Consortium
c/o University of Arkansas at Little Rock
Graduate Institute of Technology
2801 South University Avenue
Little Rock, AR 72204
(501) 569-8212 Fax: (501) 569-8039
E-mail: asgc@ualr.edu
Web: asgc.ualr.edu/documents

Summary To provide funding to African American and other underrepresented minority students at designated universities in Arkansas who are interested in working on a space-related project in fields of science, technology, engineering, and mathematics (STEM).

Eligibility This program is open to African American, Hispanic, and Native American undergraduate students at colleges and universities that participate in the Arkansas Space Grant Consortium (ASGC). Applicants must be interested in developing a project in fields of STEM that have relevance to the work of the U.S. National Aeronautics and Space Administration (NASA). Students must be U.S. citizens and have a GPA of 2.0 or higher.

Financial data The grant is $2,000. An additional $500 is available to support travel for each project.

Additional information ASGC member institutions are Arkansas State University, Arkansas Tech University, Harding University, Henderson State University, Hendrix College, Lyon College, Ouachita Baptist University, Southern Arkansas University, University of Arkansas at Fayetteville, University of Arkansas at Fort Smith, University of Arkansas at Little Rock, University of Arkansas at Montecito, University of Arkansas at Pine Bluff, University of Arkansas for Medical Sciences, University of Central Arkansas, and University of the Ozarks. This program is funded by NASA.

Number awarded Varies each year.

Deadline Applications may be submitted at any time. Grants are awarded until funds are exhausted.

[52]
ARKANSAS SPACE GRANT CONSORTIUM STEM TEACHING MAJORS UNDERREPRESENTED MINORITY STUDENT SCHOLARSHIPS

Arkansas Space Grant Consortium
c/o University of Arkansas at Little Rock
Graduate Institute of Technology
2801 South University Avenue
Little Rock, AR 72204
(501) 569-8212 Fax: (501) 569-8039
E-mail: asgc@ualr.edu
Web: asgc.ualr.edu/documents

Summary To provide funding to African American and other underrepresented minority students at designated universities in Arkansas who are interested in working on a space-related educational project in fields of science, technology, engineering, and mathematics (STEM).

Eligibility This program is open to African American, Hispanic, and Native American undergraduate students at colleges and universities that participate in the Arkansas Space Grant Consortium (ASGC). Applicants must be planning a career in STEM related disciplines at either the K-12 or college level. They must be interested in developing an educational project and/or curricula in fields of STEM that have relevance to the work of the U.S. National Aeronautics and Space Administration (NASA). Students must be U.S. citizens and have a GPA of 2.0 or higher.

Financial data The grant is $2,000. An additional $500 is available to support travel for each project.

Additional information ASGC member institutions are Arkansas State University, Arkansas Tech University, Harding University, Henderson State University, Hendrix College, Lyon College, Ouachita Baptist University, Southern Arkansas University, University of Arkansas at Fayetteville, University of Arkansas at Fort Smith, University of Arkansas at Little Rock, University of Arkansas at Montecito, University of Arkansas at Pine Bluff, University of Arkansas for Medical Sciences, University of Central Arkansas, and University of the Ozarks. This program is funded by NASA.

Number awarded Varies each year.

Deadline Applications may be submitted at any time. Grants are awarded until funds are exhausted.

[53]
ARTHUR B.C. WALKER SCHOLARSHIP

National Society of Black Physicists
Attn: Scholarship Committee Chair
1100 North Glebe Road, Suite 1010
Arlington, VA 22201
(703) 536-4207 Fax: (703) 536-4203
E-mail: scholarship@nsbp.org
Web: www.nsbp.org/scholarships

Summary To provide financial assistance to African American students majoring in physics in college.

Eligibility This program is open to African American students who are entering their junior or senior year of college and majoring in physics. Applicants must submit an essay on their academic and career objectives, information on their participation in extracurricular activities, a description of any awards and honors they have received, and 3 letters of recommendation. Financial need is not considered.

Financial data The stipend is $1,000.

Duration 1 year; nonrenewable.

Number awarded 1 each year.

Deadline November of each year.

[54]
ARTHUR H. GOODMAN MEMORIAL SCHOLARSHIPS

CDC Small Business Finance
Attn: Scholarship Program
2448 Historic Decatur Road, Suite 200
San Diego, CA 92106
(619) 291-3594 Toll Free: (800) 611-5170
Fax: (619) 291-6954
Web: cdcloans.com

Summary To provide financial assistance to African Americans, other minorities, and women who are transitioning from a community college in California or Arizona to a 4-year university in those states and interested in preparing for a career related to community development.

Eligibility This program is open to women and minorities who are residents of or attending school in California. Applicants must have completed 2 years of community college study with a GPA of 3.0 or higher and be ready to transfer to a 4-year college or university. They must be interested in preparing for a career in business, government, nonprofit, public service, or other profession that will improve their community. Along with their application, they must submit a 3-page personal statement on their community involvement and volunteerism, why they volunteer, how it has influenced them personally and their career goals, how their volunteerism has impacted individuals or the community, an individual or event that has influenced their decision to attend college and/or select their desired career, their future goals and how they include community involvement, and why they feel they are a strong candidate for this scholarship. Financial need is considered in the selection process.

Financial data Stipends range from $1,500 to $3,000.

Duration 1 year.

Additional information This program began in 1998 with a fund administered through the San Diego Foundation.

Number awarded Approximately 4 each year.

Deadline May of each year.

[55]
ASCPA EDUCATIONAL FOUNDATION DIVERSITY SCHOLARSHIPS

Alabama Society of Certified Public Accountants
Attn: ASCPA Educational Foundation
1103 South Perry Street
P.O. Box 5000
Montgomery, AL 36103
(334) 834-7650 Toll Free: (800) 227-1711
Web: www.ascpa.org

Summary To provide financial assistance to African American and other minority accounting students at colleges and universities in Alabama.

Eligibility This program is open to minority (Black or African American, Hispanic or Latino, Native American, or Asian) residents of any state enrolled at least half time at colleges and universities in Alabama with at least 1 full year of school remaining. Applicants must have declared a major in accounting and have completed intermediate accounting courses. They must have a GPA of 3.0 or higher overall and in all accounting classes. Along with their application, they must submit a 25-word essay on why the scholarship is important to them. Financial need is not considered in the selection process. Preference is given to students who have a strong interest in a career as a C.P.A. in Alabama. U.S. citizenship or permanent resident status is required.

Financial data The stipend is $2,500.

Duration 1 year.

Additional information This program began in 2012.

Number awarded 4 each year.

Deadline March of each year.

[56]
ASLA COUNCIL OF FELLOWS SCHOLARSHIPS

Landscape Architecture Foundation
Attn: Leadership in Landscape Scholarship Program
818 18th Street, N.W., Suite 810
Washington, DC 20006-3520
(202) 331-7070 Fax: (202) 331-7079
E-mail: scholarships@lafoundation.org
Web: www.lafoundation.org

Summary To provide financial assistance to upper-division students, especially African Americans and those from other disadvantaged and underrepresented groups, who are working on a degree in landscape architecture.

Eligibility This program is open to landscape architecture students in the third, fourth, or fifth year of undergraduate work. Preference is given to, and 1 scholarship is reserved for, members of underrepresented ethnic or cultural groups. Applicants must submit a 500-word essay on how they envision themselves contributing to the profession of landscape architecture, 2 letters of recommendation, documentation of financial need, and (for students applying for the scholarship reserved for underrepresented groups) a statement identifying their association with a specific ethnic or cultural group. U.S. citizenship or permanent resident status is required.

Financial data The stipend is $4,000. Students also receive a 1-year membership in the American Society of Landscape Architects (ASLA), general registration fees for the ASLA annual meeting, and a travel stipend to attend the meeting.

Duration 1 year.

Additional information This program is sponsored by ASLA and administered by the Landscape Architecture Foundation.

Number awarded 2 each year, of which 1 is reserved for a member of an underrepresented group.

Deadline February of each year.

[57]
ASSE UPS DIVERSITY SCHOLARSHIPS

American Society of Safety Engineers
Attn: ASSE Foundation
Scholarship Award Program
1800 East Oakton Street
Des Plaines, IL 60018
(847) 699-2929 Fax: (847) 768-3434
E-mail: bzylstra@asse.org
Web: www.asse.org

Summary To provide financial assistance to African American and other minority upper-division students working on a degree related to occupational safety.

Eligibility This program is open to students who are U.S. citizens and members of minority ethnic or racial groups. Applicants must be majoring in occupational safety, health, environment, industrial hygiene, occupational health nursing, or a closely-related field (e.g., industrial or environmental engineering). They must be full-time students who have completed at least 60 semester hours with a GPA of 3.0 or higher. Membership in the American Society of Safety Engineers (ASSE) is not required, but preference is given to members.

Financial data The stipend is $5,250 per year.

Duration 1 year; recipients may reapply.

Additional information Funding for this program is provided by the UPS Foundation. Recipients may also be provided with the opportunity to attend a professional development conference related to safety.

Number awarded 3 each year.

Deadline November of each year.

[58]
ASSOCIATION FOR WOMEN GEOSCIENTISTS MINORITY SCHOLARSHIP

Association for Women Geoscientists
Attn: AWG Foundation
12000 North Washington Street, Suite 285
Thornton, CO 80241
(303) 412-6219 Fax: (303) 253-9220
E-mail: minorityscholarship@awg.org
Web: www.awg.org/EAS/scholarships.html

Summary To provide financial assistance to African American and other underrepresented minority women who are interested in working on an undergraduate degree in the geosciences.

Eligibility This program is open to women who are African American, Hispanic, or Native American (including Eskimo, Hawaiian, Samoan, or American Indian). Applicants must be full-time students working on, or planning to work on, an undergraduate degree in the geosciences (including geology, geophysics, geochemistry, hydrology, meteorology, physical oceanography, planetary geology, or earth science education). They must submit a 500-word essay on their academic and career goals, 2 letters of recommendation, high school and/or college transcripts, and SAT or ACT scores. Financial need is not considered in the selection process. U.S. citizenship is required.

Financial data A total of $6,000 is available for this program each year.

Duration 1 year; may be renewed.

Additional information This program, first offered in 2004, is supported by ExxonMobil Foundation.

Number awarded 1 or more each year.

Deadline June of each year.

[59]
ATKINS NORTH AMERICA ACHIEVEMENT SCHOLARSHIP

Conference of Minority Transportation Officials
Attn: National Scholarship Program
1875 I Street, N.W., Suite 500
Washington, DC 20006
(703) 234-4072 Fax: (202) 318-0364
Web: www.comto.org/?page=Scholarships

Summary To provide financial assistance to African American and other minority high school seniors and undergraduates interested in working on a degree in transportation or a related field.

Eligibility This program is open to seniors graduating from high school with a GPA of 3.0 or higher and students currently enrolled as full-time undergraduates. Applicants must be studying or planning to study transportation, engineering, planning, management, or a related discipline They must be able to demonstrate leadership and active commitment to community service. Along with their application, they must submit a cover letter with a 500-word statement of career goals. Financial need is not considered in the selection process. U.S. citizenship or legal resident status is required.

Financial data The stipend is $2,000. Funds are paid directly to the recipient's college or university.

Duration 1 year.

Additional information The Conference of Minority Transportation Officials (COMTO) was established in 1971 to promote, strengthen, and expand the roles of minorities in all aspects of transportation. This program is sponsored by Atkins North America. Recipients are expected to attend the COMTO National Scholarship Luncheon.

Number awarded 1 each year.

Deadline May of each year.

[60]
ATKINS TRANSPORTATION YOU HIGH SCHOOL SCHOLARSHIP

Women's Transportation Seminar
Attn: WTS Foundation
1701 K Street, N.W., Suite 800
Washington, DC 20006
(202) 955-5085 Fax: (202) 955-5088
E-mail: wts@wtsinternational.org
Web: www.wtsinternational.org/education/scholarships

Summary To provide financial assistance to female high school seniors (particularly African American and other minority women) who are studying fields of science, technology, engineering, or mathematics (STEM) and planning to attend college to prepare for a career in transportation.

Eligibility This program is open to women who are high school seniors with a GPA of 3.0 or higher. Applicants must be studying STEM fields in high school and be planning to attend college to prepare for a career in transportation (e.g., civil engineering, city planning, logistics, automotive engineering, truck repair). Along with their application, they must submit a 500-word statement about their career goals after graduation and why they think they should receive the scholarship. Applications must be submitted first to a local chapter; the chapters forward selected applications for consideration on the national level. Minority women are especially encouraged to apply. Selection is based on transportation involvement and goals, job skills, academic record, and leadership potential; financial need is not considered.

Financial data The stipend is $1,000.

Duration 1 year.

Additional information Local chapters may also award additional funding to winners for their area.

Number awarded 1 each year.

Deadline Applications must be submitted by November to a local WTS chapter.

[61]
ATLANTA JAMAICAN ASSOCIATION SCHOLARSHIP

Atlanta Jamaican Association
Attn: Scholarship Committee
P.O. Box 2207
Lithonia, GA 30058
(678) 549-4876 E-mail: secretary@ajaatlanta.org
Web: www.ajaatlanta.org/Scholarship.aspx

Summary To provide financial assistance for college to high school seniors and current undergraduates who are of Jamaican heritage.

Eligibility This program is open to high school seniors and currently-enrolled undergraduates who live in any state and are of Jamaican parentage (at least 1 parent must be Jamaican). Applicants must be attending or planning to attend a 2- or 4-year college or university. They must have a GPA of 3.0 or higher. Along with their application, they must submit a 500-word essay on a topic that changes annually but relates to Jamaica; recently, students were invited to write on the proposal of the government of Jamaica to remove the Queen as Head of State. Finalists are interviewed.

Financial data A stipend is awarded (amount not specified).

Duration 1 year.

Additional information This program began in 1995.

Number awarded 1 or more each year.

Deadline April of each year.

[62]
AVIATION AND PROFESSIONAL DEVELOPMENT SCHOLARSHIPS

Airport Minority Advisory Council
Attn: AMAC Educational and Scholarship Program, Inc.
2001 Jefferson Davis Highway, Suite 500
Arlington, VA 22202
(703) 414-2622, ext. 4 Fax: (703) 414-2686
E-mail: aaron.pope@amac-org.com
Web: www.amac-org.com/scholarships.html

Summary To provide financial assistance to African American and other minority high school seniors and undergraduates who are preparing for a career in the aviation industry and are interested in participating in the Airport Minority Advisory Council (AMAC).

Eligibility This program is open to high school seniors and current undergraduates who have a GPA of 2.5 or higher and a record of involvement in community and extracurricular activities. Applicants must be working on a bachelor's degree in accounting, architecture, aviation, business administration, engineering, or finance as preparation for a career in the aviation or airport industry. They must have an endorsement from a current AMAC member and be willing to be involved in AMAC (e.g., by becoming a member if they are awarded a scholarship and communicating with AMAC once each semester during the term of the scholarship). Along with their application, they must submit a 1-page essay on their career goals and why they have chosen their particular field of study. Financial need is not considered in the selection process. U.S. citizenship is required.

Financial data The stipend is $2,000 per year.

Duration 1 year; recipients may reapply.

Number awarded 4 each semester.

Deadline August of each year for spring semester; April of each year for spring semester.

[63]
BACCALAUREATE (DIDACTIC OR COORDINATED PROGRAM) SCHOLARSHIPS

Academy of Nutrition and Dietetics
Attn: Foundation
120 South Riverside Plaza, Suite 2000
Chicago, IL 60606-6995
(312) 899-0040 Toll Free: (800) 877-1600, ext. 1133
Fax: (312) 899-4817 E-mail: scholarships@eatright.org
Web: www.eatright.org/Foundation/scholarships

Summary To provide financial assistance to underrepresented minorities and other undergraduate student members of the Academy of Nutrition and Dietetics.

Eligibility This program is open to A.N.D members enrolled at a CADE-accredited/approved college or university program for at least junior status in the dietetics program. Applicants must be U.S. citizens or permanent residents and show promise of being a valuable, contributing member of the profession. Some scholarships require membership in a specific dietetic practice group, residency in a specific state, or underrepresented minority group status. The same application form can be used for all categories.

Financial data Stipends normally range from $500 to $3,000; recently, they averaged approximately $1,870.

Duration 1 year.

Additional information The Academy of Nutrition and Dietetics was formerly the American Dietetic Association.

Number awarded Between 30 and 35 each year.

Deadline February of each year.

[64]
BARBARA JORDAN MEMORIAL SCHOLARSHIPS

Association of Texas Professional Educators
Attn: ATPE Foundation
305 East Huntland Drive, Suite 300
Austin, TX 78752-3792
Toll Free: (800) 777-ATPE Fax: (512) 302-5884
E-mail: admin@atpefoundation.org
Web: www.atpefoundation.org/scholarships.asp

Summary To provide financial assistance to upper-division and graduate students from any state who are enrolled in educator preparation programs at predominantly ethnic minority institutions in Texas.

Eligibility This program is open to juniors, seniors, and graduate students from any state who are enrolled in educator preparation programs at predominantly ethnic minority institutions in Texas. Applicants must submit a 2-page essay on their personal educational philosophy, why they want to become an educator, who influenced them the most in making their career decision, and why they are applying for the scholarship. Financial need is not considered in the selection process.

Financial data The stipend is $1,500.

Duration 1 year.

Additional information The qualifying institutions are Huston-Tillotson College, Jarvis Christian College, Our Lady of the Lake University, Paul Quinn College, Prairie View A&M University, St. Mary's University of San Antonio, Sul Ross State University, Sul Ross State University Rio Grande College, Texas A&M International University, Texas A&M University at Kingsville, Texas Southern University, University of Houston, University of Houston-Downtown, University of Texas at Brownsville and Texas Southmost College, University of Texas at El Paso, University of Texas at San Antonio, University of Texas-Pan American, University of the Incarnate Word, and Wiley College.

Number awarded Up to 6 each year.

Deadline May of each year.

[65]
BARBARA TOBE SCHOLARSHIPS

Blacks in Government-National Oceanic and Atmospheric Administration Chapter
Attn: Scholarship Committee Chair
P.O. Box 14361
Silver Spring, MD 20911-0361
(301) 713-9667 Fax: (301) 713-0372
Web: noaabig.org

Summary To provide financial assistance to African Americans who are either high school seniors in the Washington, D.C. metropolitan area or the family of employees of the U.S. National Oceanic and Atmospheric Administration (NOAA) and planning to major in selected fields in college.

Eligibility This program is open to African American high school seniors who are either attending a selected high school in the Washington, D.C. area or the family member of NOAA employees and living in that area. Applicants must be planning to attend college in any state to major or minor in a field that relates to the oceans or the atmosphere or that supports the NOAA administrative or managerial infrastructure; eligible academic disciplines include the sciences (biology, physics, chemistry, oceanography, atmospheric sciences, or meteorology), mathematics, computer science, engineering, information or management technology, business, management, administration, contracts, law, aviation, geography, medicine, or related fields. They must have a GPA of 3.0 or higher, a record of participation in school activities, demonstrated leadership abilities, involvement in community outreach activities, special talents and awards, and good moral character. Eligible graduating seniors include those at the 2 high schools in the area selected by the sponsor each year.

Eligible family members include children, grandchildren, nieces, nephews, foster children, and custodial children.

Financial data The stipend is $1,000.

Duration 1 year.

Additional information This program began in 1996.

Number awarded 1 or more each year.

Deadline June of each year.

[66]
BATTELLE COLLEGIATE NSBE SCHOLARSHIPS

National Society of Black Engineers
Attn: Programs Department
205 Daingerfield Road
Alexandria, VA 22314
(703) 549-2207 Fax: (703) 683-5312
E-mail: scholarships@nsbe.org
Web: www.nsbe.org/Programs/Scholarships.aspx

Summary To provide financial aid and summer work experience to undergraduate student members of the National Society of Black Engineers (NSBE) who are working on a degree in designated fields of science or engineering.

Eligibility This program is open to members of the society who are entering their junior or senior year of college. Applicants must be working on a degree in chemistry, computer science, materials science, mathematics, statistics, applied or engineering physics, or the following engineering specialties: chemical, civil, electrical, materials, mechanical, or software. They must be interested in a summer internship at Battelle or designated national laboratories.

Financial data The scholarship stipend is $5,000. A stipend (amount not specified) is paid for the internships.

Duration 1 year.

Additional information This program began in 2008 by Battelle Memorial Institute of Columbus, Ohio. Internships are provided at Brookhaven National Laboratory (BNL) in Upton, New York, Idaho National Laboratory (INL) in Idaho Falls, Idaho, Oak Ridge National Laboratory (ORNL) in Oak Ridge, Tennessee, and Pacific Northwest National Laboratory (PNNL) in Richland, Washington.

Number awarded 14 each year, including 6 with internships at Battelle and 2 each with internships at BNL, INL, ORNL, and PNNL.

Deadline May of each year.

[67]
BATTELLE HIGH SCHOOL SCHOLARSHIP PROGRAM

National Society of Black Engineers
Attn: Pre-College Initiative Program
205 Daingerfield Road
Alexandria, VA 22314
(703) 549-2207 Fax: (703) 683-5312
E-mail: pci@nsbe.org
Web: www.nsbe.org/Programs/Scholarships.aspx

Summary To provide financial assistance to high school seniors who are junior members of the National Society of Black Engineers (NSBE) in Ohio and planning to major in science, technology, engineering, or mathematics (STEM) at a college in any state.

Eligibility This program is open to seniors graduating from high schools in Ohio who are junior members of the society. Applicants must be planning to attend college in any state and major in a STEM-related field.

Financial data The stipend is $5,000.

Duration 1 year.

Additional information This program began in 2008 as the result of a major gift from Battelle Memorial Institute to NSBE.

Number awarded 6 each year.

Deadline May of each year.

[68]
BECHTEL UNDERGRADUATE FELLOWSHIP AWARD

National Action Council for Minorities in Engineering
Attn: University Programs
440 Hamilton Avenue, Suite 302
White Plains, NY 10601-1813
(914) 539-4010 Fax: (914) 539-4032
E-mail: scholarships@nacme.org
Web: www.nacme.org/NACME_D.aspx?pageid=105

Summary To provide financial assistance to African American and other underrepresented minority college juniors majoring in construction engineering.

Eligibility This program is open to African American, Latino, and American Indian college juniors who have a GPA of 3.0 or higher and have demonstrated academic excellence, leadership skills, and a commitment to science and engineering as a career. Applicants must be enrolled full time at an ABET-accredited engineering program and preparing for a career in a construction-related engineering discipline.

Financial data The stipend is $2,500 per year. Funds are sent directly to the recipient's university.

Duration Up to 2 years.

Additional information This program was established by the Bechtel Group Foundation.

Number awarded 2 each year.

Deadline April of each year.

[69]
BEHAVIORAL SCIENCES STUDENT FELLOWSHIPS IN EPILEPSY

Epilepsy Foundation
Attn: Research Department
8301 Professional Place
Landover, MD 20785-2353
(301) 459-3700 Toll Free: (800) EFA-1000
Fax: (301) 577-2684 TDD: (800) 332-2070
E-mail: grants@efa.org
Web: www.epilepsyfoundation.org

Summary To provide funding to undergraduate and graduate students (particularly African Americans, other minorities, women, and students with disabilities) who are interested in working on a summer research project in a behavioral science field relevant to epilepsy.

Eligibility This program is open to undergraduate and graduate students in a behavioral science program relevant to epilepsy research or clinical care, including, but not limited to, sociology, social work, psychology, anthropology, nursing, economics, vocational rehabilitation, counseling, or political science. Applicants must be interested in working on an epilepsy research project under the supervision of a qualified mentor. Because the program is designed as a training opportunity, the quality of the training plans and environment are considered in the selection process. Other selection criteria include the quality of the proposed project, the relevance of the proposed work to epilepsy, the applicant's interest in the field of epilepsy, the applicant's qualifications, and the mentor's qualifications (including his or her commitment to the student and the project), and the quality of the training environment for research related to epilepsy. U.S. citizenship is not required, but the project must be conducted in the United States. Applications from women, members of minority groups, and people with disabilities are especially encouraged. The program is not intended for students working on a dissertation research project.

Financial data The grant is $3,000.

Duration 3 months during the summer.

Additional information This program is supported by the American Epilepsy Society, Abbott Laboratories, Ortho-McNeil Pharmaceutical Corporation, and Pfizer Inc.

Number awarded Varies each year.

Deadline March of each year.

[70]
BERTHA PITTS CAMPBELL SCHOLARSHIP PROGRAM

Delta Sigma Theta Sorority, Inc.
Attn: Scholarship and Standards Committee Chair
1707 New Hampshire Avenue, N.W.
Washington, DC 20009
(202) 986-2400 Fax: (202) 986-2513
E-mail: dstemail@deltasigmatheta.org
Web: www.deltasigmatheta.org

Summary To provide financial assistance to members of Delta Sigma Theta who are working on an undergraduate degree in education.

Eligibility This program is open to current undergraduate students who are working on a degree in education. Applicants must be active, dues-paying members of Delta Sigma Theta. Selection is based on meritorious achievement.

Financial data The stipends range from $1,000 to $2,000. The funds may be used to cover tuition, fees, and living expenses.

Duration 1 year; may be renewed for 1 additional year.

Additional information This sponsor is a traditionally-African American social sorority. The application fee is $20.

Number awarded 1 or more each year.

Deadline April of each year.

[71]
BIG/FEEA SCHOLARSHIP

Blacks in Government
c/o Federal Employee Education and Assistance Fund
Attn: Scholarship Program
3333 South Wadsworth Boulevard, Suite 300
Lakewood, CO 80227
(303) 933-7580 Toll Free: (800) 323-4140
Fax: (303) 933-7587 E-mail: admin@feea.org
Web: www.feea.org

Summary To provide financial assistance for college or graduate school to dependents of members of Blacks in Government (BIG).

Eligibility This program is open to the children, stepchildren, and grandchildren of BIG members. The sponsoring BIG member must have at least 3 years of federal, state, or local government employment and 2 years of membership in BIG. Applicants must be entering or enrolled full time in an accredited 2- or 4-year postsecondary, graduate, or postgraduate program and have a GPA of 3.0 or higher. Along with their application, they must submit a 2-page essay on a topic related to a career in public service with the government, a letter of recommendation, a transcript, a list of extracurricular and community service activities, and verification of government employment; high school seniors must also submit a copy of their ACT, SAT, or other examination scores. Financial need is not considered in the selection process.

Financial data The stipend is $1,000 per year.

Duration 1 year; may be renewed.

Additional information This program, established in 2007, is jointly administered by BIG and the Federal Employee Education and Assistance Fund (FEEA).

Number awarded Up to 11 each year: 1 in each BIG region.

Deadline March of each year.

[72]
BILL BERNBACH DIVERSITY SCHOLARSHIPS

American Association of Advertising Agencies
Attn: AAAA Foundation
1065 Avenue of the Americas, 16th Floor
New York, NY 10018
(212) 262-2500 E-mail: bbscholarship@ddb.com
Web: www.aaaa.org

Summary To provide financial assistance to African American and other multicultural students who are interested in working on an undergraduate or graduate degree in advertising at designated schools.

Eligibility This program is open to African Americans, Asian Americans, Hispanic Americans, and Native Americans (including American Indians, Alaska Natives, Native Hawaiians, and other Pacific Islanders) who are interested in studying the advertising creative arts at designated institutions as a full-time student. Applicants must be working on or have already received an undergraduate degree and be able to demonstrate creative talent and promise. They must be U.S. citizens, nationals, or permanent residents. Along with their application, they must submit 10 samples of creative work in their respective field of expertise.

Financial data The stipend is $5,000.

Duration 1 year.

Additional information This program, which began in 1998, is currently sponsored by DDB Worldwide. The participating schools are the Art Center College of Design (Pasadena, California), Creative Circus (Atlanta, Georgia), Miami Ad School (Miami Beach, Florida), University of Texas at Austin, VCU Brandcenter (Richmond, Virginia), Savannah College of Art and Design (Savannah, Georgia), University of Oregon (Eugene), City College of New York, School of Visual Arts (New York, New York), Fashion Institute of Technology (New York, New York), and Brigham Young University (Provo, Utah).

Number awarded 3 each year.

Deadline October of each year.

[73]
BILL DICKEY GOLF SCHOLARSHIPS

Bill Dickey Scholarship Association
Attn: Scholarship Committee
1140 East Washington Street, Suite 103
Phoenix, AZ 85034
(602) 258-7851 Fax: (602) 258-3412
E-mail: assistant@bdscholar.org
Web: www.nmjgsa.org/scholarships.php

Summary To provide financial assistance to African American and other minority high school seniors and undergraduate students who excel at golf.

Eligibility This program is open to graduating high school seniors and current undergraduate students who are members of minority groups (African American, Asian/Pacific Islander, Hispanic, or American Indian/Alaskan Native). Applicants must submit a 500-word essay on a topic that changes annually but relates to minorities and golf. Selection is based on academic achievement; personal recommendations; participation in golf, school, and community activities; and financial need.

Financial data Stipends range from 1-time awards of $1,000 to 4-year awards of $3,500 per year. Funds are paid directly to the recipient's college.

Duration 1 year or longer.

Additional information This sponsor was established in 1984 as the National Minority Junior Golf Association and given its current name in 2006. Support is provided by the Jackie Robinson Foundation, PGA of America, Anheuser-Busch, the Tiger Woods Foundation, and other cooperating organizations.

Number awarded Varies; generally 80 or more each year.

Deadline April of each year.

[74]
BIRMINGHAM CHAPTER AABE SCHOLARSHIPS

American Association of Blacks in Energy-Birmingham Chapter
Attn: Scholarship Committee
P.O. Box 3035
Birmingham, AL 35202
(205) 325-3578 E-mail: larringt@southernco.com
Web: www.aabe.org/index.php?component=pages&id=161

Summary To provide financial assistance to African Americans and members of other underrepresented minority groups who are high school seniors in Alabama and planning to major in an energy-related field at a college in any state.

Eligibility This program is open to seniors graduating from high schools in Alabama and planning to attend a college or university in any state. Applicants must be African Americans, Hispanics, or Native Americans who have a GPA of 3.0 or higher and who can demonstrate financial need. Their intended major must be business, engineering, technology, mathematics, the physical sciences, or other energy-related field. Along with their application, they must submit a 350-word statement on why they should receive this scholarship, how their professional career objectives relate to energy, and any other relevant information.

Financial data The stipend is $5,000.

Duration 1 year.

Additional information The winner is eligible to compete for regional and national scholarships.

Number awarded 1 each year.

Deadline February of each year.

[75]
BISHOP JOSEPH B. BETHEA SCHOLARSHIPS

United Methodist Church
Attn: General Board of Higher Education and Ministry
Office of Loans and Scholarships
1001 19th Avenue South
P.O. Box 340007
Nashville, TN 37203-0007
(615) 340-7344 Fax: (615) 340-7367
E-mail: umscholar@gbhem.org
Web: www.gbhem.org

Summary To provide financial assistance for college to African American Methodist students from the southeastern states.

Eligibility This program is open to full-time undergraduate students at accredited colleges and universities who have been active, full members of a United Methodist Church for at least 1 year prior to applying. Applicants must be African Americans and members of Black Methodists for Church Renewal in the Southeastern Jurisdiction (which covers Alabama, Florida, Georgia, Kentucky, Mississippi, North Carolina, South Carolina, Tennessee, and Virginia). They must have a GPA of 2.8 or higher and be able to demonstrate financial need. U.S. citizenship or permanent resident status is required.

Financial data Stipends range from $500 to $1,000 per year.

Duration 1 year; recipients may reapply.

Number awarded 1 or more each year.

Deadline February of each year.

[76]
BISHOP T. LARRY KIRKLAND SCHOLARSHIP OF EXCELLENCE

African Methodist Episcopal Church
Fifth Episcopal District Lay Organization
4519 Admiralty Way, Suite 205
Marina del Rey, CA 90295
(310) 577-8530 Fax: (310) 577-8540
E-mail: bishoptkirkland@aol.com
Web: fifthdistrictlay.org/scholarship

Summary To provide financial assistance to members of African Methodist Episcopal (AME) churches in its Fifth Episcopal District who are high school seniors or students currently attending college in any state.

Eligibility This program is open to residents of the AME Fifth Episcopal District (Alaska, Arizona, California, Colorado, Idaho, Kansas, Missouri, Montana, Nebraska, Nevada, New Mexico, North Dakota, Oregon, South Dakota, Utah, Washington, and Wyoming) who are high school seniors or students currently enrolled at an accredited institution of higher learning in any state. Applicants must have been a member of an AME church for at least 12 months and have been an active member of its Lay Organization, the Women's Missionary Society, or the Men's Ministry. High school seniors must have a GPA of 3.0 or higher and college students must have a GPA of 2.5 or higher. Along with their application, they must submit a 500-word personal essay that describes their long-range plans, community and church involvement, accomplishments or special awards, challenges they have faced, and how they responded. Selection is based on that essay (30%), academic record (30%), letters of recommendation (15%), participation in church lay organizations (15%), and quality of application (10%).

Financial data The stipend is $1,500.

Duration 1 year.

Number awarded 1 each year.

Deadline May of each year.

[77]
BLACK DATA PROCESSING ASSOCIATES ORACLE SCHOLARSHIP

Black Data Processing Associates
Attn: Scholarship
9500 Arena Drive, Suite 106
Largo, MD 20774
(301) 584-3135 Fax: (301) 560-8300
E-mail: scholarships@bdpa.org
Web: www.bdpa.org/?page=Scholarships

Summary To provide financial assistance to members of Black Data Processing Associates (BDPA) who are working on an undergraduate degree in a field related to computer technology.

Eligibility This program is open to graduating high school seniors and current undergraduates who are BDPA members. Applicants must be enrolled or planning to enroll full time at an accredited college or university and major in engineering, computer and information science, computer engineering, or mathematics. They must have a GPA of 3.0 or higher. Along with their application, they must submit a 300-word essay that covers 1 or more of the following topics: the role that computer technology has played in their life, their dream and goal for technology in their future, how they will use their talent to give back or enrich their community, and/or how this scholarship will be used to help them with their education study and career. Financial need is not considered in the selection process.

Financial data Stipends are $4,000 or $5,000.

Duration 1 year.

Additional information This scholarship, first awarded in 2009, is sponsored by Oracle.

Number awarded Varies each year; recently, 11 of these scholarships were awarded.

Deadline July of each year.

[78]
BLACK NURSES' ASSOCIATION OF GREATER WASHINGTON FOUNDERS SCHOLARSHIP

Black Nurses' Association of Greater Washington, D.C. Area, Inc.
Attn: Scholarship Committee Chair
P.O. Box 55285
Washington, DC 20040
(202) 291-8866
Web: www.bnaofgwdca.org/scholarships.html

Summary To provide financial assistance to African American high school seniors in the Washington, D.C. area who are interested in enrolling in a nursing program at a school in any state.

Eligibility This program is open to African American seniors graduating from high schools in the District of Columbia or adjoining counties in Maryland (Anne Arundel, Calvert, Charles, Howard, Montgomery, and Prince George's). Applicants must be U.S. citizens or permanent residents and have a GPA of 2.8 or higher. They must have been accepted at a college or university in the United States that offers an NLN-accredited A.D.N., B.S.N., or L.P.N. nursing program. Along with their application, they must submit a 300-word statement that describes their personal and academic accomplishments, community service, future goals for a career in nursing, and financial need.

Financial data A stipend is awarded (amount not specified).

Duration 1 year.

Additional information This program began in 2011.

Number awarded 2 each year.

Deadline April of each year.

[79]
BLACKS AT MICROSOFT SCHOLARSHIPS

Seattle Foundation
Attn: Scholarship Administrator
1200 Fifth Avenue, Suite 1300
Seattle, WA 98101-3151
(206) 622-2294 Fax: (206) 622-7673
E-mail: scholarships@seattlefoundation.org
Web: www.seattlefoundation.org

Summary To provide financial assistance to African American high school seniors from any state who plan to major in engineering, computer science, or a business-related field in college.

Eligibility This program is open to seniors of African descent graduating from high school in any state and planning to attend a 4-year college or university. Applicants must be planning to work on a bachelor's degree in engineering, computer science, computer information systems, or selected business fields (such as finance, business administration, or marketing). They must be able to demonstrate a "passion for technology," leadership at school or in the community, a need for financial assistance to attend college, and a GPA of 3.3 or higher. Along with their application, they must submit a 500-word essay on how they plan to engage in the technology industry in their future career and a 250-word essay on their financial need for this scholarship.

Financial data The stipend is $5,000 per year.

Duration 1 year; may be renewed up to 3 additional years.

Additional information Blacks at Microsoft is an organization of African American employees of Microsoft.

Number awarded 2 each year.

Deadline February of each year.

[80]
BLANDY EXPERIMENTAL FARM RESEARCH EXPERIENCES FOR UNDERGRADUATES PROGRAM

University of Virginia
Attn: Blandy Experimental Farm
400 Blandy Farm Lane
Boyce, VA 22620
(540) 837-1758, ext. 292 Fax: (540) 837-1523
E-mail: blandy@virginia.edu
Web: blandy.virginia.edu/research/undergraduate-research

Summary To provide an opportunity for undergraduates (particularly African Americans, other underrepresented minorities, women, and students with disabilities) to conduct ecological and evolutionary research during the summer at the Blandy Experimental Farm in Clarke County, Virginia.

Eligibility This program is open to undergraduate students interested in ecological and evolutionary biology. Applicants must submit a proposal for a research project at the farm under the mentorship of a professional staff member. Current research interests of the staff include plant reproductive ecology, aquatic community ecology, biological invasions, plant population biology, conservation biology, pollination, and plant succession. Interested students should submit, along with their application, a current transcript, 2 letters of recommendation, a statement describing how this program would contribute to their education and career goals, and the names of the mentors whose research areas interest them. They must be U.S. citizens, nationals, or permanent residents. Applications are especially encouraged from underrepresented minorities, persons with disabilities, and women.

Financial data Students receive a $5,500 stipend, an additional meal budget, free housing, and a modest budget for supplies and travel.

Duration 11 weeks, from late May through mid-August.

Additional information This program, established in 1993, receives funding support from the Research Experiences for Undergraduates (REU) program of the National Science Foundation.

Number awarded 10 each year.

Deadline February of each year.

[81]
BOARD OF CORPORATE AFFILIATES SCHOLARS AWARDS

National Society of Black Engineers
Attn: Programs Department
205 Daingerfield Road
Alexandria, VA 22314
(703) 549-2207 Fax: (703) 683-5312
E-mail: scholarships@nsbe.org
Web: www.nsbe.org/Programs/Scholarships.aspx

Summary To provide financial assistance to members of the National Society of Black Engineers (NSBE) who are working on a degree in engineering.

Eligibility This program is open to members of the society who are undergraduate or graduate engineering students. Applicants must have a GPA of 3.0 or higher. Selection is based on an essay; academic achievement; service to the society at the chapter, regional, and/or national level; and other professional, campus, and community activities. Applicants for the National Society of Black Engineers Fellows Scholarship Program who rank in the highest of 3 tiers receive these awards.

Financial data The stipend is $3,000. Travel, hotel accommodations, and registration to the national convention are also provided.

Duration 1 year.

Number awarded Varies each year; recently, 50 of these scholarships were awarded.

Deadline May of each year.

[82]
BOOKER T. WASHINGTON SCHOLARSHIPS

National FFA Organization
Attn: Scholarship Office
6060 FFA Drive
P.O. Box 68960
Indianapolis, IN 46268-0960
(317) 802-4419 Fax: (317) 802-5419
E-mail: scholarships@ffa.org
Web: www.ffa.org

Summary To provide financial assistance to African American and other minority FFA members who are interested in studying agriculture in college.

Eligibility This program is open to members who are graduating high school seniors planning to enroll full time in college. Applicants must be members of a minority ethnic group (African American, Asian American, Pacific Islander, Hispanic, Alaska Native, or American Indian) planning to work on a 4-year degree in agriculture. Selection is based on academic achievement (10 points for GPA, 10 points for SAT or ACT score, 10 points for class rank), leadership in FFA activities (30 points), leadership in community activities (10 points), and participation in the Supervised Agricultural Experience (SAE) program (30 points). U.S. citizenship is required.

Financial data The stipend is $1,000. Funds are paid directly to the recipient.

Duration 1 year; nonrenewable.

Number awarded 5 each year.

Deadline February of each year.

[83]
BP NSBE CORPORATE SCHOLARSHIP PROGRAM

National Society of Black Engineers
Attn: Programs Department
205 Daingerfield Road
Alexandria, VA 22314
(703) 549-2207 Fax: (703) 683-5312
E-mail: scholarships@nsbe.org
Web: www.nsbe.org/Programs/Scholarships.aspx

Summary To provide financial assistance to members of the National Society of Black Engineers (NSBE) who are majoring in designated engineering fields.

Eligibility This program is open to members of the society who are enrolled as full-time college sophomores, juniors, or seniors and majoring in chemical, mechanical, or petroleum engineering. Applicants must have a GPA of 3.0 or higher and a demonstrated interest in employment with British Petroleum (BP). Along with their application, they must submit a 250-

word essay describing how they will use their education to make a positive impact on the world, including the African American community, and how this scholarship will advance their career goals and benefit BP.

Financial data The stipend is $2,500.

Duration 1 year.

Additional information This program is sponsored by BP.

Number awarded Varies each year; recently, 4 of these scholarships were awarded.

Deadline May of each year.

[84]
BRIGADIER GENERAL ROSCOE C. CARTWRIGHT AWARDS

The ROCKS, Inc.
c/o WSC Associates, LLP
7700 Old Branch Avenue, Suite A202
Clinton, MD 20735
(301) 856-9319 Toll Free: (877) 762-5732
Fax: (301) 856-5220 E-mail: therocks@aol.com
Web: www.rocksinc.org

Summary To provide financial assistance to students enrolled in ROTC programs at Historically Black Colleges and Universities (HBCUs).

Eligibility This program is open to Army and Air Force Cadets and Navy Midshipmen at HBCUs. Applicants must be planning to enter military service as officers following graduation from college. They must submit a letter of recommendation from their professor of military science evaluating their appearance, attitude, character, dedication, initiative, integrity, judgment, leadership potential, and written and oral communication ability. Financial need is not considered in the selection process.

Financial data The stipend is $1,200.

Duration 1 year.

Additional information This program began in 1974.

Number awarded Varies each year.

Deadline February of each year.

[85]
BRO. DR. FRANK T. SIMPSON SCHOLARSHIPS

Alpha Phi Alpha Fraternity, Inc.-Beta Sigma Lambda Chapter
Attn: BSL Educational Foundation, Inc.
P.O. Box 335
Hartford, CT 06141-0335
(203) 982-4956 E-mail: president@hartfordalphas.com
Web: www.hartfordalphas.com

Summary To provide financial assistance to high school seniors in Connecticut, especially African American males, who plan to attend college in any state.

Eligibility This program is open to seniors graduating from public and private high schools in Connecticut and planning to enroll at a 2- or 4-year college or university in any state. Preference is given to African American males. Applicants must have a GPA of 3.0 or higher and a record of community service and extracurricular activities. Along with their application, they must submit a 500-word personal essay that covers how they perceive their life 10 years after high school graduation, their personal interests, and their goals for the future. Financial need is not considered in the selection process.

Financial data The stipend is $1,500.

Duration 1 year; nonrenewable.

Number awarded Up to 4 each year.

Deadline March of each year.

[86]
BROWN AND CALDWELL MINORITY SCHOLARSHIP

Brown and Caldwell
Attn: Scholarship Program
201 North Civic Drive, Suite 115
P.O. Box 8045
Walnut Creek, CA 94596
(925) 937-9010 Fax: (925) 937-9026
E-mail: scholarships@brwncald.com
Web: www.brownandcaldwell.com/scholarships.asp

Summary To provide financial assistance to African American and other minority students working on an undergraduate or graduate degree in an environmental or engineering field.

Eligibility This program is open to members of minority groups (African Americans, Hispanics, Asians, Pacific Islanders, Native Americans, or Alaska Natives) who are full-time juniors, seniors, or graduate students at an accredited 4-year college or university. Applicants must have a GPA of 3.0 or higher and a declared major in civil, chemical, or environmental engineering or an environmental science (e.g., biology, ecology, geology, hydrogeology). They must be U.S. citizens or permanent residents. Along with their application, they must submit an essay (up to 250 words) on their future career goals in environmental science. Financial need is not considered in the selection process.

Financial data The stipend is $5,000.

Duration 1 year.

Number awarded 4 each year.

Deadline April of each year.

[87]
BUICK ACHIEVERS SCHOLARSHIP PROGRAM

Scholarship America
Attn: Scholarship Management Services
One Scholarship Way
P.O. Box 297
St. Peter, MN 56082
(507) 931-1682 Toll Free: (866) 243-4644
Fax: (507) 931-9168
E-mail: buickachievers@scholarshipamerica.org
Web: www.buickachievers.com

Summary To provide financial assistance to students (particularly African Americans, other minorities, women, and those with ties to the military) who are entering college for the first time and planning to major in specified fields related to engineering, design, or business.

Eligibility This program is open to high school seniors and graduates who are planning to enroll full time at an accredited 4-year college or university as first-time freshmen. Applicants must be planning to major in fields of engineering (chemical, computer, controls, electrical, energy, environmental, industrial, manufacturing, materials, mechanical, plastic/polymers, or software); technology (automotive technology, computer science, engineering technology, information technology);

design (graphic, industrial, product, transportation); or business (accounting, business administration, ergonomics, finance, industrial hygiene, international business, labor and industrial relations, management information systems, marketing, mathematics, occupational health and safety, production management, statistics, or supply chain/logistics). U.S. citizenship or permanent resident status is required. Selection is based on academic achievement, financial need, participation and leadership in community and school activities, work experience, educational and career goals, and other unusual circumstances. Special consideration is given to first-generation college students, women, minorities, military veterans, and dependents of military personnel.

Financial data Stipends are $25,000 or $2,000 per year.

Duration 1 year. The $25,000 awards may be renewed up to 3 additional years (or 4 years for students entering a 5-year engineering program), provided the recipient remains enrolled full time, continues to major in an eligible field, and maintains a GPA of 3.0 or higher. The $2,000 awards are nonrenewable.

Additional information This program, which began in 2011, is funded by the General Motors Foundation.

Number awarded 1,100 each year: 100 at $25,000 and 1,000 at $2,000.

Deadline February of each year.

[88] BYRON KENNETH ARMSTRONG SCHOLARS AWARD

Kappa Alpha Psi Fraternity
Attn: Grand Chapter
2322-24 North Broad Street
Philadelphia, PA 19132-4590
(215) 228-7184 Fax: (215) 228-7181
Web: www.kappaalphapsi1911.com

Summary To recognize and reward members of Kappa Alpha Psi Fraternity, a traditionally African American men's organization, who demonstrate outstanding achievement.

Eligibility This program is open to undergraduate members of the fraternity who are eligible for graduation in the term immediately preceding or during the period that the Province Council is being held. Candidates must have a GPA of 3.0 or higher. Selection is based on involvement in fraternity, college or university, and community activities.

Financial data Awards are $1,000 for first place, $750 for second place, and $500 for third place.

Duration Awards are presented annually.

Number awarded 3 each year.

Deadline Applications must be received within 14 days following the candidate's Province Council.

[89] CALDER SUMMER UNDERGRADUATE RESEARCH PROGRAM

Fordham University
Attn: Louis Calder Center Biological Field Station
53 Whippoorwill Road
P.O. Box 887
Armonk, NY 10504
(914) 273-3078, ext. 10 Fax: (914) 273-2167
E-mail: REUatCalder@fordham.edu
Web: www.fordham.edu

Summary To provide an opportunity for undergraduates (particularly African Americans, other underrepresented minorities, women, and individuals with disabilities) to pursue research activities in biology at Fordham University's Louis Calder Center Biological Field Station during the summer.

Eligibility This program is open to undergraduates interested in conducting a summer research project of their own design at the center. Applicants must be U.S. citizens, nationals, or permanent residents. Fields of interest must relate to the activities of staff who will serve as mentors on the projects; those include forest ecology, limnology, wildlife ecology, microbial ecology, Lyme disease, insect-plant interactions, evolutionary ecology, and the effects of urbanization on ecosystem processes. Applications from underrepresented minorities (African Americans, Hispanics, American Indians, Native Hawaiians, Pacific Islanders, and Alaska Natives), persons with disabilities, and women are especially encouraged.

Financial data The program provides a stipend of $5,000, housing on the site, and support for research supplies and local travel.

Duration 10 weeks during the summer.

Additional information This program has operated since 1967 with support from the Research Experiences for Undergraduates (REU) program of the National Science Foundation.

Number awarded Up to 10 each year.

Deadline February of each year.

[90] CALIFORNIA LEGISLATIVE BLACK CAUCUS YOUTH LEADERSHIP SCHOLARSHIPS

California Legislative Black Caucus
Attn: Salena Pryor-Dansby
State Capitol, Room 2057
Sacramento, CA 95814
(916) 651-4026 Fax: (916) 445-8899
Web: blackcaucus.legislature.ca.gov

Summary To provide financial assistance to residents of California who live in a state legislative district represented by a member of the California Legislative Black Caucus and are interested in attending college in any state.

Eligibility This program is open to graduating high school seniors and students currently enrolled full time at an accredited institution of higher learning in any state. Applicants must reside in a district whose member of the State Senate or General Assembly is a member of the California Legislative Black Caucus. They must have a GPA of 2.5 or higher. Along with their application, they must submit a list of extracurricular activities in which they are involved and an essay on the experiences that have influenced their decision to pursue higher education and who those experiences will help them with their career goals.

Financial data The stipend is $1,000.

Duration 1 year.

Additional information Recently, 2 state senators and 6 state assembly members constituted the California Legislative Black Caucus. Applications must be submitted directly to them. For their names and addresses, consult the caucus.

Number awarded 1 or more each year.

Deadline May of each year.

[91]
CAMMER-HILL GRANT

Wisconsin Women of Color Network, Inc.
Attn: Scholarship Committee
P.O. Box 2337
Madison, WI 53701-2337
E-mail: contact@womenofcolornetwork-wis.org
Web: www.womenofcolornetwork-wis.org/scholarship.html

Summary To provide financial assistance for vocational/technical school or community college to African American and other adult women of color from Wisconsin.

Eligibility This program is open to residents of Wisconsin who are adult women of color planning to continue their education at a vocational/technical school or community college in any state. Applicants must be a member of 1 of the following groups: African American, Asian, American Indian, or Hispanic. They must be able to demonstrate financial need. Along with their application, they must submit a 1-page essay on how this scholarship will help them accomplish their educational goal. U.S. citizenship is required.

Financial data A stipend is awarded (amount not specified).

Duration 1 year.

Additional information This program began in 1994.

Number awarded 1 each year.

Deadline May of each year.

[92]
CANFIT PROGRAM CULINARY ARTS SCHOLARSHIPS

Communities-Adolescents-Nutrition-Fitness
Attn: Scholarship Program
2140 Shattuck Avenue, Suite 610
Berkeley, CA 94704
(510) 644-1533 Toll Free: (800) 200-3131
Fax: (510) 644-1535 E-mail: info@canfit.org
Web: www.canfit.org/scholarships

Summary To provide financial assistance to African American and other minority culinary arts students in California.

Eligibility This program is open to American Indians, Alaska Natives, African Americans, Asian Americans, Pacific Islanders, and Latinos/Hispanics from California who are enrolled at a culinary arts college in the state. Applicants are not required to have completed any college units. Along with their application, they must submit 1) documentation of financial need; 2) letters of recommendation from 2 individuals; 3) a 1-to 2-page letter describing their academic goals and involvement in community nutrition and/or physical education activities; and 4) an essay of 500 to 1,000 words on a topic related to healthy foods for youth from low-income communities of color.

Financial data A stipend is awarded (amount not specified).

Number awarded 1 or more each year.

Deadline March of each year.

[93]
CANFIT PROGRAM UNDERGRADUATE SCHOLARSHIPS

Communities-Adolescents-Nutrition-Fitness
Attn: Scholarship Program
2140 Shattuck Avenue, Suite 610
Berkeley, CA 94704
(510) 644-1533 Toll Free: (800) 200-3131
Fax: (510) 644-1535 E-mail: info@canfit.org
Web: www.canfit.org/scholarships

Summary To provide financial assistance to African American and other minority undergraduate students who are working on a degree in nutrition or physical education in California.

Eligibility This program is open to American Indians, Alaska Natives, African Americans, Asian Americans, Pacific Islanders, and Latinos/Hispanics from California who are enrolled in an approved bachelor's degree program in nutrition or physical education in the state. Applicants must have completed at least 50 semester units and have a GPA of 2.5 or higher. Along with their application, they must submit 1) documentation of financial need; 2) letters of recommendation from 2 individuals; 3) a 1-to 2-page letter describing their academic goals and involvement in community nutrition and/or physical education activities; and 4) an essay of 500 to 1,000 words on a topic related to healthy foods for youth from low-income communities of color.

Financial data A stipend is awarded (amount not specified).

Number awarded 1 or more each year.

Deadline March of each year.

[94]
CAPSTONE CORPORATION SCHOLARSHIP AWARD

National Naval Officers Association-Washington, D.C. Chapter
c/o LCDR Stephen Williams
P.O. Box 30784
Alexandria, VA 22310
(703) 566-3840 Fax: (703) 566-3813
E-mail: Stephen.Williams@navy.mil
Web: dcnnoa.memberlodge.com

Summary To provide financial assistance to African American and other minority high school seniors from the Washington, D.C. area who plan to attend college in any state.

Eligibility This program is open to minority seniors graduating from high schools in the Washington, D.C. metropolitan area who plan to enroll full time at an accredited 2- or 4-year college or university in any state. Applicants must have a GPA of 3.0 or higher and be U.S. citizens or permanent residents. Selection is based on academic achievement, community involvement, and financial need.

Financial data The stipend is $1,000.

Duration 1 year; nonrenewable.

Additional information Recipients are not required to join or affiliate with the military in any way. This program is supported by Capstone Corporation, a minority-owned business incorporated in 1986 by former active-duty Navy officers.

Number awarded 1 each year.

Deadline March of each year.

[95]
CARMEN E. TURNER SCHOLARSHIPS

Conference of Minority Transportation Officials
Attn: National Scholarship Program
1875 I Street, N.W., Suite 500
Washington, DC 20006
(703) 234-4072 Fax: (202) 318-0364
Web: www.comto.org/?page=Scholarships

Summary To provide financial assistance for college or graduate school to African American and other members of the Conference of Minority Transportation Officials (COMTO).

Eligibility This program is open to undergraduate and graduate students who have been members of COMTO for at least 1 year. Applicants must be working on a degree in a field related to transportation and have a GPA of 2.5 or higher. They must be enrolled at least half time. Along with their application, they must submit a cover letter with a 500-word statement of career goals. Financial need is not considered in the selection process. U.S. citizenship or legal resident status is required.

Financial data The stipend is $3,500. Funds are paid directly to the recipient's college or university.

Duration 1 year.

Additional information COMTO was established in 1971 to promote, strengthen, and expand the roles of minorities in all aspects of transportation. Recipients are expected to attend the COMTO National Scholarship Luncheon.

Number awarded 1 each year.

Deadline May of each year.

[96]
CAROL HAYES TORIO MEMORIAL UNDERGRADUATE SCHOLARSHIP

California Dietetic Association
Attn: CDA Foundation
7740 Manchester Avenue, Suite 102
Playa del Rey, CA 90293-8499
(310) 822-0177 Fax: (310) 823-0264
E-mail: patsmith@dietitian.org
Web: www.dietitian.org/d_cdaf/cdaf_outreach.html

Summary To provide financial assistance to residents of California (particularly African Americans, other minorities, men, and individuals with physical disabilities) who are members of the Academy of Nutrition and Dietetics (AND) and interested in working on an undergraduate degree at a school in any state.

Eligibility This program is open to California residents who are AND members and 1) entering at least the second year of an accredited Coordinated Program (CP) or Didactic Program in Dietetics (DPD) in any state; or 2) accepted to an accredited Supervised Practice Program in any state to begin within 6 months. Along with their application, they must submit a letter of application that includes a discussion of their career goals. Selection is based on that letter (15%), academic ability (25%), work or volunteer experience (15%), letters of recommendation (15%), extracurricular activities (5%), and financial need (25%). Applications are especially encouraged from ethnic minorities, men, and people with physical disabilities.

Financial data The stipend is normally $1,000.

Duration 1 year.

Additional information The California Dietetic Association is the California affiliate of the AND.

Number awarded 1 each year.

Deadline April of each year.

[97]
CARROLL R. GIBSON SCHOLARSHIP AWARD

National Association of Black Narcotic Agents
c/o April Whitesell, Scholarship Award Committee Co-Chair
P.O. Box 277928
Miramar, FL 33027
E-mail: nabna1@verizon.net
Web: www.nabna.org/content/carroll-r-gibson

Summary To provide financial assistance to undergraduates working on a degree in criminal justice at an Historically Black College or University (HBCU).

Eligibility This program is open to full-time students currently enrolled at an HBCU and working on an undergraduate degree in criminal justice. Applicants must have a GPA of 2.5 or higher and a record of school and community involvement. A personal interview is required. Selection is based on merit; financial need is not considered.

Financial data Stipends range from $500 to $5,000.

Duration 1 year.

Additional information This program began in 1988.

Number awarded 1 or more each year.

Deadline Deadline not specified.

[98]
CATERPILLAR NSBE CORPORATE SCHOLARSHIPS

National Society of Black Engineers
Attn: Programs Department
205 Daingerfield Road
Alexandria, VA 22314
(703) 549-2207 Fax: (703) 683-5312
E-mail: scholarships@nsbe.org
Web: www.nsbe.org/Programs/Scholarships.aspx

Summary To provide financial assistance to members of the National Society of Black Engineers (NSBE) who are majoring in designated science and engineering fields.

Eligibility This program is open to members of the society who are enrolled as college sophomores, juniors, or seniors. Applicants must be majoring in computer science, computer information technology, materials science, applied or engineering physics, or the following fields of engineering: agricultural, chemical, civil, computer, electrical, industrial, materials, mechanical, or metallurgical. They must have a GPA of 2.8 or higher.

Financial data The stipend is $2,000.

Duration 1 year.

Additional information This program is sponsored by Caterpillar, Inc.

Number awarded 2 each year.

Deadline May of each year.

[99]
CBC SPOUSES HEINEKEN USA PERFORMING ARTS SCHOLARSHIP

Congressional Black Caucus Foundation, Inc.
Attn: Director, Educational Programs
1720 Massachusetts Avenue, N.W.
Washington, DC 20036
(202) 263-2800 Toll Free: (800) 784-2577
Fax: (202) 775-0773 E-mail: scholarships@cbcfinc.org
Web: www.cbcfinc.org/scholarships.html

Summary To provide financial assistance from the Congressional Black Caucus Foundation to undergraduate students who are interested in studying the performing arts.

Eligibility This program is open to graduating high school seniors and current undergraduates enrolled or planning to enroll full time at an accredited college or university. Applicants must be interested in preparing for a career in the performing arts, including theater, motion pictures, drama, comedy, music, dance, opera, marching bands, and other musical ensembles. They must have a GPA of 2.5 or higher. Along with their application, they must submit a 2-minute recorded sample of their performance; a 1-page resume listing their extracurricular activities, honors, employment, community service, and special skills; and a personal statement of 500 to 1,000 words on themselves and their interests. They must also be able to demonstrate financial need, leadership ability, and participation in community service activities.

Financial data The stipend is $3,000.

Duration 1 year.

Additional information This program, established in 2000, is sponsored by Heineken USA.

Number awarded Up to 10 each year.

Deadline April of each year.

[100]
CEA MINORITY STUDENT SCHOLARSHIPS

Colorado Education Association
Attn: Ethnic Minority Advisory Council
1500 Grant Street
Denver, CO 80203
(303) 837-1500 Toll Free: (800) 332-5939
Web: www.coloradoea.org

Summary To provide financial assistance to African American and other minority high school seniors in Colorado who are children of members of the Colorado Education Association (CEA) and planning to attend college in any state.

Eligibility This program is open to seniors graduating from high schools in Colorado who are members of a minority ethnic group, defined to include American Indians/Alaska Natives, Asians, Blacks, Hispanics, Native Hawaiians/Pacific Islanders, and multi-ethnic. Applicants must be the dependent child of an active, retired, or deceased CEA member. They must be planning to attend an accredited institution of higher education in any state. Along with their application, they must submit brief statements on 1) their need for this scholarship; and 2) why they plan to pursue a college education.

Financial data The stipend is $1,000.

Duration 1 year; nonrenewable.

Number awarded 4 each year.

Deadline March of each year.

[101]
CENIE "JOMO" WILLIAMS TUITION SCHOLARSHIP

National Association of Black Social Workers
Attn: NABSW Scholarships
2305 Martin Luther King Avenue, S.E.
Washington, DC 20020
(202) 678-4570 Fax: (202) 678-4572
E-mail: office-manager@nabsw.org
Web: www.nabsw.org/mserver/Forms.aspx

Summary To provide financial assistance for college or graduate school to members of the National Association of Black Social Workers (NABSW).

Eligibility This program is open to African American members of NABSW enrolled full time at an accredited social work or social welfare program with a GPA of 2.5 or higher. Applicants must be able to demonstrate community service and a research interest in the Black community. Along with their application, they must submit an essay of 2 to 3 pages on their professional interests, future social work aspirations, previous social work experiences (volunteer and professional), honors and achievements (academic and community service), and research interests within the Black community (for master's and doctoral students). Financial need is considered in the selection process.

Financial data The stipend is $2,000. Funds are sent directly to the recipient's school.

Duration 1 year.

Number awarded 2 each year.

Deadline January of each year.

[102]
CENTRAL FLORIDA CHAPTER NBMBAA SCHOLARSHIPS

National Black MBA Association-Central Florida Chapter
Attn: Scholarship Committee Chair
P.O. Box 692696
Orlando, FL 32869-2696
(321) 578-8305 E-mail: scholarships@cflblackmba.org
Web: www.cflblackmba.org

Summary To provide financial assistance to African Americans or members of another minority group who are residents of any state working on a degree in business at a university in Florida.

Eligibility This program is open to members of the following groups from any state: African American/Black, American Indian/Alaska Native, Asian American/Pacific Islander, or Hispanic/Latino. Applicants must be enrolled in a business program at an AACSB-accredited college or university in Florida. They must have a GPA of 3.0 or higher. Along with their application, they must submit a 2-page essay on a topic that changes annually but relates to minorities and business. Selection is based on that essay, transcripts, a resume, and extracurricular activities. The highest-ranked applicant receives a named scholarship sponsored by Darden Restaurants.

Financial data The Darden Named Scholarship is $5,000; a total of $10,000 in scholarships is awarded each year.

Duration 1 year.

Number awarded Varies each year.

Deadline October of each year.

[103]
CENTRAL INTELLIGENCE AGENCY UNDERGRADUATE SCHOLARSHIP PROGRAM

Central Intelligence Agency
Attn: Human Resource Management
Recruitment and Retention Center, 4B14-034 DD1
Washington, DC 20505
(703) 371-2107
Web: https:

Summary To provide college funding and work experience to high school seniors and college sophomores (particularly African Americans, other minorities, and students with disabilities) who would be interested in working for the Central Intelligence Agency (CIA) after graduation from college.

Eligibility This program is open to U.S. citizens who are either high school seniors or college freshmen or sophomores. Seniors must be at least 18 years of age by April of the year they apply and have minimum scores of 1500 on the SAT (1000 on critical reading and mathematics and 500 on writing) or 21 on the ACT. All applicants must have a GPA of 3.0 or higher and be able to demonstrate financial need (household income of $70,000 or less for a family of 4 or $80,000 or less for a family of 5 or more) and be able to meet the same employment standards as permanent employees of the CIA. This program was developed, in part, to assist minority and disabled students, but it is open to all students who meet the requirements.

Financial data Scholars are provided a salary, an optional benefits package (health, dental, and vision insurance, life insurance, and retirement), and up to $18,000 per year for tuition, fees, books, and supplies. They must agree to continue employment with the CIA after college graduation for a period 1.5 times the length of their college support.

Duration 1 year; may be renewed if the student maintains a GPA of 3.0 or higher and full-time enrollment in a 4- or 5-year college program.

Additional information Scholars work each summer at a CIA facility. In addition to a salary, they receive the cost of transportation between school and the Washington, D.C. area and a housing allowance.

Number awarded Varies each year.

Deadline October of each year.

[104]
CHARLES L. GITTENS SCHOLARSHIP AWARD

National Organization of Black Law Enforcement Executives
Attn: NOBLE Scholarships
4609 Pinecrest Office Park Drive, Suite F
Alexandria, VA 22312-1442
(703) 658-1529 Fax: (703) 658-9479
E-mail: wleach@noblenatl.org
Web: www.noblenational.org

Summary To provide financial assistance for college to African American and other high school seniors who are interested in preparing for a criminal justice career.

Eligibility This program is open to high school seniors who have a GPA of 3.7 or higher and are interested in preparing for a career in criminal justice. Applicants must be planning to attend an accredited academic institution in the United States to major in a social science (e.g. technology, forensic investigations, or other criminal investigative studies) related to a career in law enforcement or criminal justice. They must be U.S. citizens and able to demonstrate financial need. Along with their application, they must submit a 1-page essay on their career goals and interests and why they feel they should receive this scholarship. All students are eligible, but the sponsor is an organization of African American law enforcement officers.

Financial data The stipend is $1,000.

Duration 1 year; nonrenewable.

Number awarded 1 each year.

Deadline April of each year.

[105]
CHARLES S. BROWN SCHOLARSHIP IN PHYSICS

National Society of Black Physicists
Attn: Scholarship Committee Chair
1100 North Glebe Road, Suite 1010
Arlington, VA 22201
(703) 536-4207 Fax: (703) 536-4203
E-mail: scholarship@nsbp.org
Web: www.nsbp.org/scholarships

Summary To provide financial assistance to African American students working on an undergraduate or graduate degree in physics.

Eligibility This program is open to African American students who are working on an undergraduate or graduate degree in physics. Applicants must submit an essay on their academic and career objectives, information on their participation in extracurricular activities, a description of any awards and honors they have received, and 3 letters of recommendation. Financial need is not considered.

Financial data A stipend is awarded (amount not specified).

Duration 1 year; nonrenewable.

Number awarded 1 each year.

Deadline November of each year.

[106]
CHARLOTTE CHAPTER NBMBAA UNDERGRADUATE SCHOLARSHIP

National Black MBA Association-Charlotte Chapter
Attn: Director of Scholarships
P.O. Box 34613
Charlotte, NC 28234
Toll Free: (877) 732-0314
E-mail: dgibson@nbmbaacharlotte.org
Web: www.nbmbaacharlotte.org/Education.html

Summary To provide financial assistance to residents of North and South Carolina who are interested in working on a bachelor's degree at a business school in any state and submit a topic related to African Americans and business.

Eligibility This program is open to residents of North and South Carolina who are entering or enrolled full time at a college or university in any state. Applicants must be working on or planning to work on a bachelor's degree in business or management and have a GPA of 3.0 or higher. Selection is based primarily on a 2-page essay on a topic that changes annually but relates to African Americans and business.

Financial data The stipends are $5,000 or $2,000.

Duration 1 year.

Additional information The highest-ranked applicant receives the Edward G. Miller Scholarship.

Number awarded Varies each year; recently, 6 of these scholarships were awarded: 1 at $5,000 and 5 at $2,000.

Deadline August of each year.

[107] CHRISTIAN COLLEGE LEADERS SCHOLARSHIPS

Foundation for College Christian Leaders
2658 Del Mar Heights Road
PMB 266
Del Mar, CA 92014
(858) 481-0848 E-mail: LMHays@aol.com
Web: www.collegechristianleader.com

Summary To provide financial assistance for college to Christian students (particularly African Americans and other minorities) who are from California, Oregon, or Washington.

Eligibility This program is open to entering or continuing undergraduate students who reside or attend college in California, Oregon, or Washington. Applicants must have a GPA of 3.0 or higher, be able to document financial need (parents must have a combined income of less than $75,000), and be able to demonstrate Christian testimony and Christian leadership. Selection is based on identified leadership history, academic achievement, financial need, and demonstrated academic, vocational, and ministry training to further the Kingdom of Jesus Christ. Special consideration is given to minority students.

Financial data A stipend is awarded (amount not specified).

Duration 1 year; may be renewed.

Additional information The foundation, formerly known as the Eckmann Foundation, was founded in 1988.

Number awarded Varies each year.

Deadline May of each year.

[108] CIGNA HEALTHCARE UNDERGRADUATE SCHOLARSHIP

National Forum for Black Public Administrators
Attn: Scholarship Program
777 North Capitol Street, N.E., Suite 807
Washington, DC 20002
(202) 408-9300 Fax: (202) 408-8558
E-mail: vharris@nfbpa.org
Web: www.nfbpa.org/i4a/pages/index.cfm?pageid=4047

Summary To provide financial assistance to African Americans working on an undergraduate degree in public administration or a related field at an Historically Black College or University (HBCU).

Eligibility This program is open to African American undergraduate students preparing for a career in public administration. Applicants must be working full time on a degree in public administration, political science, urban affairs, public policy, or a related field at an HBCU. They must have a GPA of 3.5 or higher, excellent interpersonal and analytical abilities, and strong oral and written communication skills. Along with their application, they must submit a 3-page essay an assigned topic that relates to the public administration profession, their SAT or ACT scores, and documentation of financial need. Selection is based on academic record, leadership ability, participation in school activities, community service, and financial need.

Financial data The stipend is $10,000.

Duration 1 year.

Additional information This program is sponsored by CIGNA Healthcare. Recipients are required to attend the sponsor's annual conference to receive their scholarship; limited hotel and air accommodations are arranged and provided.

Number awarded 1 each year.

Deadline February of each year.

[109] CIRILO MCSWEEN (NEW YORK LIFE) SCHOLARSHIP

PUSH Excel
Attn: General Offices
930 East 50th Street
Chicago, IL 60615
(773) 373-3366 E-mail: pushexcel@rainbowpush.org
Web: www.pushexcel.org/pages/scholarships

Summary To provide financial assistance to African American and other high school seniors who plan to major in business and are willing to help promote the scholarship program of PUSH-Excel.

Eligibility This program is open to seniors graduating from high school and planning to major in business at an accredited 4-year college or university. Applicants must be U.S. citizens and have a GPA of 3.0 or higher. Along with their application, they must submit a 500-word essay that identifies 5 prerequisites for success, explains their personal philosophy for the pursuit of excellence, and explains how they will use their college education to achieve this pursuit of excellence. They must also agree to cooperate with the scholarship committee of PUSH-Excel by promoting its program, participating in its public relations activities, and attending its Annual National Conference luncheon and Education Leadership Conference. Selection is based on the essay, academic preparation to attend college and succeed, and ability to overcome obstacles to achieve academic and personal goals.

Financial data The stipend is $2,500 per year.

Duration 1 year; may be renewed up to 3 additional years if the recipient maintains a GPA of 3.0 or higher and fulfills the obligations to PUSH-Excel.

Additional information PUSH-Excel was founded in 1975 by the Rev. Jesse Jackson. This program is named for Cirilo McSween, the first African American agent for New York Life (which sponsors this program).

Number awarded 1 or more each year.

Deadline June of each year.

[110]
CISCO'S FUTURE SCHOLARSHIPS

Society of Women Engineers
Attn: Scholarship Selection Committee
203 North LaSalle Street, Suite 1675
Chicago, IL 60601-1269
(312) 596-5223 Toll Free: (877) SWE-INFO
Fax: (312) 644-8557 E-mail: scholarships@swe.org
Web: societyofwomenengineers.swe.org

Summary To provide financial assistance to African American and other undergraduate women, who are members of the Society of Women Engineers (SWE) and majoring in designated engineering specialties.

Eligibility This program is open to SWE members who are entering their sophomore or junior year at a 4-year ABET-accredited college or university. Preference is given to members of underrepresented ethnic or racial groups, candidates with disabilities, and veterans. Applicants must be working full time on a degree in computer science or computer or electrical engineering and have a GPA of 3.0 or higher. They must be U.S. citizens or permanent residents. Financial need is considered in the selection process.

Financial data The stipend is $5,000.

Duration 1 year.

Additional information This program is sponsored by Cisco Systems.

Number awarded 5 each year.

Deadline February of each year.

[111]
CLANSEER AND ANNA JOHNSON SCHOLARSHIPS

Community Foundation of New Jersey
Attn: Chief Operating Officer
35 Knox Hill Road
P.O. Box 338
Morristown, NJ 07963-0338
(973) 267-5533, ext. 227 Toll Free: (800) 659-5533
Fax: (973) 267-2903 E-mail: fkrueger@cfnj.org
Web: www.cfnj.org/funds/scholarship/all.php

Summary To provide financial assistance to African American high school seniors in New Jersey who plan to attend college in any state.

Eligibility This program is open to African American seniors graduating from high schools in New Jersey who have been accepted to attend an educational institution in the United States. Applicants must have earned a grade of "A" or "B" in classes related to the sciences or mathematics and have maintained above average grades in all course work. They must have been born in the United States. Selection is based primarily on financial need, but academic performance, extracurricular activities, and work experience are also considered.

Financial data Recently, the stipend was $1,550 per year. Funds are made payable jointly to the recipients and their educational institution.

Duration 4 years, provided the recipient maintains a GPA of 2.5 or higher.

Additional information Recipients must agree to donate at least 10 hours of community service per week within New Jersey for 1 year following graduation.

Number awarded 6 each year.

Deadline March of each year.

[112]
COALITION OF BLACK TRADE UNIONISTS UNDERGRADUATE SCHOLARSHIPS

Coalition of Black Trade Unionists
Attn: Scholarship Awards Committee
1150 17th Street, N.W., Suite 300
P.O. Box 66268
Washington, DC 20035-6268
(202) 778-3318 Fax: (202) 293-5308
E-mail: cbtu1@hotmail.com
Web: www.cbtu.org/bell%20ball.html

Summary To provide financial assistance to undergraduates who are members or sponsored by members of the Coalition of Black Trade Unionists (CBTU).

Eligibility This program is open to students who are enrolled or planning to enroll at a college or university. Applicants must be a CBTU member or sponsored by a member and must specify their relationship to their sponsor. Along with their application, they must submit SAT or ACT scores and a 300-word essay on assigned topics that differ, depending on the applicant's year in school. Students already enrolled in college must have a GPA of 2.5 or higher. Financial need is not considered in the selection process.

Financial data The stipend is $2,000.

Duration 1 year.

Additional information This program includes the James H. Bell Scholarship and the Leonard C. Ball Scholarship.

Number awarded 10 each year.

Deadline April of each year.

[113]
COAST GUARD HEADQUARTERS BLACKS IN GOVERNMENT SCHOLARSHIP

Blacks in Government-Coast Guard Headquarters Chapter
Attn: Scholarship Program
P.O. Box 71055
Washington, DC 20024-1055
(202) 372-1329 E-mail: Gail.M.Jackson@uscg.mil
Web: www.bignet.org/regional/CGHC

Summary To provide financial assistance to African American and other high school seniors in the Washington, D.C. metropolitan area who plan to attend college in any state.

Eligibility This program is open to seniors graduating from high schools in the Washington, D.C. metropolitan area who have a GPA of 2.0 or higher. Applicants must be planning to attend an accredited institution of higher learning. They may apply for either a general scholarship (for any field of study) or an engineering scholarship (for any field of engineering), but they may apply for only 1 of those categories. Along with their application, they must submit an essay of 350 to 500 words on 1 of the following topics: their chosen field of study and why; how their community, church, or family has influenced them; or why it is important for them to attend college. Finalists are interviewed.

Financial data The stipend ranges from $500 to $1,000.

Duration 1 year.

Additional information This program began in 2004.

Number awarded Up to 3 each year.
Deadline March of each year.

[114]
COCHRAN/GREENE SCHOLARSHIP

National Naval Officers Association-Washington, D.C. Chapter
Attn: Scholarship Program
2701 Park Center Drive, A1108
Alexandria, VA 22302
(703) 566-3840 Fax: (703) 566-3813
E-mail: Stephen.Williams@Navy.mil
Web: dcnnoa.memberlodge.com

Summary To provide financial assistance to African American and other minority female high school seniors from the Washington, D.C. area who are interested in attending college in any state.

Eligibility This program is open to female minority seniors graduating from high schools in the Washington, D.C. metropolitan area who plan to enroll full time at an accredited 2- or 4-year college or university in any state. Applicants must have a GPA of 2.5 or higher and be U.S. citizens or permanent residents. Selection is based on academic achievement, community involvement, and financial need.

Financial data The stipend is $1,500.

Duration 1 year; nonrenewable.

Additional information Recipients are not required to join or affiliate with the military in any way.

Number awarded 1 each year.

Deadline March of each year.

[115]
COKER/DAVIS SCHOLARSHIP

National Naval Officers Association-Washington, D.C. Chapter
c/o LCDR Stephen Williams
P.O. Box 30784
Alexandria, VA 22310
(703) 566-3840 Fax: (703) 566-3813
E-mail: Stephen.Williams@navy.mil
Web: dcnnoa.memberlodge.com

Summary To provide financial assistance to male African American high school seniors from the Washington, D.C. area who are interested in attending college in any state.

Eligibility This program is open to male African American seniors graduating from high schools in the Washington, D.C. metropolitan area who plan to enroll full time at an accredited 2- or 4-year college or university in any state. Applicants must have a GPA of 2.5 or higher and be U.S. citizens or permanent residents. Selection is based on academic achievement, community involvement, and financial need.

Financial data The stipend is $1,000.

Duration 1 year; nonrenewable.

Additional information Recipients are not required to join or affiliate with the military in any way.

Number awarded 1 each year.

Deadline March of each year.

[116]
COLGATE "BRIGHT SMILES, BRIGHT FUTURES" MINORITY SCHOLARSHIPS

American Dental Hygienists' Association
Attn: Institute for Oral Health
444 North Michigan Avenue, Suite 3400
Chicago, IL 60611-3980
(312) 440-8900, ext. 204 Fax: (312) 440-6726
E-mail: institute@adha.net
Web: www.adha.org/ioh/programs/scholarships.htm

Summary To provide financial assistance to 1) African American and other minority students (females or males) and 2) males of any race who are members of the Student American Dental Hygienists' Association (SADHA) or the American Dental Hygienists' Association (ADHA) and enrolled in certificate programs in dental hygiene.

Eligibility This program is open to members of groups currently underrepresented in the dental hygiene profession (Native Americans, African Americans, Hispanics, Asians, and males) who are active members of the SADHA or the ADHA. Applicants must have a GPA of 3.0 or higher, be able to document financial need of at least $1,500, and have completed at least 1 year of full-time enrollment in an accredited dental hygiene certificate program in the United States. Along with their application, they must submit a statement that covers their long-term career goals, their intended contribution to the dental hygiene profession, their professional interests, and how their extracurricular activities and their degree enhance the attainment of their goals.

Financial data The stipend ranges from $1,000 to $2,000.

Duration 1 year; nonrenewable.

Additional information These scholarships are sponsored by the Colgate-Palmolive Company.

Number awarded 2 each year.

Deadline January of each year.

[117]
COLGATE PALMOLIVE-LUBRIZOL UNDERGRADUATE RESEARCH AWARD

National Organization for the Professional Advancement of Black Chemists and Chemical Engineers
Attn: Awards Committee Chair
P.O. Box 77040
Washington, DC 20013
Toll Free: (800) 776-1419 Fax: (202) 667-1705
E-mail: awards@nobcche.org
Web: www.nobcche.org

Summary To recognize and reward African American and other minority undergraduates who have conducted outstanding research in chemistry or related fields.

Eligibility This competition is open to minority students who have completed at least 2 years of full-time work on a bachelor's degree in chemistry, materials science, polymer science, chemical engineering, or a related field. Applicants must be planning to continue on to work on a graduate degree in those fields. They must submit an abstract for a 15-minute oral presentation of their original research at the annual conference of the National Organization for the Professional Advancement of Black Chemists and Chemical Engineers (NOBCChE).

Financial data The award is $1,000. The winners also receive reimbursement of travel and lodging for the NOBCChE annual conference and an offer of a paid summer internship with Lubrizol Corporation or Colgate-Palmolive Company, the program's sponsors.

Duration 1 year; nonrenewable.

Number awarded 1 or more each year.

Deadline June of each year.

[118]
COLLABORATIVE RESEARCH EXPERIENCE FOR UNDERGRADUATES IN COMPUTER SCIENCE AND ENGINEERING

Computing Research Association
1828 L Street, N.W., Suite 800
Washington, DC 20036-5104
(202) 234-2111 Fax: (202) 667-1066
E-mail: creu@cra.org
Web: cra-w.org/undergraduate

Summary To provide funding to African American, other underrepresented minority, and female undergraduate students who are interested in conducting a research project in computer science or engineering.

Eligibility This program is open to teams of 2 or 4 undergraduates who have completed 2 years of study, including at least 4 courses in computer science or computer engineering, at a college or university in the United States. Applicants must be interested in conducting a research project directly related to computer science or computer engineering. They must apply jointly with 1 or 2 sponsoring faculty members. Teams consisting of all women or all underrepresented minorities are especially encouraged to apply; teams may also include students from non-underrepresented groups, but financial support is available only to underrepresented students. U.S. citizenship or permanent resident status is required.

Financial data The program provides a stipend of $3,000 for the academic year. Students who wish to participate in an optional summer extension receive an additional stipend of $4,000. Additional funding up to $1,500 per team may be available for purchase of supporting materials and/or travel to conferences to present the work.

Duration 1 academic year plus an optional summer extension.

Additional information This program is sponsored by the Computing Research Association's Committee on the Status of Women in Computing Research (CRA-W) and the Coalition to Diversify Computing (CDC) in cooperation with the National Science Foundation.

Number awarded Varies each year; recently, 21 teams of students received support from this program.

Deadline May of each year.

[119]
COLLEGE JOURNALISM SCHOLARSHIPS

Colorado Association of Black Journalists
Attn: Scholarship Committee
P.O. Box 40322
Denver, CO 80204
(303) 929-7299 E-mail: info@cabj-denver.org
Web: www.cabj-denver.org/awards.html

Summary To provide financial assistance to African American high school and college students from Colorado who are interested in majoring in a field related to journalism.

Eligibility This program is open to African American students currently attending a high school or college in Colorado. Applicants must be majoring or planning to major in journalism or mass communications. They must have a GPA of 3.0 or higher. Along with their application, they must submit a transcript, a letter of recommendation, and 3 samples of their media work (such as school newspaper clips, broadcast news stories, photographs, documentaries and radio excepts, or class work).

Financial data Stipends are $2,500 or $1,000. Winning students are also given a 1-year membership in the Colorado Association of Black Journalists (CABJ).

Duration 1 year.

Number awarded 3 each year: 1 at $2,500 (designated the Reynelda Muse Journalism Scholarship) and 2 at $1,000.

Deadline June of each year.

[120]
COLLEGE STUDENT PRE-COMMISSIONING INITIATIVE

U.S. Coast Guard
Attn: Recruiting Command
2300 Wilson Boulevard, Suite 500
Arlington, VA 22201
(703) 235-1775 Toll Free: (877) NOW-USCG
Fax: (703) 235-1881
E-mail: Margaret.A.Jackson@uscg.mil
Web: www.gocoastguard.com

Summary To provide financial assistance to college students at Historically Black Colleges and Universities or other minority institutions who are willing to serve in the Coast Guard following graduation.

Eligibility This program is open to students entering their junior or senior year at a college or university designated as an Historically Black College or University (HBCU), Hispanic Serving Institution (HSI), Tribal College or University (TCU), or the University of Guam, the University of Hawaii (at Manoa, Hilo, or West Oahu), Argosy University (Hawaii), or the Institute of American Indian and Alaska Native Culture (Santa Fe, New Mexico). Applicants must be U.S. citizens; have a GPA of 2.5 or higher; have scores of 1100 or higher on the critical reading and mathematics SAT, 23 or higher on the ACT, 4AQR/4PFAR on the ASTB, or 109 or higher on the SVAB GT; be between 19 and 27 years of age; and meet all physical requirements for a Coast Guard commission. They must agree to attend the Coast Guard Officer Candidate School following graduation and serve on active duty as an officer for at least 3 years.

Financial data Those selected to participate receive full payment of tuition, books, and fees; monthly housing and food allowances; medical and life insurance; special training in leadership, management, law enforcement, navigation, and marine science; 30 days of paid vacation per year; and a monthly salary of up to $2,200.

Duration Up to 2 years.

Number awarded Varies each year.

Deadline January of each year.

[121]
COLORADO EDUCATIONAL SERVICES AND DEVELOPMENT ASSOCIATION DIVERSITY SCHOLARSHIPS

Colorado Educational Services and Development Association
P.O. Box 40214
Denver, CO 80204
(303) 256-9785 E-mail: kim.medina@jwu.edu
Web: www.cesda.org/664.html

Summary To provide financial assistance to high school seniors in Colorado who are planning to attend college in the state and are either first-generation college students or members of underrepresented ethnic or racial minorities.

Eligibility This program is open to seniors graduating from high schools in Colorado who are 1) the first member of their family to attend college; 2) a member of an underrepresented ethnic or racial minority (African American, Asian/Pacific Islander, American Indian, Hispanic/Chicano/Latino); and/or 3) able to demonstrate financial need. Applicants must have a GPA of 2.8 or higher and be planning to enroll at a 2- or 4-year college or university in Colorado. U.S. citizenship or permanent resident status is required. Selection is based on leadership and community service (particularly within minority communities), past academic performance, personal and professional accomplishments, personal attributes, special abilities, academic goals, and financial need.

Financial data The stipend is $1,000.

Duration 1 year; nonrenewable.

Number awarded Varies each year.

Deadline March of each year.

[122]
COMMUNITY COLLEGE SCHOLARSHIP FOR BLACK AMERICANS

Scholarship Administrative Services, Inc.
Attn: MEFUSA Program
457 Ives Terrace
Sunnyvale, CA 94087

Summary To provide financial assistance to African American high school seniors who are interested in attending a community college.

Eligibility This program is open to African Americans graduating from high schools anywhere in the United States. Applicants must be planning to attend a community college on a full-time basis. Along with their application, they must submit a 1,000-word essay on their educational and career goals, how a community college education will help them to achieve those goals, and how they plan to serve the African American community after completing their education. Selection is based on the essay, high school GPA (2.5 or higher), SAT or ACT scores, involvement in the African American community, and financial need.

Financial data The stipend is $5,000 per year.

Duration 1 year; may be renewed 1 additional year if the recipient maintains full-time enrollment and a GPA of 2.5 or higher.

Additional information This program is sponsored by the Minority Educational Foundation of the United States of America (MEFUSA) and administered by Scholarship Administrative Services, Inc. MEFUSA was established in 2001 to meet the needs of minority students who "show a determination to get a college degree," but who, for financial or other personal reasons, are not able to attend a 4-year college or university. Requests for applications should be accompanied by a self-addressed stamped envelope, the student's e-mail address, and the name of the source where they found the scholarship information.

Number awarded Up to 100 each year.

Deadline April of each year.

[123]
CONGRESSIONAL BLACK CAUCUS SPOUSES EDUCATION SCHOLARSHIP

Congressional Black Caucus Foundation, Inc.
Attn: Director, Educational Programs
1720 Massachusetts Avenue, N.W.
Washington, DC 20036
(202) 263-2800 Toll Free: (800) 784-2577
Fax: (202) 775-0773 E-mail: scholarships@cbcfinc.org
Web: www.cbcfinc.org/scholarships.html

Summary To provide financial assistance to African American and other undergraduate and graduate students, especially those who reside or attend college in a Congressional district represented by a member of the Congressional Black Caucus (CBC).

Eligibility This program is open to 1) African American and other graduating high school seniors planning to attend an accredited institution of higher education; and 2) currently-enrolled full-time undergraduate, graduate, and doctoral students in good academic standing with a GPA of 2.5 or higher. Preference is given to applicants who reside or attend school in a Congressional district represented by a member of the CBC. Along with their application, they must a personal statement of 500 to 1,000 words on 1) their future goals, major field of study, and how that field of study will help them to achieve their future career goals; 2) involvement in school activities, community and public service, hobbies, and sports; 3) how receiving this award will affect their current and future plans; and 4) other experiences, skills, or qualifications. They must also be able to demonstrate financial need, leadership ability, and participation in community service activities.

Financial data A stipend is awarded (amount not specified).

Duration 1 year.

Additional information The program began in 1988.

Number awarded Varies each year.

Deadline June of each year.

[124]
CONNECTICUT CHAPTER AABE SCHOLARSHIPS

American Association of Blacks in Energy-Connecticut Chapter
Attn: Scholarship Committee
P.O. Box 1898
Hartford, CT 06144
(203) 499-2418 E-mail: presctchapter@gmail.com
Web: www.aabe.org/index.php?component=pages&id=827

Summary To provide financial assistance to African Americans or members of other underrepresented minority groups who are high school seniors in Connecticut and western Massachusetts and planning to major in an energy-related field at a college in any state.

Eligibility This program is open to seniors graduating from high schools in Connecticut or western Massachusetts and planning to work on a bachelor's degree at a college or university in any state. Applicants must be African Americans, Hispanics, or Native Americans who have a GPA of 3.0 or higher and who can demonstrate financial need. Their intended major must be a field of business, engineering, mathematics, or science (e.g., chemistry, geology, meteorology, physics) related to energy. Along with their application, they must submit a 350-word statement on why they should receive this scholarship, their professional career objectives, and any other relevant information.

Financial data The stipend is $2,500. Funds are disbursed directly to the students.

Duration 1 year; nonrenewable.

Additional information Winners are eligible to compete for regional and national scholarships. This program began in 2003.

Number awarded 4 or 5 each year. Since this program began, it has awarded 45 scholarships with a total value of $109,000.

Deadline April of each year.

[125]
CONNECTICUT MINORITY TEACHER INCENTIVE PROGRAM

Connecticut Office of Financial and Academic Affairs for Higher Education
Attn: Student Financial Aid
61 Woodland Street
Hartford, CT 06105-2326
(860) 947-1853 Toll Free: (800) 842-0229 (within CT)
Fax: (860) 947-1314 E-mail: mtip@ctdhe.org
Web: www.ctohe.org/SFA/default.htm

Summary To provide financial assistance to African Americans and other minority upper-division college students in Connecticut who are interested in teaching at public schools in the state.

Eligibility This program is open to juniors and seniors enrolled full time in Connecticut college and university teacher preparation programs. Applicants must be members of a minority group, defined as African American, Hispanic/Latino, Asian American, or Native American. They must be nominated by the education dean at their institution.

Financial data The maximum stipend is $5,000 per year. In addition, if recipients complete a credential and begin teaching at a public school in Connecticut within 16 months of graduation, they may receive up to $2,500 per year, for up to 4 years, to help pay off college loans.

Duration Up to 2 years.

Number awarded Varies each year.

Deadline October of each year.

[126]
CONSORTIUM FOR ENTERPRISE SYSTEMS MANAGEMENT SCHOLARSHIP FOR BDPA STUDENTS

Black Data Processing Associates
Attn: BDPA Education Technology Foundation
4423 Lehigh Road, Number 277
College Park, MD 20740
(513) 284-4968 Fax: (202) 318-2194
E-mail: scholarships@betf.org
Web: www.betf.org/scholarships/cesm.shtml

Summary To provide financial assistance to high school seniors in North or South Carolina who are members of the Black Data Processing Associates (BDPA) and interested in studying information technology at a college in those states.

Eligibility This program is open to seniors graduating from high schools in North or South Carolina and planning to enroll at an accredited 4-year college or university in their state. Applicants must be planning to work on a degree in information technology. They must have a GPA of 3.0 or higher. Along with their application, they must submit a 500-word essay on why information technology is important. Selection is based on that essay, academic achievement, leadership ability through academic or civic involvement, and participation in community service activities. U.S. citizenship or permanent resident status is required.

Financial data The stipend is $2,000. Funds may be used to pay for tuition, fees, books, room and board, or other college-related expenses.

Duration 1 year; nonrenewable.

Additional information The BDPA established its Education and Technology Foundation (BETF) in 1992 to advance the skill sets needed by African American and other minority adults and young people to compete in the information technology industry. This program is sponsored by the Consortium for Enterprise Systems Management.

Number awarded 1 or more each year.

Deadline December of each year.

[127]
CONSORTIUM OF INFORMATION AND TELECOMMUNICATIONS EXECUTIVES (CITE) TRADITIONAL SCHOLARSHIPS

Consortium of Information and Telecommunications Executives, Inc.
c/o Charlene Davis, Scholarship Committee Chair
2001 Broadway
Santa Monica, CA 90404
(310) 453-7058 E-mail: m.martin@citese.org
Web: www.forcite.org/forcite/scholarships.asp

Summary To provide financial assistance to African American high school seniors who plan to major in any field in college.

Eligibility This program is open to African American high school seniors who have been accepted by an accredited 4-year college or university in any state as a full-time student. Applicants must have a GPA of 3.0 or higher and a family income of $75,000 per year or less. They may be planning to major in any field. Along with their application, they must submit a 1-page essay on their educational and career goals. Employees of Verizon Communications or affiliated subsidiaries and their family members are ineligible. U.S. citizenship is required.

Financial data Stipends are $2,000 or $1,000.

Duration 1 year; nonrenewable.

Additional information The Consortium of Information and Telecommunications Executives (CITE) is an organization of African American employees of Verizon, founded in 1984 after the dissolution of the former Bell systems.

Number awarded 3 each year: 1 at $2,000 and 2 at $1,000. Awards are presented in each CITE Region: Southeast (Florida, Georgia, and North Carolina), Mid-Atlantic (Delaware, New Jersey, and Pennsylvania), and West (California, Illinois, and Texas).

Deadline May of each year.

[128]
CORNELL UNIVERSITY SUMMER PROGRAM IN ASTRONOMY AND ASTROPHYSICS

Cornell University
Department of Astronomy
Attn: REU Astronomy Coordinator
510 Space Sciences Building
Ithaca, NY 14853-6801
(607) 255-0288 Fax: (607) 255-1767
E-mail: pf46@cornell.edu
Web: www.astro.cornell.edu/specialprograms/reu/reu.html

Summary To provide an opportunity for undergraduate students (particularly African Americans, other underrepresented minorities, women, and individuals with disabilities) to work on astronomy research projects at Cornell University during the summer.

Eligibility This program is open to undergraduate students who have completed at least 1 year of academic training. Applicants must be interested in working with Cornell University faculty and research staff on projects covering a wide range of disciplines in radio, infrared, and radar astronomy and related theoretical topics. They must be U.S. citizens, nationals, or permanent residents. Applications are especially encouraged from underrepresented minorities, persons with disabilities, and women.

Financial data The stipend is $6,200. Other support includes $1,000 for relocation and housing and up to $1,000 round-trip transportation to Ithaca, New York.

Duration 8 weeks during the summer.

Additional information This program is funded by the National Science Foundation as part of its Research Experiences for Undergraduates (REU) Program.

Number awarded 8 each year.

Deadline February of each year.

[129]
CORPORATE PARTNER SCHOLARSHIPS

National Association of Black Accountants
Attn: National Scholarship Program
7474 Greenway Center Drive, Suite 1120
Greenbelt, MD 20770
(301) 474-NABA Fax: (301) 474-3114
E-mail: scholarships@nabainc.org
Web: www.nabainc.org

Summary To provide financial assistance to student members of the National Association of Black Accountants (NABA) who are working on an undergraduate or graduate degree in a field related to accounting.

Eligibility This program is open to minorities who are NABA members and enrolled full time as 1) an undergraduate freshman, sophomore, junior, or first-semester senior majoring in accounting, business, or finance at a 4-year college or university; or 2) a graduate student working on a master's degree in accounting. High school seniors are not eligible. Applicants must have a GPA of 3.5 or higher in their major and 3.3 or higher overall. Along with their application, they must submit a 500-word personal statement on their involvement in NABA, career objectives, leadership abilities, and community activities. Financial need is not considered in the selection process.

Financial data Stipends range from $1,000 to $5,000.

Duration 1 year.

Number awarded Varies each year.

Deadline January of each year.

[130]
CORPORATE-SPONSORED ACHIEVEMENT SCHOLARSHIPS

National Merit Scholarship Corporation
Attn: National Achievement Scholarship Program
1560 Sherman Avenue, Suite 200
Evanston, IL 60201-4897
(847) 866-5100 Fax: (847) 866-5113
Web: www.nationalmerit.org/nasp.php

Summary To provide financial assistance from corporate sponsors to African American finalists for the National Achievement Scholarship Program who are not awarded Achievement Scholarships.

Eligibility African American high school seniors who are high scorers in the National Achievement Scholarship Program but who are not awarded scholarships are considered for this program. Because winners of these scholarships must meet preferential criteria specified by sponsors, not all finalists for the National Achievement Scholarship Program are considered for this award, and the awards are not subject to regional allocation. Further, corporate sponsors frequently offer their awards to finalists who are children of their employees or residents of an area where a plant or office is located. Some companies offer scholarships to students who plan to pursue particular college majors or careers. Finalists who have qualifications that especially interest a sponsor are identified and winners are selected from among eligible candidates. Financial need is considered for some of the awards.

Financial data Most of these scholarships provide stipends that are individually determined, taking into account college costs and family financial circumstances. Variable stipend awards of this type range from at least $500 to $2,000 per year, although some have a higher annual minimum and a few range as high as $10,000 per year. Some renewable awards provide a fixed annual stipend (between $1,000 and $5,000) that is the same for every recipient of the sponsor's awards. Other corporate-sponsored scholarships are nonrenewable and provide a single payment (from $2,500 to $5,000) for the recipient's first year of college study.

Duration 1 year; most awards are renewable up to 3 additional years.

Additional information Recently, these awards were sponsored by 42 corporations, company foundations, and professional organizations.

Number awarded Approximately 100 each year.

Deadline Applicants must take the PSAT/NMSQT no later than October of their junior year.

[131]
CORRINE WILLIAMS SCHOLARSHIP

California Dietetic Association
Attn: CDA Foundation
7740 Manchester Avenue, Suite 102
Playa del Rey, CA 90293-8499
(310) 822-0177 Fax: (310) 823-0264
E-mail: patsmith@dietitian.org
Web: www.dietitian.org/d_cdaf/cdaf_outreach.html

Summary To provide financial assistance to residents of California (particularly African Americans, other minorities, men, and individuals with disabilities) who are members of the Academy of Nutrition and Dietetics (AND) and interested in participating in specified types of programs in any state.

Eligibility This program is open to California residents who are AND members and 1) entering the first or second year of an approved Dietetic Technician Program in any state; 2) entering at least the second year of an accredited Coordinated Program (CP) or Didactic Program in Dietetics (DPD) in any state; or 3) accepted to an accredited Supervised Practice Program in any state to begin within 6 months. Along with their application, they must submit a letter of application that includes a discussion of their career goals. Selection is based on that letter (15%), academic ability (25%), work or volunteer experience (15%), letters of recommendation (15%), extracurricular activities (5%), and financial need (25%). Applications are especially encouraged from ethnic minorities, men, and people with physical disabilities.

Financial data The stipend is normally $1,000.

Duration 1 year.

Additional information This program began in 2010. The California Dietetic Association is the California affiliate of the AND.

Number awarded 1 each year.

Deadline April of each year.

[132]
CRACKER BARREL-MINORITY TEACHER EDUCATION SCHOLARSHIPS

Florida Fund for Minority Teachers, Inc.
Attn: Executive Director
G415 Norman Hall
P.O. Box 117045
Gainesville, FL 32611-7045
(352) 392-9196, ext. 21 Fax: (352) 846-3011
E-mail: info@ffmt.org
Web: www.ffmt.org

Summary To provide funding to African American and other minority Florida residents who are preparing for a career as a teacher.

Eligibility This program is open to Florida residents who are African American/Black, Hispanic/Latino, Asian American/Pacific Islander, or American Indian/Alaskan Native. Applicants must be entering their junior year in a teacher education program at a participating college or university in Florida. Special consideration is given to community college graduates. Selection is based on writing ability, communication skills, overall academic performance, and evidence of commitment to the youth of America (preferably demonstrated through volunteer activities).

Financial data The stipend is $2,000 per year. Recipients are required to teach 1 year in a Florida public school for each year they receive the scholarship. If they fail to teach in a public school, they are required to repay the total amount of support received at an annual interest rate of 8%.

Duration Up to 2 consecutive years, provided the recipient remains enrolled full time with a GPA of 2.5 or higher.

Additional information For a list of the 16 participating public institutions and the 18 participating private institutions, contact the Florida Fund for Minority Teachers (FFMT). Recipients are also required to attend the annual FFMT recruitment and retention conference.

Number awarded Varies each year.

Deadline July of each year for fall semester; November of each year for spring semester.

[133]
CRCNA RACE RELATIONS MULTIRACIAL STUDENT SCHOLARSHIP

Christian Reformed Church
Attn: Office of Race Relations
2850 Kalamazoo Avenue, S.E.
Grand Rapids, MI 49560-0200
(616) 224-5883 Toll Free: (877) 279-9994
Fax: (616) 224-0834 E-mail: elugo@crcna.org
Web: www.crcna.org/race/scholarships

Summary To provide financial assistance to African American and other minority undergraduate and graduate students who are interested in attending colleges related to the Christian Reformed Church in North America (CRCNA).

Eligibility This program is open to students of color in the United States and Canada. Normally, applicants are expected to be members of CRCNA congregations who plan to pursue their educational goals at Calvin Theological Seminary or any of the colleges affiliated with the CRCNA. They must be interested in training for the ministry of racial reconciliation in church and/or in society. Students who have no prior history with the CRCNA must attend a CRCNA-related college or seminary for a full academic year before they are eligible to apply for this program. Students entering their sophomore year must have earned a GPA of 2.0 or higher as freshmen; students entering their junior year must have earned a GPA of 2.3 or higher as sophomores; students entering their senior year must have earned a GPA of 2.6 or higher as juniors.

Financial data First-year students receive $500 per semester. Other levels of students may receive up to $2,000 per academic year.

Duration 1 year.

Additional information This program was first established in 1971 and revised in 1991. Recipients are expected to train to engage actively in the ministry of racial reconciliation in church and in society. They must be able to work in the United States or Canada upon graduating and must consider working for 1 of the agencies of the CRCNA.

Number awarded Varies each year; recently, 31 students received a total of $21,000 in support.
Deadline March of each year.

[134] CTA/MARTIN LUTHER KING, JR. MEMORIAL SCHOLARSHIP FUND

California Teachers Association
Attn: CTA Foundation for Teaching and Learning
1705 Murchison Drive
P.O. Box 921
Burlingame, CA 94011-0921
(650) 697-1400 E-mail: scholarships@cta.org
Web: www.cta.org

Summary To provide financial assistance for college or graduate school to African Americans and other racial and ethnic minorities who are members of the California Teachers Association (CTA), children of members, or members of the Student CTA.
Eligibility This program is open to members of racial or ethnic minority groups (African Americans, American Indians/Alaska Natives, Asians/Pacific Islanders, and Hispanics) who are 1) active CTA members; 2) dependent children of active, retired, or deceased CTA members; or 3) members of Student CTA. Applicants must be interested in preparing for a teaching career in public education or already engaged in such a career.
Financial data Stipends vary each year; recently, they ranged from $1,000 to $4,000.
Duration 1 year.
Number awarded Varies each year; recently, 25 of these scholarships were awarded: 5 to CTA members, 10 to children of CTA members, and 10 to Student CTA members.
Deadline February of each year.

[135] CUMMINS SCHOLARSHIPS

Society of Women Engineers
Attn: Scholarship Selection Committee
203 North LaSalle Street, Suite 1675
Chicago, IL 60601-1269
(312) 596-5223 Toll Free: (877) SWE-INFO
Fax: (312) 644-8557 E-mail: scholarships@swe.org
Web: societyofwomenengineers.swe.org

Summary To provide financial assistance to minority and other women working on an undergraduate or graduate degree in computer science or designated engineering specialties.
Eligibility This program is open to women who are sophomores, juniors, seniors, or graduate students at 4-year ABET-accredited colleges and universities. Applicants must be working full time on a degree in computer science or automotive, chemical, computer, electrical, industrial, manufacturing, materials, or mechanical engineering and have a GPA of 3.5 or higher. Preference is given to members of groups underrepresented in engineering or computer science. Selection is based on merit. U.S. citizenship or permanent resident status is required.
Financial data The stipend is $1,000.
Duration 1 year.
Additional information This program is sponsored by Cummins, Inc.
Number awarded 2 each year.
Deadline February of each year.

[136] DAMON P. MOORE SCHOLARSHIP

Indiana State Teachers Association
Attn: Scholarships
150 West Market Street, Suite 900
Indianapolis, IN 46204-2875
(317) 263-3369 Toll Free: (800) 382-4037
Fax: (800) 777-6128 E-mail: mshoup@ista-in.org
Web: www.ista-in.org/dynamic.aspx?id=1212

Summary To provide financial assistance to African American and other ethnic minority high school seniors in Indiana who are interested in studying education in college.
Eligibility This program is open to ethnic minority public high school seniors in Indiana who are interested in studying education in college. Selection is based on academic achievement, leadership ability as expressed through co-curricular activities and community involvement, recommendations, and a 300-word essay on their educational goals and how they plan to use this scholarship.
Financial data The stipend is $1,000.
Duration 1 year; may be renewed for 2 additional years if the recipient maintains at least a "C+" average.
Additional information This program began in 1987.
Number awarded 1 each year.
Deadline February of each year.

[137] DAVID EVANS AND ASSOCIATES SCHOLARSHIPS

David Evans and Associates, Inc.
2100 S.W. River Parkway
Portland, OR 97201
(503) 223-2701 Toll Free: (800) 721-1916
Fax: (503) 223-6663
Web: www.deainc.com/scholarships.aspx

Summary To provide financial assistance to African Americans, other minorities, and women who are working on an undergraduate degree in civil engineering or geomatics at colleges in designated states.
Eligibility This program is open to women and minority undergraduates majoring in civil engineering (including transportation, structural, land development, or environmental) or geomatics. Applicants must be enrolled at a college or university in Arizona, California, Colorado, Idaho, New York, Oregon, or Washington. They must have a GPA of 3.0 or higher.
Financial data The stipend is $3,000.
Duration 1 year; nonrenewable.
Number awarded 2 each year.
Deadline April of each year.

[138]
DAVIS & DAVIS SCHOLARSHIP

National Naval Officers Association-Washington, D.C. Chapter
c/o LCDR Stephen Williams
P.O. Box 30784
Alexandria, VA 22310
(703) 566-3840 Fax: (703) 566-3813
E-mail: Stephen.Williams@navy.mil
Web: dcnnoa.memberlodge.com

Summary To provide financial assistance to female African American high school seniors from the Washington, D.C. area who are interested in attending college in any state.

Eligibility This program is open to female African American seniors graduating from high schools in the Washington, D.C. metropolitan area who plan to enroll full time at an accredited 2- or 4-year college or university in any state. Applicants must have a GPA of 2.5 or higher and be U.S. citizens or permanent residents. Selection is based on academic achievement, community involvement, and financial need.

Financial data The stipend is $1,000.

Duration 1 year; nonrenewable.

Additional information Recipients are not required to join or affiliate with the military in any way.

Number awarded Varies each year; recently, 2 of these scholarships were awarded.

Deadline March of each year.

[139]
DEFENSE INTELLIGENCE AGENCY UNDERGRADUATE TRAINING ASSISTANCE PROGRAM

Defense Intelligence Agency
Attn: Human Resources, HCH-4
200 MacDill Boulevard, Building 6000
Bolling AFB, DC 20340-5100
(202) 231-2736 Fax: (202) 231-4889
TDD: (202) 231-5002 E-mail: staffing@dia.mil
Web: www.dia.mil/careers/students

Summary To provide financial aid and work experience to high school seniors and lower-division students (particularly African Americans, other minorities, women, and students with disabilities) who are interested in majoring in specified fields and working for the U.S. Defense Intelligence Agency (DIA).

Eligibility This program is open to graduating high school seniors and college freshmen and sophomores interested in working full time on a baccalaureate degree in 1 of the following fields in college: biology, chemistry, computer science, engineering, foreign area studies, intelligence analysis, international relations, microbiology, pharmacology, physics, political science, or toxicology. High school seniors must have a GPA of 2.75 or higher and either 1) an SAT combined critical reading and mathematics score of 1000 or higher plus 500 or higher on the writing portion or 2) an ACT score of 21 or higher. College freshmen and sophomores must have a GPA of 3.0 or higher. All applicants must be able to demonstrate financial need (household income ceiling of $70,000 for a family of 4 or $80,000 for a family of 5 or more) and leadership abilities through extracurricular activities, civic involvement, volunteer work, or part-time employment. Students and all members of their immediate family must be U.S. citizens. Minorities, women, and persons with disabilities are strongly encouraged to apply.

Financial data Students accepted into this program receive tuition (up to $18,000 per year) at an accredited college or university selected by the student and endorsed by the sponsor; reimbursement for books and needed supplies; an annual salary to cover college room and board expenses and for summer employment; and a position at the sponsoring agency after graduation. Recipients must work for DIA after college graduation for at least 1 and a half times the length of study. For participants who leave DIA earlier than scheduled, the agency arranges for payments to reimburse DIA for the total cost of education (including the employee's pay and allowances).

Duration 4 years, provided the recipient maintains a GPA of 2.75 during the freshman year and 3.0 or higher in subsequent semesters.

Additional information Recipients are provided a challenging summer internship and guaranteed a job at the agency in their field of study upon graduation.

Number awarded Only a few are awarded each year.

Deadline October of each year.

[140]
DELLA H. RANEY NURSING SCHOLARSHIP

National Black Nurses Association, Inc.
Attn: Scholarship Committee
8630 Fenton Street, Suite 330
Silver Spring, MD 20910-3803
(301) 589-3200 Toll Free: (800) 575-6298
Fax: (301) 589-3223 E-mail: elazenby@nbna.org
Web: www.nbna.org

Summary To provide financial assistance to nursing students who apply through the Tuskegee Airmen.

Eligibility This program is open to students enrolled in at least the sophomore year of an accredited B.S.N. degree program. They must submit their application to a local chapter of the Tuskegee Airmen, a group of African Americans who served as pilots in World War II. Along with their application, they must submit a 2-page essay 1) describing their extracurricular activities and community involvement (including local chapter activities, community-based projects, school level projects, organizational efforts, state-level student nurse activities, and other activities impacting on the health and social condition of African Americans and other culturally diverse groups); 2) presenting their ideas of what they can do as an individual nurse to improve the health status and/or social condition of African Americans; and 3) stating their future goals in nursing.

Financial data The stipend ranges from $500 to $2,000 per year.

Duration 1 year; may be renewed.

Additional information This program, which began in 2012, is jointly sponsored by the National Black Nurses Association (NBNA) and the Tuskegee Airmen Scholarship Foundation.

Number awarded 1 each year.

Deadline April of each year.

[141]
DELTA BETA CHAPTER/CARMEN MERCER SCHOLARSHIP

National Sorority of Phi Delta Kappa, Inc.-Delta Beta Chapter
c/o Nancy Thompson, Chapter Scholarship Chair
4703 Broadhill Drive
Austin, TX 78723
(512) 926-6309

Summary To provide financial assistance to African American high school seniors who plan to study education in college.

Eligibility This program is open to African American graduating high school seniors who are planning to attend a 4-year college and major in the field of education. Along with their application, they must submit documentation of financial need, high school transcripts, 2 letters of recommendation, SAT and/or ACT scores, a list of honors and awards received in high school, and a list of extracurricular, community, and volunteer activities.

Financial data The stipend is $2,000.

Duration 1 year.

Number awarded 1 each year.

Deadline February of each year.

[142]
DELTA SIGMA THETA SORORITY GENERAL SCHOLARSHIPS

Delta Sigma Theta Sorority, Inc.
Attn: Scholarship and Standards Committee Chair
1707 New Hampshire Avenue, N.W.
Washington, DC 20009
(202) 986-2400 Fax: (202) 986-2513
E-mail: dstemail@deltasigmatheta.org
Web: www.deltasigmatheta.org

Summary To provide financial assistance to members of Delta Sigma Theta who are working on an undergraduate or graduate degree in any field.

Eligibility This program is open to active, dues-paying members of Delta Sigma Theta who are currently enrolled in college or graduate school. Applicants must submit an essay on their major goals and educational objectives, including realistic steps they foresee as necessary for the fulfillment of their plans. Financial need is considered in the selection process.

Financial data The stipends range from $1,000 to $2,000. The funds may be used to cover tuition, fees, and living expenses.

Duration 1 year; may be renewed for 1 additional year.

Additional information This sponsor is a traditionally-African American social sorority. The application fee is $20.

Number awarded Varies each year.

Deadline April of each year.

[143]
DENVER AREA CHAPTER/CLARKE WATSON SCHOLARSHIPS

American Association of Blacks in Energy-Denver Area Chapter
Attn: Scholarship Committee
14405 West Colfax Avenue, Suite 264
Lakewood, CO 80401-3206
E-mail: Janice.Brown@nrel.gov
Web: www.aabe.org/index.php?component=pages&id=270

Summary To provide financial assistance to African Americans and members of other underrepresented minority groups who are high school seniors in Colorado and planning to major in an energy-related field at a college in any state.

Eligibility This program is open to seniors graduating from high schools in Colorado who are planning to work on a bachelor's degree at a college or university in any state. Applicants must be African Americans, Hispanics, or Native Americans who have a GPA of 3.0 or higher and who can demonstrate financial need. They must be planning to major in a field of business, engineering, technology, physical science, or mathematics related to energy. Along with their application, they must submit a 350-word statement on why they should receive this scholarship, how their professional career objectives relate to energy, and any other relevant information. U.S. citizenship is required.

Financial data The stipend is $1,000. Funds are disbursed directly to the recipient's college or university.

Duration 1 year; may be renewed.

Additional information Winners are eligible to compete for regional and national scholarships.

Number awarded 2 each year.

Deadline February of each year.

[144]
DEPARTMENT OF HOMELAND SECURITY SUMMER FACULTY AND STUDENT RESEARCH TEAM PROGRAM

Oak Ridge Institute for Science and Education
Attn: Science and Engineering Education
P.O. Box 117
Oak Ridge, TN 37831-0117
(865) 574-1447 Fax: (865) 241-5219
E-mail: Patti.Obenour@orau.gov
Web: see.orau.org

Summary To provide an opportunity for teams of students and faculty from minority-serving educational institutions to conduct research during the summer in areas of interest to the Department of Homeland Security (DHS).

Eligibility This program is open to teams of up to 2 students (undergraduate and/or graduate) and 1 faculty from Historically Black Colleges and Universities (HBCUs), Hispanic Serving Institutions (HSIs), Tribal Colleges and Universities (TCUs), Alaska Native Serving Institutions (ANSIs), and Native Hawaiian Serving Institutions (NHSIs). Applicants must be interested in conducting research at designated DHS Centers of Excellence in science, technology, engineering, or mathematics related to homeland security (HS-STEM), including explosives detection, mitigation, and response; social and behavioral sciences; risk, economics, and decision sciences; human factors; chemical threats and countermeasures; biological threats and countermeasures; community, commerce, and infrastructure resilience; food and agricultural security; transportation security; border security; immigration studies; maritime and port security; infrastructure protection; natural disasters and related geophysical studies; emergency preparedness and response; communications and interoperability; or advanced data analysis and visualization. Faculty must have a full-time appointment at an eligible institution and have received a Ph.D. in an HS-STEM discipline no more than 7 years previously; at least 2 years of full-time research and/or teaching experience is preferred. Students must have a GPA of 3.0 or higher and be enrolled full time. Undergraduates must be entering their junior or senior year. U.S. citizenship is required. Selection is based on relevance and intrinsic merit of the research (40%), faculty applicant qualifications (30%), academic benefit to the faculty applicant and his/her institution (10%), and student applicant qualifications (20%).

Financial data Stipends are $1,200 per week for faculty, $600 per week for graduate students, and $500 per week for undergraduates. Faculty members who live more than 50 miles from their assigned site may receive a housing allowance of $1,500 and travel expenses up to an additional $500. Limited travel expenses for 1 round trip are reimbursed for undergraduate and graduate students living more than 50 miles from their assigned site.

Duration 12 weeks during the summer.

Additional information This program is funded by DHS and administered by Oak Ridge Institute for Science and Education (ORISE). Recently, the available DHS Centers of Excellence were the Center for Advancing Microbial Risk Assessment (led by Michigan State University and Drexel University); the National Center for Risk and Economic Analysis of Terrorism Events (led by University of Southern California); the National Center for Food Protection and Defense (led by University of Minnesota); the Center of Excellence for Zoonotic and Animal Disease Defense (led by Texas A&M University and Kansas State University); the National Consortium for the Study of Terrorism and Responses to Terrorism (led by University of Maryland); the Center of Excellence for Awareness and Localization of Explosives-Related Threats (led by Northeastern University and University of Rhode Island); the National Center for Border Security and Immigration (led by the University of Arizona and the University of Texas at El Paso); the Center for Maritime, Island and Remote and Extreme Environment Security (led by the University of Hawaii and Stevens Institute of Technology); the Coastal Hazards Center of Excellence (led by the University of North Carolina at Chapel Hill and Jackson State University); the National Transportation Security Center of Excellence (consisting of 7 institutions); and the Center of Excellence in Command, Control, and Interoperability (led by Purdue University and Rutgers University).

Number awarded Approximately 12 teams are selected each year.

Deadline January of each year.

[145]
DEPARTMENT OF TRANSPORTATION/ EISENHOWER GRANTS FOR RESEARCH AND INTERN FELLOWSHIPS

Department of Transportation
Federal Highway Administration
Attn: Universities and Grants Programs
4600 North Fairfax Drive, Suite 800
Arlington, VA 22203-1553
(703) 235-0538 Toll Free: (877) 558-6873
Fax: (703) 235-0593 E-mail: transportationedu@dot.gov
Web: www.fhwa.dot.gov/tpp/ddetfp.htm

Summary To enable students (particularly those at Minority Serving Institutions) to participate in transportation-related research activities either at facilities of the U.S. Department of Transportation (DOT) Federal Highway Administration in the Washington, D.C. area or as interns for private or public organizations.

Eligibility This program is open to 1) students in their junior year of a baccalaureate program who will complete their junior year before being awarded a fellowship; 2) students in their senior year of a baccalaureate program; and 3) students who have completed their baccalaureate degree and are enrolled in a program leading to a master's, Ph.D., or equivalent degree. Applicants must be enrolled full time at an accredited U.S institution of higher education and planning to enter the transportation profession after completing their higher education. They must be U.S. citizens or have an I-20 (foreign student) or I-551 (permanent resident) identification card. For research fellowships, they select 1 or more projects from a current list of research activities underway at various DOT facilities; the research is conducted with academic supervision provided by a faculty adviser from their home university (which grants academic credit for the research project) and with technical direction provided by the DOT staff. Intern fellowships provide students with opportunities to perform transportation-related research, development, technology transfer, and other activities at public and private sector organizations. Specific requirements for the target projects vary; most require engineering backgrounds, but others involve transportation planning, information management, public administration, physics, materials science, statistical analysis, operations research, chemistry, economics, technology transfer, urban studies, geography, and urban and regional planning. The DOT encourages students at Historically Black Colleges and Universities (HBCUs), Hispanic Serving Institutions (HSIs), and Tribal Colleges and Universities (TCUs) to apply for these grants. Selection is based on match of the student's qualifications with the proposed research project (including the student's ability to accomplish the project in the available time), recommendation letters regarding the nominee's qualifications to conduct the research, academic records (including class standing, GPA, and transcripts), and transportation work experience (if any), including the employer's endorsement.

Financial data Fellows receive full tuition and fees that relate to the academic credits for the approved research project (to a maximum of $10,000) and a monthly stipend of $1,450 for undergraduates, $1,700 for master's students, or $2,000 for doctoral students. An allowance for travel to and from the DOT facility where the research is conducted is also provided, but selectees are responsible for their own housing accommodations. Recipients are also provided with a 1-time allowance of up to $1,500 to attend the annual Transportation Research Board (TRB) meeting.

Duration Projects normally range from 3 to 12 months.

Number awarded Varies each year; recently, 9 students participated in this program.

Deadline Applications remain open until each project is filled.

[146]
DEVELOPMENT FUND FOR BLACK STUDENTS IN SCIENCE AND TECHNOLOGY SCHOLARSHIPS

Development Fund for Black Students in Science and Technology
2705 Bladensburg Road, N.E.
Washington, DC 20018
(202) 635-3604 E-mail: DLHinson@earthlink.net
Web: www.dfbsstscholarship.org/dfb_sch.html

Summary To provide scholarships to African American students who enroll in scientific or technical fields of study at designated Historically Black Colleges and Universities (HBCUs).

Eligibility Deans and faculty members of engineering and science departments at selected HBCUs are invited to identify students to be considered for these scholarships. Nominees must be enrolled or planning to enroll at a predominantly Black college or university or already be enrolled at the school and planning to major in a technical field (e.g., engineering, mathematics, science). U.S. citizenship or permanent resident status is required. Selection is based on academic achievement (grades and SAT scores, especially in science and mathematics), a personal essay describing career goals and relevant extracurricular activities, recommendations, and financial need.

Financial data Stipends range up to $2,000 per year.

Duration 1 year; may be renewed for up to 4 years, as long as the recipient remains in good academic standing and enrolled full time in a science or engineering curriculum.

Additional information Prior to 1995, these scholarships were awarded solely or primarily through the National Merit Scholarship Corporation's National Achievement Scholarship Program. Scholarship applications are available only through the financial aid offices of prequalified schools. Currently, these are: Bennett College, Clark Atlanta University, Elizabeth City State University, Fisk University, Florida A&M University, Fort Valley State College, Hampton University, Howard University, Langston University, Lincoln University of Pennsylvania, Morehouse University, Morgan State University, North Carolina A&T State University, Prairie View A&M University, Southern University and A&M College, Spelman College, Tennessee State University, Tuskegee University, Wilberforce University, and Xavier University of Louisiana.

Number awarded Several each year.

Deadline June of each year.

[147]
DEVERNE CALLOWAY SCHOLARSHIP

Missouri Legislative Black Caucus Foundation
c/o Senator Shalonn "Kiki" Curls
4609 Paseo Boulevard, Suite 102
Kansas City, MO 64110
Toll Free: (877) 63-MLBCF E-mail: mlbcf@aol.com
Web: www.mlbcf.com

Summary To provide financial assistance to African American and other disadvantaged residents of Missouri who are interested in working on an undergraduate degree in any field at a school in any state.

Eligibility This program is open to undergraduate students from Missouri who come from a disadvantaged background. Applicants may be attending or planning to attend a college or university in any state. They must have a GPA of 2.0 or higher. Along with their application, they must submit a 250-word personal statement on how their education will assist them in achieving their goals. Selection is based on academic excellence, community service, leadership skills, and financial need.

Financial data A stipend is awarded (amount not specified).

Duration 1 year; recipients may reapply for up to 6 years of support.

Number awarded 1 or more each year.

Deadline May of each year.

[148]
DEWAYNE WICKHAM FOUNDER'S HIGH SCHOOL SCHOLARSHIP

National Association of Black Journalists
Attn: Communications Coordinator and Program Manager
University of Maryland
1100 Knight Hall, Suite 3100
College Park, MD 20742
(301) 405-2573 Fax: (301) 314-1714
E-mail: tjohnson@nabj.org
Web: www.nabj.org/?page=SEEDScholarships

Summary To provide financial assistance to high school seniors who are members of the National Association of Black Journalists (NABJ) and planning to major in journalism.

Eligibility This program is open to African American high school senior NABJ members who are planning to attend an accredited 4-year college or university and major in journalism. Applicants must have a GPA of 2.5 to 3.0 and be able to demonstrate financial need and community involvement. Along with their application, they must submit 3 samples of their work, an official college transcript, 3 letters of recommendation, a resume, and an essay of 1,000 to 2,000 words describing their biggest challenge to their career goal of being a journalist.

Financial data The stipend is $2,500.

Duration 1 year.

Number awarded 1 each year.

Deadline March of each year.

[149]
DIETETIC TECHNICIAN PROGRAM SCHOLARSHIPS

Academy of Nutrition and Dietetics
Attn: Foundation
120 South Riverside Plaza, Suite 2000
Chicago, IL 60606-6995
(312) 899-0040 Toll Free: (800) 877-1600, ext. 1133
Fax: (312) 899-4817 E-mail: scholarships@eatright.org
Web: www.eatright.org/Foundation/scholarships

Summary To provide financial assistance to underrepresented minorities and other student members of the Academy of Nutrition and Dietetics who are in the second year of a dietetic technician program.

Eligibility This program is open to A.N.D student members in the second year of study in an accredited dietetic technician program. Applicants must be U.S. citizens or permanent residents and show promise of being a valuable, contributing member of the profession. Some scholarships require membership in a specific dietetic practice group, residency in a specific state, or underrepresented minority group status. The same application form can be used for all categories.

Financial data Stipends normally range from $500 to $3,000; recently, they averaged approximately $1,870.

Duration 1 year.

Additional information The Academy of Nutrition and Dietetics was formerly the American Dietetic Association.

Number awarded Varies each year; recently, 2 of these scholarships were awarded.

Deadline February of each year.

[150]
DISTRIBUTED RESEARCH EXPERIENCES FOR UNDERGRADUATES (DREU)

Computing Research Association
1828 L Street, N.W., Suite 800
Washington, DC 20036-5104
(202) 234-2111 Fax: (202) 667-1066
E-mail: dreu@cra.org
Web: cra-w.org/undergraduate

Summary To provide an opportunity for African American and other underrepresented undergraduate students to work on a research project in computer science or engineering during the summer.

Eligibility This program is open to members of underrepresented groups (women, Hispanics, African Americans, and American Indians) who are entering their junior or senior year of college. Applicants must be interested in conducting a summer research project directly related to computer science or computer engineering under the mentorship of a faculty member at the mentor's home university. They must be U.S. citizens or permanent residents. Selection is based on the student's potential for success in graduate school, the match between the student's experience and skills and the needs of a participating professor's research project, the student's potential gain from the experience, and the possibility that the student's participation will advance the goals of the program.

Financial data Students receive a stipend of $600 per week plus relocation travel assistance up to $500.

Duration 10 weeks during the summer.

Additional information This program began in 1994 as the Distributed Mentor Project (DMP) by the Computing Research Association's Committee on the Status of Women in Computing Research (CRA-W). In 2007, the Coalition to Diversify Computing (CDC) became a cosponsor of the program and in 2009 it was given its current name. From the beginning, funding has been provided by the National Science Foundation. Other sponsors have included the Henry Luce Foundation (current), USENIX, and AAAI.

Number awarded Varies each year; recently, 53 students were selected to participate in this program.

Deadline February of each year.

[151]
DISTRICT AND INTERNATIONAL SCHOLAR OF THE YEAR AWARDS

Omega Psi Phi Fraternity
Attn: Charles R. Drew Memorial Scholarship Commission
3951 Snapfinger Parkway
Decatur, GA 30035-3203
(404) 284-5533 Fax: (404) 284-0333
E-mail: scholarshipchairman@oppf.org
Web: www.oppf.org/scholarship

Summary To recognize and reward members of Omega Psi Phi fraternity who demonstrate outstanding academic achievement and involvement in extracurricular and community activities.

Eligibility This program is open to members of the fraternity who are enrolled as a full-time sophomore or higher at a 4-year college or university. Applicants must have a GPA of 3.3 or higher. Chapters nominate their most outstanding member to the district. Each of the 13 districts selects a District Scholar of the Year winner. Those winners become candidates for the International Scholar of the Year Award. Candidates must submit a statement of 200 to 250 words on their purpose for applying for this scholarship, how they believe funds from the fraternity can assist them in achieving their career goals, and other circumstances (including financial need) that make it important for them to receive financial assistance. Selection is based on academic excellence, participation in extracurricular activities, and campus and community involvement.

Financial data District Scholars win a certificate and $6,500. The International Scholar of the Year wins an additional $10,000.

Duration The awards are presented annually.

Additional information The winners are required to attend the Omega Psi Phi Grand Conclave or Leadership Conference. Up to $1,000 in travel expenses for attendance is provided.

Number awarded Up to 13 district winners are selected each year; 1 of those is designated International Scholar of the Year.

Deadline Applications must be submitted to the district scholarship committee chair by February of each year.

[152]
DIVERSITY COMMITTEE SCHOLARSHIP

American Society of Safety Engineers
Attn: ASSE Foundation
Scholarship Award Program
1800 East Oakton Street
Des Plaines, IL 60018
(847) 699-2929 Fax: (847) 768-3434
E-mail: bzylstra@asse.org
Web: www.asse.org

Summary To provide financial assistance to African American and other diverse upper-division or graduate students who are working on a degree related to occupational safety.

Eligibility This program is open to students who are working on an undergraduate or graduate degree in occupational safety, health, environment, industrial hygiene, occupational health nursing, or a closely-related field (e.g., industrial or environmental engineering). Applicants must be full-time students who have completed at least 60 semester hours with a GPA of 3.0 or higher as undergraduates or at least 9 semester hours as graduate students. A goal of this program is to support individuals regardless of race, ethnicity, gender, religion, personal beliefs, age, sexual orientation, physical challenges, geographic location, university, or specific area of study. U.S. citizenship is not required. Membership in the American Society of Safety Engineers (ASSE) is not required, but preference is given to members.

Financial data The stipend is $1,000 per year.

Duration 1 year; recipients may reapply.

Number awarded 1 each year.

Deadline November of each year.

[153]
DIVERSITY IN PLANNING AWARD

American Planning Association-California Chapter
Attn: California Planning Foundation
c/o Paul Wack
California Polytechnic State University at San Luis Obispo
City and Regional Planning Department
San Luis Obispo, CA 93407-0283
(805) 756-6331 Fax: (805) 756-1340
E-mail: pwack@calpoly.edu
Web: www.californiaplanningfoundation.org

Summary To provide financial assistance to African American and other undergraduate and graduate students in accredited planning programs at California universities who will increase diversity in the profession.

Eligibility This program is open to students entering their final year for an undergraduate or master's degree in an accredited planning program at a university in California. Applicants must be students who will increase diversity in the planning profession. Selection is based on academic performance, professional promise, and financial need.

Financial data The stipend is $3,000. The award includes a 1-year student membership in the American Planning Association (APA) and payment of registration for the APA California Conference.

Duration 1 year.

Additional information The accredited planning programs are at 3 campuses of the California State University system (California State Polytechnic University at Pomona, California Polytechnic State University at San Luis Obispo, and San Jose State University), 3 campuses of the University of California (Berkeley, Irvine, and Los Angeles), and the University of Southern California.

Number awarded 1 each year.

Deadline March of each year.

[154]
DIVERSITY IN PSYCHOLOGY AND LAW RESEARCH AWARD

American Psychological Association
Attn: Division 41 (American Psychology-Law Society)
c/o Diane Sivasubramaniam, Minority Affairs Committee Chair
Swinburne University of Technology
Faculty of Life and Social Sciences
Mail H31
P.O. Box 218
Hawthorn, VIC 3122
Australia
61 3 9214 5858 E-mail: dsivasubramaniam@swin.edu.au
Web: www.ap-ls.org

Summary To provide funding to African American and other student members of the American Psychology-Law Society (AP-LS) who are interested in conducting a research project related to diversity.

Eligibility This program is open to undergraduate and graduate student members of AP-LS who are interested in conducting research on issues related to psychology, law, multiculturalism, and/or diversity (e.g., research pertaining to psycholegal issues on race, gender, culture, sexual orientation). Students from underrepresented groups are strongly encouraged to apply; underrepresented groups include, but are not limited to: racial and ethnic minorities; first-generation college students; lesbian, gay, bisexual, and transgender students; and physically disabled students. Applicants must submit a project description that includes a statement of the research problem, the project's likely impact on the field of psychology and law broadly, methodology, budget, and an overview of relevant literature. Selection is based on the impact of the project on diversity and multiculturalism and the expected completion within the allocated time.

Financial data The grant is $1,000.

Duration The project must be completed within 1 year.

Number awarded Up to 4 each year.

Deadline November of each year.

[155]
DON SAHLI–KATHY WOODALL MINORITY STUDENT SCHOLARSHIP

Tennessee Education Association
801 Second Avenue North
Nashville, TN 37201-1099
(615) 242-8392 Toll Free: (800) 342-8367
Fax: (615) 259-4581 E-mail: mjohnson@tea.nea.org
Web: www.teateachers.org

Summary To provide financial assistance to African American and other minority high school seniors in Tennessee who are interested in majoring in education at a college or university in the state.

Eligibility This program is open to minority high school seniors in Tennessee who are planning to attend a college or university in the state and major in education. Application must be made either by a Future Teachers of America chapter affiliated with the Tennessee Education Association (TEA) or by the student with the recommendation of an active TEA member. Selection is based on academic record, leadership ability, financial need, and demonstrated interest in becoming a teacher.

Financial data The stipend is $1,000.

Duration 1 year.

Number awarded 1 each year.

Deadline February of each year.

[156]
DONALD AND ITASKER THORNTON MEMORIAL SCHOLARSHIP

Thornton Sisters Foundation
P.O. Box 21
Atlantic Highlands, NJ 07716-0021
(732) 872-1353 E-mail: tsfoundation2001@yahoo.com
Web: www.thornton-sisters.com/ttsf.htm

Summary To provide financial assistance for college to African American and other women of color in New Jersey.

Eligibility This program is open to women of color (defined as African Americans, Latino Americans, Caribbean Americans, and Native Americans) who are graduating from high schools in New Jersey. Applicants must have a grade average of "C+" or higher and be able to document financial need. They must be planning to attend an accredited 4-year college or university. Along with their application, they must submit a 500-word essay describing their family background, personal and financial hardships, honors or academic distinctions, and community involvement and activities.

Financial data A stipend is awarded (amount not specified). Funds are to be used for tuition and/or books.

Duration 1 year; nonrenewable.

Number awarded 1 or more each year.

Deadline May of each year.

[157]
DR. ARNITA YOUNG BOSWELL SCHOLARSHIP

National Hook-Up of Black Women, Inc.
Attn: Scholarship Committee
1809 East 71st Street, Suite 205
Chicago, IL 60649-2000
(773) 667-7061 Fax: (773) 667-7064
E-mail: info@nhbwinc.com
Web: nhbwinc.com/scholarships.html

Summary To provide financial assistance to African American high school and college students who are interested in earning an undergraduate degree.

Eligibility This program is open to African American high school seniors or currently-enrolled college students. They must be attending or preparing to attend an accredited school and have a GPA of 2.75 or higher. They must demonstrate written communication skills by preparing an essay of 300 to 500 words on a topic that changes annually but relates to current events of national interest. Selection is based on academic record, financial need, community service, concern for the African American family, and a desire to complete a college degree.

Financial data The stipend is $1,000. Funds are paid directly to the college or university of the recipient's choice.

Duration 1 year.

Number awarded 5 each year.

Deadline February of each year.

[158]
DR. BLANCA MOORE-VELEZ WOMAN OF SUBSTANCE SCHOLARSHIP

National Association of Negro Business and Professional Women's Clubs
Attn: Scholarship Committee
1806 New Hampshire Avenue, N.W.
Washington, DC 20009-3206
(202) 483-4206 Fax: (202) 462-7253
E-mail: education@nanbpwc.org
Web: www.nanbpwc.org/index-11.html

Summary To provide financial assistance to mature African American women from Nevada who are interested in working on an undergraduate degree at a college in any state.

Eligibility This program is open to African American women over 35 years of age who are residents of Nevada. Applicants must be working on an undergraduate degree at an accredited college or university in any state. They must have a GPA of 3.0 or higher. Along with their application, they must submit a 500-word essay on "Challenges to the Mature Student and How I Overcame Them." Financial need is not considered in the selection process. U.S. citizenship is required.

Financial data A stipend is awarded (amount not specified).

Duration 1 year.

Number awarded 1 each year.

Deadline February of each year.

[159]
DR. JESSE BEMLEY SCHOLARSHIP

Black Data Processing Associates
Attn: BDPA Education Technology Foundation
4423 Lehigh Road, Number 277
College Park, MD 20740
(513) 284-4968 Fax: (202) 318-2194
E-mail: scholarships@betf.org
Web: www.betf.org/scholarships/jesse-bemley.shtml

Summary To recognize and reward, with college scholarships, high school students who participate in the annual national computer competition of the Black Data Processing Associates (BDPA).

Eligibility This competition is open to students who are members of a team that participates in the High School Computer Competition at the BDPA annual conference. Each team consists of 5 students. At the end of the competition, the sponsor sends award letters to all of the eligible team members who have graduated from high school, have been accepted to a 4-year degree program, and plan to major in an information technology field. Letter recipients are invited to apply for these scholarships. Selection is based on performance at the computer competition.

Financial data Awards for each member of the top teams are $2,500 for first place, $2,000 for second place, $1,500 for third place, $1,000 for fourth place, and $500 for fifth place. Funds are paid directly to the student's college or university to be used for tuition or other school expenses.

Duration The competition is held annually.

Additional information The BDPA established its Education and Technology Foundation (BETF) in 1992 to advance the skill sets needed by African American and other minority adults and young people to compete in the information technology industry. Previously, this program was known as the Student Information Technology Education & Scholarship.

Number awarded 25 each year: 5 members of each of the top 5 teams win awards.

Deadline Deadline not specified.

[160]
DR. JOHNELLA BANKS SCHOLARSHIP FUND

Black Nurses' Association of Greater Washington, D.C. Area, Inc.
Attn: Scholarship Committee Chair
P.O. Box 55285
Washington, DC 20040
(202) 291-8866
Web: www.bnaofgwdca.org/scholarships.html

Summary To provide financial assistance to nursing students from the Washington, D.C. area who have been active in the African American community.

Eligibility This program is open to students currently enrolled as sophomores, juniors, or first-semester seniors in an NLN-accredited registered nursing or practical nursing program. Applicants must be residents of Washington, D.C. or adjoining counties in Maryland (Anne Arundel, Calvert, Charles, Howard, Montgomery, and Prince George's). They must be U.S. citizens or permanent residents and have a GPA of 2.8 or higher. Along with their application, they must submit an essay that describes their personal nursing goals and objectives, their financial need, and how Black nurses can address specific needs of the African American community. Selection is based on that essay, participation in student nurses activities and organizations, community service in the greater Washington, D.C. metropolitan area, and financial need.

Financial data A stipend is awarded (amount not specified).

Duration 1 year.

Number awarded 1 or more each year.

Deadline January of each year.

[161]
DR. JULIANNE MALVEAUX SCHOLARSHIP

National Association of Negro Business and Professional Women's Clubs
Attn: Scholarship Committee
1806 New Hampshire Avenue, N.W.
Washington, DC 20009-3206
(202) 483-4206 Fax: (202) 462-7253
E-mail: education@nanbpwc.org
Web: www.nanbpwc.org/index-11.html

Summary To provide financial assistance to African American women studying journalism, economics, or a related field in college.

Eligibility This program is open to African American women enrolled at an accredited college or university as a sophomore or junior. Applicants must have a GPA of 3.0 or higher and be majoring in journalism, economics, or a related field. Along with their application, they must submit an essay, up to 1,000 words in length, on their career plans and their relevance to the theme of the program: "Black Women's Hands Can Rock the World." U.S. citizenship is required.

Financial data The stipend is $1,000.

Duration 1 year.

Number awarded 1 or more each year.

Deadline February of each year.

[162]
DR. MARTIN LUTHER KING, JR. SCHOLARSHIP

North Carolina Association of Educators, Inc.
Attn: Minority Affairs Commission
700 South Salisbury Street
P.O. Box 27347
Raleigh, NC 27611-7347
(919) 832-3000, ext. 205
Toll Free: (800) 662-7924, ext. 205
Fax: (919) 839-8229 E-mail: joy.bradford@ncae.org
Web: www.ncae.org/get-involved/awards

Summary To provide financial assistance to minority and other high school seniors in North Carolina who plan to attend college in any state.

Eligibility This program is open to seniors graduating from high schools in North Carolina who plan to attend a college or university in any state. They must have a GPA of 2.5 or higher. Along with their application, they must submit an essay on how the philosophies and ideals of Dr. Martin Luther King influenced their life. Applications are considered and judged by members of the association's Minority Affairs Commission. Selection is based on the essay, academic record, extracurricular activities and affiliations, accomplishments (honors and awards, leadership, and work experience), and financial need.

Financial data A stipend is awarded (amount not specified).

Duration 1 year.

Number awarded 1 or more each year.

Deadline March of each year.

[163]
DUANE MOORER SCHOLARSHIP

Organization of Black Aerospace Professionals, Inc.
Attn: Scholarship Coordinator
1 Westbrook Corporate Center, Suite 300
Westchester, IL 60154
(708) 449-7755 Toll Free: (800) JET-OBAP
Fax: (708) 449-7754 E-mail: obapscholarship@obap.org
Web: www.obap.org/scholarships/scholarship-opportunities

Summary To provide financial assistance to African American high school seniors in selected states who plan to work on an aerospace degree at a school in any state.

Eligibility This program is open to African American seniors graduating from high schools within 400 miles of

Memphis (includes all of Alabama, Arkansas, Kentucky, Louisiana, Mississippi, and Missouri, plus portions of northwestern Florida, western Georgia, southern Illinois, southern Indiana, eastern Kansas, eastern Oklahoma, and eastern Texas). Applicants must be interested in enrolling in a 2- or 4-year aerospace degree program. They must have a GPA of 2.5 or higher and have participated in a program of the Organization of Black Aerospace Professionals (OBAP) within the past 3 years. Along with their application, they must submit a 250-word essay on the importance of giving back.

Financial data The stipend is $2,000.

Duration 1 year.

Additional information The OBAP was originally established in 1976 as the Organization of Black Airline Pilots to make certain Blacks and other minorities had a group that would keep them informed about opportunities for advancement within commercial aviation.

Number awarded 1 each year.

Deadline May of each year.

[164]
DWIGHT DAVID EISENHOWER HISTORICALLY BLACK COLLEGES AND UNIVERSITIES TRANSPORTATION FELLOWSHIP PROGRAM

Department of Transportation
Federal Highway Administration
Attn: Universities and Grants Programs
4600 North Fairfax Drive, Suite 800
Arlington, VA 22203-1553
(703) 235-0538 Toll Free: (877) 558-6873
Fax: (703) 235-0593 E-mail: transportationedu@dot.gov
Web: www.fhwa.dot.gov/tpp/ddetfp.htm

Summary To provide financial assistance to undergraduate and graduate students working on a degree in a transportation-related field at a designated Historically Black College or University (HBCU).

Eligibility This program is open to students working on a bachelor's, master's, or doctoral degree at 1 of 18 federally-designated 4-year HBCUs. Applicants must be working on a degree in a transportation-related field (e.g., engineering, business, aviation, architecture, public policy and analysis, urban and regional planning). They must be U.S. citizens or have an I-20 (foreign student) or I-551 (permanent resident) identification card. Undergraduates must be entering at least their junior year and have a GPA of 3.0 or higher. Graduate students must have a GPA of at least 3.25. Selection is based on their proposed plan of study, academic achievement (based on class standing, GPA, and transcripts), transportation work experience, and letters of recommendation.

Financial data Fellows receive payment of full tuition and fees (to a maximum of $10,000) and a monthly stipend of $1,450 for undergraduates, $1,700 for master's students, or $2,000 for doctoral students. They are also provided with a 1-time allowance of up to $1,500 to attend the annual Transportation Research Board (TRB) meeting.

Duration 1 year.

Additional information This program is administered by the participating HBCUs. For a list, contact the sponsor.

Number awarded Varies each year.

Deadline January of each year.

[165]
DWIGHT MOSLEY SCHOLARSHIPS

United States Tennis Association
Attn: USTA Serves
70 West Red Oak Lane
White Plains, NY 10604
(914) 696-7223 E-mail: foundation@usta.com
Web: www.usta.com

Summary To provide financial assistance to female and male high school seniors who are African American or from other diverse ethnic backgrounds, have participated in an organized community tennis program, and plan to attend college in any state.

Eligibility This program is open to high school seniors from diverse ethnic backgrounds who have excelled academically, demonstrated achievements in leadership, and participated extensively in an organized community tennis program. Applicants must be planning to enroll as a full-time undergraduate student at a 4-year college or university. They must have a GPA of 3.0 or higher and be able to demonstrate financial need and sportsmanship. Along with their application, they must submit an essay of 1 to 2 pages about how their participation in a tennis and education program has influenced their life, including examples of special mentors, volunteer service, and future goals. Females and males are considered separately.

Financial data The stipend is $2,500 per year. Funds are paid directly to the recipient's college or university.

Duration 4 years.

Number awarded 2 each year: 1 female and 1 male.

Deadline February of each year.

[166]
ED BRADLEY SCHOLARSHIP

Radio Television Digital News Foundation
Attn: Programs, Awards, and Membership Manager
529 14th Street, N.W., Suite 425
Washington, DC 20045
(202) 725-8318 Fax: (202) 223-4007
E-mail: katies@rtdna.org
Web: www.rtdna.org/pages/education/scholarship-info.php

Summary To provide financial assistance to African American and other minority undergraduate students who are preparing for a career in electronic journalism.

Eligibility This program is open to sophomore or more advanced minority undergraduate students enrolled in an electronic journalism sequence at an accredited or nationally-recognized college or university. Applicants must submit 1 to 3 examples of their journalistic skills on audio CD or DVD (no more than 15 minutes total, accompanied by scripts); a description of their role on each story and a list of who worked on each story and what they did; a 1-page statement explaining why they are preparing for a career in electronic journalism with reference to their specific career preference (radio, television, online, reporting, producing, or newsroom management); a resume; and a letter of reference from their dean or faculty sponsor explaining why they are a good candidate for the award and certifying that they have at least 1 year of school remaining.

Financial data The stipend is $10,000, paid in semiannual installments of $5,000 each.

Duration 1 year.

Additional information The Radio Television Digital News Foundation (RTDNF) also provides an all-expense paid trip to the Radio Television Digital News Association (RTDNA) annual international conference. The RTDNF was formerly the Radio and Television News Directors Foundation (RTNDF). Previous winners of any RTDNF scholarship or internship are not eligible.

Number awarded 1 each year.

Deadline May of each year.

[167]
EDITH M. ALLEN SCHOLARSHIPS

United Methodist Church
Attn: General Board of Higher Education and Ministry
Office of Loans and Scholarships
1001 19th Avenue South
P.O. Box 340007
Nashville, TN 37203-0007
(615) 340-7344 Fax: (615) 340-7367
E-mail: umscholar@gbhem.org
Web: www.gbhem.org

Summary To provide financial assistance to Methodist students who are African American and working on an undergraduate or graduate degree in specified fields.

Eligibility This program is open to full-time undergraduate and graduate students at Methodist colleges and universities (preferably Historically Black United Methodist colleges) who have been active, full members of a United Methodist Church for at least 3 years prior to applying. Applicants must be African Americans working on a degree in education, social work, medicine, and/or other health professions. They must have at least a "B+" average and be recognized as a person whose academic and vocational contributions will help improve the quality of life for others.

Financial data Stipends average $1,000.

Duration 1 year; recipients may reapply.

Number awarded Varies each year.

Deadline February of each year.

[168]
EDSA MINORITY SCHOLARSHIP

Landscape Architecture Foundation
Attn: Leadership in Landscape Scholarship Program
818 18th Street, N.W., Suite 810
Washington, DC 20006-3520
(202) 331-7070 Fax: (202) 331-7079
E-mail: scholarships@lafoundation.org
Web: www.lafoundation.org

Summary To provide financial assistance to African American and other minority college students who are interested in studying landscape architecture.

Eligibility This program is open to African American, Hispanic, Native American, and minority college students of other cultural and ethnic backgrounds. Applicants must be entering their final 2 years of undergraduate study in landscape architecture. Along with their application, they must submit a 500-word essay on a design or research effort they plan to pursue (explaining how it will contribute to the advancement of the profession and to their ethnic heritage), 3 work samples, and 2 letters of recommendation. Selection is based on professional experience, community involvement, extracurricular activities, and financial need.

Financial data The stipend is $5,000.

Additional information This scholarship was formerly designated the Edward D. Stone, Jr. and Associates Minority Scholarship.

Number awarded 1 each year.

Deadline February of each year.

[169]
EDUCATION ASSISTANCE PROGRAM

Accountancy Board of Ohio
77 South High Street, 18th Floor
Columbus, OH 43215-6128
(614) 466-4135 Fax: (614) 466-2628
Web: acc.ohio.gov/CPAExam/EducationAssistance.aspx

Summary To provide financial assistance to African American or other minority/financially disadvantaged students enrolled in an accounting education program at Ohio academic institutions approved by the Accountancy Board of Ohio.

Eligibility This program is open to minority and financially disadvantaged Ohio residents who apply as full-time juniors or seniors in an accounting program at an accredited college or university in the state. Students who remain in good standing at their institutions and who enter a qualified fifth-year program are then eligible to receive these funds. Minority is defined as people with significant ancestry from Africa (excluding the Middle East), Asia (excluding the Middle East), Central America and the Caribbean islands, South America, and the islands of the Pacific Ocean; in addition, persons with significant ancestry from the original peoples of North America who are of non-European descent. Financial disadvantage is defined according to information provided on the Free Application for Federal Student Aid (FAFSA). U.S. citizenship or permanent resident status is required.

Financial data The amount of the stipend is determined annually but does not exceed the in-state tuition at Ohio public universities (currently, $13,067).

Duration 1 year (the fifth year of an accounting program). Funds committed to students who apply as juniors must be used within 4 years and funds committed to students who apply as seniors must be used within 3 years. The award is nonrenewable and may only be used when the student enrolls in the fifth year of a program.

Number awarded Several each year.

Deadline Applications may be submitted at any time.

[170]
EDWARD S. ROTH MANUFACTURING ENGINEERING SCHOLARSHIP

Society of Manufacturing Engineers
Attn: SME Education Foundation
One SME Drive
P.O. Box 930
Dearborn, MI 48121-0930
(313) 425-3300 Toll Free: (800) 733-4763, ext. 3300
Fax: (313) 425-3411 E-mail: foundation@sme.org
Web: www.smeef.org/scholarships

Summary To provide financial assistance to African Americans and other students enrolled or planning to work on a bachelor's or master's degree in manufacturing engineering at selected universities.

Eligibility This program is open to U.S. citizens who are graduating high school seniors or currently-enrolled undergraduate or graduate students. Applicants must be enrolled or planning to enroll as a full-time student at 1 of 13 selected 4-year universities to work on a bachelor's or master's degree in manufacturing engineering. They must have a GPA of 3.0 or higher. Preference is given to 1) students demonstrating financial need; 2) minority students; and 3) students participating in a co-op program. Some preference may also be given to graduating high school seniors and graduate students. Along with their application, they must submit a 300-word essay that covers their career and educational objectives, how this scholarship will help them attain those objectives, and why they want to enter this field.

Financial data Stipend amounts vary; recently, the value of all scholarships provided by this foundation averaged approximately $2,330.

Duration 1 year; may be renewed.

Additional information The eligible institutions are California Polytechnic State University at San Luis Obispo, California State Polytechnic State University at Pomona, University of Miami (Florida), Bradley University (Illinois), Central State University (Ohio), Miami University (Ohio), Boston University, Worcester Polytechnic Institute (Massachusetts), University of Massachusetts, St. Cloud State University (Minnesota), University of Texas-Pan American, Brigham Young University (Utah), and Utah State University.

Number awarded 2 each year.

Deadline January of each year.

[171]
ELI LILLY AND COMPANY/BLACK DATA PROCESSING ASSOCIATES SCHOLARSHIP

Black Data Processing Associates
Attn: BDPA Education Technology Foundation
4423 Lehigh Road, Number 277
College Park, MD 20740
(513) 284-4968 Fax: (202) 318-2194
E-mail: scholarships@betf.org
Web: www.betf.org/scholarships/eli-lilly.shtml

Summary To provide financial assistance to African American and other minority high school seniors or current college students who are interested in studying information technology at a college in any state.

Eligibility This program is open to graduating high school seniors and current college undergraduates who are members of minority groups (African American, Hispanic, Asian, or Native American). Applicants must be enrolled or planning to enroll at an accredited 4-year college or university and work on a degree in information technology. They must have a GPA of 3.0 or higher. Along with their application, they must submit a 500-word essay on why information technology is important. Selection is based on that essay, academic achievement, leadership ability through academic or civic involvement, and participation in community service activities. U.S. citizenship or permanent resident status is required.

Financial data The stipend is $2,500. Funds may be used to pay for tuition, fees, books, room and board, or other college-related expenses.

Duration 1 year; nonrenewable.

Additional information The BDPA established its Education and Technology Foundation (BETF) in 1992 to advance the skill sets needed by African American and other minority adults and young people to compete in the information technology industry. This program is sponsored by Eli Lilly and Company.

Number awarded 1 or more each year.

Deadline July of each year.

[172]
ELIZABETH M. SMITH MEMORIAL SCHOLARSHIP

Delta Sigma Theta Sorority, Inc.-Boston Alumnae Chapter
Attn: Scholarship Committee
P.O. Box 51424
Boston, MA 02205
(617) 548-3642 E-mail: bac_dst@yahoo.com
Web: www.cityofboston.gov

Summary To provide financial assistance to African American women from Massachusetts interested in working on a degree in social sciences.

Eligibility This program is open to African American women who either live or attend an accredited college or university in Massachusetts. Applicants must be sophomores, juniors, or seniors who are majoring in the social sciences and have a GPA of 3.0 or higher. They must be able to demonstrate academic achievement, commitment to community service, motivation, character, and ability to overcome adversity and meet challenges.

Financial data The stipend is $1,000.

Duration 1 year.

Additional information The sponsor is the local alumnae chapter of a traditionally African American social sorority.

Number awarded 1 each year.

Deadline February of each year.

[173]
ELLA TACKWOOD FUND

United Methodist Higher Education Foundation
Attn: Scholarships Administrator
60 Music Square East, Suite 350
P.O. Box 340005
Nashville, TN 37203-0005
(615) 649-3990 Toll Free: (800) 811-8110
Fax: (615) 649-3980
E-mail: umhefscholarships@umhef.org
Web: www.umhef.org/scholarship-info

Summary To provide financial assistance to Methodist undergraduate and graduate students at Historically Black Colleges and Universities of the United Methodist Church.

Eligibility This program is open to students enrolling as full-time undergraduate and graduate students at the Historically Black Colleges and Universities of the United Methodist Church. Applicants must have been active, full members of a United Methodist Church for at least 1 year prior to applying. They must have a GPA of 2.5 or higher and be able to demonstrate financial need. U.S. citizenship or permanent resident status is required.

Financial data The stipend is at least $1,000 per year.

Duration 1 year; nonrenewable.

Additional information This program began in 1985. The qualifying schools are Bennett College for Women, Bethune-Cookman University, Claflin University, Clark Atlanta University, Dillard University, Huston-Tillotson College, Meharry Medical College, Paine College, Philander Smith College, Rust College, and Wiley College.

Number awarded Varies each year; recently, 2 of these scholarships were awarded.

Deadline February of each year.

[174]
ELLIS/CORLEY SCHOLARSHIP

National Naval Officers Association-Washington, D.C. Chapter
c/o LCDR Stephen Williams
P.O. Box 30784
Alexandria, VA 22310
(703) 566-3840 Fax: (703) 566-3813
E-mail: Stephen.Williams@navy.mil
Web: dcnnoa.memberlodge.com

Summary To provide financial assistance to female African American high school seniors from the Washington, D.C. area who are interested in attending an Historically Black College or University (HBCU) in any state.

Eligibility This program is open to female African American seniors graduating from high schools in the Washington, D.C. metropolitan area who plan to enroll full time at an HBCU in any state. Applicants must have a GPA of 2.5 or higher and be U.S. citizens or permanent residents. Selection is based on academic achievement, community involvement, and financial need.

Financial data The stipend is $1,000.

Duration 1 year; nonrenewable.

Additional information Recipients are not required to join or affiliate with the military in any way.

Number awarded 1 each year.

Deadline March of each year.

[175]
ELSIE MAE WHITE MEMORIAL SCHOLARSHIP FUND

Columbus Foundation
Attn: Scholarship Manager
1234 East Broad Street
Columbus, OH 43205-1453
(614) 251-4000 Fax: (614) 251-4009
E-mail: dhigginbotham@columbusfoundation.org
Web: tcfapp.org

Summary To provide financial assistance for college or graduate school to African American high school seniors and college students from any state.

Eligibility This program is open to African American high school seniors and college students. High school seniors must rank in the top third of their class; college students must have a GPA of 2.8 or higher. Applicants must be attending or planning to attend an accredited college or university in the United States as a full- or part-time undergraduate or graduate student. Preference is given to students at land grant colleges and universities. Along with their application, they must submit 300-word essays on 1) their educational and career plans and goals, why they have chosen their particular field, and why they think they will be a success; 2) why they feel they need this scholarship, especially as related to financial need; and 3) any other information that will assist the selection committee in making its decision.

Financial data The stipend is $1,000.

Duration 1 year.

Number awarded Varies each year.

Deadline May of each year.

[176]
EMMA AND MELOID ALGOOD SCHOLARSHIP

National Association of Black Social Workers
Attn: NABSW Scholarships
2305 Martin Luther King Avenue, S.E.
Washington, DC 20020
(202) 678-4570 Fax: (202) 678-4572
E-mail: office-manager@nabsw.org
Web: www.nabsw.org/mserver/Forms.aspx

Summary To provide financial assistance to members of the National Association of Black Social Workers (NABSW) who are working on a bachelor's degree.

Eligibility This program is open to African American members of NABSW working full time on a bachelor's degree at an accredited U.S. social work or social welfare program with a GPA of 2.5 or higher. Applicants must be able to demonstrate community service. Along with their application, they must submit an essay of 2 to 3 pages on their professional interests, future social work aspirations, previous social work experiences (volunteer and professional), and honors and achievements (academic and community service). Financial need is considered in the selection process.

Financial data The stipend is $1,000. Funds are sent directly to the recipient's school.

Duration 1 year.

Number awarded 1 each year.

Deadline January of each year.

[177]
EMPIRE STATE DIVERSITY HONORS SCHOLARSHIP PROGRAM

State University of New York
Attn: Office of Diversity, Equity and Inclusion
State University Plaza
353 Broadway
Albany, NY 12246
(518) 320-1189
Web: www.suny.edu/provost/odee/programs.cfm

Summary To provide financial assistance to residents of New York (particularly African Americans and other underrepresented minorities) who are attending campuses of the State University of New York (SUNY) and will contribute to the diversity of the student body.

Eligibility This program is open to U.S. citizens and permanent residents who are New York residents and enrolled as undergraduate students at any of the participating SUNY colleges. Applicants must be able to demonstrate 1) how they will contribute to the diversity of the student body, primarily by having overcome a disadvantage or other impediment to success in higher education; and 2) high academic achievement. Economic disadvantage, although not a requirement, may be the basis for eligibility. Membership in a racial or ethnic group that is underrepresented at the applicant's school or program may serve as a plus factor in making awards, but may not form the sole basis of selection.

Financial data The maximum stipend provided by the SUNY system is half the student's cost of attendance or $3,000, whichever is less. The individual campus must match the SUNY award in an equal amount.

Duration 1 year; renewable.

Number awarded Varies each year; recently, nearly 1,000 students at 46 SUNY institutions received support from this program.

Deadline Deadline not specified.

[178]
ENCOURAGE MINORITY PARTICIPATION IN OCCUPATIONS WITH EMPHASIS ON REHABILITATION

Courage Center
Attn: EMPOWER Scholarship Program
3915 Golden Valley Road
Minneapolis, MN 55422
(763) 520-0214 Toll Free: (888) 8-INTAKE
Fax: (763) 520-0562 TDD: (763) 520-0245
E-mail: empower@couragecenter.org
Web: www.couragecenter.org

Summary To provide financial assistance to African Americans and other students of color from Minnesota and western Wisconsin interested in attending college in any state to prepare for a career in the medical rehabilitation field.

Eligibility This program is open to ethnically diverse students accepted at or enrolled in an institution of higher learning in any state. Applicants must be residents of Minnesota or western Wisconsin (Burnett, Pierce, Polk, and St. Croix counties). They must be able to demonstrate a career interest in the medical rehabilitation field by a record of volunteer involvement related to health care and must have a GPA of 2.0 or higher. Along with their application, they must submit a 1-page essay that covers their experiences and interactions to date with the area of volunteering, what they have accomplished and gained from those experiences, how those experiences will assist them in their future endeavors, why education is important to them, how this scholarship will help them with their financial need and their future career goals.

Financial data The stipend is $1,500.

Duration 1 year.

Additional information This program, established in 1995, is also identified by its acronym as the EMPOWER Scholarship Award.

Number awarded 2 each year.

Deadline May of each year.

[179]
ENDOCRINE SOCIETY SUMMER RESEARCH FELLOWSHIPS

Endocrine Society
Attn: Summer Research Fellowships
8401 Connecticut Avenue, Suite 900
Chevy Chase, MD 20815
(301) 951-2616 Toll Free: (888) 363-6274
Fax: (301) 576-7787 E-mail: awards@endo-society.org
Web: www.endo-society.org

Summary To provide funding to undergraduate, medical, and graduate students (particularly African Americans and other underrepresented minorities) who are interested in conducting a research project during the summer in endocrinology.

Eligibility This program is open to full-time students who are undergraduates in the third year of study or higher, medical students beyond their first year of study, and first-year graduate students. Applicants must be interested in participating in a research project under the supervision of a mentor. The mentor must be an active member of the Endocrine Society. Each member may sponsor only 1 student. Projects must be relevant to an aspect of endocrinology and are expected to have clearly defined research goals; students should not function as aides or general research assistants. Applications on behalf of underrepresented minority students are especially encouraged.

Financial data The grant of $4,000 provides funding for a stipend, fringe benefits, and indirect costs.

Duration 10 to 12 weeks during the summer.

Additional information At the conclusion of the fellowship period, students must submit a 1-page summary of their research project explaining how the fellowship affected their consideration of a career in endocrinology.

Number awarded 20 each year.

Deadline January of each year.

[180]
ENTERTAINMENT SOFTWARE ASSOCIATION FOUNDATION SCHOLARSHIPS

Entertainment Software Association
Attn: ESA Foundation
317 Madison Avenue, 22nd Floor
New York, NY 10017
(917) 522-3250
Web: www.esafoundation.org/scholarship.asp

Summary To provide financial assistance to African Americans, other minorities, and women who are interested in attending college to prepare for a career in computer and video game arts.

Eligibility This program is open to women and members of minority groups who are high school seniors or undergraduates currently enrolled full time at an accredited 4-year college or university. Applicants must be interested in working on a degree leading to a career in computer and video game arts. They must be U.S. citizens and have a GPA of 2.75 or higher.

Financial data The stipend is $3,000.

Duration 1 year; nonrenewable.

Additional information This program began in 2007.

Number awarded Up to 30 each year: 15 to graduating high school seniors and 15 to current undergraduates.

Deadline May of each year.

[181]
ENVIRONMENTAL STUDIES SCHOLARSHIPS

Congressional Black Caucus Foundation, Inc.
Attn: Director, Educational Programs
1720 Massachusetts Avenue, N.W.
Washington, DC 20036
(202) 263-2800 Toll Free: (800) 784-2577
Fax: (202) 775-0773 E-mail: scholarships@cbcfinc.org
Web: www.cbcfinc.org/scholarships.html

Summary To provide financial assistance to African American and female upper-division students who are working on a degree in environmental science.

Eligibility This program is open to African Americans and women who are currently enrolled as full-time juniors at a 4-year college or university. Applicants must be working on a degree in environmental science and have a GPA of 2.5 or higher. They must be able to demonstrate understanding and acceptance of ServiceMaster's core values. Along with their application, they must submit a personal statement of 500 to 1,000 words on 1) their future goals, major field of study, and how that field of study will help them to achieve their future career goals; 2) involvement in school activities, community and public service, hobbies, and sports; 3) how receiving this award will affect their current and future plans; and 4) other experiences, skills, or qualifications. They must also be able to demonstrate financial need, leadership ability, and participation in community service activities. Preference is given to students who plan to complete a 4-year degree and work in an underserved community. U.S. citizenship or permanent resident status is required.

Financial data The stipend is $10,000. Funds are paid directly to the student's institution.

Duration 1 year.

Additional information This program is sponsored by ServiceMaster.

Number awarded 2 each year.

Deadline March of each year.

[182]
EPA GREATER RESEARCH OPPORTUNITIES (GRO) FELLOWSHIPS FOR UNDERGRADUATE ENVIRONMENTAL STUDY

Environmental Protection Agency
Attn: National Center for Environmental Research
Ariel Rios Building
1200 Pennsylvania Avenue, N.W.
Washington, DC 20460
(202) 347-8049 Toll Free: (800) 490-9194
E-mail: boddie.georgette@epa.gov
Web: www.epa.gov/careers/fellowships

Summary To provide financial aid and summer internships to undergraduates who are enrolled fields related to the environment at colleges and universities (particularly Minority Serving Institutions) that receive limited federal funding.

Eligibility This program is open to U.S. citizens or permanent residents who are enrolled full time at a college or university in this country that receives less than $35 million in federal research and development expenditures. Students attending eligible institutions with significant minority enrollment (defined as Minority-Serving Institutions) are particularly encouraged to apply. Applicants must have at least 2 years remaining for completion of a bachelor's degree in an environmentally-related field, such as biology, health, the social sciences, or engineering. They must be available to work as interns at an EPA facility during the summer between their junior and senior years. A goal of the program is to meet the need for scientists from underrepresented backgrounds, so the sponsor strongly encourages women, minorities, and persons with disabilities to apply. A minimum average of "B" overall is required.

Financial data The fellowship provides up to $20,700 per year for academic support and $8,600 for internship support.

Duration The final 2 years of baccalaureate study, including 12 weeks during the summer between those years.

Additional information This program began in 1982. It was formerly known as Culturally Diverse Academic Institutions Undergraduate Student Fellowships program and subsequently as Minority Academic Institutions Undergraduate Student Fellowships.

Number awarded Approximately 40 each year.

Deadline December of each year.

[183]
ETHEL LEE HOOVER ELLIS SCHOLARSHIP

National Association of Negro Business and Professional Women's Clubs
Attn: Scholarship Committee
1806 New Hampshire Avenue, N.W.
Washington, DC 20009-3206
(202) 483-4206 Fax: (202) 462-7253
E-mail: education@nanbpwc.org
Web: www.nanbpwc.org/index-11.html

Summary To provide financial assistance to African American women from designated southern states studying business at a college in any state.

Eligibility This program is open to African Americans women who are residents of Alabama, Florida, Georgia, Mississippi, North Carolina, South Carolina, Tennessee, or West Virginia. Applicants must be enrolled at an accredited college or university in any state as a sophomore or junior. They must have a GPA of 3.0 or higher and be majoring in business. Along with their application, they must submit an essay, up to 750 words in length, on the topic, "Business and Community United." U.S. citizenship is required.

Financial data A stipend is awarded (amount not specified).

Duration 1 year.

Number awarded 1 or more each year.

Deadline February of each year.

[184]
EXCELLENCE IN DIVERSITY SCHOLARSHIPS

New Jersey Utilities Association
50 West State Street, Suite 1117
Trenton, NJ 08608
(609) 392-1000 Fax: (609) 396-4231
E-mail: info@njua.com
Web: www.njua.com/html/njua_eeo_scholarship.cfm

Summary To provide financial assistance to high school seniors in New Jersey who are African Americans, members of other minority groups, females, or individuals with disabilities and interested in attending college in any state.

Eligibility This program is open to seniors graduating from high schools in New Jersey who are women, minorities (Black or African American, Hispanic or Latino, American Indian or Alaska Native, Asian, Native Hawaiian or Pacific Islander, or 2 or more races), and persons with disabilities. Applicants must be planning to work on a bachelor's degree at a college or university in any state. Along with their application, they must submit a 500-word essay explaining their career ambition and why they have chosen that career. Children of employees of any New Jersey Utilities Association-member company are ineligible. Selection is based on overall academic excellence and demonstrated financial need. U.S. citizenship or permanent resident status is required.

Financial data The stipend is $1,500 per year. Funds are paid to the recipient's college or university.

Duration 4 years.

Number awarded 2 each year.

Deadline March of each year.

[185]
EXECUTIVE LEADERSHIP COUNCIL NATIONAL ESSAY CONTEST

Executive Leadership Council
Attn: Executive Leadership Foundation
1001 North Fairfax Street, Suite 300
Alexandria, VA 22314
(703) 706-5200 E-mail: elcinfo@elcinfo.com
Web: www.elcinfo.com/higher_education.php

Summary To recognize and reward outstanding essays written by African American students on selected business topics.

Eligibility This competition is open to African American undergraduate students in good academic standing enrolled in an accredited college or university. They must write an essay between 2,000 and 3,000 words on a topic that changes each year; recently, applicants were invited to write on the topic, "Millenial Perspectives: Aligning Corporate Values."

Financial data The first-place winner receives a $7,000 award, second $6,000, third $5,000, fourth $4,000, fifth $3,000, and each sixth place $1,000. All contest winners receive a trip to New York City and Washington D.C. to participate in the foundation's Student Honors Symposium.

Duration The competition is held annually.

Additional information The Executive Leadership Foundation was founded in 1989 as an affiliate of the Executive Leadership Council, the association of African American senior executives of Fortune 500 companies. This competition is sponsored by the Coca-Cola Company.

Number awarded 10 each year: 1 for each of the first 5 places and 5 sixth-place winners.

Deadline May of each year.

[186]
EXXONMOBIL BERNARD HARRIS MATH AND SCIENCE SCHOLARSHIPS

Council of the Great City Schools
1301 Pennsylvania Avenue, N.W., Suite 702
Washington, DC 20004
(202) 393-2427 Fax: (202) 393-2400
Web: www.cgcs.org/Page/47

Summary To provide financial assistance to African American and Hispanic high school seniors interested in studying science, technology, engineering, or mathematics (STEM) in college.

Eligibility This program is open to African American and Hispanic seniors graduating from high schools in a district that is a member of the Council of the Great City Schools, a coalition of 65 of the nation's largest urban public school systems. Applicants must be planning to enroll full time at a 4-year college or university and major in a STEM field of study. They must have a GPA of 3.0 or higher. Along with their application, they must submit 1-page essays on 1) how mathematics and science education has impacted their lives so far; and 2) why they have chosen to prepare for a career in a STEM field. Selection is based on those essays; academic achievement; extracurricular activities, community service, or other experiences that demonstrate commitment to a career in a STEM field; and 3 letters of recommendation. Financial need is not considered. Males and females are judged separately.

Financial data The stipend is $5,000.

Duration 1 year; nonrenewable.

Additional information This program, which began in 2010, is sponsored by the ExxonMobil Corporation and The Harris Foundation.

Number awarded 4 each year: an African American male and female and an Hispanic male and female.

Deadline May of each year.

[187]
EXXONMOBIL NSBE CORPORATE SCHOLARSHIPS

National Society of Black Engineers
Attn: Programs Department
205 Daingerfield Road
Alexandria, VA 22314
(703) 549-2207 Fax: (703) 683-5312
E-mail: scholarships@nsbe.org
Web: www.nsbe.org/Programs/Scholarships.aspx

Summary To provide financial assistance to members of the National Society of Black Engineers (NSBE) who are majoring in designated engineering fields.

Eligibility This program is open to members of the society who are college sophomores or juniors majoring in chemical, civil, electrical, or mechanical engineering. Applicants must have a GPA of 3.5 or higher. Along with their application, they must submit essays of 300 words on 1) the advice they would offer fellow engineering students to motivate them to make academic excellence a priority in their college career; and 2) why academic excellence has been a priority in their college career.

Financial data The stipend is $2,000.

Duration 1 year.

Additional information This program is sponsored by ExxonMobil Corporation.

Number awarded Up to 10 each year.

Deadline May of each year.

[188]
FARM CREDIT EAST SCHOLARSHIPS

Farm Credit East
Attn: Scholarship Program
240 South Road
Enfield, CT 06082
(860) 741-4380 Toll Free: (800) 562-2235
Fax: (860) 741-4389
E-mail: specialoffers@famcrediteast.com
Web: www.farmcrediteast.com

Summary To provide financial assistance to African American and other residents of designated northeastern states who plan to attend school in any state to work on an undergraduate or graduate degree in a field related to agriculture, forestry, or fishing.

Eligibility This program is open to residents of Massachusetts, Connecticut, Rhode Island, New Jersey, and portions of New York and New Hampshire. Applicants must be working on or planning to work on an associate, bachelor's, or graduate degree in production agriculture, agribusiness, the forest products industry, or commercial fishing at a college or university in any state. They must submit a 200-word essay on why they wish to prepare for a career in agriculture, forestry, or fishing. Selection is based on the essay, extracurricular activities (especially farm work experience and activities indicative of an interest in preparing for a career in agriculture or agribusiness), and interest in agriculture. The program includes diversity scholarships reserved for members of minority groups (Black or African American, American Indian or Alaska Native, Asian, Native Hawaiian or other Pacific Islander, or Hispanic or Latino).

Financial data The stipend is $1,500. Funds are paid directly to the student to be used for tuition, room and board, books, and other academic charges.

Duration 1 year; nonrenewable.

Additional information Recipients are given priority for an internship with the sponsor in the summer following their junior year. Farm Credit East was formerly named First Pioneer Farm Credit.

Number awarded Up to 28 each year, including several diversity scholarships.

Deadline April of each year.

[189]
FEDERAL CITY ALUMNAE CHAPTER ACADEMIC EXCELLENCE SCHOLARSHIPS

Delta Sigma Theta Sorority, Inc.-Federal City Alumnae Chapter
Attn: Educational Development Committee
P.O. Box 1605
Washington, DC 20013
(202) 545-1913 E-mail: thefcacdst@yahoo.com
Web: thefcacdst.org

Summary To provide financial assistance to African American and other high school seniors in Washington, D.C. who plan to attend a 4-year college or university in any state.

Eligibility This program is open to seniors graduating from public or charter high schools in the District of Columbia and planning to enroll full time at an accredited 4-year college or university in any state. Applicants must have a GPA of 3.3 or higher. Along with their application, they must submit a 500-word essay on either how they plan to use their education to make the world a better place or why they should be selected to receive this scholarship.

Financial data The stipend is $5,000.

Duration 1 year.

Additional information The sponsor is the local alumnae chapter of a traditionally African American social sorority.

Number awarded 2 each year.

Deadline February of each year.

[190]
FEDERAL CITY ALUMNAE CHAPTER HBCU SCHOLARSHIPS

Delta Sigma Theta Sorority, Inc.-Federal City Alumnae Chapter
Attn: Educational Development Committee
P.O. Box 1605
Washington, DC 20013
(202) 545-1913 E-mail: thefcacdst@yahoo.com
Web: thefcacdst.org

Summary To provide financial assistance to high school seniors in Washington, D.C. who plan to attend a 4-year Historically Black College or University (HBCU) in any state.

Eligibility This program is open to seniors graduating from public or charter high schools in the District of Columbia and planning to enroll full time at an accredited 4-year HBCU in any state. Applicants must have a GPA of 2.5 or higher. Along with their application, they must submit a 500-word essay on either how they plan to use their education to make the world a better place or why they should be selected to receive this scholarship.

Financial data The stipend is $2,000.

Duration 1 year.

Additional information The sponsor is the local alumnae chapter of a traditionally African American social sorority.

Number awarded 2 each year.

Deadline February of each year.

[191]
FEDERAL EMPLOYEE EDUCATION & ASSISTANCE (FEEA)-NABNA SCHOLARSHIP FUND

National Association of Black Narcotic Agents
c/o Federal Employee Education and Assistance Fund
Attn: Scholarship Program
3333 South Wadsworth Boulevard, Suite 300
Lakewood, CO 80227
(303) 933-7580 Toll Free: (800) 323-4140
Fax: (303) 933-7587 E-mail: admin@feea.org
Web: www.nabna.org/content/feea

Summary To provide financial assistance for college or graduate school to members of the National Association of Black Narcotic Agents (NABNA) and their dependents.

Eligibility This program is open to federal employees who are NABNA members and their dependent spouses and children entering or enrolled in an accredited 2- or 4-year undergraduate, graduate, or postgraduate program. Dependents must be full-time students; federal employees may be part-time students. Applicants or their sponsoring federal employee must have at least 3 years of civilian federal service. Along with their application, they must submit a 2-page essay on a topic related to a career in public service with the federal government, a letter of recommendation, a transcript with a GPA of 3.0 or higher, and a copy of their federal "Notice of Personnel Action;" high school seniors must also submit a copy of their ACT, SAT, or other examination scores. Financial need is not considered in the selection process.

Financial data The stipend is $1,000 per year.

Duration 1 year; may be renewed.

Additional information This program is jointly administered by NABNA and the Federal Employee Education and Assistance Fund (FEEA).

Number awarded 1 or more each year.

Deadline March of each year.

[192]
FELICIA C. BRADY SCHOLARSHIP FUND

Black Nurses' Association of Greater Washington, D.C. Area, Inc.
Attn: Scholarship Committee Chair
P.O. Box 55285
Washington, DC 20040
(202) 291-8866
Web: www.bnaofgwdca.org/scholarships.html

Summary To provide financial assistance to registered nurses from the Washington, D.C. area who are members of the National Black Nurses' Association and its local affiliate, and are interested in working on an advanced degree.

Eligibility This program is open to registered nurses who are currently enrolled in an associate, bachelor's, master's, or doctoral program and have a GPA of 3.0 or higher. Applicants must be residents of Washington, D.C. or adjoining counties in Maryland (Anne Arundel, Calvert, Charles, Howard, Montgomery, and Prince George's). They must be U.S. citizens, members of the National Black Nurses' Association, and members of the Black Nurses' Association of Greater Washington, D.C. Area. Along with their application, they must submit a copy of their nursing license, an official transcript from their nursing program, 2 letters of recommendation, and a written essay that describes their personal goals and objectives, financial need, and contributions to nursing and community service involvement in the greater Washington, D.C. area.

Financial data A stipend is awarded (amount not specified).

Duration 1 year.

Number awarded 1 each year.

Deadline January of each year.

[193]
FIFTH EPISCOPAL DISTRICT/FRED J. STUART SCHOLARSHIP OF EXCELLENCE

African Methodist Episcopal Church
Fifth Episcopal District Lay Organization
4519 Admiralty Way, Suite 205
Marina del Rey, CA 90295
(310) 577-8530 Fax: (310) 577-8540
E-mail: bishoptkirkland@aol.com
Web: fifthdistrictlay.org/scholarship

Summary To provide financial assistance to members of African Methodist Episcopal (AME) churches in its Fifth Episcopal District who are interested in attending college in any state.

Eligibility This program is open to residents of the AME Fifth Episcopal District (Alaska, Arizona, California, Colorado, Idaho, Kansas, Missouri, Montana, Nebraska, Nevada, New Mexico, North Dakota, Oregon, South Dakota, Utah, Washington, and Wyoming) who are graduating high school seniors and planning to attend an accredited institution of higher learning in any state. Applicants must have been a member of an AME church for at least 12 months and have been an active member of its Lay Organization, the Women's Missionary Society, or the Men's Ministry. They must have a GPA of 3.0 or higher. Along with their application, they must submit a 250-word personal essay that describes their long-range plans, community and church involvement, accomplishments or special awards, challenges they have faced, and how they responded. Selection is based on that essay (30%), academic record (30%), letters of recommendation (15%), participation in church lay organizations (15%), and quality of application (10%).

Financial data The stipend is $1,000.

Duration 1 year.

Number awarded 1 each year.

Deadline May of each year.

[194]
FLORIDA BOARD OF ACCOUNTANCY MINORITY SCHOLARSHIPS

Florida Department of Business and Professional Regulation
Attn: Division of Certified Public Accounting
240 N.W. 76th Drive, Suite A
Gainesville, FL 32607-6656
(850) 487-1395 Fax: (352) 333-2508
Web: www.myfloridalicense.com/dbpr/cpa

Summary To provide financial assistance to minority and female residents of Florida who are entering the fifth year of an accounting program.

Eligibility This program is open to Florida residents who have completed at least 120 credit hours at a college or university in the state and have a GPA of 2.5 or higher. Applicants must be planning to remain in school as a full-time student for the fifth year required to sit for the C.P.A. examination. They must be members of a minority group, defined to include African Americans, Hispanic Americans, Asian Americans, Native Americans, or women. Selection is based on scholastic ability and performance and financial need.

Financial data The stipend is $3,000 per semester.

Duration 1 semester; may be renewed 1 additional semester.

Number awarded Varies each year; a total of $100,000 is available for this program annually.

Deadline May of each year.

[195]
FLORIDA CHAPTER AABE SCHOLARSHIPS

American Association of Blacks in Energy-Florida Chapter
c/o Atanya Lewis, Scholarship Committee
700 Universe Boulevard, JNE/JB
Juno Beach, FL 33408
E-mail: Atanya.Lewis@fpl.com
Web: www.aabe.org/index.php?component=pages&id=811

Summary To provide financial assistance to African Americans and members of other underrepresented minority groups who are high school seniors in any state and planning to major in an energy-related field at a college in Florida.

Eligibility This program is open to seniors graduating from high schools in any state and planning to attend an accredited college or university in Florida. Applicants must be African Americans, Hispanics, or Native Americans who have a GPA of 3.0 or higher and who can demonstrate financial need. Their intended major must be business, engineering, technology, mathematics, the physical sciences, or other energy-related field. Along with their application, they must submit a 350-word statement on why they should receive this scholarship, how their professional career objectives relate to energy, and any other relevant information.

Financial data A stipend is awarded (amount not specified).

Duration 1 year.

Additional information The winner is eligible to compete for regional and national scholarships.

Number awarded Varies each year; a total of $5,000 is available for this program annually.

Deadline February of each year.

[196] FLORIDA GOVERNOR'S BLACK HISTORY MONTH ESSAY CONTEST

Office of the Governor
Attn: Black History Month Committee
111 North Gadsden Street, Suite 100
Tallahassee, FL 32301
(850) 410-0696 Fax: (850) 413-0909
E-mail: blackhistoryessay@myflorida.com
Web: www.floridablackhistory.com/essay.cfm

Summary To recognize and reward, with college scholarships, students in Florida who submit outstanding essays on a topic related to Black History Month.

Eligibility This competition is open to all Florida students in 3 categories: elementary (grades 4-5), middle (grades 6-8), and high school (grades 9-12). Applicants must submit an essay, up to 500 words in length, on a topic that changes annually but relates to Black history. Recently, students were asked to look at diversity in the United States, reflect on what they have learned in their life experience, and explain if they think diversity benefits society.

Financial data Winners receive a 4-year Florida College Plan scholarship provided by the Stanley G. Tate Prepaid College Foundation.

Duration The competition is held annually. Winners receive payment of tuition for 4 years.

Additional information This program began in 2003.

Number awarded 3 each year: 1 in each of the grade categories.

Deadline February of each year.

[197] FLORIDA MINORITY TEACHER EDUCATION SCHOLARSHIPS

Florida Fund for Minority Teachers, Inc.
Attn: Executive Director
G415 Norman Hall
P.O. Box 117045
Gainesville, FL 32611-7045
(352) 392-9196, ext. 21 Fax: (352) 846-3011
E-mail: info@ffmt.org
Web: www.ffmt.org

Summary To provide funding to African Americans and members of other minority groups in Florida who are preparing for a career as a teacher.

Eligibility This program is open to Florida residents who are African American/Black, Hispanic/Latino, Asian American/Pacific Islander, or American Indian/Alaskan Native. Applicants must be entering their junior year in a teacher education program at a participating college or university in Florida. Special consideration is given to community college graduates. Selection is based on writing ability, communication skills, overall academic performance, and evidence of commitment to the youth of America (preferably demonstrated through volunteer activities).

Financial data The stipend is $4,000 per year. Recipients are required to teach 1 year in a Florida public school for each year they receive the scholarship. If they fail to teach in a public school, they are required to repay the total amount of support received at an annual interest rate of 8%.

Duration Up to 2 consecutive years, provided the recipient remains enrolled full time with a GPA of 2.5 or higher.

Additional information For a list of the 16 participating public institutions and the 18 participating private institutions, contact the Florida Fund for Minority Teachers (FFMT). Recipients are also required to attend the annual FFMT recruitment and retention conference.

Number awarded Varies each year.

Deadline July of each year for fall semester; November of each year for spring semester.

[198] FORUM FOR CONCERNS OF MINORITIES SCHOLARSHIPS

American Society for Clinical Laboratory Science
Attn: Forum for Concerns of Minorities
1861 International Drive, Suite 200
McLean, VA 22102
(571) 748-3770 E-mail: ascls@ascls.org
Web: www.ascls.org

Summary To provide financial assistance to African Americans and other minority students in clinical laboratory scientist and clinical laboratory technician programs.

Eligibility This program is open to minority students who are enrolled in a program in clinical laboratory science, including clinical laboratory science/medical technology (CLS/MT) and clinical laboratory technician/medical laboratory technician (CLT/MLT). Applicants must be able to demonstrate financial need. Membership in the American Society for Clinical Laboratory Science is encouraged but not required.

Financial data Stipends depend on the need of the recipients and the availability of funds.

Duration 1 year.

Number awarded 2 each year: 1 to a CLS/MT student and 1 to a CLT/MLT student.

Deadline March of each year.

[199]
FOURTH DISTRICT MOSAIC SCHOLARSHIP

American Advertising Federation-District 4
c/o Maria Lucas, Governor
Farah & Farah
10 West Adams Street
Jacksonville, FL 32202
(904) 807-3113 Toll Free: (800) 533-5555
Fax: (904) 355-5599 E-mail: mlucas@farahandfarah.com
Web: 4aaf.com/education/scholarships

Summary To provide financial assistance to African American and other minority undergraduate and graduate students from any state who are enrolled at colleges and universities in Florida and interested in entering the field of advertising.

Eligibility This program is open to undergraduate and graduate students from any state enrolled at accredited colleges and universities in Florida who are U.S. citizens or permanent residents of African, African American, Hispanic, Hispanic American, Indian, Native American, Asian, Asian American, or Pacific Islander descent. Applicants must be working on a bachelor's or master's degree in advertising, marketing, communications, public relations, art, graphic arts, or a related field. They must have an overall GPA of 3.0 or higher. Along with their application, they must submit a 250-word essay on why multiculturalism, diversity, and inclusion are important in the advertising, marketing, and communications industry today. Preference is given to members of the American Advertising Federation.

Financial data The stipend is $1,000.

Duration 1 year.

Number awarded 1 or more each year.

Deadline February of each year.

[200]
FRAMELINE COMPLETION FUND

Frameline
Attn: Completion Fund
145 Ninth Street, Suite 300
San Francisco, CA 94103
(415) 703-8650 Fax: (415) 861-1404
E-mail: info@frameline.org
Web: www.frameline.org/filmmaker-support

Summary To provide funding to lesbian, gay, bisexual, and transgender (LGBT) film/video artists (particularly African Americans, other film/video artists of color, and women).

Eligibility This program is open to LGBT artists who are in the last stages of the production of documentary, educational, narrative, animated, or experimental projects about or of interest to LGBT people and their communities. Applicants may be independent artists, students, producers, or nonprofit corporations. They must be interested in completion work and must have 90% of the production completed; projects in development, script-development, pre-production, or production are not eligible. Student projects are eligible only if the student maintains artistic and financial control of the project. Women and people of color are especially encouraged to apply. Selection is based on financial need, the contribution the grant will make to completing the project, assurances that the project will be completed, and the statement the project makes about LGBT people and/or issues of concern to them and their communities.

Financial data Grants range from $1,000 to $5,000.

Duration These are 1-time grants.

Additional information This program began in 1990.

Number awarded Varies each year; recently, 5 of these grants were awarded. Since this program was established, it has provided $389,200 in support to 118 films.

Deadline October of each year.

[201]
FRANCES W. HARRIS SCHOLARSHIP

New England Regional Black Nurses Association, Inc.
P.O. Box 190690
Boston, MA 02119
(617) 524-1951
Web: www.nerbna.org/org/scholarships.html

Summary To provide financial assistance to nursing students from New England who have contributed to the African American community.

Eligibility The program is open to residents of the New England states who are enrolled full time in a NLN-accredited generic diploma, associate, or bachelor's nursing program in any state. Applicants must have at least 1 full year of school remaining. Along with their application, they must submit a 3-page essay that covers their career aspirations in the nursing profession; how they have contributed to the African American or other communities of color in such areas as work, volunteering, church, or community outreach; an experience that has enhanced their personal and/or professional growth; and any financial hardships that may hinder them from completing their education.

Financial data A stipend is awarded (amount not specified).

Duration 1 year.

Number awarded 1 or more each year.

Deadline February of each year.

[202]
FRANCIS M. KEVILLE MEMORIAL SCHOLARSHIP

Construction Management Association of America
Attn: CMAA Foundation
7926 Jones Branch Drive, Suite 800
McLean, VA 22101-3303
(703) 356-2622 Fax: (703) 356-6388
E-mail: foundation@cmaanet.org
Web: www.cmaafoundation.org

Summary To provide financial assistance to minority and female undergraduate and graduate students working on a degree in construction management.

Eligibility This program is open to women and members of minority groups who are enrolled as full-time undergraduate or graduate students. Applicants must have completed at least 1 year of study and have at least 1 full year remaining for a bachelor's or master's degree in construction management or a related field. Along with their application, they must submit essays on why they are interested in a career in construction management and why they should be awarded this scholarship. Selection is based on that essay (20%), academic performance (40%), recommendation of the faculty adviser (15%), and extracurricular activities (25%); a bonus of 5% is given to student members of the Construction Management Association of America (CMAA).

Financial data The stipend is $3,000. Funds are disbursed directly to the student's university.

Duration 1 year.

Number awarded 1 each year.

Deadline June of each year.

[203]
FRANK T. MARTIN LEADERSHIP SCHOLARSHIP

Conference of Minority Transportation Officials
Attn: National Scholarship Program
1875 I Street, N.W., Suite 500
Washington, DC 20006
(703) 234-4072 Fax: (202) 318-0364
Web: www.comto.org/?page=Scholarships

Summary To provide financial assistance to African American and other minority undergraduate and graduate students working on a degree in transportation or a related field.

Eligibility This program is open to full-time undergraduate and graduate students who are working on a degree in transportation, engineering, planning, or a related discipline. They must be able to demonstrate leadership and active commitment to community service. Along with their application, they must submit a cover letter with a 500-word statement of career goals. Financial need is not considered in the selection process. U.S. citizenship or legal resident status is required.

Financial data The stipend is $3,000. Funds are paid directly to the recipient's college or university.

Duration 1 year.

Additional information The Conference of Minority Transportation Officials (COMTO) was established in 1971 to promote, strengthen, and expand the roles of minorities in all aspects of transportation. This program is sponsored by Atkins North America. Recipients are expected to attend the COMTO National Scholarship Luncheon.

Number awarded 1 each year.

Deadline May of each year.

[204]
FRANK WATTS SCHOLARSHIP

Watts Charity Association, Inc.
6245 Bristol Parkway, Suite 224
Culver City, CA 90230
(323) 671-0394 Fax: (323) 778-2613
E-mail: wattscharity@yahoo.com
Web: 4watts.tripod.com/id5.html

Summary To provide financial assistance to upper-division African Americans interested in preparing for a career as a minister.

Eligibility This program is open to U.S. citizens of African American descent who are enrolled full time as a college or university junior. Applicants must be studying to become a minister. They must have a GPA of 3.0 or higher, be between 17 and 24 years of age, and be able to demonstrate that they intend to continue their education for at least 2 years. Along with their application, they must submit 1) a 1-paragraph statement on why they should be awarded a Watts Charity Association scholarship; and 2) a 1- to 2-page essay on a specific type of cancer, based either on how it has impacted their life or on researched information.

Financial data A stipend is awarded (amount not specified).

Duration 1 year.

Additional information Royce R. Watts, Sr. established the Watts Charity Association after he learned he had cancer in 2001.

Number awarded 1 each year.

Deadline May of each year.

[205]
FREDERICK C. BRANCH MARINE CORPS LEADERSHIP SCHOLARSHIPS

U.S. Navy
Attn: Naval Education and Training Command
NSTC OD2
250 Dallas Street, Suite A
Pensacola, FL 32508-5268
(850) 452-4941, ext. 29395
Toll Free: (800) NAV-ROTC, ext. 29395
Fax: (850) 452-2486
E-mail: pnsc_nrotc.scholarship@navy.mil
Web: www.nrotc.navy.mil/hist_black.aspx

Summary To provide financial assistance to students who are entering or enrolled at specified Historically Black Colleges or Universities (HBCUs) and interested in joining Navy ROTC to prepare for service as an officer in the U.S. Marine Corps.

Eligibility This program is open to students attending or planning to attend 1 of 17 specified HBCUs with a Navy ROTC unit on campus. Applicants may either apply through their local Marine recruiter for a 4-year scholarship or be nominated by the professor of naval science at their institution and meet academic requirements set by each school for 2- or 3-year scholarships. They must be U.S. citizens between 17 and 23 years of age who are willing to serve for 4 years as active-duty Marine Corps officers following graduation from college. They must not have reached their 27th birthday by the time of college graduation and commissioning; applicants who have prior active-duty military service may be eligible for age adjustments for the amount of time equal to their prior service, up to a maximum of 36 months. The qualifying scores are 1000 composite on the SAT or 22 composite on the ACT. Current enlisted and former military personnel are also eligible if they will complete the program by the age of 30.

Financial data These scholarships provide payment of full tuition and required educational fees, as well as a specified amount for textbooks, supplies, and equipment. The program also provides a stipend for 10 months of the year that is $250 per month as a freshman, $300 per month as a sophomore, $350 per month as a junior, and $400 per month as a senior.

Duration Scholarships are available for 2-, 3-, or 4-year terms.

Additional information Recipients must complete 4 years of study in naval science classes as students at 1 of the following HBCUs: Allen University, Clark Atlanta University, Dillard University, Florida A&M University, Hampton University, Howard University, Huston-Tillotson University, Morehouse College, Norfolk State University, Prairie View A&M University, Savannah State University, Southern University and A&M College, Spelman College, Tennessee State University, Texas Southern University, Tuskegee University, or Xavier University. After completing the program, all participants are commissioned as second lieutenants in the Marine Corps Reserve with an 8-year service obligation, including 4 years of active duty. Current military personnel who are accepted into this program are released from active duty and are not eligible for active-duty pay and allowances, medical benefits, or other active-duty entitlements.

Number awarded Varies each year.

Deadline January of each year for students applying for a 4-year scholarship through their local Marine recruiter; July of each year if applying for a 2- or 3-year scholarship through the Navy ROTC unit at their institution.

[206] FULFILLING THE LEGACY SCHOLARSHIPS

National Society of Black Engineers
Attn: Programs Department
205 Daingerfield Road
Alexandria, VA 22314
(703) 549-2207 Fax: (703) 683-5312
E-mail: scholarships@nsbe.org
Web: www.nsbe.org/Programs/Scholarships.aspx

Summary To provide financial assistance to members of the National Society of Black Engineers (NSBE) who are or will be working on an undergraduate or graduate degree in engineering.

Eligibility This program is open to members of the society who are undergraduate or graduate engineering students. High school seniors are also eligible. Applicants must epitomize the society's mission of producing culturally responsible Black engineers who excel academically, succeed professionally, and positively impact the community. Selection is based on an essay; academic achievement; service to the society at the chapter, regional, and/or national level; and other professional, campus, and community activities.

Financial data The stipend is $1,000.

Duration 1 year; may be renewed.

Number awarded Varies each year, depending on the availability of funds. Recently, 10 of these scholarships were awarded to undergraduate and graduate students and 5 to high school seniors.

Deadline May of each year.

[207] GATES MILLENNIUM SCHOLARS PROGRAM

Bill and Melinda Gates Foundation
P.O. Box 10500
Fairfax, VA 22031-8044
Toll Free: (877) 690-GMSP Fax: (703) 205-2079
Web: www.gmsp.org

Summary To provide financial assistance to African American and other outstanding low-income minority students, particularly those interested in majoring in specific fields in college.

Eligibility This program is open to African Americans, Alaska Natives, American Indians, Hispanic Americans, and Asian Pacific Islander Americans who are graduating high school seniors with a GPA of 3.3 or higher. Principals, teachers, guidance counselors, tribal higher education representatives, and other professional educators are invited to nominate students with outstanding academic qualifications, particularly those likely to succeed in the fields of computer science, education, engineering, library science, mathematics, public health, or science. Nominees should have significant financial need and have demonstrated leadership abilities through participation in community service, extracurricular, or other activities. U.S. citizenship, nationality, or permanent resident status is required. Nominees must be planning to enter an accredited college or university as a full-time, degree-seeking freshman in the following fall.

Financial data The program covers the cost of tuition, fees, books, and living expenses not paid for by grants and scholarships already committed as part of the recipient's financial aid package.

Duration 4 years or the completion of the undergraduate degree, if the recipient maintains at least a 3.0 GPA.

Additional information This program, established in 1999, is funded by the Bill and Melinda Gates Foundation and administered by the United Negro College Fund with support from the American Indian Graduate Center, the Hispanic Scholarship Fund, and the Asian & Pacific Islander American Scholarship Fund.

Number awarded 1,000 new scholarships are awarded each year.

Deadline January of each year.

[208] GATEWAYS TO THE LABORATORY PROGRAM

Cornell University
Attn: Weill Cornell/Rockefeller/Sloan-Kettering Tri-Institutional MD-PhD Program
Gateways to the Laboratory Program
1300 York Avenue, Room C-103
New York, NY 10065-4805
(212) 746-6023 Fax: (212) 746-8678
E-mail: mdphd@med.cornell.edu
Web: www.med.cornell.edu/mdphd/summerprogram

Summary To provide African American and other underrepresented minority or disadvantaged college freshmen and sophomores with an opportunity to participate in a summer research project in New York City through the Tri-Institutional MD-PhD Program of Weill Cornell Medical College, Rockefeller University, and Sloan-Kettering Institute.

Eligibility This program is open to college freshmen and sophomores who are defined by the National Institutes of Health (NIH) as in need of special recruitment and retention, i.e., members of racial and ethnic groups underrepresented in health-related sciences (American Indians or Alaska Natives, Blacks or African Americans, Hispanics or Latinos, and Native Hawaiians or Other Pacific Islanders), persons with disabilities, and individuals from disadvantaged backgrounds (low-income or from a rural or inner-city environment). Applicants must be interested in continuing on to a combined M.D./Ph.D. program following completion of their undergraduate degree. They should have a GPA of 3.0 or higher and have completed a college level calculus class. Along with their application, they must submit an essay summarizing their laboratory experience, research interests, and goals. U.S. citizenship or permanent resident status is required.

Financial data Students receive a research stipend of $4,300 and reimbursement of travel expenses. At the end of the summer, 1 family member receives airfare and hotel accommodations to come to New York for the final presentations.

Duration 10 weeks, during the summer.

Additional information Interns work independently on a research project at Weill Cornell Medical College, Rockefeller University, or Memorial Sloan-Kettering Cancer Center, all located across the street from each other on the Upper East Side of New York City.

Number awarded 15 each year.

Deadline January of each year.

[209]
GAUFF/TYRANCE SCHOLARSHIP

National Naval Officers Association-Washington, D.C. Chapter
c/o LCDR Stephen Williams
P.O. Box 30784
Alexandria, VA 22310
(703) 566-3840 Fax: (703) 566-3813
E-mail: Stephen.Williams@navy.mil
Web: dcnnoa.memberlodge.com

Summary To provide financial assistance to African American high school seniors from the Washington, D.C. area who are interested in attending an Historically Black College or University (HBCU) in any state.

Eligibility This program is open to African American seniors graduating from high schools in the Washington, D.C. metropolitan area who plan to enroll full time at an HBCU in any state. Applicants must have a GPA of 3.0 or higher and be U.S. citizens or permanent residents. Selection is based on academic achievement, community involvement, and financial need.

Financial data The stipend is $1,000.

Duration 1 year; nonrenewable.

Additional information Recipients are not required to join or affiliate with the military in any way.

Number awarded 1 each year.

Deadline March of each year.

[210]
GENERAL MILLS HEALTH SCHOLARSHIP

Congressional Black Caucus Foundation, Inc.
Attn: Director, Educational Programs
1720 Massachusetts Avenue, N.W.
Washington, DC 20036
(202) 263-2800 Toll Free: (800) 784-2577
Fax: (202) 775-0773 E-mail: scholarships@cbcfinc.org
Web: www.cbcfinc.org/scholarships.html

Summary To provide financial assistance to undergraduate and graduate students who are interested in preparing for a health-related career, especially those who reside in a Congressional district represented by a member of the Congressional Black Caucus (CBC).

Eligibility This program is open to students attending or planning to attend an accredited institution of higher education as a full-time undergraduate or graduate student. Preference is given to those who reside or attend school in a Congressional district represented by a member of the CBC. Applicants must be interested in preparing for a career in a medical or other health-related field, including medicine, nursing, technology, nutrition, or engineering. They must have a GPA of 2.5 or higher. Along with their application, they must submit transcripts; a 1-page resume listing their extracurricular activities, honors, employment, community service, and special skills; and a personal statement of 500 to 1,000 words on themselves and their interests. They must also be able to demonstrate financial need, leadership ability, and participation in community service activities.

Financial data A stipend is awarded (amount not specified).

Duration 1 year.

Additional information The program was established in 1998 with support from General Mills, Inc.

Number awarded Varies each year.

Deadline February of each year.

[211]
GENERAL MILLS NSBE CORPORATE SCHOLARSHIP PROGRAM

National Society of Black Engineers
Attn: Programs Department
205 Daingerfield Road
Alexandria, VA 22314
(703) 549-2207 Fax: (703) 683-5312
E-mail: scholarships@nsbe.org
Web: www.nsbe.org/Programs/Scholarships.aspx

Summary To provide financial assistance to members of the National Society of Black Engineers (NSBE) who are majoring in food-related fields of engineering.

Eligibility This program is open to members of the society who are entering their sophomore or junior year in college and majoring in biological, chemical, electrical, food-processing, industrial, or mechanical engineering. Applicants must have a GPA of 3.0 or higher and be a U.S. citizen or authorized to work in the United States. Along with their application, they must submit an essay of 300 to 500 words describing how engineers nourish lives. Financial need is not considered in the selection process.

Financial data The stipend is $3,000.

Duration 1 year.

Additional information This program is sponsored by General Mills.

Number awarded 6 each year.

Deadline May of each year.

[212]
GENERATION GOOGLE SCHOLARSHIPS

Google Inc.
Attn: Scholarships
1600 Amphitheatre Parkway
Mountain View, CA 94043-8303
(650) 253-0000 Fax: (650) 253-0001
E-mail: generationgoogle@google.com
Web: www.google.com

Summary To provide financial assistance to African Americans and members of other underrepresented groups planning to work on a bachelor's degree in a computer-related field.

Eligibility This program is open to high school seniors planning to enroll full time at a college or university in the United States or Canada. Applicants must be members of a group underrepresented in computer science: African Americans, Hispanics, American Indians, women, or people with a disability. They must be interested in working on a bachelor's degree in computer science, computer engineering, software engineering, or a related field. Selection is based on academic achievement (GPA of 3.2 or higher), leadership, commitment to and passion for computer science and technology through involvement in their community, and financial need.

Financial data The stipend is $10,000 per year for U.S. students or $C5,000 for Canadian students.

Duration 1 year; may be renewed for up to 3 additional years or until graduation, whichever comes first.

Additional information Recipients are also invited to attend Google's Computer Science Summer Institute at either Mountain View, California or Cambridge, Massachusetts in the summer.

Number awarded Varies each year.

Deadline February of each year.

[213]
GEOGRAPHICALLY-BASED SCHOLARSHIPS OF THE UNCF

United Negro College Fund
Attn: Scholarships and Grants Department
8260 Willow Oaks Corporate Drive
P.O. Box 10444
Fairfax, VA 22031-8044
(703) 205-3466 Toll Free: (800) 331-2244
Fax: (703) 205-3574
Web: www.uncf.org

Summary To provide financial assistance to high school juniors or seniors from designated areas who are interested in attending a member institution of the United Negro College Fund (UNCF).

Eligibility These programs are open to seniors graduating from high schools in designated geographical areas with a GPA of 2.5 or higher. Students who have completed their junior year in high school with a record of distinction may also be considered. Financial need must be demonstrated. Applications should be submitted directly to the UNCF-member institution the student plans to attend.

Financial data The awards are intended to cover tuition and range from a minimum of $500 to a maximum of $7,500 per year.

Duration 1 year; may be renewed.

Additional information Recipients must attend a UNCF-member institution of higher learning. These are: Miles College, Oakwood College, Stillman College, Talladega College, and Tuskegee University in Alabama; Philander Smith College in Arkansas; Bethune-Cookman University, Edward Waters College, and Florida Memorial University in Florida; Clark Atlanta University, Interdenominational Theological Center, Morehouse College, Paine College, and Spelman College in Georgia; Dillard University and Xavier University in Louisiana; Rust College and Tougaloo College in Mississippi; Bennett College, Johnson C. Smith University, Livingstone College, Saint Augustine's University, and Shaw University in North Carolina; Wilberforce University in Ohio; Allen University, Benedict College, Claflin University, Morris College, and Voorhees College in South Carolina; Fisk University, Lane College, and LeMoyne-Owen College in Tennessee; Huston-Tillotson College, Jarvis Christian College, Texas College, and Wiley College in Texas; and Virginia Union University in Virginia.

Number awarded A total of nearly 1,200 UNCF scholarships are awarded each year.

Deadline Deadline dates vary, depending upon the individual institution's requirements.

[214]
GEORGE A. LOTTIER GOLF FOUNDATION INTERNSHIP AND SCHOLARSHIP AWARD

Atlanta Tribune: The Magazine
Attn: Editor
875 Old Roswell Road, Suite C-100
Roswell, GA 30076-1660
(770) 587-0501, ext. 202 Fax: (770) 642-6501
E-mail: kmines@atlantatribune.com
Web: www.atlantatribune.com

Summary To provide financial aid and summer work experience at the *Atlanta Tribune: The Magazine* to African American and other minority upper-division and graduate students from any state interested in a career in print journalism.

Eligibility This program is open to minority college students from any state entering their junior or senior year of college or enrolled in a graduate program with a GPA of 3.0 or higher. Applicants must be majoring in a field related to print media, including communications, English, graphic design (with an emphasis on publication layout and design), journalism, marketing, or sales. Along with their application, they must submit a 500-word personal essay.

Financial data The program provides a paid internship and a scholarship stipend of $2,500.

Duration 1 year, including 10 weeks during the summer for the internship.

Number awarded Varies each year; recently, 4 of these scholarships and internships were awarded.

Deadline April of each year.

[215]
GEORGE CAMPBELL, JR. FELLOWSHIP IN ENGINEERING

National Action Council for Minorities in Engineering
Attn: University Programs
440 Hamilton Avenue, Suite 302
White Plains, NY 10601-1813
(914) 539-4010 Fax: (914) 539-4032
E-mail: scholarships@nacme.org
Web: www.nacme.org/NACME_D.aspx?pageid=105

Summary To provide financial assistance to African American and other underrepresented minority college sophomores majoring in engineering or related fields.

Eligibility This program is open to African American, Latino, and American Indian college sophomores who have a GPA of 3.0 or higher and have demonstrated academic excellence, leadership skills, and a commitment to science and engineering as a career. Applicants must be enrolled full time at an ABET-accredited engineering program. Fields of study include all areas of engineering as well as computer science, materials science, mathematics, operations research, or physics.

Financial data The stipend is $5,000 per year. Funds are sent directly to the recipient's university.

Duration Up to 3 years.

Number awarded 1 each year.

Deadline April of each year.

[216]
GEORGE GENG ON LEE MINORITIES IN LEADERSHIP SCHOLARSHIP

Capture the Dream, Inc.
Attn: Scholarship Program
484 Lake Park Avenue, Suite 15
Oakland, CA 94610
(510) 343-3635 E-mail: info@capturethedream.org
Web: www.capturethedream.org/programs/scholarship.php

Summary To provide financial assistance to African Americans and other minorities in California who can demonstrate leadership and are interested in attending college in any state.

Eligibility This program is open to residents of California who are members of minority groups and either graduating high school seniors or current full-time undergraduates at 4-year colleges and universities in any state. Applicants must submit a 1,000-word essay on why they should be selected to receive this scholarship, using their experiences within school, work, and home to display the challenges they have faced as a minority and how they overcame adversity to assume a leadership role. They should also explain how their career goals and future aspirations will build them as a future minority leader. Selection is based on academic performance, community service, leadership history, professional recommendations, and financial need. U.S. citizenship or permanent resident status is required.

Financial data The stipend is $1,000.

Duration 1 year.

Number awarded 1 or more each year.

Deadline July of each year.

[217]
GEORGIA FUNERAL SERVICE PRACTITIONERS ASSOCIATION SCHOLARSHIPS

Georgia Funeral Service Practitioners Association
Attn: Office of the Education and Research Director
346 Athens Avenue
P.O. Box 1069
Athens, GA 30601
(706) 548-5671 Fax: (706) 548-1975
E-mail: hopeiglehart@aol.com
Web: gfspa.net/edu.htm

Summary To provide financial assistance to students at mortuary schools in any state who are recommended by a member of the Georgia Funeral Service Practitioners Association, successor to the Georgia Colored Funeral Directors and Embalmers Association.

Eligibility This program is open to full-time students who have completed at least 1 of the last 3 quarters of an accredited program of mortuary science or funeral service at a school in any state. Applicants must have a GPA of 3.0 or higher and demonstrated qualities of professionalism that are needed for success in funeral service. Along with their application, they must submit an essay on their interest in funeral service, 2 letters of recommendation (including 1 from an active member of the Georgia Funeral Service Practitioners Association), transcripts, and information on their financial situation. U.S. citizenship is required.

Financial data A stipend is awarded (amount not specified).

Duration 1 year.

Additional information The Georgia Funeral Service Practitioners Association was established in 1925 as the Georgia Colored Funeral Directors and Embalmers Association, the Georgia affiliate of the National Negro Funeral Directors Association.

Number awarded 1 or more each year.

Deadline April of each year.

[218]
GLOSTER B. CURRENT, SR. SCHOLARSHIP

United Methodist Church-New York Annual Conference
Attn: Gloster B. Current Scholarship Committee
c/o Rev. Andrew Peck-McClain
Cornwall United Methodist Church
196 Main Street
Cornwall, NY 12518
(845) 534-2794 Fax: (914) 235-7313
E-mail: pastor.conwallumc@gmail.com
Web: www.nyac.com/pages/detail/1725

Summary To provide financial assistance to Methodist undergraduate students of African descent from any state who are preparing for a career in public service.

Eligibility This program is open to members of United Methodist Church (UMC) congregations in any state who are of African descent. Applicants must be enrolled or planning to enroll at an accredited institution of higher education in any state to work on an undergraduate degree in a field of public service (e.g., the ministry, social work, health care, or government service). They must be between 16 and 25 years of age and have a GPA of at least "C" in high school and/or 2.75 or higher in college. Along with their application, they must submit a 1-page essay on their interest in a career of public service. Selection is based on academic record, leadership potential, a letter of recommendation from a UMC local pastor, and financial need.

Financial data The stipend is $1,000.

Duration 1 year; nonrenewable.

Additional information This program began in 2003.

Number awarded 1 or more each year.

Deadline April of each year.

[219]
GO RED MULTICULTURAL SCHOLARSHIP FUND

American Heart Association
Attn: Go Red for Women
7272 Greenville Avenue
Dallas, TX 75231-4596
Toll Free: (800) AHA-USA1
E-mail: GoRedScholarship@heart.org
Web: www.goredforwomen.org/goredscholarship.aspx

Summary To provide financial assistance to women from multicultural backgrounds who are preparing for a career in a field of health care.

Eligibility This program is open to women who are currently enrolled at an accredited college, university, health care institution, or program and have a GPA of 3.0 or higher. Applicants must be undergraduates of Hispanic, African American, or other minority origin. They must be preparing for a career as a nurse, physician, or allied health care worker. Selection is based on community involvement, a personal letter, transcripts, and 2 letters of recommendation.

Financial data The stipend is $2,500.

Duration 1 year.

Additional information This program, which began in 2012, is supported by Macy's.

Number awarded Varies each year; recently, 16 of these scholarships were awarded.

Deadline November of each year.

[220]
GOLDEN APPLE SCHOLARS OF ILLINOIS

Golden Apple Foundation
Attn: Scholars Program
8 South Michigan Avenue, Suite 700
Chicago, IL 60603-3463
(312) 407-0006 Fax: (312) 407-0344
E-mail: info@goldenapple.org
Web: www.goldenapple.org/golden-apple-scholars

Summary To provide funding to high school seniors in Illinois (particularly minority and bilingual students) who wish to study education at an Illinois college and teach in the state.

Eligibility This program is open to high school seniors at schools in Illinois. Students must be nominated by a teacher, principal, guidance counselor, or other non-family adult; self-nominations are also accepted. Nominees must be committed to teaching as a profession and must be interested in attending 1 of 53 designated colleges and universities in Illinois. A limited number of openings are also available to sophomores at those designated Illinois institutions. The program strongly encourages nomination of prospective teachers for which there is currently a shortage, especially minority and bilingual teachers. Selection is based on 7 essays included on the application, ACT scores and transcripts, letters of reference, and an interview.

Financial data Scholars receive a scholarship/loan of $2,500 per year for their freshman and sophomore year and $5,000 per year for their junior and senior year. They also receive a stipend of $2,000 per year for participating in a summer teaching internship. If they complete a bachelor's degree and teach for 5 years in an Illinois school of need, the loan is forgiven. Schools of need are defined as those either having Chapter I status by the U.S. Department of Education or having mediocre to poor PSAE or ISAT scores.

Duration 4 years, provided the recipient maintains a GPA of 2.0 or higher during the freshman year and 2.5 or higher in subsequent years. Students who enter the program as sophomores receive 2 years of support.

Additional information During the annual summer institutes, scholars participate in teaching internships and seminars on the art and craft of teaching. This program was established in 1988.

Number awarded Varies each year; recently, 110 of these scholarships were awarded.

Deadline Nominations must be submitted by November of each year.

[221]
GOLDEN TORCH AWARDS

National Society of Black Engineers
Attn: Pre-College Initiative Program
205 Daingerfield Road
Alexandria, VA 22314
(703) 549-2207 Fax: (703) 683-5312
E-mail: pci@nsbe.org
Web: www.nsbe.org/Programs/Scholarships.aspx

Summary To provide financial assistance to high school seniors who are junior members of the National Society of Black Engineers (NSBE) and planning to major in a field related to engineering in college.

Eligibility This program is open to junior members of the society who are high school seniors. Applicants must have been accepted as a full-time student at a 4-year college or university to major in engineering, computer science, mathematics, or technology. They must have a GPA of 3.0 or higher. Along with their application, they must submit an essay, up to 500 words in length, on how they will continue the legacy of NSBE and how they will serve as role models in their community after college.

Financial data The stipend is $1,000 per year.

Duration 1 year; may be renewed 3 additional years if the recipient maintains a GPA of 2.75 or higher in college.

Number awarded Varies each year; recently, 5 of these awards were presented.

Deadline May of each year.

[222]
GOLDMAN SACHS SCHOLARSHIP FOR EXCELLENCE

Goldman Sachs
Attn: Human Capital Management
200 West Street, 25th Floor
New York, NY 10282
E-mail: Iris.Birungi@gs.com
Web: www.goldmansachs.com

Summary To provide financial aid and work experience to African American and other underrepresented minority students preparing for a career in the financial services industry.

Eligibility This program is open to undergraduate students of Black, Latino, or Native American heritage. Applicants must be entering their sophomore or junior year and have a GPA of 3.4 or higher. Students with all majors and disciplines are encouraged to apply, but they must be able to demonstrate an interest in the financial services industry. Along with their application, they must submit 2 essays of 500 words or fewer on the following topics: 1) why they are interested in the financial services industry; and 2) how they have demonstrated team-oriented leadership through their involvement with a campus-based or community-based organization. Selection is based on academic achievement, interest in the financial services industry, community involvement, and demonstrated leadership and teamwork capabilities.

Financial data Sophomores receive a stipend of $5,000, a summer internship at Goldman Sachs, an opportunity to receive a second award upon successful completion of the internship, and an offer to return for a second summer internship. Juniors receive a stipend of $10,000 and a summer internship at Goldman Sachs.

Duration Up to 2 years.

Additional information This program was initiated in 1994 when it served only students at 4 designated Historically Black Colleges and Universities: Florida A&M University, Howard University, Morehouse College, and Spelman College. It has since been expanded to serve underrepresented minority students in all states.

Number awarded 1 or more each year.

Deadline January of each year.

[223] GORDON STAFFORD SCHOLARSHIP IN ARCHITECTURE

Gordon Stafford Scholarship
Attn: Scholarship Selection Committee
622 20th Street
Sacramento, CA 95814
(916) 930-5900 Fax: (916) 930-5800
E-mail: scholarship@gsscholarship.com
Web: www.skwarchitects.com/about/scholarship

Summary To provide financial assistance to African Americans and members of other minority groups from California who are interested in studying architecture at a college in any state.

Eligibility This program is open to California residents accepted by an accredited school of architecture in any state as first-year or transfer students. Applicants must be U.S. citizens or permanent residents who are persons of color (defined as Black, Hispanic, Native American, Pacific-Asian, or Asian-Indian). They must submit a 500-word statement expressing their desire to study architecture. Finalists are interviewed and must travel to Sacramento, California at their own expense for the interview.

Financial data The stipend is $2,000 per year. That includes $1,000 deposited in the recipient's school account and $1,000 paid to the recipient directly.

Duration 1 year; may be renewed up to 4 additional years.

Additional information This program began in 1995 to celebrate the 50th anniversary of the architectural firm that sponsors it, Stafford King Wiese Architects.

Number awarded Up to 5 of these scholarships may be active at a time.

Deadline June of each year.

[224] GRADY-RAYAM PRIZE IN SACRED MUSIC

"Negro Spiritual" Scholarship Foundation
P.O. Box 547728
Orlando, FL 32854-7728
(407) 841-NSSF
Web: www.negrospiritual.org/competition

Summary To recognize and reward, with college scholarships, African American high school students in selected eastern states who excel at singing "Negro spirituals."

Eligibility This competition is open to high school juniors and seniors of Afro-ethnic heritage in 6 districts: 1) Florida; 2) Southeast (Georgia, North Carolina, and South Carolina); 3) Mid-south (Alabama, Arkansas, Louisiana, Mississippi, and Tennessee); 4) Northeast (New Jersey, New York, and Pennsylvania; 5) New England (Connecticut, Maine, Massachusetts, New Hampshire, Rhode Island, and Vermont); and 6) Capital (Delaware, Maryland, Virginia, Washington, D.C., and West Virginia). Participants must perform 2 "Negro spiritual" songs, 1 assigned and 1 selected. Selection is based on technique (tone quality, intonation, and vocal production), musicianship and artistry (inflection, diction, authenticity, rhythmic energy, and memorization), and stage presence (demeanor, posture, and sincerity of delivery). U.S. citizenship or permanent resident status is required.

Financial data Winners earn tuition assistance grants for college of $3,000 and cash prizes of $300. Other finalists receive cash prizes of $100.

Duration The competition is held annually at a site in each of the 5 regions.

Additional information This program began in Florida in 1997, in the Mid-south district in 2006, in the New England and Capital districts in 2008, in the Southeast district in 2010, and in the Northeast district in 2012. The entry fee is $20.

Number awarded 12 tuition assistance grants and cash prizes (1 to a male and 1 to a female in each of the 6 districts) are awarded each year. The number of other cash prizes awarded to finalists varies each year.

Deadline December of each year.

[225] GREAT LAKES SECTION IFT DIVERSITY SCHOLARSHIP

Institute of Food Technologists-Great Lakes Section
c/o Janice Harte, Scholarship Chair
Michigan State University
Department of Food Science and Human Nutrition
106 Malcolm Trout Building
East Lansing, MI 48824-1224
(517) 355-8474, ext. 105 Fax: (517) 353-8963
E-mail: harteja@msu.edu
Web: www.greatlakesift.org

Summary To provide financial assistance to African Americans and other minorities who are members of the Great Lakes Section of the Institute of Food Technologists (IFT) from any state and working on an undergraduate or graduate degree related to food technology at a college in Michigan.

Eligibility This program is open to minority residents of any state who are members of the IFT Great Lakes Section (GLS) and working full time on an undergraduate or graduate degree in food science, nutrition, food engineering, food packaging, or food service courses at a college or university in Michigan. Applicants must have a GPA of 3.0 or higher and plans for a career in the food industry. Along with their application, they must submit a 1-page personal statement that covers their academic program, future plans and career goals, extracurricular activities (including involvement in community, university, GLS, or national IFT activities), and work experience. Financial need is not considered in the selection process.

Financial data The stipend is $1,000.

Duration 1 year; nonrenewable.

Number awarded 1 each year.

Deadline January of each year.

[226]
GULF COAST CHAPTER AABE SCHOLARSHIPS

American Association of Blacks in Energy-Gulf Coast Chapter
Attn: Scholarship Committee
P.O. Box 1115
Gulfport, MS 39502
(850) 505-2294 E-mail: TELocket@southernco.com
Web: www.aabe.org/index.php?component=pages&id=322

Summary To provide financial assistance to African Americans and members of other underrepresented minority groups who are high school seniors in southern Alabama, Florida, or Mississippi and planning to major in an energy-related field at a college in any state.

Eligibility This program is open to seniors graduating from high schools in southern Alabama, Florida, or Mississippi and planning to attend a college or university in any state. Applicants must be African Americans, Hispanics, or Native Americans who have a GPA of 3.0 or higher and who can demonstrate financial need. Their intended major must be business, engineering, technology, mathematics, the physical sciences, or other energy-related field. Along with their application, they must submit a 350-word statement on why they should receive this scholarship, how their professional career objectives relate to energy, and any other relevant information.

Financial data The stipend is $1,500.

Duration 1 year.

Additional information The winner is eligible to compete for regional and national scholarships.

Number awarded 6 each year.

Deadline February of each year.

[227]
HAITIAN AMERICAN NURSES ASSOCIATION SCHOLARSHIPS

Haitian American Nurses Association
Attn: Chair of the Education Committee
666 N.E. 125 Street, Suite 238
P.O. Box 695069
Miami, FL 33269
(786) 360-6888 E-mail: education@hanaofflorida.org
Web: www.hanaofflorida.org/scholarshipinfo.html

Summary To provide financial assistance to students who are of Haitian descent and enrolled in an accredited nursing program.

Eligibility This program is open to nursing students who are of Haitian descent and enrolled at a school in any state. Applicants must have a GPA of 3.0 or higher. Along with their application, they must submit a 1-page essay on why they selected nursing as a career. An interview is required.

Financial data A stipend is awarded (amount not specified).

Duration 1 year; nonrenewable.

Number awarded Varies each year; recently, 3 of these scholarships were awarded.

Deadline March of each year.

[228]
HALLIE Q. BROWN SCHOLARSHIP

National Association of Colored Women's Clubs
1601 R Street, N.W.
Washington, DC 20009
(202) 667-4080 Fax: (202) 667-2574
E-mail: cearly@nacwcya.org
Web: www.nacwc.org/programs/educational.html

Summary To provide financial assistance for college to students who are nominated by a member of the National Association of Colored Women's Clubs.

Eligibility This program is open to students who have completed at least 1 semester of postsecondary education. Candidates must be nominated by a member of the National Association of Colored Women's Clubs; the nomination must be endorsed by the member's club and the club's region. Nominees must have a GPA of 2.0 or higher and be able to demonstrate financial need.

Financial data The amount awarded varies, according to financial need, and has ranged from $1,000 to $2,000 per year.

Duration The award is presented biennially, in even-numbered years.

Additional information In the past, recipients were to attend 1 of the United Negro College Fund universities or colleges; now, recipients may enroll in any accredited postsecondary institution of their choice.

Number awarded Approximately 20 every other year.

Deadline March of even-numbered years.

[229]
HAMPTON ROADS BLACK MEDIA PROFESSIONALS SCHOLARSHIPS

Hampton Roads Black Media Professionals
Attn: Vice President, Print
P.O. Box 2622
Norfolk, VA 23501-2622
(757) 446-2273 E-mail: larry.rubama@pilotonline.com
Web: www.hrbmp.us/scholarships

Summary To provide financial assistance to outstanding African American undergraduate students in Virginia who are preparing for a career in journalism.

Eligibility This program is open to 1) African American undergraduate students working on media-related degrees at a Virginia college or university; and 2) African American students who are residents of Hampton Roads and pursuing media-related degrees at a college or university anywhere in Virginia. Applicants must have a GPA of 3.0 or higher in their major and 2.5 or higher overall. Along with their application, they must submit a college transcript, a list of extracurricular activities, 2 letters of recommendation, an essay of 700 to

1,000 words on an assigned topic related to current issues in journalism, another essay of 700 to 1,000 words on their commitment to a career in journalism or other media-related fields, and samples of their work in their student newspaper or broadcast program.

Financial data Stipends range from $500 to $1,500.

Duration 1 year; may be renewed.

Number awarded Varies; generally 5 to 6 each year. Since 1989, when the award was initiated, more than $70,000 in scholarships has been awarded.

Deadline April of each year.

[230]
HANDY SIMMONS SCHOLARSHIP

African Methodist Episcopal Church
Women's Missionary Society
c/o Loretta Howell Lillard
3781 The Great Drive
Atlanta, GA 30349
(404) 771-5713 Fax: (404) 254-1171
E-mail: lorettalillard@wmsscholarship.com
Web: www.wmsscholarship.com/application

Summary To provide financial assistance to members of African Methodist Episcopal (AME) churches who are attending college.

Eligibility This program is open to active members of AME churches and its Young People's Department (YPD). Applicants must be currently enrolled as college freshmen, sophomores, or juniors and working on an associate, technical, or bachelor's degree in any field. They must have a GPA of 2.5 or higher. Along with their application, they must submit an essay of 500 to 1,000 words on a topic that changes annually but relates to Christian themes. Selection is based on that essay, academic performance, quality and level of church participation, leadership and extracurricular activities, letters of reference, and financial need.

Financial data Stipends range from $300 to $1,000.

Duration 1 year.

Number awarded 1 or more each year.

Deadline April of each year.

[231]
HAROLD HAYDEN MEMORIAL SCHOLARSHIP

National Organization of Black County Officials
1425 K Street, N.W., Suite 350
Washington, DC 20005
(202) 350-6696 Fax: (202) 350-6699
E-mail: nobco@nocboinc.org
Web: www.nobcoinc.org/scholarship.html

Summary To provide financial assistance for college to high school and currently-enrolled college students nominated by members of the National Association of Black County Officials (NABCO).

Eligibility This program is open to high school seniors and currently-enrolled college students. Applicants must submit an endorsement from a NABCO member and a brief (up to 3 pages) autobiographical essay. Selection is based on academic record, leadership record, character and personality, personal achievement, interest in government and politics, and commitment to human and civil rights. Financial need is not considered in the selection process.

Financial data A stipend is awarded (amount not specified).

Duration 1 year.

Additional information This fund was established in 1984 to honor a co-founder of the NABCO.

Number awarded Varies each year; recently, 5 of these scholarships were awarded.

Deadline June of each year.

[232]
HARRY L. MORRISON SCHOLARSHIP

National Society of Black Physicists
Attn: Scholarship Committee Chair
1100 North Glebe Road, Suite 1010
Arlington, VA 22201
(703) 536-4207 Fax: (703) 536-4203
E-mail: scholarship@nsbp.org
Web: www.nsbp.org/scholarships

Summary To provide financial assistance to African American students majoring in physics in college.

Eligibility This program is open to African American students who are entering their junior or senior year of college and majoring in physics. Applicants must submit an essay on their academic and career objectives, information on their participation in extracurricular activities, a description of any awards and honors they have received, and 3 letters of recommendation. Financial need is not considered.

Financial data The stipend is $1,000.

Duration 1 year; nonrenewable.

Number awarded 1 each year.

Deadline November of each year.

[233]
HARRY R. KENDALL LEADERSHIP DEVELOPMENT SCHOLARSHIPS

United Methodist Church
General Board of Global Ministries
Attn: United Methodist Committee on Relief
Health and Welfare Ministries
475 Riverside Drive, Room 330
New York, NY 10115
(212) 870-3871 Toll Free: (800) UMC-GBGM
E-mail: jyoung@gbgm-umc.org
Web: new.gbgm-umc.org/umcor/work/health/scholarships

Summary To provide financial assistance to African Americans who are Methodists or other Christians and preparing for a career in a health-related field.

Eligibility This program is open to undergraduate and graduate students who are U.S. citizens or permanent residents of African American descent. Applicants must be professed Christians, preferably United Methodists. They must be planning to enter a health care field or already be a practitioner in such a field. Financial need is considered in the selection process.

Financial data The stipend is $2,000.

Duration 1 year.

Additional information This program began in 1980.

Number awarded Varies each year.

Deadline June of each year.

[234]
HARVARD SCHOOL OF PUBLIC HEALTH SUMMER PROGRAM IN BIOLOGICAL SCIENCES IN PUBLIC HEALTH

Harvard School of Public Health
Attn: Division of Biological Sciences
655 Huntington Avenue, Building 2, Room 111
Boston, MA 02115
(617) 432-4397 Fax: (617) 432-0433
E-mail: BPH@hsph.harvard.edu
Web: www.hsph.harvard.edu

Summary To enable African American and other minority or disadvantaged college science students to participate in a summer research project in biological sciences at Harvard School of Public Health.

Eligibility This program is open to U.S. citizens, nationals, and permanent residents who are 1) members of ethnic groups underrepresented in graduate education (African Americans, Hispanics/Latinos, American Indians, Alaskan Natives, Pacific Islanders, and Native Hawaiians); 2) first-generation college students; and 3) students from an economically disadvantaged background. Applicants must be entering their junior or senior year with a GPA of 3.0 or higher and be interested in preparing for a research career in the biological sciences. They must be interested in participating in a summer research project related to biological science questions that are important to the prevention of disease, especially such public health questions as cancer, infections (malaria, tuberculosis, parasites), lung diseases, common diseases of aging, diabetes, and obesity.

Financial data The program provides a stipend of at least $3,600, a travel allowance of up to $500, and free dormitory housing.

Duration 9 weeks, beginning in mid-June.

Additional information Recipients conduct research under the mentorship of Harvard faculty members who are specialists in cancer cell biology, immunology and infectious diseases, molecular and cellular toxicology, environmental health sciences, nutrition, and cardiovascular research. Funding for this program is provided by the National Institutes of Health.

Number awarded Up to 10 each year.

Deadline January of each year.

[235]
HARVARD-SMITHSONIAN CENTER FOR ASTROPHYSICS SOLAR SUMMER INTERN PROGRAM

Harvard-Smithsonian Center for Astrophysics
Attn: Solar REU Program
60 Garden Street, Mail Stop 70
Cambridge, MA 02138
(617) 496-7703 E-mail: dnickerson-at-cfa@harvard.edu
Web: www.cfa.harvard.edu/opportunities/solar_reu

Summary To provide an opportunity for undergraduates (particularly African Americans, other underrepresented minorities, women, and students with disabilities) to participate in a summer research program at the Harvard-Smithsonian Center for Astrophysics (CfA).

Eligibility This program is open to U.S. citizens, nationals, and permanent residents who are full-time undergraduates, preferably those entering their junior or senior year. Applicants must be interested in working during the summer on a project in either of 2 CfA divisions: high energy astrophysics (which focuses on X-ray astronomy) or solar, stellar, and planetary sciences (which focuses on understanding star and planet formation and the physical processes in the Sun, stars, and stellar systems). Applications from underrepresented minorities, persons with disabilities, and women are encouraged.

Financial data The stipend is $5,000. Housing and travel expenses are also covered.

Duration 10 weeks during the summer.

Number awarded 8 each year.

Deadline February of each year.

[236]
HARVEY WASHINGTON BANKS SCHOLARSHIP IN ASTRONOMY

National Society of Black Physicists
Attn: Scholarship Committee Chair
1100 North Glebe Road, Suite 1010
Arlington, VA 22201
(703) 536-4207 Fax: (703) 536-4203
E-mail: scholarship@nsbp.org
Web: www.nsbp.org/scholarships

Summary To provide financial assistance to African American students majoring in astronomy in college.

Eligibility This program is open to African American students who are entering their junior or senior year of college and majoring in astronomy. Applicants must submit an essay on their academic and career objectives, information on their participation in extracurricular activities, a description of any awards and honors they have received, and 3 letters of recommendation. Financial need is not considered.

Financial data The stipend is $1,000.

Duration 1 year; nonrenewable.

Additional information This program is offered in partnership with the American Astronomical Society.

Number awarded 1 each year.

Deadline November of each year.

[237]
HATTIE J. HILLIARD SCHOLARSHIP

Wisconsin Women of Color Network, Inc.
Attn: Scholarship Committee
P.O. Box 2337
Madison, WI 53701-2337
E-mail: contact@womenofcolornetwork-wis.org
Web: www.womenofcolornetwork-wis.org/scholarship.html

Summary To provide financial assistance to African Americans and other women of color from Wisconsin who are interested in studying art at a school in any state.

Eligibility This program is open to residents of Wisconsin who are women of color enrolled or planning to enroll at a college, university, or vocational/technical school in any state. Applicants must be a member of 1 of the following groups: African American, Asian, American Indian, or Hispanic. Their field of study must be art, graphic art, commercial art, or a related area. They must be able to demonstrate financial need. Along with their application, they must submit a 1-page essay on how this scholarship will help them accomplish their educational goal. U.S. citizenship is required.

Financial data A stipend is awarded (amount not specified).

Duration 1 year.

Additional information This program began in 1995.

Number awarded 1 each year.

Deadline May of each year.

[238]
HAYNES/HETTING AWARD

Philanthrofund Foundation
Attn: Scholarship Committee
1409 Willow Street, Suite 109
Minneapolis, MN 55403-2241
(612) 870-1806 Toll Free: (800) 435-1402
Fax: (612) 871-6587 E-mail: info@PfundOnline.org
Web: www.pfundonline.org/scholarships.html

Summary To provide financial aid for college to African American and Native American undergraduate or graduate students in Minnesota who have supported gay, lesbian, bisexual, and transgender (GLBT) activities.

Eligibility This program is open to residents of Minnesota and students attending a Minnesota educational institution who are African American or Native American. Applicants must be self-identified as GLBT or from a GLBT family. They may be attending or planning to attend a trade school, technical college, college, or university (as an undergraduate or graduate student). Selection is based on the applicant's 1) affirmation of GLBT or allied identity; 2) evidence of experience and skills in service and leadership; and 3) evidence of service, leading, and working for change in GLBT communities, including serving as a role model, mentor, and/or adviser.

Financial data The stipend is $5,000. Funds must be used for tuition, books, fees, or dissertation expenses.

Duration 1 year.

Number awarded 1 each year.

Deadline January of each year.

[239]
HBCUCONNECT MINORITY SCHOLARSHIPS

HBCUConnect.com, LLC.
Attn: Scholarship Administrator
750 Cross Pointe Road, Suite Q
Columbus, OH 43230
Toll Free: (877) 864-4446
E-mail: culpepper@hbcuconnect.com
Web: www.hbcuconnect.com/scholarships/?page=1

Summary To provide financial assistance to underrepresented minority students attending or planning to attend an Historically Black College or University (HBCU).

Eligibility This program is open to high school seniors and current full-time college students who are members of an underrepresented minority group (African American, Hispanic American, Native American). Applicants must be attending or interested in attending an HBCU to work on a 4-year degree. Along with their application, they must submit a 350-word essay on why they chose to attend an HBCU. Selection is based on quality of content in their online registration with HBCUConnect and financial need.

Financial data The stipend is $1,000.

Duration 1 year.

Number awarded Up to 4 each year.

Deadline May of each year.

[240]
HEALTH RESEARCH AND EDUCATIONAL TRUST SCHOLARSHIPS

New Jersey Hospital Association
Attn: Health Research and Educational Trust
760 Alexander Road
P.O. Box 1
Princeton, NJ 08543-0001
(609) 275-4224 Fax: (609) 452-8097
Web: www.njha.com/education/scholarships

Summary To provide financial assistance to New Jersey residents (particularly African Americans, other minorities, and women) who are working on an undergraduate or graduate degree in a field related to health care administration at a school in any state.

Eligibility This program is open to residents of New Jersey enrolled in an upper-division or graduate program in hospital or health care administration, public administration, nursing, or other allied health profession at a school in any state. Graduate students working on an advanced degree to prepare to teach nursing are also eligible. Applicants must have a GPA of 3.0 or higher and be able to demonstrate financial need. Along with their application, they must submit a 2-page essay (on which 50% of the selection is based) describing their academic plans for the future. Minorities and women are especially encouraged to apply.

Financial data The stipend is $2,000.

Duration 1 year.

Additional information This program began in 1983.

Number awarded Varies each year; recently, 3 of these scholarships were awarded.

Deadline July of each year.

[241]
HECUA SCHOLARSHIPS FOR SOCIAL JUSTICE

Higher Education Consortium for Urban Affairs
Attn: Student Services
2233 University Avenue West, Suite 210
St. Paul, MN 55114-1698
(651) 287-3300 Toll Free: (800) 554-1089
Fax: (651) 659-9421 E-mail: hecua@hecua.org
Web: www.hecua.org/programs/scholarships

Summary To provide financial assistance to African Americans and other students from targeted groups who are enrolled in programs of the Higher Education Consortium for Urban Affairs (HECUA) at participating colleges and universities.

Eligibility This program is open to students at member colleges and universities who are participating in HECUA programs. Applicants must be a first-generation college student, from a low-income family, and/or a student of color. Along with their application, they must submit a reflective essay, drawing on their life experiences and their personal and academic goals, on what they believe they can contribute to the mission of HECUA to equip students with the knowledge, experiences, tools, and passion to address issues of social justice and social change. The essay should also explain how the HECUA program will benefit them and the people, issues, and communities they care about.

Financial data The stipend is $1,500. Funds are applied as a credit to the student's HECUA program fees for the semester.

Duration 1 semester.

Additional information This program began in 2006. Consortium members include Augsburg College (Minneapolis, Minnesota), Augustana College (Sioux Falls, South Dakota), Carleton College (Northfield, Minnesota), College of Saint Scholastica (Duluth, Minnesota), Colorado College (Colorado Springs, Colorado), Denison University (Granville, Ohio), Gustavus Adolphus College (St. Peter, Minnesota), Hamline University (St. Paul, Minnesota), Macalester College (St. Paul, Minnesota), Saint Mary's University (Winona, Minnesota), Saint Catherine University (St. Paul, Minnesota), Saint Olaf College (Northfield, Minnesota), Swarthmore College (Swarthmore, Pennsylvania), University of Minnesota (Twin Cities, Duluth, Morris, Crookston, Rochester), University of Saint Thomas (St. Paul, Minnesota), and Viterbo University (La Crosse, Wisconsin).

Number awarded Several each year.

Deadline April of each year for summer and fall programs; November of each year for January and spring programs.

[242]
HENRY ARTHUR CALLIS SCHOLARSHIP FUND

Alpha Phi Alpha Fraternity, Inc.-Mu Lambda Chapter
Attn: Mu Lambda Foundation
2405 First Street, N.W.
Washington, DC 20001
Web: www.mulambda.org/henry-arthur-callis-scholarship

Summary To provide financial assistance to African American high school seniors from the Washington, D.C. metropolitan area who plan to attend college in any state.

Eligibility This program is open to African American seniors graduating from high schools in Washington, D.C. and neighboring school districts. Applicants must be planning to attend a college or university in any state. Along with their application, they must submit 2 letters of recommendation, a transcript, a copy of their SAT and/or ACT scores, documentation of financial need, and a personal essay describing their involvement in extracurricular and community activities.

Financial data The stipend is $1,000.

Duration 1 year.

Additional information Alpha Phi Alpha is the first collegiate fraternity established primarily for African American men. Mu Lambda is the alumni chapter for Washington, D.C.

Number awarded 1 or more each year.

Deadline February of each year.

[243]
HERBERT LEHMAN EDUCATION FUND

NAACP Legal Defense and Educational Fund
Attn: Director of Scholarship Programs
99 Hudson Street, Suite 1600
New York, NY 10013-2897
(212) 965-2265 Fax: (212) 219-1595
E-mail: scholarships@naacpldf.org
Web: www.naacpldf.org/scholarships

Summary To provide financial assistance for college to African American and other high school seniors and recent graduates who are committed to civil rights.

Eligibility This program is open to high school seniors, high school graduates, and college freshmen attending or planning to attend 4-year colleges and universities. Applicants must be dedicated to advancing the cause of civil rights, excel academically, show exceptional leadership potential, and have made an impact on their communities through service to others. They must also be able to demonstrate financial need.

Financial data The stipend is $2,000 per year.

Duration 1 year; may be renewed for up to 3 additional years if the student remains enrolled full time, maintains good academic standing, and fulfills all program requirements.

Additional information The NAACP Legal Defense and Educational Fund established this program in 1964 so African American students in the South could attend formerly segregated schools. It is currently open to all students, regardless of race, color, ethnicity, national origin, religion, creed, sex, age, marital status, parental status, physical disability, learning disability, political affiliation, veteran status, sexual orientation, or gender identity.

Number awarded Varies each year; recently, a total of 79 new and renewal scholarships were awarded.

Deadline March of each year.

[244]
HERMAN J. NEAL SCHOLARSHIP PROGRAM

Illinois CPA Society
Attn: CPA Endowment Fund of Illinois
550 West Jackson, Suite 900
Chicago, Il 60661-5716
(312) 993-0407 Toll Free: (800) 993-0407 (within IL)
Fax: (312) 993-9954
Web: www.icpas.org/hc-students.aspx?id=2724

Summary To provide financial assistance to African American residents of Illinois enrolled as upper-division or graduate students in accounting at a college or university in the state.

Eligibility This program is open to African American residents of Illinois enrolled as juniors, seniors, or graduate student at a college or university in the state. Applicants must be studying accounting and have a GPA of 3.0 or higher. They must be able to demonstrate a commitment to becoming a C.P.A. and financial need. U.S. citizenship or permanent resident status is required.

Financial data The maximum stipend is $4,000 for payment of tuition and fees. Awards include up to $500 in expenses for books and required classroom materials.

Duration 1 year.

Additional information The scholarship does not cover the cost of C.P.A. examination review courses. Recipients may not receive a full graduate assistantship, fellowship, or scholarship from a college or university, participate in a full-tuition reimbursement cooperative education or internship program, or participate in an employee full-tuition reimbursement program during the scholarship period.

Number awarded Varies each year; recently, 4 of these scholarships were awarded.

Deadline March of each year.

[245]
HERMAN S. DREER SCHOLARSHIP/ LEADERSHIP AWARD

Omega Psi Phi Fraternity
Attn: Charles R. Drew Memorial Scholarship Commission
3951 Snapfinger Parkway
Decatur, GA 30035-3203
(404) 284-5533 Fax: (404) 284-0333
E-mail: scholarshipchairman@oppf.org
Web: www.oppf.org/scholarship

Summary To provide financial assistance to undergraduate Omega Psi Phi Fraternity men who can demonstrate leadership and humanitarian accomplishments.

Eligibility This program is open to members of Omega Psi Phi at 4-year colleges and universities who are full-time sophomores or higher and have a GPA of 3.0 or higher. Each of the fraternity's 12 district representatives may nominate 1 member. Candidates must submit 1) a statement of 200 to 250 words on their purpose for applying for this scholarship, how they believe funds from the fraternity can assist them in achieving their career goals, and other circumstances (including financial need) that make it important for them to receive financial assistance; and 2) a 500-word essay detailing their leadership and humanitarian accomplishments. The award is given to the undergraduate student best exemplifying the fraternity's principles of manhood, scholarship, perseverance, and uplift.

Financial data The stipend is $5,000.

Duration 1 year.

Additional information The winner is required to attend the Omega Psi Phi Grand Conclave or Leadership Conference. Up to $1,000 in travel expenses for attendance is provided.

Number awarded 1 each year.

Deadline April of each year.

[246]
HILIARY H. HOLLOWAY MEMORIAL SCHOLARSHIPS

Kappa Alpha Psi Fraternity
Attn: Foundation
2322 North Broad Street
Philadelphia, PA 19132
(215) 225-6566 Fax: (215) 225-2205
E-mail: info@thekappafoundation.org
Web: www.thekappafoundation.org

Summary To provide financial assistance to members of Kappa Alpha Psi Fraternity, a traditionally African American men's organization, who demonstrate outstanding achievement.

Eligibility This program is open to undergraduate members of the fraternity who apply to their regional Province. Each Province determines its own criteria for selection, but they normally consider academic performance, extracurricular activities, and fraternity and community involvement.

Financial data A stipend is awarded (amount not specified).

Duration 1 year.

Number awarded Up to 12 each year: 1 for each of the fraternity's provinces.

Deadline Each Province establishes its own deadline.

[247]
HILTON NSBE CORPORATE SCHOLARSHIP PROGRAM

National Society of Black Engineers
Attn: Programs Department
205 Daingerfield Road
Alexandria, VA 22314
(703) 549-2207 Fax: (703) 683-5312
E-mail: scholarships@nsbe.org
Web: www.nsbe.org/Programs/Scholarships.aspx

Summary To provide financial assistance to undergraduate members of the National Society of Black Engineers (NSBE) who are working on a degree in engineering, science, or technology.

Eligibility This program is open to members of the society who are working on a technical undergraduate degree in any field of engineering. Applicants must have a GPA of 3.0 or higher. Along with their application, they must submit official transcripts, a list of leadership examples, a resume, and a 350-word essay on an assigned topic.

Financial data The stipend is $10,000 per year.

Duration 1 year; may be renewed.

Additional information This program is sponsored by Hilton.

Number awarded 1 each year.

Deadline May of each year.

[248]
HISTORICALLY BLACK COLLEGE SCHOLARSHIPS

U.S. Navy
Attn: Naval Education and Training Command
NSTC OD2
250 Dallas Street, Suite A
Pensacola, FL 32508-5268
(850) 452-4941, ext. 29395
Toll Free: (800) NAV-ROTC, ext. 29395
Fax: (850) 452-2486
E-mail: pnsc_nrotc.scholarship@navy.mil
Web: www.nrotc.navy.mil/scholarship_criteria.aspx

Summary To provide financial assistance to students at specified Historically Black Colleges or Universities (HBCUs) who are interested in joining Navy ROTC to prepare for service as an officer in the U.S. Navy.

Eligibility This program is open to students attending or planning to attend 1 of 17 specified HBCUs with a Navy ROTC unit on campus. Applicants must be nominated by the professor of naval science at their institution and meet academic requirements set by each school. They must be U.S. citizens between 17 and 23 years of age who are willing to serve for 4 years as active-duty Navy officers following graduation from college. They must not have reached their 27th birthday by the time of college graduation and commissioning; applicants who have prior active-duty military service may be eligible for age adjustments for the amount of time equal to their prior service, up to a maximum of 36 months. The qualifying scores are 530 critical reading and 520 mathematics on the SAT or 22 on English and 21 on mathematics on the ACT. Current enlisted and former military personnel are also eligible if they will complete the program by the age of 30.

Financial data These scholarships provide payment of full tuition and required educational fees, as well as a specified amount for textbooks, supplies, and equipment. The program also provides a stipend for 10 months of the year that is $250 per month as a freshman, $300 per month as a sophomore, $350 per month as a junior, and $400 per month as a senior.

Duration Up to 4 years.

Additional information Recipients must complete 4 years of study in naval science classes as students at 1 of the following HBCUs: Allen University, Clark Atlanta University, Dillard University, Florida A&M University, Hampton University, Howard University, Huston-Tillotson University, Morehouse College, Norfolk State University, Prairie View A&M University, Savannah State University, Southern University and A&M College, Spelman College, Tennessee State University, Texas Southern University, Tuskegee University, or Xavier University. After completing the program, all participants are commissioned as ensigns in the Naval Reserve with an 8-year service obligation, including 4 years of active duty. Current military personnel who are accepted into this program are released from active duty and are not eligible for active-duty pay and allowances, medical benefits, or other active-duty entitlements.

Number awarded Varies each year.

Deadline January of each year.

[249]
HOLY FAMILY MEMORIAL SCHOLARSHIP PROGRAM

Holy Family Memorial
Attn: Human Resources
2300 Western Avenue
P.O. Box 1450
Manitowoc, WI 54221-1450
(920) 320-4031 Toll Free: (800) 994-3662, ext. 4031
Fax: (920) 320-8522 E-mail: recruiter@hfmhealth.org
Web: www.hfmhealth.org/scholarships

Summary To provide funding to students (particularly African Americans and other minorities) who are working on a degree in a health-related area and willing to work at a designated hospital in Wisconsin following completion of their degree.

Eligibility This program is open to students working on a degree in health-related areas that include, but are not limited to, nursing, pharmacy, sonography, occupational therapy, physical therapy, speech/language pathology, respiratory therapy, or radiology. Applicants must have a GPA of 3.0 or higher. Selection is based on a personal interview, likelihood for professional success, customer service orientation, work ethic, enthusiasm, and professionalism. Minorities are especially encouraged to apply.

Financial data Stipends are $800 per semester ($1,600 per year) for students at technical colleges, $2,000 per semester ($4,000 per year) for students at public universities, or $2,500 per semester ($5,000 per year) for students at private universities. Recipients must commit to working 6 months for each semester of support received at Holy Family Memorial in Manitowoc, Wisconsin following completion of their degree.

Duration 1 semester; renewable.

Number awarded Varies each year.

Deadline Deadline not specified.

[250]
HONEYWELL INTERNATIONAL SCHOLARSHIPS

Society of Women Engineers
Attn: Scholarship Selection Committee
203 North LaSalle Street, Suite 1675
Chicago, IL 60601-1269
(312) 596-5223 Toll Free: (877) SWE-INFO
Fax: (312) 644-8557 E-mail: scholarships@swe.org
Web: societyofwomenengineers.swe.org

Summary To provide financial assistance to women (particularly minority women) who are interested in studying specified fields of engineering in college.

Eligibility This program is open to women who are graduating high school seniors or rising college sophomores, juniors, or seniors. Applicants must be enrolled or planning to enroll full time at an ABET-accredited 4-year college or university and major in computer science or aerospace, chemical, computer, electrical, industrial, manufacturing, materials, or mechanical engineering. They must have a GPA of 3.5 or higher. Preference is given to members of groups underrepresented in computer science and engineering. U.S. citizenship or permanent resident status is required. Financial need is considered in the selection process.

Financial data The stipend is $5,000.

Duration 1 year.

Additional information This program is sponsored by Honeywell International Inc.

Number awarded 3 each year.

Deadline February of each year for current college students; May of each year for high school seniors.

[251]
HONORABLE ERNESTINE WASHINGTON LIBRARY SCIENCE/ENGLISH LANGUAGE ARTS SCHOLARSHIP

African-American/Caribbean Education Association, Inc.
P.O. Box 1224
Valley Stream, NY 11582-1224
(718) 949-6733 E-mail: aaceainc@yahoo.com
Web: www.aaceainc.com/Scholarships.html

Summary To provide financial assistance to high school seniors of African American or Caribbean heritage who plan to study a field related to library science or English language arts in college.

Eligibility This program is open to graduating high school seniors who are U.S. citizens of African American or Caribbean heritage. Applicants must be planning to attend a college or university and major in a field related to library science or English language arts. They must have completed 4 years of specified college preparatory courses with a grade of 90 or higher and have an SAT score of at least 1790. They must also have completed at least 200 hours of community service during their 4 years of high school, preferably in the field that they plan to study in college. Financial need is not considered in the selection process. New York residency is not required, but applicants must be available for an interviews in the Queens, New York area.

Financial data The stipend ranges from $1,000 to $2,500. Funds are paid directly to the recipient.

Duration 1 year.

Number awarded 1 each year.

Deadline April of each year.

[252]
HOUSTON SUN SCHOLARSHIP

National Association of Negro Business and Professional Women's Clubs
Attn: Scholarship Committee
1806 New Hampshire Avenue, N.W.
Washington, DC 20009-3206
(202) 483-4206 Fax: (202) 462-7253
E-mail: education@nanbpwc.org
Web: www.nanbpwc.org/index-11.html

Summary To provide financial assistance to African Americans from designated states studying journalism at a college in any state.

Eligibility This program is open to African Americans (men or women) who are residents of Arkansas, Kansas, Louisiana, Missouri, New Mexico, Oklahoma, or Texas. Applicants must be enrolled at an accredited college or university in any state as a sophomore or junior. They must have a GPA of 3.0 or higher and be majoring in journalism. Along with their application, they must submit an essay, up to 750 words in length, on the topic, "Credo of the Black Press." U.S. citizenship is required.

Financial data The stipend is $1,000.

Duration 1 year.

Number awarded 1 or more each year.

Deadline February of each year.

[253]
HUBERTUS W.V. WILLEMS SCHOLARSHIP FOR MALE STUDENTS

National Association for the Advancement of Colored People
Attn: Education Department
4805 Mt. Hope Drive
Baltimore, MD 21215-3297
(410) 580-5760 Toll Free: (877) NAACP-98
E-mail: youth@naacpnet.org
Web: www.naacp.org/pages/naacp-scholarships

Summary To provide funding to males, particularly male members of the National Association for the Advancement of Colored People (NAACP), who are interested in undergraduate or graduate education in selected scientific fields.

Eligibility This program is open to males who are high school seniors, college students, or graduate students. Applicants must be majoring (or planning to major) in 1 of the following fields: engineering, chemistry, physics, or mathematics. Preference is given to members of the NAACP. The required minimum GPA is 2.5 for graduating high school seniors and undergraduate students or 3.0 for graduate students. Undergraduates must be enrolled full time but graduate students may be full- or part-time students. Applicants must be able to demonstrate financial need, defined as a family income of less than $16,245 for a family of 1 ranging to less than $49,905 for a family of 7. Along with their application, they must submit a 1-page essay on their interest in their major and a career, their life's ambition, what they hope to accomplish in their lifetime, and what position they hope to attain. Full-time enrollment is required for undergraduate students, although graduate students may be enrolled full or part time. U.S. citizenship is required.

Financial data The stipend is $2,000 per year for undergraduate students or $3,000 per year for graduate students.

Duration 1 year; may be renewed.

Number awarded Varies each year; recently, 7 of these scholarships were awarded.

Deadline March of each year.

[254]
HURSTON/WRIGHT AWARD FOR COLLEGE WRITERS

Zora Neale Hurston/Richard Wright Foundation
Attn: Hurston/Wright Awards
12138 Central Avenue, Suite 953
Bowie, MD 20721
(301) 459-2108 E-mail: info@hurstonwright.org
Web: www.hurstonwright.org/#!college-awards/cs3d

Summary To recognize and reward the best fiction written by undergraduate or graduate students of African descent.

Eligibility This program is open to students of African descent who are enrolled full time as undergraduate or graduate students at a college or university in the United States. Applicants should submit a manuscript of a short story (up to 25 pages) or novel excerpt (up to 15 pages). They should indicate whether it is a short story or novel excerpt. Only 1 entry may be submitted per applicant. Writers who have already published a book (in any genre) are ineligible.

Financial data The first-place award is $1,000; finalist awards are $500.

Duration The prizes are awarded annually.

Additional information There is a $10 processing fee.

Number awarded 3 awards are presented each year: 1 first-place award and 2 finalist awards.

Deadline January of each year.

[255]
I EMPOWER SCHOLARSHIP

Greater Washington Urban League
Attn: Thursday Network
c/o Samantha Davis
P.O. Box 12023
Washington, DC 20005
E-mail: scholarship@thursdaynetwork.org
Web: www.thursdaynetwork.org/volunteer.html

Summary To provide financial assistance to African American and other high school seniors in the service area of the Greater Washington Urban League (GWUL) who plan to attend college in any state.

Eligibility This program is open to seniors graduating from high schools in Washington, D.C., Prince George's County (Maryland), or Montgomery County (Maryland) and planning to enroll at a 4-year college or university in any state. Applicants must have a GPA of 2.8 or higher. Along with their application, they must submit copies of their SAT or ACT scores, documentation of financial need, a 500-word essay on what they consider to be the single most important societal problem, and other 500-word essay on what they have done to make their community a better place to live.

Financial data The stipend is $2,000. Funds are paid directly to the recipient's institution.

Duration 1 year.

Additional information This program, which began in 1992, is operated by the Thursday Network, the young professionals' auxiliary of the GWUL, as part of its Young Blacks Give Back (YBGB) Month.

Number awarded 1 each year.

Deadline February of each year.

[256]
IABA SCHOLARSHIPS

International Association of Black Actuaries
Attn: IABA Foundation Scholarship Committee
P.O. Box 369
Windsor, CT 06095
(860) 906-1286 Fax: (860) 906-1369
E-mail: iaba@blackactuaries.org
Web: www.blackactuaries.org/scholarships

Summary To provide financial assistance to Black upper-division and graduate students preparing for an actuarial career.

Eligibility This program is open to full-time juniors, seniors, and graduate students who are of African descent, originating from the United States, Canada, the Caribbean, or African nations. Applicants must have been admitted to a college or university offering either a program in actuarial science or courses that will prepare them for an actuarial career. They must be citizens or permanent residents of the United States or Canada or eligible to study in those countries under a U.S. student visa or Canadian student authorization. Other requirements include a GPA of 3.0 or higher, a mathematics SAT score of at least 600 or a mathematics ACT score of at least 28, completion of probability and calculus courses, attempting or passing an actuarial examination, completion of Validation by Educational Experience (VEE) requirements, and familiarity with actuarial profession demands. Selection is based on merit and financial need.

Financial data Stipends range from $3,500 to $5,000 per year.

Duration 1 year; may be renewed.

Additional information Support for this program is provided by Ernst & Young, Liberty Mutual, New York Life, Prudential, and Towers Watson.

Number awarded Varies each year; recently, 16 of these scholarships, with a total value of $59,000, were awarded.

Deadline May of each year.

[257]
IBM CORPORATION SWE SCHOLARSHIPS

Society of Women Engineers
Attn: Scholarship Selection Committee
203 North LaSalle Street, Suite 1675
Chicago, IL 60601-1269
(312) 596-5223 Toll Free: (877) SWE-INFO
Fax: (312) 644-8557 E-mail: scholarships@swe.org
Web: societyofwomenengineers.swe.org

Summary To provide financial assistance to undergraduate women (particularly African American women and those from other underrepresented minority groups) who are majoring in designated engineering specialties.

Eligibility This program is open to women who are entering their sophomore or junior year at a 4-year ABET-accredited college or university. Applicants must be working full time on a degree in computer science or electrical or computer engineering and have a GPA of 3.4 or higher. Preference is given to members of groups underrepresented in engineering or computer science. Selection is based on merit. U.S. citizenship or permanent resident status is required.

Financial data The stipend is $1,000.

Duration 1 year.

Additional information This program is sponsored by the IBM Corporation.

Number awarded 5 each year.

Deadline February of each year.

[258]
ILLINOIS NURSES FOUNDATION CENTENNIAL SCHOLARSHIP

Illinois Nurses Association
Attn: Illinois Nurses Foundation
105 West Adams Street, Suite 1420
Chicago, IL 60603
(312) 419-2900 Fax: (312) 419-2920
E-mail: inf@illinoisnurses.com
Web: www.illinoisnurses.com

Summary To provide financial assistance to nursing undergraduate and graduate students who are African American or members of other underrepresented groups.

Eligibility This program is open to students working on an associate, bachelor's, or master's degree at an accredited NLNAC or CCNE school of nursing. Applicants must be members of a group underrepresented in nursing (African Americans, Hispanics, American Indians, Asians, and males). Undergraduates must have earned a passing grade in all nursing courses taken to date and have a GPA of 2.85 or higher. Graduate students must have completed at least 12 semester hours of graduate work and have a GPA of 3.0 or higher. All applicants must be willing to 1) act as a spokesperson to other student groups on the value of the scholarship to continuing their nursing education; and 2) be profiled in any media or marketing materials developed by the Illinois Nurses Foundation. Along with their application, they must submit a narrative of 250 to 500 words on how they, as nurses, plan to affect policy at either the state or national level that impacts on nursing or health care generally, or how they believe they will impact the nursing profession in general.

Financial data A stipend is awarded (amount not specified).

Duration 1 year.

Number awarded 1 or more each year.

Deadline March of each year.

[259]
INDIANA CHAPTER AABE SCHOLARSHIPS

American Association of Blacks in Energy-Indiana Chapter
Attn: Scholarship Committee
P.O. Box 44531
Indianapolis, IN 46244
(317) 684-4934 E-mail: aabram@nisource.com
Web: www.aabe.org/index.php?component=pages&id=348

Summary To provide financial assistance to African Americans and members of other underrepresented minority groups who are high school seniors in Indiana and planning to major in an energy-related field at a college in any state.

Eligibility This program is open to seniors graduating from high schools in Indiana and planning to work on a bachelor's degree at a college or university in any state. Applicants must be African Americans, Hispanics, or Native Americans who have a GPA of 3.0 or higher and are able to demonstrate financial need. Their intended major must be a field of business, engineering, physical science, mathematics, or technology related to energy. Along with their application, they must submit a 350-word statement on why they should receive this scholarship, their professional career objectives, and any other relevant information.

Financial data The stipend is $1,000 or $500.

Duration 1 year; nonrenewable.

Additional information Winners are eligible to compete for regional and national scholarships.

Number awarded 3 each year: 1 at $1,000 and 2 at $500.

Deadline February of each year.

[260]
INDIANA INDUSTRY LIAISON GROUP SCHOLARSHIP

Indiana Industry Liaison Group
c/o Tony Pickell, Vice Chair
AAP Precision Planning, LLC
6215 Meridian Street West Drive
Indianapolis, IN 46260
(317) 590-4797 E-mail: vchair@indianailg.org
Web: www.indianailg.org/scholardetails.html

Summary To provide financial assistance to African American and other students from any state who are enrolled at colleges and universities in Indiana and have been involved in activities to promote diversity.

Eligibility This program is open to residents of any state currently enrolled at an accredited college or university in Indiana. Applicants must either 1) be enrolled in programs or classes related to diversity/Affirmative Action (AA)/Equal Employment Opportunity (EEO); or 2) have work or volunteer experience with diversity/AA/EEO organizations. Along with their application, they must submit an essay of 400 to 500 words on 1 of the following topics: 1) their personal commitment to diversity/AA/EEO within their community or business; 2) a time or situation in which they were able to establish and/or sustain a commitment to diversity; 3) a time when they have taken a position in favor of affirmative action and/or diversity; or 4) activities in which they have participated within their community that demonstrate their personal commitment to moving the community's diversity agenda forward. Financial need is not considered in the selection process.

Financial data The stipend is $1,000.

Duration 1 year.

Number awarded 1 each year.

Deadline January of each year.

[261]
INDIANA MINORITY TEACHER/SPECIAL EDUCATION SERVICES SCHOLARSHIP

State Student Assistance Commission of Indiana
Attn: Grants and Scholarships
W462 Indiana Government Center South
402 West Washington Street
Indianapolis, IN 46204
(317) 232-2355 Toll Free: (888) 528-4719 (within IN)
Fax: (317) 232-3260 E-mail: grants@ssaci.in.gov
Web: www.in.gov/ssaci/2342.htm

Summary To provide funding to Black and Hispanic undergraduate students in Indiana interested in preparing for a teaching career and to other residents of the state preparing for a career in special education, occupational therapy, or physical therapy.

Eligibility This program is open to 1) Black and Hispanic students seeking teacher certification; 2) students seeking special education teaching certification; or 3) students seeking occupational or physical therapy certification. Applicants must be Indiana residents and U.S. citizens who are enrolled or accepted for enrollment as full-time students at an academic institution in Indiana. Students who are already enrolled in college must have a GPA of 2.0 or higher. Applicants must be preparing to teach in an accredited elementary or secondary school in Indiana or to work as an occupational or physical therapist at a school or rehabilitation facility. Financial need may be considered, but it is not a requirement. In the selection process, awards are presented in the following priority order: 1) minority students seeking a renewal scholarship; 2) newly-enrolling minority students; 3) non-minority students seeking a renewal scholarship; and 4) newly-enrolling non-minority students.

Financial data Minority students demonstrating financial need may receive up to $4,000 per year. For non-minority students, the maximum award is $1,000. For 3 out of the 5 years following graduation, recipients must teach full time in an elementary or secondary school in Indiana or practice as an occupational or physical therapist at a school or rehabilitation facility in the state. If they fail to meet that service requirement, they are required to reimburse the state of Indiana for all funds received.

Duration 1 year; may be renewed up to 3 additional years if recipients maintain a 2.0 GPA. They may, however, take up to 6 years to complete the program from the start of receiving the first scholarship.

Additional information This program began in 1988 to address the critical shortage of Black and Hispanic teachers in Indiana. An amendment in 1990 added the field of special education, and in 1991 the fields of occupational and physical therapy were added. Participating colleges in Indiana select the recipients. Students must submit their application to the financial aid office of the college they plan to attend (not to the State Student Assistance Commission of Indiana).

Number awarded Varies each year.

Deadline Each participating college or university establishes its own filing deadline for this program.

[262]
INDIANAPOLIS CHAPTER NBMBAA UNDERGRADUATE SCHOLARSHIP PROGRAM

National Black MBA Association-Indianapolis Chapter
Attn: Scholarship Program
P.O. Box 2325
Indianapolis, IN 46206-2325
(317) 308-6447 E-mail: scholarship@nbmbaa-indy.org
Web: www.nbmbaa-indy.org/nbmbaa_education.htm

Summary To provide financial assistance to African American students from any state working on an undergraduate degree in business or management.

Eligibility This program is open to African American students enrolled full time in an undergraduate business or management program and working on a bachelor's degree at a college or university in any state. Applicants must submit a 2-page essay on a current events topic that changes annually; recently, students were invited to write on how social networking has influenced the way companies conduct business in today's market. Selection is based on the essay, transcripts, and a list of extracurricular activities; financial need is not considered.

Financial data The stipend is $1,000.

Duration 1 year.

Number awarded 1 each year.

Deadline October of each year.

[263]
INTERMOUNTAIN SECTION AWWA DIVERSITY SCHOLARSHIP

American Water Works Association-Intermountain Section
Attn: Member Services Coordinator
3430 East Danish Road
Sandy, UT 94093
(801) 712-1619, ext. 2 Fax: (801) 487-6699
E-mail: nicoleb@ims-awwa.org
Web: ims-awwa.site-ym.com/group/StudentPO

Summary To provide financial assistance to African Americans, other minorities, and women who are interested in working on an undergraduate or graduate degree in the field of water quality, supply, and treatment at a university in Idaho or Utah.

Eligibility This program is open to 1) women; and 2) students who identify as Hispanic or Latino, Black or African American, Native Hawaiian or other Pacific Islander, Asian, or American Indian or Alaska Native. Applicants must be entering or enrolled in an undergraduate or graduate program at a college or university in Idaho or Utah that relates to water quality, supply, or treatment. Along with their application, they must submit a 2-page essay on their academic interests and career goals and how those relate to water quality, supply, or treatment. Selection is based on that essay, letters of recommendation, and potential to contribute to the field of water quality, supply, and treatment in the Intermountain West.

Financial data The stipend is $1,000. The winner also receives a 1-year student membership in the Intermountain Section of the American Water Works Association (AWWA) and a 1-year subscription to *Journal AWWA.*

Duration 1 year; nonrenewable.

Number awarded 1 each year.

Deadline October of each year.

[264]
INTERPUBLIC GROUP SCHOLARSHIP AND INTERNSHIP

New York Women in Communications, Inc.
Attn: NYWICI Foundation
355 Lexington Avenue, 15th Floor
New York, NY 10017-6603
(212) 297-2133 Fax: (212) 370-9047
E-mail: nywicipr@nywici.org
Web: www.nywici.org/foundation/scholarships

Summary To provide financial aid and work experience to African American and other minority women who are residents of designated eastern states and enrolled as juniors at a college in any state to prepare for a career in advertising or public relations.

Eligibility This program is open to female residents of New York, New Jersey, Connecticut, or Pennsylvania who are from ethnically diverse groups and currently enrolled as juniors at a college or university in any state. Also eligible are women who reside outside the 4 states but are currently enrolled at a college or university within 1 of the 5 boroughs of New York City. Applicants must be preparing for a career in advertising or public relations and have a GPA of 3.2 or higher. They must be available for a summer internship with Interpublic Group (IPG) in New York City. Along with their application, they must submit a 2-page resume; a personal essay of 300 words on an assigned topic that changes annually; 2 letters of recommendation; and an official transcript. Selection is based on academic record, need, demonstrated leadership, participation in school and community activities, honors and other awards or recognition, work experience, goals and aspirations, and unusual personal and/or family circumstances. U.S. citizenship is required.

Financial data The scholarship stipend ranges up to $10,000; the internship is salaried (amount not specified).

Duration 1 year.

Additional information This program is sponsored by IPG, a holding company for a large number of firms in the advertising industry.

Number awarded 2 each year.

Deadline January of each year.

[265]
IRA DORSEY SCHOLARSHIP ENDOWMENT FUND

Alpha Phi Alpha Fraternity, Inc.-Xi Alpha Lambda Chapter
Attn: Director of Education
P.O. Box 10371
Alexandria, VA 22310
(540) 657-6523 E-mail: xal_education@apaxal.com
Web: apaxal.com

Summary To provide financial assistance to African American and other male high school seniors in the Washington, D.C. metropolitan area who plan to attend college in any state.

Eligibility This program is open to male seniors graduating from high schools in the metropolitan Washington area of Virginia, Maryland, and the District of Columbia. Applicants must have a GPA of 2.5 or higher and be planning to attend a 4-year college or university in any state. Along with their application, they must submit a 500-word essay on a topic that changes annually; recently, they were invited to comment on whether affirmative action programs are still needed in this country. Selection is based on the quality of that essay, academic achievement, participation in school and community clubs and organizations, honors and awards, and financial need.

Financial data The stipend is $1,500.

Duration 1 year; nonrenewable.

Additional information Alpha Phi Alpha is the first collegiate fraternity established primarily for African American men. Xi Alpha Lambda is the alumni chapter for northern Virginia.

Number awarded Several each year.

Deadline May of each year.

[266]
IRLET ANDERSON SCHOLARSHIP AWARD

National Organization of Black Law Enforcement Executives
Attn: NOBLE Scholarships
4609 Pinecrest Office Park Drive, Suite F
Alexandria, VA 22312-1442
(703) 658-1529 Fax: (703) 658-9479
E-mail: wleach@noblenatl.org
Web: www.noblenational.org

Summary To provide financial assistance for college to high school seniors, especially African Americans, who are interested in preparing for a criminal justice career.

Eligibility This program is open to high school seniors who have a GPA of 3.7 or higher and are interested in preparing for a career in criminal justice. Applicants must be planning to attend an accredited academic institution in the United States to major in a social science (e.g. technology, forensic investigations, or other criminal investigative studies) related to a career in law enforcement or criminal justice. They must be U.S. citizens and able to demonstrate financial need. Along with their application, they must submit a 1-page essay on their career goals and interests and why they feel they should receive this scholarship.

Financial data The stipend is $3,500.

Duration 1 year; nonrenewable.

Additional information The sponsor is an organization of African American law enforcement officers.

Number awarded 1 each year.

Deadline April of each year.

[267]
ISBA SCHOLARSHIPS

Idaho State Broadcasters Association
1674 West Hill Road, Suite 3
Boise, ID 83702
(208) 345-3072 Fax: (208) 343-8946
E-mail: isba@qwestoffice.net
Web: bestinbroadcasting.com

Summary To provide financial assistance to students (particularly minority and other diverse students) at Idaho colleges and universities who are preparing for a career in the broadcasting field.

Eligibility This program is open to full-time students at Idaho schools who are preparing for a career in broadcasting, including business administration, sales, journalism, or engineering. Applicants must have a GPA of at least 2.0 for the first 2 years of school or 2.5 for the last 2 years. Along with their application, they must submit a letter of recommendation from the general manager of a broadcasting station that is a member of the Idaho State Broadcasters Association and a 1-page essay describing their career plans and why they want the scholarship. Applications are encouraged from a broad and diverse student population. Financial need is not considered in the selection process.

Financial data The stipend is $1,000.

Duration 1 year.

Number awarded At least 2 each year.

Deadline March of each year.

[268]
ITW SCHOLARSHIPS

Society of Women Engineers
Attn: Scholarship Selection Committee
203 North LaSalle Street, Suite 1675
Chicago, IL 60601-1269
(312) 596-5223 Toll Free: (877) SWE-INFO
Fax: (312) 644-8557 E-mail: scholarships@swe.org
Web: societyofwomenengineers.swe.org

Summary To provide financial assistance to African Americans and other undergraduate women majoring in designated engineering specialties.

Eligibility This program is open to women who are entering their junior year at a 4-year ABET-accredited college or university. Applicants must be working full time on a degree in computer science, electrical or mechanical engineering, or polymer science. They must have a GPA of 3.0 or higher. Preference is given to members of groups underrepresented in engineering or computer science. Selection is based on merit. U.S. citizenship or permanent resident status is required.

Financial data The stipend is $2,500 per year.

Duration 1 year; may be renewed 1 additional year.

Additional information This program is sponsored by Illinois Tool Works, Inc.

Number awarded 2 each year.

Deadline February of each year.

[269]
J. PARIS MOSLEY SCHOLARSHIP

Cleveland Foundation
Attn: Scholarship Processing
1422 Euclid Avenue, Suite 1300
Cleveland, OH 44115-2001
(216) 861-3810 Fax: (216) 861-1729
E-mail: Hello@clevefdn.org
Web: www.clevelandfoundation.org

Summary To provide financial assistance for college to high school seniors in any state who are deaf (preference given to African Americans and other underrepresented minority applicants) or whose primary caregivers are deaf.

Eligibility This program is open to high school seniors in any state who are deaf or hard of hearing or the children or grandchildren of deaf or hard of hearing parents or grandparents. Applicants must be planning to attend a college, university, vocational school, or other postsecondary program in any state. They must use some form of sign language, have a GPA of 2.5 or higher, and be able to demonstrate financial need. Preference is given to students of African American, Latino American, or Native American descent.

Financial data A stipend is awarded (amount not specified).

Duration 1 year.

Number awarded 1 or more each year.

Deadline April of each year.

[270] JACK AND JILL SCHOLARSHIPS

Jack and Jill Foundation of America
1930 17th Street, N.W.
Washington, DC 20009
(202) 232-5290 Fax: (202) 232-1747
Web: www.jackandjillfoundation.org/scholarships

Summary To provide financial assistance to African American high school seniors who plan to attend college in any state.

Eligibility This program is open to African American seniors graduating from high schools in any state with a GPA of 3.0 or higher. Applicants must be planning to enroll full time at an accredited 4-year college or university. Dependents of members of Jack and Jill of America are not eligible.

Financial data Stipends range from $1,500 to $2,500. Funds may be used for tuition or room and board.

Duration 1 year.

Additional information Jack and Jill of America was established in 1938 as an organization for African American mothers who wished to ensure greater opportunity for their children.

Number awarded Varies each year.

Deadline March of each year.

[271] JACKIE ROBINSON SCHOLARSHIPS

Jackie Robinson Foundation
Attn: Education and Leadership Development Program
75 Varick Street, Second Floor
New York, NY 10013-1917
(212) 290-8600 Fax: (212) 290-8081
E-mail: general@jackierobinson.org
Web: www.jackierobinson.org

Summary To provide financial assistance for college to African American and other minority high school seniors.

Eligibility This program is open to members of an ethnic minority group who are high school seniors accepted at a 4-year college or university. Applicants must have a mathematics and critical reading SAT score of 1000 or higher or ACT score of 21 or higher. Selection is based on academic achievement, financial need, dedication towards community service, and leadership potential. U.S. citizenship is required.

Financial data The maximum stipend is $7,500 per year.

Duration 4 years.

Additional information The program also offers personal and career counseling on a year-round basis, a week of interaction with other scholarship students from around the country, and assistance in obtaining summer jobs and permanent employment after graduation. It was established in 1973 by a grant from Chesebrough-Pond.

Number awarded Varies each year; recently, 181 of these scholarships were awarded.

Deadline March of each year.

[272] JAMES B. MORRIS SCHOLARSHIPS

James B. Morris Scholarship Fund
Attn: Scholarship Selection Committee
P.O. Box 12145
Des Moines, IA 50312
(515) 864-0922
Web: www.morrisscholarship.org

Summary To provide financial assistance to African American and other minority undergraduate, graduate, and law students from Iowa.

Eligibility This program is open to minority students (African Americans, Asian/Pacific Islanders, Hispanics, or Native Americans) who are interested in working on an undergraduate or graduate degree. Applicants must be either Iowa residents attending a college or university anywhere in the United States or non-Iowa residents who are attending a college or university in Iowa. Along with their application, they must submit an essay of 250 to 500 words on why they are applying for this scholarship, activities or organizations in which they are involved, and their future plans. Selection is based on the essay, academic achievement (GPA of 2.5 or higher), community service, and financial need. U.S. citizenship is required.

Financial data The stipend ranges from $1,000 to $2,500 per year.

Duration 1 year; may be renewed.

Additional information This fund was established in 1978 in honor of the J.B. Morris family, who founded the Iowa branch of the National Association for the Advancement of Colored People and published the *Iowa Bystander* newspaper. The program includes the Ann Chapman Scholarships, the Vincent Chapman, Sr. Scholarships, and the Brittany Hall Memorial Scholarships.

Number awarded Varies each year; recently, 19 of these scholarships were awarded.

Deadline March of each year.

[273] JAMES CARLSON MEMORIAL SCHOLARSHIP

Oregon Student Access Commission
Attn: Grants and Scholarships Division
1500 Valley River Drive, Suite 100
Eugene, OR 97401-2146
(541) 687-7395 Toll Free: (800) 452-8807, ext. 7395
Fax: (541) 687-7414 TDD: (800) 735-2900
E-mail: awardinfo@osac.state.or.us
Web: www.oregonstudentaid.gov/scholarships.aspx

Summary To provide financial assistance to Oregon residents from diverse environments (including African Americans) who are majoring in education on the undergraduate or graduate school level at a school in any state.

Eligibility This program is open to residents of Oregon who are U.S. citizens or permanent residents and enrolled at a college or university in any state. Applicants must be either 1) college seniors or fifth-year students majoring in elementary or secondary education; or 2) graduate students working on an elementary or secondary certificate. Full-time enrollment and financial need are required. Priority is given to 1) students who come from diverse environments and submit an essay of 250 to 350 words on their experience living or working in diverse environments; 2) dependents of members of the Oregon Education Association; and 3) applicants committed to teaching autistic children.

Financial data Stipends for scholarships offered by the Oregon Student Access Commission (OSAC) range from $200 to $10,000 but recently averaged $2,300.

Duration 1 year.

Additional information This program is administered by the OSAC with funds provided by the Oregon Community Foundation.

Number awarded Varies each year; recently, 3 of these scholarships were awarded.

Deadline February of each year.

[274]
JAMES J. WYCHOR SCHOLARSHIPS

Minnesota Broadcasters Association
Attn: Scholarship Program
3033 Excelsior Boulevard, Suite 440
Minneapolis, MN 55416
(612) 926-8123 Toll Free: (800) 245-5838
Fax: (612) 926-9761
E-mail: llasere@minnesotabroadcasters.com
Web: www.minnesotabroadcasters.com/membership

Summary To provide financial assistance to minority or other Minnesota residents interested in studying broadcasting at a college in any state.

Eligibility This program is open to residents of Minnesota who are accepted or enrolled at an accredited postsecondary institution in any state offering a broadcast-related curriculum. Applicants must have a high school or college GPA of 3.0 or higher and must submit a 500-word essay on why they wish to prepare for a career in broadcasting or electronic media. Employment in the broadcasting industry is not required, but students who are employed must include a letter from their general manager describing the duties they have performed as a radio or television station employee and evaluating their potential for success in the industry. Financial need is not considered in the selection process. Some of the scholarships are awarded only to minority or women candidates.

Financial data The stipend is $1,500.

Duration 1 year; recipients who are college seniors may reapply for an additional 1-year renewal as a graduate student.

Number awarded 10 each year, distributed as follows: 3 within the 7-county metro area, 5 allocated geographically throughout the state (northeast, northwest, central, southeast, southwest), and 2 reserved specifically for women and minority applicants.

Deadline June of each year.

[275]
JAMES WILCOX AFRICAN AMERICAN FIFTH-YEAR SCHOLARSHIP

Florida Institute of CPAs
Attn: FICPA Educational Foundation
325 West College Avenue
P.O. Box 5437
Tallahassee, FL 32314
(850) 224-2727, ext. 0
Toll Free: (800) 342-3197, ext. 0 (within FL)
Fax: (850) 222-8190 E-mail: wilsonb@ficpa.org
Web: www.ficpa.org

Summary To provide financial assistance to African American residents of Florida who are completing their fifth year of accounting study at a school in the state.

Eligibility This program is open to African American residents of Florida who have completed their senior year of an accounting program at a college or university in the state. Applicants must be entering the fifth year of study to complete the 150-hour requirement and sit for the C.P.A. exam. They must indicate a desire to work in Florida. Selection is based on financial need, educational achievement, and demonstrated professional, social, and charitable activities. U.S. citizenship or permanent resident status is required.

Financial data A stipend is awarded (amount not specified).

Duration 1 year.

Number awarded 1 or more each year.

Deadline April of each year.

[276]
JAMYE COLEMAN WILLIAMS AND JOSEPH C. MCKINNEY SCHOLARSHIPS

African Methodist Episcopal Church
Connectional Lay Organization
Attn: Scholarship Chair
P.O. Box 7682
Tallahassee, FL 32314
(850) 580-1400 Fax: (850) 224-3139
E-mail: hdbo12@yahoo.com
Web: www.connectionallay-amec.org

Summary To provide financial assistance to members of the African Methodist Episcopal (AME) Church who are interested in attending a college or university, especially those interested preparing for leadership in the denomination.

Eligibility This program is open to members of AME churches who are working on or planning to work on a bachelor's degree in any field at a college or university. Applicants must submit a 500-word essay on the importance of a college education in the 21st century. Preference is given to students who desire to serve the AME Church in a leadership capacity. Selection is based on academic record, qualities of leadership, extracurricular activities and accomplishments, reference letters, and financial need.

Financial data The stipend is $5,000. Funds are sent directly to the student.

Duration 1 year.

Number awarded 2 each year.
Deadline March of each year.

[277]
J.D. WILLIAMS SCHOLARSHIP

African Methodist Episcopal Church
Connectional Lay Organization
Attn: Scholarship Chair
P.O. Box 7682
Tallahassee, FL 32314
(850) 580-1400 Fax: (850) 224-3139
E-mail: hdbo12@yahoo.com
Web: www.connectionallay-amec.org

Summary To provide financial assistance to members of the African Methodist Episcopal (AME) Church who are interested in working on an undergraduate or graduate degree at a college or university affiliated with the denomination.

Eligibility This program is open to members of AME churches who are working on or planning to work on a bachelor's, M.Div., or D.Min. degree at an AME college or university. Applicants must submit a 500-word essay on the importance of a college education in the 21st century. Selection is based on academic record, qualities of leadership, extracurricular activities and accomplishments, reference letters, and financial need.

Financial data The stipend is $5,000. Funds are sent directly to the student.

Duration 1 year.

Number awarded 1 or more each year.

Deadline March of each year.

[278]
JDOS-INTERNATIONALE SCHOLARSHIP

National Forum for Black Public Administrators
Attn: Scholarship Program
777 North Capitol Street, N.E., Suite 807
Washington, DC 20002
(202) 408-9300 Fax: (202) 408-8558
E-mail: vharris@nfbpa.org
Web: www.nfbpa.org/i4a/pages/index.cfm?pageid=4047

Summary To provide financial assistance to African Americans working on a undergraduate or graduate degree in public administration or a related field.

Eligibility This program is open to African American undergraduate and graduate students preparing for a career in public service. Applicants must be working full time on a degree in public administration, political science, urban affairs, public policy, or a related field. They must have excellent interpersonal and analytical abilities and strong oral and written communication skills. Along with their application, they must submit a 3-page autobiographical essay that includes their academic and career goals and objectives. Selection is based on academic record, leadership ability, participation in school activities, community service, and financial need.

Financial data The stipend is $2,500.

Duration 1 year.

Additional information This program is sponsored by the construction management firm JDos-Internationalé of Washington, D.C. Recipients are required to attend the sponsor's annual conference to receive their scholarship; limited hotel and air accommodations are arranged and provided.

Number awarded 1 each year.

Deadline February of each year.

[279]
JERRY MORRIS AND SUMMER HOUSTON MEMORIAL SCHOLARSHIP

Union Pacific Railroad Black Employee Network
1400 Douglas Street
Mailstop 0780
Omaha, NE 68179
(402) 544-1183 Toll Free: (888) 870-8777
Web: www.uprr.com

Summary To provide financial assistance to African Americans from designated states who plan to attend college in their state.

Eligibility This program is open to U.S. citizens who are African American residents of Arkansas, California, Colorado, Illinois, Louisiana, Missouri, Nebraska, Nevada, or Texas. Applicants must be seniors in high school or full-time freshmen or sophomores at a college or university in those states. They must have a GPA of 2.75 or higher, a record of active involvement in school and community activities, and demonstrated social awareness and involvement. Along with their application, they must submit a 500-word essay on a topic that changes annually but relates to leadership. Selection is based on that essay, GPA, SAT/ACT scores, letters of recommendation, and financial need.

Financial data Stipends range from $500 to $1,000.

Duration 1 year; may be renewed 1 additional year.

Number awarded 1 or more each year.

Deadline February of each year.

[280]
JESSE L. JACKSON SR. FELLOWS SCHOLARSHIP AWARD

PUSH Excel
Attn: General Offices
930 East 50th Street
Chicago, IL 60615
(773) 373-3366 E-mail: pushexcel@rainbowpush.org
Web: www.pushexcel.org/pages/scholarships

Summary To provide financial assistance to high school seniors who plan to attend college and are willing to help promote the scholarship program of PUSH-Excel.

Eligibility This program is open to seniors graduating from high school and planning to enroll at an accredited 4-year college or university. Applicants must be U.S. citizens and have a GPA of 3.0 or higher. Along with their application, they must submit a 500-word essay that identifies 5 prerequisites for success, explains their personal philosophy for the pursuit of excellence, and explains how they will use their college education to achieve this pursuit of excellence. They must also agree to cooperate with the scholarship committee of PUSH-Excel by promoting its program, participating in its public relations activities, and attending its Annual National Conference luncheon and Education Leadership Conference. Selection is based on the essay, academic preparation to attend college and succeed, and ability to overcome obstacles to achieve academic and personal goals.

Financial data The stipend is $5,000 per year.
Duration 1 year; nonrenewable.
Additional information PUSH-Excel was founded in 1975 by the Rev. Jesse Jackson. This program is sponsored by Toyota.
Number awarded 1 or more each year.
Deadline June of each year.

[281] JESSICA M. BLANDING MEMORIAL SCHOLARSHIP

New England Regional Black Nurses Association, Inc.
P.O. Box 190690
Boston, MA 02119
(617) 524-1951
Web: www.nerbna.org/org/scholarships.html

Summary To provide financial assistance to licensed practical nurses from New England who are working on an undergraduate nursing degree and have contributed to the African American community.
Eligibility The program is open to residents of the New England states who are licensed practical nurses working on an associate or bachelor's degree in nursing at a school in any state. Applicants must have at least 1 full year of school remaining. Along with their application, they must submit a 3-page essay that covers their career aspirations in the nursing profession; how they have contributed to the African American or other communities of color in such areas as work, volunteering, church, or community outreach; an experience that has enhanced their personal and/or professional growth; and any financial hardships that may hinder them from completing their education.
Financial data A stipend is awarded (amount not specified).
Duration 1 year.
Number awarded 1 or more each year.
Deadline February of each year.

[282] JIMMY A. YOUNG MEMORIAL EDUCATION RECOGNITION AWARD

American Association for Respiratory Care
Attn: American Respiratory Care Foundation
9425 North MacArthur Boulevard, Suite 100
Irving, TX 75063-4706
(972) 243-2272 Fax: (972) 484-2720
E-mail: info@arcfoundation.org
Web: www.arcfoundation.org

Summary To provide financial assistance to college students, especially African Americans and other minorities, interested in becoming respiratory therapists.
Eligibility Candidates must be enrolled in an accredited respiratory therapy program, have completed at least 1 semester/quarter of the program, and have a GPA of 3.0 or higher. Preference is given to nominees of minority origin. Applications must include 6 copies of an original referenced paper on some aspect of respiratory care and letters of recommendation. The foundation prefers that the candidates be nominated by a school or program, but any student may initiate a request for sponsorship by a school (in order that a deserving candidate is not denied the opportunity to compete simply because the school does not initiate the application).
Financial data The stipend is $1,000. The award also provides airfare, 1 night's lodging, and registration for the association's international congress.
Duration 1 year.
Number awarded 1 each year.
Deadline June of each year.

[283] JOANNE ROBINSON MEMORIAL SCHOLARSHIP

JoAnne Robinson Memorial Scholarship Fund
c/o WEWS
3001 Euclid Avenue
Cleveland, OH 44115
(216) 431-5555

Summary To provide financial assistance to African American undergraduates who are majoring in broadcast journalism.
Eligibility This program is open to full-time college students who are African American and majoring in broadcast journalism. Applicants must exemplify the following characteristics: hard working, detail oriented, outstanding communication and interpersonal skills, and dedication to excellence (personally and professionally). Along with their application, they must submit a statement on the goals, values, and characteristics that make them worthy of this scholarship. Financial need is not considered in the selection process.
Financial data The stipend is $1,000. Funds may be used for tuition, books, and other educational expenses.
Duration 1 year; nonrenewable.
Additional information This scholarship is administered by the Scripps Howard Foundation, which forwards the stipend to the recipient's institution.
Number awarded 1 each year.
Deadline February of each year.

[284] JOHN AND MURIEL LANDIS SCHOLARSHIPS

American Nuclear Society
Attn: Scholarship Coordinator
555 North Kensington Avenue
La Grange Park, IL 60526-5535
(708) 352-6611 Toll Free: (800) 323-3044
Fax: (708) 352-0499 E-mail: outreach@ans.org
Web: www.new.ans.org/honors/scholarships

Summary To provide financial assistance to undergraduate or graduate students (particularly African Americans, other minorities, and women) who are interested in preparing for a career in nuclear-related fields and can demonstrate financial need.
Eligibility This program is open to undergraduate and graduate students at colleges or universities located in the United States who are preparing for, or planning to prepare for, a career in nuclear science, nuclear engineering, or a nuclear-related field. Qualified high school seniors are also eligible. Applicants must have greater than average financial need and have experienced circumstances that render them disadvantaged. Along with their application, they must submit an essay on their academic and professional goals, experiences that have affected those goals, etc. Selection is based

on that essay, academic achievement, letters of recommendation, and financial need. Women and members of minority groups are especially urged to apply. U.S. citizenship is not required.

Financial data The stipend is $5,000, to be used to cover tuition, books, fees, room, and board.

Duration 1 year; nonrenewable.

Number awarded Up to 9 each year.

Deadline January of each year.

[285]
JOHN B. MCLENDON SCHOLARSHIP FUND

North Carolina State Education Assistance Authority
Attn: Scholarship and Grant Services
10 Alexander Drive
P.O. Box 13663
Research Triangle Park, NC 27709-3663
(919) 549-8614 Toll Free: (800) 700-1775
Fax: (919) 248-4687 E-mail: information@ncseaa.edu
Web: www.ncseaa.edu/McLendon.htm

Summary To provide financial assistance to residents of North Carolina who are male or female varsity athletes enrolled at designated Historically Black Colleges and Universities (HBCUs) in the state.

Eligibility This program is open to residents of North Carolina who have been enrolled for at least 2 semesters at Bennett College for Women, Elizabeth City State University, Fayetteville State University, Johnson C. Smith University, Livingstone College, North Carolina A&T State University, North Carolina Central University, Shaw University, St. Augustine's College, or Winston-Salem State University. Applicants must be varsity athletes at their campus. Selection is made by the institution and based on leadership qualities, academics, and involvement in the institution's community. Men and women are considered separately.

Financial data The stipend is $1,250 per year.

Duration 1 year; nonrenewable.

Additional information The North Carolina General Assembly established this program in 2007.

Number awarded 20 each year: 2 (1 man and 1 woman) at each participating institution (except Bennett College for Women, which selects 2 women).

Deadline Each institution sets its own deadline.

[286]
JOHN GLOUCESTER MEMORIAL PRESBYTERIAN CHURCH SCHOLARSHIP

Presbytery of Boston
Attn: John Gloucester Memorial Presbyterian Church Scholarship Fund
P.O. Box 200160
Boston, MA 02120
E-mail: jgscholarship@yahoo.com
Web: www.presbyteryofboston.org/resources

Summary To provide financial assistance to African American and other undergraduate students who meet specified preferences.

Eligibility This program is open to students accepted or enrolled at a college or university for undergraduate study. The following categories of people are strongly encouraged to apply: minorities, members or descendants of members of the John Gloucester Memorial Presbyterian Church, residents of the Mission Hill area of Boston, members of the Presbyterian Church (USA), and those who desire to attend a Presbyterian Church (USA) educational institution. Applicants must have a GPA of 2.5 or higher and be able to demonstrate financial need.

Financial data The stipend is $1,000 per year.

Duration 1 year; recipients may reapply.

Additional information The John Gloucester Memorial Presbyterian Church was established in 1920 as the first Black Presbyterian church in New England. When the church closed in 2000 and its property was sold, the proceeds were used to establish this scholarship.

Number awarded 1 or more each year.

Deadline May of each year.

[287]
JOHN T. SMITH SCHOLARSHIPS

Kentucky Community and Technical College System
Attn: Financial Aid
300 North Main Street
Versailles, KY 40383
(859) 256-3100 Toll Free: (877) 528-2748 (within KY)
Web: www.kctcs.edu

Summary To provide financial assistance to African American and other minority students attending or planning to attend participating institutions within the Kentucky Community and Technical College System (KCTCS).

Eligibility This program is open to minority residents of Kentucky who are attending or planning to attend a participating KCTCS institution. Applicants must be enrolled or planning to enroll in a transfer program to a 4-year institution. They must be able to demonstrate unmet financial need and a GPA of 2.5 or higher. Most colleges require full-time enrollment.

Financial data Stipends vary at each participating college, but they are intended to provide full payment of tuition and required fees.

Duration 1 year; may be renewed 1 additional year.

Number awarded Varies each year.

Deadline Each college sets its own deadline.

[288]
JOHN W. WORK III MEMORIAL FOUNDATION SCHOLARSHIP

Community Foundation of Middle Tennessee
Attn: Scholarship Committee
3833 Cleghorn Avenue, Suite 400
Nashville, TN 37215-2519
(615) 321-4939 Toll Free: (888) 540-5200
Fax: (615) 327-2746 E-mail: grants@cfmt.org
Web: www.cfmt.org/request/scholarships/allscholarships

Summary To provide financial assistance to upper-division and graduate students from Tennessee, especially African Americans who are working on a degree in music at a school in any state.

Eligibility This program is open to residents of Tennessee, especially African Americans, enrolled as juniors, seniors, or graduate students at an accredited college, university, or institute in any state. Applicants must be working on a degree in music and have a GPA of 3.0 or higher. Selection is based on demonstrated potential for excellence in music, academic record, standardized test scores, extracurricular activities, work experience, community involvement, recommendations, and financial need.

Financial data Stipends range from $500 to $2,500 per year. Funds are paid to the recipient's school and must be used for tuition, fees, books, supplies, room, board, or miscellaneous expenses.

Duration 1 year.

Number awarded 1 or more each year.

Deadline March of each year.

[289]
JOHNNIE L. COCHRAN, JR./MWH SCHOLARSHIP

National Forum for Black Public Administrators
Attn: Scholarship Program
777 North Capitol Street, N.E., Suite 807
Washington, DC 20002
(202) 408-9300 Fax: (202) 408-8558
E-mail: vharris@nfbpa.org
Web: www.nfbpa.org/i4a/pages/index.cfm?pageid=4047

Summary To provide financial assistance to African Americans working on a undergraduate or graduate degree in public administration.

Eligibility This program is open to African American undergraduate and graduate students preparing for a career in public service. Applicants must be working full time on a degree in public administration, political science, urban affairs, public policy, or a related field. They must have a GPA of 3.0 or higher, excellent interpersonal and analytical abilities, and strong oral and written communication skills. Along with their application, they must submit a 3-page autobiographical essay that includes their academic and career goals and objectives. Selection is based on academic record, leadership ability, participation in school activities, community service, and financial need.

Financial data The stipend is $5,000.

Duration 1 year.

Additional information This program is sponsored by the engineering and financial consulting firm MWH. Recipients are required to attend the sponsor's annual conference to receive their scholarship; limited hotel and air accommodations are arranged and provided.

Number awarded 1 each year.

Deadline February of each year.

[290]
JOSHUA DAVID GARDNER MEMORIAL SCHOLARSHIP

Joshua David Gardner Memorial Scholarship Endowment, Inc.
4196 Merchant Plaza, Suite 816
Lake Ridge, VA 22192-5085
(719) 433-8101
E-mail: gardner@joshgardnerendowment.org
Web: www.joshgardnerendowment.org

Summary To provide financial assistance to undergraduates enrolled or planning to enroll at an Historically Black College or University (HBCU).

Eligibility This program is open to U.S. citizens between 17 and 25 years of age who are enrolled or planning to enroll at an accredited 4-year HBCU. Applicants must have a GPA of 3.0 or higher and scores of at least 1500 on the SAT or 23 on the ACT. Along with their application, they must submit a 500-word essay on the importance of personal integrity for leaders. Financial need is considered in the selection process.

Financial data The stipend is $2,000.

Duration 1 year; nonrenewable.

Additional information This program began in 2007.

Number awarded At least 1 each year.

Deadline April of each year.

[291]
JOYCE WASHINGTON SCHOLARSHIP

Watts Charity Association, Inc.
6245 Bristol Parkway, Suite 224
Culver City, CA 90230
(323) 671-0394 Fax: (323) 778-2613
E-mail: wattscharity@yahoo.com
Web: 4watts.tripod.com/id5.html

Summary To provide financial assistance to upper-division African Americans majoring in child development, teaching, or social services.

Eligibility This program is open to U.S. citizens of African American descent who are enrolled full time as a college or university junior. Applicants must be majoring in child development, teaching, or social services. They must have a GPA of 3.0 or higher, be between 17 and 24 years of age, and be able to demonstrate that they intend to continue their education for at least 2 years. Along with their application, they must submit 1) a 1-paragraph statement on why they should be awarded a Watts Charity Association scholarship; and 2) a 1- to 2-page essay on a specific type of cancer, based either on how it has impacted their life or on researched information.

Financial data A stipend is awarded (amount not specified).

Duration 1 year.

Additional information Royce R. Watts, Sr. established the Watts Charity Association after he learned he had cancer in 2001.

Number awarded 1 each year.

Deadline May of each year.

[292]
J.P. MORGAN LAUNCHING LEADERS UNDERGRADUATE SCHOLARSHIP

J.P. Morgan
Campus Recruiting
Attn: Launching Leaders
277 Park Avenue, Second Floor
New York, NY 10172
(212) 270-6000
E-mail: bronwen.x.baumgardner@jpmorgan.com
Web: careers.jpmorgan.com

Summary To provide financial aid and work experience to African American and other underrepresented minority undergraduate students interested in a career in financial services.

Eligibility This program is open to Black, Hispanic, and Native American students enrolled as sophomores or juniors and interested in financial services. Applicants must have a GPA of 3.5 or higher. Along with their application, they must submit 500-word essays on 1) why they should be considered potential candidates for CEO of the sponsoring bank in 2020; and 2) the special background and attributes they would contribute to the sponsor's diversity agenda. They must be interested in a summer associate position in the sponsor's investment banking, sales and trading, or research divisions.

Financial data The stipend is $5,000 for recipients accepted as sophomores or $10,000 for recipients accepted as juniors. For students accepted as sophomores and whose scholarship is renewed for a second year, the stipend is $15,000. The summer internship is a paid position.

Duration 1 year; may be renewed 1 additional year if the recipient successfully completes the 10-week summer intern program and maintains a GPA of 3.5 or higher.

Number awarded Approximately 12 each year.

Deadline October of each year.

[293] JUANITA KIDD STOUT SCHOLARSHIP PROGRAM

Delta Sigma Theta Sorority, Inc.
Attn: Scholarship and Standards Committee Chair
1707 New Hampshire Avenue, N.W.
Washington, DC 20009
(202) 986-2400 Fax: (202) 986-2513
E-mail: dstemail@deltasigmatheta.org
Web: www.deltasigmatheta.org

Summary To provide financial assistance to members of Delta Sigma Theta who are working on an undergraduate degree in criminal justice.

Eligibility This program is open to current undergraduate students who are working on a degree in criminal justice. Applicants must be active, dues-paying members of Delta Sigma Theta. Selection is based on meritorious achievement.

Financial data The stipends range from $1,000 to $2,000. The funds may be used to cover tuition, fees, and living expenses.

Duration 1 year; may be renewed for 1 additional year.

Additional information This sponsor is a traditionally-African American social sorority. The application fee is $20.

Number awarded 1 or more each year.

Deadline April of each year.

[294] JULIUS S., JR. AND IANTHIA H. SCOTT ENDOWED SCHOLARSHIP

United Methodist Higher Education Foundation
Attn: Scholarships Administrator
60 Music Square East, Suite 350
P.O. Box 340005
Nashville, TN 37203-0005
(615) 649-3990 Toll Free: (800) 811-8110
Fax: (615) 649-3980
E-mail: umhefscholarships@umhef.org
Web: www.umhef.org/scholarship-info

Summary To provide financial assistance to Methodist undergraduate students at designated Historically Black Colleges and Universities of the United Methodist Church.

Eligibility This program is open to students entering their sophomore year at the following Historically Black Colleges and Universities of the United Methodist Church: Wiley College, Paine College, or Philander Smith College. Applicants must have been active, full members of a United Methodist Church for at least 1 year prior to applying. They must have a GPA of 3.0 or higher and be able to demonstrate financial need. U.S. citizenship or permanent resident status is required.

Financial data The stipend is at least $1,000 per year.

Duration 1 year; nonrenewable.

Additional information This program began in 1999.

Number awarded 1 scholarship is awarded each year on a rotational basis among the 3 participating institutions.

Deadline February of each year.

[295] JUSTINE E. GRANNER MEMORIAL SCHOLARSHIP

Iowa United Methodist Foundation
2301 Rittenhouse Street
Des Moines, IA 50321
(515) 974-8927
Web: www.iumf.org/generalscholarships.html

Summary To provide financial assistance to African Americans and other ethnic minorities in Iowa interested in majoring in a health-related field.

Eligibility This program is open to ethnic minority students preparing for a career in nursing, public health, or a related field at a college or school of nursing in Iowa. Applicants must have a GPA of 3.0 or higher. They must submit transcripts, 3 letters of recommendation, ACT and/or SAT scores, and documentation of financial need. Preference is given to graduates of Iowa high schools.

Financial data The stipend is $1,000.

Duration 1 year.

Number awarded 1 each year.

Deadline March of each year.

[296] K. LEROY IRVIS UNDERGRADUATE SCHOLARSHIPS

Pennsylvania Black Conference on Higher Education
c/o Judith A.W. Thomas, Scholarship Committee Chair
Lincoln University, School of Social Sciences and Behavioral Studies
1570 Old Baltimore Pike
P.O. Box 179
Lincoln University, PA 19352
(484) 365-8159 E-mail: scholarships@pbcohe.org
Web: www.phcohe.org

Summary To provide financial assistance to African American residents of any state who are enrolled as undergraduates at colleges in Pennsylvania.

Eligibility This program is open to African Americans from any state who have completed at least the first semester as an undergraduate at a college or university in Pennsylvania. Applicants must have a GPA of 3.0 or higher. Along with their application, they must submit an essay, up to 5 pages in length, on why they should receive this scholarship. Selection is based on that essay, academics, extracurricular activity participation, leadership qualities, and interpersonal qualities.

Financial data The stipend is $1,000.

Duration 1 year.

Number awarded 6 each year: 2 in each of 3 regions (eastern, central, and western) in Pennsylvania.

Deadline December of each year.

[297]
KAISER PERMANENTE NORTHWEST HEALTH CARE CAREER SCHOLARSHIPS

Kaiser Permanente Northwest
c/o Oregon Health Career Center
Attn: Scholarship Program Coordinator
25195 S.W. Parkway Avenue, Suite 204
Wilsonville, OR 97070
(503) 682-1300, ext. 113 Fax: (503) 682-1311
E-mail: kpnwscholarship@gmail.com
Web: kpnwscholarship.com

Summary To provide financial assistance to seniors (particularly African Americans or members of other minority groups underrepresented in the health professions) who are enrolled at more than 100 designated high schools in Oregon or Washington and plan to attend college in any state to prepare for a career as a health care professional.

Eligibility This program is open to seniors graduating from approved high schools in Oregon and Washington and planning to enroll full time at a college or university in any state. Applicants must be planning to prepare for a career as a medical or dental health care professional. They must be a U.S. citizen, national, or permanent resident and have a GPA of 2.5 or higher. Preference is given to students who 1) can demonstrate financial need; 2) are the first member of their family to attend college; 3) are bilingual; or 4) are a member of an ethnic or racial group underrepresented in the health professions.

Financial data The stipend is $2,000 per year.

Duration 1 year (the freshman year of college); recipients may apply for 1 additional year (the junior year of college) of funding.

Additional information This program, which began in 2008, is offered jointly by Kaiser Permanente Northwest and the Oregon Health Career Center at the Oregon Health & Science University.

Number awarded At least 1 at each of the 113 approved high schools.

Deadline January of each year.

[298]
KANSAS ETHNIC MINORITY SCHOLARSHIP PROGRAM

Kansas Board of Regents
Attn: Student Financial Assistance
1000 S.W. Jackson Street, Suite 520
Topeka, KS 66612-1368
(785) 296-3518 Fax: (785) 296-0983
E-mail: dlindeman@ksbor.org
Web: www.kansasregents.org/scholarships_and_grants

Summary To provide financial assistance to African Americans and other minority students in Kansas who are interested in attending college in the state.

Eligibility Eligible to apply are Kansas residents who fall into 1 of these minority groups: American Indian, Alaskan Native, African American, Asian, Pacific Islander, or Hispanic. Applicants may be current college students (enrolled in community colleges, colleges, or universities in Kansas), but high school seniors graduating in the current year receive priority consideration. Minimum academic requirements include 1 of the following: 1) ACT score of 21 or higher or combined mathematics and critical reading SAT score of 990 or higher; 2) cumulative GPA of 3.0 or higher; 3) high school rank in upper 33%; 4) completion of the Kansas Scholars Curriculum (4 years of English, 3 years of mathematics, 3 years of science, 3 years of social studies, and 2 years of foreign language); 5) selection by the National Merit Corporation in any category; or 6) selection by the College Board as a Hispanic Scholar. Selection is based primarily on financial need.

Financial data A stipend of up to $1,850 is provided, depending on financial need and availability of state funds.

Duration 1 year; may be renewed for up to 3 additional years (4 additional years for designated 5-year programs), provided the recipient maintains a 2.0 cumulative GPA and has financial need.

Additional information There is a $12 application fee.

Number awarded Approximately 200 each year.

Deadline April of each year.

[299]
KANSAS SPJ MINORITY STUDENT SCHOLARSHIP

Society of Professional Journalists-Kansas Professional Chapter
c/o Denise Neil, Scholarship Committee
Wichita Eagle
825 East Douglas Avenue
P.O. Box 820
Wichita, KS 67201-0820
(316) 268-6327 E-mail: dneil@wichitaeagle.com

Summary To provide financial assistance to African American and other minority residents of any state who are enrolled at colleges and universities in Kansas and interested in a career in journalism.

Eligibility This program is open to residents of any state who are members of a racial or ethnic minority group and entering their junior or senior year at colleges and universities in Kansas. Applicants do not have to be journalism or communication majors, but they must demonstrate a strong and sincere interest in print journalism, broadcast journalism, online journalism, or photojournalism. They must have a GPA of 2.5 or higher. Along with their application, they must submit a professional resume, 4 to 6 examples of their best work (clips or stories, copies of photographs, tapes or transcripts of broadcasts, printouts of web pages) and a 1-page cover letter about themselves, how they came to be interested in journalism, their professional goals, and (if appropriate) their financial need for this scholarship.

Financial data The stipend is $1,000.

Duration 1 year.

Number awarded 1 each year.
Deadline March of each year.

[300]
KAPPA SCHOLARSHIP ENDOWMENT FUND AWARDS

Kappa Alpha Psi Fraternity-Washington (DC) Alumni Chapter
Attn: Kappa Scholarship Endowment Fund, Inc.
P.O. Box 29331
Washington, DC 20017-0331
Toll Free: (866) 671-5295 E-mail: info@ksef-inc.com
Web: www.ksef-inc.com

Summary To provide financial assistance to African American and other high school seniors in Washington, D.C. who plan to attend college in any state.

Eligibility This program is open to seniors graduating from public or charter high schools in Washington, D.C. with a GPA of 2.5 or higher. Applicants must be planning to enroll full time at an accredited 4-year institution of higher learning in any state. They must be able to demonstrate involvement in school and community activities and financial need.

Financial data Stipend amounts vary; recently, they averaged $4,000.

Duration 1 year.

Additional information The sponsor is an historically African American social fraternity, but both women and men are eligible for these scholarships.

Number awarded Varies each year; recently, 28 of these scholarships were awarded.

Deadline March of each year.

[301]
KATHY MANN MEMORIAL SCHOLARSHIP

Wisconsin Education Association Council
Attn: Scholarship Committee
33 Nob Hill Drive
P.O. Box 8003
Madison, WI 53708-8003
(608) 276-7711 Toll Free: (800) 362-8034, ext. 278
Fax: (608) 276-8203 E-mail: BrisackM@weac.org
Web: www.weac.org

Summary To provide financial assistance to African American and other minority high school seniors whose parent is a member of the Wisconsin Education Association Council (WEAC) and who plan to study education at a college in any state.

Eligibility This program is open to high school seniors whose parent is an active WEAC member, an active retired member, or a person who died while holding a WEAC membership. Applicants must be members of a minority group (American Indian, Eskimo or Aleut, Hispanic, Asian or Pacific Islander, or Black). They must rank in the top 25% of their graduating class or have a GPA of 3.0 or higher, plan to major or minor in education at a college in any state, and intend to teach in Wisconsin. Along with their application, they must submit a 300-word essay on why they want to enter the education profession and what they hope to accomplish. Selection is based primarily on that essay, GPA, letters of recommendation, and school and community activities. Secondary consideration may be given to other factors, including financial need.

Financial data The stipend is $1,450 per year.

Duration 4 years, provided the recipient maintains a GPA of 3.0 or higher.

Number awarded 1 each year.

Deadline February of each year.

[302]
KATU THOMAS R. DARGAN SCHOLARSHIP

KATU-TV
Attn: Human Resources
2153 N.E. Sandy Boulevard
P.O. Box 2
Portland, OR 97207-0002
(503) 231-4222
Web: www.katu.com/about/scholarship

Summary To provide financial assistance to African American and other minority students from Oregon and Washington who are studying broadcasting or communications in college.

Eligibility This program is open to minority (Asian, Black/African American, Hispanic or Latino, Native Hawaiian or Pacific Islander, American Indian or Alaska Native) U.S. citizens, currently enrolled as a sophomore or higher at a 4-year college or university or an accredited community college in Oregon or Washington. Residents of Oregon or Washington enrolled at a school in any state are also eligible. Applicants must be majoring in broadcasting or communications and have a GPA of 3.0 or higher. Community college students must be enrolled in a broadcast curriculum that is transferable to a 4-year accredited university. Finalists are interviewed. Selection is based on financial need, academic achievement, and an essay on personal and professional goals.

Financial data The stipend is $6,000. Funds are sent directly to the recipient's school.

Duration 1 year; recipients may reapply if they have maintained a GPA of 3.0 or higher.

Additional information Winners are also eligible for a paid internship in selected departments at Fisher Broadcasting/KATU in Portland, Oregon.

Number awarded 1 each year.

Deadline April of each year.

[303]
KAY MADRY SULLIVAN FELLOWSHIP

Alpha Kappa Alpha Sorority, Inc.
Attn: Educational Advancement Foundation
5656 South Stony Island Avenue
Chicago, IL 60637
(773) 947-0026 Toll Free: (800) 653-6528
Fax: (773) 947-0277 E-mail: akaeaf@akaeaf.net
Web: www.akaeaf.org/fellowships_endowments.htm

Summary To provide financial assistance to residents of designated states (especially African American women) who have been involved in foster care and are interested in attending college in any state.

Eligibility This program is open to undergraduate students who are enrolled full time as sophomores or higher in an accredited degree-granting institution in any state. Applicants must have been involved in the foster care system and be residents of Florida; if no residents of Florida apply, the scholarship may be awarded to a resident of Georgia or South Carolina. Along with their application, they must submit 1) a list of honors, awards, and scholarships received; 2) a list of organizations in which they have memberships, especially minority organizations; and 3) a statement of their personal and career goals, including how this scholarship will enhance their ability to attain those goals. The sponsor is a traditionally African American women's sorority.

Financial data A stipend is awarded (amount not specified).

Duration 1 year.

Number awarded 1 or more each even-numbered year.

Deadline April of each even-numbered year.

[304]
KENTUCKY LIBRARY ASSOCIATION SCHOLARSHIP FOR MINORITY STUDENTS

Kentucky Library Association
c/o Executive Secretary
1501 Twilight Trail
Frankfort, KY 40601
(502) 223-5322 Fax: (502) 223-4937
E-mail: info@kylibasn.org
Web: www.klaonline.org/scholarships965.cfm

Summary To provide financial assistance to African Americans and other minorities who are residents of Kentucky or attending school there and are working on an undergraduate or graduate degree in library science.

Eligibility This program is open to members of minority groups (defined as American Indian, Alaskan Native, Black, Hispanic, Pacific Islander, or other ethnic group) who are entering or continuing at a graduate library school accredited by the American Library Association (ALA) or an undergraduate library program accredited by the National Council of Teacher Education (NCATE). Applicants must be residents of Kentucky or a student in a library program in the state. Along with their application, they must submit a statement of their career objectives, why they have chosen librarianship as a career, and their reasons for applying for this scholarship. Selection is based on that statement, cumulative undergraduate and graduate GPA (if applicable), academic merit and potential, and letters of recommendation. U.S. citizenship or permanent resident status is required.

Financial data The stipend is $1,000.

Duration 1 year; nonrenewable.

Number awarded 1 or more each year.

Deadline June of each year.

[305]
KENTUCKY MINORITY EDUCATOR RECRUITMENT AND RETENTION SCHOLARSHIPS

Kentucky Department of Education
Attn: Minority Educator Recruitment and Retention
500 Mero Street, 8th Floor
Frankfort, KY 40601
(502) 564-1479, ext. 4014 Fax: (502) 564-6952
TDD: (502) 564-4970
E-mail: monica.davis@education.ky.gov
Web: www.education.ky.gov

Summary To provide funding to African American and other minority undergraduate and graduate students enrolled in Kentucky public institutions who want to become teachers.

Eligibility This program is open to residents of Kentucky who are undergraduate or graduate students pursuing initial teacher certification at a public university or community college in the state. Applicants must have a GPA of 2.5 or higher and either maintain full-time enrollment or be a part-time student within 18 semester hours of receiving a teacher education degree. They must be U.S. citizens and meet the Kentucky definition of a minority student.

Financial data Stipends are $5,000 per year at the 8 state universities in Kentucky or $2,000 per year at community and technical colleges. Recipients are required to teach 1 semester in Kentucky for each semester or summer term the scholarship is received. If they fail to fulfill that requirement, the scholarship converts to a loan with severe penalties for nonpayment.

Duration 1 year; may be renewed up to 3 additional years.

Additional information The Kentucky General Assembly established this program in 1992.

Number awarded Varies each year.

Deadline Each state college of teacher education sets its own deadline.

[306]
KERMIT B. NASH ACADEMIC SCHOLARSHIP

Sickle Cell Disease Association of America
Attn: Scholarship Committee
231 East Baltimore Street, Suite 800
Baltimore, MD 21202
(410) 528-1555 Toll Free: (800) 421-8453
Fax: (410) 528-1495
E-mail: scdaa@sicklecelldisease.org
Web: www.sicklecelldisease.org

Summary To provide financial assistance for college to graduating high school seniors who have sickle cell disease and are members of the Sickle Cell Disease Association of America (SCDAA).

Eligibility This program is open to graduating high school seniors who are SCDAA members and have sickle cell disease (not just the trait). Applicants must have a GPA of 3.0 or higher and be U.S. citizens or permanent residents planning to attend an accredited 4-year college or university as a full-time student. They must submit a personal essay, up to 1,000 words, on an aspect of the impact of the disease on their lives or on society. Selection is based on GPA, general academic achievement and promise, SAT scores, leadership and community service, severity of academic challenges and obstacles posed by sickle cell disease, and the quality of their essay.

Financial data The stipend is $5,000 per year.

Duration Up to 4 years, provided the recipient maintains a GPA of 2.5 or higher.

Additional information The Sickle Cell Disease Association of America (SCDAA) was formerly the National Association for Sickle Cell Disease. It established this program in 1999.

Number awarded 1 each year.

Deadline May of each year.

[307]
KIMBALL OFFICE SCHOLARSHIP

International Interior Design Association
Attn: IIDA Foundation
222 Merchandise Mart, Suite 567
Chicago, IL 60654
(312) 467-1950 Toll Free: (888) 799-4432
Fax: (312) 467-0779 E-mail: iidahq@iida.org
Web: www.iida.org

Summary To provide financial assistance to African American and other minority students enrolled in the senior year of an interior design program.

Eligibility This program is open to college seniors of African, Asian, Latino, or Native American heritage. Applicants must be working on a degree in interior design. Selection is based on excellence in academics and promising design talent.

Financial data The stipend is $4,000.

Duration 1 year.

Additional information This program began in 2006 by Kimball Office, a unit of Kimball International, Inc.

Number awarded 1 each year.

Deadline Deadline not specified.

[308]
LAGRANT FOUNDATION UNDERGRADUATE SCHOLARSHIPS

Lagrant Foundation
Attn: Senior Programs and Outreach Manager
600 Wilshire Boulevard, Suite 1520
Los Angeles, CA 90017
(323) 469-8680, ext. 223 Fax: (323) 469-8683
E-mail: erickainiguez@lagrant.com
Web: www.lagrantfoundation.org

Summary To provide financial assistance to African American and other minority college students who are interested in majoring in advertising, public relations, or marketing.

Eligibility This program is open to African Americans, Asian Americans/Pacific Islanders, Hispanics/Latinos, and Native Americans/American Indians who are full-time students at a 4-year accredited institution. Applicants must have a GPA of 2.75 or higher and be either majoring in advertising, marketing, or public relations or minoring in communications with plans to prepare for a career in advertising, marketing, or public relations. Along with their application, they must submit 1) a 1- to 2-page essay outlining their career goals; what steps they will take to increase ethnic representation in the fields of advertising, marketing, and public relations; and the role of an advertising, marketing, or public relations practitioner; 2) a paragraph describing the college and/or community activities in which they are involved; 3) a brief paragraph describing any honors and awards they have received; 4) a letter of reference; 5) a resume; and 6) an official transcript. U.S. citizenship or permanent resident status is required.

Financial data The stipend is $5,000.

Duration 1 year.

Number awarded Varies each year; recently, 16 of these scholarships were awarded.

Deadline February of each year.

[309]
LANDMARK SCHOLARS PROGRAM

Landmark Media Enterprises LLC
c/o Ann Morris, Managing Editor
Greensboro News & Record
200 East Market Street
Greensboro, NC 27401
(540) 981-3211 Toll Free: (800) 346-1234
E-mail: amorris@news-record.com
Web: company.news-record.com/intern.htm

Summary To provide financial aid and work experience to African American and other minority undergraduates who are interested in preparing for a career in journalism.

Eligibility This program is open to minority (Asian, Hispanic, African American, Native American) college sophomores, preferably those with ties to the mid-Atlantic states (Delaware, Maryland, North Carolina, South Carolina, Virginia, and Washington, D.C.). Applicants must be full-time students with a GPA of 2.5 or higher in a 4-year degree program. They must be interested in preparing for a career in print journalism and participating in an internship in news, features, sports, copy editing, photography, or graphics/illustration. U.S. citizenship or permanent resident status is required. Selection is based on grades, work samples, recommendations, targeted selection interview skills, and financial need.

Financial data The stipend is $5,000 per year. During the summers following their sophomore and junior years, recipients are provided with paid internships. Following graduation, they are offered a 1-year internship with full benefits and the possibility of continued employment.

Duration 2 years (the junior and senior years of college).

Additional information The internships are offered at the *News & Record* in Greensboro, North Carolina, the *Virginian-Pilot* in Norfolk, Virginia, or the *Roanoke Times* in Roanoke, Virginia.

Number awarded 1 or more each year.

Deadline January of each year.

[310]
LARONA J. MORRIS SCHOLARSHIP

Sigma Gamma Rho Sorority, Inc.
Attn: National Education Fund
1000 Southhill Drive, Suite 200
Cary, NC 27513
(919) 678-9720 Toll Free: (888) SGR-1922
Fax: (919) 678-9721 E-mail: info@sgrho1922.org
Web: www.sgrho1922.org/nef

Summary To provide financial assistance to African American and other undergraduate students working on a degree in hotel and restaurant management.

Eligibility This program is open to undergraduates working on a degree in hotel and restaurant management. The sponsor is a traditionally African American sorority, but support is available to males and females of all races. Applicants must have a GPA of "C" or higher and be able to demonstrate financial need.

Financial data A stipend is awarded (amount not specified).

Duration 1 year.

Additional information A processing fee of $20 is required.

Number awarded 1 each year.

Deadline April of each year.

[311]
LARRY AND CAROLYN SUAREZ FELLOWSHIP

Alpha Kappa Alpha Sorority, Inc.
Attn: Educational Advancement Foundation
5656 South Stony Island Avenue
Chicago, IL 60637
(773) 947-0026 Toll Free: (800) 653-6528
Fax: (773) 947-0277 E-mail: akaeaf@akaeaf.net
Web: www.akaeaf.org/fellowships_endowments.htm

Summary To provide financial assistance to undergraduates (especially African American women) who are working on a degree in business and entrepreneurship.

Eligibility This program is open to undergraduate students who are enrolled full time as sophomores or higher in an accredited degree-granting institution in any state. Applicants must be majoring in business and/or entrepreneurship. Along with their application, they must submit 1) a list of honors, awards, and scholarships received; 2) a list of organizations in which they have memberships, especially minority organizations; and 3) a statement of their personal and career goals, including how this scholarship will enhance their ability to attain those goals. The sponsor is a traditionally African American women's sorority.

Financial data A stipend is awarded (amount not specified).

Duration 1 year.

Number awarded 1 or more each even-numbered year.

Deadline April of each even-numbered year.

[312]
LARRY W. CARTER SCHOLARSHIP

Greater Des Moines Community Foundation
Finkbine Mansion
1915 Grand Avenue
Des Moines, IA 50309
(515) 883-2626 Fax: (515) 309-0704
E-mail: trettin@desmoinesfoundation.org
Web: www.desmoinesfoundation.org/article.aspx?id=82

Summary To provide financial assistance to African American undergraduate and graduate students in Iowa.

Eligibility Eligible to apply are African Americans who reside in Iowa and are enrolled in college or graduate school on a full- or part-time basis. Applicants must submit a personal statement that explains why they feel they should be selected to receive this scholarship and describes their personal and educational goals, motivations, and reasons for pursuing higher education. Financial need is considered in the selection process.

Financial data The stipend is $3,000.

Duration 1 year.

Number awarded Varies each year; recently, 3 of these scholarships were awarded.

Deadline May of each year.

[313]
LARRY W. MCCORMICK COMMUNICATIONS SCHOLARSHIP FOR UNDERREPRESENTED STUDENTS

The Lullaby Guild, Inc.
Attn: Scholarship Committee
6709 La Tijera, Suite 116
Los Angeles, CA 90045
(310) 335-5655 E-mail: mail@lullabyguild.org
Web: www.lullabyguild.org

Summary To provide financial assistance to African American and other underrepresented upper-division students who are working on a degree in a field related to mass communications.

Eligibility This program is open to underrepresented (e.g., African American, Hispanic American, Native American, Alaskan American, Pacific Islander, Asian) students entering their junior or senior year at an accredited college or university. Applicants must be working on a degree in a field related to mass communications, including audiovisual and electronic and print journalism. Along with their application, they must submit a personal statement regarding their volunteer services, official transcripts, 3 letters of recommendation, 3 samples of their journalistic work, and a 500-word personal statement about their interest in journalism or mass communication. Selection is based on academic achievement, letters of recommendation, journalistic experience and/or evidence of journalistic talent, clarity of purpose in plans and goals for a future in journalism or mass communications, and involvement in volunteer community service.

Financial data The stipend is $2,500.

Duration 1 year.

Number awarded 1 each year.

Deadline February of each year.

[314]
LARRY WHITESIDE SCHOLARSHIP

National Association of Black Journalists
Attn: Communications Coordinator and Program Manager
University of Maryland
1100 Knight Hall, Suite 3100
College Park, MD 20742
(301) 405-2573 Fax: (301) 314-1714
E-mail: tjohnson@nabj.org
Web: www.nabj.org/?page=SEEDScholarships

Summary To provide financial assistance to undergraduate or graduate student members of the National Association of Black Journalists (NABJ) who are preparing for a career in sports journalism.

Eligibility This program is open to African American undergraduate or graduate student members of NABJ who are currently enrolled full time at an accredited 4-year college or university. Applicants must be studying journalism as preparing for a career in sports journalism and have a GPA of 2.5 or higher in their major and 2.0 overall. They must be able to demonstrate financial need. Along with their application, they must submit 5 samples of their work, an official college transcript, 3 letters of recommendation, a resume, and an essay of 1,000 to 2,000 words on a sports journalist (living or deceased) whom they admire and why that person has inspired them to prepare for a career in sports journalism.

Financial data The stipend is $2,500. Funds are paid directly to the recipient's college or university.

Duration 1 year; nonrenewable.

Number awarded 1 each year.

Deadline March of each year.

[315]
LAURENCE R. FOSTER MEMORIAL SCHOLARSHIPS

Oregon Student Access Commission
Attn: Grants and Scholarships Division
1500 Valley River Drive, Suite 100
Eugene, OR 97401-2146
(541) 687-7395 Toll Free: (800) 452-8807, ext. 7395
Fax: (541) 687-7414 TDD: (800) 735-2900
E-mail: awardinfo@osac.state.or.us
Web: www.oregonstudentaid.gov/scholarships.aspx

Summary To provide financial assistance to African Americans and other residents of Oregon who come from a diverse environment and are enrolled at a college or graduate school in any state to prepare for a public health career.

Eligibility This program is open to residents of Oregon who are enrolled at least half time at a 4-year college or university in any state to prepare for a career in public health (not private practice). Preference is given first to applicants from diverse environments; second to persons employed in, or graduate students working on a degree in, public health; and third to juniors and seniors majoring in a health program (e.g., nursing, medical technology, physician assistant). Applicants must be able to demonstrate financial need. Along with their application, they must submit essays of 250 to 350 words on 1) what public health means to them; 2) the public health aspect they intend to practice and the health and population issues impacted by that aspect; and 3) their experience living or working in diverse environments.

Financial data Stipends for scholarships offered by the Oregon Student Access Commission (OSAC) range from $200 to $10,000 but recently averaged $2,300.

Duration 1 year.

Additional information This program is administered by the OSAC with funds provided by the Oregon Community Foundation.

Number awarded Varies each year; recently, 6 of these scholarships were awarded.

Deadline February of each year.

[316]
LCDR EIFFERT FOSTER STUDENT SCHOLARSHIP

National Naval Officers Association-Washington, D.C. Chapter
c/o LCDR Stephen Williams
P.O. Box 30784
Alexandria, VA 22310
(703) 566-3840 Fax: (703) 566-3813
E-mail: Stephen.Williams@navy.mil
Web: dcnnoa.memberlodge.com

Summary To provide financial assistance to female African American high school seniors from the Washington, D.C. area who have been in foster care and are interested in attending college in any state.

Eligibility This program is open to female African American seniors graduating from high schools in the Washington, D.C. metropolitan area who plan to enroll full time at an accredited 2- or 4-year college or university in any state. Applicants must have lived in a foster home. They must have a GPA of 2.5 or higher and be U.S. citizens or permanent residents. Selection is based on academic achievement, community involvement, and financial need.

Financial data The stipend is $1,000.

Duration 1 year; nonrenewable.

Additional information Recipients are not required to join or affiliate with the military in any way.

Number awarded 1 each year.

Deadline March of each year.

[317]
LCDR MICHAEL FLIES EAGLE SCOUT LEADERSHIP SCHOLARSHIP

National Naval Officers Association-Washington, D.C. Chapter
c/o LCDR Stephen Williams
P.O. Box 30784
Alexandria, VA 22310
(703) 566-3840 Fax: (703) 566-3813
E-mail: Stephen.Williams@navy.mil
Web: dcnnoa.memberlodge.com

Summary To provide financial assistance to male African American high school seniors from the Washington, D.C. area who are Eagle Scouts and interested in attending college in any state.

Eligibility This program is open to male African American seniors graduating from high schools in the Washington, D.C. metropolitan area who plan to enroll full time at an accredited 2- or 4-year college or university in any state. Applicants must be Eagle Scouts. They must have a GPA of 3.0 or higher and be U.S. citizens or permanent residents. Selection is based on academic achievement, community involvement, and financial need.

Financial data The stipend is $1,000.

Duration 1 year; nonrenewable.

Additional information Recipients are not required to join or affiliate with the military in any way.

Number awarded 1 each year.

Deadline March of each year.

[318]
LEADERSHIP FOR DIVERSITY SCHOLARSHIP

California School Library Association
Attn: CSL Foundation
6444 East Spring Street, Number 237
Long Beach, CA 90815-1553
Toll Free: (888) 655-8480 Fax: (888) 655-8480
E-mail: info@csla.net
Web: www.csla.net

Summary To provide financial assistance to African American and other students who reflect the diversity of California's population and are interested in earning a credential as a library media teacher in the state.

Eligibility This program is open to students who are members of a traditionally underrepresented group enrolled in a college or university library media teacher credential program in California. Applicants must intend to work as a library media teacher in a California school library media center for a minimum of 3 years. Along with their application, they must submit a 250-word statement on their school library media career interests and goals, why they should be considered, what they can contribute, their commitment to serving the needs of multicultural and multilingual students, and their financial situation.

Financial data The stipend is $1,500.

Duration 1 year.

Number awarded 1 each year.

Deadline May of each year.

[319]
LEGACY PARK FOUNDATION SCHOLARSHIPS

Legacy Park Foundation
Attn: Scholarship Director
5240 Tennyson Parkway, Suite 207
Plano, TX 75024
E-mail: info@legacyparkfoundation.org
Web: www.legacyparkfoundation.org

Summary To provide financial assistance to African American and other minority or economically disadvantaged high school seniors who plan to attend college and major in any field.

Eligibility This program is open to graduating high school seniors who qualify as members of minority or other economically disadvantaged groups. Applicants must be U.S. citizens or permanent residents planning to enroll at a college or university in any state and major in any field. They must have a GPA of 3.7 or higher and scores of at least 2000 on the SAT or 29 on the ACT. Selection is based on academic achievement, extracurricular and community participation, and financial need.

Financial data The stipend is $1,000.

Duration 1 year.

Additional information This program began in 2007.

Number awarded 5 each year.

Deadline April of each year.

[320]
LEONARD M. PERRYMAN COMMUNICATIONS SCHOLARSHIP FOR ETHNIC MINORITY STUDENTS

United Methodist Communications
Attn: Communications Resourcing Team
810 12th Avenue South
P.O. Box 320
Nashville, TN 37202-0320
(615) 742-5481 Toll Free: (888) CRT-4UMC
Fax: (615) 742-5485 E-mail: scholarships@umcom.org
Web: crt.umc.org/interior.asp?ptid=44&mid=10270

Summary To provide financial assistance to African American and other minority students at United Methodist colleges who are interested in careers in religious communications.

Eligibility This program is open to United Methodist ethnic minority students enrolled in accredited institutions of higher education as juniors or seniors. Applicants must be interested in preparing for a career in religious communications. For the purposes of this program, "communications" is meant to cover audiovisual, electronic, and print journalism. Selection is based on Christian commitment and involvement in the life of the United Methodist church, academic achievement, journalistic experience, clarity of purpose, and professional potential as a religion communicator.

Financial data The stipend is $2,500 per year.

Duration 1 year.

Additional information The scholarship may be used at any accredited institution of higher education.

Number awarded 1 each year.

Deadline March of each year.

[321]
LEONARDO WATTS SCHOLARSHIP

Watts Charity Association, Inc.
6245 Bristol Parkway, Suite 224
Culver City, CA 90230
(323) 671-0394 Fax: (323) 778-2613
E-mail: wattscharity@yahoo.com
Web: 4watts.tripod.com/id5.html

Summary To provide financial assistance to upper-division African Americans working on a degree in classical music.

Eligibility This program is open to U.S. citizens of African American descent who are enrolled full time as a college or university junior. Applicants must be studying classical music, including voice and/or instrumental. They must have a GPA of 3.0 or higher, be between 17 and 24 years of age, and be able to demonstrate that they intend to continue their education for at least 2 years. Along with their application, they must submit 1) a 1-paragraph statement on why they should be awarded a Watts Charity Association scholarship; and 2) a 1- to 2-page essay on a specific type of cancer, based either on how it has impacted their life or on researched information.

Financial data A stipend is awarded (amount not specified).

Duration 1 year.

Additional information Royce R. Watts, Sr. established the Watts Charity Association after he learned he had cancer in 2001.

Number awarded 1 each year.

Deadline May of each year.

[322]
LEROY APKER AWARD

American Physical Society
Attn: Honors Program
One Physics Ellipse
College Park, MD 20740-3844
(301) 209-3268 Fax: (301) 209-0865
E-mail: honors@aps.org
Web: www.aps.org/programs/honors/awards/apker.cfm

Summary To recognize and reward undergraduate students (particularly African Americans, other underrepresented minorities, and women) for outstanding work in physics.

Eligibility This program is open to undergraduate students at colleges and universities in the United States. Nominees should have completed or be completing the requirements for an undergraduate degree with an excellent academic record and should have demonstrated exceptional potential for scientific research by making an original contribution to physics. Each department of physics in the United States may nominate only 1 student. Each nomination packet should include the student's academic transcript, a description of the original contribution written by the student (such as a manuscript or reprint of a research publication or senior thesis), a 1,000-word summary, and 2 letters of recommendation. Nominations of qualified women and members of underrepresented minority groups are especially encouraged.

Financial data The award consists of a $5,000 honorarium for the student, a certificate citing the work and school of the recipient, and an allowance for travel expenses to the meeting of the American Physical Society (APS) at which the prize is presented. Each of the finalists receives an honorarium of $2,000 and a certificate. Each of the physics departments whose nominees are selected as recipients and finalists receives a certificate and an award; the departmental award is $5,000 for recipients and $1,000 for finalists.

Duration The award is presented annually.

Additional information This award was established in 1978.

Number awarded 2 recipients each year: 1 to a student at a Ph.D. granting institution and 1 at a non-Ph.D. granting institution.

Deadline June of each year.

[323]
LEROY SCHMIDT MINORITY 150-HOUR UNDERGRADUATE ACCOUNTING SCHOLARSHIP

Wisconsin Institute of Certified Public Accountants
Attn: WICPA Educational Foundation
235 North Executive Drive, Suite 200
Brookfield, WI 53005
(262) 785-0445, ext. 3025
Toll Free: (800) 772-6939 (within WI)
Fax: (262) 785-0838 E-mail: jessica@wicpa.org
Web: www.wicpa.org

Summary To provide financial assistance to African American and other underrepresented minority residents of Wisconsin who are enrolled at a college or university in the state and working to meet the requirements to sit for the Certified Public Accountant (C.P.A.) examination.

Eligibility This program is open to residents of Wisconsin who are African American, Native American/Alaskan Native, of Pacific Island races, or of Hispanic ethnic origin. Applicants must be entering the fifth year of academic work leading to an undergraduate degree in accounting at a college or university in the state. They must be working full time to complete the 150-hour accounting education requirement to sit for the C.P.A. examination. Along with their application, they must submit a 1-page personal statement on their career objectives, most significant accomplishment, and strongest personal attribute. Selection is based on that statement, honors and awards, academic achievement, extracurricular and volunteer activities, work experience, and letters of recommendation. U.S. citizenship is required.

Financial data The stipend is $2,500.

Duration 1 year.

Number awarded 1 or more each year.

Deadline February of each year.

[324]
LES PAYNE FOUNDER'S SCHOLARSHIP

National Association of Black Journalists
Attn: Communications Coordinator and Program Manager
University of Maryland
1100 Knight Hall, Suite 3100
College Park, MD 20742
(301) 405-2573 Fax: (301) 314-1714
E-mail: tjohnson@nabj.org
Web: www.nabj.org/?page=SEEDScholarships

Summary To provide financial assistance to undergraduate and graduate student members of the National Association of Black Journalists (NABJ) who are working on a degree in print journalism.

Eligibility This program is open to African American undergraduate or graduate student members of NABJ who are currently enrolled full time at an accredited 4-year college or university. Applicants must be working on a degree in print journalism and have a GPA of 3.0 or higher. They must be able to demonstrate financial need. Along with their application, they must submit 5 samples of their work, an official college transcript, 3 letters of recommendation, a resume, and an essay of 1,000 to 2,000 words describing 3 issues about which they are passionate and which they hope to cover as a professional journalist.

Financial data The stipend is $2,500.

Duration 1 year.

Number awarded 1 each year.

Deadline March of each year.

[325]
LIFE TECHNOLOGIES SCHOLARSHIPS

Society of Women Engineers
Attn: Scholarship Selection Committee
203 North LaSalle Street, Suite 1675
Chicago, IL 60601-1269
(312) 596-5223 Toll Free: (877) SWE-INFO
Fax: (312) 644-8557 E-mail: scholarships@swe.org
Web: societyofwomenengineers.swe.org

Summary To provide financial assistance to African American and other undergraduate women who are majoring in designated engineering specialties.

Eligibility This program is open to society members who are entering their sophomore, junior, or senior year at an ABET-accredited 4-year college or university. Applicants must be working full time on a degree in computer science or biomedical, chemical, civil, computer, electrical, industrial, manufacturing, materials, mechanical, or software engineering and have a GPA of 3.0 or higher. They must be U.S. citizens or permanent residents. Selection is based on merit. Preference is given to groups underrepresented in computer science and engineering.

Financial data The stipend is $7,500 or $2,500.

Duration 1 year.

Number awarded 3 each year: 1 at $7,500 and 2 at $2,500.

Deadline February of each year.

[326]
LIN MEDIA MINORITY SCHOLARSHIP AND TRAINING PROGRAM

LIN Television Corporation
Attn: Vice President, Human Resources
One West Exchange Street, Suite 5A
Providence, RI 02903-1064
(401) 454-2880 Fax: (401) 454-6990
Web: www.linmedia.com

Summary To provide funding to African American and other minority undergraduates interested in earning a degree in a field related to broadcast journalism and working at a station owned by LIN Television Corporation.

Eligibility This program is open to U.S. citizens and permanent residents of non-white origin who are enrolled as a sophomore or higher at a college or university. Applicants must have a declared major in broadcast journalism, digital multimedia, mass/speech/digital communication, television production, or marketing and a GPA of 3.0 or higher. Along with their application, they must submit a list of organizations and activities in which they have held leadership positions, 3 references, a 50-word description of their career goals, a list of personal achievements and honors, and a 500-word essay about themselves. Financial need is not considered in the selection process.

Financial data The program pays for tuition and fees, books, and room and board, to a maximum of $10,000 per year. Recipients must sign an employment agreement that guarantees them part-time employment as an intern during school and a 2-year regular position at a television station owned by LIN Television Corporation following graduation. If they fail to honor the employment agreement, they must repay all scholarship funds received.

Duration 2 years.

Additional information LIN Television Corporation owns 28 television stations in 17 media markets in the United States. Recipients of these scholarships must work at a station selected by LIN management.

Number awarded 2 each year: 1 for a student in broadcast television and 1 for a student in digital media.

Deadline March of each year.

[327]
LOCKHEED MARTIN NSBE CORPORATE SCHOLARSHIP PROGRAM

National Society of Black Engineers
Attn: Programs Department
205 Daingerfield Road
Alexandria, VA 22314
(703) 549-2207 Fax: (703) 683-5312
E-mail: scholarships@nsbe.org
Web: www.nsbe.org/Programs/Scholarships.aspx

Summary To provide financial assistance to members of the National Society of Black Engineers (NSBE) who are majoring in fields related to engineering.

Eligibility This program is open to members of the society who are entering their junior or senior year in college and majoring in computer science, mathematics, or the following fields of engineering: aerospace, computer, electrical, mechanical, or systems. Applicants must have a GPA of 3.0 or higher and a demonstrated interest in employment with Lockheed Martin Corporation. Along with their application, they must submit a 250-word essay describing their career goals and how they can make a community and professional impact as a Lockheed Martin employee. Selection is based on that essay; NSBE and university academic achievement; professional development; service to the society at the chapter, regional, and/or national level; and campus and community activities.

Financial data The stipend is $2,000.

Duration 1 year.

Additional information This program is sponsored by Lockheed Martin Corporation.

Number awarded 5 each year.

Deadline May of each year.

[328]
LORRAINE HANSBERRY PLAYWRITING AWARD

John F. Kennedy Center for the Performing Arts
Education Department
Attn: Kennedy Center American College Theater Festival
2700 F Street, N.W.
Washington, DC 20566
(202) 416-8857 Fax: (202) 416-8860
E-mail: KCACTF@kennedy-center.org
Web: www.kcactf.org

Summary To recognize and reward student authors of plays on the African American experience in America.

Eligibility Students at any accredited junior or senior college in the United States are eligible to compete, provided their college agrees to participate in the Kennedy Center American College Theater Festival (KCACTF). Undergraduate students must be carrying at least 6 semester hours, graduate students must be enrolled in at least 3 semester hours, and continuing part-time students must be enrolled in a regular degree or certificate program. These awards are presented to the best plays written by students of African or Diasporan descent on the subject of the African American experience.

Financial data The first-place award is $1,000 and the second-place award is $500. In addition, grants of $750 and $500 are made to the theater departments of the colleges or universities producing the first- and second-place plays. The winning playwright also receives an all-expense paid professional development opportunity.

Duration The awards are presented annually.

Additional information This program is supported by the Kennedy Center and Dramatic Publishing Company. It honors the first African American playwright to win the New York Drama Critics Award who died in 1965 at the age of 34. First presented in 1977, it is part of the Michael Kanin Playwriting Awards Program. The sponsoring college or university must pay a registration fee of $275 for each production.

Number awarded 2 students and 2 sponsoring institutions receive awards each year.

Deadline November of each year.

[329]
LOUIS B. RUSSELL, JR. MEMORIAL SCHOLARSHIP

Indiana State Teachers Association
Attn: Scholarships
150 West Market Street, Suite 900
Indianapolis, IN 46204-2875
(317) 263-3369 Toll Free: (800) 382-4037
Fax: (800) 777-6128 E-mail: mshoup@ista-in.org
Web: www.ista-in.org/dynamic.aspx?id=1038

Summary To provide financial assistance to African American and other minority high school seniors in Indiana who are interested in attending vocational school in any state.

Eligibility This program is open to ethnic minority high school seniors in Indiana who are interested in continuing their education in the area of industrial arts, vocational education, or technical preparation at an accredited postsecondary institution in any state. Selection is based on academic achievement, leadership ability as expressed through co-curricular activities and community involvement, recommendations, and a 300-word essay on their educational goals and how they plan to use this scholarship.

Financial data The stipend is $1,000.

Duration 1 year; may be renewed for 1 additional year, provided the recipient maintains a GPA of "C+" or higher.

Number awarded 1 each year.

Deadline February of each year.

[330]
LOUIS STOKES HEALTH SCHOLARS PROGRAM

Congressional Black Caucus Foundation, Inc.
Attn: Director, Educational Programs
1720 Massachusetts Avenue, N.W.
Washington, DC 20036
(202) 263-2800 Toll Free: (800) 784-2577
Fax: (202) 775-0773 E-mail: scholarships@cbcfinc.org
Web: www.cbcfinc.org/scholarships.html

Summary To provide financial assistance to African American and other underrepresented undergraduate students who are interested in preparing for a health-related career.

Eligibility This program is open to 1) underrepresented graduating high school seniors planning to attend an accredited institution of higher education; and 2) currently-enrolled full-time undergraduate students in good academic standing with a GPA of 3.0 or higher. Applicants must be planning to work on a degree in a subject that will lead to a degree in a health field. Along with their application, they must submit a personal statement of 500 to 1,000 words on 1) their future goals, major field of study, and how that field of study will help them to achieve their future career goals; 2) involvement in school activities, community and public service, hobbies, and sports; 3) how receiving this award will affect their current and future plans; and 4) other experiences, skills, or qualifications. They must also be able to demonstrate financial need, leadership ability, and participation in community service activities. Preference is given to students who demonstrate an interest in working with underserved communities. Students currently attending 2-year institutions are strongly encouraged to apply. U.S. citizenship or permanent resident status is required.

Financial data The stipend is $8,000. Funds are paid directly to the student's institution.

Duration 1 year.

Additional information This program is sponsored by UnitedHealth Group.

Number awarded 10 each year.

Deadline March of each year.

[331]
LOUISE JANE MOSES/AGNES DAVIS MEMORIAL SCHOLARSHIP

California Librarians Black Caucus-Greater Los Angeles Chapter
Attn: Scholarship Committee
P.O. Box 882276
Los Angeles, CA 90009
E-mail: scholarship@clbc.org
Web: www.clbc.org/scholar.html

Summary To provide financial assistance to African Americans in California who are interested in becoming librarians or library paraprofessionals.

Eligibility This program is open to African American residents of California who are working on a degree from an accredited library/information science program or an accredited library/information science paraprofessional program in the state. Applicants must submit an essay of 300 to 500 words on their professional goals and their interest in a library or information-related career. Selection is based on demonstrated financial need, scholastic achievement, and commitment to the goals of encouraging and supporting African American library professionals and improving library service to the African American community. Interviews are required.

Financial data Stipends range from $750 to $1,500.

Duration 1 year.

Number awarded 2 to 3 each year.

Deadline October of each year.

[332]
LOUISE MORITZ MOLITORIS LEADERSHIP AWARD

Women's Transportation Seminar
Attn: WTS Foundation
1701 K Street, N.W., Suite 800
Washington, DC 20006
(202) 955-5085 Fax: (202) 955-5088
E-mail: wts@wtsinternational.org
Web: www.wtsinternational.org/education/scholarships

Summary To provide financial assistance to undergraduate women (particularly minority women) who are interested in a career in transportation.

Eligibility This program is open to women who are working on an undergraduate degree in transportation or a transportation-related field (e.g., transportation engineering, planning, finance, or logistics). Applicants must have a GPA of 3.0 or higher. Along with their application, they must submit a 500-word statement about their career goals after graduation and why they think they should receive the scholarship award; their statement should specifically address the issue of leadership. Applications must be submitted first to a local chapter; the chapters forward selected applications for consideration on the national level. Minority women are especially encouraged to apply. Selection is based on transportation involvement and goals, job skills, academic record, and leadership potential; financial need is not considered.

Financial data The stipend is $5,000.

Duration 1 year.

Additional information Local chapters may also award additional funding to winners for their area.

Number awarded 1 each year.

Deadline Applications must be submitted by November to a local WTS chapter.

[333]
LOVETTE HOOD JR. SCHOLARSHIP

Sigma Gamma Rho Sorority, Inc.
Attn: National Education Fund
1000 Southhill Drive, Suite 200
Cary, NC 27513
(919) 678-9720 Toll Free: (888) SGR-1922
Fax: (919) 678-9721 E-mail: info@sgrho1922.org
Web: www.sgrho1922.org/nef

Summary To provide financial assistance to African American and other undergraduate students working on a degree in theology.

Eligibility This program is open to undergraduates working on a degree in theology. The sponsor is a traditionally African American sorority, but support is available to males and females of all races. Applicants must have a GPA of "C" or higher and be able to demonstrate financial need.

Financial data A stipend is awarded (amount not specified).

Duration 1 year.

Additional information A processing fee of $20 is required.

Number awarded 1 each year.

Deadline April of each year.

[334]
LTK SCHOLARSHIP

Conference of Minority Transportation Officials
Attn: National Scholarship Program
1875 I Street, N.W., Suite 500
Washington, DC 20006
(703) 234-4072 Fax: (202) 318-0364
Web: www.comto.org/?page=Scholarships

Summary To provide financial assistance to African American and other minority upper-division and graduate students in engineering or other fields related to transportation.

Eligibility This program is open to full-time minority juniors, seniors, and graduate students in engineering of other technical transportation-related disciplines. Applicants must have a GPA of 3.0 or higher. Along with their application, they must submit a cover letter with a 500-word statement of career goals. Financial need is not considered in the selection process. U.S. citizenship or legal resident status is required.

Financial data The stipend is $6,000. Funds are paid directly to the recipient's college or university.

Duration 1 year.

Additional information The Conference of Minority Transportation Officials (COMTO) was established in 1971 to promote, strengthen, and expand the roles of minorities in all aspects of transportation. This program is sponsored by LTK Engineering Services. Recipients are required to become members of COMTO if they are not already members and attend the COMTO National Scholarship Luncheon.

Number awarded 1 or more each year.

Deadline May of each year.

[335]
LUBRIZOL CORPORATION SCHOLARSHIP PROGRAM

College Now Greater Cleveland, Inc.
Attn: Managed Scholarships
200 Public Square, Suite 3820
Cleveland, OH 44114
(216) 241-5587 Fax: (216) 241-6184
E-mail: info@collegenowgc.org
Web: www.collegenowgc.org

Summary To provide financial assistance to African Americans, other minorities, and women who are working on a degree in specified fields of science and business at college in any state.

Eligibility This program is open to members of minority ethnic groups (American Indians, African Americans, Asian Pacific Americans, and Hispanic Americans) and women. Applicants must be enrolled full time at a 4-year college or university in any state and majoring in chemistry, computer information systems, computer science, engineering (chemical, computer, or mechanical), business, marketing, accounting, or finance. They must have a GPA of 3.0 or higher and be able to demonstrate financial need. Along with their application, they must submit a 500-word essay describing their academic and career goals.

Financial data The stipend is $4,000 per year.

Duration 1 year; may be renewed, provided the recipient maintains a GPA of 3.0 or higher.

Additional information This program is sponsored by the Lubrizol Corporation.

Number awarded Varies each year.

Deadline March of each year.

[336]
LUBRIZOL NSBE CORPORATE SCHOLARSHIP PROGRAM

National Society of Black Engineers
Attn: Programs Department
205 Daingerfield Road
Alexandria, VA 22314
(703) 549-2207 Fax: (703) 683-5312
E-mail: scholarships@nsbe.org
Web: www.nsbe.org/Programs/Scholarships.aspx

Summary To provide financial assistance to members of the National Society of Black Engineers (NSBE) who are majoring in specified fields of engineering.

Eligibility This program is open to members of the society, including domestic and international students, who are currently enrolled as freshmen, sophomores, or juniors at a college or university in the United States and majoring in chemical, computer, or mechanical engineering. Applicants must have a GPA of 3.0 or higher. Along with their application, they must submit an essay on how they will use this scholarship opportunity to advance their career goals. Financial need is not considered in the selection process.

Financial data The stipend is $3,000.

Duration 1 year.

Additional information This program is sponsored by Lubrizol Corporation.

Number awarded 1 each year.

Deadline May of each year.

[337]
MABEL D. RUSSELL BLACK COLLEGE FUND

United Methodist Higher Education Foundation
Attn: Scholarships Administrator
60 Music Square East, Suite 350
P.O. Box 340005
Nashville, TN 37203-0005
(615) 649-3990 Toll Free: (800) 811-8110
Fax: (615) 649-3980
E-mail: umhefscholarships@umhef.org
Web: www.umhef.org/scholarship-info

Summary To provide financial assistance to Methodist undergraduate and graduate students at Historically Black Colleges and Universities of the United Methodist Church.

Eligibility This program is open to students enrolling as full-time undergraduate and graduate students at the Historically Black Colleges and Universities of the United Methodist Church. Applicants must have been active, full members of a United Methodist Church for at least 1 year prior to applying. They must have a GPA of 3.0 or higher and be able to demonstrate financial need. U.S. citizenship or permanent resident status is required.

Financial data The stipend is at least $1,000 per year.

Duration 1 year; nonrenewable.

Additional information This program began in 1978. The qualifying schools are Bennett College for Women, Bethune-Cookman University, Claflin University, Clark Atlanta University, Dillard University, Huston-Tillotson College, Meharry Medical College, Paine College, Philander Smith College, Rust College, and Wiley College.

Number awarded 1 each year.

Deadline February of each year.

[338]
MABEL SMITH MEMORIAL SCHOLARSHIP

Wisconsin Women of Color Network, Inc.
Attn: Scholarship Committee
P.O. Box 2337
Madison, WI 53701-2337
E-mail: contact@womenofcolornetwork-wis.org
Web: www.womenofcolornetwork-wis.org/scholarship.html

Summary To provide financial assistance for vocational/technical school or community college to African American and other minority residents of Wisconsin.

Eligibility This program is open to residents of Wisconsin who are high school or GED-equivalent graduating seniors planning to continue their education at a vocational/technical school or community college in any state. Applicants must be a member of 1 of the following groups: African American, Asian, American Indian, Latina, or biracial. They must have a GPA of 2.0 or higher and be able to demonstrate financial need. Along with their application, they must submit a 1-page essay on how this scholarship will help them accomplish their educational goal. U.S. citizenship is required.

Financial data A stipend is awarded (amount not specified).

Duration 1 year.

Additional information This program began in 1990.

Number awarded 1 each year.

Deadline May of each year.

[339]
MAHLON MARTIN FELLOWSHIPS

Arkansas Department of Higher Education
Attn: Financial Aid Division
114 East Capitol Avenue
Little Rock, AR 72201-3818
(501) 371-2050 Toll Free: (800) 54-STUDY
Fax: (501) 371-2001 E-mail: finaid@adhe.edu
Web: www.adhe.edu

Summary To provide funding to African American undergraduate students in Arkansas interested in conducting a research project.

Eligibility This program is open to African American undergraduate students at Arkansas colleges and universities who are interested in conducting a research project in their field of study under the mentorship of a faculty member. Applicants must have completed at least 30 semester credit hours toward their degree and have a GPA of 3.25 or higher. Their institution may be a public or private institution of higher education in Arkansas that offers 2 or more years of college study. The faculty member must be tenured or tenure-track; temporary instructors and adjunct faculty are not eligible. Students must be U.S. citizens or permanent residents.

Financial data The maximum grant is $1,250. Students are also eligible for a travel grant up to $750 to attend a meeting of experts in their research area. Faculty mentors are eligible for grants up to $750.

Duration Grants are available for academic year only, summer only, or academic year and summer; students may compete for up to 2 years of additional funding.

Number awarded 2 to 4 each year.

Deadline October of each year.

[340]
MAINE SECTION ASCE HIGH SCHOOL SCHOLARSHIP

American Society of Civil Engineers-Maine Section
c/o Leslie L. Corrow, Scholarship Chair
Kleinschmidt Associates
75 Main Street
P.O. Box 576
Pittsfield, ME 04967
(207) 487-3328 Fax: (207) 487-3124
E-mail: scholarships@maineasce.org
Web: www.maineasce.org

Summary To provide financial assistance to high school seniors in Maine (particularly African Americans, other minorities, and women) who are interested in studying civil engineering in college.

Eligibility This program is open to graduating high school seniors who are Maine residents and who intend to study civil engineering in college. Women and minorities are especially encouraged to apply. Applicants must submit a 200-word statement describing why they have chosen civil engineering as a career and what they hope to accomplish by being a civil engineer. Selection is based on the statement, academic performance, extracurricular activities, and letters of recommendation.

Financial data The stipend is $2,000.

Duration 1 year; nonrenewable.

Number awarded 1 each year.

Deadline January of each year.

[341]
MAMIE W. MALLORY NATIONAL SCHOLARSHIP PROGRAM

National Black Coalition of Federal Aviation Employees
Attn: Tamisha Thomas
P.O. Box 87216
Atlanta, GA 30337
E-mail: tlarue@gmail.com
Web: www.nbcfae.org

Summary To provide financial assistance to undergraduate students, especially African Americans and those from other underrepresented groups, who are interested in preparing for a career in a field related to aviation.

Eligibility This program is open to undergraduate students preparing for a career in aviation, science, or technology. The program encourages applications from women, minorities, and people with disabilities. Selection is based on academic achievement, leadership, community involvement, and financial need.

Financial data The stipend is $2,000.

Duration 1 year.

Additional information This program began in 2005.

Number awarded 24 each year: 3 in each of the sponsor's regions.

Deadline April of each year.

[342]
MARATHON OIL CORPORATION COLLEGE SCHOLARSHIP PROGRAM OF THE HISPANIC SCHOLARSHIP FUND

Hispanic Scholarship Fund
Attn: Selection Committee
1411 West 190th Street, Suite 325
Gardena, CA 90248
Toll Free: (877) HSF-INFO E-mail: scholar1@hsf.net
Web: www.hsf.net/Scholarship-Programs.aspx

Summary To provide financial assistance to African American and other minority upper-division and graduate students working on a degree in a field related to the oil and gas industry.

Eligibility This program is open to U.S. citizens and permanent residents (must have a permanent resident card or a passport stamped I-551) who are of Hispanic American, African American, Asian Pacific Islander American, or American Indian/Alaskan Native heritage. Applicants must be currently enrolled full time at an accredited 4-year college or university in the United States, Puerto Rico, Guam, or the U.S. Virgin Islands with a GPA of 3.0 or higher. They must be 1) sophomores majoring in accounting, chemical engineering, computer engineering, computer science, electrical engineering, environmental engineering, geology, geosciences, information technology/management information systems, mechanical engineering, or petroleum engineering; or 2) seniors planning to work on a master's degree in geology, geosciences, or petroleum engineering. Selection is based on academic achievement, personal strengths, interest and commitment to a career in the oil and gas industry, leadership, and financial need.

Financial data The stipend is $15,000 per year.

Duration 2 years (the junior and senior undergraduate years or the first 2 years of a master's degree program).

Additional information This program is jointly sponsored by Marathon Oil Corporation and the Hispanic Scholarship Fund (HSF). Recipients may be offered a paid 8- to 10-week summer internship at various Marathon Oil Corporation locations.

Number awarded 1 or more each year.

Deadline November of each year.

[343]
MARATHON PETROLEUM CORPORATION COLLEGE SCHOLARSHIP PROGRAM OF THE HISPANIC SCHOLARSHIP FUND

Hispanic Scholarship Fund
Attn: Selection Committee
1411 West 190th Street, Suite 325
Gardena, CA 90248
Toll Free: (877) HSF-INFO E-mail: scholar1@hsf.net
Web: www.hsf.net/Scholarship-Programs.aspx

Summary To provide financial assistance to African American and other minority upper-division, graduate, or law students working on a degree in specified fields, especially at designated universities.

Eligibility This program is open to U.S. citizens and permanent residents (must have a permanent resident card or a passport stamped I-551) who are of Hispanic American, African American, Asian Pacific Islander American, or American Indian/Alaskan Native heritage. Applicants must be currently enrolled full time at an accredited 4-year college or university and have a GPA of 3.0 or higher. They must be 1) juniors, seniors, or fifth-year students majoring in accounting, chemical engineering, civil engineering, computer science, electrical engineering, environmental engineering, finance, industrial engineering, information technology/management information systems, marketing, or mechanical engineering; 2) first-year graduate students working on a degree in human resource management; or 3) first-year law students. Preference is given to students attending 1 of the following institutions: Bowling Green State University, Central Michigan University, Indiana University, Louisiana State University, Miami University of Ohio, Michigan State University, North Carolina A&T University, Ohio Northern University, Ohio State University, Purdue University, Tiffin University, University of Cincinnati, University of Dayton, University of Findlay, University of Illinois at Urbana-Champaign, University of Louisville, University of Michigan, University of Toledo, West Virginia University, or Western Michigan University. Selection is based on academic achievement, personal strengths, leadership, and financial need. Military veterans and ROTC students are especially encouraged to apply.

Financial data The stipend is $7,500.

Duration 1 year.

Additional information This program is jointly sponsored by Marathon Petroleum Corporation and the Hispanic Scholarship Fund (HSF). Recipients may be offered a paid 8- to 10-week summer internship at various Marathon Petroleum Corporation locations.
Number awarded 1 or more each year.
Deadline October of each year.

[344]
MARCIA SILVERMAN MINORITY STUDENT AWARD

Public Relations Student Society of America
Attn: Vice President of Member Services
33 Maiden Lane, 11th Floor
New York, NY 10038-5150
(212) 460-1474 Fax: (212) 995-0757
E-mail: prssa@prsa.org
Web: www.prssa.org/scholarships_competitions/individual

Summary To provide financial assistance to African American and other minority college seniors who are interested in preparing for a career in public relations.
Eligibility This program is open to minority (African American/Black, Hispanic/Latino, Asian, Native American, Alaskan Native, or Pacific Islander) students who are entering their senior year at an accredited 4-year college or university. Applicants must have a GPA of 3.0 or higher and be working on a degree in public relations, journalism, or other field to prepare for a career in public relations. Along with their application, they must submit an essay on their view of the public relations profession and their public relations career goals. Selection is based on academic achievement, demonstrated leadership, practical experience, commitment to public relations, writing skills, and letters of recommendation.
Financial data The stipend is $5,000.
Duration 1 year.
Additional information This program began in 2010.
Number awarded 1 each year.
Deadline June of each year.

[345]
MARGARET A. PEMBERTON SCHOLARSHIP FUND

Black Nurses' Association of Greater Washington, D.C. Area, Inc.
Attn: Scholarship Committee Chair
P.O. Box 55285
Washington, DC 20040
(202) 291-8866
Web: www.bnaofgwdca.org/scholarships.html

Summary To provide financial assistance to African American high school seniors in the Washington, D.C. area who are interested in working on a baccalaureate degree in nursing at a school in any state.
Eligibility This program is open to African American seniors graduating from high schools in the District of Columbia or adjoining counties in Maryland (Anne Arundel, Calvert, Charles, Howard, Montgomery, and Prince George's). Applicants must be U.S. citizens or permanent residents and have a GPA of 2.8 or higher. They must have been accepted into a baccalaureate nursing program at a college or university in the United States. Along with their application, they must submit a 1-page essay that describes their personal and educational goals, reasons why they should be selected (including evidence of financial need), and current and projected contributions to the community (including high school service and/or volunteer activities).
Financial data A stipend is awarded (amount not specified).
Duration 1 year.
Additional information This program began in 2002.
Number awarded 1 each year.
Deadline April of each year.

[346]
MARJORIE BOWENS-WHEATLEY SCHOLARSHIPS

Unitarian Universalist Association
Attn: UU Women's Federation
25 Beacon Street
Boston, MA 02108-2800
(617) 948-4692 Fax: (617) 742-2402
E-mail: uuwf@uua.org
Web: www.uuwf.org

Summary To provide financial assistance to African American and other women of color who are working on an undergraduate or graduate degree to prepare for Unitarian Universalist ministry or service.
Eligibility This program is open to women of color who are either 1) aspirants or candidates for the Unitarian Universalist ministry; or 2) candidates in the Unitarian Universalist Association's professional religious education or music leadership credentialing programs. Applicants must submit a 1- to 2-page narrative that covers their call to UU ministry, religious education, or music leadership; their passions; how their racial/ethnic/cultural background influences their goals for their calling; and how the work of the program's namesake relates to their dreams and plans for their UU service.
Financial data Stipends from $1,500 to $2,000.
Duration 1 year.
Additional information This program began in 2009.
Number awarded Varies each year; recently, 4 of these scholarships were awarded.
Deadline March of each year.

[347]
MARK MILLER AWARD

National Association of Black Accountants
Attn: National Scholarship Program
7474 Greenway Center Drive, Suite 1120
Greenbelt, MD 20770
(301) 474-NABA Fax: (301) 474-3114
E-mail: scholarships@nabainc.org
Web: www.nabainc.org

Summary To provide financial assistance to student members of the National Association of Black Accountants (NABA) who have overcome hardships and are working on an undergraduate or graduate degree in a field related to accounting.
Eligibility This program is open to NABA members who are ethnic minorities enrolled full time as 1) an undergraduate freshman, sophomore, junior, or first-semester senior majoring in accounting, business, or finance at a 4-year college or

university; or 2) a graduate student working on a master's degree in accounting. High school seniors are not eligible. Applicants must have a GPA of 2.0 or higher in their major and 2.5 or higher overall. Along with their application, they must submit 1) a 500-word personal statement on their involvement in NABA, career objectives, leadership abilities, and community activities; and 2) a 500-word statement on how they overcame personal, family, or financial hardship to persevere in their pursuit of their degree.

Financial data The stipend is $2,500.

Duration 1 year.

Number awarded 1 each year.

Deadline January of each year.

[348]
MARY A. MCDOWELL FELLOWSHIP

Alpha Kappa Alpha Sorority, Inc.
Attn: Educational Advancement Foundation
5656 South Stony Island Avenue
Chicago, IL 60637
(773) 947-0026 Toll Free: (800) 653-6528
Fax: (773) 947-0277 E-mail: akaeaf@akaeaf.net
Web: www.akaeaf.org/fellowships_endowments.htm

Summary To provide financial assistance to undergraduates (especially African American women) who are working on a degree in special needs education.

Eligibility This program is open to undergraduate students who are enrolled full time as sophomores or higher in an accredited degree-granting institution in any state. Applicants must be majoring in special needs education. Along with their application, they must submit 1) a list of honors, awards, and scholarships received; 2) a list of organizations in which they have memberships, especially minority organizations; and 3) a statement of their personal and career goals, including how this scholarship will enhance their ability to attain those goals. The sponsor is a traditionally African American women's sorority.

Financial data A stipend is awarded (amount not specified).

Duration 1 year.

Number awarded 1 or more each even-numbered year.

Deadline April of each even-numbered year.

[349]
MARY E. WOOD SCHOLARSHIP

Greater Des Moines Community Foundation
Finkbine Mansion
1915 Grand Avenue
Des Moines, IA 50309
(515) 883-2626 Fax: (515) 309-0704
E-mail: trettin@desmoinesfoundation.org
Web: www.desmoinesfoundation.org/article.aspx?id=82

Summary To provide financial assistance to African American residents of Iowa working on an undergraduate degree at a school in any state.

Eligibility Eligible to apply are African Americans who reside in Iowa and have received either a high school diploma or a GED diploma. Applicants must be attending a college, university, or trade school in any state. Along with their application, they must submit a personal statement that explains why they feel they should be selected to receive this scholarship and describes their personal and educational goals, motivations, and reasons for pursuing higher education. Financial need is considered in the selection process.

Financial data A stipend is awarded (amount not specified).

Duration 1 year.

Number awarded 1 or more each year.

Deadline May of each year.

[350]
MARY ELIZA MAHONEY SCHOLARSHIP

New England Regional Black Nurses Association, Inc.
P.O. Box 190690
Boston, MA 02119
(617) 524-1951
Web: www.nerbna.org/org/scholarships.html

Summary To provide financial assistance to high school seniors New England who have contributed to the African American community and are interested in studying nursing at a school in any state.

Eligibility The program is open to seniors graduating from high schools in New England who are planning to enroll full time in an NLN-accredited baccalaureate program in nursing in any state. Applicants must have at least 1 full year of school remaining. Along with their application, they must submit a 3-page essay that covers their career aspirations in the nursing profession; how they have contributed to the African American or other communities of color in such areas as work, volunteering, church, or community outreach; an experience that has enhanced their personal and/or professional growth; and any financial hardships that may hinder them from completing their education.

Financial data A stipend is awarded (amount not specified).

Duration 1 year.

Number awarded 1 or more each year.

Deadline February of each year.

[351]
MARY HILL DAVIS ETHNIC/MINORITY STUDENT SCHOLARSHIP PROGRAM

Baptist General Convention of Texas
Attn: Institutional Ministries Department
333 North Washington
Dallas, TX 75246-1798
(214) 828-5252 Toll Free: (888) 244-9400
Fax: (214) 828-5261 E-mail: institutions@bgct.org
Web: texasbaptists.org

Summary To provide financial assistance for college to African American and other ethnic minority residents of Texas who are members of Texas Baptist congregations.

Eligibility This program is open to members of Texas Baptist congregations who are of African American, Hispanic, Native American, or other intercultural heritage. Applicants must be attending or planning to attend a university affiliated with the Baptist General Convention of Texas to work on a bachelor's degree as preparation for service as a future lay or vocational ministry leader in a Texas Baptist ethnic/minority church. They must have been active in their respective ethnic/minority community. Along with their application, they must submit a letter of recommendation from their pastor and transcripts. Students still in high school must have a GPA of at least 3.0; students previously enrolled in a college must have at least a 2.0 GPA. U.S. citizenship or permanent resident status is required.

Financial data Stipends are $800 per semester ($1,600 per year) for full-time students or $400 per semester ($800 per year) for part-time students.

Duration 1 semester; may be renewed up to 7 additional semesters.

Additional information The scholarships are funded through the Week of Prayer and the Mary Hill Davis Offering for state missions sponsored annually by Women's Missionary Union of Texas. The eligible institutions are Baptist University of The Americas, Baylor University, Dallas Baptist University, East Texas Baptist University, Hardin Simmons University, Houston Baptist University, Howard Payne University, University of Mary Hardin Baylor, and Wayland Baptist University.

Number awarded Varies each year.

Deadline April of each year.

[352] MARY L. KIRKLAND YOUTH EDUCATION SCHOLARSHIP AWARD

African Methodist Episcopal Church
Midwest Conference
Attn: Women's Missionary Society
YES Scholarship Committee
P.O. Box 171488
Kansas City, KS 66117-0488
Web: www.midwestwms.org/ypd.html

Summary To provide financial assistance to members of African Methodist Episcopal (AME) churches in its Midwest Conference who are interested in attending college in any state.

Eligibility This program is open to high school seniors and students already enrolled at a college, university, junior college, or vocational school in any state. Applicants must be a member of an AME church and its Young People's Department (YPD) in the Midwest Conference (Kansas, Nebraska, and northwest Missouri).

Financial data Stipends recently were $2,500 or $400.

Duration 1 year.

Number awarded Varies each year; recently, 5 of these scholarships were awarded: 1 at $2,500 and 4 at $400.

Deadline June of each year.

[353] MARY MCLEOD BETHUNE SCHOLARSHIPS

Florida Department of Education
Attn: Office of Student Financial Assistance
325 West Gaines Street
Tallahassee, FL 32399-0400
(850) 410-5160 Toll Free: (888) 827-2004
Fax: (850) 487-1809 E-mail: osfa@fldoe.org
Web: www.floridastudentfinancialaid.org

Summary To provide financial assistance to high school seniors interested in attending Historically Black Colleges and Universities (HBCUs) in Florida.

Eligibility Eligible are high school seniors who wish to attend Florida A&M University, Bethune-Cookman University, Edward Waters College, or Florida Memorial University for a minimum of 12 credit hours per term. Applicants must be Florida residents, be U.S. citizens or eligible noncitizens, have a GPA of 3.0 or higher, be able to demonstrate financial need, and not be in default or owe repayment on any federal or state grant, scholarship, or loan program. Priority may be given to students with the lowest total family resources.

Financial data The stipend is $3,000 per year.

Duration 1 year; may be renewed up to 3 additional years if the student maintains full-time enrollment and a GPA of 3.0 or higher and continues to demonstrate financial need.

Number awarded Varies each year; recently, this program awarded 120 new and 105 renewal grants.

Deadline Deadlines are established by the participating institutions.

[354] MARYLAND CHAPTER/ELIZABETH KNIGHT SCHOLARSHIP AWARDS

Consortium of Information and Telecommunications Executives-Maryland Chapter
P.O. Box 1286
Baltimore, MD 21203
(410) 393-2337 E-mail: scholarship@cite-md.org
Web: www.cite-md.org

Summary To provide financial assistance to African American high school seniors in Maryland who plan to attend college in any state.

Eligibility This program is open to African American seniors graduating from high schools in Maryland with a GPA of 3.0 or higher. Applicants must have been accepted by an accredited college or university in any state and be able to document financial need. Employees and immediate family members of employees of the Verizon Corporation or an affiliated subsidiary are ineligible.

Financial data The stipend is $1,000.

Duration 1 year.

Additional information The Consortium of Information and Telecommunications Executives (CITE) is an organization of African American employees of Verizon, founded in 1984 after the dissolution of the former Bell systems.

Number awarded 3 each year.

Deadline March of each year.

[355] MARYLAND CHAPTER NFBPA SCHOLARSHIP

National Forum for Black Public Administrators
Attn: Scholarship Program
777 North Capitol Street, N.E., Suite 807
Washington, DC 20002
(202) 408-9300 Fax: (202) 408-8558
E-mail: vharris@nfbpa.org
Web: www.nfbpa.org/i4a/pages/index.cfm?pageid=4047

Summary To provide financial assistance to African American undergraduate students from Maryland working on a degree in public administration or a related field.

Eligibility This program is open to African Americans who reside or attend school in Maryland. Applicants must be working full time on an undergraduate degree in public administration, public policy, political science, or a related field. Along with their application, they must submit a 3-page essay on a public administration/public policy issue of concern and interest and outlining a set of recommended goals and strategies to respond to the issue. Selection is based on academic record, leadership ability, participation in school activities, community service, and financial need.

Financial data The stipend is $1,500.

Duration 1 year.

Additional information This program is sponsored by the Maryland Chapter of the National Forum for Black Public Administrators (NFBPA). Recipients are required to attend the sponsor's annual conference to receive their scholarship; limited hotel and air accommodations are arranged and provided.

Number awarded 2 each year.

Deadline February of each year.

[356]
MARYLAND SEA GRANT RESEARCH EXPERIENCES FOR UNDERGRADUATES

Maryland Sea Grant College
c/o University of Maryland
4321 Hartwick Road, Suite 300
College Park, MD 20740
(301) 405-7500 Fax: (301) 314-5780
E-mail: mallen@mdsg.umd.edu
Web: www.mdsg.umd.edu

Summary To provide undergraduate students (particularly minority and disadvantaged students) with an opportunity to conduct summer research on Chesapeake Bay in fields related to marine biology.

Eligibility This program is open to undergraduate students who have completed at least 2 years of study towards a bachelor's degree. Applicants must be interested in conducting individual research projects (under the mentorship of scientists at laboratories of the University of Maryland Center for Environmental Sciences on Chesapeake Bay) in biology, chemistry, ecology, environmental science, engineering, marine science, mathematics, or physics. U.S. citizenship or permanent resident status is required. Selection is based on a 1-page description of interests, course work and grades, letters of recommendation, and the potential benefits students will gain from the research experience. Preference is given to rising seniors. Students from underrepresented groups and from institutions with limited research opportunities are especially encouraged to apply.

Financial data Fellows receive a stipend of $6,000, payment of dormitory costs, round-trip travel expenses, and funding to assist in publishing or presenting the results of summer research.

Duration 12 weeks during the summer.

Additional information This program is supported by the National Science Foundation as part of the Research Experiences for Undergraduates Program.

Number awarded 14 each year.

Deadline February of each year.

[357]
MASSMUTUAL SCHOLARS PROGRAM

Massachusetts Mutual Life Insurance Company
1295 State Street
Springfield, MA 01111-0001
Toll Free: (800) 542-6767
Web: www.act.org/massmutual

Summary To provide financial assistance to African American and other minority undergraduates preparing for a career in the insurance and financial services industry.

Eligibility This program is open to full-time students of African American, Asian/Pacific Islander, or Hispanic descent who are entering their sophomore, junior, senior, or fifth-year senior year at an accredited college or university in the United States, Puerto Rico, U.S. Virgin Islands, or Guam. Applicants must be U.S. citizens or permanent residents and have a GPA of 3.0 or higher. They may be majoring in any field, but preference is given to students who demonstrate 1) an interest in preparing for a career in the insurance and financial services industry; and 2) leadership and participation in extracurricular activities. Financial need is considered in the selection process.

Financial data The stipend is $5,000.

Duration 1 year.

Number awarded 30 each year.

Deadline May of each year.

[358]
MAUDE DAVIS/JOSEPH C. MCKINNEY SCHOLARSHIP

African Methodist Episcopal Church
Second Episcopal District Lay Organization
c/o Dr. V. Susie Oliphant, District Coordinator
910 Luray Place
Hyattsville, MD 20783
(301) 559-9488 E-mail: vsfo@verizon.net

Summary To provide financial assistance to members of the African Methodist Episcopal (AME) Church in its Second Episcopal District who are interested in attending college in any state.

Eligibility This program is open to AME members in the Second Episcopal District, which includes the Conferences of Baltimore, Washington, Virginia, North Carolina, and Western North Carolina. Applicants must be graduating high school seniors or college freshmen who are attending or planning to attend a college or university in any state to work on an undergraduate degree or certification. Along with their application, they must submit a high school transcript and SAT scores, 3 letters of recommendation, a 1-page biographical statement that includes career goals, and documentation of financial need.

Financial data A stipend is awarded (amount not specified).

Duration 1 year.

Number awarded Each of the 5 Conferences may award 1 or more of these scholarships each year.

Deadline June of each year.

[359]
MAUREEN L. AND HOWARD N. BLITMAN, P.E. SCHOLARSHIP TO PROMOTE DIVERSITY IN ENGINEERING

National Society of Professional Engineers
Attn: NSPE Educational Foundation
1420 King Street
Alexandria, VA 22314-2794
(703) 684-2833 Toll Free: (888) 285-NSPE
Fax: (703) 836-4875 E-mail: education@nspe.org
Web: www.nspe.org/Students/Scholarships/index.html

Summary To provide financial assistance for college to African Americans and members of other underrepresented ethnic minority groups who are interested in preparing for a career in engineering.

Eligibility This program is open to members of underrepresented ethnic minorities (African Americans, Hispanics, or Native Americans) who are high school seniors accepted into an ABET-accredited engineering program at a 4-year college or university. Applicants must have a GPA of 3.5 or higher, verbal SAT score of 600 or higher, and math SAT score of 700 or higher (or English ACT score of 29 or higher and math ACT score of 29 or higher). They must submit brief essays on 4 assigned topics. Selection is based on those essays, GPA, internship/co-op experience and community involvement, 2 faculty recommendations, and honors/scholarships/awards. U.S. citizenship is required.

Financial data The stipend is $5,000 per year; funds are paid directly to the recipient's institution.

Duration 1 year; nonrenewable.

Number awarded 1 each year.

Deadline February of each year.

[360]
MAXINE V. FENNELL MEMORIAL SCHOLARSHIP

New England Regional Black Nurses Association, Inc.
P.O. Box 190690
Boston, MA 02119
(617) 524-1951
Web: www.nerbna.org/org/scholarships.html

Summary To provide financial assistance to licensed practical nurses from New England who are studying to become a registered nurse (R.N.) and have contributed to the African American community.

Eligibility The program is open to residents of the New England states who are licensed practical nurses and currently enrolled in an NLN-accredited R.N. program (diploma, associate, baccalaureate) at a school in any state. Applicants must have at least 1 full year of school remaining. Along with their application, they must submit a 3-page essay that covers their career aspirations in the nursing profession; how they have contributed to the African American or other communities of color in such areas as work, volunteering, church, or community outreach; an experience that has enhanced their personal and/or professional growth; and any financial hardships that may hinder them from completing their education.

Financial data A stipend is awarded (amount not specified).

Duration 1 year.

Number awarded 1 or more each year.

Deadline February of each year.

[361]
MAYNARD H. JACKSON/FULL CIRCLE COMMUNICATIONS SCHOLARSHIP

National Forum for Black Public Administrators
Attn: Scholarship Program
777 North Capitol Street, N.E., Suite 807
Washington, DC 20002
(202) 408-9300 Fax: (202) 408-8558
E-mail: vharris@nfbpa.org
Web: www.nfbpa.org/i4a/pages/index.cfm?pageid=4047

Summary To provide financial assistance to African American undergraduate and graduate students preparing for a career in public service or a business field that supports the administration of public service.

Eligibility This program is open to African American undergraduate and graduate students preparing for a career in public service or a business field that supports the administration of public service. Applicants must be working full time on a degree in public administration, political science, urban affairs, public policy, business administration, or a related field. They must have a GPA of 3.0 or higher, a well-balanced focus of academic excellence and volunteerism/community involvement, and strong leadership and communication (oral and written) skills. Along with their application, they must submit a 3-page autobiographical essay that includes their academic and career goals and objectives. Selection is based on academic record, leadership ability, participation in school activities, community service, and financial need.

Financial data The stipend is $2,000.

Duration 1 year.

Additional information This program is sponsored by Full Circle Communications, a media management consulting firm based in Puerto Rico. Recipients are required to attend the sponsor's annual conference to receive their scholarship; limited hotel and air accommodations are arranged and provided.

Number awarded 1 each year.

Deadline February of each year.

[362]
MEDICAL COLLEGE OF WISCONSIN DIVERSITY SUMMER HEALTH-RELATED RESEARCH EDUCATION PROGRAM

Medical College of Wisconsin
Attn: Office of Student Diversity Affairs
8701 Watertown Plank Road
Milwaukee, WI 53226
(414) 955-8735 Fax: (414) 955-0129
E-mail: studentdiversity@mcw.edu
Web: www.mcw.edu

Summary To provide an opportunity for African American and other undergraduate residents of any state who come from diverse backgrounds to participate in a summer research training program at the Medical College of Wisconsin.

Eligibility This program is open to U.S. citizens and permanent residents who come from an ethnically, economically, and/or educationally disadvantaged backgrounds. The program targets African Americans, Mexican-Americans, Native Americans (American Indians, Alaska Natives, and Native Hawaiians), Pacific Islanders, Hmong, mainland Puerto

Ricans, and individuals with disabilities. Applicants must be interested in participating in a summer research training program at the Medical College of Wisconsin. They must have completed at least 1 year of undergraduate study at an accredited college or university (or be a community college student enrolled in at least 3 courses per academic term) and have a GPA of 3.4 or higher.

Financial data The stipend is $10 per hour for a 40-hour week. Housing is provided for students who live outside Milwaukee County and travel expenses are paid for those who live outside Wisconsin.

Duration 10 weeks during the summer.

Additional information Students are "matched" with a full-time faculty investigator to participate in a research project addressing the causes, prevention, and treatment of cardiovascular, pulmonary, or hematological diseases. This program is funded by the National Heart, Lung, and Blood Institute (NHLBI) of the National Institutes of Health (NIH). Participants are required to prepare an abstract of their research and make a brief oral presentation of their project at the conclusion of the summer.

Number awarded Approximately 12 each year.

Deadline February of each year.

[363]
MEDICAL SCIENTIST TRAINING PROGRAM

University of California at San Diego
Attn: School of Medicine
Summer Undergraduate Research Fellowship Program
9500 Gilman Drive, MC 0661
La Jolla, CA 92093-0661
(858) 822-5631 Toll Free: (800) 925-8704
Fax: (858) 822-3067 E-mail: mstp@ucsd.edu
Web: mstp.ucsd.edu/surf/Pages/default.aspx

Summary To provide an opportunity for African Americans and other college students from underrepresented groups to work during the summer on a research project in the biomedical sciences at the University of California at San Diego (UCSD).

Eligibility This program is open to undergraduate students at colleges in any state who are members of an underrepresented group (racial and ethnic groups that have been shown to be underrepresented in health-related sciences, individuals with disabilities, or individuals from a disadvantaged background). Applicants must be interested in working on a research project in the laboratory of a UCSD faculty member in the biomedical sciences. They must be U.S. citizens, permanent residents, or nationals. Along with their application, they must submit brief essays on 1) why they consider themselves an individual from a disadvantaged ethnicity or background or are underrepresented in the biomedical sciences; 2) their past research experiences; 3) the areas of research they wish to pursue in the program; 4) their educational and career plans and how this program will advance them towards their goals; and 5) anything else that might help to evaluate their application.

Financial data The program provides a stipend of $1,600 per month, room (but not board), and a $500 travel allowance.

Duration 8 weeks during the summer.

Additional information This program is sponsored by the National Heart, Lung, and Blood Institute (NHLBI) of the National Institutes of Health (NIH).

Number awarded Varies each year; recently, 11 students participated in this program.

Deadline January of each year.

[364]
MELLON MAYS UNDERGRADUATE FELLOWSHIP PROGRAM

United Negro College Fund
Attn: Director, Mellon Programs
350 Spelman Lane
Box 333
Atlanta, GA 30314
(404) 270-5685 Fax: (404) 270-5687
E-mail: cspence@spelman.edu
Web: www.uncfmellon.org/programs1

Summary To provide financial assistance and loan repayment to upper-division students at member institutions of the United Negro College Fund (UNCF) who are majoring in designated fields and planning to prepare for a career as a college professor.

Eligibility This program is open to students who are entering their junior year at a UNCF institution (or Hampton University) and have a GPA of 3.2 or higher. Applicants must be majoring in designated fields of the social sciences that use historical or philosophical methods, the humanities, or the sciences. They must be planning to enroll in a Ph.D. program following completion of their bachelor's degree and prepare for a career as a college professor. The chief academic officer of their college or the UNCF/Mellon programs campus coordinator must submit a nomination on their behalf; each institution may nominate only 5 students. During their junior and senior years and the summers following those years, they must engage in supervised research or other comparable activities arranged by a mentor. Students enrolled in professional programs (e.g., law, engineering, journalism, education) are not eligible. U.S. citizenship or permanent resident status is required.

Financial data Students receive a stipend of $3,600 for their research activity during the academic year and $3,900 for summer research. If they enroll in a Ph.D. program within 39 months after completing their bachelor's degree, the program will repay one-eighth or up to $1,250 per year of their undergraduate Guaranteed Student Loan for the first 4 years of full-time graduate study. If they complete a Ph.D. degree, an additional $5,000 of their undergraduate loan will be repaid.

Duration Up to 2 years of undergraduate tuition support and up to 4 years of loan repayment are provided.

Additional information This program is sponsored by the Andrew W. Mellon Foundation.

Number awarded Varies each year.

Deadline Letters of nomination must be submitted by January of each year.

[365]
MERCK UNDERGRADUATE SCIENCE RESEARCH SCHOLARSHIPS

United Negro College Fund
Attn: Merck Science Initiative
8260 Willow Oaks Corporate Drive, Suite 110
P.O. Box 10444
Fairfax, VA 22031-4511
(703) 205-3503 Fax: (703) 205-3574
E-mail: uncfmerck@uncf.org
Web: umsi.uncf.org

Summary To provide financial aid and summer work experience to African American undergraduates who are interested in preparing for a career in biomedical research.

Eligibility This program is open to African American students currently enrolled as full-time juniors and planning to graduate in the coming year. Applicants must be majoring in a life or physical science or engineering, be interested in biomedical research, and have a GPA of 3.3 or higher; physical science majors have completed 2 semesters of organic chemistry. All applicants must be interested in working at Merck as a summer intern. Candidates for professional (Pharm.D., D.V.M., D.D.S., etc.) degrees are ineligible. U.S. citizenship or permanent resident status is required. Selection is based on GPA, demonstrated interest in a scientific education and a career in scientific research, and interest in and ability to perform laboratory work.

Financial data The total award is $30,000, including up to $25,000 for tuition, fees, room, and board, and at least $5,000 for a summer internship stipend. In addition, the department of the recipient may receive a grant of up to $10,000. The department grant may not be used to support salaries, travel, or indirect costs.

Duration 1 academic year plus an internship of 10 to 12 weeks during the summer.

Additional information This program, established in 1995, is funded by the Merck Company Foundation.

Number awarded At least 15 each year.

Deadline December of each year.

[366]
MERITER MINORITY HEALTH CAREERS SCHOLARSHIP

Meriter Health Services
Attn: Human Resources
202 South Park Street
Madison, WI 53715-1596
(608) 417-6567 E-mail: rthrall@meriter.com
Web: www.meriter.com/wordpress/?p=2241

Summary To provide financial assistance to African Americans and members of other minority groups who are preparing for a career in a health care occupation.

Eligibility This program is open to members of minority groups (African American, Hispanic, Asian or Pacific Islander, and Native American) who are U.S. citizens or permanent residents. Applicants must have completed at least 1 semester in a college or technical school and be working on a college degree, professional degree, or certification in a health care occupation. Along with their application, they must submit a 2-page essay on their reasons for selecting a health career, any unique experiences that have prepared them for such a career, and how their contributions to the health care field can enhance the fabric of life in our community. Selection is based on demonstrated history of academic success and demonstrated commitment to community service.

Financial data The stipend is $4,000. Funds are paid directly to the student for assistance with tuition.

Duration 1 year.

Number awarded 1 or more each year.

Deadline April of each year.

[367]
METRO DC CHAPTER NABA SCHOLARSHIP

National Association of Black Accountants-Metro Washington DC Chapter
Attn: Student Member Services Directors
P.O. Box 18602
Washington, DC 20036-8602
(202) 455-LIFT
E-mail: studentservices@nabametrodc.org
Web: www.nabametrodc.org

Summary To provide financial assistance to members of the Metro Washington DC chapter of the National Association of Black Accountants (NABA) who are working on an undergraduate or graduate degree in accounting, business, or finance.

Eligibility This program is open to NABA members who live or attend school in the Metropolitan Washington D.C. area (Maryland, northern Virginia, and the District of Columbia). Applicants must be 1) full-time freshmen, sophomores, juniors, or first-year seniors majoring in accounting, business, or finance; or 2) graduate students enrolled in a C.P.A. review program. They must have an overall GPA of 3.0 or higher. Along with their application, they must submit an essay of 500 to 750 words on a topic that changes annually but relates to minorities in finance. Financial need is not considered in the selection process.

Financial data A stipend is awarded (amount not specified).

Duration 1 year.

Number awarded 1 or more each year.

Deadline February of each year.

[368]
METRO NEW YORK CHAPTER NBMBAA UNDERGRADUATE SCHOLARSHIP

National Black MBA Association-Metro New York Chapter
Attn: Scholarship Committee
P.O. Box 8135
New York, NY 10116
(212) 202-7544 Fax: (212) 202-7544
E-mail: studentrelations@nyblackmba.org
Web: www.nyblackmba.org/scholarshipapplication.php

Summary To provide financial assistance to African American and other minority students from any state working on an undergraduate degree in business or management at a school in the New York metropolitan area.

Eligibility This program is open to minority students who may be residents of any state but must be enrolled full time in an accredited New York metropolitan area business or management program and working on bachelor's degree. Applicants must have a GPA of 2.5 or higher and a record of at least 5 hours of community service or extracurricular activities each semester. Along with their application, they must submit 3 essays on assigned topics that change annually but relate to African Americans in business. Financial need is not considered in the selection process.

Financial data The stipend is $1,000.

Duration 1 year.

Number awarded Varies each year; recently, 2 of these scholarships were awarded.

Deadline October of each year.

[369] MIAMI CHAPTER BLACK NURSES' ASSOCIATION UNDERGRADUATE SCHOLARSHIPS

Black Nurses' Association, Inc.-Miami Chapter
Attn: Scholarship Committee
P.O. Box 472826
Miami, FL 33147-2826
(305) 754-2280 E-mail: info@bna-miami.org
Web: bna-miami.org

Summary To provide financial assistance to members of the National Black Nurses' Association (NBNA) from Florida who are enrolled in an undergraduate program in nursing at a school in any state.

Eligibility This program is open to NBNA members who are residents of Florida and have completed at least 1 semester of an R.N. or L.P.N. program in any state. Applicants must have a GPA of 2.5 or higher and be able to demonstrate financial need. Along with their application, they must submit a brief statement about themselves, their future goals in nursing, and their particular qualifications for this award. U.S. citizenship or permanent resident status is required.

Financial data The stipend is $1,500 per year.

Duration 1 year; may be renewed 1 additional, provided the recipient maintains a GPA of 2.5 or higher.

Number awarded 1 to 3 each year.

Deadline April of each year.

[370] MICHAEL BAKER CORPORATION SCHOLARSHIP PROGRAM FOR DIVERSITY IN ENGINEERING

Association of Independent Colleges and Universities of Pennsylvania
101 North Front Street
Harrisburg, PA 17101-1405
(717) 232-8649 Fax: (717) 233-8574
E-mail: info@aicup.org
Web: www.aicup.org

Summary To provide financial assistance to African Americans, other minorities, and women from any state enrolled at member institutions of the Association of Independent Colleges and Universities of Pennsylvania (AICUP) who are majoring in designated fields of engineering.

Eligibility This program is open to full-time undergraduate students from any state enrolled at designated AICUP colleges and universities who are women and/or members of the following minority groups: American Indians, Alaska Natives, Asians, Blacks/African Americans, Hispanics/Latinos, Native Hawaiians, or Pacific Islanders. Applicants must be juniors majoring in architectural, civil, or environmental engineering with a GPA of 3.0 or higher. Along with their application, they must submit a 2-page essay on what they believe will be the greatest challenge facing the engineering profession over the next decade, and why.

Financial data The stipend is $2,500 per year.

Duration 1 year; may be renewed 1 additional year if the recipient maintains appropriate academic standards.

Additional information This program, sponsored by the Michael Baker Corporation, is available at the 83 private colleges and universities in Pennsylvania that comprise the AICUP.

Number awarded 1 each year.

Deadline April of each year.

[371] MICHAEL P. ANDERSON SCHOLARSHIP IN SPACE SCIENCE

National Society of Black Physicists
Attn: Scholarship Committee Chair
1100 North Glebe Road, Suite 1010
Arlington, VA 22201
(703) 536-4207 Fax: (703) 536-4203
E-mail: scholarship@nsbp.org
Web: www.nsbp.org/scholarships

Summary To provide financial assistance to African American students majoring in space science in college.

Eligibility This program is open to African American students who are entering their junior or senior year of college and majoring in space science. Applicants must submit an essay on their academic and career objectives, information on their participation in extracurricular activities, a description of any awards and honors they have received, and 3 letters of recommendation. Financial need is not considered.

Financial data The stipend is $1,000.

Duration 1 year; nonrenewable.

Additional information This program is offered in partnership with the American Astronomical Society.

Number awarded 1 each year.

Deadline November of each year.

[372] MICHIGAN CHAPTER AABE SCHOLARSHIPS

American Association of Blacks in Energy-Michigan Chapter
Attn: Sheila Patterson
Consumers Energy
One Energy Plaza 7-253
Jackson, MI 49201
(517) 788-1893 E-mail: sheila.patterson@cmsenergy.com
Web: www.aabe.org/index.php?component=pages&id=572

Summary To provide financial assistance to African Americans and members of other underrepresented minority groups who are high school seniors in Michigan and planning to major in an energy-related field at a college in any state.

Eligibility This program is open to seniors graduating from high schools in Michigan and planning to work on a bachelor's degree at a college or university in any state. Applicants must be African Americans, Hispanics, or Native Americans who have a GPA of 3.0 or higher and are able to demonstrate financial need. Their intended major must be a field of business, engineering, physical science, mathematics, or technology related to energy. Along with their application, they must submit a 350-word statement on why they should receive this scholarship, their professional career objectives, and any other relevant information.

Financial data The stipend is $1,000.

Duration 1 year; nonrenewable.

Additional information Winners are eligible to compete for regional and national scholarships.

Number awarded At least 1 each year.

Deadline February of each year.

[373]
MIKE SHINN DISTINGUISHED MEMBER OF THE YEAR AWARDS

National Society of Black Engineers
Attn: Programs Department
205 Daingerfield Road
Alexandria, VA 22314
(703) 549-2207 Fax: (703) 683-5312
E-mail: scholarships@nsbe.org
Web: www.nsbe.org/Programs/Scholarships.aspx

Summary To provide financial assistance to male and female members of the National Society of Black Engineers (NSBE) who are working on a degree in engineering.

Eligibility This program is open to members of the society who are undergraduate or graduate engineering students. Applicants must have a GPA of 3.2 or higher. Selection is based on an essay; NSBE and university academic achievement; professional development; service to the society at the chapter, regional, and/or national level; and campus and community activities. The male and female applicants for the NSBE Fellows Scholarship Program who are judged most outstanding receive these awards.

Financial data The stipend is $7,500. Travel, hotel accommodations, and registration to the national convention are also provided.

Duration 1 year.

Number awarded 2 each year: 1 male and 1 female.

Deadline November of each year.

[374]
MILDRED COLLINS NURSING/HEALTH SCIENCE/MEDICINE SCHOLARSHIP

African-American/Caribbean Education Association, Inc.
P.O. Box 1224
Valley Stream, NY 11582-1224
(718) 949-6733 E-mail: aaceainc@yahoo.com
Web: www.aaceainc.com/Scholarships.html

Summary To provide financial assistance to high school seniors of African American or Caribbean heritage who plan to study a field related to nursing, health science, or medicine in college.

Eligibility This program is open to graduating high school seniors who are U.S. citizens of African American or Caribbean heritage. Applicants must be planning to attend a college or university and major in a field related to nursing, health science, or medicine. They must have completed 4 years of specified college preparatory courses with a grade of 90 or higher and have an SAT score of at least 1790. They must also have completed at least 200 hours of community service during their 4 years of high school, preferably in the field that they plan to study in college. Financial need is not considered in the selection process. New York residency is not required, but applicants must be available for an interviews in the Queens, New York area.

Financial data The stipend ranges from $1,000 to $2,500. Funds are paid directly to the recipient.

Duration 1 year.

Number awarded 1 each year.

Deadline April of each year.

[375]
MILDRED TOWLE SCHOLARSHIP FOR AFRICAN AMERICANS

Hawai'i Community Foundation
Attn: Scholarship Department
827 Fort Street Mall
Honolulu, HI 96813
(808) 566-5570 Toll Free: (888) 731-3863
Fax: (808) 521-6286
E-mail: scholarships@hcf-hawaii.org
Web: www.hawaiicommunityfoundation.org/scholarships

Summary To provide financial assistance to African Americans from any state studying at colleges and universities in Hawaii.

Eligibility This program is open to African Americans from any state enrolled full time at a college or university in Hawaii. Applicants are not required to be residents of Hawaii. They must be able to demonstrate academic achievement (GPA of 3.0 or higher), good moral character, and financial need. Along with their application, they must submit a short statement indicating their reasons for attending college, their planned course of study, their career goals, and what community service means to them.

Financial data The amounts of the awards depend on the availability of funds and the need of the recipient. Recently, the average value of each of the scholarships awarded by the foundation was $2,200.

Duration 1 year.

Number awarded Varies each year; recently, 11 of these scholarships were awarded.

Deadline February of each year.

[376]
MINORITIES IN GOVERNMENT FINANCE SCHOLARSHIP

Government Finance Officers Association
Attn: Scholarship Committee
203 North LaSalle Street, Suite 2700
Chicago, IL 60601-1210
(312) 977-9700 Fax: (312) 977-4806
Web: www.gfoa.org

Summary To provide financial assistance to African American and other minority upper-division and graduate students who are preparing for a career in state and local government finance.

Eligibility This program is open to upper-division and graduate students who are preparing for a career in public finance by working on a degree in public administration, accounting, finance, political science, economics, or business administration (with a specific focus on government or nonprofit management). Applicants must be members of a minority group, citizens or permanent residents of the United States or Canada, and able to provide a letter of recommendation from a representative of their school. Selection is based on career plans, academic record, plan of study, letters of recommendation, and GPA. Financial need is not considered.

Financial data The stipend is $5,000.

Duration 1 year.

Additional information This program defines minorities as Blacks or African Americans, American Indians or Alaskan Natives, Hispanics or Latinos, Native Hawaiians or other Pacific Islanders, or Asians.

Number awarded 1 or more each year.

Deadline February of each year.

[377]
MINORITIES IN HOSPITALITY SCHOLARS PROGRAM

International Franchise Association
Attn: IFA Educational Foundation
1501 K Street, N.W., Suite 350
Washington, DC 20005
(202) 662-0784 Fax: (202) 628-0812
E-mail: mbrewer@franchise.org
Web: www.franchise.org/Scholarships.aspx

Summary To provide financial assistance to African American and other minority students working on an undergraduate degree related to hospitality.

Eligibility This program is open to college sophomores, juniors, and seniors who are U.S. citizens and members of a minority group (defined as African Americans, American Indians, Hispanic Americans, and Asian Americans). Applicants must be working on a degree in a field related to the hospitality industry. Along with their application, they must submit a 500-word essay on why they should be selected to receive this scholarship. Financial need is not considered in the selection process.

Financial data The stipend is $2,000.

Duration 1 year.

Additional information This program is cosponsored by the IFA Educational Foundation and Choice Hotels International.

Number awarded 1 or more each year.

Deadline January of each year.

[378]
MINORITY AFFAIRS COMMITTEE AWARD FOR OUTSTANDING SCHOLASTIC ACHIEVEMENT

American Institute of Chemical Engineers
Attn: Minority Affairs Committee
Three Park Avenue
New York, NY 10016-5991
(646) 495-1348 Fax: (646) 495-1504
E-mail: awards@aiche.org
Web: www.aiche.org

Summary To recognize and reward African American and other underrepresented minority students majoring in chemical engineering who serve as role models for other minority students.

Eligibility Members of the American Institute of Chemical Engineers (AIChE) may nominate any chemical engineering student who serves as a role model for minority students in that field. Nominees must be members of a minority group that is underrepresented in chemical engineering (i.e., African American, Hispanic, Native American, Alaskan Native). They must have a GPA of 3.0 or higher. Along with their application, they must submit a 300-word essay on their immediate plans after graduation, areas of chemical engineering of most interest, and long-range career plans. Selection is based on that essay, academic record, participation in AIChE student chapter and professional or civic activities, and financial need.

Financial data The award consists of a plaque and a $1,500 honorarium.

Duration The award is presented annually.

Additional information This award was first presented in 1996.

Number awarded 1 each year.

Deadline Nominations must be submitted by May of each year.

[379]
MINORITY AND "AT RISK" STUDENT SCHOLARSHIP

Idaho State Board of Education
Len B. Jordan Office Building
650 West State Street, Room 307
P.O. Box 83720
Boise, ID 83720-0037
(208) 332-1574 Fax: (208) 334-2632
E-mail: scholarshiphelp@osbe.idaho.gov
Web: www.boardofed.idaho.gov/scholarship/minority.asp

Summary To provide financial assistance to African Americans and other "at risk" high school seniors in Idaho who plan to attend college in the state.

Eligibility This program is open to residents of Idaho who are graduates of high schools in the state. Applicants must meet at least 3 of the following 5 requirements: 1) have a disability; 2) be a member of an ethnic minority group historically underrepresented in higher education in Idaho (Native Americans, African Americans, Hispanic Americans); 3) have substantial financial need; 4) be a first-generation college student; 5) be a migrant farm worker or a dependent of a farm worker. U.S. citizenship is required.

Financial data The maximum stipend is $3,000 per year.

Duration 1 year; may be renewed for up to 3 additional years.

Additional information This program began in 1991 by the Idaho state legislature. Information is also available from high school counselors and financial aid offices of colleges and universities in Idaho. Recipients must plan to attend or be attending 1 of 11 participating colleges and universities in the state on a full-time basis. For a list of those schools, write to the State of Idaho Board of Education.

Number awarded Approximately 40 each year.

Deadline Deadline not specified.

[380]
MINORITY AND UNDERREPRESENTED ENVIRONMENTAL LITERACY PROGRAM

Missouri Department of Higher Education
Attn: Minority and Underrepresented Environmental Literacy Program
205 Jefferson Street
P.O. Box 1469
Jefferson City, MO 65102-1469
(573) 751-2361 Toll Free: (800) 473-6757
Fax: (573) 751-6635 E-mail: info@dhe.mo.gov
Web: dhe.mo.gov/ppc/grants/muelp_0310_final.php

Summary To provide financial assistance to African American and other underrepresented students from Missouri who are or will be working on a bachelor's or master's degree in an environmental field.

Eligibility This program is open to residents of Missouri who are high school seniors or current undergraduate or graduate students enrolled or planning to enroll full time at a college or university in the state. Priority is given to members of the following underrepresented minority ethnic groups: African Americans, Hispanic or Latino Americans, Native Americans and Alaska Natives, and Native Hawaiians and Pacific Islanders. Applicants must be working on or planning to work on a bachelor's or master's degree in 1) engineering (civil, chemical, environmental, mechanical, or agricultural); 2) environmental studies (geology, biology, wildlife management, natural resource planning, natural resources, or a closely-related course of study); 3) environmental chemistry; or 4) environmental law enforcement. They must be U.S. citizens or permanent residents or otherwise lawfully present in the United States. Graduating high school seniors must have a GPA of 3.0 or higher; students currently enrolled in college or graduate school must have a GPA of 2.5 or higher. Along with their application, they must submit a 1-page essay on their environmental education and career goals, 3 letters of recommendation, a resume of school and community activities, and transcripts that include SAT or ACT scores. Financial need is not considered in the selection process.

Financial data Stipends vary each year; recently, they averaged approximately $3,996 per year.

Duration 1 year; may be renewed if the recipient maintains a GPA of 2.5 or higher and full-time enrollment.

Additional information This program was established by the Missouri Department of Natural Resources but transferred to the Department of Higher Education in 2009.

Number awarded Varies each year.

Deadline May of each year.

[381]
MINORITY LEAP SCHOLARSHIPS

Missouri Society of Certified Public Accountants
Attn: LEAP Program
540 Maryville Centre Drive, Suite 200
P.O. Box 419042
St. Louis, MO 63141-9042
(314) 997-7966, ext. 125
Toll Free: (800) 264-7966, ext. 125 (within MO)
Fax: (314) 997-2592 E-mail: lsimpson@mocpa.org
Web: www.mocpa.org/students/scholarships

Summary To provide financial assistance to African American and other minority residents of Missouri who are working on an undergraduate or graduate degree in accounting at a university in the state.

Eligibility This program is open to members of minority groups underrepresented in the accounting profession (Black/African American, Hispanic/Latino, Native American, Asian American) who are currently working full time on an undergraduate or graduate degree in accounting at a college or university in Missouri. Applicants must either be residents of Missouri or the children of members of the Missouri Society of Certified Public Accountants (MSCPA). They must be U.S. citizens, have completed at least 30 semester hours of college work, have a GPA of 3.3 or higher, and be student members of the MSCPA. Selection is based on the GPA, involvement in MSCPA, educator recommendations, and leadership potential. Financial need is not considered.

Financial data The stipend is $1,250 per year.

Duration 1 year; may be renewed.

Additional information These scholarships are offered through the sponsor's Lead and Enhance the Accounting Profession (LEAP) program, established in 2001.

Number awarded Varies each year; recently, 2 of these scholarships were awarded.

Deadline February of each year.

[382]
MINORITY NURSE MAGAZINE SCHOLARSHIP PROGRAM

Minority Nurse Magazine
c/o Alloy Education
2 LAN Drive, Suite 100
Westford, MA 01886
Toll Free: (877) ASK-ALLO
E-mail: editor@minoritynurse.com
Web: www.minoritynurse.com

Summary To provide financial assistance to African Americans and members of other minority groups who are working on a bachelor's or master's degree in nursing.

Eligibility This program is open to racial and ethnic minority nursing students currently enrolled in 1) the third or fourth year of an accredited B.S.N. program; 2) an accelerated program leading to a B.S.N. degree (e.g., R.N. to B.S.N., B.A. to B.S.N.); or 3) an accelerated master's entry nursing program (e.g., B.A. to M.S.N.) for students with bachelor's degrees in fields other than nursing. Graduate students who already have a bachelor's degree in nursing are not eligible. Along with their application, they must submit a 250-word essay on their academic and personal accomplishments, community service, and goals for their future nursing career. Selection is based on academic excellence (GPA of 3.0 or higher), demonstrated commitment of service to the student's minority community, and financial need. U.S. citizenship of permanent resident status is required.

Financial data The stipends are $3,000 or $1,000.

Duration 1 year.

Additional information This program began in 2000. Winners are announced in the summer issue of *Minority Nurse* magazine.

Number awarded 3 each year: 1 at $3,000 and 2 at $1,000.

Deadline January of each year.

[383] MINORITY SCHOLARSHIP AWARD FOR ACADEMIC EXCELLENCE IN PHYSICAL THERAPY

American Physical Therapy Association
Attn: Honors and Awards Program
1111 North Fairfax Street
Alexandria, VA 22314-1488
(703) 684-APTA Toll Free: (800) 999-APTA
Fax: (703) 684-7343 TDD: (703) 683-6748
E-mail: honorsandawards@apta.org
Web: www.apta.org

Summary To provide financial assistance to African American and other minority students who are interested in becoming a physical therapist or physical therapy assistant.

Eligibility This program is open to U.S. citizens and permanent residents who are members of the following minority groups: African American or Black, Asian, Native Hawaiian or other Pacific Islander, American Indian or Alaska Native, or Hispanic/Latino. Applicants must be in the final year of a professional physical therapy or physical therapy assistant education program. They must submit a personal essay outlining their professional goals and minority service. U.S. citizenship or permanent resident status is required. Selection is based on 1) demonstrated evidence of contributions in the area of minority affairs and services with an emphasis on contributions made while enrolled in a physical therapy program; 2) potential to contribute to the profession of physical therapy; and 3) scholastic achievement.

Financial data The stipend varies; recently, minimum awards were $6,000 for physical therapy students or $2,500 for physical therapy assistant students.

Duration 1 year.

Number awarded Varies each year; recently, 7 of these awards were granted.

Deadline November of each year.

[384] MINORITY SCHOLARSHIP AWARDS FOR COLLEGE STUDENTS IN CHEMICAL ENGINEERING

American Institute of Chemical Engineers
Attn: Minority Affairs Committee
Three Park Avenue
New York, NY 10016-5991
(646) 495-1348 Fax: (646) 495-1504
E-mail: awards@aiche.org
Web: www.aiche.org

Summary To provide financial assistance for the undergraduate study of chemical engineering to African American and other underrepresented minority college student members of the American Institute of Chemical Engineers (AIChE).

Eligibility This program is open to undergraduate student AIChE members who are also members of a minority group that is underrepresented in chemical engineering (African Americans, Hispanics, Native Americans, and Alaskan Natives). They must have a GPA of 3.0 or higher. Along with their application, they must submit a 300-word essay on their immediate plans after graduation, areas of chemical engineering of most interest, and long-range career plans. Selection is based on that essay, academic record, participation in AIChE student chapter and professional or civic activities, and financial need.

Financial data The stipend is $1,000.

Duration 1 year; nonrenewable.

Number awarded Approximately 10 each year.

Deadline June of each year.

[385] MINORITY SCHOLARSHIP AWARDS FOR INCOMING COLLEGE FRESHMEN IN CHEMICAL ENGINEERING

American Institute of Chemical Engineers
Attn: Minority Affairs Committee
Three Park Avenue
New York, NY 10016-5991
(646) 495-1348 Fax: (646) 495-1504
E-mail: awards@aiche.org
Web: www.aiche.org

Summary To provide financial assistance to African American and other incoming minority freshmen interested in studying science or engineering in college.

Eligibility Eligible are members of a minority group that is underrepresented in chemical engineering (African Americans, Hispanics, Native Americans, and Alaskan Natives). Applicants must be graduating high school seniors planning to enroll at a 4-year university with a major in science or engineering. They must be nominated by an American Institute of Chemical Engineers (AIChE) local section. Selection is based on academic record (including a GPA of 3.0 or higher), participation in school and work activities, a 300-word letter outlining the reasons for choosing science or engineering, and financial need.

Financial data The stipend is $1,000.

Duration 1 year; nonrenewable.

Number awarded Approximately 10 each year.

Deadline Nominations must be submitted by June of each year.

[386] MINORITY SCHOLARSHIP IN CLASSICS AND CLASSICAL ARCHAEOLOGY

American Philological Association
Attn: Executive Director
University of Pennsylvania
220 South 40th Street, Suite 201E
Philadelphia, PA 19104-3512
(215) 898-4975 Fax: (215) 573-7874
E-mail: apaclassics@sas.upenn.edu
Web: www.apaclassics.org

Summary To provide African American and other minority undergraduates with summer training as preparation for advanced work in the classics or classical archaeology.

Eligibility Eligible to apply are minority (African American, Hispanic American, Asian American, and Native American) undergraduate students who wish to engage in summer study as preparation for graduate work in the classics or classical archaeology. Applicants may propose participation in summer programs in Italy, Greece, Egypt, or other classical centers; language training at institutions in the United States, Canada, or Europe; or other relevant courses of study. Selection is based on academic qualifications, especially in classics; demonstrated ability in at least 1 classical language; quality of the proposal for study with respect to preparation for a career in classics; and financial need. Applications must be endorsed by a member of the American Philological Association (APA).

Financial data The maximum award is $4,000.

Duration 1 summer.

Additional information This program includes 1 scholarship supported by the Gladys Krieble Delmas Foundation.

Number awarded 2 each year.

Deadline December of each year.

[387]
MINORITY TEACHERS OF ILLINOIS SCHOLARSHIP PROGRAM

Illinois Student Assistance Commission
Attn: Scholarship and Grant Services
1755 Lake Cook Road
Deerfield, IL 60015-5209
(847) 948-8550 Toll Free: (800) 899-ISAC
Fax: (847) 831-8549 TDD: (800) 526-0844
E-mail: isac.studentservices@isac.illinois.gov
Web: www.collegeillinois.org

Summary To provide funding to African American and other minority students in Illinois who plan to become teachers at the preschool, elementary, or secondary level.

Eligibility Applicants must be Illinois residents, U.S. citizens or eligible noncitizens, members of a minority group (African American/Black, Hispanic American, Asian American, or Native American), and high school graduates or holders of a General Educational Development (GED) certificate. They must be enrolled at least half time as an undergraduate or graduate student, have a GPA of 2.5 or higher, not be in default on any student loan, and be enrolled or accepted for enrollment in a teacher education program.

Financial data Grants up to $5,000 per year are awarded. Recipients must agree to teach full time 1 year for each year of support received. The teaching agreement may be fulfilled at a public, private, or parochial preschool, elementary school, or secondary school in Illinois; at least 30% of the student body at those schools must be minority. It must be fulfilled within the 5-year period following the completion of the undergraduate program for which the scholarship was awarded. The time period may be extended if the recipient serves in the U.S. armed forces, enrolls full time in a graduate program related to teaching, becomes temporarily disabled, is unable to find employment as a teacher at a qualifying school, or takes additional courses on at least a half-time basis to obtain certification as a teacher in Illinois. Recipients who fail to honor this work obligation must repay the award with 5% interest.

Duration 1 year; may be renewed for a total of 8 semesters or 12 quarters.

Number awarded Varies each year.

Deadline Priority consideration is given to applications received by February of each year.

[388]
MIRIAM WEINSTEIN PEACE AND JUSTICE EDUCATION AWARD

Philanthrofund Foundation
Attn: Scholarship Committee
1409 Willow Street, Suite 109
Minneapolis, MN 55403-2241
(612) 870-1806 Toll Free: (800) 435-1402
Fax: (612) 871-6587 E-mail: info@PfundOnline.org
Web: www.pfundonline.org/scholarships.html

Summary To provide financial assistance to African American and other minority students from Minnesota who have supported gay, lesbian, bisexual, and transgender (GLBT) activities and are interested in working on a degree in education.

Eligibility This program is open to residents of Minnesota and students attending a Minnesota educational institution who are members of a religious, racial, or ethnic minority. Applicants must be self-identified as GLBT or from a GLBT family and have demonstrated a commitment to peace and justice issues. They may be attending or planning to attend trade school, technical college, college, or university (as an undergraduate or graduate student). Preference is given to students who have completed at least 2 years of college and are working on a degree in education. Selection is based on the applicant's 1) affirmation of GLBT or allied identity; 2) evidence of experience and skills in service and leadership; and 3) evidence of service, leading, and working for change in GLBT communities, including serving as a role model, mentor, and/or adviser.

Financial data The stipend is $3,000. Funds must be used for tuition, books, fees, or dissertation expenses.

Duration 1 year.

Number awarded 1 each year.

Deadline January of each year.

[389]
MISS BLACK AMERICA

Miss Black America Pageant
P.O. Box 25668
Philadelphia, PA 19144
(215) 844-8872 E-mail: Contact@MissBlackAmerica.com
Web: www.missblackamerica.com

Summary To recognize and reward beautiful and talented Black American women.

Eligibility All African American women between 18 and 29 years of age, including married contestants and contestants with children, are eligible. Finalists who compete in the national pageant are selected after competitions on the local and state levels. The winner at the national pageant is chosen by a panel of judges on the basis of a swimsuit competition, a 2-minute talent presentation, and a question and answer session.

Financial data Miss Black America receives a cash award of at least $2,000 and an array of prizes.

Duration The competition is held annually.

Additional information This competition began in 1968. There is a $50 application fee and an $800 sponsorship fee.

Number awarded 1 each year.

Deadline December of each year.

[390]
MISSISSIPPI CHAPTER AABE SCHOLARSHIPS

American Association of Blacks in Energy-Mississippi Chapter
Attn: Scholarship Committee Chair
P.O. Box 986
Jackson, MS 39205
E-mail: rkent@entergy.com
Web: www.aabe.org/index.php?component=pages&id=387

Summary To provide financial assistance to African Americans and members of other underrepresented minority groups who are high school seniors in Mississippi and planning to major in an energy-related field at a college in any state.

Eligibility This program is open to seniors graduating from high schools in Mississippi and planning to attend a 4-year college or university in any state. Applicants must be African Americans, Hispanics, or Native Americans who have a GPA of 3.0 or higher and are able to demonstrate financial need. Their intended major must be computer technology, engineering, technology, mathematics, the physical sciences (chemistry, geology, meteorology, or physics only), or other energy-related field. Along with their application, they must submit a 350-word statement on why they should receive this scholarship, how their professional career objectives relate to energy, and any other relevant information.

Financial data Stipends are $2,000 or $1,000.

Duration 1 year.

Additional information Winners are eligible to compete for regional and national scholarships.

Number awarded 4 or more each year: 1 at $2,000 and 3 or more at $1,000.

Deadline March of each year.

[391]
MISSOURI MINORITY TEACHING SCHOLARSHIP PROGRAM

Missouri Department of Higher Education
Attn: Student Financial Assistance
205 Jefferson Street
P.O. Box 1469
Jefferson City, MO 65102-1469
(573) 526-7958 Toll Free: (800) 473-6757
Fax: (573) 751-6635 E-mail: info@dhe.mo.gov
Web: www.dhe.mo.gov/ppc/grants/minorityteaching.php

Summary To provide scholarships and other funding to African American and other minority high school seniors, high school graduates, and college students in Missouri who are interested in preparing for a teaching career in mathematics or science.

Eligibility This program is open to Missouri residents who are African American, Asian American, Hispanic American, or Native American. Applicants must be 1) high school seniors, college students, or returning adults (without a degree) who rank in the top 25% of their high school class and scored at or above the 75th percentile on the ACT or SAT examination (recently, that meant a composite score of 24 or higher on the ACT or 1340 or higher on the composite critical reading and mathematics SAT); 2) individuals who have completed 30 college hours and have a cumulative GPA of 3.0 or better; or 3) baccalaureate degree-holders who are returning to an approved mathematics or science teacher education program. They must be a U.S. citizen or permanent resident or otherwise lawfully present in the United States. All applicants must be enrolled full time in an approved teacher education program at a community college, 4-year college, or university in Missouri. Selection is based on high school class rank, ACT or SAT scores, school and community activities, career interest in teaching, leadership skills, employment experience, and recommendations.

Financial data The stipend is $3,000 per year, of which $2,000 is provided by the state as a forgivable loan and $1,000 is provided by the school as a scholarship. Recipients must commit to teaching in a Missouri public elementary or secondary school for 5 years following graduation. If they fail to fulfill that obligation, they must repay the state portion of the scholarship with interest at 9.5%.

Duration Up to 4 years.

Number awarded Up to 100 each year.

Deadline June of each year.

[392]
MONSANTO BDPA NATIONAL SCHOLARSHIPS

Black Data Processing Associates
Attn: BDPA Education Technology Foundation
4423 Lehigh Road, Number 277
College Park, MD 20740
(513) 284-4968 Fax: (202) 318-2194
E-mail: scholarships@betf.org
Web: www.betf.org/scholarships/monsanto.shtml

Summary To provide financial assistance to members of the Black Data Processing Associates (BDPA) who are interested in studying information technology at a college in any state.

Eligibility This program is open to BDPA members who are either graduating high school seniors or college students with at least 1 year remaining in a 4-year degree program. Applicants must be working on or planning to work on a degree in information technology. They must have a GPA of 3.0 or higher. Along with their application, they must submit a 500-word essay on how information technology is impacting agriculture. Selection is based on that essay, academic achievement, leadership ability through academic or civic involvement, and participation in community service activities. U.S. citizenship or permanent resident status is required.

Financial data The stipend is $2,500 per year. Funds may be used to pay for tuition, fees, books, room and board, or other college-related expenses.

Duration 4 years.

Additional information The BDPA established its Education and Technology Foundation (BETF) in 1992 to advance the skill sets needed by African American and other minority adults and young people to compete in the information technology industry. This program is sponsored by the Monsanto Company.

Number awarded 2 each year.

Deadline July of each year.

[393]
MONTFORD POINT MARINE ASSOCIATION SCHOLARSHIP

Montford Point Marine Association
c/o James Maillard, National Scholarship Director
7714 113th Street, Number 2G
Forest Hills, NY 11375-7119
(718) 261-9640 Fax: (718) 261-3021
E-mail: Scholarships@montfordpointmarines.com
Web: www.montfordpointmarines.com

Summary To provide financial assistance to high school seniors, high school graduates, and current undergraduates who have a connection to the Montford Point Marine Association (MPMA).

Eligibility This program is open to high school seniors, high school graduates, or current college students who have a connection to the MPMA. Along with their application, they must submit academic transcripts, information on their connection to MPMA, and a 500-word essay on a topic that changes periodically. Only undergraduate study is supported. The family income of applicants must be less than $90,000 per year.

Financial data Stipends depend on the need of the recipient and the availability of funds, but generally range from $500 to $2,500 per year.

Duration 1 year.

Additional information Membership in the MPMA is restricted to former Marines and the families of Marines who served at Camp Montford Point, North Carolina where African Americans trained during the days of segregation from 1942 to 1949. This scholarship program, which began in 2003, operates in coordination with the Marine Corps Scholarship Foundation.

Number awarded 1 or more each year.

Deadline Deadline not specified.

[394]
MONTGOMERY SUMMER RESEARCH DIVERSITY FELLOWSHIPS

American Bar Foundation
Attn: Summer Research Diversity Fellowship
750 North Lake Shore Drive
Chicago, IL 60611-4403
(312) 988-6515 Fax: (312) 988-6579
E-mail: fellowships@abfn.org
Web: www.americanbarfoundation.org

Summary To provide an opportunity for African American and other undergraduate students from diverse backgrounds to work on a summer research project in the field of law and social science.

Eligibility This program is open to U.S. citizens and permanent residents who are African Americans, Hispanic/Latinos, Asians, Puerto Ricans, Native Americans, or other individuals who will add diversity to the field of law and social science. Applicants must be sophomores or juniors in college, have a GPA of 3.0 or higher, be majoring in the social sciences or humanities, and be willing to consider an academic or research career. Along with their application, they must submit a 200-word essay on their future plans and why this fellowship would contribute to them, another essay on an assigned topic, official transcripts, and a letter of recommendation from a faculty member familiar with their work.

Financial data Participants receive a stipend of $3,600.

Duration 35 hours per week for 8 weeks during the summer.

Additional information Students are assigned to an American Bar Foundation Research Professor who involves the student in the design and conduct of the professor's research project and who acts as mentor during the student's tenure.

Number awarded 4 each year.

Deadline February of each year.

[395]
MOSS ADAMS FOUNDATION SCHOLARSHIP

Educational Foundation for Women in Accounting
Attn: Foundation Administrator
136 South Keowee Street
Dayton, OH 45402
(937) 424-3391 Fax: (937) 222-5749
E-mail: info@efwa.org
Web: www.efwa.org/scholarships_MossAdams.php

Summary To provide financial support to women (preference given to African American and other minority women) who are working on an accounting degree.

Eligibility This program is open to women who are enrolled in an accounting degree program at an accredited college or university. Applicants must meet 1 of the following criteria: 1) women pursuing a fifth-year requirement either through general studies or within a graduate program; 2) women returning to school as current or reentry juniors or seniors; or 3) minority women. Selection is based on aptitude for accounting and business, commitment to the goal of working on a degree in accounting (including evidence of continued commitment after receiving this award), clear evidence that the candidate has established goals and a plan for achieving those goals (both personal and professional), financial need, and a demonstration of how the scholarship will impact her life. U.S. citizenship is required.

Financial data The stipend is $1,000.

Duration 1 year.

Additional information This program was established by Rowling, Dold & Associates LLP, a woman-owned C.P.A. firm based in San Diego. It was renamed when that firm merged with Moss Adams LLP.

Number awarded 1 each year.

Deadline April of each year.

[396]
MR. COLLEGIATE AFRICAN AMERICAN SCHOLARSHIP PROGRAM

Mr. Collegiate African American Scholarship Pageant
P.O. Box 5433
Prairie View, TX 77446
E-mail: mrcollegiateafricanamerican@gmail.com
Web: mrcollegiatepageant.blogspot.com

Summary To recognize and reward, with college scholarships, outstanding African American men who participate in a pageant.

Eligibility This competition is open to African American men between 18 and 30 years of age attending 4-year colleges and universities, especially Historically Black Colleges and Universities. Applicants must be interested in participating in a pageant where they are judged on a personal and private interview (20%), platform expression (25%), talent (35%), evening wear (10%), and on-stage interview (10%).

Financial data A total of $8,000 in scholarships and prizes is awarded.

Duration The pageant is held annually.

Additional information This program began in 1990. The pageant is held in Prairie View, Texas.

Number awarded Varies each year.

Deadline February of each year.

[397]
MRS. PATRICIA THOMPSON SCHOLARSHIP

National Naval Officers Association-Washington, D.C. Chapter
c/o LCDR Stephen Williams
P.O. Box 30784
Alexandria, VA 22310
(703) 566-3840 Fax: (703) 566-3813
E-mail: Stephen.Williams@navy.mil
Web: dcnnoa.memberlodge.com

Summary To provide financial assistance to male African American high school seniors from the Washington, D.C. area who are interested in attending college in any state.

Eligibility This program is open to male African American seniors graduating from high schools in the Washington, D.C. metropolitan area who plan to enroll full time at an accredited 2- or 4-year college or university in any state. Applicants must have a GPA of 2.5 or higher and be U.S. citizens or permanent residents. Selection is based on academic achievement, community involvement, and financial need.

Financial data The stipend is $1,000.

Duration 1 year; nonrenewable.

Additional information Recipients are not required to join or affiliate with the military in any way.

Number awarded 1 each year.

Deadline March of each year.

[398]
MSCPA/NABA SCHOLARSHIPS

Massachusetts Society of Certified Public Accountants
Attn: MSCPA Educational Foundation
105 Chauncy Street, Tenth Floor
Boston, MA 02111
(617) 556-4000 Toll Free: (800) 392-6145
Fax: (617) 556-4126 E-mail: info@mscpaonline.org
Web: www.cpatrack.com/scholarships

Summary To provide financial assistance to members of the National Association of Black Accountants (NABA) from Massachusetts who are working on an undergraduate or graduate degree in accounting at a college or university in the state.

Eligibility This program is open to African American students from any state who are members of the Boston Metropolitan Chapter of NABA and enrolled at a college or university in Massachusetts. Applicants must be undergraduates who have completed at least the first semester of their sophomore year or graduate students. They must be able to demonstrate financial need, academic excellence, and an intention to prepare for a career as a Certified Public Accountant (C.P.A.) at a firm in Massachusetts.

Financial data The stipend is $2,500.

Duration 1 year.

Additional information This program is sponsored by the Boston Metropolitan Chapter of NABA and the Massachusetts Society of Certified Public Accountants (MSCPA).

Number awarded 2 each year.

Deadline March of each year.

[399]
MUSIC AND CHRISTIAN ARTS MINISTRY SCHOLARSHIP

African Methodist Episcopal Church
Attn: Christian Education Department
Music and Christian Arts Ministry
500 Eighth Avenue South
Nashville, TN 37203
Toll Free: (800) 525-7282 Fax: (615) 726-1866
E-mail: cedoffice@ameced.com
Web: www.ameced.com/music.shtml

Summary To provide financial assistance to members of African Methodist Episcopal (AME) churches who are interested in working on an undergraduate degree in music at a Black-related college in any state.

Eligibility This program is open to graduating high school seniors who are members of an AME congregation. Applicants must be planning to attend an AME-supported college or university or an Historically Black College or University (HBCU) in any state to study music. They must be planning to assume a music leadership position in a local AME church. Along with their application, they must submit a current high school transcript, 3 letters of recommendation (including 1 from their music teacher or director and 1 from their pastor), a 1-page essay on why they should be awarded this scholarship, and a CD or cassette recording of a musical performance. Selection is based on academic achievement, school involvement, music involvement and performance genre, community involvement, and other honors and awards.

Financial data The stipend is $2,000 per year. Funds are sent directly to the student upon proof of enrollment.

Duration 1 year; recipients may apply for 1 additional year if they earn a GPA of 3.3 or higher in their first year.

Number awarded 1 or more each year.

Deadline April of each year.

[400]
MUTUAL OF OMAHA ACTUARIAL SCHOLARSHIP FOR MINORITY STUDENTS

Mutual of Omaha
Attn: Strategic Staffing-Actuarial Recruitment
Mutual of Omaha Plaza
Omaha, NE 68175
(402) 351-3300 E-mail: diversity@mutualofomaha.com
Web: www.mutualofomaha.com

Summary To provide financial aid and work experience to African American and other minority undergraduate students who are preparing for an actuarial career.

Eligibility This program is open to members of minority groups (African American, Hispanic, Native American, Asian or Pacific Islander, or Alaskan Eskimo) who have completed at least 24 semester hours of full-time study. Applicants must be working on an actuarial or mathematics-related degree with the goal of preparing for an actuarial career. They must have a GPA of 3.0 or higher and have passed at least 1 actuarial examination. Prior to accepting the award, they must be available to complete a summer internship at the sponsor's home office in Omaha, Nebraska. Along with their application, they must submit a 1-page personal statement on why they are interested in becoming an actuary and how they are preparing themselves for an actuarial career. Status as a U.S. citizen, permanent resident, asylee, or refugee must be established.

Financial data The scholarship stipend is $5,000 per year. Funds are paid directly to the student. For the internship, students receive an hourly rate of pay, subsidized housing, and financial incentives for successful examination results received during the internship period.

Duration 1 year. Recipients may reapply if they maintain a cumulative GPA of 3.0 or higher.

Number awarded Varies each year.

Deadline October of each year.

[401]
NABA 20 PEARLS SCHOLARSHIP

National Association of Black Accountants
Attn: National Scholarship Program
7474 Greenway Center Drive, Suite 1120
Greenbelt, MD 20770
(301) 474-NABA Fax: (301) 474-3114
E-mail: scholarships@nabainc.org
Web: www.nabainc.org

Summary To provide financial assistance to student members of the National Association of Black Accountants (NABA) who are also members of Alpha Kappa Alpha sorority and working on an undergraduate or graduate degree in a field related to accounting.

Eligibility This program is open to NABA members who are also Alpha Kappa Alpha members and enrolled full time as 1) an undergraduate freshman, sophomore, junior, or first-semester senior majoring in accounting, business, or finance at a 4-year college or university; or 2) a graduate student working on a master's degree in accounting. High school seniors are not eligible. Applicants must have a GPA of 3.5 or higher in their major and 3.3 or higher overall. Along with their application, they must submit a 500-word personal statement on their involvement in NABA, career objectives, leadership abilities, and community activities. Financial need is not considered in the selection process.

Financial data The stipend is $1,500.

Duration 1 year.

Number awarded 1 each year.

Deadline January of each year.

[402]
NABJ/CAROLE SIMPSON SCHOLARSHIP

National Association of Black Journalists
Attn: Communications Coordinator and Program Manager
University of Maryland
1100 Knight Hall, Suite 3100
College Park, MD 20742
(301) 405-2573 Fax: (301) 314-1714
E-mail: tjohnson@nabj.org
Web: www.nabj.org/?page=SEEDScholarships

Summary To provide financial assistance to undergraduate or graduate student members of the National Association of Black Journalists (NABJ) who are working on a degree in broadcast journalism.

Eligibility This program is open to African American undergraduate or graduate student members of NABJ who are currently enrolled full time at an accredited 4-year college or university. Applicants must be studying broadcast journalism as preparation for a career in television news and have a GPA of 2.5 or higher. They must be able to demonstrate financial need. Along with their application, they must submit 5 samples of their work, an official college transcript, 3 letters of recommendation, a resume, and an essay of 1,000 to 2,000 words on how the career of this program's namesake inspired them to prepare for a career in broadcast journalism and what they hope their legacy will be.

Financial data The stipend is $2,500. Funds are paid directly to the recipient's college or university.

Duration 1 year; nonrenewable.

Number awarded 1 each year.

Deadline March of each year.

[403]
NACME PRE-ENGINEERING STUDENT SCHOLARSHIPS

National Action Council for Minorities in Engineering
Attn: Pre-Engineering Department
440 Hamilton Avenue, Suite 302
White Plains, NY 10601-1813
(914) 539-4010 Fax: (914) 539-4032
E-mail: scholarships@nacme.org
Web: www.nacmebacksme.org/NBM_C.aspx?pageid=153

Summary To provide financial assistance to African American and other underrepresented minority high school seniors interested in studying engineering in college.

Eligibility This program is open to African American, Latino, and American Indian high school seniors who have participated in an Academy of Engineering or other pre-college or high school program focused on mathematics, science, and engineering. Applicants must have been accepted as a full-time student at 1 of 51 ABET-accredited engineering programs at universities that have partnered with this sponsor. They must have a GPA of 3.0 or higher and minimum scores of 1650 on the SAT (including 550 on mathematics) or 24 on the ACT composite (including 24 on the mathematics section). Along with their application, they must submit documentation of financial need and 2 brief essays on assigned topics. U.S. citizenship or permanent resident status is required.

Financial data The stipend is $2,500. Funds are sent directly to the recipient's university.

Duration 1 year; nonrenewable.

Additional information For a list of the 51 partner institutions, contact the sponsor.

Number awarded Varies each year; recently, 95 of these scholarships were awarded.

Deadline March of each year.

[404]
NANBPWC NATIONAL SCHOLARSHIPS

National Association of Negro Business and Professional Women's Clubs
Attn: Scholarship Committee
1806 New Hampshire Avenue, N.W.
Washington, DC 20009-3206
(202) 483-4206 Fax: (202) 462-7253
E-mail: education@nanbpwc.org
Web: www.nanbpwc.org/index-11.html

Summary To provide financial assistance for college to African American high school seniors.

Eligibility This program is open to African American high school seniors planning to enroll in an accredited college or university. Applicants must have a GPA of 3.0 or higher. Along with their application, they must submit an essay (at least 300 words) on "Why Education is Important to Me." Financial need is not considered in the selection process. U.S. citizenship is required.

Financial data The stipend is $1,000.

Duration 1 year.

Number awarded 10 each year.

Deadline February of each year.

[405]
NASA UNDERGRADUATE STUDENT RESEARCH PROGRAM

Universities Space Research Association
Attn: NASA USRP Project Administrator
2101 NASA Parkway, AE2 Education Office
Houston, TX 77058
(281) 244-2036 E-mail: garza@epo.usra.edu
Web: usrp.usra.edu

Summary To provide an opportunity for undergraduate students (particularly those who represented diversity) to participate in a research project at centers of the U.S. National Aeronautics and Space Administration (NASA).

Eligibility This program is open to sophomores, juniors, and seniors enrolled full time at accredited U.S. colleges and universities. Applicants must have a GPA of 3.0 or higher with an academic major or demonstrated course work concentration in engineering, mathematics, computer science, or physical/life sciences. They must be interested in participating in a mentored research experience at a designated NASA center. The program seeks participation from students who represent America's rich and diverse population: female and male students of all races, creeds, colors, national origins, ages, and disabilities. U.S. citizenship is required.

Financial data The stipend is $6,500 for the summer session or $9,500 for the fall or spring semester. Participants also receive round-trip airfare or ground transportation costs to and from the NASA host center.

Duration 10 weeks during the summer or 15 weeks during the fall or spring semester.

Additional information The participating NASA centers include Ames Research Center (Moffett Field, California), Dryden Flight Research Center (Edwards, California), Glenn Research Center (Cleveland, Ohio), Goddard Space Flight Center (Greenbelt, Maryland), Jet Propulsion Laboratory (Pasadena, California), Johnson Space Center (Houston, Texas), Kennedy Space Center (Florida), Langley Research Center (Hampton, Virginia), Marshall Space Flight Center (Huntsville, Alabama), Stennis Space Center (Mississippi), Wallops Flight Facility (Virginia), and White Sands Test Facility (Las Cruces, New Mexico).

Number awarded Approximately 330 each year.

Deadline Deadline not specified.

[406]
NATIONAL ACHIEVEMENT SCHOLARSHIP PROGRAM

National Merit Scholarship Corporation
Attn: National Achievement Scholarship Program
1560 Sherman Avenue, Suite 200
Evanston, IL 60201-4897
(847) 866-5100 Fax: (847) 866-5113
Web: www.nationalmerit.org/nasp.php

Summary To provide financial assistance for college to Black American high school seniors with exceptional scores on the SAT and/or PSAT/NMSQT.

Eligibility This program is open to Black American seniors who are enrolled full time in a secondary school and progressing normally toward graduation or completion of high school requirements. Applicants must be U.S. citizens (or intend to become a citizen as soon as qualified) and be planning to attend an accredited college or university in the United States. They must take the PSAT/NMSQT at the proper time in high school (no later than the 11th grade) and mark section 14 on the PSAT/NMSQT answer sheet, which identifies them as a Black American who is requesting consideration in the Achievement Program. Final selection is based on the student's academic record, a self-description, PSAT/NMSQT and SAT scores, and a recommendation written by the principal or another official. Financial information is not considered, nor are college choice, course of study, or career plans.

Financial data The stipend is $2,500.

Duration 1 year.

Additional information A sizable group of each year's Achievement Program's non-winners are brought to the attention of U.S. institutions of higher education for the College-Sponsored Achievement Program or for the Corporate-Sponsored Achievement Program. Each winner must enroll as a full-time day student in a course of study leading to 1 of the traditional baccalaureate degrees. Recipients must meet the standards of performance and terms set forth in their scholarship offer. Students who have completed high school, or who are now enrolled in college or have attended college in the past, are not eligible for consideration.

Number awarded Approximately 700 each year.

Deadline Applicants must take the PSAT/NMSQT no later than October of their junior year.

[407]
NATIONAL ASSOCIATION OF BLACK ACCOUNTANTS MEMBER SCHOLARSHIP AWARDS

National Association of Black Accountants
Attn: National Scholarship Program
7474 Greenway Center Drive, Suite 1120
Greenbelt, MD 20770
(301) 474-NABA Fax: (301) 474-3114
E-mail: scholarships@nabainc.org
Web: www.nabainc.org

Summary To provide financial assistance to student members of the National Association of Black Accountants (NABA) who are working on an undergraduate or graduate degree in a field related to accounting.

Eligibility This program is open to minorities who are NABA members and enrolled full time as 1) an undergraduate freshman, sophomore, junior, or first-semester senior majoring in accounting, business, or finance at a 4-year college or university; or 2) a graduate student working on a master's degree in accounting. High school seniors are not eligible. Applicants must have a GPA of 3.5 or higher in their major and 3.3 or higher overall. Along with their application, they must submit a 500-word personal statement on their involvement in NABA, career objectives, leadership abilities, and community activities. Financial need is not considered in the selection process.

Financial data The stipend ranges from $1,000 to $3,000.

Duration 1 year.

Additional information This program includes named scholarships that vary from time to time. Recently, those included the Ralph and Valerie Thomas Scholarship, the Thomas S. Watson, Jr. Memorial Scholarship, the Travis C. Tomlin Memorial Scholarship, and the Walter and Victoria Smith Award.

Number awarded Varies each year.

Deadline January of each year.

[408]
NATIONAL ASSOCIATION OF BLACK ACCOUNTANTS NATIONAL SCHOLARSHIP

National Association of Black Accountants
Attn: National Scholarship Program
7474 Greenway Center Drive, Suite 1120
Greenbelt, MD 20770
(301) 474-NABA Fax: (301) 474-3114
E-mail: scholarships@nabainc.org
Web: www.nabainc.org

Summary To provide financial assistance to student members of the National Association of Black Accountants (NABA) who are working on an undergraduate or graduate degree in a field related to accounting.

Eligibility This program is open to minorities who are NABA members and enrolled full time as 1) an undergraduate freshman, sophomore, junior, or first-semester senior majoring in accounting, business, or finance at a 4-year college or university; or 2) a graduate student working on a master's degree in accounting. High school seniors are not eligible. Applicants must have a GPA of 3.5 or higher in their major and 3.3 or higher overall. Along with their application, they must submit a 500-word personal statement on their involvement in NABA, career objectives, leadership abilities, and community activities. Financial need is not considered in the selection process.

Financial data The stipend is $3,000.

Duration 1 year.

Number awarded 1 each year.

Deadline January of each year.

[409]
NATIONAL ASSOCIATION OF BLACK JOURNALISTS SCHOLARSHIP

National Association of Black Journalists
Attn: Communications Coordinator and Program Manager
University of Maryland
1100 Knight Hall, Suite 3100
College Park, MD 20742
(301) 405-2573 Fax: (301) 314-1714
E-mail: tjohnson@nabj.org
Web: www.nabj.org/?page=SEEDScholarships

Summary To provide financial assistance to undergraduate or graduate student members of the National Association of Black Journalists (NABJ) who are working on a degree in a field related to journalism.

Eligibility This program is open to African American undergraduate or graduate student members of NABJ who are currently enrolled full time at an accredited 4-year college or university. Applicants must be working on a degree in journalism or other communications-related field and have a GPA of 2.5 or higher. They must be able to demonstrate financial need. Along with their application, they must submit 5 samples of their work, an official college transcript, 3 letters of recommendation, a resume, and an essay of 1,000 to 2,000 words on how they see themselves as a journalist and what they would improve about the media business.

Financial data The stipend is $2,500. Funds are paid directly to the recipient's college or university.

Duration 1 year; nonrenewable.

Number awarded 1 each year.

Deadline March of each year.

[410]
NATIONAL ASSOCIATION OF NEGRO MUSICIANS SCHOLARSHIP CONTEST

National Association of Negro Musicians, Inc.
Attn: National Scholarship Chair
11551 South Laflin Street
P.O. Box 43053
Chicago, IL 60643
(773) 568-3818 Fax: (773) 785-5388
E-mail: nanm@nanm.org
Web: www.nanm.org/Scholarship

Summary To recognize and reward (with scholarships for additional study) young musicians who are sponsored by a branch of the National Association of Negro Musicians.

Eligibility This competition is open to musicians between 18 and 30 years of age. Contestants must be sponsored by a branch in good standing, although they do not need to be a member of a local branch or the national organization. For each category of the competition, they must select 2 compositions from assigned lists to perform, of which 1 list consists of works by African American composers. People ineligible to compete include former first-place winners of this competition; full-time public school teachers and college faculty (although graduate students holding teaching assistantships are still eligible if they receive less than 50% of their employment from that appointment); vocalists who have contracts as full-time solo performers in operatic, oratorio, or other types of professional singing organizations; instrumentalists with contractual full-time orchestral or ensemble jobs; and professional performers under management. Local branches nominate competitors for regional competitions. Regional winners advance to the national competition. Selection is based on musical accuracy (20 points), intonation (20 points), interpretation (20 points), tone quality (20 points), technical proficiency (10 points), and memorization (10 points). The category of the competition rotates on a 5-year schedule as follows: 2013: organ; 2014: winds and percussion; 2015: piano; 2016: voice; 2017: strings.

Financial data In the national competition, awards are at least $2,000 for first place, $1,500 for second, $1,000 for third, $750 for fourth, and $500 for fifth. All funds are paid directly to the winner's teacher/coach or institution.

Duration The competition is held annually.

Additional information The National Association of Negro Musicians was founded in 1919. Students must submit a $5 fee to enter a local branch competition. The branch must submit a $10 fee to enter the student in the regional competition. The region must submit a $15 fee to enter the student in the national competition.

Number awarded 5 each year.

Deadline Deadline not specified.

[411] NATIONAL BLACK MBA ASSOCIATION UNDERGRADUATE SCHOLARSHIP PROGRAM

National Black MBA Association
Attn: Scholarship Program
1 East Wacker Drive, Suite 3500
Chicago, IL 60601
(312) 236-BMBA Fax: (312) 580-8717
E-mail: Scholarship@nbmbaa.org
Web: www.nbmbaa.org

Summary To provide financial assistance to students interested in working on a bachelor's degree in a field related to business and becoming involved in activities of the National Black MBA Association (NBMBAA).

Eligibility This program is open to minority students who are currently enrolled full time in the first, second, third, or fourth year of a bachelor's degree program in business, management, or related field in the United States or Canada. Applicants must submit a 300-word essay on an assigned topic that relates to minorities in business. They must have a GPA of 3.0 or higher. Selection is based on the quality of the paper, academic excellence, leadership potential, communication skills, and involvement in local communities through service to others. U.S. citizenship is required.

Financial data Stipends range from $1,000 to $5,000. Membership in the NBMBAA is also included. Some recipients are provided with complimentary registration, round-trip airfare, housing, and special VIP access to receptions and events at the NBMBAA annual conference and exposition.

Duration 1 year.

Additional information Recipients must agree to become a member of the NBMBAA Scholarship Advisory Team and Scholarship Alumni Club, become an active member of their local NBMBAA chapter, and participate in limited public relations activities at the convention.

Number awarded Varies each year; recently, the sponsor awarded 18 undergraduate and graduate scholarships.

Deadline June of each year.

[412] NATIONAL OCEANIC AND ATMOSPHERIC ADMINISTRATION EDUCATIONAL PARTNERSHIP PROGRAM WITH MINORITY SERVING INSTITUTIONS UNDERGRADUATE SCHOLARSHIPS

National Oceanic and Atmospheric Administration
Attn: Office of Education
1315 East-West Highway
SSMC3, Room 10703
Silver Spring, MD 20910
(301) 713-9437, ext. 150 Fax: (301) 713-9465
E-mail: studentscholarshipprograms@noaa.gov
Web: www.epp.noaa.gov/ssp_undergrad_page.html

Summary To provide financial aid and research experience to undergraduate students at Minority Serving Institutions who are majoring in scientific fields of interest to the National Oceanic and Atmospheric Administration (NOAA).

Eligibility This program is open to full-time juniors at Minority Serving Institutions, including Hispanic Serving Institutions (HSIs), Historically Black Colleges and Universities (HBCUs), and Tribal Colleges and Universities (TCUs). Applicants must have a GPA of 3.0 or higher and a major in atmospheric science, biology, computer science, engineering, environmental science, geography, hydrology, mathematics, oceanography, physical science, physics, remote sensing, social science, or other field that supports NOAA's programs and mission. They must also be interested in participating in a research internship at an NOAA site. Selection is based on relevant course work (30%), education plan and statement of career interest (40%), recommendations (20%), and additional experience related to diversity of education, extracurricular activities, honors and awards, non-academic and volunteer work, and communication skills (10%). U.S. citizenship is required.

Financial data This program provides payment of tuition and fees (to a maximum of $8,000 per year) and a stipend during the internship of $650 per week.

Duration 2 academic years and 2 summer internships.

Number awarded Up to 15 each year.

Deadline February of each year.

[413]
NATIONAL ORGANIZATION OF PROFESSIONAL BLACK NATURAL RESOURCES CONSERVATION SERVICE EMPLOYEES SCHOLARSHIPS

National Organization of Professional Black Natural Resources Conservation Service Employees
c/o HBCU Scholarship Committee Chair
25 Underwood Street, N.W.
Washington, DC 20012
(202) 720-1088 E-mail: kim.bradford@wdc.usda.gov
Web: www.nopbnrcse.memberlodge.org/scholarships

Summary To provide financial assistance to students working on a bachelor's degree in agriculture, natural resource sciences, or a related field at an 1890 Historically Black Land-Grant Institution.

Eligibility This program is open to students enrolled or planning to enroll at 1 of the 18 universities designated as an 1890 Historically Black Land-Grant Institution. Applicants must be interested in working on a bachelor's degree in 1 of the following fields: agriculture, agricultural business/management, agricultural economics, agricultural engineering/mechanics, agricultural production and technology, agronomy or crop science, animal science, botany, farm and range management, forestry, horticulture, natural resource management, soil conservation and science, or wildlife management. They must have a GPA of 2.8 or higher. Along with their application, they must submit 250-word essays on 1) the reason they are majoring in their selected field; 2) their short- and long-term career goals and objectives; and 3) why they need financial assistance to continue their education. U.S. citizenship is required.

Financial data The stipend is $1,000.

Duration 1 year; nonrenewable.

Additional information The eligible 1890 Historically Black Land-Grant Institutions are Alabama A&M University, Alcorn State University (Mississippi), Delaware State University, Florida A&M University, Fort Valley State University (Georgia), Kentucky State University, Langston University (Oklahoma), Lincoln University (Missouri), North Carolina A&T State University, Prairie View A&M University (Texas), South Carolina State University, Southern University (Louisiana), Tennessee State University, Tuskegee University (Alabama), University of Arkansas at Pine Bluff, University of Maryland Eastern Shore, Virginia State University, and West Virginia State University.

Number awarded 10 each year.

Deadline January of each year.

[414]
NATIONAL PRESS CLUB SCHOLARSHIP FOR JOURNALISM DIVERSITY

National Press Club
Attn: Executive Director's Office
529 14th Street, N.W., 13th Floor
Washington, DC 20045
(202) 662-7599
Web: www.press.org/about/students

Summary To provide funding to African Americans and other high school seniors who are planning to major in journalism in college and who will bring diversity to the field.

Eligibility This program is open to high school seniors who have been accepted to college and plan to prepare for a career in journalism. Applicants must submit 1) a 500-word essay explaining how they would add diversity to U.S. journalism; 2) up to 5 work samples demonstrating an ongoing interest in journalism through work on a high school newspaper or other media; 3) letters of recommendation from 3 people; 4) a copy of their high school transcript; 5) documentation of financial need; 6) a letter of acceptance from the college or university of their choice; and 7) a brief description of how they have pursued journalism in high school.

Financial data The stipend is $2,000 for the first year and $2,500 for each subsequent year. The program also provides an additional $500 book stipend, designated the Ellen Masin Persina Scholarship, for the first year.

Duration 4 years.

Additional information The program began in 1990.

Number awarded 1 each year.

Deadline February of each year.

[415]
NATIONAL SCHOLARSHIP PROGRAM OF 100 BLACK MEN OF AMERICA

100 Black Men of America, Inc.
Attn: National Scholarship Administrator
141 Auburn Avenue
Atlanta, GA 30303
(404) 688-5100 Toll Free: (800) 598-3411
Fax: (404) 688-1028 E-mail: info@100bmoa.org
Web: www.100blackmen.org/education.aspx

Summary To provide financial assistance for college to African American males and other high school seniors or current undergraduates who submit essays on topics related to African Americans.

Eligibility This program is open to high school seniors and undergraduates who are attending or planning to attend an accredited postsecondary institution as a full-time student. Applicants must have a GPA of 2.5 or higher and have completed at least 50 hours of active community service within the past 12 months. Along with their application, they must submit a 600-word essay on their choice of a topic that changes annually; recently, students were invited to write on 1 of the following: 1) the link between obesity and health issues; 2) the importance of higher education; 3) gang violence in America; 4) hazing in high schools and colleges; or 5) the rise in student loans instead of scholarship applications. Financial need is not considered in the selection process.

Financial data Stipends range from $1,000 to $3,000.

Duration 1 year.

Number awarded Varies each year; recently, 79 of these scholarships were awarded.

Deadline February of each year.

[416]
NATIONAL SOCIETY OF BLACK ENGINEERS MAJOR SPONSORS SCHOLARS AWARDS

National Society of Black Engineers
Attn: Programs Department
205 Daingerfield Road
Alexandria, VA 22314
(703) 549-2207 Fax: (703) 683-5312
E-mail: scholarships@nsbe.org
Web: www.nsbe.org/Programs/Scholarships.aspx

Summary To provide financial assistance to members of the National Society of Black Engineers (NSBE) who are working on a degree in engineering.

Eligibility This program is open to members of the society who are undergraduate or graduate engineering students. Applicants must have a GPA of 3.0 or higher. Selection is based on an essay; academic achievement; service to the society at the chapter, regional, and/or national level; and other professional, campus, and community activities. Applicants for the National Society of Black Engineers Fellows Scholarship Program who rank in the second of 3 tiers receive these awards.

Financial data The stipend is $1,500. Travel, hotel accommodations, and registration to the national convention are also provided.

Duration 1 year.

Number awarded Varies each year; recently, 17 of these scholarships were awarded.

Deadline May of each year.

[417]
NATIONAL SORORITY OF PHI DELTA KAPPA SCHOLARSHIPS

National Sorority of Phi Delta Kappa, Inc.
Attn: Perpetual Scholarship Foundation
8233 South King Drive
Chicago, IL 60619
(773) 783-7379 Fax: (773) 783-7354
E-mail: nspdkhq@aol.com

Summary To provide financial assistance to African American high school seniors interested in studying education in college.

Eligibility This program is open to African American high school seniors who are interested in working on a 4-year college degree in education. Men and women compete separately. Financial need is considered in the selection process.

Financial data The stipend is $1,500 per year.

Duration 4 years, provided the recipient maintains a GPA of 2.5 or higher and a major in education.

Additional information The sponsor was founded in 1923 as an organization of female African American educators.

Number awarded 10 each year: 1 male and 1 female in each of the organization's 5 regions.

Deadline Applications must be submitted to a local chapter of the organization by January of each year.

[418]
NATIONAL SPACE GRANT COLLEGE AND FELLOWSHIP PROGRAM

National Aeronautics and Space Administration
Attn: Office of Education
300 E Street, S.W.
Mail Suite 6M35
Washington, DC 20546-0001
(202) 358-1069 Fax: (202) 358-7097
E-mail: Diane.D.DeTroye@nasa.gov
Web: www.nasa.gov

Summary To provide financial assistance to undergraduate and graduate students (particularly African Americans, other underrepresented minorities, and women) who are interested in preparing for a career in a space-related field.

Eligibility This program is open to undergraduate and graduate students at colleges and universities that participate in the National Space Grant program of the U.S. National Aeronautics and Space Administration (NASA) through their state consortium. Applicants must be interested in a program of study and/or research in a field of science, technology, engineering, or mathematics (STEM) related to space. A specific goal of the program is to recruit and train U.S. citizens, especially underrepresented minorities, women, and persons with disabilities, for careers in aerospace science and technology. Financial need is not considered in the selection process.

Financial data Each consortium establishes the terms of the fellowship program in its state.

Additional information NASA established the Space Grant program in 1989. It operates through 52 consortia in each state, the District of Columbia, and Puerto Rico. Each consortium includes selected colleges and universities in that state as well as other affiliates from industry, museums, science centers, and state and local agencies.

Number awarded Varies each year.

Deadline Each consortium sets its own deadlines.

[419]
NAVY/MARINE CORPS JROTC SCHOLARSHIP

National Naval Officers Association-Washington, D.C. Chapter
c/o LCDR Stephen Williams
P.O. Box 30784
Alexandria, VA 22310
(703) 566-3840 Fax: (703) 566-3813
E-mail: Stephen.Williams@navy.mil
Web: dcnnoa.memberlodge.com

Summary To provide financial assistance to African American and other minority high school seniors from the Washington, D.C. area who have participated in Navy or Marine Corps Junior Reserve Officers Training Corps (JROTC) and are planning to attend college in any state.

Eligibility This program is open to minority seniors graduating from high schools in the Washington, D.C. metropolitan area who have participated in Navy or Marine Corps JROTC. Applicants must be planning to enroll full time at an accredited 2- or 4-year college or university in any state. They must have a GPA of 2.5 or higher. Selection is based on academic achievement, community involvement, and financial need. U.S. citizenship or permanent resident status is required.

Financial data The stipend is $1,000.

Duration 1 year; nonrenewable.

Additional information Recipients are not required to join or affiliate with the military in any way after college.

Number awarded 1 each year.

Deadline March of each year.

[420]
NBNA SCHOLARSHIPS

National Black Nurses Association, Inc.
Attn: Scholarship Committee
8630 Fenton Street, Suite 330
Silver Spring, MD 20910-3803
(301) 589-3200 Toll Free: (800) 575-6298
Fax: (301) 589-3223 E-mail: elazenby@nbna.org
Web: www.nbna.org

Summary To provide financial assistance for undergraduate nursing education to members of the National Black Nurses Association (NBNA).

Eligibility This program is open to members of the association who are currently enrolled in a B.S.N., A.D., diploma, or L.P.N./L.V.N. program with at least 1 full year of school remaining. Along with their application, they must submit a 2-page essay 1) describing their extracurricular activities and community involvement (including local chapter activities, community-based projects, school level projects, organizational efforts, state-level student nurse activities, and other activities impacting on the health and social condition of African Americans and other culturally diverse groups); 2) presenting their ideas of what they can do as an individual nurse to improve the health status and/or social condition of African Americans; and 3) stating their future goals in nursing.

Financial data The stipend ranges from $500 to $2,000 per year.

Duration 1 year; may be renewed.

Additional information This program includes the following named scholarships: the Dr. Lauranne Sams Scholarship, the Martha R. Dudley Scholarship, the Maria Dudley Advanced Scholarship, the NBNA Board of Directors Scholarship, the Rita E. Miller Scholarship, the Martha A. Dawson Genesis Scholarship, the Margaret Pemberton Scholarship, the Reverend Pauline L. Cole Scholarship, the Sheila Haley Scholarship, the United Health Foundation Scholarship, and the Esther Colliflower/VITAS Innovative Hospice Care Scholarship.

Number awarded Varies each year.

Deadline April of each year.

[421]
NELLIE STONE JOHNSON SCHOLARSHIP

Nellie Stone Johnson Scholarship Program
P.O. Box 40309
St. Paul, MN 55104
(651) 738-1404 Toll Free: (866) 738-5238
E-mail: info@nelliestone.org
Web: www.nelliestone.org

Summary To provide financial assistance to African American and other minority union members or their families who are interested in working on an undergraduate or graduate degree in any field at a Minnesota state college or university.

Eligibility This program is open to students in undergraduate and graduate programs at a 2- or 4-year institution that is a component of Minnesota State Colleges and Universities (MnSCU). Applicants must be a minority (Asian, American Indian, Alaska Native, Black/African American, Hispanic/Latino, Native Hawaiian, or Pacific Islander) union member or the child, grandchild, or spouse of a minority union member. They must submit a 2-page essay about their background, educational goals, career goals, and other activities that may impact the cause of human or civil rights. Undergraduates must have a GPA of 2.0 or higher; graduate students must have a GPA of 3.0 or higher. Preference is given to Minnesota residents. Selection is based on the essay, commitment to human or civil rights, extracurricular activities, volunteer activities, community involvement, academic standing, and financial need.

Financial data Stipends range from $500 to $2,000 per year.

Duration 1 year; may be renewed up to 3 additional years for students working on a bachelor's degree, 1 additional year for students working on a master's degree, or 1 additional year for students in a community or technical college program.

Number awarded Varies each year; recently, 18 of these scholarships were awarded.

Deadline April of each year.

[422]
NELSON MANDELA SCHOLARSHIPS

National Black Law Students Association
Attn: Director of Education and Career Development
1225 11th Street, N.W.
Washington, DC 20001-4217
(202) 618-2572 E-mail: educationcareer@nblsa.org
Web: www.nblsa.org/scholarships

Summary To provide financial assistance to members of the National Black Law Students Association (NBLSA) who are currently enrolled as undergraduate students.

Eligibility This program is open to NBLSA Pre-Law Division members who are of African descent and currently enrolled as undergraduates planning to attend law school. Applicants must submit an essay on a topic that changes annually; recently, students were asked to present their thoughts on a quotation from Nelson Mandela on education as a weapon to change the world.

Financial data The stipend is $1,000.

Duration 1 year.

Number awarded 2 each year.

Deadline January of each year.

[423]
NEW ENGLAND CITE SCHOLARSHIPS

Consortium of Information and Telecommunications Executives-New England Chapter
Attn: Scholarship Committee
Verizon Communications
65 Crescent Street
Brockton, MA 02301
(508) 921-2144 E-mail: Scholar@cite-newengland.org
Web: www.cite-newengland.org

Summary To provide financial assistance to African American residents of New England states who are attending or planning to attend college in any state.

Eligibility This program is open to African American residents of Maine, Massachusetts, New Hampshire, Rhode Island, or Vermont who are graduating high school seniors or current college freshmen, sophomores, or juniors. Applicants must be attending or planning to attend a 4-year college or university in any state and have a GPA of 3.0 or higher. Along with their application, they must submit a 300-word essay on a topic that changes annually but relates to the legacy of the sponsoring organization in serving the African American community of New England. Financial need is not considered in the selection process. U.S. citizenship is required.

Financial data The stipend is $1,000.

Duration 1 year; nonrenewable.

Additional information The Consortium of Information and Telecommunications Executives (CITE) is an organization of African American employees of Verizon, founded in 1984 after the dissolution of the former Bell systems. Recipients are required to attend the sponsor's presentation ceremony.

Number awarded 1 or more each year.

Deadline April of each year.

[424] NEW JERSEY CHAPTER NBMBAA UNDERGRADUATE SCHOLARSHIPS

National Black MBA Association-New Jersey Chapter
Attn: Scholarship Program
P.O. Box 28023
Newark, NJ 07101
(732) 246-2878
Web: www.nbmbaa-newjersey.org/scholarships.asp?id=7

Summary To provide financial assistance to African American students from New Jersey interested in working on an undergraduate degree in business or management at a school in any state.

Eligibility This program is open to African American residents of New Jersey who are graduating high school seniors or full-time undergraduates enrolled in their first, second, or third year at an accredited college or university in any state. Applicants must be working on or planning to work on a bachelor's degree in business or management. Along with their application, they must submit a 2-page essay on a topic that changes annually but relates to African Americans in business. Selection is based on that essay, transcripts, a resume of work experience and extracurricular or volunteer activities, and 2 letters of recommendation.

Financial data A stipend is awarded (amount not specified).

Duration 1 year.

Number awarded Varies each year.

Deadline July of each year.

[425] NEW YORK CITE TRADITIONAL SCHOLARSHIPS

Consortium of Information and Telecommunications Executives-New York Chapter
Attn: Diane Lewis, Scholarship Committee Chair
Church Street Station
P.O. Box 3452
New York, NY 10008
(212) 962-1730 E-mail: diane.c.lewis@verizon.com
Web: www.citeny.org/scholarship.html

Summary To provide financial assistance to African American high school seniors from New York who plan to major in selected business- or engineering-related fields in college.

Eligibility This program is open to African American seniors graduating from high schools in New York who have been accepted by an accredited 4-year college or university in any state as a full-time student. Applicants must have a GPA of 3.0 or higher and a family income of $75,000 per year or less. They must be planning to major in 1 of the following fields: accounting, advertising, business, computer science, electrical engineering, finance, industrial engineering, information technology, marketing, or mathematics. Along with their application, they must submit a 1-page essay on their educational and career goals. Employees of Verizon Communications or affiliated subsidiaries and their family members are ineligible. U.S. citizenship is required.

Financial data The stipend is $1,500.

Duration 1 year; nonrenewable.

Additional information The Consortium of Information and Telecommunications Executives (CITE) is an organization of African American employees of Verizon, founded in 1984 after the dissolution of the former Bell systems.

Number awarded 2 each year.

Deadline April of each year.

[426] NIDDK/OMHRC SUMMER INTERNSHIP PROGRAM FOR UNDERREPRESENTED GROUPS

National Institute of Diabetes and Digestive and Kidney Diseases
Attn: Office of Minority Health Research Coordination
6707 Democracy Boulevard, Room 906A
Bethesda, MD 20892-5454
(301) 435-2988 Fax: (301) 594-9358
E-mail: MartinezW@mail.nih.gov
Web: www2.niddk.nih.gov/Funding

Summary To provide African American and other underrepresented minority undergraduate students with an opportunity to conduct research in the laboratory of a National Institute of Diabetes and Digestive and Kidney Diseases (NIDDK) intramural scientist during the summer.

Eligibility This program is open to undergraduate students who are members of underrepresented minority groups (African Americans, Hispanic Americans, Native Americans, Native Hawaiians, other Pacific Islanders, and Alaska Natives). Applicants must be interested in participating in a research project conducted at an intramural research laboratory of NIDDK in Bethesda, Maryland or Phoenix, Arizona. They must have completed at least 1 year at an accredited institution and have a GPA of 3.0 or higher. Along with their application, they must submit a 2-page personal statement of their research interest, career goals, and reasons for applying to training at NIDDK. U.S. citizenship or permanent resident status is required.

Financial data Students receive a stipend of $2,500, housing, and (for those who live outside the Washington metropolitan area or the state of Arizona) a travel allowance of $500.

Duration 10 weeks during the summer.

Number awarded Varies each year.

Deadline February of each year.

[427]
NLGJA/KAY LONGCOPE SCHOLARSHIP AWARD

National Lesbian & Gay Journalists Association
2120 L Street, N.W., Suite 850
Washington, DC 20037
(202) 588-9888 Fax: (202) 588-1818
E-mail: info@nlgfa.org
Web: www.nlgja.org/students/longcope

Summary To provide financial assistance to African American and other lesbian, gay, bisexual, and transgender (LGBT) undergraduate and graduate students of color who are interested in preparing for a career in journalism.

Eligibility This program is open to LGBT students of color who are 1) high school seniors accepted to a U.S. community college or 4-year university and planning to enroll full time; 2) full-time undergraduate students at U.S. community colleges and 4-year universities; or 3) undergraduate students who have been accepted for their first year at a U.S. graduate school. Applicants must be planning a career in journalism and be committed to furthering the sponsoring organization's mission of fair and accurate coverage of the LGBT community. They must demonstrate an awareness of the issues facing the LGBT community and the importance of fair and accurate news coverage. For undergraduates, a declared major in journalism and/or communications is desirable but not required; non-journalism majors may demonstrate their commitment to a journalism career through work samples, internships, and work on a school news publication, online news service, or broadcast affiliate. Graduate students must be enrolled in a journalism program. Along with their application, they must submit a 1-page resume, 5 work samples, official transcripts, 3 letters of recommendation, and a 750-word news story on a designated subject involving the LGBT community. U.S. citizenship or permanent resident status is required. Selection is based on journalistic and scholastic ability.

Financial data The stipend is $3,000.

Duration 1 year.

Additional information This program began in 2008.

Number awarded 1 each year.

Deadline June of each year.

[428]
NORTH CAROLINA CHAPTER AABE SCHOLARSHIPS

American Association of Blacks in Energy-North Carolina Chapter
Attn: Scholarship Committee
P.O. Box 207
Raleigh, NC 27602-0207
E-mail: jgraves73@gmail.com
Web: www.aabe.org/index.php?component=pages&id=416

Summary To provide financial assistance to African Americans and members of other underrepresented minority groups who are high school seniors in North Carolina and planning to major in an energy-related field at a college in any state.

Eligibility This program is open to seniors graduating from high schools in North Carolina and planning to work on a bachelor's degree at a college or university in any state. Applicants must be African Americans, Hispanics, or Native Americans who have a GPA of 3.0 or higher and are able to demonstrate financial need. Their intended major must be a field of business, engineering, physical science, mathematics, or technology related to energy. Along with their application, they must submit a 350-word statement on why they should receive this scholarship, their professional career objectives, and any other relevant information.

Financial data The stipend is $1,000.

Duration 1 year; nonrenewable.

Additional information Winners are eligible to compete for regional and national scholarships.

Number awarded 1 or more each year.

Deadline February of each year.

[429]
NORTH CAROLINA CPA FOUNDATION OUTSTANDING MINORITY ACCOUNTING STUDENT SCHOLARSHIPS

North Carolina Association of Certified Public Accountants
Attn: North Carolina CPA Foundation, Inc.
3100 Gateway Centre Boulevard
P.O. Box 80188
Raleigh, NC 27623-0188
(919) 469-1040, ext. 130 Toll Free: (800) 722-2836
Fax: (919) 378-2000 E-mail: jtahler@ncacpa.org
Web: ncacpa.org

Summary To provide financial assistance to African American and other minority undergraduate and graduate students working on a degree in accounting at colleges and universities in North Carolina.

Eligibility This program is open to North Carolina residents who have completed at least 36 semester hours, including at least 4 accounting courses, at a college or university in the state. Applicants must be members of a minority group, defined as Black, Native American/Alaskan Native, Middle-Eastern, Asian or Pacific Islander, or Hispanic. They must be enrolled full time in an academic program leading to a degree in accounting or its equivalent and have a GPA of 3.0 or higher. Along with their application, they must submit a 500-word essay on 1 of the following questions: 1) what the profession can do to educate minorities about understanding the impact of and ways to survive the national financial crisis; 2) how they will impact minority communities by becoming a C.P.A.; or 3) the challenges that minority C.P.A.s face in the profession. Selection is based on GPA (30%), extracurricular activities (20%), essay content (25%), and essay grammar (25%).

Financial data Stipends are $2,000 or $1,000.

Duration 1 year; may be renewed up to 2 additional years.

Number awarded 2 each year: 1 at $2,000 and 1 at $1,000.

Deadline March of each year.

[430]
NORTH CAROLINA MILLENNIUM TEACHER SCHOLARSHIP/LOAN PROGRAM

North Carolina State Education Assistance Authority
Attn: Millennium Teacher Scholarship Program
10 Alexander Drive
P.O. Box 13663
Research Triangle Park, NC 27709-3663
(919) 549-8614 Toll Free: (800) 700-1775
Fax: (919) 248-4687 E-mail: eew@ncseaa.edu
Web: www.ncseaa.edu/MTSLP.htm

Summary To provide funding to high school seniors in North Carolina who are interested in attending designated public Historically Black Colleges and Universities (HBCUs) in the state to work on a degree in education.

Eligibility This program is open to seniors graduating from high schools in North Carolina who have been accepted at Elizabeth City State University, Fayetteville State University, or Winston-Salem State University. Applicants must have a combined mathematics and critical reading SAT score of at least 900, have a GPA of at least 2.5, and be able to demonstrate at least $3,000 worth of financial aid need. They must be interested in teaching at a North Carolina public school after graduation; priority is given to applicants planning to teach in designated critical shortage licensure areas.

Financial data The stipend is $6,500 per year. This is a loan-for-service program. Recipients are required to teach 1 year in a North Carolina public school for each year of support they receive. If they fail to fulfill that service obligation, they must repay all funds received with 10% interest. Repayment in service or cash must be completed within 10 years.

Duration 1 year; may be renewed up to 3 additional years.

Additional information The North Carolina General Assembly established this program in 2004.

Number awarded Up to 20 students are accepted at each of the 3 participating universities each year; recently, a total of 46 students were receiving $285,015 through this program.

Deadline Deadline not specified.

[431]
NORTHROP GRUMMAN NSBE CORPORATE SCHOLARSHIPS

National Society of Black Engineers
Attn: Programs Department
205 Daingerfield Road
Alexandria, VA 22314
(703) 549-2207 Fax: (703) 683-5312
E-mail: scholarships@nsbe.org
Web: www.nsbe.org/Programs/Scholarships.aspx

Summary To provide financial assistance to members of the National Society of Black Engineers (NSBE) who are working on an undergraduate degree in designated science and engineering fields.

Eligibility This program is open to members of the society who are U.S. citizens currently enrolled as college sophomores, juniors, or seniors. Applicants must be majoring in computer engineering, computer science, electrical engineering, naval architecture, or systems engineering. They must have a GPA of 3.0 or higher and a demonstrated interest in employment with Northrop Grumman.

Financial data The stipend is $5,000.

Duration 1 year.

Additional information This program is sponsored by Northrop Grumman Corporation.

Number awarded 5 each year.

Deadline May of each year.

[432]
NORTHWEST JOURNALISTS OF COLOR SCHOLARSHIP AWARDS

Northwest Journalists of Color
c/o Caroline Li
1433 12th Avenue, Suite A1
Seattle, WA 98122
E-mail: Caroline@SoMuchGoodMusic.com
Web: www.aajaseattle.org/scholarships

Summary To provide financial assistance to African American and other minority students from Washington state who are interested in careers in journalism.

Eligibility This program is open to members of minority groups (Asian American, African American, Native American, and Latino) who are 1) residents of Washington attending an accredited college or university in any state; 2) residents of any state attending a Washington college or university; or 3) seniors graduating from Washington high schools and planning to attend an accredited college in any state. Applicants must be planning a career in broadcast, photo, or print journalism. Along with their application, they must submit 1) a 500-word essay about their interest in a career as a journalist; 2) a current resume; 3) up to 3 work samples; 4) reference letters; and 5) documentation of financial need.

Financial data Stipends range up to $2,500 per year.

Duration 1 year; may be renewed.

Additional information This program, established in 1986, is sponsored by the Seattle chapters of the Asian American Journalists Association, the Native American Journalists Association, the National Association of Black Journalists, and the Latino Media Association. It includes the Walt and Milly Woodward Memorial Scholarship donated by the Western Washington Chapter of the Society of Professional Journalists.

Number awarded Varies each year.

Deadline April of each year.

[433]
NSBE FELLOWS SCHOLARSHIP PROGRAM

National Society of Black Engineers
Attn: Programs Department
205 Daingerfield Road
Alexandria, VA 22314
(703) 549-2207 Fax: (703) 683-5312
E-mail: scholarships@nsbe.org
Web: www.nsbe.org/Programs/Scholarships.aspx

Summary To provide financial assistance to members of the National Society of Black Engineers (NSBE) who are working on a degree in engineering.

Eligibility This program is open to members of the society who are undergraduate or graduate engineering students. Applicants must have a GPA of 2.7 or higher. Selection is based on an essay; academic achievement; service to the society at the chapter, regional, and/or national level; and other professional, campus, and community activities. Applicants for this program who rank in the third of 3 tiers receive these awards.

Financial data The stipend is $1,000.

Duration 1 year.

Number awarded Varies each year; recently, 9 of these scholarships were awarded.

Deadline May of each year.

[434]
NSBP/ELMER S. IMES SCHOLARSHIP IN PHYSICS

National Society of Black Physicists
Attn: Scholarship Committee Chair
1100 North Glebe Road, Suite 1010
Arlington, VA 22201
(703) 536-4207 Fax: (703) 536-4203
E-mail: scholarship@nsbp.org
Web: www.nsbp.org/scholarships

Summary To provide financial assistance to African American students majoring in physics in college.

Eligibility This program is open to African American students who are entering their junior or senior year of college and majoring in physics. Applicants must submit an essay on their academic and career objectives, information on their participation in extracurricular activities, a description of any awards and honors they have received, and 3 letters of recommendation. Financial need is not considered.

Financial data A stipend is awarded (amount not specified).

Duration 1 year; nonrenewable.

Number awarded 1 each year.

Deadline November of each year.

[435]
NSCA MINORITY SCHOLARSHIPS

National Strength and Conditioning Association
Attn: Grants and Scholarships Program
1885 Bob Johnson Drive
Colorado Springs, CO 80906-4000
(719) 632-6722, ext. 152 Toll Free: (800) 815-6826
Fax: (719) 632-6367 E-mail: foundation@nsca-lift.org
Web: www.nsca-lift.org/Foundation/grants-and-scholarships

Summary To provide financial assistance to African Americans and other minorities who are interested in working on an undergraduate or graduate degree in strength training and conditioning.

Eligibility This program is open to Blacks, Hispanics, Asian Americans, and Native Americans who are 17 years of age and older. Applicants must have been accepted into an accredited postsecondary institution to work on an undergraduate or graduate degree in the strength and conditioning field. Along with their application, they must submit a 500-word essay on their personal and professional goals and how receiving this scholarship will assist them in achieving those goals. Selection is based on that essay, academic achievement, strength and conditioning experience, honors and awards, community involvement, letters of recommendation, and involvement in the National Strength and Conditioning Association (NSCA).

Financial data The stipend is $1,500.

Duration 1 year.

Additional information The NSCA is a nonprofit organization of strength and conditioning professionals, including coaches, athletic trainers, physical therapists, educators, researchers, and physicians. This program was first offered in 2003.

Number awarded Varies each year; recently, 9 of these scholarships were awarded.

Deadline March of each year.

[436]
NSNA/BREAKTHROUGH TO NURSING SCHOLARSHIPS

National Student Nurses' Association
Attn: Foundation
45 Main Street, Suite 606
Brooklyn, NY 11201
(718) 210-0705 Fax: (718) 797-1186
E-mail: nsna@nsna.org
Web: www.nsna.org

Summary To provide financial assistance to African American and other minority undergraduate and graduate students who wish to prepare for careers in nursing.

Eligibility This program is open to students currently enrolled in state-approved schools of nursing or pre-nursing associate degree, baccalaureate, diploma, generic master's, generic doctoral, R.N. to B.S.N., R.N. to M.S.N., or L.P.N./L.V.N. to R.N. programs. Graduating high school seniors are not eligible. Support for graduate education is provided only for a first degree in nursing. Applicants must be members of a racial or ethnic minority underrepresented among registered nurses (American Indian or Alaska Native, Hispanic or Latino, Native Hawaiian or other Pacific Islander, Black or African American, or Asian). They must be committed to providing quality health care services to underserved populations. Along with their application, they must submit a 200-word description of their professional and educational goals and how this scholarship will help them achieve those goals. Selection is based on academic achievement, financial need, and involvement in student nursing organizations and community health activities. U.S. citizenship or permanent resident status is required.

Financial data Stipends range from $1,000 to $2,500.

Duration 1 year.

Additional information Applications must be accompanied by a $10 processing fee.

Number awarded Varies each year; recently, 13 of these scholarships were awarded: 10 sponsored by the American Association of Critical-Care Nurses and 3 sponsored by the Mayo Clinic.

Deadline January of each year.

[437]
NUCLEAR REGULATORY COMMISSION HISTORICALLY BLACK COLLEGES AND UNIVERSITIES STUDENT RESEARCH PARTICIPATION PROGRAM

Oak Ridge Institute for Science and Education
Attn: Science and Engineering Education
P.O. Box 117
Oak Ridge, TN 37831-0117
(865) 576-3937 Fax: (865) 241-5220
E-mail: michael.hubbard@orau.gov
Web: see.orau.org

Summary To provide funding to students at Historically Black Colleges and Universities (HBCUs) who wish to participate in research at various facilities of the U.S. Nuclear Regulatory Commission (NRC).

Eligibility This program is open to undergraduate and graduate students at HBCUs who are U.S. citizens or permanent residents. Applicants must be studying computer science, engineering, earth or geosciences, health physics, materials science, mathematics, molecular/radiation biology, performance and risk assessments, physical sciences, or statistics-related nuclear material control and accounting. They must be interested in participating in a research project at a laboratory where NRC research is being conducted, on an HBCU campus, or at a host university under the guidance of a principal investigator who has an NRC research grants.

Financial data The stipend is $700 per week for graduate students or $600 per week for undergraduates. Also provided is limited travel reimbursement for round-trip transportation between the facility and home or campus.

Duration 10 to 12 weeks during the summer. Some 1-year appointments at participating facilities or on campus are also available.

Additional information This program is funded by the NRC and administered by Oak Ridge Institute for Science and Education (ORISE).

Number awarded Varies each year.

Deadline Applications may be submitted at any time.

[438]
NWA/DAVID SANKEY MINORITY SCHOLARSHIP IN METEOROLOGY

National Weather Association
Attn: Executive Director
228 West Millbrook Road
Raleigh, NC 27609-4304
(919) 845-1546 Fax: (919) 845-2956
E-mail: exdir@nwas.org
Web: www.nwas.org

Summary To provide financial assistance to African Americans and other members of minority groups who are working on an undergraduate or graduate degree in meteorology.

Eligibility This program is open to members of minority ethnic groups who are either entering their sophomore or higher year of undergraduate study or enrolled as graduate students. Applicants must be working on a degree in meteorology. Along with their application, they must submit a 1-page statement explaining why they are applying for this scholarship. Selection is based on that statement, academic achievement, and 2 letters of recommendation.

Financial data The stipend is $1,000.

Duration 1 year.

Additional information This program began in 2002.

Number awarded 1 each year.

Deadline April of each year.

[439]
OFFICE OF STUDENT AFFAIRS COMMUNITY LEADERSHIP TUITION SCHOLARSHIP

National Association of Black Social Workers
Attn: NABSW Scholarships
2305 Martin Luther King Avenue, S.E.
Washington, DC 20020
(202) 678-4570 Fax: (202) 678-4572
E-mail: office-manager@nabsw.org
Web: www.nabsw.org/mserver/Forms.aspx

Summary To provide financial assistance to members of the National Association of Black Social Workers (NABSW) who have provided outstanding community service and are working on an undergraduate or graduate degree.

Eligibility This program is open to African American members of NABSW who are enrolled at least half time at an accredited U.S. institution. Applicants must be working on an associate, bachelor's, master's, or Ph.D. degree in social work, sociology, or other field of human services. They must have a GPA of 3.0 or higher and a record of volunteer service to the African American community. Along with their application, they must submit a letter of recommendation from a prestigious community leader that highlights their volunteer work and leadership efforts within the African American community. Financial need is considered in the selection process.

Financial data The stipend is $1,000. Funds are sent directly to the recipient's school.

Duration 1 year.

Number awarded 1 each year.

Deadline January of each year.

[440]
OHIO HIGH SCHOOL ATHLETIC ASSOCIATION ETHNIC MINORITY SCHOLARSHIPS

Ohio High School Athletic Association
Attn: Foundation
4080 Roselea Place
Columbus, OH 43214
(614) 267-2502 Fax: (614) 267-1677
Web: www.ohsaa.org/members/scholar/application.htm

Summary To provide financial assistance to African American and other minority high school seniors in Ohio who have participated in athletics and plan to attend college in any state.

Eligibility This program is open to minority seniors graduating from high schools in Ohio that are members of the Ohio High School Athletic Association (OHSAA). Applicants must have received at least 3 varsity letters in 1 sport or 4 letters in 2 sports and have a GPA of 3.25 or higher. They must be planning to attend a college or university in any state. Along with their application, they must submit a 1-page essay on the role that interscholastic athletics has played in their life and how such participation will benefit them in the future. Selection is based on that essay, GPA, ACT and SAT scores, varsity letters earned, and athletic honors.

Financial data The stipend is $1,000.

Duration 1 year.

Additional information Recipients of athletic scholarships in NCAA Division I or II institutions or appointees to military academies are not eligible to apply for this scholarship.

Number awarded 6 each year: 1 in each OHSSA District.

Deadline March of each year.

[441] OHIO NEWSPAPERS FOUNDATION MINORITY SCHOLARSHIPS

Ohio Newspapers Foundation
Attn: Foundation
1335 Dublin Road, Suite 216-B
Columbus, OH 43215-7038
(614) 486-6677, ext. 1010 Fax: (614) 486-4940
E-mail: ariggs@ohionews.org
Web: www.ohionews.org/foundation/scholarships

Summary To provide financial assistance to African American and other minority high school seniors in Ohio planning to attend college in the state to prepare for a career in journalism.

Eligibility This program is open to high school seniors in Ohio who are members of minority groups (African American, Hispanic, Asian American, or American Indian) and planning to prepare for a career in newspaper journalism. Applicants must have a high school GPA of 2.5 or higher and demonstrate writing ability in an autobiography of 750 to 1,000 words that describes their academic and career interests, awards, extracurricular activities, and journalism-related activities. They must be planning to attend a college or university in Ohio.

Financial data The stipend is $1,500.

Duration 1 year; nonrenewable.

Additional information This program began in 1990.

Number awarded 1 each year.

Deadline March of each year.

[442] OMEGA MASON/MAUDE BISSON NURSING SCHOLARSHIP

Auxiliary to the National Medical Association
8403 Colesville Road, Suite 920
Silver Spring, MD 20910
(301) 495-3779 Fax: (301) 495-0037
E-mail: anmanationaloffice@earthlink.net
Web: www.anmanet.org

Summary To provide financial assistance to African American nursing students.

Eligibility Applicants must be African American, be currently enrolled in an accredited nursing school, have earned a GPA of 3.2 or higher, be able to demonstrate financial need, and have a record of community involvement. For 2-year nursing programs, applicants must be second-year students; for 4-year programs, applicants must be entering their third year. In addition to completing a formal application, students must submit a 1-page essay detailing their educational goals and reasons for requesting this scholarship. The scholarship is awarded to a student nurse in the city where the national convention of the Auxiliary to the National Medical Association (ANMA) is held each year.

Financial data A stipend is awarded (amount not specified).

Duration 1 year.

Number awarded 1 each year.

Deadline April of each year.

[443] OMEGA PSI PHI FOUNDERS' MEMORIAL SCHOLARSHIPS

Omega Psi Phi Fraternity
Attn: Charles R. Drew Memorial Scholarship Commission
3951 Snapfinger Parkway
Decatur, GA 30035-3203
(404) 284-5533 Fax: (404) 284-0333
E-mail: scholarshipchairman@oppf.org
Web: www.oppf.org/scholarship

Summary To provide financial assistance to outstanding undergraduate and graduate members of Omega Psi Phi fraternity.

Eligibility This program is open to members of the fraternity who are enrolled full time as sophomores, juniors, or graduate students and have a GPA of 3.0 or higher. Each chapter may nominate 1 undergraduate and 1 graduate member to the district. Candidates must submit a statement of 200 to 250 words on their purpose for applying for this scholarship, how they believe funds from the fraternity can assist them in achieving their career goals, and other circumstances (including financial need) that make it important for them to receive financial assistance. Selection is based on academic achievement, extracurricular activities, and community and campus involvement.

Financial data The stipend is $5,000.

Duration The scholarships are offered annually.

Additional information The winners are required to attend the Omega Psi Phi Grand Conclave or Leadership Conference. Up to $1,000 in travel expenses for attendance is provided.

Number awarded 4 each year: 3 to undergraduates and 1 to a graduate student.

Deadline Applications must be submitted to the district scholarship committee chair by January of each year.

[444] OMEGA PSI PHI UNDERGRADUATE AND GRADUATE SCHOLARSHIPS

Omega Psi Phi Fraternity
Attn: Charles R. Drew Memorial Scholarship Commission
3951 Snapfinger Parkway
Decatur, GA 30035-3203
(404) 284-5533 Fax: (404) 284-0333
E-mail: scholarshipchairman@oppf.org
Web: www.oppf.org/scholarship

Summary To provide financial assistance for undergraduate, graduate, or professional education to members of Omega Psi Phi who have an outstanding academic record.

Eligibility This program is open to members of the fraternity who are either 1) a sophomore, junior, or senior planning to continue on to graduate or professional school; or 2) currently attending graduate or professional school. Applicants must be enrolled full time at a 4-year college or university and have a GPA of 3.0 or higher. Along with their application, they must submit a statement of 200 to 250 words on their purpose for applying for this scholarship, how they believe funds from the fraternity can assist them in achieving their career goals, and other circumstances (including financial need) that make it important for them to receive financial assistance.

Financial data The stipend is $4,000.

Duration 1 year.

Additional information The winners are required to attend the Omega Psi Phi Grand Conclave or Leadership Conference. Up to $1,000 in travel expenses for attendance is provided.

Number awarded 2 each year: 1 to an undergraduate and 1 to a graduate student.

Deadline April of each year.

[445]
OPERATION JUMP START III SCHOLARSHIPS

American Association of Advertising Agencies
Attn: AAAA Foundation
1065 Avenue of the Americas, 16th Floor
New York, NY 10018
(212) 262-2500 E-mail: ameadows@aaaa.org
Web: www.aaaa.org

Summary To provide financial assistance to African American and other multicultural art directors and copywriters interested in working on an undergraduate or graduate degree in advertising.

Eligibility This program is open to African Americans, Asian Americans, Hispanic Americans, and Native Americans who are U.S. citizens or permanent residents. Applicants must be incoming graduate students at 1 of 6 designated portfolio schools or full-time juniors at 1 of 2 designated colleges. They must be able to demonstrate extreme financial need, creative talent, and promise. Along with their application, they must submit 10 samples of creative work in their respective field of expertise.

Financial data The stipend is $5,000 per year.

Duration Most awards are for 2 years.

Additional information Operation Jump Start began in 1997 and was followed by Operation Jump Start II in 2002. The current program began in 2006. The 6 designated portfolio schools are the AdCenter at Virginia Commonwealth University, the Creative Circus in Atlanta, the Portfolio Center in Atlanta, the Miami Ad School, the University of Texas at Austin, and Pratt Institute. The 2 designated colleges are the Minneapolis College of Art and Design and the Art Center College of Design at Pasadena, California.

Number awarded 20 each year.

Deadline Deadline not specified.

[446]
ORA LEE SANDERS SCHOLARSHIP

PUSH Excel
Attn: General Offices
930 East 50th Street
Chicago, IL 60615
(773) 373-3366 E-mail: pushexcel@rainbowpush.org
Web: www.pushexcel.org/pages/scholarships

Summary To provide financial assistance to high school seniors who plan to attend college and are willing to help promote the scholarship program of PUSH-Excel.

Eligibility This program is open to seniors graduating from high school and planning to enroll at an accredited 4-year college or university. Applicants must be U.S. citizens and have a GPA of 2.5 or higher. Along with their application, they must submit a 500-word essay that identifies 5 prerequisites for success, explains their personal philosophy for the pursuit of excellence, and explains how they will use their college education to achieve this pursuit of excellence. They must also agree to cooperate with the scholarship committee of PUSH-Excel by promoting its program, participating in its public relations activities, and attending its Annual National Conference luncheon and Education Leadership Conference. Selection is based on the essay, academic preparation to attend college and succeed, ability to overcome obstacles to achieve academic and personal goals, and financial need.

Financial data The stipend is $1,000 per year.

Duration 1 year; may be renewed up to 3 additional years if the recipient maintains a GPA of 2.5 or higher and fulfills the obligations to PUSH-Excel.

Additional information PUSH-Excel was founded in 1975 by the Rev. Jesse Jackson.

Number awarded Varies each year; recently, 50 of these scholarships were awarded.

Deadline June of each year.

[447]
ORACLE AMERICA NSBE CORPORATE SCHOLARSHIP PROGRAM

National Society of Black Engineers
Attn: Programs Department
205 Daingerfield Road
Alexandria, VA 22314
(703) 549-2207 Fax: (703) 683-5312
E-mail: scholarships@nsbe.org
Web: www.nsbe.org/Programs/Scholarships.aspx

Summary To provide financial assistance to high school seniors and current undergraduates who are members of the National Society of Black Engineers (NSBE) and interested in studying engineering or a related field.

Eligibility This program is open to members of the society who are either high school seniors or current college freshmen, sophomores, juniors, or seniors. Applicants must be majoring or planning to major in engineering, computer or information science, computer engineering, or mathematics. They must have a GPA of 3.0 or higher and be U.S. citizens. Selection is based on academic standing, leadership skills, focus on the applications of engineering in the work world, and financial need.

Financial data The stipend is $4,500.

Duration 1 year.

Additional information This program is sponsored by Oracle America, Inc.

Number awarded 2 each year.

Deadline May of each year.

[448]
PAGE EDUCATION FOUNDATION GRANTS

Page Education Foundation
P.O. Box 581254
Minneapolis, MN 55458-1254
(612) 332-0406 E-mail: info@page-ed.org
Web: www.page-ed.org

Summary To provide funding to African Americans and other high school seniors of color in Minnesota who plan to attend college in the state.

Eligibility This program is open to students of color who are graduating from high schools in Minnesota and planning to enroll full time at a postsecondary school in the state. Applicants must submit a 500-word essay that deals with why they believe education is important, their plans for the future, and the service-to-children project they would like to complete in the coming school year. Selection is based on the essay, 3 letters of recommendation, and financial need.

Financial data Stipends range from $1,000 to $2,500 per year.

Duration 1 year; may be renewed up to 3 additional years.

Additional information This program was founded in 1988 by Alan Page, a former football player for the Minnesota Vikings. While attending college, the Page Scholars fulfill a 50-hour service-to-children contract that brings them into contact with K-8 students of color.

Number awarded Varies each year; recently, 503 Page Scholars (210 new recipients and 293 renewals) were enrolled, of whom 260 were African American, 141 Asian American, 70 Chicano/Latino, 13 American Indian, and 19 biracial or multiracial.

Deadline April of each year.

[449]
PARSONS BRINCKERHOFF ENGINEERING SCHOLARSHIP

Conference of Minority Transportation Officials
Attn: National Scholarship Program
1875 I Street, N.W., Suite 500
Washington, DC 20006
(703) 234-4072 Fax: (202) 318-0364
Web: www.comto.org/?page=Scholarships

Summary To provide financial assistance to African Americans and other members of the Conference of Minority Transportation Officials (COMTO) who are working on an undergraduate degree in engineering.

Eligibility This program is open to undergraduate students who have been members of COMTO for at least 1 year. Applicants must be working on a degree in engineering with a GPA of 3.0 or higher. Along with their application, they must submit a cover letter with a 500-word statement of career goals. Financial need is not considered in the selection process. U.S. citizenship or legal resident status is required.

Financial data The stipend is $2,500. Funds are paid directly to the recipient's college or university.

Duration 1 year.

Additional information COMTO was established in 1971 to promote, strengthen, and expand the roles of minorities in all aspects of transportation. This program is sponsored by Parsons Brinckerhoff, Inc. Recipients are expected to attend the COMTO National Scholarship Luncheon.

Number awarded 2 each year.

Deadline May of each year.

[450]
PARSONS BRINCKERHOFF GOLDEN APPLE SCHOLARSHIP

Conference of Minority Transportation Officials
Attn: National Scholarship Program
1875 I Street, N.W., Suite 500
Washington, DC 20006
(703) 234-4072 Fax: (202) 318-0364
Web: www.comto.org/?page=Scholarships

Summary To provide financial assistance to African American and other members of the Conference of Minority Transportation Officials (COMTO) and their children who are high school seniors planning to attend college to prepare for a career in the business aspects of the transportation industry.

Eligibility This program is open to graduating high school seniors who are members of COMTO or whose parents are members. Applicants must be planning to attend an accredited college, university, or vocational/technical institution to prepare for a career in transportation in the fields of communications, finance, or marketing. They must have a GPA of 2.0 or higher. Along with their application, they must submit a cover letter with a 500-word statement of career goals. Financial need is not considered in the selection process. U.S. citizenship or legal resident status is required.

Financial data The stipend is $2,500. Funds are paid directly to the recipient's college or university.

Duration 1 year.

Additional information COMTO was established in 1971 to promote, strengthen, and expand the roles of minorities in all aspects of transportation. This program is sponsored by Parsons Brinckerhoff, Inc. Recipients are expected to attend the COMTO National Scholarship Luncheon.

Number awarded 1 each year.

Deadline May of each year.

[451]
PDA FOUNDATION DIVERSITY SCHOLARSHIP

Pennsylvania Dietetic Association
Attn: Foundation
96 Northwoods Boulevard, Suite B2
Columbus, OH 43235
(614) 436-6136 Fax: (614) 436-6181
E-mail: padafoundation@eatrightpa.org
Web: www.eatrightpa.org/scholarshipapp.cfm

Summary To provide financial assistance to African American and other minority members of the Pennsylvania Dietetic Association (PDA) who are working on an associate or bachelor's degree in dietetics.

Eligibility This program is open to PDA members who are Black, Hispanic, Asian or Pacific Islander, or Native American (Alaskan Native, American Indian, or Hawaiian Native). Applicants must be 1) enrolled in the first year of study in an accredited dietetic technology program; or 2) enrolled in the third year of study in an accredited undergraduate or coordinated program in dietetics. They must have a GPA of 2.5 or higher. Along with their application, they must submit a letter indicating their intent and the reason they are applying for the scholarship, including a description of their personal financial situation. Selection is based on academic achievement (20%), commitment to the dietetic profession (30%), leadership ability (30%), and financial need (20%).

Financial data The stipend is $1,000.

Duration 1 year.

Additional information The Pennsylvania Dietetic Association is the Pennsylvania affiliate of the Academy of Nutrition and Dietetics.

Number awarded 1 or more each year.

Deadline March of each year.

[452]
PDEF MICKEY WILLIAMS MINORITY STUDENT SCHOLARSHIPS

Society of Nuclear Medicine and Molecular Imaging
Attn: Grants and Awards
1850 Samuel Morse Drive
Reston, VA 20190-5316
(703) 708-9000, ext. 1253 Fax: (703) 708-9015
E-mail: kpadleyh@snmmi.org
Web: www.snm.org/index.cfm?pageid=1083

Summary To provide financial support to African American and other minority students working on an associate or bachelor's degree in nuclear medicine technology.

Eligibility This program is open to students accepted or enrolled in a baccalaureate or associate degree program in nuclear medicine technology. Applicants must be members of a minority group: African American, Native American (including American Indian, Eskimo, Hawaiian, and Samoan), Hispanic American, Asian American, or Pacific Islander. They must have a cumulative GPA of 2.5 or higher and be able to demonstrate financial need. Along with their application, they must submit an essay on their reasons for entering the nuclear medicine technology field, their career goals, and their financial need. U.S. citizenship or permanent resident status is required.

Financial data The stipend is $2,500.

Duration 1 year; may be renewed for 1 additional year.

Additional information This program is supported by corporate sponsors of the Professional Development and Education Fund (PDEF) of the Society of Nuclear Medicine and Molecular Imaging Technologist Section (SNMMITS).

Number awarded Varies each year; recently, 2 of these scholarships were awarded.

Deadline April of each year.

[453]
PDK/DR. JO ANN OTA FUJIOKA SCHOLARSHIP

Phi Delta Kappa International
Attn: PDK Educational Foundation
320 West Eighth Street, Suite 216
P.O. Box 7888
Bloomington, IN 47407-7888
(812) 339-1156 Toll Free: (800) 766-1156
Fax: (812) 339-0018 E-mail: scholarships@pdkintl.org
Web: pdkintl.org

Summary To provide financial assistance to African American and other high school seniors of color who plan to study education at a college in any state and have a connection to Phi Delta Kappa (PDK).

Eligibility This program is open to high school seniors of color who are planning to major in education and can meet 1 of the following criteria: 1) is a member of a Future Educators Association (FEA) chapter; 2) is the child or grandchild of a PDK member; 3) has a reference letter written by a PDK member; or 4) is selected to represent the local PDK chapter. Applicants must submit a 500-word essay on a topic related to education that changes annually; recently, they were invited to explain what caused them to choose a career in education, what they hope to accomplish during their career as an educator, and how they will measure their success. Selection is based on the essay, academic standing, letters of recommendation, service activities, educational activities, and leadership activities; financial need is not considered.

Financial data The stipend depends on the availability of funds; recently, it was $2,000.

Duration 1 year.

Additional information This program began in 2006.

Number awarded 1 each year.

Deadline March of each year.

[454]
PFATS-NFL CHARITIES MINORITY SCHOLARSHIPS

Professional Football Athletic Trainers Society
c/o Britt Brown, ATC, Associate Athletic Trainer
Dallas Cowboys
One Cowboys Parkway
Irving, TX 75063
(972) 497-4992 E-mail: bbrown@dallascowboys.net
Web: www.pfats.com/about/scholarships

Summary To provide financial assistance to African American and other minority undergraduate and graduate students working on a degree in athletic training.

Eligibility This program is open to ethnic minority students who are working on an undergraduate or graduate degree in athletic training. Applicants must have a GPA of 2.5 or higher. Along with their application, they must submit a cover letter, a curriculum vitae, and a letter of recommendation from their supervising athletic trainer.

Financial data A stipend is awarded (amount not specified).

Duration 1 year.

Additional information Recipients also have an opportunity to work at summer training camp of a National Football League (NFL) team. Support for this program, which began in 1993, is provided by NFL Charities.

Number awarded 1 or more each year.

Deadline March of each year.

[455]
PHIL B. CURLS, SR. SCHOLARSHIP

Missouri Legislative Black Caucus Foundation
c/o Senator Shalonn "Kiki" Curls
4609 Paseo Boulevard, Suite 102
Kansas City, MO 64110
Toll Free: (877) 63-MLBCF E-mail: mlbcf@aol.com
Web: www.mlbcf.com

Summary To provide financial assistance to African Americans and other residents of Missouri who come from a disadvantaged background and are interested in working on an undergraduate or graduate degree in a health-related field at a school in any state.

Eligibility This program is open to undergraduate and graduate students from Missouri who are preparing for a career as a physician, nurse, dentist, health researcher, hospital administrator, or other health-related professional. Applicants must come from a disadvantaged background and have a GPA of 2.0 or higher. They may be attending a college or university in any state. Along with their application, they must submit a 250-word personal statement on how their education will assist them in achieving their goals. Selection is based on academic excellence, community service, leadership skills, and financial need.

Financial data A stipend is awarded (amount not specified).

Duration 1 year; recipients may reapply for up to 6 years of support.

Additional information This foundation was established in 1989 to provide scholarships and other assistance to disadvantaged youths in Missouri. Its motto is, "Building a Brighter Future for African American families."

Number awarded 1 or more each year.

Deadline May of each year.

[456]
PHILLIP D. REED UNDERGRADUATE ENDOWMENT FELLOWSHIP

National Action Council for Minorities in Engineering
Attn: University Programs
440 Hamilton Avenue, Suite 302
White Plains, NY 10601-1813
(914) 539-4010 Fax: (914) 539-4032
E-mail: scholarships@nacme.org
Web: www.nacme.org/NACME_D.aspx?pageid=105

Summary To provide financial assistance to African American and other underrepresented minority college sophomores majoring in engineering or related fields.

Eligibility This program is open to African American, Latino, and American Indian college sophomores who have a GPA of 3.0 or higher and have demonstrated academic excellence, leadership skills, and a commitment to science and engineering as a career. Applicants must be enrolled full time at an ABET-accredited engineering program. Fields of study include all areas of engineering as well as computer science, materials science, mathematics, operations research, or physics.

Financial data The stipend is $5,000 per year. Funds are sent directly to the recipient's university.

Duration Up to 3 years.

Number awarded 1 each year.

Deadline April of each year.

[457]
PHYLLIS G. MEEKINS SCHOLARSHIP

Ladies Professional Golf Association
Attn: LPGA Foundation
100 International Golf Drive
Daytona Beach, FL 32124-1082
(386) 274-6200 Fax: (386) 274-1099
E-mail: foundation.scholarships@lpga.com
Web: www.lpgafoundation.org/scholarships?

Summary To provide financial assistance to African American and other minority female graduating high school seniors who played golf in high school and plan to continue to play in college.

Eligibility This program is open to female high school seniors who are members of a recognized minority group. Applicants must have a GPA of 3.0 or higher and a background in golf. They must be planning to enroll full time at a college or university in the United States and play competitive golf. Along with their application, they must submit a letter that describes how golf has been an integral part of their lives and includes their personal, academic, and professional goals; their chosen discipline of study; and how this scholarship will be of assistance. Financial need is considered in the selection process. U.S. citizenship or legal resident status is required.

Financial data The stipend is $1,250.

Duration 1 year.

Additional information This program began in 2006.

Number awarded 1 each year.

Deadline May of each year.

[458]
PHYSICAL AND LIFE SCIENCES DIRECTORATE INTERNSHIPS

Lawrence Livermore National Laboratory
Physical and Life Sciences Directorate
Attn: Education Coordinator
7000 East Avenue, L-418
Livermore, CA 94550
(925) 422-0455 E-mail: hutcheon3@llnl.gov
Web: www-pls.llnl.gov

Summary To provide an opportunity for undergraduate and graduate students (particularly African Americans, other minorities, and women) to work on summer research projects within the Physical and Life Sciences Directorate (PLS) of Lawrence Livermore National Laboratory (LLNL).

Eligibility This program is open to full-time undergraduate and graduate students who are interested in working on research projects within the PLS Directorate of LLNL. Openings are currently available in chemistry (organic, inorganic, synthetic, analytical, computational, nuclear, and environmental) and materials science (theory, simulation and modeling, synthesis and processing, materials under extreme conditions, dynamic materials science, metallurgy, nuclear fuels, optical materials, and surface science). Applicants must have a GPA of 3.0 or higher. Selection is based on academic record, aptitude, research interests, and recommendations of instructors. Women and minorities are encouraged to apply.

Financial data The stipend is $14 to $20 per hour for undergraduates or $4,100 to $4,900 per month for graduate students. Living accommodations and arrangements are the responsibility of the intern.

Duration 2 or 3 months, during the summer.

Number awarded Varies each year.

Deadline February of each year.

[459]
P.O. PISTILLI SCHOLARSHIPS

Design Automation Conference
c/o Andrew B. Kahng, Scholarship Director
University of California at San Diego-Jacobs School of Engineering
Jacobs Hall, EBU3B, Rpp, 2134
9500 Gilman Drive
La Jolla, CA 92093-0404
(858) 822-4884 Fax: (858) 534-7029
E-mail: abk@cs.ucsd.edu
Web: www.dac.com

Summary To provide financial assistance to African Americans, other minorities, females, and individuals with disabilities who are high school seniors and interested in preparing for a career in computer science or electrical engineering.

Eligibility This program is open to graduating high school seniors who are members of underrepresented groups: women, African Americans, Hispanics, Native Americans, and persons with disabilities. Applicants must be interested in preparing for a career in electrical engineering, computer engineering, or computer science. They must have at least a 3.0 GPA, have demonstrated high achievements in math and science courses, have demonstrated involvement in activities associated with the underrepresented group they represent, and be able to demonstrate significant financial need. U.S. citizenship is not required, but applicants must be U.S. residents when they apply and must plan to attend an accredited U.S. college or university. Along with their application, they must submit 3 letters of recommendation, official transcripts, ACT/SAT and/or PSAT scores, a personal statement outlining future goals and why they think they should receive this scholarship, and documentation of financial need.

Financial data Stipends are $4,000 per year. Awards are paid each year in 2 equal installments.

Duration 1 year; may be renewed up to 4 additional years.

Additional information This program is funded by the Design Automation Conference of the Association for Computing Machinery's Special Interest Group on Design Automation.

Number awarded 2 to 7 each year.

Deadline January of each year.

[460]
PRAXAIR SCHOLARSHIPS

Society of Women Engineers
Attn: Scholarship Selection Committee
203 North LaSalle Street, Suite 1675
Chicago, IL 60601-1269
(312) 596-5223 Toll Free: (877) SWE-INFO
Fax: (312) 644-8557 E-mail: scholarships@swe.org
Web: societyofwomenengineers.swe.org

Summary To provide financial assistance to undergraduate women (particularly African Americans and other underrepresented minorities) who are majoring in chemical or mechanical engineering.

Eligibility This program is open to society members who are entering their sophomore, junior, or senior year at an ABET-accredited 4-year college or university. Applicants must be working full time on a degree in computer science or chemical or mechanical engineering and have a GPA of 3.2 or higher. Selection is based on merit. Preference is given to groups underrepresented in computer science and engineering.

Financial data The stipend is $1,000.

Duration 1 year.

Additional information This program began in 2011 by Praxair, Inc.

Number awarded 10 each year.

Deadline February of each year.

[461]
PREACHER'S KID SCHOLARSHIP

African Methodist Episcopal Church
Connectional Ministers' Spouses, Widows and Widowers Organization
c/o Jennifer Green, Scholarship Committee Chair
2386 S.W. 102nd Avenue
Miramar, FL 33025-6509
E-mail: ConnMSWAWOPk@aol.com
Web: www.amemswwpk.org/pr01.htm

Summary To provide financial assistance for college to children of ministers in the African Methodist Episcopal (AME) Church.

Eligibility This program is open to dependent children under 21 years of age who are entering college freshmen and whose parent or legal guardian is an AME minister. Applicants must be a member of the AME Church, have a score on the SAT of 850 or higher or on the ACT of 20 or higher, rank in the top 50% of their high school class, and have a cumulative GPA of 2.5 or higher. Along with their application, they must submit an essay of 300 to 350 words on how the AME Church has made a difference in their life and what they will do to support their church. Their minister parent must have been a member of the Connectional AME Ministers' Spouses, Widows and Widowers Organization for at least 1 year.

Financial data The scholarship stipend is $2,500. Book awards are $500.

Duration 1 year.

Number awarded Varies each year; recently, the program awarded 1 scholarship and 4 book awards.

Deadline April of each year.

[462]
PRE-MED ENRICHMENT PROGRAM FOR UNDERREPRESENTED MINORITY UNDERGRADUATES

University of Pennsylvania
Perelman School of Medicine
Attn: Center of Excellence for Diversity in Health Education and Research
3508 Market Street, Suite 234
Philadelphia, PA 19104-3357
(215) 898-3980 Fax: (215) 573-2793
E-mail: tyeshiak@mail.med.upenn.edu
Web: www.uphs.upenn.edu/coeomh/premed.htm

Summary To provide an opportunity for African American and other underrepresented minority undergraduates to gain research experience in medicine during a summer program at the University of Pennsylvania.

Eligibility This program is open to undergraduate students who are members of ethnic or racial groups underrepresented in medicine. Applicants must have completed at least 60 credits of a pre-medical program and have a GPA of 2.75 or higher. They must be interested in participating in a program at the University of Pennsylvania that includes research, clinical observations, classroom exercises, and teaching observation designed to stimulate and cultivate their interest in academic medicine. U.S. citizenship or permanent resident status is required.

Financial data The program provides a stipend (amount not specified), housing, and 2 meals per day.

Duration 10 weeks during the summer.

Additional information This program, which began in 1993, is sponsored by the Bureau of Health Professions of the U.S. Health Resources and Services Administration.

Number awarded 10 to 12 each year.

Deadline January of each year.

[463]
PRESIDENTIAL CHOICE SCHOLARSHIP AWARD

PUSH Excel
Attn: General Offices
930 East 50th Street
Chicago, IL 60615
(773) 373-3366 E-mail: pushexcel@rainbowpush.org
Web: www.pushexcel.org/pages/scholarships

Summary To provide financial assistance for college to high school seniors who have demonstrated a commitment to social justice and are willing to help promote the scholarship program of PUSH-Excel.

Eligibility This program is open to seniors graduating from high school and planning to enroll at an accredited 4-year college or university. Applicants must be U.S. citizens and have a GPA of 3.0 or higher. They must have demonstrated 1) a commitment to addressing and advocating for social justice issues; and 2) an understanding and practice of the gift of service. Along with their application, they must submit a 500-word essay that identifies 5 prerequisites for success, explains their personal philosophy for the pursuit of excellence, and explains how they will use their college education to achieve this pursuit of excellence. They must also agree to cooperate with the scholarship committee of PUSH-Excel by promoting its program, participating in its public relations activities, and attending its Annual National Conference luncheon and Education Leadership Conference. Selection is based on the essay, academic preparation to attend college and succeed, ability to overcome obstacles to achieve academic and personal goals, character, persistence and dedication to service, and financial need.

Financial data The stipend is $1,000 per year.

Duration 1 year; may be renewed up to 3 additional years if the recipient maintains a GPA of 3.0 or higher and fulfills the obligations to PUSH-Excel.

Additional information PUSH-Excel was founded in 1975 by the Rev. Jesse Jackson.

Number awarded Varies each year.

Deadline June of each year.

[464]
PRINCETON SUMMER UNDERGRADUATE RESEARCH EXPERIENCE

Princeton University
Attn: Graduate School
Office of Academic Affairs and Diversity
Clio Hall
Princeton, NJ 08544-0255
(609) 258-2066 E-mail: diverse@princeton.edu
Web: www.princeton.edu

Summary To provide an opportunity for African American and other minority or disadvantaged students to assist Princeton faculty in any area during the summer.

Eligibility This program is open to full-time sophomores and juniors at all colleges and universities in the United States who are majoring in any academic discipline and have a GPA of 3.5 or higher in their major. Current college freshmen and graduating seniors are not eligible. Applicants must be interested in working during the summer with a Princeton faculty member. They should have a goal of continuing on for a Ph.D. and preparing for a career in college or university teaching and research. Students in the sciences and engineering normally work in a laboratory group on an aspect of the faculty member's current research. Students in the humanities and social sciences might assist a faculty member engaged in a particular research, editing, bibliographical, or course-preparation project; alternatively, they may work on a research paper under faculty supervision. Members of racial and ethnic minority groups underrepresented in doctoral research programs, students from socioeconomically disadvantaged backgrounds, and students at small liberal arts colleges are especially encouraged to apply.

Financial data Participants receive a stipend of $3,750, housing in a campus dormitory, a $150 meal card, and up to $500 in reimbursement of travel costs.

Duration 8 weeks during the summer.

Number awarded Up to 20 each year.

Deadline January of each year.

[465]
PROFESSIONAL GOLF MANAGEMENT DIVERSITY SCHOLARSHIP

Professional Golfers' Association of America
Attn: PGA Foundation
100 Avenue of the Champions
Palm Beach Gardens, FL 33418
Toll Free: (888) 532-6661
Web: www.pgafoundation.com

Summary To provide financial assistance to African Americans, other minorities, and women who are interested in attending a designated college or university to prepare for a career as a golf professional.

Eligibility This program is open to women and minorities interested in becoming a licensed PGA Professional. Applicants must be interested in attending 1 of 20 colleges and universities that offer the Professional Golf Management (PGM) curriculum sanctioned by the PGA.

Financial data The stipend is $3,000 per year.

Duration 1 year; may be renewed.

Additional information This program began in 1993. Programs are offered at 20 designated universities; for a list, contact the PGA.

Number awarded Varies each year; recently, 20 of these scholarships were awarded.

Deadline Deadline not specified.

[466]
PROMISING SCHOLARS FUND EDWARD A. BOUCHET SCHOLARSHIPS

Community Foundation for Greater New Haven
Attn: Scholarships
70 Audubon Street
New Haven, CT 06510-9755
(203) 777-7076 Fax: (203) 777-6584
E-mail: dcanning@cfgnh.org
Web: www.cfgnh.org

Summary To provide financial assistance to African American high school seniors and graduates in Connecticut who plan to attend college in any state.

Eligibility This program is open to African American high school seniors and recent graduates in Connecticut who are planning to enter an accredited 2- or 4-year college or university in any state as a full-time undergraduate. Applicants must be U.S. citizens and have a GPA of 2.5 or higher. Selection is based on academic record, demonstrated leadership, and participation in school and community activities. Some consideration is given to honors, work experience, a statement of goals and aspirations, and unusual personal or family circumstances. Preference is given to males and to residents of New Haven County.

Financial data Stipends range from $1,000 to $4,000 per year.

Duration 1 year; recipients may reapply.

Additional information This program, established in 2007, is funded by the Beta Tau Boulé (the New Haven chapter) of Sigma Pi Phi and administered by the Scholarship Management Services division of Scholarship America, One Scholarship Way, P.O. Box 297, St. Peter, MN 56082, (507) 931-1682, (800) 537-4180, Fax: (507) 931-9168.

Number awarded Up to 20 each year.

Deadline March of each year.

[467]
PROVIDENCE ALUMNAE CHAPTER SCHOLASTIC ACHIEVEMENT AWARD

Delta Sigma Theta Sorority, Inc.-Providence Alumnae Chapter
Attn: Scholarship Committee
P.O. Box 40175
Providence, RI 02940-0175
(401) 351-1332 E-mail: mestel@verizon.net
Web: www.dstprovidencealumnae.org

Summary To provide financial assistance to female African American residents of Rhode Island who are attending college in any state.

Eligibility This program is open to African American women who are residents of Rhode Island. Applicants must be attending a 4-year college or university in any state and have a GPA of 3.0 or higher. Along with their application, they must submit a current official transcript, a letter of recommendation, and an essay describing their career goals, community service activities, educational accomplishments, and personal interests and talents.

Financial data The stipend is $1,000.

Duration 1 year.

Number awarded 1 or more each year.

Deadline March of each year.

[468]
PROVIDENCE ALUMNAE MEMORIAL AWARD

Delta Sigma Theta Sorority, Inc.-Providence Alumnae Chapter
Attn: Scholarship Committee
P.O. Box 40175
Providence, RI 02940-0175
(401) 351-1332 E-mail: mestel@verizon.net
Web: www.dstprovidencealumnae.org

Summary To provide financial assistance to African American female high school seniors from Rhode Island who are planning to attend college in any state.

Eligibility This program is open to African American women who are seniors graduating from high schools in Rhode Island. Applicants must be planning to enroll at a college in any state. Along with their application, they must submit a current official transcript, a letter of recommendation, and an essay describing their career goals, community service activities, educational accomplishments, and personal interests and talents.

Financial data The stipend is $1,250.

Duration 1 year.

Number awarded 1 or more each year.

Deadline March of each year.

[469]
PRSSA DIVERSITY MULTICULTURAL SCHOLARSHIPS

Public Relations Student Society of America
Attn: Vice President of Member Services
33 Maiden Lane, 11th Floor
New York, NY 10038-5150
(212) 460-1474 Fax: (212) 995-0757
E-mail: prssa@prsa.org
Web: www.prssa.org/scholarships_competitions/individual

Summary To provide financial assistance to African American and other minority college students who are interested in preparing for a career in public relations.

Eligibility This program is open to minority (African American/Black, Hispanic/Latino, Asian, Native American, Alaskan Native, or Pacific Islander) students who are at least juniors at an accredited 4-year college or university. Applicants must be enrolled full time, be able to demonstrate financial need, and have a GPA of 3.0 or higher. Membership in the Public Relations Student Society of America is preferred but not required. A major or minor in public relations is preferred; students who attend a school that does not offer a public relations degree or program must be enrolled in a communications degree program (e.g., journalism, mass communications).

Financial data The stipend is $1,500.

Duration 1 year.

Additional information This program began in 1989.

Number awarded 2 each year.

Deadline May of each year.

[470]
PUGET SOUND CHAPTER/HORACE AND SUSIE REVELS CAYTON SCHOLARSHIP

Public Relations Society of America-Puget Sound Chapter
c/o Amy Turner
EnviroIssues
101 Stewart Street, Suite 1200
Seattle, WA 98101
(206) 269-5041 Fax: (206) 269-5046
E-mail: prsascholarship@asi-seattle.net
Web: www.prsapugetsound.org/Page.aspx?cid=127

Summary To provide financial assistance to African American and other minority upperclassmen from Washington who are interested in preparing for a career in public relations.

Eligibility This program is open to U.S. citizens who are members of minority groups, defined as African Americans, Asian Americans, Hispanic/Latino Americans, Native Americans, and Pacific Islanders. Applicants must be full-time juniors or seniors attending a college in Washington or Washington students (who graduated from a Washington high school or whose parents live in the state year-round) attending college elsewhere. They must be able to demonstrate aptitude in public relations and related courses, activities, and/or internships.

Financial data The stipend is $2,500.

Duration 1 year.

Additional information This program began in 1992.

Number awarded 1 each year.

Deadline April of each year.

[471]
PUGET SOUND CHAPTER SHARON D. BANKS MEMORIAL UNDERGRADUATE SCHOLARSHIP

Women's Transportation Seminar-Puget Sound Chapter
c/o Jennifer Barnes, Scholarship Co-Chair
Heffron Transportation, Inc.
532 27th Avenue
Seattle, WA 98122
(206) 324-3623 Fax: (877) 314-9959
E-mail: jennifer@hefftrans.com
Web: www.wtsinternational.org

Summary To provide financial assistance to women (especially African American and other minority women) who are undergraduate students from Washington working on a degree related to transportation.

Eligibility This program is open to women who are residents of Washington, studying at a college in the state, or working as an intern in the state. Applicants must be currently enrolled in an undergraduate degree program in a transportation-related field, such as engineering, planning, finance, or logistics. They must have a GPA of 3.0 or higher and plans to prepare for a career in a transportation-related field. Minority women are especially encouraged to apply. Along with their application, they must submit a 500-word statement about their career goals after graduation and why they think they should receive this scholarship award. Selection is based on that statement, academic record, and transportation-related activities or job skills. Financial need is not considered.

Financial data The stipend is $4,000.

Duration 1 year.

Additional information The winner is also nominated for scholarships offered by the national organization of the Women's Transportation Seminar.

Number awarded 1 each year.

Deadline November of each year.

[472]
RA CONSULTING SERVICES/MARIA RILEY SCHOLARSHIP

National Forum for Black Public Administrators
Attn: Scholarship Program
777 North Capitol Street, N.E., Suite 807
Washington, DC 20002
(202) 408-9300 Fax: (202) 408-8558
E-mail: vharris@nfbpa.org
Web: www.nfbpa.org/i4a/pages/index.cfm?pageid=4047

Summary To provide financial assistance to African Americans working on an undergraduate or graduate degree in engineering or information technology.

Eligibility This program is open to African American undergraduate and graduate students preparing for a career as a public administrator serving the engineering and information technology fields. Applicants must be working full time on a degree in engineering or information technology. They must have a GPA of 3.0 or higher, excellent interpersonal and analytical abilities, and strong oral and written communication skills. Along with their application, they must submit a 3-page autobiographical essay that includes their academic and career goals and objectives. Selection is based on academic record, leadership ability, participation in school activities, community service, and financial need.

Financial data The stipend is $2,500.

Duration 1 year.

Additional information This program is sponsored by RA Consulting Services. Recipients are required to attend the sponsor's annual conference to receive their scholarship; limited hotel and air accommodations are arranged and provided.

Number awarded 1 each year.

Deadline February of each year.

[473]
RDW GROUP, INC. MINORITY SCHOLARSHIP FOR COMMUNICATIONS

Rhode Island Foundation
Attn: Funds Administrator
One Union Station
Providence, RI 02903
(401) 427-4017 Fax: (401) 331-8085
E-mail: lmonahan@rifoundation.org
Web: www.rifoundation.org

Summary To provide financial assistance to African Americans and other residents of color from Rhode Island who are working on a undergraduate or graduate degree in communications in any state.

Eligibility This program is open to undergraduate and graduate students at colleges and universities in any state who are Rhode Island residents of color. Applicants must intend to work on a degree in communications (including computer graphics, art, cinematography, or other fields that would prepare them for a career in advertising). They must be able to demonstrate financial need and a commitment to a career in communications. Along with their application, they must submit an essay (up to 300 words) on the impact they would like to have on the communications field.

Financial data The stipend is approximately $2,000 per year.

Duration 1 year; recipients may reapply.

Additional information This program is sponsored by the RDW Group, Inc.

Number awarded 1 each year.

Deadline April of each year.

[474]
REAR ADMIRAL BENJAMIN T. HACKER, USN MEMORIAL SCHOLARSHIP

National Naval Officers Association-Washington, D.C. Chapter
c/o LCDR Stephen Williams
P.O. Box 30784
Alexandria, VA 22310
(703) 566-3840 Fax: (703) 566-3813
E-mail: Stephen.Williams@navy.mil
Web: dcnnoa.memberlodge.com

Summary To provide financial assistance to African American and other minority high school seniors from the Washington, D.C. area who are interested in attending an Historically Black College or University (HBCU) in any state and enrolling in the Navy Reserve Officers Training Corps (NROTC) program.

Eligibility This program is open to minority seniors graduating from high schools in the Washington, D.C. metropolitan area who plan to enroll full time at an HBCU in any state that has an NROTC program; they may enroll at another college or university that shares the NROTC unit located at an HBCU. Applicants must have a GPA of 2.5 or higher and be U.S. citizens or permanent residents. Selection is based on academic achievement, community involvement, and financial need.

Financial data The stipend is $1,000.

Duration 1 year; nonrenewable.

Additional information If the recipient fails to enroll in the NROTC unit, all scholarship funds must be returned.

Number awarded 1 each year.

Deadline March of each year.

[475]
REJESTA V. PERRY SCHOLARSHIP

Sigma Gamma Rho Sorority, Inc.
Attn: National Education Fund
1000 Southhill Drive, Suite 200
Cary, NC 27513
(919) 678-9720 Toll Free: (888) SGR-1922
Fax: (919) 678-9721 E-mail: info@sgrho1922.org
Web: www.sgrho1922.org/nef

Summary To provide financial assistance to African American and other undergraduate students working on a degree in education.

Eligibility This program is open to undergraduates working on a degree in education. The sponsor is a traditionally African American sorority. Applicants must have a GPA of "C" or higher and be able to demonstrate financial need.

Financial data A stipend is awarded (amount not specified).

Duration 1 year.

Additional information A processing fee of $20 is required.

Number awarded 1 each year.

Deadline April of each year.

[476]
RESEARCH AND ENGINEERING APPRENTICESHIP PROGRAM (REAP) FOR HIGH SCHOOL STUDENTS

Academy of Applied Science
Attn: REAP
1 Maple Street
Concord, NH 03301
(603) 228-4520 Fax: (603) 228-0210
E-mail: renie@aas-world.org
Web: www.aas-world.org/interest-pages/for-students.html

Summary To provide an opportunity for African American and other high school students from groups historically underrepresented in science, technology, engineering, and science (STEM) who want to participate in a summer research apprenticeship.

Eligibility This program is open to high school students from groups historically underrepresented or underserved in STEM; that includes 1) Blacks/African Americans; 2) Hispanics; 3) Native Americans/Alaskan Natives; 4) low-income according to federal TRIO criteria; and 5) women in physical science, computer science, mathematics, or engineering. Applicants must be interested in working as an apprentice on a research project in the laboratory of a mentor scientist at a college or university near their home. Selection is based on demonstrated interests in STEM research and demonstrated potential for a successful career in STEM. They must be at least 16 years of age.

Financial data The stipend is $1,300.

Duration Summer months.

Additional information The program provides intensive summer training for high school students in the laboratories of scientists. The program, established in 1980, is funded by a grant from the U.S. Army Research Office. Students must live at home while they participate in the program and must live in the area of an approved college or university. The program does not exist in every state.

Number awarded Varies; recently, approximately 120 students were funded at 44 universities nationwide.

Deadline February of each year.

[477]
RESEARCH EXPERIENCES FOR UNDERGRADUATES PROGRAM IN SOLAR AND SPACE PHYSICS

University of Colorado
Attn: Laboratory for Atmospheric and Space Physics
1234 Innovation Drive
Boulder, CO 80303-7814
(303) 735-2143 E-mail: martin.snow@lasp.colorado.edu
Web: lasp.colorado.edu/home/education/reu

Summary To provide an opportunity for upper-division students (particularly African Americans, other minorities, women, and students with disabilities) to work on research projects related to solar and space physics at laboratories in Boulder, Colorado during the summer.

Eligibility This program is open to students currently enrolled as sophomores and juniors at colleges and universities in any state. Applicants must be interested in participating on a research project related to solar and space physics at a participating laboratory in Boulder, Colorado. They must be U.S. citizens, nationals, or permanent residents. Applications are especially encouraged from underrepresented minorities, persons with disabilities, and women.

Financial data The stipend is $500 per week. Students also receive dormitory housing, a food allowance, and a travel stipend of $500.

Duration 8 weeks, starting in June.

Additional information The participating laboratories are the Laboratory for Atmospheric and Space Physics (LASP) of the University of Colorado, the High Altitude Observatory (HAO) of the National Center for Atmospheric Research (NCAR), the Space Weather Prediction Center (SWPC) of the National Oceanic and Atmospheric Administration (NOAA), the Planetary Science Directorate of the Southwest Research Institute (SwRI), and NorthWest Research Associates (NWRA). This program is funded by the National Science Foundation as part of its Research Experiences for Undergraduates (REU) Program.

Number awarded Varies each year; recently, 16 of these internships were awarded.

Deadline January of each year.

[478]
RESEARCH IN SCIENCE AND ENGINEERING PROGRAM

Rutgers University
Attn: Graduate School
25 Bishop Place
New Brunswick, NJ 08901-1181
(848) 932-6584 Fax: (732) 932-7407
E-mail: rise@rci.rutgers.edu
Web: rise.rutgers.edu/index.php

Summary To provide an opportunity for undergraduate students from any state (particularly African Americans and members of other underrepresented or disadvantaged groups) to work on a summer research project in science, mathematics, or engineering at Rutgers University in New Jersey.

Eligibility This program is open to undergraduates majoring in science (especially the biomedical sciences), mathematics, or engineering at a college or university in any state. Applicants must be interested in participating in a summer research project under the guidance of a faculty member at the graduate school of Rutgers University in New Brunswick. They should have completed at least the sophomore year and have a GPA of 3.0 or higher. Applications are especially encouraged from members of groups underrepresented in the sciences, mathematics, or engineering; students from economically or educationally disadvantaged backgrounds; members of the first generation in their family to attend college; undergraduates attending schools that do not offer opportunities for independent research or mentoring by research-active faculty; nontraditional students; and individuals who have faced life challenges. U.S. citizenship or permanent residents status is required.

Financial data The program provides a stipend of $4,000, free housing, and up to $500 of reimbursement for travel expenses.

Duration 8 or 10 weeks during the summer.

Additional information This program is administered by the Rutgers University Graduate School. Support is provided by many sponsors, including the National Science Foundation, the Federation of American Societies for Experimental Biology, Merck Research Laboratories, Public Service Electric and Gas, the New Jersey Space Grant Consortium, the New Jersey Commission on Cancer Research, and the McNair Scholars Program.

Number awarded 20 to 25 each year.

Deadline Applications are accepted on a rolling basis; selection begins in January and continues until all places are filled.

[479]
RHO MU OMEGA CHAPTER GENERAL SCHOLARSHIPS

Alpha Kappa Alpha Sorority, Inc.-Rho Mu Omega Chapter
Attn: DC Pearls III Foundation
Program Chair
P.O. Box 91436
Washington, DC 20090-1436
E-mail: programs@rhomuomega.org
Web: www.whomuomega.org/scholarship

Summary To provide financial assistance to high school seniors in Washington, D.C. who plan to attend an Historically Black College or University (HBCU) and major in any field.

Eligibility This program is open to seniors graduating from high schools in Washington, D.C. and planning to attend an HBCU. Applicants may be majoring in any field.

Financial data The stipend is $1,000.

Duration 1 year.

Number awarded 5 each year.

Deadline March of each year.

[480]
RICHARD B. FISHER SCHOLARSHIP

Morgan Stanley
Attn: Diversity Recruiting
1585 Broadway
New York, NY 10036
(212) 762-0211 Toll Free: (888) 454-3965
Fax: (212) 507-4972
E-mail: richardbfisherprogram@morganstanley.com
Web: www.morganstanley.com

Summary To provide financial aid and work experience to African Americans and members of other underrepresented groups who are preparing for a career in technology within the financial services industry.

Eligibility This program is open to African American, Hispanic, Native American and lesbian/gay/bisexual/transgender students who are enrolled in their sophomore or junior year of college (or the third or fourth year of a 5-year program). Applicants must be enrolled full time and have a GPA of 3.4 or higher. They must be willing to commit to a paid summer internship in the Morgan Stanley Information Technology Division. All majors and disciplines are eligible, but preference is given to students preparing for a career in technology within the financial services industry. Along with their application, they must submit 1-page essays on 1) why they are applying for this scholarship and why they should be selected as a recipient; 2) a technical project on which they worked, either through a university course or previous work experience, their role in the project, and how they contributed to the end result; and 3) a software, hardware, or new innovative application of existing technology that they would create if they could and the impact it would have. Financial need is not considered in the selection process.

Financial data The stipend is $7,500 per year.

Duration 1 year (the junior year); may be renewed for the senior year.

Additional information The program, established in 1993, includes a paid summer internship in the Morgan Stanley Information Technology Division in the summer following the time of application. Since its establishment, nearly 400 students have received assistance through the program.

Number awarded 1 or more each year.

Deadline December of each year.

[481]
RICHARD HECKERT FELLOWSHIP

National Action Council for Minorities in Engineering
Attn: University Programs
440 Hamilton Avenue, Suite 302
White Plains, NY 10601-1813
(914) 539-4010 Fax: (914) 539-4032
E-mail: scholarships@nacme.org
Web: www.nacme.org/NACME_D.aspx?pageid=105

Summary To provide financial assistance to African Americans and other underrepresented minority high school seniors interested in studying engineering or related fields in college.

Eligibility This program is open to African American, Latino, and American Indian high school seniors who are in the top 10% of their graduating class, have a GPA of 3.0 or higher, and have demonstrated academic excellence, leadership skills, and a commitment to science and engineering as a career. Candidates must have been accepted as a full-time student at an ABET-accredited engineering program. They must be nominated by their school (each high school may nominate only 1 student). Fields of study include all areas of engineering as well as computer science, materials science, mathematics, operations research, or physics. Letters of nomination must be accompanied by a transcript, SAT or ACT report form, resume, and 100-word statement of why the student should receive this scholarship.

Financial data The stipend is $5,000 per year. Funds are sent directly to the recipient's university.

Duration 4 years.

Number awarded 1 each year.

Deadline April of each year.

[482]
RICHARD S. SMITH SCHOLARSHIP

United Methodist Church
Attn: General Board of Discipleship
Young People's Ministries
P.O. Box 340003
Nashville, TN 37203-0003
(615) 340-7184 Toll Free: (877) 899-2780, ext. 7184
Fax: (615) 340-7063 E-mail: ypm@gbod.org
Web: globalyoungpeople.org

Summary To provide financial assistance to African American and other minority high school seniors who wish to prepare for a Methodist church-related career.

Eligibility This program is open to graduating high school seniors who are members of racial/ethnic minority groups and have been active members of a United Methodist Church for at least 1 year. Applicants must have been admitted to an accredited college or university to prepare for a church-related career. They must have maintained at least a "C" average throughout high school and be able to demonstrate financial need. Along with their application, they must submit brief essays on their participation in church projects and activities, a leadership experience, the role their faith plays in their life, the church-related vocation to which God is calling them, and their extracurricular interests and activities. U.S. citizenship or permanent resident status is required.

Financial data The stipend is $1,000.

Duration 1 year; nonrenewable.

Additional information This program began in 1997. Recipients must enroll full time in their first year of undergraduate study.

Number awarded 2 each year.

Deadline May of each year.

[483]
ROBERT A. ELLIS SCHOLARSHIP IN PHYSICS

National Society of Black Physicists
Attn: Scholarship Committee Chair
1100 North Glebe Road, Suite 1010
Arlington, VA 22201
(703) 536-4207 Fax: (703) 536-4203
E-mail: scholarship@nsbp.org
Web: www.nsbp.org/scholarships

Summary To provide financial assistance to African American students majoring in physics in college.

Eligibility This program is open to African American students who are entering their junior or senior year of college and majoring in physics. Applicants must submit an essay on their academic and career objectives, information on their participation in extracurricular activities, a description of any awards and honors they have received, and 3 letters of recommendation. Financial need is not considered.

Financial data A stipend is awarded (amount not specified).

Duration 1 year; nonrenewable.

Number awarded 1 each year.

Deadline November of each year.

[484]
ROBERT D. LYNCH LEADERSHIP SCHOLARSHIP

Pennsylvania Black Conference on Higher Education
c/o Judith A.W. Thomas, Scholarship Committee Chair
Lincoln University, School of Social Sciences and Behavioral Studies
1570 Old Baltimore Pike
P.O. Box 179
Lincoln University, PA 19352
(484) 365-8159 E-mail: scholarships@pbcohe.org
Web: www.phcohe.org

Summary To provide financial assistance to African American residents of any state who are enrolled as undergraduates at colleges in Pennsylvania and have demonstrated outstanding leadership skills.

Eligibility This program is open to African Americans from any state who have completed at least the first semester as an undergraduate at a college or university in Pennsylvania. Applicants must have a GPA of 3.0 or higher. Along with their application, they must submit an essay, up to 5 pages in length, on why they should receive this scholarship. Selection is based on leadership skills and academic record.

Financial data The stipend is $1,000.

Duration 1 year.

Number awarded 1 each year.

Deadline December of each year.

[485]
ROBERT P. MADISON SCHOLARSHIP IN ARCHITECTURE

Cleveland Foundation
Attn: Scholarship Processing
1422 Euclid Avenue, Suite 1300
Cleveland, OH 44115-2001
(216) 861-3810 Fax: (216) 861-1729
E-mail: Hello@clevefdn.org
Web: www.clevelandfoundation.org

Summary To provide financial assistance to African American high school seniors and undergraduates from any state who are interested in studying architecture.

Eligibility This program is open to African American high school seniors and current undergraduates from any state. Applicants must be accepted or enrolled at an accredited college or university that has a degree-granting program in architecture. They must have a GPA of 3.0 or higher and be able to demonstrate financial need. Along with their application, they must submit a brief essay on why they want to be an architect. Selection is based on evidence of commitment to a career as an architect, academic performance, and special skill or talent related to excelling in architectural course work.

Financial data The stipend is $1,000. Funds are paid directly to the recipient's institution to be used for tuition, fees, books, supplies, and/or equipment required for courses.

Duration 1 year; nonrenewable.

Additional information This program began in 2004 by the firm of Robert P. Madison International to honor its founder, the first African American registered to practice architecture in Ohio.

Number awarded Varies each year.

Deadline April of each year.

[486]
ROCHON/DAVIS SCHOLARSHIP

National Naval Officers Association-Washington, D.C. Chapter
c/o LCDR Stephen Williams
P.O. Box 30784
Alexandria, VA 22310
(703) 566-3840 Fax: (703) 566-3813
E-mail: Stephen.Williams@navy.mil
Web: dcnnoa.memberlodge.com

Summary To provide financial assistance to African American high school seniors from the Washington, D.C. area who are interested in attending an Historically Black College or University (HBCU) in any state.

Eligibility This program is open to African American seniors graduating from high schools in the Washington, D.C. metropolitan area who plan to enroll full time at an HBCU in any state. Applicants must have a GPA of 3.0 or higher and be U.S. citizens or permanent residents. Selection is based on academic achievement, community involvement, and financial need.

Financial data The stipend is $1,000.

Duration 1 year; nonrenewable.

Additional information Recipients are not required to join or affiliate with the military in any way.

Number awarded 1 each year.

Deadline March of each year.

[487]
ROCKWELL AUTOMATION SCHOLARSHIPS

Society of Women Engineers
Attn: Scholarship Selection Committee
203 North LaSalle Street, Suite 1675
Chicago, IL 60601-1269
(312) 596-5223 Toll Free: (877) SWE-INFO
Fax: (312) 644-8557 E-mail: scholarships@swe.org
Web: societyofwomenengineers.swe.org

Summary To provide financial assistance to upper-division women (particularly African Americans and other underrepresented minorities) who are majoring in computer science or selected engineering specialties.

Eligibility This program is open to women who are entering their junior year at an ABET-accredited college or university. Applicants must be working full time on a degree in computer science or computer, electrical, industrial, manufacturing, mechanical, or software engineering and have a GPA of 3.0 or higher. Selection is based on merit and demonstrated leadership potential. Preference is given to students attending designated universities and to members of groups underrepresented in computer science and engineering.

Financial data The stipend is $2,500.

Duration 1 year.

Additional information This program, established in 1991, is supported by Rockwell Automation, Inc. For a list of the preferred universities, check the web site of the Society of Women Engineers.

Number awarded 2 each year.

Deadline February of each year.

[488]
ROCKWELL COLLINS NSBE CORPORATE SCHOLARSHIPS

National Society of Black Engineers
Attn: Programs Department
205 Daingerfield Road
Alexandria, VA 22314
(703) 549-2207 Fax: (703) 683-5312
E-mail: scholarships@nsbe.org
Web: www.nsbe.org/Programs/Scholarships.aspx

Summary To provide financial aid and work experience to members of the National Society of Black Engineers (NSBE) who are majoring in computer science or designated engineering fields.

Eligibility This program is open to members of the society who are enrolled as college sophomores or juniors and majoring in computer science or engineering (aerospace, computer, electrical, industrial, or mechanical). Applicants must have a GPA of 3.0 or higher and a demonstrated interest in employment with Rockwell Collins. They must be U.S. citizens or otherwise eligible to work in the United States.

Financial data The stipend is $2,500.

Duration 1 year.

Additional information This program is sponsored by Rockwell Collins, Inc. Recipients must be available to accept, if offered, an internship or co-op with Rockwell Collins prior to completion of their undergraduate program.

Number awarded 3 each year.

Deadline May of each year.

[489]
ROCKWELL COLLINS SWE SCHOLARSHIPS

Society of Women Engineers
Attn: Scholarship Selection Committee
203 North LaSalle Street, Suite 1675
Chicago, IL 60601-1269
(312) 596-5223 Toll Free: (877) SWE-INFO
Fax: (312) 644-8557 E-mail: scholarships@swe.org
Web: societyofwomenengineers.swe.org

Summary To provide financial assistance to undergraduates (particularly African Americans and other underrepresented minorities) who are members of the Society of Women Engineers (SWE) and majoring in computer science or selected engineering specialties.

Eligibility This program is open to members of the society who are entering their sophomore or junior year at a 4-year ABET-accredited college or university. Applicants must be working full time on a degree in computer science or computer, electrical, or software engineering and have a GPA of 3.0 or higher. Selection is based on merit. They must be available to accepted 1 Rockwell Collins co-op or internship prior to completing their degree. Preference is given to members of groups underrepresented in computer science and engineering.

Financial data The stipend is $2,500.

Duration 1 year.

Additional information This program, established in 1991, is supported by Rockwell Collins, Inc.

Number awarded 3 each year.

Deadline February of each year.

[490]
RON BROWN SCHOLAR PROGRAM

CAP Charitable Foundation
Attn: Ron Brown Scholar Program
1160 Pepsi Place, Suite 206
Charlottesville, VA 22901
(434) 964-1588 Fax: (434) 964-1589
E-mail: info@ronbrown.org
Web: www.ronbrown.org

Summary To provide financial assistance for college to African American high school seniors.

Eligibility This program is open to academically-talented African American high school seniors who have demonstrated social commitment and leadership potential. They must be interested in attending a 4-year college or university as a full-time student. U.S. citizenship or permanent resident status is required. Finalists are invited to participate in a weekend selection program in Washington, D.C.; their expenses are reimbursed. Final selection is based on academic excellence, leadership, skills, school and community involvement, and financial need.

Financial data The stipend is $10,000 per year. Funds may be used to cover tuition, fees, books, room, board, and other college-related expenses. Payment is made directly to the recipient's school.

Duration 4 years.

Additional information Established in 1996, this program honors a former Secretary of Commerce who served during the Clinton administration. During college, recipients are required to pursue 1 or more summer internships devoted to community service (e.g., in education, health, government, politics) and 1 pre-professional internship.

Number awarded 10 to 20 each year.

Deadline January of each year.

[491]
RON HERNDON SCHOLARSHIPS

Black United Fund of Oregon
Attn: ACCESS Scholarship Committee
2828 N.E. Alberta
Portland, OR 97211
(503) 282-7973 Fax: (503) 282-3482
E-mail: bufor@bufor.org
Web: bufor.org

Summary To provide financial assistance to African American high school seniors from Oregon and southwestern Washington who plan to attend college in any state.

Eligibility This program is open to African American seniors graduating from high schools in Oregon and southwestern Washington and planning to attend a college or university in any state. They must have a GPA of 2.75 or higher and a record of community service. Along with their application, they must submit a resume that includes information on extracurricular school activities, paid work experience, volunteer activities outside of school, and awards or honors attained. Financial need is considered in the selection process.

Financial data The stipend is $1,500.

Duration 1 year; nonrenewable.

Additional information This program began in 1994.

Number awarded 3 each year.

Deadline January of each year.

[492]
RONALD E. MCNAIR SCHOLARSHIP IN SPACE AND OPTICAL PHYSICS

National Society of Black Physicists
Attn: Scholarship Committee Chair
1100 North Glebe Road, Suite 1010
Arlington, VA 22201
(703) 536-4207 Fax: (703) 536-4203
E-mail: scholarship@nsbp.org
Web: www.nsbp.org/scholarships

Summary To provide financial assistance to African American students majoring in space or optical physics in college.

Eligibility This program is open to African American students who are entering their junior or senior year of college and majoring in space or optical physics. Applicants must submit an essay on their academic and career objectives, information on their participation in extracurricular activities, a description of any awards and honors they have received, and 3 letters of recommendation. Financial need is not considered.

Financial data The stipend is $1,000.

Duration 1 year; nonrenewable.

Additional information This program is offered in partnership with the American Astronomical Society.

Number awarded 1 each year.

Deadline November of each year.

[493]
RONALD E. MCNAIR SCIENTIFIC ACHIEVEMENT AWARD

Omega Psi Phi Fraternity
Attn: Charles R. Drew Memorial Scholarship Commission
3951 Snapfinger Parkway
Decatur, GA 30035-3203
(404) 284-5533 Fax: (404) 284-0333
E-mail: scholarshipchairman@oppf.org
Web: www.oppf.org/scholarship

Summary To provide financial assistance to undergraduate Omega Psi Phi Fraternity brothers who are majoring in the sciences.

Eligibility This program is open to fraternity brothers in good standing who are at least sophomores in college and are majoring in a field of science, including (but not limited to) chemistry, physics, biology, engineering, or mathematics. Applicants must be enrolled full time and have a GPA of 3.5 or higher. Along with their application, they must submit a statement of 200 to 250 words on their purpose for applying for this scholarship, how they believe funds from the fraternity can assist them in achieving their career goals, and other circumstances (including financial need) that make it important for them to receive financial assistance.

Financial data The stipend is $6,000.

Duration 1 year.

Additional information The winner is required to attend the Omega Psi Phi Grand Conclave or Leadership Conference. Up to $1,000 in travel expenses for attendance is provided.

Number awarded 1 or more each year.

Deadline April of each year.

[494]
ROSA L. PARKS SCHOLARSHIPS

Conference of Minority Transportation Officials
Attn: National Scholarship Program
1875 I Street, N.W., Suite 500
Washington, DC 20006
(703) 234-4072 Fax: (202) 318-0364
Web: www.comto.org/?page=Scholarships

Summary To provide financial assistance for college to children of members of the Conference of Minority Transportation Officials (COMTO) and to other students interested in working on a bachelor's or master's degree in transportation.

Eligibility This program is open to 1) college-bound high school seniors whose parent has been a COMTO member for at least 1 year; 2) undergraduates who have completed at least 60 semester credit hours in a transportation discipline; and 3) students working on a master's degree in transportation who have completed at least 15 credits. Applicants must have a GPA of 3.0 or higher. Along with their application, they must submit a cover letter with a 500-word statement of career goals. Financial need is not considered in the selection process. U.S. citizenship or legal resident status is required.

Financial data The stipend is $4,500. Funds are paid directly to the recipient's college or university.

Duration 1 year.

Additional information COMTO was established in 1971 to promote, strengthen, and expand the roles of minorities in all aspects of transportation. Recipients are expected to attend the COMTO National Scholarship Luncheon.

Number awarded 1 each year.

Deadline May of each year.

[495]
ROSEWOOD FAMILY SCHOLARSHIP FUND

Florida Department of Education
Attn: Office of Student Financial Assistance
325 West Gaines Street
Tallahassee, FL 32399-0400
(850) 410-5160 Toll Free: (888) 827-2004
Fax: (850) 487-1809 E-mail: osfa@fldoe.org
Web: www.floridastudentfinancialaid.org

Summary To provide financial assistance for college to African American or other minority students who can demonstrate financial need and wish to study in Florida.

Eligibility This program is open to residents of any state who wish to enroll full time at a state university, public community college, or public postsecondary vocational/technical school in Florida. Applicants must be a descendant of an African American Rosewood family (whose members were killed by a mob in January 1923). Other minority undergraduate students are considered if funds remain available after awarding Rosewood descendants. Financial need must be demonstrated.

Financial data Stipends depend on the need of the recipient; recently, they averaged $3,620 for students at public state universities and $1,998 for students at public community colleges.

Duration 1 year; may be renewed up to 3 additional years, provided the student maintains full-time enrollment and a GPA of 2.0 or higher.

Number awarded Varies each year; recently, this program presented 11 new and 9 renewal awards.

Deadline March of each year.

[496]
ROYCE OSBORN MINORITY STUDENT SCHOLARSHIPS

American Society of Radiologic Technologists
Attn: ASRT Education and Research Foundation
15000 Central Avenue, S.E.
Albuquerque, NM 87123-3909
(505) 298-4500, ext. 2541
Toll Free: (800) 444-2778, ext. 2541
Fax: (505) 298-5063 E-mail: foundation@asrt.org
Web: www.asrtfoundation.org

Summary To provide financial assistance to African American and other minority students enrolled in entry-level radiologic sciences programs.

Eligibility This program is open to Blacks or African Americans, American Indians or Alaska Natives, Hispanics or Latinos, Asians, and Native Hawaiians or other Pacific Islanders who are enrolled in an accredited entry-level program in radiography, sonography, magnetic resonance, or nuclear medicine. Applicants must be able to finish their degree or certificate in the year for which they are applying. They must be U.S. citizens, nationals, or permanent residents have a GPA of 3.0 or higher. Along with their application, they must submit 9 essays of 200 words each on assigned topics related to their personal situation and interest in a career in radiologic science. Selection is based on those essays, academic and professional achievements, recommendations, and financial need.

Financial data The stipend is $4,000. Funds are paid directly to the recipient's institution.

Duration 1 year.

Number awarded 5 each year.

Deadline January of each year.

[497]
ROYCE R. WATTS SR. SCHOLARSHIP

Watts Charity Association, Inc.
6245 Bristol Parkway, Suite 224
Culver City, CA 90230
(323) 671-0394 Fax: (323) 778-2613
E-mail: wattscharity@yahoo.com
Web: 4watts.tripod.com/id5.html

Summary To provide financial assistance to upper-division African American college students interested in health, civil rights, or administration.

Eligibility This program is open to U.S. citizens of African American descent who are enrolled full time as a college or university junior. Applicants must have an interest in health and pre-medicine, community activities and civil rights, or administration. They must have a GPA of 3.0 or higher, be between 17 and 24 years of age, and be able to demonstrate that they intend to continue their education for at least 2 years. Along with their application, they must submit 1) a 1-paragraph statement on why they should be awarded a Watts Charity Association scholarship; and 2) a 1- to 2-page essay on a specific type of cancer, based either on how it has impacted their life or on researched information.

Financial data A stipend is awarded (amount not specified).

Duration 1 year.

Additional information Royce R. Watts, Sr. established the Watts Charity Association after he learned he had cancer in 2001.

Number awarded 1 each year.

Deadline May of each year.

[498]
RTDNF/CAROLE SIMPSON SCHOLARSHIP

Radio Television Digital News Foundation
Attn: Programs, Awards, and Membership Manager
529 14th Street, N.W., Suite 425
Washington, DC 20045
(202) 725-8318 Fax: (202) 223-4007
E-mail: katies@rtdna.org
Web: www.rtdna.org/pages/education/scholarship-info.php

Summary To provide financial assistance to African American and other minority undergraduate students who are interested in preparing for a career in electronic journalism.

Eligibility This program is open to sophomore or more advanced minority undergraduate students enrolled in an electronic journalism sequence at an accredited or nationally-recognized college or university. Applicants must submit 1 to 3 examples of their journalistic skills on audio CD or DVD (no more than 15 minutes total, accompanied by scripts); a description of their role on each story and a list of who worked on each story and what they did; a 1-page statement explaining why they are preparing for a career in electronic journalism with reference to their specific career preference (radio, television, online, reporting, producing, or newsroom management); a resume; and a letter of reference from their dean or faculty sponsor explaining why they are a good candidate for the award and certifying that they have at least 1 year of school remaining.

Financial data The stipend is $2,000, paid in semiannual installments of $1,000 each.

Duration 1 year.

Additional information The Radio Television Digital News Foundation (RTDNF) also provides an all-expense paid trip to the Radio Television Digital News Association (RTDNA) annual international conference. The RTDNF was formerly the Radio and Television News Directors Foundation (RTNDF). Previous winners of any RTDNF scholarship or internship are not eligible.

Number awarded 1 each year.

Deadline May of each year.

[499]
RUTH M. BATSON SCHOLARSHIPS

Ruth M. Batson Educational Foundation
250 Cambridge Street, Suite 701
Boston, MA 02114
(617) 742-1070 E-mail: dao5753@aol.com

Summary To provide financial assistance to African American college students who face serious financial need.

Eligibility This program is open to African American college students who need aid as a supplement to other financial assistance. Emergency grants are also available to students who need assistance to remain in school. Selection is based on academic achievement, character, extracurricular activities, and financial need.

Financial data Assistance ranges from $500 to $1,500.

Duration 1 year.

Number awarded Varies each year.

Deadline June of each year.

[500]
SACHS FOUNDATION SCHOLARSHIPS

Sachs Foundation
90 South Cascade Avenue, Suite 1410
Colorado Springs, CO 80903-1691
(719) 633-2353
Web: www.sachsfoundation.org

Summary To provide financial assistance to African American high school seniors in Colorado who plan to attend college in any state.

Eligibility This program is open to African American graduating high school seniors who are U.S. citizens and have been residents of Colorado for at least 5 years. Applicants must be planning to attend a college or university in any state. Along with their application, they must submit a 1-page personal biography, transcripts, 3 references, and documentation of financial need. Once accepted as undergraduate scholars, students may later apply for support in graduate school.

Financial data The average annual stipend recently was $5,000 for undergraduates or $6,000 for graduate students. Funds are sent to the financial aid office of the recipient's school.

Duration Normally, undergraduate students receive 4 years of support, as long as they maintain full-time enrollment and a current GPA of 2.5 or higher per term. Graduate students receive up to an additional 4 years of support.

Additional information This foundation was established in 1931. Since its founding, it has provided more than 8,000 scholarships to African Americans in Colorado.

Number awarded Approximately 35 each year.

Deadline March of each year.

[501]
SANDISK SCHOLARS PROGRAM

SanDisk Foundation
951 SanDisk Drive
Milpitas, CA 97034-7933
(408) 801-1240 Fax: (408) 801-8657
E-mail: Mike.wong@sandisk.com
Web: www.sandisk.com

Summary To provide financial assistance to African Americans, Latinos, and women who are interested in attending college to study a field of science, technology, engineering, or mathematics (STEM).

Eligibility This program is open to women, African Americans, and Latinos who are high school seniors or freshmen, sophomores, or juniors at a 2- or 4-year college or university. Applicants must be interested in working full time on an undergraduate degree in a field of STEM. Selection is based on academic achievements and records, community involvement, an essay, and financial need.

Financial data The stipend is $2,500 per year.

Duration 1 year; may be renewed up to 3 additional years.

Additional information This program, which began in 2012, is offered in partnership with the United Negro College Fund (UNCF), the Hispanic Scholarship Fund (HSF), the Silicon Valley Community Foundation (SVCF), and International Scholarship and Tuition Services (ISTS). The program also offers scholarships to dependents of SanDisk employees and provides grants to specified universities for their scholarships.

Number awarded Varies each year; recently, 29 of these scholarships were awarded to the general public.

Deadline March of each year.

[502]
SANDRA R. SPAULDING MEMORIAL SCHOLARSHIPS

California Nurses Association
Attn: California Nurses Foundation
2030 Franklin Street, Suite 610
Oakland, CA 94612
(510) 622-8311 Fax: (510) 663-4825
E-mail: info@calnursesfoundation.org
Web: www.nationalnursesunited.org/pages/1074

Summary To provide financial assistance to African Americans and other students from diverse ethnic backgrounds who are enrolled in an associate degree in nursing (A.D.N.) program in California.

Eligibility This program is open to students who have been admitted to a second-year accredited A.D.N. program in California and plan to complete the degree within 2 years. Along with their application, they must submit a 1-page essay describing their personal and professional goals. Selection is based on that essay, commitment and active participation in nursing and health-related organizations, professional vision and direction, and financial need. A goal of this scholarship program is to encourage ethnic and socioeconomic diversity in nursing.

Financial data A stipend is awarded (amount not specified).

Duration 1 year; nonrenewable.

Additional information This program began in 1985.

Number awarded 1 or more each year.

Deadline July of each year.

[503]
SAO SUMMER INTERN PROGRAM

Harvard-Smithsonian Center for Astrophysics
Attn: Summer Intern Program
60 Garden Street, Mail Stop 70
Cambridge, MA 02138
(617) 496-7063 E-mail: intern-at-cfa@harvard.edu
Web: hea-www.harvard.edu/REU/REU.html

Summary To enable undergraduates (particularly African Americans, other underrepresented minorities, women, and students with disabilities) who are interested in a physical science career or science education to obtain research experience at the Smithsonian Astrophysical Observatory (SAO) at Harvard University.

Eligibility This program is open to U.S. citizens, nationals, and permanent residents enrolled in a program leading to a bachelor's degree. Applicants must be interested in a career in astronomy, astrophysics, physics, or related physical sciences. Along with their application, they must submit an essay of 600 to 800 words describing academic and career goals, scientific interests, relevant work experience, why they would like to be in the program, and why they would be a good candidate. Graduating seniors are not eligible. Applications are especially encouraged from underrepresented minorities, persons with disabilities, and women.

Financial data The stipend is $4,500. Housing and travel expenses are provided.

Duration 10 weeks during the summer.

Additional information Each intern works with a scientist on an individual research project. Potential areas of research include observational and theoretical cosmology, extragalactic and galactic astronomy, interstellar medium and star formation, laboratory astrophysics, supernovae and supernova remnants, planetary science, and solar and stellar astrophysics. Also included in the program are weekly lectures, field trips, and workshops specifically designed for the participants. This program is supported by the National Science Foundation as part of its Research Experiences for Undergraduates (REU) Program.

Number awarded 10 each year.

Deadline January of each year.

[504]
SCHOLARSHIPS FOR MINORITY ACCOUNTING STUDENTS

American Institute of Certified Public Accountants
Attn: Academic and Career Development Division
220 Leigh Farm Road
Durham, NC 27707-8110
(919) 402-4931 Fax: (919) 419-4705
E-mail: scholarships@aicpa.org
Web: www.aicpa.org

Summary To provide financial assistance to African Americans and other minorities interested in studying accounting at the undergraduate or graduate school level.

Eligibility This program is open to minority undergraduate and graduate students, enrolled full time, who have a GPA of 3.3 or higher (both cumulatively and in their major) and intend to pursue a C.P.A. credential. The program defines minority students as those whose heritage is Black or African American, Hispanic or Latino, Native American, or Asian American. Undergraduates must have completed at least 30 semester hours, including at least 6 semester hours of a major in accounting. Graduate students must be working on a master's degree in accounting, finance, taxation, or a related program. Applicants must be U.S. citizens or permanent residents and student affiliate members of the American Institute of Certified Public Accountants (AICPA). Along with their application, they must submit 500-word essays on 1) why they want to become a C.P.A. and how attaining that licensure will contribute to their goals; and 2) how they would spread the message about accounting and the C.P.A. profession in their community and school. In the selection process, some consideration is given to financial need.

Financial data Stipends range from $1,500 to $3,000 per year. Funds are disbursed directly to the recipient's school.

Duration 1 year; may be renewed up to 3 additional years or until completion of a bachelor's or master's degree, whichever is earlier.

Additional information This program began in 1969.

Number awarded Varies each year; recently, 78 students received funding through this program.

Deadline March of each year.

[505]
SCHOLARSHIPS FOR RACIAL JUSTICE

Higher Education Consortium for Urban Affairs
Attn: Student Services
2233 University Avenue West, Suite 210
St. Paul, MN 55114-1698
(651) 287-3300 Toll Free: (800) 554-1089
Fax: (651) 659-9421 E-mail: hecua@hecua.org
Web: www.hecua.org/programs/scholarships

Summary To provide financial assistance to African American and other students of color who are enrolled in programs of the Higher Education Consortium for Urban Affairs (HECUA) at participating colleges and universities and are committed to undoing institutionalized racism.

Eligibility This program is open to students at member colleges and universities who are participating in HECUA programs. Applicants must be a student of color who can demonstrate a commitment to undoing institutionalized racism. Along with their application, they must submit a reflective essay on the personal, social, or political influences in their lifetime that have motivated them to work on racial justice issues.

Financial data The stipend is $4,000. Funds are applied as a credit to the student's HECUA program fees for the semester.

Duration 1 semester.

Additional information This program began in 2006. Consortium members include Augsburg College (Minneapolis, Minnesota), Augustana College (Sioux Falls, South Dakota), Carleton College (Northfield, Minnesota), College of Saint Scholastica (Duluth, Minnesota), Colorado College (Colorado Springs, Colorado), Denison University (Granville, Ohio), Gustavus Adolphus College (St. Peter, Minnesota), Hamline University (St. Paul, Minnesota), Macalester College (St. Paul, Minnesota), Saint Mary's University (Winona, Minnesota), Saint Catherine University (St. Paul, Minnesota), Saint Olaf College (Northfield, Minnesota), Swarthmore College (Swarthmore, Pennsylvania), University of Minnesota (Twin Cities, Duluth, Morris, Crookston, Rochester), University of Saint Thomas (St. Paul, Minnesota), and Viterbo University (La Crosse, Wisconsin).

Number awarded Several each year.

Deadline April of each year for summer and fall programs; November of each year for January and spring programs.

[506]
SCHOLARSHIPS SUPPORTING POST-SECONDARY EDUCATION FOR A CAREER IN THE AUDIOVISUAL INDUSTRY

InfoComm International
International Communications Industries Foundation
11242 Waples Mill Road, Suite 200
Fairfax, VA 22030
(703) 273-7200 Toll Free: (800) 659-7469
Fax: (703) 278-8082 E-mail: jhardwick@infocomm.org
Web: www.infocomm.org

Summary To provide financial assistance to undergraduate and graduate students (particularly African Americans, other minorities, and women) who are interested in preparing for a career in the audiovisual (AV) industry.

Eligibility This program is open to second-year students at 2-year colleges, juniors and seniors at 4-year institutions, and graduate students. Applicants must have a GPA of 2.75 or higher and be majoring or planning to major in audiovisual subjects or related fields, including audio, video, audiovisual, radio/television/film, or other field related to a career in the audiovisual industry. Students in other programs, such as journalism, may be eligible if they can demonstrate a relationship to career goals in the AV industry. Along with their application, they must submit 1) an essay of 150 to 200 words on the career path they plan to pursue in the audiovisual industry in the next 5 years; and 2) an essay of 250 to 300 words on the experience or person influencing them the most in selecting the audiovisual industry as their career of choice. Minority and women candidates are especially encouraged to apply. Selection is based on the essays, presentation of the application, GPA, AV-related experience, work experience, and letters of recommendation.

Financial data The stipend is $4,000. Funds are sent directly to the school.

Duration 1 year.

Additional information InfoComm International, formerly the International Communications Industries Association, established the International Communications Industries Foundation (ICIF) to manage its charitable and educational activities.

Number awarded Varies each year.

Deadline April of each year.

[507]
SCIENCE LEADERSHIP SCHOLARSHIPS

Washington Science Teachers Association
c/o Sonia Siegel Vexler
Pacific Science Center
200 Second Avenue North
Seattle, WA 98109
(206) 443-2001 Fax: (206) 443-3631
TDD: (206) 443-2887 E-mail: ssiegelvexler@pacsci.org
Web: www.wsta.net/awards

Summary To provide financial assistance to upper-division students and teachers in Washington (particularly African Americans, other underrepresented minorities, and women) who are interested in training in science education.

Eligibility This program is open to juniors and seniors at colleges and universities in Washington who are working on certification in science education or in elementary education with an emphasis on science. Preference is given to African Americans, Hispanics, Native Americans, and women. Applicants must submit a 1-page essay on why they are applying for this scholarship.

Financial data The stipend is $2,000.

Duration 1 year; nonrenewable.

Additional information This program began in 2003 as the Peggy Vatter Memorial Scholarships.

Number awarded 1 or more each year.

Deadline June of each year.

[508]
S.D. BECHTEL JR. FOUNDATION ENGINEERING SCHOLARSHIPS

National Society of Black Engineers
Attn: Programs Department
205 Daingerfield Road
Alexandria, VA 22314
(703) 549-2207 Fax: (703) 683-5312
E-mail: scholarships@nsbe.org
Web: www.nsbe.org/Programs/Scholarships.aspx

Summary To provide financial assistance to undergraduate members of the National Society of Black Engineers (NSBE) who are studying civil or mechanical engineering.

Eligibility This program is open to members of the society who are current college sophomores, juniors, or seniors. Applicants must be majoring in civil or mechanical engineering. They must have a GPA of 3.0 or higher. Along with their application, they must submit 3 essays of 300 words each on assigned topics. Selection is based on academic standing, leadership skills, focus on engineering in the work world, and financial need.

Financial data The stipend is $15,000 per year.

Duration 1 year; may be renewed, depending on academic performance and progress toward graduation.

Additional information This program is sponsored by the S.D. Bechtel, Jr. Foundation.

Number awarded 3 each year.

Deadline May of each year.

[509]
SEATTLE CHAPTER AWIS SCHOLARSHIPS

Association for Women in Science-Seattle Chapter
c/o Fran Solomon, Scholarship Committee Chair
5805 16th Avenue, N.E.
Seattle, WA 98105
(206) 522-6441 E-mail: scholarship@seattleawis.org
Web: seattleawis.org/award/scholarships

Summary To provide financial assistance to African American and other women undergraduates from any state majoring in science, mathematics, or engineering at colleges and universities in Washington.

Eligibility This program is open to women from any state entering their junior or senior year at a 4-year college or university in Washington. Applicants must have a declared major in science (e.g., biological sciences, environmental science, biochemistry, chemistry, pharmacy, geology, computer science, physics), mathematics, or engineering. Along with their application, they must submit essays on the events that led to their choice of a major, their current career plans and long-term goals, and their volunteer and community activities. Selection is based on academic excellence, motivation to prepare for a science-based career, record of giving back to their communities, and financial need. At least 1 scholarship is reserved for a woman from a group that is underrepresented in science, mathematics, and engineering careers, including Native American Indians and Alaska Natives, Black/African Americans, Mexican Americans/Chicanas/Latinas, Native Pacific Islanders (Polynesians, Melanesians, and Micronesians), adult learners (returning students), and women with disabilities.

Financial data Stipends range from $1,000 to $1,500.

Duration 1 year.

Additional information This program includes the following named awards: the Virginia Badger Scholarship, the Angela Paez Memorial Scholarship, and the Fran Solomon Scholarship. Support for the program is provided by several sponsors, including the American Chemical Society, Iota Sigma Pi, Rosetta Inpharmatics, and ZymoGenetics, Inc.

Number awarded 4 to 6 each year.

Deadline April of each year.

[510]
SEATTLE CHAPTER NABA SCHOLARSHIPS

National Association of Black Accountants-Seattle Chapter
Attn: Scholarship Committee
P.O. Box 18105
Seattle, WA 98118
E-mail: naba.seattle@live.com
Web: www.nabaseattle.org

Summary To provide financial assistance to members of the National Association of Black Accountants (NABA) from any state who are working on an undergraduate degree in a business-related field at colleges and universities in Washington.

Eligibility This program is open to full-time sophomores, juniors, and seniors working on a degree in accounting, finance, or other business-related field at colleges and universities in Washington. Applicants must be ethnic minorities and active NABA members. They must have a GPA of 3.0 or higher. Financial need is not considered in the selection process.

Financial data Stipends range from $1,000 to $2,000.

Duration 1 year.

Number awarded Varies each year.

Deadline April of each year.

[511]
SECOND EPISCOPAL DISTRICT KITTRELL-ALLEN-ADAMS SCHOLARSHIP

African Methodist Episcopal Church
Second Episcopal District
c/o Gail P. Radcliff, District Coordinator
9285 Berry Road
Waldorf, MD 20603
(301) 870-8492

Summary To provide financial assistance to members of the African Methodist Episcopal (AME) Church in its Second Episcopal District who are interested in attending college in any state.

Eligibility This program is open to AME members in the Second Episcopal District, which includes the Conferences of Baltimore, Washington, Virginia, North Carolina, and Western North Carolina. Applicants must be graduating high school seniors or students already working on an undergraduate degree at a college or university in any state. Along with their application, they must submit an autobiographical essay of 1 to 2 pages that includes information about their future goals and family, school, church, and community involvements. Selection is based on that essay, high school grades and SAT scores, letters of recommendation, and financial need.

Financial data A stipend is awarded (amount not specified).

Duration 1 year.

Number awarded 1 or more each year.

Deadline July of each year.

[512]
SELMO BRADLEY SCHOLARSHIP

African Methodist Episcopal Church
Eleventh Episcopal District Lay Organization
c/o Loretta S. Coppock
11499 Sir Barton Court
Jacksonville, FL 32218
(904) 751-7300 E-mail: eedlo@eedlo.org
Web: www.eedlo.org/scholarships.html

Summary To provide financial assistance to members of African Methodist Episcopal (AME) churches in Florida who are interested in attending college in any state.

Eligibility This program is open to seniors graduating from public or private high schools in Florida who are members of AME churches. Applicants must be planning to enroll full time at an institution of higher learning in any state: an AME-supported college, a Predominantly Black College or University, or an accredited trade school. They must have a GPA of 2.5

or higher. Along with their application, they must submit a 1-page essay on why a college education is important and a statement regarding their financial need.

Financial data A stipend is awarded (amount not specified).

Duration 1 year.

Number awarded 1 or more each year.

Deadline April of each year.

[513] SHARON D. BANKS MEMORIAL UNDERGRADUATE SCHOLARSHIP

Women's Transportation Seminar
Attn: WTS Foundation
1701 K Street, N.W., Suite 800
Washington, DC 20006
(202) 955-5085 Fax: (202) 955-5088
E-mail: wts@wtsinternational.org
Web: www.wtsinternational.org/education/scholarships

Summary To provide financial assistance to undergraduate women (particularly African Americans and other minorities) who are interested in a career in transportation.

Eligibility This program is open to women who are working on an undergraduate degree in transportation or a transportation-related field (e.g., transportation engineering, planning, finance, or logistics). Applicants must have a GPA of 3.0 or higher and be interested in a career in transportation. Along with their application, they must submit a 500-word statement about their career goals after graduation and why they think they should receive the scholarship award. Applications must be submitted first to a local chapter; the chapters forward selected applications for consideration on the national level. Minority women are especially encouraged to apply. Selection is based on transportation involvement and goals, job skills, and academic record; financial need is not considered.

Financial data The stipend is $5,000.

Duration 1 year.

Additional information This program began in 1992. Local chapters may also award additional funding to winners in their area.

Number awarded 1 each year.

Deadline Applications must be submitted by November to a local WTS chapter.

[514] SHELL INCENTIVE FUND SCHOLARSHIPS

Shell Oil Company
Attn: Scholarship Administrator
910 Louisiana, Suite 4476C
Houston, TX 77002
(713) 241-6314 E-mail: terry.garland@shell.com
Web: www.shell.us

Summary To provide financial assistance to African American and other underrepresented minority students majoring in specified engineering and geosciences fields at designated universities.

Eligibility This program is open to students enrolled full time as sophomores, juniors, or seniors at 22 participating universities. Applicants must be U.S. citizens or authorized to work in the United States and members of a race or ethnicity underrepresented in the technical and scientific academic areas (Black, Hispanic/Latino, American Indian, or Alaskan Native). They must have a GPA of 3.2 or higher with a major in engineering (chemical, civil, electrical, geological, geophysical, mechanical, or petroleum) or geosciences (geology, geophysics, or physics). Along with their application, they must submit a 100-word essay on the kind of work they plan to be doing in 10 years, both in their career and in their community. Financial need is not considered in the selection process.

Financial data The stipend is $5,000 per year.

Duration 1 year; may be renewed up to 3 additional years, provided the recipient remains qualified and accepts a Shell Oil Company internship (if offered).

Additional information This program is administered by Educational Testing Service, Scholarship and Recognition Programs, P.O. Box 6730, Princeton, NJ 08541, (609) 771-7878. The participating institutions are Colorado School of Mines, Cornell University, Florida A&M University, Georgia Institute of Technology, Louisiana State University, Massachusetts Institute of Technology, Michigan State University, North Carolina A&T State University, Ohio State University, Pennsylvania State University, Prairie View A&M University, Purdue University, Rice University, Stanford University, Texas A&M University, University of Colorado at Boulder, University of Houston, University of Illinois at Urbana-Champaign, University of Michigan, University of Oklahoma, University of Texas at Austin, and University of Texas at El Paso.

Number awarded Approximately 20 each year.

Deadline May of each year.

[515] SHIRLEY DELIBERO SCHOLARSHIP

American Public Transportation Association
Attn: American Public Transportation Foundation
1666 K Street, N.W., Suite 1100
Washington, DC 20006
(202) 496-4803 Fax: (202) 496-4323
E-mail: yconley@apta.com
Web: www.aptfd.org/work/scholarship.htm

Summary To provide financial assistance to African American undergraduate and graduate students who are preparing for a career in the public transportation industry.

Eligibility This program is open to African American sophomores, juniors, seniors, and graduate students who are preparing for a career in the transit industry. Any member organization of the American Public Transportation Association (APTA) can nominate and sponsor candidates for this scholarship. Nominees must be enrolled in a fully-accredited institution, have and maintain at least a 3.0 GPA, and be either employed by or demonstrate a strong interest in entering the business administration or management area of the public transportation industry. They must submit a 1,000-word essay on the topic, "In what segment of the public transportation industry will you make a career and why?" Selection is based on demonstrated interest in the transit field as a career, need for financial assistance, academic achievement, essay content and quality, and involvement in extracurricular citizenship and leadership activities.

Financial data The stipend is $2,500.

Duration 1 year; may be renewed.

Number awarded 1 each year.

Deadline May of each year.

[516]
SIGMA GAMMA RHO SCHOLARSHIPS/ FELLOWSHIPS

Sigma Gamma Rho Sorority, Inc.
Attn: National Education Fund
1000 Southhill Drive, Suite 200
Cary, NC 27513
(919) 678-9720 Toll Free: (888) SGR-1922
Fax: (919) 678-9721 E-mail: info@sgrho1922.org
Web: www.sgrho1922.org/nef

Summary To provide financial assistance for undergraduate or graduate study to African American and other applicants who can demonstrate financial need.

Eligibility This program is open to high school seniors, undergraduates, and graduate students who can demonstrate financial need. The sponsor is a traditionally African American sorority, but support is available to males and females of all races. Applicants must have a GPA of "C" or higher.

Financial data A stipend is awarded (amount not specified).

Duration 1 year.

Additional information This program includes the following named awards: the Lorraine A. Williams Scholarship, the Philo Sallie A. Williams Scholarship, the Cleo W. Higgins Scholarship (limited to doctoral students), the Angela E. Randall Scholarship, the Inez Colson Memorial Scholarship (limited to students majoring in education or mathematics at Savannah State University), and the Philo Geneva Young Scholarship. A processing fee of $20 is required.

Number awarded Varies each year.

Deadline April of each year.

[517]
SISTER THEA BOWMAN FOUNDATION KNIGHTS OF COLUMBUS SCHOLARSHIPS

Knights of Columbus
Attn: Department of Scholarships
P.O. Box 1670
New Haven, CT 06507-0901
(203) 752-4332 Fax: (203) 772-2696
E-mail: info@kofc.org
Web: www.kofc.org/un/en/scholarships/bowman.html

Summary To provide financial assistance to African American high school seniors interested in attending a Catholic college.

Eligibility This program is open to African American seniors graduating from high schools in the United States. Applicants must be planning to attend a Catholic college or university. They are not required to be the children of members of the Knights of Columbus.

Financial data The stipend is $9,375 per year.

Duration 1 year; may be renewed up to 3 additional years.

Additional information This program began in 1996.

Number awarded Scholarships are offered when funds are available.

Deadline February of the year when available.

[518]
SMITHSONIAN MINORITY AWARDS PROGRAM

Smithsonian Institution
Attn: Office of Fellowships and Internships
470 L'Enfant Plaza, Suite 7102
P.O. Box 37012, MRC 902
Washington, DC 20013-7012
(202) 633-7070 Fax: (202) 633-7069
E-mail: siofi@si.edu
Web: www.smithsonianofi.com

Summary To provide funding to African American and other minority undergraduate and graduate students who are interested in conducting research at the Smithsonian Institution.

Eligibility This program is open to members of U.S. minority groups underrepresented in the Smithsonian's scholarly programs. Applicants must be undergraduates or beginning graduate students interested in conducting research in the Institution's disciplines and in the museum field. They must be U.S. citizens or permanent residents and have a GPA of 3.0 or higher.

Financial data Students receive a grant of $600 per week.

Duration Up to 10 weeks.

Additional information Recipients must carry out independent research projects in association with the Smithsonian's research staff. Eligible fields of study currently include animal behavior, ecology, and environmental science (including an emphasis on the tropics); anthropology (including archaeology); astrophysics and astronomy; earth sciences and paleobiology; evolutionary and systematic biology; history of science and technology; history of art (especially American, contemporary, African, Asian, and 20th-century art); American crafts and decorative arts; social and cultural history of the United States; and folk life. Students are required to be in residence at the Smithsonian for the duration of the fellowship.

Number awarded Varies each year; recently, 25 of these awards were granted: 2 for fall, 19 for summer, and 4 for spring.

Deadline January of each year for summer and fall residency; September of each year for spring residency.

[519]
SOUTH CAROLINA CHAPTER JOSIE K. CLAIBORNE MEMORIAL SCHOLARSHIPS

American Association of Blacks in Energy-South Carolina Chapter
Attn: Scholarship Committee
P.O. Box 7696
Columbia, SC 29202
(803) 933-7252 E-mail: mpriester-clarke@scana.com
Web: www.aabe.org/index.php?component=pages&id=920

Summary To provide financial assistance to African Americans and members of other underrepresented minority groups who are high school seniors in South Carolina and planning to major in an energy-related field at a college in any state.

Eligibility This program is open to seniors graduating from high schools in South Carolina and planning to work on a bachelor's degree at a college or university in any state. Applicants must be African Americans, Hispanics, or Native Americans who have a GPA of 3.0 or higher and are able to demonstrate financial need. Their intended major must be a field of business, engineering, physical science (e.g., astronomy, chemistry, geology, mineralogy, meteorology, physics), mathematics, or technology related to energy. Along with their application, they must submit a 350-word statement on why they should receive this scholarship, their professional career objectives, and any other relevant information.

Financial data The stipend is $1,000.

Duration 1 year; nonrenewable.

Additional information Winners are eligible to compete for regional and national scholarships.

Number awarded Up to 2 each year.

Deadline February of each year.

[520]
SOUTH EASTERN REGION FELLOWSHIP FOR LIFE-LONG LEARNING

Alpha Kappa Alpha Sorority, Inc.
Attn: Educational Advancement Foundation
5656 South Stony Island Avenue
Chicago, IL 60637
(773) 947-0026 Toll Free: (800) 653-6528
Fax: (773) 947-0277 E-mail: akaeaf@akaeaf.net
Web: www.akaeaf.org/fellowships_endowments.htm

Summary To provide financial assistance to members of Alpha Kappa Alpha (a traditionally African American women's sorority) in southeastern states who are engaged in a program of lifelong learning.

Eligibility This program is open to sorority m who are enrolled full time as sophomores or higher in an accredited degree-granting institution and are planning to continue their program of education. Applicants must be residents of Alabama, Mississippi, or Tennessee and enrolled in a program of lifelong learning at a college or university in those states. Along with their application, they must submit 1) a list of honors, awards, and scholarships received; 2) a list of organizations in which they have memberships, especially minority organizations; and 3) a statement of their personal and career goals, including how this scholarship will enhance their ability to attain those goals. The sponsor is a traditionally African American women's sorority.

Financial data A stipend is awarded (amount not specified).

Duration 1 year.

Number awarded 1 each even-numbered year.

Deadline April of each even-numbered year.

[521]
SPHINX COMPETITION AWARDS

Sphinx Organization
Attn: Screening Committee
400 Renaissance Center, Suite 2550
Detroit, MI 48243
(313) 877-9100 Fax: (313) 877-0164
E-mail: Competition@sphinxmusic.org
Web: www.sphinxmusic.org

Summary To recognize and reward outstanding junior high, high school, and college-age Black and Latino string instrumentalists.

Eligibility This competition is open to Black and Latino instrumentalists in 2 divisions: junior, for participants who are younger than 18 years of age, and senior, for participants who are between 18 and 27 years of age. All entrants must be current U.S. residents who can compete in the instrumental categories of violin, viola, cello, and double bass. Along with their applications, they must submit a preliminary audition tape that includes all of the required preliminary repertoire for their instrument category. Based on those tapes, qualifiers are invited to participate in the semifinals and finals competitions, held at sites in Detroit and Ann Arbor, Michigan.

Financial data In the senior division, the first-place winner receives a $10,000 cash prize, solo appearances with major orchestras, and a performance with the Sphinx Symphony; the second-place winner receives a $5,000 cash prize and a performance with the Sphinx Symphony; the third-place winner receives a $3,500 cash prize and a performance with the Sphinx Symphony. In the junior division, the first-place winner receives a $5,000 cash prize, solo appearances with major orchestras, a national radio debut, and 2 performances with the Sphinx Symphony; the second-place winner receives a $3,500 cash prize and a performance with the Sphinx Symphony; the third-place winner receives a $2,000 cash prize and a performance with the Sphinx Symphony. All semifinalists receive scholarships to attend designated summer programs. They also receive full tuition scholarships for their instrumental studies at selected colleges and universities from the Sphinx Music Assistance Fund (MAF) of the League of American Orchestras.

Duration The competition is held annually.

Additional information The sponsoring organization was incorporated in 1996 to hold this competition, first conducted in 1998. The Sphinx Symphony is an African American/Latino orchestra that performs at Orchestra Hall in Detroit. The MAF program was established by the New York Philharmonic in 1965, transferred to the American Symphony Orchestra League in 1994, and to the League of American Orchestras in 2001. In 2002, it partnered with the Sphinx Organization to provide scholarships to all 18 semifinalists. Applications must be accompanied by a $35 fee. That fee may be waived from both divisions and all instrumental categories if demonstrable need is shown.

Number awarded 18 semifinalists (9 from each age division) are selected each year. Of those, 3 junior and 3 senior competitors win cash prizes.

Deadline November of each year.

[522]
SPIE SCHOLARSHIP PROGRAM

SPIE-The International Society for Optical Engineering
Attn: Scholarship Committee
1000 20th Street
P.O. Box 10
Bellingham, WA 98227-0010
(360) 676-3290 Toll Free: (888) 504-8171
Fax: (360) 647-1445 E-mail: scholarships@spie.org
Web: spie.org/x7236.xml

Summary To provide financial assistance to entering or continuing undergraduate and graduate student members of SPIE-The International Society for Optical Engineering (particularly African Americans, other minorities, women, and veterans) who are preparing for a career in optical science or engineering.

Eligibility This program is open to high school seniors planning to attend college, current undergraduate students, and current graduate students. Applicants must be society members majoring or planning to enroll full or part time and major in optics, optoelectronics, photonics, imaging, or a related discipline (e.g., physics, electrical engineering) at a college or university anywhere in the world. Along with their application, they must submit a 500-word essay on their academic work, career objectives, how this scholarship would help them attain their goals, and what they have achieved and learned through their studies and activities. Financial need is not considered in the selection process. Women, minorities, and veterans are encouraged to apply.

Financial data Stipends range from $2,000 to $11,000. Special awards include the D.J. Lovell Scholarship at $11,000; the John Kiel Scholarship at $10,000; the Laser Technology, Engineering, and Applications Scholarship at $5,000; the Optical Design and Engineering Scholarship at $5,000, and the BACUS Scholarship at $5,000.

Duration 1 year.

Additional information The International Society for Optical Engineering was founded in 1955 as the Society of Photo-Optical Instrumentation Engineers (SPIE). This program includes the following special named scholarships: the D.J. Lovell Scholarship, sponsored by SPIE (the most prestigious of the scholarships); the John Kiel Scholarship, awarded for a student's potential for long-term contribution to the field of optics and optical engineering; the Optical Design and Engineering Scholarship in Optical Engineering, established to honor Bill Price and Warren Smith and awarded to a full-time graduate or undergraduate student in the field of optical design and engineering; the Laser Technology, Engineering, and Applications Scholarship (formerly the F-MADE Scholarship), sponsored by the Forum for Military Applications of Directed Energy (F-MADE) in recognition of a student's scholarly achievement in laser technology, engineering, or applications; and the BACUS Scholarship, awarded to a full-time undergraduate or graduate student in the field of microlithography with an emphasis on optical tooling and/or semiconductor manufacturing technologies, sponsored by BACUS (SPIE's photomask international technical group).

Number awarded Varies each year; recently, this program awarded 140 scholarships with a value of $353,000. Since the program was established, it has awarded more than $3.8 million to nearly 2,000 students in 86 countries.

Deadline February of each year.

[523]
ST. PHILIP'S EPISCOPAL CHURCH/ABSALOM JONES SCHOLARSHIP FUND

St. Philip's Episcopal Church
Attn: Absalom Jones Scholarship Selection Committee
522 Main Street
Laurel, MD 20707-4118
(301) 776-5151 Fax: (301) 776-6337
E-mail: absalomjonesfund@stphilipslaurel.org
Web: www.stphilipslaurel.org/about/ministries

Summary To provide financial assistance to African American and other undergraduate and graduate students at schools in any state who have a tie to the Episcopal Diocese of Washington, D.C.

Eligibility This program is open to students who reside, work, attend school, or are members of a parish in the Episcopal Diocese of Washington. Applicants must be attending or planning to attend a college, seminary, or vocational/technical institute in any state as an undergraduate or graduate student. They must be able to demonstrate the qualities for which Absalom Jones, the first African American priest in the Episcopal Church, was noted: compassion, service, leadership, and an emphasis on education. Financial need is considered in the selection process.

Financial data The stipend is $1,000.

Duration 1 year.

Additional information The Episcopal Diocese of Washington serves the District of Columbia and the Maryland counties of Charles, St. Mary's, Prince George's, and Montgomery.

Number awarded 2 each year.

Deadline April of each year.

[524]
STAN BECK FELLOWSHIP

Entomological Society of America
Attn: Entomological Foundation
9332 Annapolis Road, Suite 210
Lanham, MD 20706-3150
(301) 459-9082 Fax: (301) 459-9084
E-mail: melodie@entfdn.org
Web: www.entfdn.org/awards_education.php

Summary To assist minority and other "needy" students working on an undergraduate or graduate degree in entomology who are nominated by members of the Entomological Society of America (ESA).

Eligibility This program is open to students working on an undergraduate or graduate degree in entomology at a college or university in Canada, Mexico, or the United States. Candidates must be nominated by members of the society. They must be "needy" students; for the purposes of this program, need may be based on physical limitations, or economic, minority, or environmental conditions.

Financial data The stipend is $2,000 per year.

Duration 1 year; may be renewed up to 3 additional years.

Additional information This fellowship was first awarded in 1996. Recipients are expected to be present at the society's annual meeting, where the award will be presented.

Number awarded 1 each year.

Deadline June of each year.

[525]
STANFORD SUMMER RESEARCH PROGRAM/ AMGEN SCHOLARS PROGRAM

Stanford University
School of Medicine
Attn: Office of Graduate Education
M.S.O.B. Second Floor
251 Campus Drive
Stanford, CA 94305-5421
(650) 725-8791 E-mail: ssrpmail@stanford.edu
Web: ssrp.stanford.edu

Summary To provide African American and other underrepresented minority undergraduate students with a summer research experience at Stanford University in biological and biomedical sciences.

Eligibility This program is open to sophomores, juniors, and non-graduating seniors at 4-year colleges and universities in the United States, Puerto Rico, and U.S. territories. Students from all ethnic backgrounds are eligible, but the program especially encourages applications from African Americans, Latino/Hispanic Americans, Native Americans, Pacific Islanders, and other undergraduates who, by reason of their culture, class, race, ethnicity, background, work and life experiences, skills, and interests would bring diversity to graduate study in the biological and biomedical sciences (biochemistry, bioengineering, biology, biomedical informatics, biophysics, cancer biology, chemical and systems biology, developmental biology, genetics, immunology, microbiology, molecular and cellular physiology, neurosciences, stem cell and regenerative medicine, and structural biology). Applicants must have at least 1 year of undergraduate education remaining before graduation and should be planning to prepare for and enter a Ph.D. program in the biological or biomedical sciences. They must have a GPA of 3.2 or higher. U.S. citizenship or permanent resident status is required.

Financial data The program provides a stipend of $3,500, housing, meals, and transportation to and from the San Francisco Bay area.

Duration 9 weeks during the summer.

Additional information This program currently serves as the Stanford component of the Amgen Scholars Program, which operates at 9 other U.S. universities and is funded by the Amgen Foundation.

Number awarded Up to 25 each year.

Deadline January of each year.

[526]
STUDENT OPPORTUNITY SCHOLARSHIPS OF THE PRESBYTERIAN CHURCH (USA)

Presbyterian Church (USA)
Attn: Office of Financial Aid for Studies
100 Witherspoon Street, Room M-052
Louisville, KY 40202-1396
(502) 569-5224 Toll Free: (800) 728-7228, ext. 5224
Fax: (502) 569-8766 TDD: (800) 833-5955
E-mail: finaid@pcusa.org
Web: gamc.pcusa.org

Summary To provide financial assistance to Presbyterian college students, especially African Americans and other racial/ethnic minorities.

Eligibility This program is open to active members of the Presbyterian Church (USA) who are entering their sophomore, junior, or senior year of college as full-time students. Preference is given to applicants who are members of racial/ethnic minority groups (Asian American, African American, Hispanic American, Native American, Alaska Native). Applicants must have a GPA of 2.5 or higher and be able to demonstrate financial need.

Financial data Stipends range up to $2,000 per year, depending upon the financial need of the recipient.

Duration 1 year; may be renewed for up to 3 additional years if the recipient continues to need financial assistance and demonstrates satisfactory academic progress.

Number awarded Varies each year.

Deadline May of each year.

[527]
SUMMER HONORS UNDERGRADUATE RESEARCH PROGRAM

Harvard Medical School
Attn: Division of Medical Sciences
Diversity Programs Office
260 Longwood Avenue, Room 432
Boston, MA 02115-5720
(617) 432-1342 Toll Free: (800) 367-9019
Fax: (617) 432-2644 E-mail: SHURP@hms.harvard.edu
Web: www.hms.harvard.edu/dms/diversity/shurp

Summary To provide an opportunity for African American and other underrepresented minority students to engage in research at Harvard Medical School during the summer.

Eligibility This program at Harvard Medical School is open to undergraduate students belonging to minority groups that are underrepresented in the sciences. Applicants must have had at least 1 summer (or equivalent) of experience in a research laboratory and have taken at least 1 upper-level biology course that includes molecular biology. They should be considering a career in biological or biomedical research. U.S. citizenship or permanent resident status is required.

Financial data The program provides a stipend of $420 per week, dormitory housing, travel costs, a meal card, and health insurance if it is needed.

Duration 10 weeks during the summer.

Number awarded Varies each year.

Deadline January of each year.

[528]
SUMMER RESEARCH OPPORTUNITIES PROGRAM (SROP)

Committee on Institutional Cooperation
Attn: Academic and International Programs
1819 South Neil Street, Suite D
Champaign, IL 61820-7271
(217) 333-8475 Fax: (217) 244-7127
E-mail: cic@staff.cic.net
Web: www.cic.net/Home/Students/SROP/Home.aspx

Summary To provide an opportunity for African Americans and other undergraduates from diverse backgrounds to gain research experience at member institutions of the Committee on Institutional Cooperation (CIC) during the summer.

Eligibility This program is open to students currently enrolled in a degree-granting program at a college or university who have a GPA of 3.0 or higher and an interest in continuing on to graduate school. Applicants must be interested in conducting a summer research project under the supervision of a faculty mentor at a CIC member institution. The program is designed to increase educational access for students from diverse backgrounds; members of racial and ethnic minority groups and low-income first-generation students are especially encouraged to apply. U.S. citizenship or permanent resident status is required.

Financial data Participants are paid a stipend that depends on the participating CIC member institution, but ranges from $3,000 to $6,000. Faculty mentors receive a $500 research allowance for the cost of materials.

Duration 8 to 10 weeks during the summer.

Additional information Participants work directly with faculty mentors at the institution of their choice and also engage in other enrichment activities, such as workshops and social gatherings. In July, all participants come together at 1 of the CIC campuses for the annual SROP conference. The participating CIC member institutions are University of Illinois at Urbana-Champaign, University of Iowa, University of Michigan, University of Minnesota, University of Nebraska at Lincoln, University of Wisconsin at Madison, Michigan State University, Northwestern University, Ohio State University, Pennsylvania State University, and Purdue University. Students are required to write a paper and an abstract describing their projects and to present the results of their work at a campus symposium.

Number awarded Varies each year.

Deadline February of each year.

[529]
SUMMER UNDERGRADUATE RESEARCH FELLOWSHIPS IN ORGANIC CHEMISTRY

American Chemical Society
Division of Organic Chemistry
1155 16th Street, N.W.
Washington, DC 20036
(202) 872-4401 Toll Free: (800) 227-5558, ext. 4401
E-mail: division@acs.org
Web: www.organicdivision.org/?nd=p_surf_program

Summary To provide an opportunity for college juniors (particularly African Americans and other minorities) to work on a research project in organic chemistry during the summer.

Eligibility This program is open to students who are currently enrolled as juniors at a college or university in the United States and are nominated by their school. Nominees must be interested in conducting a research project in organic chemistry at the home institution during the following summer. The project must be mentored by a member of the Organic Division of the American Chemical Society. Along with their application, students must submit brief statements on the project they propose to undertake, their background that has prepared them to do this work, their proposed methodology, and how a summer research project fits into their long-range plans. U.S. citizenship or permanent resident status is required. Selection is based on demonstrated interest and talent in organic chemistry, merit and feasibility of the research project, commitment of a faculty mentor to support the student, academic record (particularly in organic chemistry and related sciences), and importance of the award in facilitating the personal and career plans of the student. Applications from minorities are especially encouraged.

Financial data Grants range up to $5,000. The program also covers the costs of a trip by all participants to an industrial campus in the fall for a dinner, award session, scientific talks, a tour of the campus, and a poster session where the results of the summer research investigations are presented.

Duration Summer months.

Additional information Current corporate sponsors of this program include Pfizer, Merck, and Genentech.

Number awarded 12 each year.

Deadline February of each year.

[530]
SURETY AND FIDELITY INDUSTRY SCHOLARSHIP PROGRAM

The Surety Foundation
Attn: Scholarship Program for Minority Students
1101 Connecticut Avenue, N.W., Suite 800
Washington, DC 20036
(202) 463-0600 Fax: (202) 463-0606
E-mail: scarradine@surety.org
Web: www.thesuretyfoundation.org

Summary To provide financial assistance to African American and other minority undergraduates working on a degree in a field related to insurance.

Eligibility This program is open to full-time undergraduates who are U.S. citizens and members of a minority group (Black, Native American/Alaskan Native, Asian/Pacific Islander, Hispanic). Applicants must have completed at least 30 semester hours of study at an accredited 4-year college or university and have a declared major in insurance/risk management, accounting, business, or finance. They must have a GPA of 3.0 or higher and be able to demonstrate financial need. Along with their application, they must submit an essay of 500 to 1,000 words on the role of surety bonding and the surety industry in public sector construction.

Financial data The stipend is $2,500 per year.

Duration 1 year; recipients may reapply.

Additional information This program, established in 2003 by The Surety & Fidelity Association of America, includes the Adrienne Alexander Scholarship and the George W. McClellan Scholarship.

Number awarded Varies each year.

Deadline April of each year.

[531]
SYNOD OF LAKES AND PRAIRIES RACIAL ETHNIC SCHOLARSHIPS

Synod of Lakes and Prairies
Attn: Committee on Racial Ethnic Ministry
2115 Cliff Drive
Eagen, MN 55122-3327
(651) 357-1140 Toll Free: (800) 328-1880, ext. 202
Fax: (651) 357-1141 E-mail: mkes@lakesandprairies.org
Web: www.lakesandprairies.org

Summary To provide financial assistance to African American and other minority residents of the Presbyterian Church (USA) Synod of Lakes and Prairies who are working on an undergraduate or graduate degree at a college or seminary in any state in preparation for service to the church.

Eligibility This program is open to members of Presbyterian churches who reside within the Synod of Lakes and Prairies (Iowa, Minnesota, Nebraska, North Dakota, South Dakota, and Wisconsin). Applicants must be members of ethnic minority groups studying at least half time for service in the Presbyterian Church (USA) as a teaching elder, ordained minister, commissioned ruling elder, lay professional, or volunteer. They must be in good academic standing, making progress toward an undergraduate or graduate degree, and able to demonstrate financial need. Along with their application, they must submit essays of 200 to 500 words on 1) what the church needs to do to be faithful to its mission in the world today; and 2) the people, practices, or events that influence their commitment to Christ in ways that renew their fair and strengthen their service.

Financial data Stipends range from $850 to $3,500.

Duration 1 year.

Number awarded Varies each year; recently, 9 of these scholarships were awarded.

Deadline September of each year.

[532]
SYNOD OF THE TRINITY RACIAL ETHNIC EDUCATIONAL SCHOLARSHIPS

Synod of the Trinity
Attn: Scholarships
3040 Market Street
Camp Hill, PA 17011-4599
(717) 737-0421, ext. 233
Toll Free: (800) 242-0534, ext. 233
Fax: (717) 737-8211 E-mail: mhumer@syntrinity.org
Web: www.syntrinity.org

Summary To provide financial assistance to African American and other ethnic minority students in Pennsylvania, West Virginia, and designated counties in Ohio who are interested in attending college in any state.

Eligibility This program is open to members of a racial minority group (African American, Asian, Hispanic, Latino, Middle Eastern, or Native American) who are enrolled or planning to enroll full time at an accredited college or vocational school in any state. Applicants may be of any religious denomination, but they must be residents of the area covered by the Presbyterian Church (USA) Synod of the Trinity, which covers all of Pennsylvania; West Virginia except for the counties of Berkeley, Grant, Hampshire, Hardy, Jefferson, Mineral, Morgan, and Pendleton; and the Ohio counties of Belmont, Columbiana, Harrison, Jefferson, and Monroe. They must have total income of less than $85,000 for a family of 4. U.S. citizenship or permanent resident status is required.

Financial data Awards range from $100 to $1,000 per year, depending on the need of the recipient.

Duration 1 year; recipients may reapply.

Number awarded Varies each year.

Deadline April of each year.

[533]
TDC SCHOLARSHIP

National Association of Black Accountants
Attn: National Scholarship Program
7474 Greenway Center Drive, Suite 1120
Greenbelt, MD 20770
(301) 474-NABA Fax: (301) 474-3114
E-mail: scholarships@nabainc.org
Web: www.nabainc.org

Summary To provide financial assistance to student members of the National Association of Black Accountants (NABA) who are working on an undergraduate or graduate degree in a field related to accounting.

Eligibility This program is open to minorities who are NABA members and enrolled full time as 1) an undergraduate freshman, sophomore, junior, or first-semester senior majoring in accounting, business, or finance at a 4-year college or university; or 2) a graduate student working on a master's degree in accounting. High school seniors are not eligible. Applicants must have a GPA of 2.0 or higher in their major and 2.5 or higher overall. Along with their application, they must submit a 500-word personal statement on their involvement in NABA, career objectives, leadership abilities, and community activities. Financial need is not considered in the selection process.

Financial data The stipend is $1,000.

Duration 1 year.

Number awarded 1 each year.

Deadline January of each year.

[534]
TECHNICAL RESEARCH EXHIBITION AWARDS

National Society of Black Engineers
Attn: Programs Department
205 Daingerfield Road
Alexandria, VA 22314
(703) 549-2207 Fax: (703) 683-5312
E-mail: programs@nsbe.org
Web: www.nsbe.org

Summary To recognize and reward outstanding technical papers by undergraduate and graduate student members of the National Society of Black Engineers (NSBE).

Eligibility This competition is open to undergraduate and graduate student members of the society. Candidates must submit technical papers that are between 10 and 20 pages in length and that follow a standard style for such work. All papers must include an abstract and a high degree of technical content. International members who are unable to attend the national convention may also apply through an online procedure. Undergraduate students (both domestic and international) are encouraged to submit results from hands-on project based research as well as theoretical research with an academic or project-based focus. Graduate students (both domestic and international) are encouraged to submit topics demonstrating theoretical research with an academic focus. Domestic applicants must specify whether they wish to participate in a poster session, oral presentation (10 minutes, followed by a 10-minute question and answer session), or both at the NSBE national convention. Based on the abstracts, 50 members are selected to present their research at the convention. Winners are selected, either from presentations at the convention or from posts on the web site. Selection is based on format (15 points), organization (10 points), technical content (40 points), clarity (10 points), grammar (15 points), and use of visual aids (10 points).

Financial data In the oral presentations category, first prize is $2,000, second $1,000, and third $500. In the posters category, first prize is $1,600, second $800, and third $400.

Duration The competition is held annually.

Number awarded 6 cash awards (3 for oral presentations and 3 for posters) are presented each year.

Deadline January of each year.

[535]
TENNESSEE MINORITY TEACHING FELLOWS PROGRAM

Tennessee Student Assistance Corporation
Parkway Towers
404 James Robertson Parkway, Suite 1510
Nashville, TN 37243-0820
(615) 741-1346 Toll Free: (800) 342-1663
Fax: (615) 741-6101 E-mail: TSAC.Aidinfo@tn.gov
Web: www.tn.gov

Summary To provide funding to African American and other minority residents of Tennessee who wish to attend college in the state to prepare for a career in the teaching field.

Eligibility This program is open to minority residents of Tennessee who are either high school seniors planning to enroll full time at a college or university in the state or continuing college students at a Tennessee college or university. High school seniors must have a GPA of 2.75 or higher and an ACT score of at least 18 or a combined mathematics and critical reading SAT score of at least 860. Continuing college students must have a college GPA of 2.5 or higher. All applicants must agree to teach at the K-12 level in a Tennessee public school following graduation from college. Along with their application, they must submit a 250-word essay on why they chose teaching as a profession. U.S. citizenship is required.

Financial data The scholarship/loan is $5,000 per year. Recipients incur an obligation to teach at the preK-12 level in a Tennessee public school 1 year for each year the award is received.

Duration 1 year; may be renewed for up to 3 additional years, provided the recipient maintains full-time enrollment and a cumulative GPA of 2.5 or higher.

Additional information This program began in 1989.

Number awarded 20 new awards are granted each year.

Deadline April of each year.

[536]
THETA OMEGA OMEGA CHAPTER IVY VINE CHARITIES SCHOLARSHIPS

Alpha Kappa Alpha Sorority, Inc.-Theta Omega Omega Chapter
Attn: Ivy Vine Charities, Inc.
43 Randolph Road
PMB 102
Silver Spring, MD 20904
(301) 368-2105 E-mail: ivcscholarship@gmail.com
Web: www.ivyvinecharities.org/scholarship.html

Summary To provide financial assistance to high school seniors from the Washington, D.C. metropolitan area who plan to attend college, especially an Historically Black College or University (HBCU), in any state.

Eligibility This program is open to seniors graduating from high schools in Washington, D.C. or the Maryland counties of Montgomery or Prince George's. Applicants must have a GPA of 2.7 or higher and a record of participation in school and community activities. They must have been accepted by a 4-year college or university in any state; for some of the awards, that must be an HBCU.

Financial data Scholarship stipends are $4,000; book awards are $1,000.

Duration 1 year.

Additional information Alpha Kappa Alpha was founded in 1908 at Howard University and is currently 1 of the largest social sororities whose membership is predominantly African American women. The Theta Omega Omega chapter serves alumnae members in the Washington, D.C. metropolitan area.

Number awarded 3 scholarships (2 for students attending an HBCU and 1 for a student at another college or university) are awarded each year. The number of book awards varies; recently, 4 were presented.

Deadline March of each year.

[537]
THIRD EPISCOPAL DISTRICT RAYMOND R. DAVIS SCHOLARSHIP

African Methodist Episcopal Church
Third Episcopal District Lay Organization
c/o Lenora Brogdon-Wyatt, Second Vice President
1113 West Second Street
Xenia, OH 45385
(937) 554-7585 E-mail: lenora.brogdon@yahoo.com
Web: www.thirddistrictame.org/raydavis.htm

Summary To provide financial assistance to members of African Methodist Episcopal (AME) churches in its Third Episcopal District who are interested in attending college in any state.

Eligibility This program is open to members of Third Episcopal District AME churches (in Ohio, western Pennsylvania, and West Virginia). Applicants must be high school seniors or students already enrolled in a bachelor's degree program in any field at an accredited college or university in any state. Along with their application, they must submit an essay of 800 to 1,000 words on a theme that changes annually but relates to their personal development. Selection is based on that essay, academic achievement, quality and level of church participation, leadership, extracurricular activities, honors, and letters of recommendation.

Financial data Stipends range from $500 to $1,000.

Duration 1 year.

Number awarded 1 or more each year.

Deadline February of each year.

[538]
THOMARA LATIMER CANCER FOUNDATION SCHOLARSHIPS

Thomara Latimer Cancer Foundation
Attn: Scholarship Committee
Franklin Plaza Center
29193 Northwestern Highway, Suite 528
Southfield, MI 48034
(248) 557-2346 Fax: (248) 557-9230
E-mail: info@thomlatimercares.org
Web: www.thomlatimercares.org

Summary To provide financial assistance to African American residents of Michigan (especially those who have had cancer) who are interested in studying a medically-related field at a college in any state.

Eligibility This program is open to African American residents of Michigan between 17 and 30 years of age. Applicants must be 1) a high school senior accepted at an accredited college or university in any state in a medically-related program (e.g., medical technician, physician assistant); or 2) a student admitted to a medically-related professional program (e.g., nursing, medicine, physical or occupational therapy) at a college or university in any state. They must have a GPA of 3.0 or higher. Along with their application, they must submit a brief essay on why they should be awarded this scholarship. Financial need is not considered in the selection process. Special consideration is given to students who are cancer survivors.

Financial data The stipend is $1,000.

Duration 1 year; may be renewed 1 additional year.

Number awarded 10 each year.

Deadline December of each year.

[539]
THOMAS G. NEUSOM SCHOLARSHIPS

Conference of Minority Transportation Officials
Attn: National Scholarship Program
1875 I Street, N.W., Suite 500
Washington, DC 20006
(703) 234-4072 Fax: (202) 318-0364
Web: www.comto.org/?page=Scholarships

Summary To provide financial assistance for college or graduate school to African American and other members of the Conference of Minority Transportation Officials (COMTO).

Eligibility This program is open to undergraduate and graduate students who have been members of COMTO for at least 1 year. Applicants must be working (either full or part time) on a degree in a field related to transportation and have a GPA of 2.5 or higher. Along with their application, they must submit a cover letter with a 500-word statement of career goals. Financial need is not considered in the selection process. U.S. citizenship or legal resident status is required.

Financial data The stipend is $5,500. Funds are paid directly to the recipient's college or university.

Duration 1 year.

Additional information COMTO was established in 1971 to promote, strengthen, and expand the roles of minorities in all aspects of transportation. Recipients are expected to attend the COMTO National Scholarship Luncheon.

Number awarded 1 each year.

Deadline May of each year.

[540]
THOMAS R. LEE, JR. SCHOLARSHIPS

Knights of Peter Claver, Inc.
Attn: National Scholarship Committee
1825 Orleans Avenue
New Orleans, LA 70116-2894
(504) 821-4225 Fax: (504) 821-4253
E-mail: info@kofpc.org
Web: www.kofpc.org

Summary To provide financial assistance for college to high school seniors with a connection of the Knights of Peter Claver (an organization for Catholic men of color).

Eligibility This program is open to practicing Catholics who are graduating high school seniors. Applicants, or at least 1 of their parents, must be a member of the Knights of Peter Claver or its Ladies Auxiliary.

Financial data The stipend is $2,000 per year.

Duration 2 years, provided the recipient maintains a GPA of 3.0 or higher during the freshman year of college.

Additional information The Knights of Peter Claver was founded in 1909 at Mobile, Alabama as a Catholic fraternal society for men of color. The sponsor also offers another scholarship to high school seniors with a connection of the Knights of Peter Claver: the $1,000 Willie Polk, Jr. Memorial Scholarships.

Number awarded 2 each year.

Deadline June of each year.

[541]
THURGOOD MARSHALL SCHOLARSHIPS

Thurgood Marshall College Fund
Attn: Campus Relations Associate
901 F Street, N.W., Suite 300
Washington, DC 20004
(202) 507-4851 Fax: (202) 652-2934
E-mail: info@tmcfund.org
Web: www.thurgoodmarshallfund.net

Summary To provide financial assistance to high school seniors or graduates who are interested in working on a degree at a college or university that is a member of the Thurgood Marshall College Fund (TMCF).

Eligibility This program is open to full-time students enrolled or accepted at 1 of 47 designated TMCF institutions, most of which are public Historically Black Colleges and Universities (HBCUs) or other schools with large African American enrollments. Applicants must be U.S. citizens or permanent residents with a valid permanent resident card or passport stamped I-551. They must have a current GPA of 3.0 or higher and be able to demonstrate financial need. Along with their application, they must submit 1) a resume that includes community service, leadership activities, and employment/internship experience; 2) their Student Aid report from their FAFSA; 3) their most recent transcript; 4) a recommendation from a current school faculty member; and 5) a 500-word essay on their choice of 3 assigned topics.

Financial data Stipends average $3,100 per semester ($6,200 per year), depending on the need of the recipient. Funds are awarded through the institution to be used for tuition, room, board, books, and fees.

Duration 1 year; may be renewed for up to 3 additional years if the recipient maintains a GPA of 3.0 or higher in college.

Additional information This program was founded in 1987 by the Miller Brewing Company (now MillerCoors) in cooperation with the American Association of State Colleges and Universities and the Office for the Advancement of Public Black Colleges of the National Association of State Universities and Land-Grant Colleges. Other major sponsors include Wells Fargo Bank, Walmart Stores, Altria Group, Costco Wholesale, Ford Motor Company, and the United Student Aid Fund. Contact TMCF for a list of participating institutions.

Number awarded Varies each year; recently, nearly 230 students were receiving support from this program.

Deadline April of each year.

[542]
TOYOTA NSBE CORPORATE SCHOLARSHIPS

National Society of Black Engineers
Attn: Programs Department
205 Daingerfield Road
Alexandria, VA 22314
(703) 549-2207 Fax: (703) 683-5312
E-mail: scholarships@nsbe.org
Web: www.nsbe.org/Programs/Scholarships.aspx

Summary To provide financial assistance to members of the National Society of Black Engineers (NSBE) who are majoring in designated engineering fields.

Eligibility This program is open to members of the society who are enrolled as college sophomores, juniors, or seniors and majoring in chemical, electrical, industrial, materials, or mechanical engineering. Applicants must have a GPA of 3.0 or higher and a demonstrated interest in employment with Toyota.

Financial data The stipend is $2,500.

Duration 1 year.

Additional information This program is sponsored by Toyota Motor Sales, U.S.A., Inc.

Number awarded 2 each year.

Deadline May of each year.

[543]
TRAILBLAZER SCHOLARSHIP

Conference of Minority Transportation Officials
Attn: National Scholarship Program
1875 I Street, N.W., Suite 500
Washington, DC 20006
(703) 234-4072 Fax: (202) 318-0364
Web: www.comto.org/?page=Scholarships

Summary To provide financial assistance to African American and other minority undergraduate and graduate students working on a degree in a field related to transportation.

Eligibility This program is open to minority undergraduate and graduate students who are working (either full or part time) on a degree in a field related to transportation and have a GPA of 2.5 or higher. Along with their application, they must submit a cover letter with a 500-word statement of career goals. Financial need is not considered in the selection process. U.S. citizenship or legal resident status is required.

Financial data The stipend is $2,500. Funds are paid directly to the recipient's college or university.

Duration 1 year.

Additional information The Conference of Minority Transportation Officials (COMTO) was established in 1971 to promote, strengthen, and expand the roles of minorities in all aspects of transportation. Recipients are expected to attend the COMTO National Scholarship Luncheon.

Number awarded 1 each year.

Deadline May of each year.

[544]
TUSKEGEE AIRMEN SCHOLARSHIPS

Tuskegee Airmen Scholarship Foundation
P.O. Box 83395
Los Angeles, CA 90045
(310) 215-3985 E-mail: anoldwarrior@msn.com
Web: www.taisf.org/scholar.htm

Summary To provide financial assistance for college to high school seniors and graduates who submit an essay on the history of Tuskegee Airmen, a group of African Americans who served as pilots in World War II.

Eligibility This program is open to students who have graduated or will graduate from high school in the current year with a GPA of 3.0 or higher. Applicants must submit a 1-page essay entitled "The Tuskegee Airmen" that reflects an overview of their history. They must also submit documentation of financial need and a 2-page essay that includes a brief autobiographical sketch, educational aspirations, career goals, and an explanation of why financial assistance is essential. Applications must be submitted to individual chapters of Tuskegee Airmen, Inc. which verify them as appropriate, evaluate them, and forward those considered worthy of further consideration to the national competition. Selection is based on academic achievement, extracurricular and community activities, financial need, recommendations, and both essays.

Financial data The stipend is $1,500.

Duration 1 year; nonrenewable.

Number awarded 40 each year.

Deadline January of each year.

[545]
UNCF CORPORATE SCHOLARS PROGRAMS

United Negro College Fund
Attn: Corporate Scholars Program
P.O. Box 1435
Alexandria, VA 22313-9998
Toll Free: (866) 671-7237 E-mail: internship@uncf.org
Web: www.uncf.org

Summary To provide financial aid and work experience to African Americans and other minority students working on a degree in designated fields of business, science, and engineering.

Eligibility A number of corporate sponsors provides funding for this program; each establishes its own specifications. All are open to undergraduates; some are also available to graduate students. Some allow students to be enrolled at the college or university of their choice, others are limited to students at Historically Black Colleges and Universities (HBCUs), and others are restricted to UNCF member institutions. Some are open to minority (African American, Alaskan Native, American Indian, Asian Pacific Islander American, Hispanic) students in general, but others are more restrictive. Fields of study vary, but most focus on areas of business, science, and engineering of interest to the corporate sponsor. All include summer internships at the corporate sponsor's facilities. GPA requirements vary; some are as high as 3.0.

Financial data The students selected for this program receive paid internships and need-based scholarships that range up to $15,000 per year.

Duration 8 to 10 weeks for the internships; 1 year for the scholarships, which may be renewed.

Number awarded Varies each year.

Deadline Each sponsor sets its own deadline.

[546]
UNDERGRADUATE STUDENT RESEARCH EXPERIENCES AT FDA

National Science Foundation
Directorate for Engineering
Attn: Division of Chemical, Bioengineering, Environmental, and Transport Systems
4201 Wilson Boulevard, Room 565S
Arlington, VA 22230
(703) 292-7942 Fax: (703) 292-9098
TDD: (800) 281-8749 E-mail: lesterow@nsf.gov
Web: www.nsf.gov/funding/pgm_summ.jsp?pims_id=5605

Summary To provide an opportunity for undergraduate students (particularly African Americans, other underrepresented minorities, and students with disabilities) to be part of research studies at an intramural laboratory of the U.S. Food and Drug Administration (FDA).

Eligibility This program is open to undergraduate students in science, engineering, and mathematics fields of interest to the National Science Foundation (NSF). Applicants must be U.S. citizens, nationals, or permanent residents. They must be proposing a program of full- or part-time work at an FDA laboratory in an area related to their academic program under the guidance of an academic adviser and an FDA mentor. The program encourages applications from all citizens, including women and men, underrepresented minorities, and persons with disabilities.

Financial data Undergraduate students may receive stipends up to $450 per week; they may also receive some assistance with housing or travel expenses, or both. No indirect costs are allowed. The total award may be up to $8,000 for a fellowship for a single student. FDA provides office space, research facilities, research costs in the form of expendable and minor equipment purchases in the host laboratory, and the time of its research staff.

Duration Support may be provided for a summer project, or for 1 or 2 semesters of part- or full-time work.

Additional information This program is also offered by the NSF Directorate for Computer and Information Science and Engineering.

Number awarded A total of 3 to 10 grants for all FDA programs is awarded each year; total funding is approximately $500,000.

Deadline March of each year.

[547]
UNITED AIRLINES PILOT SCHOLARSHIPS

Organization of Black Aerospace Professionals, Inc.
Attn: Scholarship Coordinator
1 Westbrook Corporate Center, Suite 300
Westchester, IL 60154
(708) 449-7755 Toll Free: (800) JET-OBAP
Fax: (708) 449-7754 E-mail: obapscholarship@obap.org
Web: www.obap.org/scholarships/scholarship-opportunities

Summary To provide financial assistance to members of the Organization of Black Aerospace Professionals (OBAP) who are enrolled in a collegiate aviation program.

Eligibility This program is open to OBAP members who have a commercial certificate and instrument rating, preferably for multi-engine. Applicants must be enrolled in an accredited collegiate aviation program. They must have a GPA of 3.0 or higher. Along with their application, they must submit a 500-word essay on how this award will help advance their aviation career and a copy of their first class medical certificate.

Financial data The stipend is $4,000. Funds are paid directly to the college.

Duration 1 year.

Additional information The OBAP was originally established in 1976 as the Organization of Black Airline Pilots to make certain Blacks and other minorities had a group that would keep them informed about opportunities for advancement within commercial aviation. This program is sponsored by United Airlines.

Number awarded 2 each year.

Deadline May of each year.

[548]
UNITED HEALTH FOUNDATION SCHOLARSHIPS OF THE THURGOOD MARSHALL COLLEGE FUND

Thurgood Marshall College Fund
Attn: Campus Relations Associate
901 F Street, N.W., Suite 300
Washington, DC 20004
(202) 507-4851 Fax: (202) 652-2934
E-mail: info@tmcfund.org
Web: www.thurgoodmarshallfund.net

Summary To provide financial assistance to African American upper-division students working on a degree in health-related fields at public Historically Black Colleges and Universities (HBCUs) that are members of the Thurgood Marshall College Fund (TMCF).

Eligibility This program is open to students currently enrolled as juniors at any of the 47 TMCF member institutions. Applicants must be majoring in a health-related field. They must have a GPA of 3.0 or higher and be able to demonstrate financial need. Along with their application, they must submit a 500-word essay on 1 of the following topics: 1) a significant setback, challenge, or opportunity in their life and the impact it has had on them; 2) what inspired them to pursue a degree in their current field of study and the impact it will have on our society; or 3) what it means to be the first person in their family to receive a college degree. U.S. citizenship or permanent resident status is required.

Financial data The stipend $6,200.

Duration 1 year; nonrenewable.

Additional information This program is sponsored by United Health Foundation.

Number awarded Varies each year.

Deadline April of each year.

[549]
UNITED METHODIST ETHNIC MINORITY SCHOLARSHIPS

United Methodist Church
Attn: General Board of Higher Education and Ministry
Office of Loans and Scholarships
1001 19th Avenue South
P.O. Box 340007
Nashville, TN 37203-0007
(615) 340-7344 Fax: (615) 340-7367
E-mail: umscholar@gbhem.org
Web: www.gbhem.org

Summary To provide financial assistance to African Americans and other undergraduate Methodist students of ethnic minority ancestry.

Eligibility This program is open to full-time undergraduate students at accredited colleges and universities in the United States who have been active, full members of a United Methodist Church for at least 1 year prior to applying. Applicants must have at least 1 parent who is African American, Hispanic, Asian, Native American, or Pacific Islander. They must have a GPA of 2.5 or higher and be able to demonstrate financial need. U.S. citizenship, permanent resident status, or membership in a central conference of the United Methodist Church is required. Selection is based on church membership, involvement in church and community activities, GPA, and financial need.

Financial data Stipends range from $500 to $1,000.

Duration 1 year; recipients may reapply.

Number awarded Varies each year.

Deadline February of each year.

[550]
UNITED NEGRO COLLEGE FUND ACADEMIC MAJOR-BASED SCHOLARSHIPS

United Negro College Fund
Attn: Scholarships and Grants Department
8260 Willow Oaks Corporate Drive
P.O. Box 10444
Fairfax, VA 22031-8044
(703) 205-3466 Toll Free: (800) 331-2244
Fax: (703) 205-3574
Web: www.uncf.org

Summary To provide financial assistance to students who are interested in majoring in specified fields at academic institutions affiliated with the United Negro College Fund (UNCF).

Eligibility These programs are open to students planning to pursue designated majors at UNCF-member institutions. Applicants must be high school seniors or graduates with strong academic backgrounds (minimum GPA of 2.5). Students who have completed their junior year in high school with a record of distinction may also be considered. Financial need must be demonstrated. Applications should be submitted directly to the UNCF-member institution the student plans to attend.

Financial data The awards are intended to cover tuition and range from a minimum of $500 to a maximum of $7,500 per year.

Duration 1 year; may be renewed.

Additional information Recipients must attend a UNCF-member institution of higher learning. These are: Miles College, Oakwood College, Stillman College, Talladega College, and Tuskegee University in Alabama; Philander Smith College in Arkansas; Bethune-Cookman University, Edward Waters College, and Florida Memorial College in Florida; Clark Atlanta University, Interdenominational Theological Center, Morehouse College, Paine College, and Spelman College in Georgia; Dillard University and Xavier University in Louisiana; Rust College and Tougaloo College in Mississippi; Bennett College, Johnson C. Smith University, Livingstone College, Saint Augustine's University, and Shaw University in North Carolina; Wilberforce University in Ohio; Allen University, Benedict College, Claflin University, Morris College, and Voorhees College in South Carolina; Fisk University, Lane College, and LeMoyne-Owen College in Tennessee; Huston-Tillotson College, Jarvis Christian College, Texas College, and Wiley College in Texas; and Virginia Union University in Virginia.

Number awarded A total of nearly 1,200 UNCF scholarships are awarded each year.

Deadline Deadline dates vary, depending upon the individual institution's requirements.

[551]
UNITED PARCEL SERVICE SCHOLARSHIP FOR MINORITY STUDENTS

Institute of Industrial Engineers
Attn: Scholarship Coordinator
3577 Parkway Lane, Suite 200
Norcross, GA 30092
(770) 449-0461, ext. 105 Toll Free: (800) 494-0460
Fax: (770) 441-3295 E-mail: bcameron@iienet.org
Web: www.iienet2.org/Details.aspx?id=857

Summary To provide financial assistance to African American and other minority undergraduates who are studying industrial engineering at a school in the United States, Canada, or Mexico.

Eligibility Eligible to be nominated are minority undergraduate students enrolled at any school in the United States or its territories, Canada, or Mexico, provided the school's engineering program is accredited by an agency recognized by the Institute of Industrial Engineers (IIE) and the student is pursuing a full-time course of study in industrial engineering with a GPA of at least 3.4. Nominees must have at least 5 full quarters or 3 full semesters remaining until graduation. Students may not apply directly for these awards; they must be nominated by the head of their industrial engineering department. Nominees must be IIE members. Selection is based on scholastic ability, character, leadership, and potential service to the industrial engineering profession.

Financial data The stipend is $4,000.

Duration 1 year.

Additional information Funding for this program is provided by the UPS Foundation.

Number awarded 1 each year.

Deadline Schools must submit nominations by November of each year.

[552]
UNIVERSITY OF CALIFORNIA AT BERKELEY AMGEN SCHOLARS PROGRAM

University of California at Berkeley
Attn: Amgen Scholars Program
158 Barrows Hall
MC 2990
Berkeley, CA 94720-2990
(510) 642-0280 Fax: (510) 643-6762
E-mail: amgenscholars@berkeley.edu
Web: amgenscholars.berkeley.edu

Summary To provide undergraduate students (particularly African Americans and others from diverse backgrounds) with a summer research experience at the University of California at Berkeley in biological and biomedical sciences.

Eligibility This program is open to sophomores, juniors, and non-graduating seniors at 4-year colleges and universities in the United States, Puerto Rico, and U.S. territories. Applicants must be interested in a summer research experience at UC Berkeley in biochemistry, bioengineering, biophysics, cell and developmental biology, chemical biology, chemical and biomedical engineering, chemistry, computational biology, genetics, genomics and development, immunology, integrative biology, microbiology, molecular and cell biology, neuroscience, plant and microbial biology, structural biology, or synthetic biology. They must have a GPA of 3.2 or higher and an interest in continuing on to a Ph.D. or M.D./Ph.D. (but not M.D.) program. Applications are especially encouraged from students from diverse populations and backgrounds. U.S. citizenship or permanent resident status is required.

Financial data Housing, travel to and from Berkeley, meals, and a stipend of $4,000 are provided.

Duration 10 weeks during the summer.

Additional information This program serves as the UC Berkeley component of the Amgen Scholars Program, which operates at 9 other U.S. universities and is funded by the Amgen Foundation.

Number awarded 25 each year.

Deadline January of each year.

[553]
UNIVERSITY OF CALIFORNIA AT SAN FRANCISCO SUMMER RESEARCH OPPORTUNITIES

University of California at San Francisco
Office of Graduate Outreach
Attn: Outreach and Student Programs Coordinator
1675 Owens Street, Room 310
Box 0523
San Francisco, CA 94143-0523
(415) 514-3510 Fax: (415) 514-0844
E-mail: gdsummerprogram@ucsf.edu
Web: graduate.ucsf.edu

Summary To provide undergraduate students (particularly African Americans and others from diverse backgrounds) with a summer research experience at the University of California at San Francisco in biological and biomedical sciences.

Eligibility This activity consists of 3 separate programs, but they operate together and have a common application and requirements. The 3 programs are the Amgen Scholars Program, the Molecular Biosciences Research Experiences for Undergraduates (REU), and the Summer Research Training Program (SRTP). The activity is open to sophomores, juniors, and non-graduating seniors at 4-year colleges and universities in the United States, Puerto Rico, and U.S. territories. Applicants must be interested in a summer research experience at UC San Francisco in biochemistry, bioengineering, bioinformatics, biology (molecular, cell, and developmental), biopsychology, biotechnology, chemical and biomedical engineering, chemistry, immunology, medical pharmacology, microbiology, molecular genetics, molecular medicine, molecular pharmacology, neurobiology, neuroscience, pathology, physiological psychology, physiological science, statistics, or toxicology. They must be U.S. citizens, nationals, or permanent residents. The Amgen Scholars Program requires a GPA of 3.2 or higher but the other 2 components have no minimum GPA requirement; all programs require an interest in continuing on to a Ph.D. or M.D./Ph.D. (but not M.D.) program. Applications are especially encouraged from underrepresented minority, socioeconomically disadvantaged, and first-generation college students and from students with limited access to research laboratories.

Financial data The program provides a stipend of $4,000, a $500 allowance for travel to and from San Francisco, housing in the city, health insurance, and a public transportation pass.

Duration 10 weeks during the summer.

Additional information This program is comprised of 1) the UC San Francisco component of the Amgen Scholars Program, which operates at 9 other U.S. universities and is funded by the Amgen Foundation; 2) the REU program, funded by the National Science Foundation; and 3) the SRTP, which is a UCSF program with supplemental funding from Genentech and the Howard Hughes Medical Institute.

Number awarded Approximately 60 each year.

Deadline January of each year.

[554]
URBAN LEAGUE OF NEBRASKA SCHOLARSHIPS

Urban League of Nebraska
Attn: Program Director
3040 Lake Street
Omaha, NE 68111
(402) 451-1066, ext. 39
E-mail: rsmith@urbanleagueneb.org
Web: www.urbanleagueneb.org

Summary To provide financial assistance to African American and other high school seniors in Nebraska who plan to attend college in any state.

Eligibility This program is open to seniors graduating from high schools in Nebraska and planning to enroll at a college or university in any state. Applicants must have a GPA of 2.5 or higher and a record of at least 10 hours of documented community involvement. Along with their application, they must submit an essay of 250 to 500 words on their educational and career goals, ambitions, and reasons why they should receive this scholarship. Financial need is also considered in the selection process.

Financial data A stipend is awarded (amount not specified).

Duration 1 year.

Additional information These scholarships are available to all Nebraska high school seniors, but the sponsor's historic mission has been to assist African Americans to improve their lives and careers.

Number awarded 1 or more each year.

Deadline March of each year.

[555]
USDA/1890 NATIONAL SCHOLARS PROGRAM

Department of Agriculture
Office of Advocacy and Outreach
Attn: 1890 Programs
1400 Independence Avenue, S.W.
Mail Stop 0170
Washington, DC 20250
(202) 205-4307 Fax: (202) 720-7136
E-mail: 1890init@usda.gov
Web: www.outreach.usda.gov/education/1890/index.htm

Summary To provide financial assistance to high school seniors and graduates interested in majoring in a field related to agriculture or agribusiness at 1 of the 18 Historically Black 1890 Land Grant Institutions.

Eligibility This program is open to U.S. citizens who have or will have a high school diploma or GED certificate with a GPA of 3.0 or higher and a combined critical reading and mathematics score of at least 1000 on the SAT or a composite score of at least 21 on the ACT. They must be planning to attend 1 of the 18 Historically Black 1890 Land Grant Institutions and study such fields as agriculture, agricultural business/management, agricultural economics, agricultural engineering/mechanics, agricultural production and technology, agronomy or crop science, animal sciences, botany, farm and range management, food sciences/technology, forestry and related services, home economics and nutrition, horticulture, natural resources management, soil conservation/soil science, wildlife management, or other related disciplines. Currently-enrolled undergraduate students attending an 1890 institution are not eligible.

Financial data Each award provides annual tuition, employment, employee benefits, use of a laptop computer and software while receiving the scholarship, fees, books, and room and board. Following graduation, scholars are required to perform 1 year of service to the U.S. Department of Agriculture for each year of support received.

Duration 4 years, provided the scholar maintains normal progress toward the bachelor's degree and satisfactory performance.

Additional information The Historically Black 1890 Land Grant institutions are: Alabama A&M University, Alcorn State University, University of Arkansas at Pine Bluff, Delaware State University, Florida A&M University, Fort Valley State University, Kentucky State University, Lincoln University of Missouri, Langston University, University of Maryland-Eastern Shore, North Carolina A&T State University, Prairie View A&M University, South Carolina State University, Southern University and A&M College, Tennessee State University, Tuskegee University, Virginia State University, and West Virginia State University. Applications must be submitted to the Liaison Officer of the U.S. Department of Agriculture at a participating 1890 institution.

Number awarded 36 or more each year: at least 2 at each of the participating universities.

Deadline May of each year.

[556]
VADM SAMUEL L. GRAVELY, JR., USN (RET.) MEMORIAL SCHOLARSHIPS

Armed Forces Communications and Electronics Association
Attn: AFCEA Educational Foundation
4400 Fair Lakes Court
Fairfax, VA 22033-3899
(703) 631-6138 Toll Free: (800) 336-4583, ext. 6138
Fax: (703) 631-4693 E-mail: scholarshipsinfo@afcea.org
Web: www.afcea.org

Summary To provide funding to students majoring in specified scientific fields at an Historically Black College or University (HBCU).

Eligibility This program is open to sophomores and juniors enrolled full or part time at an accredited 2- or 4-year HBCU or in a distance learning or online degree program affiliated with those institutions. They must be working toward a bachelor's degree in engineering (aerospace, computer, electrical, or systems), computer science, computer engineering technology, computer information systems, mathematics, physics, information systems management, or other field directly related to the support of U.S. intelligence or homeland security enterprises. Special consideration is given to military enlisted personnel and veterans.

Financial data The stipend is $5,000.

Duration 1 year; may be renewed.

Additional information This program began in 2009 with support from American Systems.

Number awarded At least 2 each year.

Deadline April of each year.

[557]
VALERIE RUSSELL SCHOLARSHIP

United Church of Christ
Justice and Witness Ministries
Attn: Grants, Scholarships, and Resources
700 Prospect Avenue East
Cleveland, OH 44115-1100
(216) 736-3839 Toll Free: (866) 822-8224, ext. 3839
Fax: (216) 736-3783 E-mail: jeffersv@ucc.org
Web: www.ucc.org/women/the-valerie-russell.html

Summary To provide financial assistance to African American laywomen who are members of a United Church of Christ (UCC) congregation and working on an undergraduate or graduate degree to advance the justice ministries of the denomination.

Eligibility This program is open to African American laywomen who have a strong theologically-grounded commitment to the justice ministries of the UCC but are not a member in discernment, licensed, commissioned, or ordained. Applicants must be 1) working on an undergraduate or graduate degree in a field that will affirm the values of the UCC and promote its justice commitments; or 2) already professionally engaged in justice work either in the church or in a secular organization and seeking funds for continuing education activities (e.g., classes, workshops, travel) that will assist in personal skill building.

Financial data Stipends range from $1,500 to $2,000 per year. Funds may be used for tuition for undergraduate or graduate study or for continuing education activities.

Duration 1 year; may be renewed.

Number awarded 1 or more each year.

Deadline April of each year.

[558]
VANGUARD MINORITY SCHOLARSHIP PROGRAM

Scholarship America
Attn: Scholarship Management Services
One Scholarship Way
P.O. Box 297
St. Peter, MN 56082
(507) 931-1682 Toll Free: (800) 537-4180
Fax: (507) 931-9168
Web: sms.scholarshipamerica.org/vanguard/index.html

Summary To provide financial assistance to African American and other minority students working on an undergraduate degree in specified fields.

Eligibility This program is open to U.S. citizens and permanent residents who are members of racial or ethnic minorities. Applicants must be entering their junior or senior year as a full-time student at an accredited 4-year college or university in the United States and have a GPA of 3.0 or higher. They must be working on a degree in accounting, business, economics, or finance. Selection is based on academic record, demonstrated leadership and participation in school and community activities, honors, work experience, a statement of goals and aspirations, unusual personal or family circumstances, recommendations, and a resume; financial need is not considered. Students who attended a 2-year college while working on a bachelor's degree are not eligible.

Financial data The stipend ranges up to $10,000.

Duration 1 year; nonrenewable.

Additional information This program, established in 2004, is sponsored by Vanguard Group, Inc.

Number awarded Up to 10 each year.

Deadline November of each year.

[559]
VERIZON NSBE CORPORATE SCHOLARSHIPS

National Society of Black Engineers
Attn: Programs Department
205 Daingerfield Road
Alexandria, VA 22314
(703) 549-2207 Fax: (703) 683-5312
E-mail: scholarships@nsbe.org
Web: www.nsbe.org/Programs/Scholarships.aspx

Summary To provide financial assistance to members of the National Society of Black Engineers (NSBE) who are working on an undergraduate or graduate degree in specified fields of science, engineering, or business.

Eligibility This program is open to members of the society who are undergraduate or graduate students working on a degree in computer engineering, computer science, electric engineering, wireless communication, or business (M.B.A. degree only). Applicants must have a GPA of 3.0 or higher and a demonstrated interest in employment with Verizon and its affiliated companies in the fields of wireless, business, or telecommunications.

Financial data Stipends are $6,500 or $5,000.

Duration 1 year.

Additional information This program is supported by Verizon.

Number awarded 3 each year: 1 at $6,500 and 2 at $5,000.

Deadline May of each year.

[560]
VIRGINIA CHAPTER AABE SCHOLARSHIPS

American Association of Blacks in Energy-Virginia Chapter
Attn: Scholarship Committee
120 Tredegar Street
Richmond, VA 23219
E-mail: aabe@dom.com
Web: www.aabe.org

Summary To provide financial assistance to African Americans and members of other underrepresented minority groups who are high school seniors in Virginia and planning to major in an energy-related field at a college in any state.

Eligibility This program is open to seniors graduating from high schools in Virginia and planning to attend a college or university in any state. Applicants must be African Americans, Hispanics, or Native Americans who have a GPA of 3.0 or higher and who can demonstrate financial need. Their intended major must be business, engineering, technology, mathematics, the physical sciences, or other energy-related field. Along with their application, they must submit a 350-word statement on why they should receive this scholarship, how their professional career objectives relate to energy, and any other relevant information.

Financial data The stipend is $1,000.

Duration 1 year.

Additional information The winner is eligible to compete for regional and national scholarships.

Number awarded 4 each year.

Deadline February of each year.

[561]
VIRGINIA CITE TRADITIONAL SCHOLARSHIPS

Consortium of Information and Telecommunications Executives-Virginia Chapter
c/o Rhonda Stanford, Scholarship Committee
P.O. Box 950
Glen Allen, VA 23065-0950
(804) 756-5286
E-mail: Rhonda.s.stanford@citevirginia.org
Web: www.citevirginia.org/scholarship.html

Summary To provide financial assistance to African American high school seniors in Virginia who plan to attend college in any state and major in designated business- and engineering-related fields.

Eligibility This program is open to African American seniors graduating from high schools in Virginia with a GPA of 3.0 or higher. Applicants must have been accepted by an accredited college or university in any state as a full-time student. They must be planning to major in 1 of the following fields: accounting, advertising, business, computer science, electrical engineering, finance, industrial engineering, information technology, marketing, or mathematics. Their family income must be $75,000 per year or less. Along with their application, they must submit a 1-page essay on their educational and career goals. Employees and immediate family members of employees of the Verizon Corporation or an affiliated subsidiary are ineligible. U.S. citizenship is required.

Financial data The stipend is $1,000.

Duration 1 year.

Additional information The Consortium of Information and Telecommunications Executives (CITE) is an organization of African American employees of Verizon, founded in 1984 after the dissolution of the former Bell systems. Recipients must attend the sponsor's scholarship event in June.

Number awarded 1 or more each year.

Deadline April of each year.

[562] VIRGINIA NURSE PRACTITIONER/NURSE MIDWIFE SCHOLARSHIP PROGRAM

Virginia Department of Health
Attn: Office of Minority Health and Public Health Policy
109 Governor Street, Suite 1016 East
Richmond, VA 23219
(804) 864-7435 Fax: (804) 864-7440
E-mail: IncentivePrograms@vdh.virginia.gov
Web: www.vdh.virginia.gov

Summary To provide funding to nursing students in Virginia (particularly African Americans and other minorities) who are willing to work as nurse practitioners and/or midwives in the state following graduation.

Eligibility This program is open to residents of Virginia who are enrolled or accepted for enrollment full or part time at a nurse practitioner program in the state or a nurse midwifery program in Virginia or a nearby state. Applicants must have a cumulative GPA of at least 3.0 in undergraduate and/or graduate courses. Preference is given to 1) residents of designated medically underserved areas of Virginia; 2) students enrolled in family practice, obstetrics and gynecology, pediatric, adult health, and geriatric nurse practitioner programs; and 3) minority students. Selection is based on scholastic achievement, character, and stated commitment to postgraduate employment in a medically underserved area of Virginia.

Financial data The stipend is $5,000 per year. Recipients must agree to serve in a designated medically underserved area of Virginia for a period of years equal to the number of years of scholarship support received. The required service must begin within 2 years of the recipient's graduation and must be in a facility that provides services to persons who are unable to pay for the service and that participates in all government-sponsored insurance programs designed to assure full access to medical care service for covered persons. If the recipient fails to complete the course of study, or pass the licensing examination, or provide the required service, all scholarship funds received must be repaid with interest and a penalty.

Duration 1 year; may be renewed for 1 additional year.

Number awarded Up to 5 each year.

Deadline June of each year.

[563] VISUAL ARTS SCHOLARSHIP

Congressional Black Caucus Foundation, Inc.
Attn: Director, Educational Programs
1720 Massachusetts Avenue, N.W.
Washington, DC 20036
(202) 263-2800 Toll Free: (800) 784-2577
Fax: (202) 775-0773 E-mail: scholarships@cbcfinc.org
Web: www.cbcfinc.org/scholarships.html

Summary To provide financial assistance from the Congressional Black Caucus Foundation to undergraduate students who are interested in studying the visual arts.

Eligibility This program is open to graduating high school seniors and current undergraduates enrolled or planning to enroll full time at an accredited college or university. Applicants must be interested in preparing for a career in the visual arts, including architecture, ceramics, drawing, fashion, graphic design, illustration, interior design, painting, photography, sketching, video production, or other decorative arts. They must have a GPA of 2.5 or higher. Along with their application, they must submit 5 samples of their work in the art genre for which they are applying; a 1-page resume listing their extracurricular activities, honors, employment, community service, and special skills; and a personal statement of 500 to 1,000 words on themselves and their interests. They must also be able to demonstrate financial need, leadership ability, and participation in community service activities.

Financial data The stipend is $3,000.

Duration 1 year.

Additional information This program began in 2006.

Number awarded Up to 10 each year.

Deadline April of each year.

[564] VISUAL TASK FORCE SCHOLARSHIPS

National Association of Black Journalists
Attn: Communications Coordinator and Program Manager
University of Maryland
1100 Knight Hall, Suite 3100
College Park, MD 20742
(301) 405-2573 Fax: (301) 314-1714
E-mail: tjohnson@nabj.org
Web: www.nabj.org/?page=SEEDScholarships

Summary To provide financial assistance to high school seniors and undergraduate or graduate student members of the National Association of Black Journalists (NABJ) who are interested in a career in visual journalism.

Eligibility This program is open to African American high school seniors and undergraduate and graduate student members of NABJ who are currently enrolled or planning to enroll full time at an accredited 4-year college or university. Applicants must be interested in working on a degree in a field related to visual journalism (e.g., photojournalism, design and informational graphics, broadcast photojournalism) to prepare for a career in newspaper, magazine, broadcast, or online journalism. They must have a GPA of 2.75 or higher and be able to demonstrate financial need. Along with their application, they must submit samples of their work, an official college transcript, 3 letters of recommendation, a resume, and an essay of 1,000 to 2,000 words on the reasons they wish to prepare for a career in visual journalism and how they use their visual skills to tell a story effectively and creatively.

Financial data The stipend is $1,500. Funds are paid directly to the recipient's college or university.

Duration 1 year; nonrenewable.

Number awarded 2 each year.

Deadline March of each year.

[565]
VIVIAN D. TILLMAN SCHOLARSHIP

Sigma Gamma Rho Sorority, Inc.
Attn: National Education Fund
1000 Southhill Drive, Suite 200
Cary, NC 27513
(919) 678-9720 Toll Free: (888) SGR-1922
Fax: (919) 678-9721 E-mail: info@sgrho1922.org
Web: www.sgrho1922.org/nef

Summary To provide financial assistance to African American and other undergraduate students working on a degree in journalism or communications.

Eligibility This program is open to undergraduates working on a degree in journalism or communications. The sponsor is a traditionally African American sorority, but support is available to males and females of all races. Applicants must have a GPA of "C" or higher and be able to demonstrate financial need. Along with their application, they must submit a 500-word essay on how they will use their communication or journalism skills for the betterment of the country.

Financial data A stipend is awarded (amount not specified).

Duration 1 year.

Additional information A processing fee of $20 is required.

Number awarded 1 each year.

Deadline April of each year.

[566]
VSCPA MINORITY ACCOUNTING SCHOLARSHIPS

Virginia Society of Certified Public Accountants
Attn: Educational Foundation
4309 Cox Road
Glen Allen, VA 23060
(804) 612-9427 Toll Free: (800) 733-8272
Fax: (804) 273-1741 E-mail: info@vscpafoundation.com
Web: www.vscpa.com

Summary To provide financial assistance to African American and other minority students enrolled in an undergraduate accounting program in Virginia.

Eligibility Applicants must be minority students (African American or Black, Hispanic or Latino, American Indian or Native Alaskan, Asian, Native Hawaiian or other Pacific Islander) currently enrolled in a Virginia college or university undergraduate accounting program. They must be U.S. citizens, be majoring in accounting, have completed at least 3 hours of accounting, be currently registered for 3 more credit hours of accounting and have a GPA of 3.0 or higher. Along with their application, they must submit a 500-word essay on assigned topics. Selection is based on the essay, their most recent transcript, a current resume, a faculty letter of recommendation, and financial need.

Financial data The stipend is $1,000.

Duration 1 year.

Number awarded Varies each year; recently, 2 of these scholarships were awarded.

Deadline March of each year.

[567]
WAKE FOREST UNIVERSITY SCHOOL OF MEDICINE EXCELLENCE IN CARDIOVASCULAR SCIENCES SUMMER RESEARCH PROGRAM

Wake Forest University School of Medicine
Attn: Hypertension and Vascular Research Center
Medical Center Boulevard
Winston-Salem, NC 27157-1032
(336) 716-1080 Fax: (336) 716-2456
E-mail: nsarver@wakehealth.edu
Web: www.wakehealth.edu

Summary To provide African American and other underrepresented or disadvantaged students with an opportunity to engage in a summer research project in cardiovascular science at Wake Forest University in Winston-Salem, North Carolina.

Eligibility This program is open to undergraduates and master's degree students who are members of underrepresented minority groups (African Americans, Alaskan Natives, Asian Americans, Native Americans, Pacific Islanders, and Hispanics) or who come from disadvantaged backgrounds (e.g., rural areas, first-generation college students). Applicants must be interested in participating in a program of summer research in the cardiovascular sciences that includes "hands-on" laboratory research, a lecture series by faculty and guest speakers, and a research symposium at which students present their research findings. U.S. citizenship or permanent resident status is required.

Financial data The stipend is $1,731 per month, housing in a university dormitory, and round-trip transportation expense.

Duration 2 months during the summer.

Additional information This program is sponsored by the National Heart, Lung, and Blood Institute (NHLBI) of the National Institutes of Health (NIH).

Number awarded Approximately 12 each year.

Deadline February of each year.

[568]
WALMART FIRST-GENERATION SCHOLARSHIPS OF THE THURGOOD MARSHALL COLLEGE FUND

Thurgood Marshall College Fund
Attn: Campus Relations Associate
901 F Street, N.W., Suite 300
Washington, DC 20004
(202) 507-4851 Fax: (202) 652-2934
E-mail: info@tmcfund.org
Web: www.thurgoodmarshallfund.net

Summary To provide financial assistance to African Americans who are interested in enrolling at any of the public Historically Black Colleges and Universities (HBCUs) that are members of the Thurgood Marshall College Fund (TMCF) and are the first in their family to enroll in college.

Eligibility This program is open to African American students currently enrolled full time at 1 of the 47 colleges and universities that are TMCF members. Applicants must be the first member of their family to attend any college. They must have a GPA of 2.5 or higher and be able to demonstrate financial need. Along with their application, they must submit a 500-word essay on 1 of the following topics: 1) a significant setback, challenge, or opportunity in their life and the impact it has had on them; 2) what inspired them to pursue a degree in their current field of study and the impact it will have on our society; or 3) what it means to be the first person in their family to receive a college degree. U.S. citizenship or permanent resident status is required.

Financial data The stipend is $3,100 per semester ($6,200 per year).

Duration 1 year.

Additional information This program is sponsored by Walmart Corporation.

Number awarded Approximately 100 each year.

Deadline April of each year.

[569] WALTER SAMUEL MCAFEE SCHOLARSHIP IN SPACE PHYSICS

National Society of Black Physicists
Attn: Scholarship Committee Chair
1100 North Glebe Road, Suite 1010
Arlington, VA 22201
(703) 536-4207 Fax: (703) 536-4203
E-mail: scholarship@nsbp.org
Web: www.nsbp.org/scholarships

Summary To provide financial assistance to African American students majoring in space physics in college.

Eligibility This program is open to African American students who are entering their junior or senior year of college and majoring in space physics. Applicants must submit an essay on their academic and career objectives, information on their participation in extracurricular activities, a description of any awards and honors they have received, and 3 letters of recommendation. Financial need is not considered.

Financial data The stipend is $1,000.

Duration 1 year; nonrenewable.

Additional information This program is offered in partnership with the American Astronomical Society.

Number awarded 1 each year.

Deadline November of each year.

[570] WALTER VAUGHN EXCELLENCE IN HUMAN RESOURCES SCHOLARSHIP

National Forum for Black Public Administrators
Attn: Scholarship Program
777 North Capitol Street, N.E., Suite 807
Washington, DC 20002
(202) 408-9300 Fax: (202) 408-8558
E-mail: vharris@nfbpa.org
Web: www.nfbpa.org/i4a/pages/index.cfm?pageid=4047

Summary To provide financial assistance to African Americans working on an undergraduate or graduate degree in public administration with an emphasis on human resource management.

Eligibility This program is open to African American undergraduate and graduate students preparing for a career in public service. Applicants must be working full time on a degree in public administration, human resource management, or a related field. They must have a GPA of 3.0 or higher, a record of involvement in extracurricular activities (excluding athletics), excellent interpersonal and leadership abilities, and strong oral and written communication skills. Along with their application, they must submit a 3-page autobiographical essay that includes their academic and career goals and objectives. Selection is based on academic record, leadership ability, participation in school activities, community service, and financial need.

Financial data The stipend is $2,500.

Duration 1 year.

Additional information This program is sponsored by CPS Human Resource Services. Recipients are required to attend the sponsor's annual conference to receive their scholarship; limited hotel and air accommodations are arranged and provided.

Number awarded 1 each year.

Deadline February of each year.

[571] WARNER NORCROSS & JUDD PARALEGAL ASSISTANT SCHOLARSHIP

Grand Rapids Community Foundation
Attn: Education Program Officer
185 Oakes Street S.W.
Grand Rapids, MI 49503-4008
(616) 454-1751, ext. 103 Fax: (616) 454-6455
E-mail: rbishop@grfoundation.org
Web: www.grfoundation.org/scholarshipslist

Summary To provide financial assistance to African and other minority residents of Michigan who are interested in working on a paralegal studies degree at an institution in the state.

Eligibility This program is open to residents of Michigan who are students of color attending or planning to attend an accredited public or private 2- or 4-year college or university in the state. Applicants must have a declared major in paralegal/legal assistant studies. They must be U.S. citizens or permanent residents and have a GPA of 2.5 or higher. Financial need is considered in the selection process.

Financial data The stipend is $2,000. Funds are paid directly to the recipient's institution.

Duration 1 year.

Additional information Funding for this program is provided by the law firm Warner Norcross & Judd LLP.

Number awarded 1 each year.

Deadline March of each year.

[572] WASA/PEMCO 21ST CENTURY EDUCATOR SCHOLARSHIP

Washington Association of School Administrators
825 Fifth Avenue, S.E.
Olympia, WA 98501
(360) 943-5717 Toll Free: (800) 859-9272
Fax: (360) 352-2043 E-mail: admin@wasa-oly.org
Web: www.wasa-oly.org

Summary To provide financial assistance to minority and other high school seniors in the state of Washington who are interested in majoring in education in college.

Eligibility This program is open to high school seniors who are enrolled in a Washington public or accredited private school, have a GPA of 3.0 or higher, and intend to major and prepare for a career in K-12 education. Applicants must submit a completed application form, a criteria essay, a goals essay, 3 reference letters, and an official grades transcript. They compete in 3 applicant pools: eastern Washington, western Washington, and minority. Along with their application, they must submit a 1-page essay on why they have chosen K-12 education as their future profession. Selection is based on that essay, leadership, community service, honors and awards, and student activities.

Financial data The stipend is $1,000 per year.

Duration 4 years.

Additional information This program is sponsored jointly by the Washington Association of School Administrators (WASA) and the PEMCO Foundation.

Number awarded 3 each year: 1 to a student from eastern Washington, 1 to a student from western Washington, and 1 to a minority student.

Deadline March of each year.

[573]
WASHINGTON ADMIRAL'S FUND SCHOLARSHIP

National Naval Officers Association-Washington, D.C. Chapter
c/o LCDR Stephen Williams
P.O. Box 30784
Alexandria, VA 22310
(703) 566-3840 Fax: (703) 566-3813
E-mail: Stephen.Williams@navy.mil
Web: dcnnoa.memberlodge.com

Summary To provide financial assistance to African American and other minority high school seniors from the Washington, D.C. area who are interested in attending a college or university in any state and enrolling in the Navy Reserve Officers Training Corps (NROTC) program.

Eligibility This program is open to minority seniors graduating from high schools in the Washington, D.C. metropolitan area who plan to enroll full time at an accredited 2- or 4-year college or university in any state. Applicants must be planning to enroll in the NROTC program. They must have a GPA of 2.5 or higher and be U.S. citizens or permanent residents. Selection is based on academic achievement, community involvement, and financial need.

Financial data The stipend is $1,000.

Duration 1 year; nonrenewable.

Additional information If the recipient fails to enroll in the NROTC unit, all scholarship funds must be returned.

Number awarded 1 each year.

Deadline March of each year.

[574]
WASHINGTON CHAPTER CONCERNED BLACK MEN SCHOLARSHIP AWARDS

Concerned Black Men, Inc.-Washington DC Chapter
Thurgood Marshall Center
1816 12th Street, N.W., Suite 203
Washington, DC 20009-4422
(202) 797-7444 Fax: (202) 797-7447
E-mail: office@cbmdc.org
Web: www.cbmdc.org

Summary To provide financial assistance to African American and other high school seniors in Washington, D.C. who plan to attend college in any state.

Eligibility This program is open to seniors who are graduating from high schools in Washington, D.C. and planning to enroll at a college or university in any state. Applicants must have a GPA of 2.5 or higher. Along with their application, they must submit a 500-word essay on why they should be a recipient of this scholarship. Financial need may also be considered in the selection process.

Financial data A stipend is awarded (amount not specified).

Duration 1 year.

Additional information The sponsor is an organization of African American men, but both men and women are eligible for this scholarship.

Number awarded 1 or more each year.

Deadline May of each year.

[575]
WASHINGTON DC ALUMNAE CHAPTER SCHOLARSHIPS

Delta Sigma Theta Sorority, Inc.-Washington DC Alumnae Chapter
Attn: Scholarship Committee
P.O. Box 90202
Washington, DC 20090-0202
Toll Free: (201) 388-1912
E-mail: scholarship@wdcac.org
Web: www.wdcac.org/scholarship

Summary To provide financial assistance to African American and other high school seniors in Washington, D.C. who plan to attend college in any state.

Eligibility This program is open to seniors graduating from public, charter, parochial, and private high schools in Washington, D.C. and planning to enroll full time at a 2- or 4-year college or university in any state. Applicants must submit an official high school transcript, a copy of their SAT or ACT scores, documentation of financial need, 2 letters of recommendation, and a 1-page autobiographical essay including their academic and career goals, community service involvement, why the scholarship is important, and its expected benefit.

Financial data Stipends range from $1,050 to $2,500 per year.

Duration 1 year; may be renewed.

Additional information The sponsor is the local alumnae chapter of a traditionally African American social sorority.

Number awarded Varies each year.

Deadline February of each year.

[576]
WASHINGTON DC AREA SUPPLY OFFICERS SCHOLARSHIP

National Naval Officers Association-Washington, D.C. Chapter
c/o LCDR Stephen Williams
P.O. Box 30784
Alexandria, VA 22310
(703) 566-3840 Fax: (703) 566-3813
E-mail: Stephen.Williams@navy.mil
Web: dcnnoa.memberlodge.com

Summary To provide financial assistance to African American and other minority high school seniors from the Washington, D.C. area who are interested in attending college in any state.

Eligibility This program is open to minority seniors graduating from high schools in the Washington, D.C. metropolitan area who plan to enroll full time at an accredited 2- or 4-year college or university in any state. Applicants must have a GPA of 3.0 or higher and be U.S. citizens or permanent residents. Selection is based on academic achievement, community involvement, and financial need.

Financial data The stipend is $3,000.

Duration 1 year; nonrenewable.

Number awarded 1 each year.

Deadline March of each year.

[577]
WASHINGTON, D.C. CHAPTER NNOA SCHOLARSHIPS

National Naval Officers Association-Washington, D.C. Chapter
c/o LCDR Stephen Williams
P.O. Box 30784
Alexandria, VA 22310
(703) 566-3840 Fax: (703) 566-3813
E-mail: Stephen.Williams@navy.mil
Web: dcnnoa.memberlodge.com

Summary To provide financial assistance to African American high school seniors from the Washington, D.C. area who are interested in attending college in any state.

Eligibility This program is open to African American seniors graduating from high schools in the Washington, D.C. metropolitan area who plan to enroll full time at an accredited 2- or 4-year college or university in any state. Applicants must have a GPA of 2.5 or higher and be U.S. citizens or permanent residents. Selection is based on academic achievement, community involvement, and financial need.

Financial data The stipend is $1,000.

Duration 1 year; nonrenewable.

Additional information Recipients are not required to join or affiliate with the military in any way. In addition to a number of scholarships with additional requirements, this program includes the following named general scholarships: the David and Sheila Garnett Leadership Scholarship, the Ester Boone Memorial Scholarships, the Mr. Charlie Tompkins Scholarship, the Navy Federal Credit Union Scholarship, the Pringle & Pringle Higher Education Scholarship, the Rear Admiral Mack and Nancy Gaston Leadership Scholarship, the Rear Admiral Michelle Howard Excellence in Leadership Scholarship, the Vice Admiral Samuel L. Gravely, Jr. Memorial Scholarship, and the William A. Borders Jr. Justice Scholarship.

Number awarded Varies each year; recently, 15 of these scholarships were awarded.

Deadline March of each year.

[578]
WASHINGTON, D.C. CHAPTER UNDERGRADUATE SCHOLARSHIP PROGRAM

National Black MBA Association-Washington, DC Chapter
Attn: Scholarship Program
P.O. Box 14042
Washington, DC 20044
(202) 628-0138 E-mail: outreach@dcbmbaa.org
Web: www.dcbmbaa.org/zpindex.zpl

Summary To provide financial assistance to African American and other minority students from Washington, D.C., Maryland, or Virginia who are working on an undergraduate degree in business or management at a school in any state.

Eligibility This program is open to minority residents of Washington, D.C., Maryland, or Virginia who are graduating high school seniors or current full-time undergraduates at a college or university in any state. Applicants must be working on or planning to work on a bachelor's degree in business or management. Along with their application, they must submit an essay (from 500 to 600 words) on a topic that changes annually but focuses on minorities in business. Selection is based the essay, GPA, extracurricular activity, and community involvement.

Financial data The stipend is $1,500 or $1,000.

Duration 1 year.

Additional information This program began in 2000.

Number awarded 2 each year: 1 at $1,500 and 1 at $1,000.

Deadline June of each year.

[579]
WASHINGTON DC METROPOLITAN AREA CHAPTER AABE SCHOLARSHIPS

American Association of Blacks in Energy-Washington DC Metropolitan Area Chapter
Attn: Scholarship Committee
P.O. Box 77263
Washington, DC 20013
E-mail: dcaabeschl@aol.com
Web: www.aabe.org

Summary To provide financial assistance to African Americans and members of other underrepresented minority groups who are high school seniors in the Washington, D.C. metropolitan area and planning to major in an energy-related field at a college in any state.

Eligibility This program is open to seniors graduating from high schools in the Washington, D.C. metropolitan area who are planning to work on a bachelor's degree at a college or university in any state. Applicants must be African Americans, Hispanics, or Native Americans who have a GPA of 3.0 or higher and who can demonstrate financial need. Their intended major must be a field of business, engineering, physical science, mathematics, or technology related to energy. Along with their application, they must submit a 350-word statement on why they should receive this scholarship, their professional career objectives, and any other relevant information.

Financial data Stipends range from $1,500 to $2,500.

Duration 1 year; nonrenewable.

Additional information Winners are eligible to compete for regional and national scholarships.

Number awarded 3 each year: 1 each at $2,500, $2,000, and $1,500.

Deadline February of each year.

[580]
WASHINGTON HEADQUARTERS REGION NBCFAE SCHOLARSHIP

National Black Coalition of Federal Aviation Employees-Washington Headquarters Region
c/o Deames Bynum, President
4905 Cranford Terrace
Upper Marlboro, MD 20772
(301) 627-5277
Web: www.nbcfaehq.org/indexs.html

Summary To provide financial assistance to residents of Washington, D.C., especially those with a tie to the National Black Coalition of Federal Aviation Employees (NBCFAE), who are interested in attending college or graduate school in any state to work on a degree in any field.

Eligibility This program is open to graduating high school seniors, current undergraduates, college seniors entering graduate school, and first-year graduate students. Applicants must meet 1 of the following requirements: 1) reside in Washington, D.C.; 2) work for or be a family member of an employee of the Department of Transportation within the District of Columbia; 3) be a member or a family member of the Washington Headquarters Region of NBCFAE; or 4) be referred by a member of the Washington Headquarters Region of NBCFAE. They must be working on or planning to work on an associate, bachelor's, or master's degree in any field at a school in any state and have a GPA of 2.5 or higher. Along with their application, they must submit an essay of 300 to 500 words describing 1 or more of the following: career goals, personal goals, overcoming the odds, or someone they admire. Financial need is not considered in the selection process.

Financial data A stipend is awarded (amount not specified).

Duration 1 year.

Number awarded 1 or more each year.

Deadline May of each year.

[581]
WASHINGTON POST URBAN JOURNALISM WORKSHOP

Washington Post
Attn: Young Journalists Development Program
P.O. Box 77130
Washington, DC 20013
(202) 334-4917 E-mail: yjdp@washpost.com
Web: www.washingtonpost.com/youngjournalists

Summary To provide financial assistance to African American and other high school students in the Washington D.C. area who are interested in preparing for a career in journalism.

Eligibility This program is open to high school seniors in 19 designated public school systems in the Washington, D.C. area. Applicants must have an interest in a journalism career and strong writing skills. The program is not limited to African Americans; all interested students are encouraged to apply. Along with their application, they must submit 1) an autobiography of 200 to 250 words, including what is important to them, why they want to participate in the program, and what they have to share with other students who will participate in the workshop; 2) a 1-page essay on the topic of what makes a good journalist; and 3) a news report based on a set of hypothetical facts. Students who are accepted to the program attend workshops on 8 consecutive Saturdays. They are assigned to 1 of 3 segments: newspaper, radio, or television. Scholarship recipients are selected on the basis of participation in those sessions and their application information.

Financial data The stipend is $2,500.

Duration 1 year; nonrenewable.

Additional information The eligible public school systems are those in Washington, D.C.; the counties of Anne Arundel, Calvert, Charles, Frederick, Howard, Montgomery, Prince George's, and St. Mary's in Maryland; the cities of Alexandria, Falls Church, Manassas, and Manassas Park in Virginia; and the counties of Arlington, Fairfax, Fauquier, Loudoun, Prince William, and Stafford in Virginia. This program, which began in 1986, is offered in collaboration with the Washington Association of Black Journalists (WABJ).

Number awarded Recently, 32 students were selected to participate in the workshop. >From among those, 3 were chosen to receive scholarships (1 each in the newspaper, radio, and television segments).

Deadline January of each year.

[582]
WASHINGTON UNIVERSITY AMGEN SCHOLARS PROGRAM

Washington University
Division of Biology and Biomedical Sciences
Attn: Summer Research Admissions
660 South Euclid Avenue
Campus Box 8226
St. Louis, MO 63110-1093
(314) 362-7963 Toll Free: (800) 852-9074
E-mail: DBBS-summerresearch@wusm.wustl.edu
Web: dbbs.wustl.edu

Summary To provide undergraduate students (particularly African Americans, other underrepresented minorities, women, and students with disabilities) with a summer research experience at Washington University in St. Louis in biological and biomedical sciences.

Eligibility This program is open to sophomores, juniors, and non-graduating seniors at 4-year colleges and universities in the United States, Puerto Rico, and U.S. territories. Applicants must be interested in a summer research experience at Washington University in biochemistry, bioengineering, bioinformatics, biology (molecular, cell, and developmental), biopsychology, biotechnology, chemical and biomedical engineering, chemistry, immunology, medical pharmacology, microbiology, molecular genetics, molecular medicine, molecular pharmacology, neurobiology, neuroscience, pathology, physiological psychology, physiological science, statistics, or toxicology. They must have a GPA of 3.2 or higher and an interest in continuing on to a Ph.D. or M.D./Ph.D. (but not M.D.) program. Applications are especially encouraged from students from economically disadvantaged backgrounds, those who attend small liberal arts colleges, and from members of groups traditionally underrepresented in biomedical research (African Americans, Hispanic Americans, Native Americans, Pacific Islanders, women, and people with disabilities). U.S. citizenship or permanent resident status is required.

Financial data Housing, travel to and from St. Louis, meals, and a stipend of $4,000 are provided.

Duration 10 weeks during the summer.

Additional information This program serves as the Washington University component of the Amgen Scholars Program, which operates at 9 other U.S. universities and is funded by the Amgen Foundation.

Number awarded 25 each year.

Deadline January of each year.

[583]
WATSON MIDWIVES OF COLOR SCHOLARSHIP

American College of Nurse-Midwives
Attn: ACNM Foundation, Inc.
8403 Colesville Road, Suite 1550
Silver Spring, MD 20910-6374
(240) 485-1850 Fax: (240) 485-1818
E-mail: fdn@acnm.org
Web: www.midwife.org

Summary To provide financial assistance for midwifery education to African Americans and other students of color who belong to the American College of Nurse-Midwives (ACNM).

Eligibility This program is open to ACNM members of color who are currently enrolled in an accredited basic midwife education program and have successfully completed 1 academic or clinical semester/quarter or clinical module. Applicants must submit a 150-word essay on their 5-year midwifery career plans and a 100-word essay on their intended future participation in the local, regional, and/or national activities of the ACNM. Selection is based on leadership potential, financial need, academic history, and potential for future professional contribution to the organization.

Financial data The stipend is $3,000.

Duration 1 year.

Number awarded Varies each year; recently, 3 of these scholarships were awarded.

Deadline March of each year.

[584]
WAYNE D. CORNILS SCHOLARSHIP

Idaho State Broadcasters Association
1674 West Hill Road, Suite 3
Boise, ID 83702
(208) 345-3072 Fax: (208) 343-8946
E-mail: isba@qwestoffice.net
Web: bestinbroadcasting.com

Summary To provide financial assistance to African Americans and other less advantaged students at Idaho colleges and universities who are preparing for a career in the broadcasting field.

Eligibility This program is open to full-time students at Idaho schools who are preparing for a career in broadcasting, including business administration, sales, journalism, or engineering. Applicants must have a GPA of at least 2.0 for the first 2 years of school or 2.5 for the last 2 years. Along with their application, they must submit a letter of recommendation from the general manager of a broadcasting station that is a member of the Idaho State Broadcasters Association and a 1-page essay describing their career plans and why they want the scholarship. Applications are encouraged from a broad and diverse student population. This scholarship is reserved for a less advantaged applicant.

Financial data The stipend depends on the need of the recipient.

Duration 1 year.

Number awarded 1 each year.

Deadline March of each year.

[585]
WEISMAN SCHOLARSHIPS

Connecticut Office of Financial and Academic Affairs for Higher Education
Attn: Student Financial Aid
61 Woodland Street
Hartford, CT 06105-2326
(860) 947-1853 Toll Free: (800) 842-0229 (within CT)
Fax: (860) 947-1314 E-mail: mtip@ctdhe.org
Web: www.ctohe.org/SFA/default.htm

Summary To provide financial assistance to African Americans and other minority upper-division college students from any state who are enrolled at a college in Connecticut and interested in teaching mathematics or science at public middle and high schools in the state.

Eligibility This program is open to residents of any state who are enrolled full time as juniors or seniors at Connecticut colleges and universities and preparing to become a mathematics or science teacher at the middle or high school level. Applicants must be members of a minority group, defined as African American, Hispanic/Latino, Asian American, or Native American. They must be nominated by the education dean at their institution.

Financial data The maximum stipend is $5,000 per year. In addition, if recipients complete a credential and begin teaching mathematics or science at a public school in Connecticut within 16 months of graduation, they may receive up to $2,500 per year, for up to 4 years, to help pay off college loans.

Number awarded Varies each year.

Deadline October of each year.

[586]
WESTCHESTER/GREATER CONNECTICUT CHAPTER NBMBAA HIGH SCHOOL SCHOLARSHIP

National Black MBA Association-Westchester/Greater Connecticut Chapter
Attn: Scholarship Chair
P.O. Box 3586
Stamford, CT 06905
Toll Free: (866) 966-9942 E-mail: info@nbmbaa-wgc.org
Web: www.nbmbaa-wgc.org/education/scholarship.html

Summary To provide financial assistance to African Americans and other underrepresented minority high school seniors from Connecticut and Westchester County, New York who plan to study a business-related field at a college in any state.

Eligibility This program is open to seniors graduating from high schools in Connecticut or Westchester County, New York who are members of underrepresented minority groups. Applicants must be planning to enroll full time at an accredited college or university in any state to work on a degree in accounting, business, economics, entrepreneurship, management, marketing, or a related area. They must be U.S. citizens (or in possession of a current student visa) and have a GPA of 3.0 or higher. Selection is based on an essay on an assigned topic, academic ability, demonstrated leadership ability, and participation in high school and community activities.

Financial data The stipend is $1,000.

Duration 1 year.

Number awarded 1 or more each year.

Deadline December of each year.

[587]
WESTCHESTER/GREATER CONNECTICUT CHAPTER NBMBAA UNDERGRADUATE SCHOLARSHIP

National Black MBA Association-Westchester/Greater Connecticut Chapter
Attn: Scholarship Chair
P.O. Box 3586
Stamford, CT 06905
Toll Free: (866) 966-9942 E-mail: info@nbmbaa-wgc.org
Web: www.nbmbaa-wgc.org/education/scholarship.html

Summary To provide financial assistance to African Americans and other underrepresented minority residents of Connecticut and Westchester County, New York who are working on a business-related undergraduate degree at a college in any state.

Eligibility This program is open to residents of Connecticut or Westchester County, New York who are members of underrepresented minority groups. Applicants must be enrolled full time at an accredited college or university in any state and working on an undergraduate degree in accounting, business, economics, entrepreneurship, management, marketing, or a related area. They must be U.S. citizens (or in possession of a current student visa) and have a GPA of 3.0 or higher. Selection is based on an essay on an assigned topic, academic ability, demonstrated leadership ability, and participation in college and community activities.

Financial data The stipend is $1,000.

Duration 1 year.

Number awarded 1 or more each year.

Deadline December of each year.

[588]
WILLIAM K. SCHUBERT M.D. MINORITY NURSING SCHOLARSHIP PROGRAM

Cincinnati Children's Hospital Medical Center
Attn: Office of Diversity and Inclusion, MLC 9008
3333 Burnet Avenue
Cincinnati, OH 45229-3039
(513) 803-6416 Toll Free: (800) 344-2462
Fax: (513) 636-5643 TDD: (513) 636-4900
E-mail: diversity@cchmc.org
Web: www.cincinnatichildrens.org

Summary To provide financial assistance to African Americans and members of other underrepresented groups who are interested in working on a bachelor's or master's degree in nursing to prepare for licensure in Ohio.

Eligibility This program is open to members of groups underrepresented in the nursing profession (males, American Indians or Alaska Natives, Blacks or African Americans, Hawaiian Natives or other Pacific Islanders, Hispanics or Latinos, or Asians). Applicants must be enrolled or accepted in a professional bachelor's or master's registered nurse program at an accredited school of nursing to prepare for initial licensure in Ohio. They must have a GPA of 2.75 or higher. Along with their application, they must submit a 750-word essay that covers 1) their long-range personal, educational, and professional goals; 2) why they chose nursing as a profession; 3) how their experience as a member of an underrepresented group has influenced a major professional and/or personal decision in their life; 4) any unique qualifications, experiences, or special talents that demonstrate their creativity; and 5) how their work experience has contributed to their personal development.

Financial data The stipend is $2,750 per year.

Duration 1 year. May be renewed up to 3 additional years for students working on a bachelor's degree or 1 additional year for students working on a master's degree; renewal requires that students maintain a GPA of 2.75 or higher.

Number awarded 1 or more each year.

Deadline April of each year.

[589]
WILLIAM RANDOLPH HEARST ENDOWMENT SCHOLARSHIPS

National Action Council for Minorities in Engineering
Attn: University Programs
440 Hamilton Avenue, Suite 302
White Plains, NY 10601-1813
(914) 539-4010 Fax: (914) 539-4032
E-mail: scholarships@nacme.org
Web: www.nacme.org/NACME_D.aspx?pageid=105

Summary To provide financial assistance to African American and other underrepresented minority college freshmen or sophomores majoring in engineering or related fields.

Eligibility This program is open to African American, Latino, and American Indian college freshmen and sophomores who have a GPA of 2.8 or higher and have demonstrated academic excellence, leadership skills, and a commitment to science and engineering as a career. Applicants must be enrolled full time at an ABET-accredited engineering program. Fields of study include all areas of engineering as well as computer science, materials science, mathematics, operations research, or physics.

Financial data The stipend is $2,500 per year. Funds are sent directly to the recipient's university.

Duration Up to 4 years.

Additional information This program was established by the William Randolph Hearst Foundation.

Number awarded 2 each year.

Deadline April of each year.

[590]
WILLIAM SAMBER SR. AVIATION/MATH AND SCIENCE SCHOLARSHIP

African-American/Caribbean Education Association, Inc.
P.O. Box 1224
Valley Stream, NY 11582-1224
(718) 949-6733 E-mail: aaceainc@yahoo.com
Web: www.aaceainc.com/Scholarships.html

Summary To provide financial assistance to high school seniors of African American or Caribbean heritage who plan to study a field related to aviation, mathematics, or science in college.

Eligibility This program is open to graduating high school seniors who are U.S. citizens of African American or Caribbean heritage. Applicants must be planning to attend a college or university and major in a field related to a career in aviation, mathematics, or science. They must have completed 4 years of specified college preparatory courses with a grade of 90 or higher and have an SAT score of at least 1790. They must also have completed at least 200 hours of community service during their 4 years of high school, preferably in the field that they plan to study in college. Financial need is not considered in the selection process. New York residency is not required, but applicants must be available for an interview in the Queens, New York area.

Financial data The stipend ranges from $1,000 to $2,500. Funds are paid directly to the recipient.

Duration 1 year.

Number awarded 2 each year.

Deadline April of each year.

[591]
WILLIAM TOWNSEND PORTER FELLOWSHIP FOR MINORITY INVESTIGATORS

Marine Biological Laboratory
Attn: Chief Academic and Scientific Officer
7 MBL Street
Woods Hole, MA 02543-1015
(508) 289-7173 Fax: (508) 457-1924
E-mail: casoofice@mbl.edu
Web: hermes.mbl.edu

Summary To support African Americans and other underrepresented minorities who wish to conduct research during the summer at the Marine Biological Laboratory (MBL) in Woods Hole, Massachusetts.

Eligibility This program is open to young scientists (undergraduates, senior graduate students, and postdoctoral trainees) who are from an underrepresented minority group (African American, Hispanic American, or Native American), are U.S. citizens or permanent residents, and are interested in conducting research with senior investigators at MBL. Applicants must submit a statement of the potential impact of this award on their career development. Fields of study include, but are not limited to, cell biology, developmental biology, ecology, evolution, microbiology, neurobiology, physiology, regenerative biology, and tissue engineering.

Financial data Grants range from $5,000 to $25,000, typically to cover laboratory rental and/or housing costs. Awardees are responsible for other costs, such as supplies, shared resource usage, affiliated staff who accompany them, or travel.

Duration 8 to 10 weeks during the summer.

Additional information This fellowship was first awarded in 1921. Funding is provided by the Harvard Apparatus Foundation.

Number awarded 1 or more each year.

Deadline December of each year.

[592]
WILLIE HOBBS MOORE SCHOLARSHIP

National Society of Black Physicists
Attn: Scholarship Committee Chair
1100 North Glebe Road, Suite 1010
Arlington, VA 22201
(703) 536-4207 Fax: (703) 536-4203
E-mail: scholarship@nsbp.org
Web: www.nsbp.org/scholarships

Summary To provide financial assistance to African American students majoring in physics in college.

Eligibility This program is open to African American students who are entering their junior or senior year of college and majoring in physics. Applicants must submit an essay on their academic and career objectives, information on their participation in extracurricular activities, a description of any awards and honors they have received, and 3 letters of recommendation. Financial need is not considered.

Financial data The stipend is $1,000.

Duration 1 year; nonrenewable.

Number awarded 1 each year.

Deadline November of each year.

[593]
WILLIE J. WILLIAMS MUSIC SCHOLARSHIP

African Methodist Episcopal Church
Eleventh Episcopal District Lay Organization
c/o Loretta S. Coppock
11499 Sir Barton Court
Jacksonville, FL 32218
(904) 751-7300 E-mail: eedlo@eedlo.org
Web: www.eedlo.org/scholarships.html

Summary To provide financial assistance to members of African Methodist Episcopal (AME) churches in Florida who are interested in studying music at an Historically Black College or University (HBCU).

Eligibility This program is open to seniors graduating from public or private high schools in Florida who are members of AME churches. Applicants must be planning to enroll at an HBCU and major in music; preference may be given to students at AME church college or university. Along with their application, they must submit a 1-page essay on why they should be awarded this scholarship and a statement regarding their financial need.

Financial data A stipend is awarded (amount not specified).

Duration 1 year.
Number awarded 1 or more each year.
Deadline April of each year.

[594]
WILLIE T. LOUD-CH2M HILL SCHOLARSHIP

National Forum for Black Public Administrators
Attn: Scholarship Program
777 North Capitol Street, N.E., Suite 807
Washington, DC 20002
(202) 408-9300 Fax: (202) 408-8558
E-mail: vharris@nfbpa.org
Web: www.nfbpa.org/i4a/pages/index.cfm?pageid=4047

Summary To provide financial assistance to African Americans working on a bachelor's or master's degree in public administration.

Eligibility This program is open to African American graduate students preparing for a career in public service. Applicants must be working full time on a bachelor's or master's degree in public administration, urban affairs, or a related field. They must have a GPA of 3.0 or higher, strong interpersonal skills, and excellent writing, analytical, and oral communication abilities. Along with their application, they must submit a 3-page autobiographical essay that includes their academic and career goals and objectives. Selection is based on academic record, leadership ability, participation in school activities, community service, and financial need.

Financial data The stipend is $5,000.

Duration 1 year.

Additional information This program, established in 1997, is sponsored by CH2M Hill. Recipients are required to attend the sponsor's annual conference to receive their scholarship; limited hotel and air accommodations are arranged and provided.

Number awarded 1 each year.

Deadline February of each year.

[595]
WINGS FINANCIAL SCHOLARSHIPS

Organization of Black Aerospace Professionals, Inc.
Attn: Scholarship Coordinator
1 Westbrook Corporate Center, Suite 300
Westchester, IL 60154
(708) 449-7755 Toll Free: (800) JET-OBAP
Fax: (708) 449-7754 E-mail: obapscholarship@obap.org
Web: www.obap.org/scholarships/scholarship-opportunities

Summary To provide financial assistance to African American high school seniors and college students who are interested in working on an aerospace degree at a school in any state.

Eligibility This program is open to African American high school seniors and current college students who are enrolled or planning to enroll in an aerospace program at an accredited college or university. Applicants must have a GPA of 2.7 or higher. Along with their application, they must submit a 500-word essay describing how this scholarship would impact their career goals.

Financial data The stipend is $1,000.

Duration 1 year.

Additional information This program is sponsored by Wings Financial Credit Union.

Number awarded 2 each year.

Deadline May of each year.

[596]
WISCONSIN MINORITY TEACHER LOANS

Wisconsin Higher Educational Aids Board
131 West Wilson Street, Suite 902
P.O. Box 7885
Madison, WI 53707-7885
(608) 267-2212 Fax: (608) 267-2808
E-mail: deanna.schulz@wisconsin.gov
Web: heab.state.wi.us/programs.html

Summary To provide funding to African Americans and other minorities in Wisconsin who are interested in teaching in Wisconsin school districts with large minority enrollments.

Eligibility This program is open to residents of Wisconsin who are African Americans, Hispanic Americans, American Indians, or southeast Asians (students who were admitted to the United States after December 31, 1975 and who are a former citizen of Laos, Vietnam, or Cambodia or whose ancestor was a citizen of 1 of those countries). Applicants must be enrolled at least half time as juniors, seniors, or graduate students at an independent or public institution in the state in a program leading to teaching licensure and have a GPA of 2.5 or higher. They must agree to teach in a Wisconsin school district in which minority students constitute at least 29% of total enrollment or in a school district participating in the interdistrict pupil transfer program. Financial need is not considered in the selection process.

Financial data Loans are provided up to $2,500 per year. For each year the student teaches in an eligible school district, 25% of the loan is forgiven; if the student does not teach in an eligible district, the loan must be repaid at an interest rate of 5%.

Duration 1 year; may be renewed 1 additional year.

Additional information Eligible students should apply through their school's financial aid office.

Number awarded Varies each year.

Deadline Deadline dates vary by institution; check with your school's financial aid office.

[597]
WISCONSIN MINORITY UNDERGRADUATE RETENTION GRANTS

Wisconsin Higher Educational Aids Board
131 West Wilson Street, Suite 902
P.O. Box 7885
Madison, WI 53707-7885
(608) 267-2212 Fax: (608) 267-2808
E-mail: deanna.schulz@wisconsin.gov
Web: heab.state.wi.us/programs.html

Summary To provide financial assistance to African Americans and other minorities in Wisconsin who are currently enrolled at a college in the state.

Eligibility This program is open to residents of Wisconsin who are African Americans, Hispanic Americans, American Indians, or southeast Asians (students who were admitted to the United States after December 31, 1975 and who are a former citizen of Laos, Vietnam, or Cambodia or whose ancestor was a citizen of 1 of those countries). Applicants must be enrolled at least half time as sophomores, juniors, seniors, or fifth-year undergraduates at a Wisconsin technical college, tribal college, or independent college or university in the state. They must be nominated by their institution and be able to demonstrate financial need.

Financial data Stipends range from $250 to $2,500 per year, depending on the need of the recipient.

Duration Up to 4 years.

Additional information The Wisconsin Higher Educational Aids Board administers this program for students at private nonprofit institutions, technical colleges, and tribal colleges. The University of Wisconsin has a similar program for students attending any of the branches of that system. Eligible students should apply through their school's financial aid office.

Number awarded Varies each year.

Deadline Deadline dates vary by institution; check with your school's financial aid office.

[598]
WISCONSIN TALENT INCENTIVE PROGRAM (TIP) GRANTS

Wisconsin Higher Educational Aids Board
131 West Wilson Street, Suite 902
P.O. Box 7885
Madison, WI 53707-7885
(608) 266-1665 Fax: (608) 267-2808
E-mail: colettem1.brown@wi.gov
Web: heab.state.wi.us/programs.html

Summary To provide financial assistance for college to African Americans and other needy and educationally disadvantaged students in Wisconsin.

Eligibility This program is open to residents of Wisconsin entering a college or university in the state who meet the requirements of both financial need and educational disadvantage. Financial need qualifications include 1) family contribution (a dependent student whose expected parent contribution is $200 or less or an independent student whose maximum academic year contribution is $200 or less); 2) Temporary Assistance to Needy Families (TANF) or Wisconsin Works (W2) benefits (a dependent student whose family is receiving TANF or W2 benefits or an independent student who is receiving TANF or W2 benefits); or 3) unemployment (a dependent student whose parents are ineligible for unemployment compensation and have no current income from employment, or an independent student and spouse, if married, who are ineligible for unemployment compensation and have no current income from employment). Educational disadvantage qualifications include students who are 1) minorities (African American, Native American, Hispanic, or southeast Asian); 2) enrolled in a special academic support program due to insufficient academic preparation; 3) a first-generation college student (neither parent graduated from a 4-year college or university); 4) disabled according to the Department of Workforce Development, the Division of Vocational Rehabilitation, or a Wisconsin college or university that uses the Americans with Disabilities Act definition; 5) currently or formerly incarcerated in a correctional institution; or 6) from an environmental and academic background that deters the pursuit of educational plans. Students already in college are not eligible.

Financial data Stipends range up to $1,800 per year.

Duration 1 year; may be renewed up to 4 additional years, provided the recipient continues to be a Wisconsin resident enrolled at least half time in a degree or certificate program, makes satisfactory academic progress, demonstrates financial need, and remains enrolled continuously from semester to semester and from year to year. If recipients withdraw from school or cease to attend classes for any reason (other than medical necessity), they may not reapply.

Number awarded Varies each year.

Deadline Deadline not specified.

[599]
WOMEN'S TRANSPORTATION SEMINAR JUNIOR COLLEGE SCHOLARSHIP

Women's Transportation Seminar
Attn: WTS Foundation
1701 K Street, N.W., Suite 800
Washington, DC 20006
(202) 955-5085 Fax: (202) 955-5088
E-mail: wts@wtsinternational.org
Web: www.wtsinternational.org/education/scholarships

Summary To provide financial assistance to women (particularly minority women) who are enrolled at a community college or trade school to prepare for a career in transportation.

Eligibility This program is open to women who are working on an associate or technical degree in transportation or a transportation-related field (e.g., transportation engineering, planning, finance, or logistics). Applicants must have a GPA of 3.0 or higher. Along with their application, they must submit a 500-word statement about their career goals after graduation and why they think they should receive the scholarship award. Applications must be submitted first to a local chapter; the chapters forward selected applications for consideration on the national level. Minority women are especially encouraged to apply. Selection is based on transportation involvement and goals, job skills, academic record, and leadership potential; financial need is not considered.

Financial data The stipend is $1,000.

Duration 1 year.

Additional information Local chapters may also award additional funding to winners for their area.

Number awarded 1 each year.

Deadline Applications must be submitted by November to a local WTS chapter.

[600]
XEROX TECHNICAL MINORITY SCHOLARSHIP PROGRAM

Xerox Corporation
Attn: Technical Minority Scholarship Program
150 State Street, Fourth Floor
Rochester, NY 14614
(585) 422-7689 E-mail: GlobalCareers@xerox.com
Web: www.xerox.com/jobs/minority-scholarships/enus.html

Summary To provide financial assistance to African Americans and other minorities interested in undergraduate or graduate education in the sciences and/or engineering.

Eligibility This program is open to minorities (people of African American, Asian, Pacific Islander, Native American, Native Alaskan, or Hispanic descent) working full time on a bachelor's, master's, or doctoral degree in chemistry, computing and software systems, engineering (chemical, computer, electrical, imaging, manufacturing, mechanical, optical, or software), information management, laser optics, materials science, physics, or printing management science. Applicants must be U.S. citizens or permanent residents with a GPA of 3.0 or higher and attending a 4-year college or university.

Financial data Stipends range from $1,000 to $10,000.

Duration 1 year.

Number awarded Varies each year, recently, 130 of these scholarships were awarded.

Deadline September of each year.

[601] XI PSI OMEGA CHAPTER SCHOLARSHIPS

Alpha Kappa Alpha Sorority, Inc.-Xi Psi Omega Chapter
Attn: President
P.O. Box 140894
Anchorage, AK 99514
(907) 346-3998 E-mail: akaxpo@gmail.com
Web: xipsiomega.com/scholarship.html

Summary To provide financial assistance to high school seniors (especially African American women) from Alaska who plan to attend college in any state.

Eligibility This program is open to seniors graduating from high schools in Alaska who are planning to attend a 2- or 4-year accredited college or university in any state. Applicants must have a GPA of 2.5 or higher and a record of active participation in school and community activities. Alpha Kappa Alpha (AKA) is currently 1 of the largest social sororities whose membership is predominantly African American women.

Financial data A stipend is awarded (amount not specified).

Duration 1 year; nonrenewable.

Additional information The Xi Psi Omega chapter of AKA serves alumnae members in Alaska.

Number awarded 1 or more each year.

Deadline March of each year.

[602] XI ZETA OMEGA FELLOWSHIP

Alpha Kappa Alpha Sorority, Inc.
Attn: Educational Advancement Foundation
5656 South Stony Island Avenue
Chicago, IL 60637
(773) 947-0026 Toll Free: (800) 653-6528
Fax: (773) 947-0277 E-mail: akaeaf@akaeaf.net
Web: www.akaeaf.org/fellowships_endowments.htm

Summary To provide financial assistance to undergraduates (especially African American women) who are working on a degree in early childhood education.

Eligibility This program is open to undergraduate students who are enrolled full time as sophomores or higher in an accredited degree-granting institution in any state. Applicants must be majoring in early childhood education. Along with their application, they must submit 1) a list of honors, awards, and scholarships received; 2) a list of organizations in which they have memberships, especially minority organizations; and 3) a statement of their personal and career goals, including how this scholarship will enhance their ability to attain those goals. The sponsor is a traditionally African American women's sorority.

Financial data A stipend is awarded (amount not specified).

Duration 1 year.

Number awarded 1 or more each even-numbered year.

Deadline April of each even-numbered year.

[603] YOUTH PARTNERS ACCESSING CAPITAL SCHOLARSHIPS

Alpha Kappa Alpha Sorority, Inc.
Attn: Educational Advancement Foundation
5656 South Stony Island Avenue
Chicago, IL 60637
(773) 947-0026 Toll Free: (800) 653-6528
Fax: (773) 947-0277 E-mail: akaeaf@akaeaf.net
Web: www.akaeaf.org/undergraduate_scholarships.htm

Summary To provide financial assistance to undergraduate members of Alpha Kappa Alpha sorority who demonstrate outstanding community service.

Eligibility This program is open to members of the organization, a traditionally African American women's sorority, who are working at least as sophomores on an undergraduate degree at an accredited degree-granting institution. Applicants must have a GPA of 3.0 or higher and a record of demonstrated participation in leadership, volunteer, civic, or campus activities. They must be able to demonstrate exceptional academic achievement or extreme financial need.

Financial data Stipends vary; recently, they averaged $1,300.

Duration 1 year.

Number awarded Varies each year; recently, 10 of these scholarships were awarded.

Deadline April of each year.

[604] ZANNONI INDIVIDUAL SUMMER UNDERGRADUATE RESEARCH FELLOWSHIPS

American Society for Pharmacology and Experimental Therapeutics
9650 Rockville Pike
Bethesda, MD 20814-3995
(301) 634-7060 Fax: (301) 634-7061
E-mail: djordan@aspet.org
Web: www.aspet.org/awards/SURF

Summary To provide funding to undergraduate students (particularly African Americans, other minorities, and women) who are interested in participating in a summer research project at a laboratory affiliated with the American Society for Pharmacology and Experimental Therapeutics (ASPET).

Eligibility This program is open to undergraduate students interested in working during the summer in the laboratory of a society member who must agree to act as a sponsor. Applications must be submitted jointly by the student and the sponsor, and they must include 1) a letter from the sponsor with a brief description of the proposed research, a statement of the qualifications of the student, the degree of independence the student will have, a description of complementary activities available to the student, and a description of how the student will report on the research results; 2) a letter from the student indicating the nature of his or her interest in the project and a description of future plans; 3) a copy of the sponsor's updated curriculum vitae; and 4) copies of all the student's undergraduate transcripts. Selection is based on the nature of the research opportunities provided, student and sponsor qualifications, and the likelihood the student will prepare for a career in pharmacology. Applications from underrepresented minorities and women are particularly encouraged.

Financial data The stipend is $2,800. Funds are paid directly to the institution but may be used only for student stipends.

Duration 10 weeks during the summer.

Additional information Some of these awards are funded through the Glenn E. Ullyot Fund; those recipients are designated as the Ullyot Fellows.

Number awarded Varies each year; recently, 4 of these fellowships were awarded.

Deadline February of each year.

Graduate Students

Listed alphabetically by program title and described in detail here are 479 fellowships, forgivable loans, grants, awards, and other sources of "free money" set aside for African Americans who are incoming, continuing, or returning graduate students working on a master's, doctoral, or professional degree. This funding is available to support study, training, research, and/or creative activities in the United States.

[605]
A. GRACE LEE MIMS VOCAL SCHOLARSHIP

Cleveland Foundation
Attn: Scholarship Processing
1422 Euclid Avenue, Suite 1300
Cleveland, OH 44115-2001
(216) 861-3810 Fax: (216) 861-1729
E-mail: Hello@clevefdn.org
Web: www.clevelandfoundation.org

Summary To provide financial assistance to African Americans who have a connection to Ohio and are interested in working on a master's degree in vocal music or education with an emphasis on Negro spirituals.

Eligibility This program is open to African American graduate students born, reared, or residing in Ohio. Applicants must be working on a master's degree at an institution (college, university, conservatory) in any state in vocal performance or music education with an emphasis on voice. They must have a GPA of 2.0 or higher. Along with their application, they must submit 1) 3 letters of recommendation from voice teachers or music professors attesting to their musical talent, moral character, and dedication to the survival of the Negro spiritual; 2) a personal statement describing their commitment to ensure the preservation of the Negro spiritual through their performance or teaching career; 3) an audio tape or CD of a recent performance (concert or recital); 4) 3 music programs over at least a 2-year span including their performance of Negro spirituals; and 5) a detailed budget for their academic year's educational expenses. U.S. citizenship is required.

Financial data The stipend is $10,000 per year. Funds must be applied to tuition, fees, books, supplies, and equipment required for the program.

Duration 1 year; recipients may reapply.

Number awarded 1 or more each year.

Deadline April of each year.

[606]
A. KAY STANFIELD SPINKS LAW STUDENT SCHOLARSHIP

D. Augustus Straker Bar Foundation
c/o Shirley A. Kaigler
27777 Franklin Road, Suite 2500
Southfield, MI 48034
(248) 351-3000 E-mail: StrakerFoundation@jaffelaw.com
Web: www.strakerlaw.org

Summary To provide financial assistance to African American and other minority students from any state who are enrolled at law schools in Michigan.

Eligibility This program is open to minority students from any state who are entering their second or third year at a certified law school program within the state of Michigan. Applicants must demonstrate scholarly dedication, involvement in school and community activities, and the ability to articulate a vision that indicates prospects for long-term success in the practice of law, especially as it relates to representing minority viewpoints within the system of jurisprudence.

Financial data The stipend is $2,500.

Duration 1 year.

Additional information The D. Augustus Straker Bar Association was founded in 1990 as a proactive organization for African American attorneys. It was named in honor of the first African American attorney to argue a case before the Michigan Supreme Court (in 1890). That association established this foundation and began awarding scholarships in 1999. Following the death of the foundation's first president in 2012, the scholarship was named after her.

Number awarded 1 or more each year.

Deadline April of each year.

[607]
ABA LEGAL OPPORTUNITY SCHOLARSHIP

American Bar Association
Attn: Fund for Justice and Education
321 North Clark Street, 21st Floor
Chicago, IL 60654-7598
(312) 988-5927 Fax: (312) 988-6392
E-mail: legalosf@staff.abanet.org
Web: www.americanbar.org

Summary To provide financial assistance to African Americans and other racial and ethnic minority students who are interested in attending law school.

Eligibility This program is open to racial and ethnic minority college graduates who are interested in attending an ABA-accredited law school. Only students beginning law school may apply; students who have completed 1 or more semesters of law school are not eligible. Applicants must have a cumulative GPA of 2.5 or higher and be citizens or permanent residents of the United States. Along with their application, they must submit a 1,000-word statement describing their personal and family background, community service activities, and other connections to their racial and ethnic minority community. Financial need is also considered in the selection process.

Financial data The stipend is $5,000 per year.

Duration 1 year; may be renewed for 2 additional years if satisfactory performance in law school has been achieved.

Additional information This program began in the 2000-01 academic year.

Number awarded Approximately 20 each year.

Deadline February of each year.

[608]
ACA/MARTIN LUTHER KING JR. SCHOLARSHIP AWARDS

American Correctional Association
Attn: Scholarship Award Committee
206 North Washington Street, Suite 200
Alexandria, VA 22314
(703) 224-0000 Toll Free: (800) ACA-JOIN
Fax: (703) 224-0179 E-mail: jenniferb@aca.org
Web: www.aca.org/pastpresentfuture/awards.asp

Summary To provide financial assistance for undergraduate or graduate study to African Americans and other minorities interested in a career in the criminal justice field.

Eligibility Members of the American Correctional Association (ACA) may nominate a minority person for these awards. Nominees do not need to be ACA members, but they must have been accepted to or be enrolled in an undergraduate or graduate program in criminal justice at a 4-year college or university. Along with the nomination package, they must submit a 250-word essay describing their reflections on the ideals and philosophies of Dr. Martin Luther King and how they have attempted to emulate those qualities in their lives. They must provide documentation of financial need, academic achievement, and commitment to the principles of Dr. King.

Financial data A stipend is awarded (amount not specified). Funds are paid directly to the recipient's college or university.

Number awarded 1 each year.

Deadline May of each year.

[609]
ACADEMY OF NUTRITION AND DIETETICS GRADUATE SCHOLARSHIPS

Academy of Nutrition and Dietetics
Attn: Foundation
120 South Riverside Plaza, Suite 2000
Chicago, IL 60606-6995
(312) 899-0040 Toll Free: (800) 877-1600, ext. 1133
Fax: (312) 899-4817 E-mail: scholarships@eatright.org
Web: www.eatright.org/Foundation/scholarships

Summary To provide financial assistance to African American and other graduate student members of the Academy of Nutrition and Dietetics.

Eligibility This program is open to members of the academy who are enrolled in the second year of a master's or doctoral degree program in dietetics. Applicants who are currently completing a dietetic internship or preprofessional practice program that is combined with a graduate program may also apply. The graduate scholarships are available only to U.S. citizens and permanent residents. Applicants should intend to practice in the field of dietetics. Some scholarships require specific areas of study (e.g., public health nutrition, food service administration) and status as a registered dietitian. Others may require membership in a specific dietetic practice group, residency in a specific state, or underrepresented minority group status. The same application form can be used for all categories.

Financial data Stipends normally range from $500 to $3,000; recently, they averaged approximately $1,870.

Duration 1 year.

Additional information The Academy of Nutrition and Dietetics was formerly the American Dietetic Association.

Number awarded Approximately 60 each year.

Deadline February of each year.

[610]
ACOUSTICAL SOCIETY OF AMERICA MINORITY FELLOWSHIP

Acoustical Society of America
Attn: Office Manager
2 Huntington Quadrangle, Suite 1NO1
Melville, NY 11747-4502
(516) 576-2360 Fax: (516) 576-2377
E-mail: asa@aip.org
Web: www.acousticalsociety.org

Summary To provide financial assistance to African Americans and other underrepresented minorities who are working on a graduate degree involving acoustics.

Eligibility This program is open to U.S. and Canadian citizens and permanent residents who are members of a minority group that is underrepresented in the sciences (Hispanic, African American, or Native American). Applicants must be enrolled in or accepted to a graduate degree program as a full-time student. Their program of study may be in any field of pure or applied science and engineering directly related to acoustics, including acoustical oceanography, architectural acoustics, animal bioacoustics, biomedical ultrasound, bioresponse to vibration, engineering acoustics, musical acoustics, noise, physical acoustics, psychological acoustics, physiological acoustics, signal processing in acoustics, speech communication, structural acoustics and vibration, and underwater acoustics. Along with their application, student must submit a statement on why they are enrolled in their present academic program, including how they intend to use their graduate education to develop a career and how the study of acoustics is relevant to their career objectives.

Financial data The stipend is $20,000 per year. The sponsor strongly encourages the host educational institution to waive all tuition costs and assessed fees. Fellows also receive $1,000 for travel to attend a national meeting of the sponsor.

Duration 1 year; may be renewed for 1 additional year if the recipient is making normal progress toward a degree and is enrolled full time.

Additional information This program began in 1992.

Number awarded 1 each year.

Deadline March of each year.

[611]
ACS/ORGANIC CHEMISTRY GRADUATE STUDENT FELLOWSHIPS

American Chemical Society
Division of Organic Chemistry
1155 16th Street, N.W.
Washington, DC 20036
(202) 872-4401 Toll Free: (800) 227-5558, ext. 4401
E-mail: division@acs.org
Web: www.organicdivision.org/?nd=graduate_fellowship

Summary To provide funding for research to members (particularly minority and female members) of the Division of Organic Chemistry of the American Chemical Society (ACS) who are working on a doctoral degree in organic chemistry.

Eligibility This program is open to members of the division who are entering the third or fourth year of a Ph.D. program in organic chemistry. Applicants must submit 3 letters of recommendation, a resume, and a short essay on a research area of their choice. U.S. citizenship or permanent resident status is required. Selection is based primarily on evidence of research accomplishment. Applications from women and minorities are especially encouraged.

Financial data The stipend is $26,000; that includes $750 for travel support to present a poster of their work at the National Organic Symposium.

Duration 1 year.

Additional information This program began in 1982. It includes the Emmanuil Troyansky Fellowship. Current corporate sponsors include Genentech, Organic Syntheses, Boehringer Ingelheim, and Amgen.

Number awarded Varies each year; recently, 8 of these fellowships were awarded.

Deadline May of each year.

[612]
ADDIE B. MORRIS SCHOLARSHIP

American Association of Railroad Superintendents
P.O. Box 200
La Fox, IL 60147
(630) 762-0754 E-mail: aars@supt.org
Web: www.railroadsuperintendents.org/Scholarships

Summary To provide financial assistance to undergraduate and graduate students, with preference given to African Americans and other minorities working on a degree in transportation.

Eligibility This program is open to full-time undergraduate and graduate students enrolled at accredited colleges and universities in Canada or the United States. Applicants must have completed enough credits to have standing as a sophomore and must have a GPA of 2.75 or higher. Preference is given to minority students enrolled in the transportation field who can demonstrate financial need.

Financial data The stipend is $1,000. Funds are sent directly to the recipient's institution.

Duration 1 year.

Number awarded 1 or more each year.

Deadline May of each year.

[613]
ADLER POLLOCK & SHEEHAN DIVERSITY SCHOLARSHIP

Adler Pollock & Sheehan P.C.
Attn: Diversity Committee Chair
175 Federal Street
Boston, MA 02110-2210
(617) 482-0600 Fax: (617) 482-0604
E-mail: Diversitycomm@apslaw.com
Web: www.apslaw.com/firm-diversity.html

Summary To provide financial assistance to African Americans and other residents of Massachusetts and Rhode Island who are members of diverse groups and plan to attend law school in any state.

Eligibility This program is open to residents of Massachusetts and Rhode Island who are members of a diverse group, including African American, American Indian, Hispanic, Asian/Pacific Islander, gay/lesbian, or other minority group. Applicants must be entering their first year at an ABA-accredited law school in the United States. They must be able to demonstrate academic achievement, a desire to work and reside in Massachusetts or Rhode Island after graduation, a demonstrated commitment to the community, a vision of contributions to the profession and community after graduation, and financial need.

Financial data The stipend is $10,000.

Duration 1 year.

Number awarded 1 each year.

Deadline May of each year.

[614]
ADRIENNE M. AND CHARLES SHELBY ROOKS FELLOWSHIP FOR RACIAL AND ETHNIC THEOLOGICAL STUDENTS

United Church of Christ
Attn: Local Church Ministries
700 Prospect Avenue East
Cleveland, OH 44115-1100
(216) 736-3865 Toll Free: (866) 822-8224, ext. 3865
Fax: (216) 736-3783 E-mail: lcm@ucc.org
Web: www.ucc.org/seminarians/ucc-scholarships-for.html

Summary To provide financial assistance to African American and other minority students who are either enrolled at an accredited seminary preparing for a career of service in the United Church of Christ (UCC) or working on a doctoral degree in the field of religion.

Eligibility This program is open to members of underrepresented ethnic groups (African American, Hispanic American, Asian American, Native American Indian, or Pacific Islander) who have been a member of a UCC congregation for at least 1 year. Applicants must be either 1) enrolled in an accredited school of theology in the United States or Canada and working on an M.Div. degree with the intent of becoming a pastor or teacher within the UCC; or 2) doctoral (Ph.D., Th.D., or Ed.D.) students within a field related to religious studies. Seminary students must have a GPA in all postsecondary work of 3.0 or higher and must have begun the in-care process; preference is given to students who have demonstrated leadership (through a history of service to the church) and scholarship (through exceptional academic performance). For doctoral students, preference is given to applicants who have demonstrated academic excellence, teaching effectiveness, and commitment to the UCC and who intend to become professors in colleges, seminaries, or graduate schools.

Financial data Grants range from $500 to $5,000 per year.

Duration 1 year; may be renewed.

Number awarded Varies each year; recently, 16 of these scholarships, including 10 for M.Div. students and 6 for doctoral students, were awarded.

Deadline February of each year.

[615]
AETNA FOUNDATION-NMF HEALTHCARE LEADERSHIP PROGRAM

National Medical Fellowships, Inc.
Attn: Scholarship Program
347 Fifth Avenue, Suite 510
New York, NY 10016
(212) 483-8880, ext. 304 Toll Free: (877) NMF-1DOC
Fax: (212) 483-8897 E-mail: mbrito@nmfonline.org
Web: www.nmfonline.org/programs/aetna-foundation

Summary To provide financial assistance to African Americans and other underrepresented minorities who are medical students at schools in selected states.

Eligibility This program is open to members of underrepresented minority groups (African American, Hispanic/Latino, American Indian, Native Hawaiian, Alaska Native, Vietnamese, Cambodian, or Native Pacific Islander) who are currently enrolled in their second or third year of medical school. U.S. citizenship is required. Applicants must be attending medical school in southern California (particularly Los Angeles), Connecticut, Illinois (particularly Chicago), New Jersey, New York City, or Philadelphia. Along with their application, they must submit an essay of 500 to 1,000 words on what leadership means for physicians. Selection is based on that essay, letters of recommendation, community service and leadership activities, and financial need.

Financial data The stipend is $5,000.

Duration 1 year.

Additional information Funding for this program, which is administered by National Medical Fellowships (NMF), is provided by the Aetna Foundation.

Number awarded 10 each year.

Deadline February of each year for Illinois; March of each year for Connecticut, New Jersey, New York City, and Philadelphia; or April of each year for southern California.

[616]
AFRICAN AMERICAN LAW STUDENT FELLOWSHIP PROGRAM

National Bar Institute
1225 11th Street, N.W.
Washington, DC 20001-4217
(202) 842-3900 Fax: (202) 289-6170
Web: www.nationalbar.org/nbi/nbigrants.html

Summary To provide financial assistance to African American students working on a law degree.

Eligibility This program is open to African Americans who have completed at least 2 consecutive years of full-time study at a U.S. law school. Applicants must have demonstrated a commitment to creating equality and justice for African Americans through work in their law schools, neighborhoods, and community and must intend to return to a Black community to practice law once their legal training is completed. U.S. citizenship or permanent resident status and membership in the National Bar Association (NBA) are required. Selection is based on the applicant's academic qualifications, potential to make a significant contribution to the field, commitment to African American issues in the field of study and/or community, and financial need.

Financial data Stipends range from $1,000 to $10,000, but most are approximately $2,500.

Duration 1 year.

Additional information The National Bar Institute was established in 1982 as the philanthropic arm of the National Bar Association, an organization of African American lawyers.

Number awarded Up to 3 each year.

Deadline May of each year.

[617]
AFRICAN AMERICAN SCHOLARSHIP FUND OF DISCIPLES HOME MISSIONS

Christian Church (Disciples of Christ)
Attn: Disciples Home Missions
130 East Washington Street
P.O. Box 1986
Indianapolis, IN 46206-1986
(317) 713-2652 Toll Free: (888) DHM-2631
Fax: (317) 635-4426 E-mail: mail@dhm.disciples.org
Web: www.discipleshomemissions.org

Summary To provide financial assistance to African Americans interested in preparing for a career in the ministry of the Christian Church (Disciples of Christ).

Eligibility This program is open to African American ministerial students who are members of a Christian Church (Disciples of Christ) congregation in the United States or Canada. Applicants must plan to prepare for the ordained ministry, be working on an M.Div. or equivalent degree, provide evidence of financial need, be enrolled full time at an accredited school or seminary, provide a transcript of academic work, and be under the care of a regional Commission on the Ministry or in the process of coming under care.

Financial data A stipend is awarded (amount not specified).

Duration 1 year; recipients may reapply.

Additional information This program began in 1939 as the Negro Student Scholarship Fund of the United Christian Missionary Society. Its current name was adopted in 2009.

Number awarded 1 each year.

Deadline March of each year.

[618]
AFRICAN HERITAGE CAUCUS SCHOLARSHIPS

African Heritage Caucus
c/o Stephanie Haiba Collier, Scholarship Chair
3100 Sasparilla Cove
Austin, TX 78748
E-mail: swcollier@swmail.sw.org
Web: www.africanheritagecaucus.org

Summary To provide financial assistance to members of the African Heritage Caucus within the American Academy of Physician Assistants (AAPA).

Eligibility This program is open to physician assistant students entering their clinical phase of training and members of both the AAPA and its African Heritage Caucus. Applicants must submit an essay of 500 to 750 words on 1 of the following topics: 1) their opinion on the impact of universal health care in addressing the issues of racial health care disparities in our country; or 2) the major health care disparities facing the African American community and how they will address those as a practicing physician assistant. Selection is based on academic progress, financial need, community and/or professional activities, and knowledge of health care issues and the physician assistant's role.

Financial data Stipends range from $500 to $1,000.

Duration 1 year.

Number awarded Up to 2 each year.

Deadline April of each year.

[619]
AFRL/DAGSI OHIO STUDENT-FACULTY RESEARCH FELLOWSHIP PROGRAM

Dayton Area Graduate Studies Institute
3155 Research Boulevard, Suite 205
Kettering, OH 45420
(937) 781-4001 Fax: (937) 781-4005
E-mail: kelam@dagsi.org
Web: www.dagsi.org/pages/osrfp_proinforeq.html

Summary To provide funding to faculty and graduate students (particularly African Americans and other minorities, women, and individuals with disabilities) at designated universities in Ohio who are from any state and interested in conducting research in aerospace technologies of interest to the U.S. Air Force.

Eligibility This program is open to research teams of full-time graduate students and faculty at 18 designated Ohio universities. Applicants must be interested in conducting research that will utilize the facilities of the Air Force Research Laboratory (AFRL) at Wright-Patterson Air Force Base. All 6 directorates at the AFRL (air vehicles, propulsion, sensors, materials and manufacturing, human effectiveness, and information) participate in this program. Applications from Ph.D. candidates must be developed and written largely by the student, with support, guidance, and input as necessary from the faculty partner. For master's projects, the proposal can be developed and written jointly by the faculty member and the student. All participants (faculty and student) must be U.S. citizens. Underrepresented minorities, women, and persons with disabilities are strongly urged to apply.

Financial data Grants provide stipends of $23,500 for students who have a master's degree and are working on a Ph.D. or $18,500 for students who have a bachelor's degree and are working on a master's; student's tuition for 1 academic year; a faculty stipend of $11,000; student and faculty allowances of $3,000 each for program-related travel or other approved expenses; and overhead at a maximum off-campus rate of 26% of student and faculty stipends and miscellaneous allowances.

Duration 1 year; may be renewed for 1 additional year by master's students and for 2 additional years by Ph.D. candidates. Students are expected to spend 8 consecutive weeks conducting research at AFRL and faculty members are expected to spend at least 1 month conducting research at AFRL.

Additional information DAGSI was established in 1994 as a consortium of graduate engineering schools at the University of Dayton, Wright State University, and the Air Force Institute of Technology. The Ohio State University and the University of Cincinnati joined as affiliated members in 1996 and Miami University and Ohio University joined as associate members in 2001. Students from the following universities are also eligible to participate in this program: University of Akron, Bowling Green State University, Central State University, Cleveland State University, Kent State University, Shawnee State University, University of Toledo, Youngstown State University, Medical College of Ohio, Northeastern Ohio Universities College of Medicine, and Case Western Reserve University.

Number awarded At least 20 each year.

Deadline January of each year.

[620]
AGA INVESTING IN THE FUTURE STUDENT RESEARCH FELLOWSHIPS

American Gastroenterological Association
Attn: AGA Research Foundation
Research Awards Manager
4930 Del Ray Avenue
Bethesda, MD 20814-2512
(301) 222-4012 Fax: (301) 654-5920
E-mail: awards@gastro.org
Web: www.gastro.org/aga-foundation/grants

Summary To provide funding for research on digestive diseases or nutrition to undergraduate and medical students who are African Americans or from other underrepresented minority groups.

Eligibility This program is open to undergraduate and medical students at accredited U.S. institutions who are African Americans, Hispanic/Latino Americans, Alaska Natives, American Indians, or Natives of the U.S. Pacific Islands. Applicants must be interested in conducting research on digestive diseases or nutrition. They may not hold similar salary support awards from other agencies (e.g., American Liver Foundation, Crohn's and Colitis Foundation). Research must be conducted under the supervision of a preceptor who is a full-time faculty member at an institution in a state other than the student's, directing a research project in a gastroenterology-related area, and a member of the American Gastroenterological Association (AGA).

Financial data Fellowships provide payment of housing, travel, and a stipend of $5,000.

Duration 8 to 10 weeks. The work may take place at any time during the year.

Number awarded 10 each year.

Deadline February of each year.

[621]
AGING RESEARCH DISSERTATION AWARDS TO INCREASE DIVERSITY

National Institute on Aging
Attn: Office of Extramural Affairs
7201 Wisconsin Avenue, Suite 2C-218
Bethesda, MD 20814
(301) 402-4158 Fax: (301) 402-2945
TDD: (301) 451-0088 E-mail: hunterc@nia.nih.gov
Web: www.grants.nih.gov

Summary To provide financial assistance to doctoral candidates from underrepresented groups (particularly African Americans, other minorities, and students with disabilities) who wish to conduct research on aging.

Eligibility This program is open to doctoral candidates conducting research on a dissertation with an aging-related focus, including the basic biology of aging; chronic, disabling, and degenerative diseases of aging, with a particular focus on Alzheimer's Disease; multiple mobidities; individual behavioral and social changes with aging; caregiving; longevity; and the consequences for society of an aging population. Applicants must be 1) members of an ethnic or racial group underrepresented in biomedical or behavioral research (African Americans, Hispanic Americans, American Indians, Alaska Natives, Native Hawaiians, and other Pacific Islanders); 2) individuals with disabilities; or 3) individuals from socially, culturally, economically, or educationally disadvantaged backgrounds that have inhibited their ability to prepare for a career in health-related research. They must be U.S. citizens, nationals, or permanent residents.

Financial data Grants provide $22,032 per year for stipend and up to $20,000 for additional expenses. No funds may be used to pay for tuition or fees associated with completion of doctoral studies. The institution may receive up to 8% of direct costs as facilities and administrative costs per year.

Duration Up to 2 years.

Number awarded Up to 5 each year.

Deadline Applications must be submitted by February, June, or October of each year.

[622]
AGNES JONES JACKSON SCHOLARSHIPS

National Association for the Advancement of Colored People
Attn: Education Department
4805 Mt. Hope Drive
Baltimore, MD 21215-3297
(410) 580-5760 Toll Free: (877) NAACP-98
E-mail: youth@naacpnet.org
Web: www.naacp.org/pages/naacp-scholarships

Summary To provide financial assistance to members of the National Association for the Advancement of Colored People (NAACP) who are attending or planning to attend college or graduate school.

Eligibility This program is open to members of the NAACP who are younger than 25 years of age and full-time undergraduates or full- or part-time graduate students. The minimum GPA is 2.5 for graduating high school seniors and undergraduate students or 3.0 for graduate students. All applicants must be able to demonstrate financial need (family income must be less than $16,245 for a family of 1, ranging up to $49,905 for a family of 7) and U.S. citizenship. Along with their application, they must submit a 1-page essay on their interest in their major and a career, their life's ambition, what they hope to accomplish in their lifetime, and what position they hope to attain.

Financial data The stipend is $1,500 per year for undergraduate students or $2,500 per year for graduate students.

Duration 1 year; recipients may apply for renewal.

Number awarded Varies each year; recently, 5 of these scholarships were awarded.

Deadline March of each year.

[623]
AHRQ GRANTS FOR HEALTH SERVICES RESEARCH DISSERTATIONS

Agency for Healthcare Research and Quality
Attn: Office of Extramural Research, Education, and Priority Populations
540 Gaither Road
Rockville, MD 20850
(301) 427-1869 Fax: (301) 427-1561
TDD: (301) 451-0088 E-mail: Ali.Azadegan@ahrq.hhs.gov
Web: grants.nih.gov/grants/guide/pa-files/PA-12-256.html

Summary To provide funding to doctoral candidates (particularly African Americans, other underrepresented minorities, and students with disabilities) who are engaged in research for a dissertation that examines an aspect of the health care system.

Eligibility This program is open to citizens, nationals, and permanent residents who are enrolled full time in an accredited research doctoral degree program at an institution in the United States. Applicants must have completed all requirements for the doctoral degree except for the dissertation in such fields as the social or behavioral sciences, mathematics, engineering, health services, nursing, epidemiology, biostatistics, health policy, or health informatics. Their proposed dissertation topic must relate to the strategic goals of the Agency for Healthcare Research and Quality (AHRQ): 1) reducing the risk of harm from health care services by promoting the delivery of appropriate care that achieves the best quality outcomes; 2) achieving wider access to effective health care services and reducing health care costs; and 3) assuring that providers and consumers/patients use beneficial and timely health care information to make informed decisions. Priority is given to proposals that address health services research issues critical to such priority population as individuals living in inner city and rural (including frontier) areas; low-income and minority groups; women, children, and the elderly; and individuals with special health care needs, including those with disabilities and those who need chronic or end-of-life health care. Members of underrepresented racial and ethnic groups, individuals from disadvantaged backgrounds, and individuals with disabilities are especially encouraged to apply.

Financial data Up to $40,000 is awarded for the investigator's salary, direct project expenses (travel, data purchasing, data processing, and supplies), and matriculation fees. The institution will receive facilities and administrative costs of 8% of total allowable direct costs, exclusive of tuition and related fees, health insurance, and expenditures for equipment.

Duration 9 to 17 months.

Number awarded Up to 30 each year.

Deadline January, April, July, or October of each year.

[624]
AICPA FELLOWSHIPS FOR MINORITY DOCTORAL STUDENTS

American Institute of Certified Public Accountants
Attn: Academic and Career Development Division
220 Leigh Farm Road
Durham, NC 27707-8110
(919) 402-4931 Fax: (919) 419-4705
E-mail: scholarships@aicpa.org
Web: www.aicpa.org

Summary To provide financial assistance to African American and other underrepresented minority doctoral students who wish to prepare for a career teaching accounting at the college level.

Eligibility This program is open to underrepresented minority students who have applied to and/or been accepted into a doctoral program with a concentration in accounting. Applicants must have earned a master's degree or completed a minimum of 3 years of full-time work in accounting. They must be attending or planning to attend school full time and agree not to work full time in a paid position, teach more than 1 course as a teaching assistant, or work more than 25% as a research assistant. U.S. citizenship or permanent resident status is required. Preference is given to applicants who have attained a C.P.A. designation and/or are members of the American Institute of Certified Public Accountants (AICPA) and those who perform AICPA committee service. For purposes of this program, the AICPA defines minority students as those whose heritage is Black or African American, Hispanic or Latino, or Native American. Selection is based on academic and professional achievement, commitment to earning an accounting doctoral degree, and financial need.

Financial data The stipend is $12,000 per year.

Duration 1 year; may be renewed up to 4 additional years.

Number awarded Varies each year; recently, 21 of these fellowships were awarded.

Deadline March of each year.

[625]
AIR FORCE SUMMER FACULTY FELLOWSHIP PROGRAM

American Society for Engineering Education
Attn: AFSFF Program
1818 N Street, N.W., Suite 600
Washington, DC 20036-2479
(202) 649-3834 Fax: (202) 265-8504
E-mail: sffp@asee.org
Web: sffp.asee.org

Summary To provide funding to science and engineering faculty and graduate students (particularly African Americans and other underrepresented minorities) who are interested in conducting research during the summer at Air Force facilities.

Eligibility This program is open to U.S. citizens and permanent residents who have a full-time faculty appointment at a U.S. college or university in a field of engineering or science of interest to the Air Force. Applicants must be interested in conducting a research project, under the direction of an Air Force research adviser, at an Air Force Research Laboratory, the U.S. Air Force Academy, or the Air Force Institute of Technology. A graduate student may accompany the faculty member. Faculty and students at Historically Black Colleges and Universities ((HBCUs), Minority Institutions (MIs), American Indian Tribal Colleges and Universities (TCUs), and Hispanic Serving Institutions (HSIs) are especially encouraged to apply.

Financial data Stipends are $1,700 per week for full professors, $1,500 per week for associate professors, $1,300 per week for assistant professors, $884 per week for graduate students working on a master's degree, or $1,037 per week for graduate students working on a doctoral degree. Relocation reimbursement and a daily expense allowance of $50 (for fellows with a commute distance greater than 50 miles) are also available.

Duration 8 to 12 weeks during the summer. May be renewed for a second and third summer, but recipients may not reapply for 2 years after completing a third summer.

Additional information This program began operating in 2005. Research must be conducted in residence at an Air Force facility.

Number awarded Approximately 100 each year.

Deadline December of each year.

[626]
AKA/EAF ENDOWMENT AWARDS

Alpha Kappa Alpha Sorority, Inc.
Attn: Educational Advancement Foundation
5656 South Stony Island Avenue
Chicago, IL 60637
(773) 947-0026 Toll Free: (800) 653-6528
Fax: (773) 947-0277 E-mail: akaeaf@akaeaf.net
Web: www.akaeaf.org/fellowships_endowments.htm

Summary To provide financial assistance to undergraduate and graduate students (especially African American women) who meet designated requirements.

Eligibility This program is open to undergraduate and graduate students who are enrolled full time as sophomores or higher in an accredited degree-granting institution and are planning to continue their program of education. Applicants may apply for scholarships that include specific requirements established by the donor of the endowment that supports it. Along with their application, they must submit 1) a list of honors, awards, and scholarships received; 2) a list of organizations in which they have memberships, especially minority organizations; and 3) a statement of their personal and career goals, including how this scholarship will enhance their ability to attain those goals. The sponsor is a traditionally African American women's sorority.

Financial data Award amounts are determined by the availability of funds from the particular endowment. Recently, stipends averaged more than $1,700 per year.

Duration 1 year or longer.

Additional information Each endowment establishes its own requirements. Examples of requirements include residence of the applicant, major field of study, minimum GPA, attendance at an Historically Black College or University (HBCU) or member institution of the United Negro College Fund (UNCF), or other personal feature. For further information on all endowments, contact the sponsor.

Number awarded Varies each year; recently, 32 of these scholarships, with a total value of nearly $76,00, were awarded.

Deadline April of each year.

[627]
AKA/EAF GRADUATE SCHOLARSHIPS

Alpha Kappa Alpha Sorority, Inc.
Attn: Educational Advancement Foundation
5656 South Stony Island Avenue
Chicago, IL 60637
(773) 947-0026 Toll Free: (800) 653-6528
Fax: (773) 947-0277 E-mail: akaeaf@akaeaf.net
Web: www.akaeaf.org/graduate_scholarships.htm

Summary To provide financial assistance for study or research to graduate students (especially African American women).

Eligibility This program is open to students who are working full time on a graduate degree in any state. Applicants may apply either for a scholarship based on merit (requires a GPA of 3.0 or higher) or on financial need (requires a GPA of 2.5 or higher). Along with their application, they must submit 1) a list of honors, awards, and scholarships received; 2) a list of organizations in which they have memberships, especially minority organizations; 3) a description of the project or research on which they are currently working, or (if they are not involved in a project or research) the aspects of their field that interest them; and 4) a statement of their personal and career goals, including how this scholarship will enhance their ability to attain those goals. The sponsor is a traditionally African American women's sorority.

Financial data Stipends range up to $3,000.

Duration 1 year; nonrenewable.

Number awarded Varies each year; recently, 74 of these scholarships, with a total value of $62,050, were awarded.

Deadline August of each year.

[628]
ALA SPECTRUM SCHOLARSHIP PROGRAM

American Library Association
Attn: Office for Diversity
50 East Huron Street
Chicago, IL 60611-2795
(312) 280-5048 Toll Free: (800) 545-2433, ext. 5048
Fax: (312) 280-3256 TDD: (888) 814-7692
E-mail: spectrum@ala.org
Web: www.ala.org/offices/diversity/spectrum

Summary To provide financial assistance to African American and other minority students interested in working on a degree in librarianship.

Eligibility This program is open to ethnic minority students (African American or Black, Asian, Native Hawaiian or other Pacific Islander, Latino or Hispanic, and American Indian or Alaska Native). Applicants must be U.S. or Canadian citizens or permanent residents who have completed no more than a third of the requirements for a master's or school library media degree. They must be enrolled full or part time at an ALA-accredited school of library and information studies or an ALA-recognized NCATE school library media program. Selection is based on academic leadership, outstanding service, commitment to a career in librarianship, statements indicating the nature of the applicant's library and other work experience, letters of reference, and personal presentation.

Financial data The stipend is $5,000.

Duration 1 year; nonrenewable.

Additional information This program began in 1998. It is administered by a joint committee of the American Library Association (ALA).

Number awarded Varies each year; recently, 69 of these scholarships were awarded.

Deadline February of each year.

[629]
ALAO DIVERSITY SCHOLARSHIP

Academic Library Association of Ohio
c/o Diane Kolosionek, Diversity Committee Chair
Cleveland State University, Michael Schwartz Library
2121 Euclid Avenue
RT 110D
Cleveland, OH 44115-2214
(216) 802-3358 E-mail: d.kolosionek44@csuohio.edu
Web: www.alaoweb.org

Summary To provide financial assistance to African American and other residents of Ohio who are working on a master's degree in library science at a school in any state and will contribute to diversity in the profession.

Eligibility This program is open to residents of Ohio who are enrolled or entering an ALA-accredited program for a master's degree in library science, either on campus or via distance education. Applicants must be able to demonstrate how they will contribute to diversity in the profession, including (but not limited to) race or ethnicity, sexual orientation, life experience, physical ability, and a sense of commitment to those and other diversity issues. Along with their application, they must submit 1) a list of participation in honor societies or professional organizations, awards, scholarships, prizes, honors, or class offices; 2) a list of their community, civic, organizational, or volunteer experiences; and 3) an essay on their understanding of and commitment to diversity in libraries, including how they, as library school students and future professionals, might address the issue.

Financial data The stipend is $1,500.

Duration 1 year.

Number awarded 1 each year.

Deadline March of each year.

[630]
ALBERT W. DENT STUDENT SCHOLARSHIP

American College of Healthcare Executives
Attn: Scholarship Committee
One North Franklin Street, Suite 1700
Chicago, IL 60606-3529
(312) 424-2800 Fax: (312) 424-0023
E-mail: geninfo@ache.org
Web: www.ache.org

Summary To provide financial assistance for college to African American and other minority graduate student members of the American College of Healthcare Executives (ACHE).

Eligibility This program is open to ACHE student associates entering their final year of classroom work in a health care management master's degree program. Applicants must be minority students, enrolled full time, able to demonstrate financial need, and U.S. or Canadian citizens. Along with their application, they must submit an 1- to 2-page essay describing their leadership abilities and experiences, their community and volunteer involvement, their goals as a health care executive, and how this scholarship can help them achieve their career goals.

Financial data The stipend is $5,000.

Duration 1 year.

Additional information The program was established and named in honor of Dr. Albert W. Dent, the foundation's first African American fellow and president emeritus of Dillard University.

Number awarded Varies each year; the sponsor awards up to 20 scholarships through this and its other scholarship program.

Deadline March of each year.

[631]
ALLISON E. FISHER SCHOLARSHIP

National Association of Black Journalists
Attn: Communications Coordinator and Program Manager
University of Maryland
1100 Knight Hall, Suite 3100
College Park, MD 20742
(301) 405-2573 Fax: (301) 314-1714
E-mail: tjohnson@nabj.org
Web: www.nabj.org/?page=SEEDScholarships

Summary To provide financial assistance to undergraduate or graduate student members of the National Association of Black Journalists (NABJ) who are working on a degree in journalism.

Eligibility This program is open to African American undergraduate or graduate student members of NABJ who are currently enrolled full time at an accredited 4-year college or university. Applicants must be majoring in journalism or another communications-related discipline and have a GPA of 3.0 or higher. They must be able to demonstrate financial need. Along with their application, they must submit 5 samples of their work, an official college transcript, 3 letters of recommendation, a resume, and an essay of 1,000 to 2,000 words on the reasons why they are preparing for a career in journalism and what they hope their legacy as a journalist will be.

Financial data The stipend is $2,500. Funds are paid directly to the recipient's college or university.

Duration 1 year; nonrenewable.

Number awarded 1 each year.

Deadline March of each year.

[632]
ALMA WELLS GIVENS SCHOLARSHIP

Auxiliary to the National Medical Association
8403 Colesville Road, Suite 920
Silver Spring, MD 20910
(301) 495-3779 Fax: (301) 495-0037
E-mail: anmanationaloffice@earthlink.net
Web: www.anmanet.org

Summary To provide financial assistance to African American medical students attending selected schools.

Eligibility This program is open to African American medical school students who have completed their sophomore year at 1 of the following medical schools: Howard University College of Medicine (Washington, D.C.), Meharry Medical College (Nashville, Tennessee), Morehouse School of Medicine (Atlanta, Georgia), or Charles R. Drew University (Los Angeles, California). Selection is based on medical aptitude, academic record, personal record, and need.

Financial data A stipend is awarded (amount not specified).

Duration 1 year.

Additional information This program was originally established in 1942. The first scholarships were presented to students at Howard University and Meharry Medical College in 1948-49, at Morehouse College in 1980, and at Charles R. Drew University in 1983.

Number awarded 1 each year.

Deadline Deadline not specified.

[633]
ALPHA PHI ALPHA FRATERNITY SCHOLARSHIPS

Alpha Phi Alpha Fraternity, Inc.
Attn: Education Foundation
2313 St. Paul Street
Baltimore, MD 21218-5211
(410) 554-0040 Fax: (410) 554-0054
E-mail: apaef@apa1906.net
Web: www.alpha-phi-alpha.com/Page.php?id=102

Summary To provide financial assistance for college or graduate school to brothers of Alpha Phi Alpha Fraternity.

Eligibility This program is open to brothers of the fraternity who either 1) are working full time on an undergraduate degree; or 2) have been admitted to a graduate or professional program. Applicants must have a GPA of 3.5 or higher. Along with their application, they must submit a resume, a list of their involvement in the fraternity's national programs and special projects, an official transcript, 3 letters of recommendation, and an essay on their career ambitions, goals, and why they should be awarded the scholarship.

Financial data The stipend is $1,500.

Duration 1 year.

Additional information Alpha Phi Alpha is the first collegiate fraternity established primarily for African American men.

Number awarded 15 each year: 3 in each of the fraternity's 5 geographic regions.

Deadline April of each year.

[634]
ALUMNI EXTENSION TECHNICAL SCHOLARSHIPS

National Society of Black Engineers
Attn: Programs Department
205 Daingerfield Road
Alexandria, VA 22314
(703) 549-2207 Fax: (703) 683-5312
E-mail: scholarships@nsbe.org
Web: www.nsbe.org/Programs/Scholarships.aspx

Summary To provide financial assistance to members of the National Society of Black Engineers (NSBE) who are entering or enrolled in a graduate program in engineering or science.

Eligibility This program is open to members of the society who are either graduating college seniors planning to enter graduate school or current graduate students with at least 1 academic year remaining. All technical fields of engineering and science are eligible. Preference is given to members of the NSBE Alumni Extension (AE) or an NSBE Special Interest Group (SIG). Applicants must submit an essay of 200 to 250 words on a topic that changes annually; recently, they were invited to describe a technical design, process, or program that NSBE technical professionals (alumni) or specialists (graduate students) can implement via a new or existing SIG to improve the quality of life in the Black community.

Financial data The stipend is $2,000.

Duration 1 year.

Number awarded 2 each year.

Deadline May of each year.

[635]
AMA FOUNDATION MINORITY SCHOLARS AWARDS

American Medical Association
Attn: AMA Foundation
515 North State Street
Chicago, IL 60610
(312) 464-4193 Fax: (312) 464-4142
E-mail: amafoundation@ama-assn.org
Web: www.ama-assn.org

Summary To provide financial assistance to medical school students who are African American or members of other underrepresented minority groups.

Eligibility This program is open to first- and second-year medical students who are members of the following minority groups: African American, American Indian, Native Hawaiian, Alaska Native, or Hispanic. Only nominations are accepted. Each medical school is invited to submit 2 nominees. U.S. citizenship or permanent resident status is required.

Financial data The stipend is $10,000.

Duration 1 year.

Additional information This program is offered by the AMA Foundation of the American Medical Association in collaboration with the Minority Affairs Consortium (MAC) and with support from the Pfizer Medical Humanities Initiative.

Number awarded Up to 12 each year.

Deadline April of each year.

[636]
AMELIA KEMP MEMORIAL SCHOLARSHIP

Women of the Evangelical Lutheran Church in America
Attn: Scholarships
8765 West Higgins Road
Chicago, IL 60631-4101
(773) 380-2741 Toll Free: (800) 638-3522, ext. 2741
Fax: (773) 380-2419 E-mail: valora.starr@elca.org
Web: www.womenoftheelca.org

Summary To provide financial assistance to African American and other lay women of color who are members of Evangelical Lutheran Church of America (ELCA) congregations and who wish to study on the undergraduate, graduate, professional, or vocational school level.

Eligibility This program is open to ELCA lay women of color who are at least 21 years of age and have experienced an interruption of at least 2 years in their education since high school. Applicants must have been admitted to an educational institution to prepare for a career in other than ordained ministry. U.S. citizenship is required.

Financial data The maximum stipend is $1,000.

Duration Up to 2 years.

Number awarded 1 or more each year.

Deadline February of each year.

[637]
AMERICAN ANTHROPOLOGICAL ASSOCIATION MINORITY DISSERTATION FELLOWSHIP PROGRAM

American Anthropological Association
Attn: Director of Academic Relations
2200 Wilson Boulevard, Suite 600
Arlington, VA 22201-3357
(703) 528-1902 Fax: (703) 528-3546
E-mail: academic@aaanet.org
Web: www.aaanet.org/cmtes/minority/Minfellow.cfm

Summary To provide funding to African Americans and other minorities who are working on a Ph.D. dissertation in anthropology.

Eligibility This program is open to Native American, African American, Latino(a), Pacific Islander, and Asian American doctoral students who have been admitted to degree candidacy in anthropology. Applicants must be U.S. citizens, enrolled in a full-time academic program leading to a doctoral degree in anthropology, and members of the American Anthropological Association. They must have a record of outstanding academic success, have had their dissertation proposal approved by their dissertation committee prior to application, be writing a dissertation in an area of anthropological research, and need funding to complete the dissertation. Along with their application, they must submit a cover letter, a research plan summary, a curriculum vitae, a statement regarding employment, a disclosure statement providing information about other sources of available and pending financial support, 3 letters of recommendation, and an official transcript from their doctoral program. Selection is based on the quality of the submitted information and the judged likelihood that the applicant will have a good chance of completing the dissertation.

Financial data The grant is $10,000. Funds are sent in 2 installments (in September and in January) directly to the recipient.

Duration 1 year; nonrenewable.

Number awarded 1 each year.

Deadline February of each year.

[638]
AMERICAN ASSOCIATION OF NURSE ANESTHETISTS FOUNDATION SCHOLARSHIPS

American Association of Nurse Anesthetists
Attn: AANA Foundation
222 South Prospect Avenue
Park Ridge, IL 60068-4001
(847) 655-1170 Fax: (847) 692-6968
E-mail: foundation@aana.com
Web: www.aanafoundation.com

Summary To provide financial assistance to African and African American members of the American Association of Nurse Anesthetists (AANA) who are interested in obtaining further education.

Eligibility This program is open to African and African American members of the association who are currently enrolled in an accredited nurse anesthesia education program. First-year students must have completed 6 months of nurse anesthesia classes; second-year students must have completed 12 months of nurse anesthesia classes. Along with their application, they must submit a 250-word essay describing why they have chosen nurse anesthesia as a profession and their professional goals for the future. Financial need is also considered in the selection process.

Financial data The stipend is $3,000.

Duration 1 year.

Additional information This program began in 2004.

Number awarded 3 each year.

Deadline March of each year.

[639]
AMERICAN ASSOCIATION OF UNIVERSITY WOMEN CAREER DEVELOPMENT GRANTS

American Association of University Women
Attn: AAUW Educational Foundation
301 ACT Drive, Department 60
P.O. Box 4030
Iowa City, IA 52243-4030
(319) 337-1716, ext. 60 Fax: (319) 337-1204
E-mail: aauw@act.org
Web: www.aauw.org

Summary To provide financial assistance to African American and other women who are seeking career advancement, career change, or reentry into the workforce.

Eligibility This program is open to women who are U.S. citizens or permanent residents, have earned a bachelor's degree, received their most recent degree more than 4 years ago, and are making career changes, seeking to advance in current careers, or reentering the workforce. Applicants must be interested in working toward a master's degree, second bachelor's or associate degree, professional degree (e.g., M.D., J.D.), certification program, or technical school certificate. They must be planning to undertake course work at an accredited 2- or 4-year college or university (or a technical school that is licensed, accredited, or approved by the U.S. Department of Education). Primary consideration is given to women of color and women pursuing their first advanced degree or credentials in nontraditional fields. Support is not provided for prerequisite course work or for Ph.D. course work or dissertations. Selection is based on demonstrated commitment to education and equity for women and girls, reason for seeking higher education or technical training, degree to which study plan is consistent with career objectives, potential for success in chosen field, documentation of opportunities in chosen field, feasibility of study plans and proposed time schedule, validity of proposed budget and budget narrative (including sufficient outside support), and quality of written proposal.

Financial data Grants range from $2,000 to $12,000. Funds may be used for tuition, fees, books, supplies, local transportation, dependent child care, or purchase of a computer required for the study program.

Duration 1 year, beginning in July; nonrenewable.

Additional information The filing fee is $35.

Number awarded Varies each year; recently, 63 of these grants, with a value of $670,000, were awarded.

Deadline December of each year.

[640]
AMERICAN BAPTIST CHURCHES OF OHIO/FAYE AND ROBERT LETT SCHOLARSHIP

American Baptist Churches of Ohio
Attn: Ohio Baptist Education Society
647 South Diamond Street
Mansfield, OH 44907
(419) 524-4761 E-mail: pastorchris@neo.rr.com
Web: www.abc-ohio.org/index.php/menu-obes

Summary To provide funding to African American upper-division and graduate students from Ohio who are interested in preparing for the Baptist ministry at a college or seminary in any state.

Eligibility This program is open to African American residents of Ohio who have completed at least 2 years of study at an accredited college or university in any state and are interested in continuing their education as an upper-division or seminary student. Applicants must 1) hold active membership in a church affiliated with the American Baptist Churches of Ohio or a church dually-aligned with the American Baptist Churches of Ohio; 2) be in the process of preparing for a professional career in Christian ministry (such as a local church pastor, church education, youth or young adult ministries, church music, specialized ministry, chaplaincy, ministry in higher education, or missionary service); 3) be committed to working professionally within the framework of the American Baptist Churches USA; and 4) acknowledge a personal commitment to the Gospel of Jesus Christ, an understanding of the Christian faith, and a definite call to professional Christian ministry as a life work. Financial need must be demonstrated.

Financial data Stipends generally range from $1,000 to $1,500 a year.

Duration 1 year.

Additional information This program began in 1990.

Number awarded 1 or more each year.

Deadline March of each year.

[641]
AMERICAN EDUCATIONAL RESEARCH ASSOCIATION DISSERTATION GRANTS PROGRAM

American Educational Research Association
1430 K Street, N.W., Suite 1200
Washington, DC 20005
(202) 238-3200 Fax: (202) 238-3250
E-mail: fellowships@aera.net
Web: www.aera.net

Summary To provide funding to doctoral students (particularly African Americans and other underrepresented minorities) who are writing their dissertation on educational policy.

Eligibility This program is open to advanced graduate students who are writing their dissertations in such disciplines as (but not limited to) education, sociology, economics, psychology, demography, statistics, or psychometrics. Applicants may be U.S. citizens, U.S. permanent residents, or non-U.S. citizens working at a U.S. institution. Underrepresented minority researchers are strongly encouraged to apply. Dissertation topics may cover a wide range of policy-related issues, but priority is given to proposals that 1) develop or benefit from new quantitative measures or methodological approaches for addressing education issues; 2) incorporate subject matter expertise, especially when studying science, technology, engineering, or mathematics (STEM) learning; 3) analyze TIMSS, PISA, or other international data resources; or 4) include the integration and analysis of more than 1 data set. The research project must include the analysis of data from at least 1 of the large-scale nationally or internationally representative data sets, such as those of the National Science Foundation (NSF), National Center for Education Statistics (NCES), or National Institutes of Health (NIH). Selection is based on the importance of the proposed policy issue, strength of the methodological model and proposed statistical analysis of the study, and relevant experience or research record of the applicant.

Financial data The maximum grant is $20,000 per year. No support is provided for indirect costs to institutions. Funding is linked to approval of the recipient's progress report and final report. Grantees receive one-third of the total award at the beginning of the grant period, one-third upon acceptance of the progress report, and one-third upon acceptance of the final report. Funds can be sent either to the recipients or to their institutions.

Duration 1 year; nonrenewable.

Additional information Funding for this program is provided by the NSF and the NCES. Grantees must submit a brief (3 to 6 pages) progress report midway through the grant period. A final report must be submitted at the end of the grant period. The final report may be either an article suitable for publication in a scholarly journal or a copy of the dissertation.

Number awarded Approximately 15 each year.

Deadline January, March, or August of each year.

[642]
AMERICAN GEOPHYSICAL UNION GRADUATE FELLOWSHIP IN THE HISTORY OF SCIENCE

American Geophysical Union
Attn: History of Geophysics
2000 Florida Avenue, N.W.
Washington, DC 20009-1277
(202) 462-6900 Toll Free: (800) 966-2481
Fax: (202) 328-0566
E-mail: HistoryofGeophysics@agu.org
Web: education.agu.org/grants/research-grants-awards

Summary To provide funding to doctoral candidates (particularly African Americans, other minorities, women, and students with disabilities) who are conducting dissertation research in the history of geophysics.

Eligibility This program is open to doctoral candidates at U.S. institutions who have passed all preliminary examinations. Applicants must be completing a dissertation in the history of the geophysical sciences, including topics related to atmospheric sciences, biogeosciences, geodesy, geomagnetism and paleomagnetism, hydrology, ocean sciences, planetary sciences, seismology, space physics, aeronomy, tectonophysics, volcanology, geochemistry, and petrology. They must submit a cover letter with a vita, undergraduate and graduate transcripts, a 10-page description of the dissertation topic and proposed research plan, and 3 letters of recommendation. U.S. citizenship or permanent resident status is required. Applications are encouraged from women, minorities, and students with disabilities who are traditionally underrepresented in the geophysical sciences.

Financial data The grant is $5,000; funds are to be used to assist with the costs of travel to obtain archival or research materials.

Number awarded 1 each year.

Deadline September of each year.

[643]
AMERICAN HEALTH INFORMATION MANAGEMENT ASSOCIATION FOUNDATION DIVERSITY SCHOLARSHIPS

American Health Information Management Association
Attn: AHIMA Foundation
233 North Michigan Avenue, 21st Floor
Chicago, IL 60601-5809
(312) 233-1175 Fax: (312) 233-1475
E-mail: info@ahimafoundation.org
Web: www.ahimafoundation.org

Summary To provide financial assistance to African American and other members of the American Health Information Management Association (AHIMA) who are interested in working on an undergraduate or graduate degree in health information management (HIM) or health information technology (HIT) and will contribute to diversity in the profession.

Eligibility This program is open to AHIMA members who are enrolled at least half time in a program accredited by the Commission on Accreditation for Health Informatics and Information Management Education (CAHIM). Applicants must be working on a degree in HIM or HIT at the associate, bachelor's, post-baccalaureate, master's, or doctoral level. They must have a GPA of 3.5 or higher and at least 1 full semester remaining after the date of the award. To qualify for this support, applicants must demonstrate how they will contribute to diversity in the health information management profession; diversity is defined as differences in race, ethnicity, nationality, gender, sexual orientation, socioeconomic status, age, physical capabilities, and religious beliefs. Selection is based on GPA and academic achievement, volunteer and work experience, commitment to the HIM profession, quality and relevance of references, and completeness and clarity of thought.

Financial data Stipends are $1,000 for associate degree students, $1,500 for bachelor's degree or post-baccalaureate certificate students, $2,000 for master's degree students, or $2,500 for doctoral degree students.

Duration 1 year.

Number awarded Varies each year; recently, 9 of these scholarships were awarded: 6 to undergraduates and 3 to graduate students.

Deadline September of each year.

[644]
AMERICAN METEOROLOGICAL SOCIETY GRADUATE FELLOWSHIP IN THE HISTORY OF SCIENCE

American Meteorological Society
Attn: Development and Student Program Manager
45 Beacon Street
Boston, MA 02108-3693
(617) 227-2426, ext. 3907 Fax: (617) 742-8718
E-mail: dFernandez@ametsoc.org
Web: www.ametsoc.org

Summary To provide funding to graduate students (particularly African Americans, other minorities, women, and individuals with disabilities) who are members of the American Meteorological Society (AMS) and interested in conducting dissertation research on the history of meteorology.

Eligibility This program is open to AMS members and student members who are planning to complete a doctoral dissertation on the history of the atmospheric or related oceanic or hydrologic sciences. Applicants must be U.S. citizens or permanent residents and working on a degree at a U.S. institution. Fellowships may be used to support research at a location away from the student's institution, provided the plan is approved by the student's thesis adviser. In such an instance, an effort is made to place the student into a mentoring relationship with a member of the society at an appropriate institution. The sponsor specifically encourages applications from women, minorities, and students with disabilities who are traditionally underrepresented in the atmospheric and related oceanic sciences.

Financial data The stipend is $15,000.

Duration 1 year.

Number awarded 1 each year.

Deadline February of each year.

[645]

AMERICAN PEDIATRIC SOCIETY/SOCIETY FOR PEDIATRIC RESEARCH STUDENT RESEARCH PROGRAM

American Pediatric Society/Society for Pediatric Research
3400 Research Forest Drive, Suite B-7
The Woodlands, TX 77381
(281) 419-0052 Fax: (281) 419-0082
E-mail: student-research@aps-spr.org
Web: www.aps-spr.org/get-involved/student-research

Summary To provide financial assistance to medical students (particularly African Americans and members of other underrepresented groups) who are considering careers in research related to pediatrics.

Eligibility This program is open to students seeking a pediatric research opportunity at an institution (in the United States or Canada) other than their own medical school. Applicants must be enrolled in a medical school in good standing at the time of their application. If they already have a medical degree, they are ineligible. Letters of recommendation are required. Members of underrepresented groups are encouraged to apply.

Financial data The stipend is $61.20 per day, to a maximum of $5,508.

Duration 2 to 3 months.

Additional information Participants choose or are assigned to 1 of more than 300 leading research laboratories in the United States or Canada to work under the direct supervision of experienced scientists in the field of pediatrics.

Number awarded Varies each year.

Deadline January of each year.

[646]

AMERICAN PLANNING ASSOCIATION/JUDITH MCMANUS PRICE SCHOLARSHIPS

American Planning Association
Attn: Leadership Affairs Associate
205 North Michigan Avenue, Suite 1200
Chicago, IL 60601
(312) 431-9100 Fax: (312) 786-6700
E-mail: fellowship@planning.org
Web: www.planning.org/scholarships/apa

Summary To provide financial assistance to African Americans, other underrepresented minority students, and women enrolled in undergraduate or graduate degree programs at recognized planning schools.

Eligibility This program is open to undergraduate and graduate students in urban and regional planning who are women or members of the following minority groups: African American, Hispanic American, or Native American. Applicants must be citizens of the United States and able to document financial need. They must intend to work as practicing planners in the public sector. Along with their application, they must submit a 2-page personal and background statement describing how their education will be applied to career goals and why they chose planning as a career path. Selection is based (in order of importance), on: 1) commitment to planning as reflected in their personal statement and on their resume; 2) academic achievement and/or improvement during the past 2 years; 3) letters of recommendation; 4) financial need; and 5) professional presentation.

Financial data Stipends range from $2,000 to $4,000 per year. The money may be applied to tuition and living expenses only. Payment is made to the recipient's university and divided by terms in the school year.

Duration 1 year; recipients may reapply.

Additional information This program began in 2002.

Number awarded Varies each year; recently, 3 of these scholarships were awarded.

Deadline April of each year.

[647]

AMERICAN POLITICAL SCIENCE ASSOCIATION MINORITY FELLOWS PROGRAM

American Political Science Association
Attn: APSA Minority Fellows Program
1527 New Hampshire Avenue, N.W.
Washington, DC 20036-1206
(202) 349-9362 Fax: (202) 483-2657
E-mail: sragland@apsanet.org
Web: www.apsanet.org/content_3284.cfm

Summary To provide financial assistance to African Americans and other underrepresented minorities interested in working on a doctoral degree in political science.

Eligibility This program is open to African Americans, Asian Pacific Americans, Latino(a)s, and Native Americans who are in their senior year at a college or university or currently enrolled in a master's degree program. Applicants must be planning to enroll in a doctoral program in political science to prepare for a career in teaching and research. They must be U.S. citizens and able to demonstrate financial need. Along with their application, they must submit a 500-word personal statement that includes why they are interested in attending graduate school in political science, what specific fields within the discipline they plan to study, and how they intend to contribute to research within the discipline. Selection is based on interest in teaching and potential for research in political science.

Financial data The stipend is $2,000 per year.

Duration 2 years.

Additional information In addition to the fellows who receive stipends from this program, students who are selected as fellows without stipend are recommended for admission and financial support to every doctoral political science program in the country. This program was established in 1969.

Number awarded Up to 12 fellows receive stipends each year.

Deadline October of each year.

[648]

AMERICAN PSYCHOLOGICAL ASSOCIATION PREDOCTORAL FELLOWSHIP IN MENTAL HEALTH AND SUBSTANCE ABUSE SERVICES

American Psychological Association
Attn: Minority Fellowship Program
750 First Street, N.E.
Washington, DC 20002-4242
(202) 336-6127 Fax: (202) 336-6012
TDD: (202) 336-6123 E-mail: mfp@apa.org
Web: www.apa.org

Summary To provide financial assistance to doctoral students (particularly African Americans and members of other ethnic minority groups) who are committed to providing mental health and substance abuse services to ethnic minority populations.

Eligibility Applicants must be U.S. citizens, nationals, or permanent residents, enrolled full time in an accredited doctoral program, and committed to a career in psychology related to ethnic minority mental health and substance abuse services. Members of ethnic minority groups (African Americans, Hispanics/Latinos, American Indians, Alaskan Natives, Asian Americans, Native Hawaiians, and other Pacific Islanders) are especially encouraged to apply. Preference is given to students specializing in clinical, school, and counseling psychology. Selection is based on commitment to ethnic minority behavioral health services or policy, knowledge of ethnic minority behavioral health services, the fit between career goals and training environment selected, potential as a future leader in ethnic minority psychology as demonstrated through accomplishments and goals, scholarship and grades, and letters of recommendation.

Financial data The stipend varies but is based on the amount established by the National Institutes of Health for predoctoral students; recently that was $22,032 per year.

Duration 1 academic or calendar year; may be renewed for up to 2 additional years.

Additional information Funding is provided by the U.S. Substance Abuse and Mental Health Services Administration.

Number awarded Varies each year.

Deadline January of each year.

[649] AMERICAN SOCIETY OF CRIMINOLOGY FELLOWSHIPS FOR ETHNIC MINORITIES

American Society of Criminology
Attn: Awards Committee
1314 Kinnear Road, Suite 212
Columbus, OH 43212-1156
(614) 292-9207 Fax: (614) 292-6767
E-mail: asc@asc41.com
Web: www.asc41.com/awards/GradMinorityFellowship.html

Summary To provide financial assistance to African American and other ethnic minority doctoral students in criminology and criminal justice.

Eligibility This program is open to students of color, especially members of ethnic groups underrepresented in the field of criminology and criminal justice, including (but not limited to) Asians, Blacks, Indigenous peoples, and Hispanics. Applicants must have been accepted into a doctoral program in the field. Along with their application, they must submit an up-to-date curriculum vitae; an indication of race or ethnicity; copies of undergraduate and graduate transcripts; a statement of need and prospects for other financial assistance; a letter describing career plans, salient experiences, and nature of interest in criminology and criminal justice; and 3 letters of reference.

Financial data The stipend is $6,000.

Duration 1 year.

Additional information This fellowship was first awarded in 1989.

Number awarded 3 each year.

Deadline February of each year.

[650] AMERICAN SOCIOLOGICAL ASSOCIATION MINORITY FELLOWSHIP PROGRAM GENERAL FELLOWSHIP

American Sociological Association
Attn: Minority Affairs Program
1430 K Street, N.W., Suite 600
Washington, DC 20005-2504
(202) 383-9005, ext. 322 Fax: (202) 638-0882
TDD: (202) 638-0981 E-mail: minority.affairs@asanet.org
Web: www.asanet.org/funding/mfp.cfm

Summary To provide financial assistance to doctoral students in sociology who are African American or members of other minority groups.

Eligibility This program is open to U.S. citizens, permanent residents, and noncitizen nationals who are Blacks/African Americans, Latinos (e.g., Mexican Americans, Puerto Ricans, Cubans), American Indians or Alaskan Natives, Asian Americans (e.g., southeast Asians, Japanese, Chinese, Koreans), or Pacific Islanders (e.g., Filipinos, Samoans, Hawaiians, Guamanians). Applicants must be entering or continuing students in sociology at the doctoral level. Along with their application, they must submit 3-page essays on 1) the reasons why they decided to undertake graduate study in sociology, their primary research interests, and why they hope to do with a Ph.D. in sociology; and 2) what led them to select the doctoral program they attend or hope to attend and how they see that doctoral program preparing them for a professional career in sociology. Selection is based on commitment to research, focus of research experience, academic achievement, writing ability, research potential, and financial need.

Financial data The stipend is $18,000 per year.

Duration 1 year; may be renewed up to 2 additional years.

Additional information This program, which began in 1974, is supported by individual members of the American Sociological Association (ASA) and by several affiliated organizations (Alpha Kappa Delta, Sociologists for Women in Society, the Association of Black Sociologists, the Midwest Sociological Society, and the Southwestern Sociological Association).

Number awarded Varies each year; since the program began, approximately 500 of these fellowships have been awarded.

Deadline January of each year.

[651] AMERICAN SPEECH-LANGUAGE-HEARING FOUNDATION SCHOLARSHIP FOR MINORITY STUDENTS

American Speech-Language-Hearing Foundation
Attn: Programs Administrator
2200 Research Boulevard
Rockville, MD 20850-3289
(301) 296-8703 Fax: (301) 296-8567
E-mail: foundationprograms@asha.org
Web: www.ashfoundation.org/grants/GraduateScholarships

Summary To provide financial assistance to African American and other minority graduate students in communication sciences and disorders programs.

Eligibility This program is open to full-time graduate students who are enrolled in communication sciences and disorders programs, with preference given to U.S. citizens who are members of a racial or ethnic minority group. Applicants must submit an essay, up to 5 pages in length, on a topic that relates to the future of leadership in the discipline. Selection is based on academic promise and outstanding academic achievement.

Financial data The stipend is $5,000. Funds must be used for educational support (e.g., tuition, books, school living expenses), not for personal or conference travel.

Duration 1 year.

Number awarded 1 each year.

Deadline June of each year.

[652]
AMS GRADUATE FELLOWSHIPS

American Meteorological Society
Attn: Development and Student Program Manager
45 Beacon Street
Boston, MA 02108-3693
(617) 227-2426, ext. 3907 Fax: (617) 742-8718
E-mail: dFernandez@ametsoc.org
Web: www.ametsoc.org

Summary To encourage students (particularly African Americans, other minorities, women, and individuals with disabilities) who are entering their first year of graduate school to work on an advanced degree in the atmospheric and related oceanic and hydrologic sciences.

Eligibility This program is open to students entering their first year of graduate study and planning to work on an advanced degree in the atmospheric or related oceanic or hydrologic sciences. Applicants must be U.S. citizens or permanent residents and have a GPA of 3.25 or higher. Along with their application, they must submit 200-word essays on 1) their most important achievements that qualify them for this scholarship; and 2) their career goals in the atmospheric or related sciences. Selection is based on academic record as an undergraduate. The sponsor specifically encourages applications from women, minorities, and students with disabilities who are traditionally underrepresented in the atmospheric and related sciences.

Financial data The stipend is $24,000 per academic year.

Duration 9 months.

Additional information This program was initiated in 1991. It is funded by high-technology firms and government agencies.

Number awarded Varies each year; recently, 13 of these scholarships were awarded.

Deadline January of each year.

[653]
ANAPATA DIVERSITY SCHOLARSHIP CONTEST

Ms. JD
Attn: Chief Financial Officer
3207 Jackson Street
Houston, TX 77004
E-mail: staff@ms-jd.org
Web: ms-jd.org/anapata-student-scholarship

Summary To provide financial assistance to law students who are African American or members of other groups traditionally underrepresented in the legal profession.

Eligibility This program is open to students currently enrolled at ABA-approved law schools in the United States. Members of groups traditionally underrepresented in the legal profession are especially encouraged to apply. They must submit a resume, transcript, personal introduction paragraph, 2 recommendations, and a 750-word essay demonstrating their personal philosophy regarding diversity in the legal profession. Selection is based on academic achievement, leadership ability, writing and interpersonal skills, and interest in promoting diversity in the legal profession.

Financial data The stipend is $1,000.

Duration 1 year.

Additional information This program is offered by Ms. JD in partnership with Anapata, Inc.

Number awarded 1 or more each year.

Deadline February of each year.

[654]
ANL LABORATORY–GRADUATE RESEARCH APPOINTMENTS

Argonne National Laboratory
Division of Educational Programs
Attn: Graduate Student Program Office
9700 South Cass Avenue/DEP 223
Argonne, IL 60439-4845
(630) 252-3366 Fax: (630) 252-3193
E-mail: lisareed@anl.gov
Web: www.dep.anl.gov/p_graduate/labgrad.htm

Summary To offer opportunities for qualified graduate students (particularly African Americans, other underrepresented minorities, and women) to carry out their master's or doctoral thesis research at the Argonne National Laboratory (ANL).

Eligibility Appointments are available for graduate students at U.S. universities who wish to carry out their thesis research under the co-sponsorship of an Argonne National Laboratory staff member and a faculty member. Research may be conducted in the basic physical and life sciences, mathematics, computer science, and engineering, as well as in a variety of applied areas relating to energy, conservation, environmental impact and technology, nanomaterials, and advanced nuclear energy systems. Applicants must be U.S. citizens or permanent residents. The laboratory encourages applications from all qualified persons, especially women and members of underrepresented minority groups.

Financial data Support consists of a stipend, tuition payments up to $5,000 per year, and payment of certain travel expenses. In addition, the student's faculty sponsor may receive payment for limited travel expenses.

Duration 1 year; may be renewed.

Additional information This program, which is also referred to as the Lab–Grad Program, is sponsored by the U.S. Department of Energy. In certain cases, students may be awarded support for pre-thesis studies on campus, provided that they intend to carry out their thesis research at Argonne.

Number awarded Varies each year.

Deadline Applications may be submitted at any time, but a complete application should be submitted at least 2 months prior to the proposed starting date.

[655]
ANNA M. WINSTON AWARD

National Association of Black Accountants
Attn: National Scholarship Program
7474 Greenway Center Drive, Suite 1120
Greenbelt, MD 20770
(301) 474-NABA Fax: (301) 474-3114
E-mail: scholarships@nabainc.org
Web: www.nabainc.org

Summary To provide financial assistance to student members of the National Association of Black Accountants (NABA) who are attending an Historically Black College or University (HBCU) to work on an undergraduate or graduate degree in a field related to accounting.

Eligibility This program is open to minorities who are NABA members and enrolled full time as 1) an undergraduate freshman, sophomore, junior, or first-semester senior majoring in accounting, business, or finance at an HBCU; or 2) a graduate student working on a master's degree in accounting at an HBCU. High school seniors are not eligible. Applicants must have a GPA of 2.0 or higher in their major and 2.5 or higher overall. Along with their application, they must submit a 500-word personal statement on their involvement in NABA, career objectives, leadership abilities, and community activities. Financial need is not considered in the selection process.

Financial data The stipend ranges from $500 to $1,000.

Duration 1 year.

Additional information Applicants for this scholarship are required to sign a pledge form with a promise to fund it within 5 years of graduation from college.

Number awarded 1 each year.

Deadline January of each year.

[656]
APAGS COMMITTEE ON ETHNIC MINORITY AFFAIRS GRANT PROGRAM

American Psychological Association
Attn: American Psychological Association of Graduate Students
750 First Street, N.E.
Washington, DC 20002-4242
(202) 336-6014 Fax: (202) 336-5694
E-mail: apags@apa.org
Web: www.apa.org

Summary To provide funding to graduate students (particularly African Americans and other ethnic minorities) who are members of the American Psychological Association of Graduate Students (APAGS) and who wish to develop a project that increases membership and participation of ethnic minority students within the association.

Eligibility This program is open to members of APAGS who are enrolled at least half time in a master's or doctoral program at an accredited university. Applicants must be interested in developing a project to increase the membership and participation of ethnic minority graduate students within APAGS, advertise education and training opportunities for ethnic minorities, and enhance the recruitment and retention efforts for ethnic minority students in psychology. Examples include, but are not limited to, workshops, conferences, speaker series, mentorship programs, and the development of student organizations with a focus on multiculturalism or ethnic minority concerns.

Financial data The grant is $1,000.

Duration The grant is presented annually.

Additional information This grant was first awarded in 1997.

Number awarded 5 each year.

Deadline Deadline not specified.

[657]
APF/COGDOP GRADUATE RESEARCH SCHOLARSHIPS

American Psychological Foundation
750 First Street, N.E.
Washington, DC 20002-4242
(202) 336-5843 Fax: (202) 336-5812
E-mail: foundation@apa.org
Web: www.apa.org/apf/funding/cogdop.aspx

Summary To provide funding for research to graduate students (particularly African Americans and other diverse students) who are working on a graduate degree in psychology.

Eligibility Each department of psychology that is a member in good standing of the Council of Graduate Departments of Psychology (COGDOP) may nominate up to 3 candidates for these scholarships. Nominations must include a completed application form, a letter of nomination from the department chair or director of graduate studies, a letter of recommendation from the nominee's graduate research adviser, a transcript of all graduate course work completed by the nominee, a curriculum vitae, and a brief outline of the nominee's thesis or dissertation research project. Selection is based on the context for the research, the clarity and comprehensibility of the research question, the appropriateness of the research design, the general importance of the research, and the use of requested funds. The sponsor encourages applications from individuals who represent diversity in race, ethnicity, gender, age, disability, and sexual orientation.

Financial data Awards range from $1,000 to $5,000 per year. A total of $28,000 is available for these scholarships each year.

Duration 1 year.

Additional information The highest rated nominees receive the Harry and Miriam Levinson Scholarship of $5,000 and the William and Dorothy Bevan Scholarship of $5,000. The next highest rated nominee receives the Ruth G. and Joseph D. Matarazzo Scholarship of $3,000. The next highest rated nominee receives the Clarence Rosecrans Scholarship of $2,000. The next highest rated nominees receive the William C. Howell Scholarship and the Peter and Malina James and Dr. Louis P. James Legacy Scholarship of $1,000 each. Another 9 scholarships of $1,000 each are also awarded.

Number awarded 15 each year: 2 at $5,000, 1 at $3,000, 1 at $2,000, and 11 at $1,000.

Deadline June of each year.

[658]
AP-GOOGLE JOURNALISM AND TECHNOLOGY SCHOLARSHIP PROGRAM

Online News Association
Attn: Scholarship Manager
P.O. Box 65741
Washington, DC 20035
(646) 290-7900 E-mail: irving@journalists.org
Web: journalists.org/next-gen/ap-google-scholarship

Summary To recognize and reward undergraduate and graduate students (especially African Americans and those from other diverse backgrounds) who propose outstanding projects "at the intersection of journalism and technology."

Eligibility This program is open to full-time undergraduates (at least sophomores) and graduate students at U.S. institutions who have at least 1 year of study remaining and a GPA of 3.0 or higher. Students from diverse backgrounds (defined as ethnic and racial minorities, members of the lesbian, gay, bisexual, and transgender (LGBT) community, and students with disabilities) and those attending rural area institutions are strongly encouraged to apply. Some scholarships are reserved for students who can demonstrate financial need. Applicants must develop original journalistic content with computer science elements; they should explain how their strategy moves digital journalism forward or provides valuable lessons or outcomes. Examples include data visualization, data mining, mobile devices and applications, 3-D storytelling, digital ethics, or microcomputers. In the selection process, emphasis is placed on innovation and creativity. U.S. citizenship is required.

Financial data The award is a $20,000 scholarship, of which half is paid to the winner's institution at the beginning of the first semester and half at the beginning of the second semester, provided the recipient earns a GPA of 3.0 or higher for the first semester.

Duration The competition is held annually.

Additional information This competition is supported by Google.

Number awarded 6 each year.

Deadline February of each year.

[659]
ARENT FOX DIVERSITY SCHOLARSHIPS

Arent Fox LLP
Attn: Attorney Recruitment and Professional Development Coordinator
1717 K Street, N.W.
Washington, DC 20036
(202) 857-6000 Fax: (202) 857-6395
E-mail: dcattorneyrecruit@arentfox.com
Web: www.arentfox.com

Summary To provide financial aid and work experience to African American and other minority law students.

Eligibility This program is open to first-year law students who are members of a diverse population that historically has been underrepresented in the legal profession. Applicants must be U.S. citizens or otherwise authorized to work in the United States. They must also be willing to work as a summer intern at the sponsoring law firm's offices in Los Angeles, New York City, or Washington, D.C. Along with their application, they must submit a resume, an undergraduate transcript and law school grades when available, a 5- to 10-page legal writing sample, 3 letters of recommendation, and an essay on how their background, skills, experience, and interest equip them to meet the sponsor's goal of commitment to diversity. Selection is based on academic performance during college and law school, oral and writing communication skills, leadership qualities, and community involvement.

Financial data The scholarship stipend is $15,000. The summer salary is $2,500 per week.

Duration 1 year.

Additional information These scholarships were first offered in 2006. Recipients are also offered summer internships with Arent Fox: 1 in Los Angeles, 1 in New York City, and 1 in Washington, D.C. Students interested in the summer program in Los Angeles should contact Attorney Recruitment Manager, 555 West Fifth Street, 48th Floor, Los Angeles, CA 90013, (213) 629-7400, Fax: (213) 629-7401, E-mail: laattorneyrecruit@arentfox.com. Students interested in the summer program in New York should contact Attorney Recruitment Coordinator, 1675 Broadway, New York, NY 10019, (212) 484-3983, Fax: (212) 484-3990, E-mail: nyattorneyrecruit@arentfox.com.

Number awarded 3 each year.

Deadline January of each year.

[660]
ASCA FOUNDATION SCHOLARSHIPS

American School Counselor Association
Attn: ASCA Foundation
1101 King Street, Suite 625
Alexandria, VA 22314
(703) 683-ASCA Toll Free: (800) 306-4722
Fax: (703) 683-1619 E-mail: asca@schoolcounselor.org
Web: www.schoolcounselor.org/content.asp?contentid=176

Summary To provide financial assistance for graduate school to members of the American School Counselor Association (ASCA), especially African Americans, other minorities, and males.

Eligibility This program is open to ASCA members working full time on a master's degree in school counseling. Applicants must submit a 2-page essay on a topic that changes annually but relates to the role of counselors in schools. Males and minorities are especially encouraged to apply.

Financial data The stipend is $1,000.

Duration 1 year.

Additional information Support for this program is provided by Anheuser-Busch.

Number awarded Up to 10 each year.

Deadline October of each year.

[661]
ASME GRADUATE TEACHING FELLOWSHIP

ASME International
Attn: Centers Administrator
Two Park Avenue
New York, NY 10016-5675
(212) 591-8131 Toll Free: (800) THE-ASME
Fax: (212) 591-7143 E-mail: LefeverB@asme.org
Web: www.asme.org

Summary To provide funding to members of the American Society of Mechanical Engineers (ASME) who are working on a doctorate in mechanical engineering (particularly those who are African Americans, other minority group members, and female).

Eligibility This program is open to U.S. citizens or permanent residents who have an undergraduate degree from an ABET-accredited program, belong to the society as a student member, are currently employed as a teaching assistant with lecture responsibility, and are working on a Ph.D. in mechanical engineering. Along with their application, they must submit a statement about their interest in a faculty career. Applications from women and minorities are particularly encouraged.

Financial data Fellowship stipends are $5,000 per year.

Duration Up to 2 years.

Additional information Recipients must teach at least 1 lecture course.

Number awarded Up to 4 each year.

Deadline February of each year.

[662]
BAKER DONELSON DIVERSITY SCHOLARSHIPS

Baker, Donelson, Bearman, Caldwell & Berkowitz, P.C.
Attn: Director of Attorney Recruiting
3414 Peachtree Road N.E., Suite 1600
Atlanta, GA 30326
(404) 577-6000 Fax: (404) 221-6501
E-mail: lklein@bakerdonelson.com
Web: www.bakerdonelson.com

Summary To provide financial assistance to law students who are African American or members of other groups underrepresented at large law firms.

Eligibility This program is open to students who have completed the first year at an ABA-accredited law school. Applicants must be members of a group traditionally underrepresented at large law firms (American Indian or Alaskan Native, Native Hawaiian or Pacific Islander, Hispanic or Latino, Black, or Asian). Along with their application, they must submit a 10-page legal writing sample and a 1-page personal statement on challenges they have faced in pursuit of their legal career that have helped them to understand the value of diversity and its inclusion in the legal profession. Finalists are interviewed.

Financial data The stipend is $10,000.

Duration 1 year.

Additional information Recipients are also offered summer internships at Baker Donelson offices in Atlanta (Georgia), Baton Rouge (Louisiana), Birmingham (Alabama), Chattanooga (Tennessee), Jackson (Mississippi), Johnson City (Tennessee), Knoxville (Tennessee), Memphis (Tennessee), Nashville (Tennessee), and New Orleans (Louisiana).

Number awarded 3 each year.

Deadline June of each year.

[663]
BAKERHOSTETLER DIVERSITY FELLOWSHIP PROGRAM

BakerHostetler LLP
Attn: Attorney Recruitment and Development Manager
PNC Center
1900 East Ninth Street, Suite 3200
Cleveland, OH 44114-3482
(216) 621-0200 Fax: (216) 696-0740
E-mail: ddriscole@bakerlaw.com
Web: www.bakerlaw.com/diversityfellowshipprogram

Summary To provide financial aid and summer work experience to African American and other minority law school students who are interested in employment with BakerHostetler.

Eligibility This program is open to full-time second-year students at ABA-accredited law schools who are members of underrepresented groups (Black/African American, Hispanic, Asian American/Pacific Islander, American Indian/Alaskan Native, 2 or more races, or gay, lesbian, bisexual, transgender). Applicants must be interested in a summer associate position with BakerHostetler and possible full-time employment following graduation. They must be U.S. citizens or otherwise authorized to work in the United States. Along with their application, they must submit a 500-word personal statement presenting their views of or experience with diversity, including why they are interested in Baker Hostetler and how they will be able to contribute to the diversity objectives of the firm. Selection is based on academic performance in college and law school, personal achievements, community involvement, oral and written communication skills, demonstrated leadership achievements, and a sincere interest and commitment to join BakerHostetler.

Financial data The stipend is $25,000, of which $10,000 is paid within the first 30 days of starting a summer associate position with the firm and the remaining $15,000 is contingent upon receiving and accepting a full-time offer with the firm.

Duration Summer associate positions are for 8 weeks.

Additional information Summer associate positions may be performed at any of the firm's offices in Chicago, Cincinnati, Cleveland, Columbus, Costa Mesa, Denver, Houston, Los Angeles, New York, Orlando, or Washington, D.C.

Number awarded 1 or more each year.

Deadline October of each year.

[664]
BALFOUR PHI DELTA PHI MINORITY SCHOLARSHIP PROGRAM

Phi Delta Phi International Legal Fraternity
1426 21st Street, N.W., First Floor
Washington, DC 20036
(202) 223-6801 Toll Free: (800) 368-5606
Fax: (202) 223-6808 E-mail: info@phideltaphi.org
Web: www.phideltaphi.org

Summary To provide financial assistance to African Americans and other minorities who are members of Phi Delta Phi International Legal Fraternity.

Eligibility This program is open to ethnic minority members of the legal fraternity. Applicants must affirm that they intend to practice law in inner-cities of the United States, especially in New England. They must submit a 750-word essay on why they consider themselves qualified to serve as role models for minority youth. Selection is based on participation, ethics, and scholastics.

Financial data The stipend is $3,000.

Duration 1 year.

Additional information This program began in 1997 with funding from the Lloyd G. Balfour Foundation.

Number awarded 1 each year.

Deadline October of each year.

[665]
BARBARA JORDAN MEMORIAL SCHOLARSHIPS

Association of Texas Professional Educators
Attn: ATPE Foundation
305 East Huntland Drive, Suite 300
Austin, TX 78752-3792
Toll Free: (800) 777-ATPE Fax: (512) 302-5884
E-mail: admin@atpefoundation.org
Web: www.atpefoundation.org/scholarships.asp

Summary To provide financial assistance to upper-division and graduate students from any state who are enrolled in educator preparation programs at predominantly ethnic minority institutions in Texas.

Eligibility This program is open to juniors, seniors, and graduate students from any state who are enrolled in educator preparation programs at predominantly ethnic minority institutions in Texas. Applicants must submit a 2-page essay on their personal educational philosophy, why they want to become an educator, who influenced them the most in making their career decision, and why they are applying for the scholarship. Financial need is not considered in the selection process.

Financial data The stipend is $1,500.

Duration 1 year.

Additional information The qualifying institutions are Huston-Tillotson College, Jarvis Christian College, Our Lady of the Lake University, Paul Quinn College, Prairie View A&M University, St. Mary's University of San Antonio, Sul Ross State University, Sul Ross State University Rio Grande College, Texas A&M International University, Texas A&M University at Kingsville, Texas Southern University, University of Houston, University of Houston-Downtown, University of Texas at Brownsville and Texas Southmost College, University of Texas at El Paso, University of Texas at San Antonio, University of Texas-Pan American, University of the Incarnate Word, and Wiley College.

Number awarded Up to 6 each year.

Deadline May of each year.

[666]
BEHAVIORAL SCIENCES STUDENT FELLOWSHIPS IN EPILEPSY

Epilepsy Foundation
Attn: Research Department
8301 Professional Place
Landover, MD 20785-2353
(301) 459-3700 Toll Free: (800) EFA-1000
Fax: (301) 577-2684 TDD: (800) 332-2070
E-mail: grants@efa.org
Web: www.epilepsyfoundation.org

Summary To provide funding to undergraduate and graduate students (particularly African Americans, other minorities, women, and students with disabilities) who are interested in working on a summer research project in a behavioral science field relevant to epilepsy.

Eligibility This program is open to undergraduate and graduate students in a behavioral science program relevant to epilepsy research or clinical care, including, but not limited to, sociology, social work, psychology, anthropology, nursing, economics, vocational rehabilitation, counseling, or political science. Applicants must be interested in working on an epilepsy research project under the supervision of a qualified mentor. Because the program is designed as a training opportunity, the quality of the training plans and environment are considered in the selection process. Other selection criteria include the quality of the proposed project, the relevance of the proposed work to epilepsy, the applicant's interest in the field of epilepsy, the applicant's qualifications, and the mentor's qualifications (including his or her commitment to the student and the project), and the quality of the training environment for research related to epilepsy. U.S. citizenship is not required, but the project must be conducted in the United States. Applications from women, members of minority groups, and people with disabilities are especially encouraged. The program is not intended for students working on a dissertation research project.

Financial data The grant is $3,000.

Duration 3 months during the summer.

Additional information This program is supported by the American Epilepsy Society, Abbott Laboratories, Ortho-McNeil Pharmaceutical Corporation, and Pfizer Inc.

Number awarded Varies each year.

Deadline March of each year.

[667]
BELFER CENTER FOR SCIENCE AND INTERNATIONAL AFFAIRS FELLOWSHIPS

Harvard University
John F. Kennedy School of Government
Belfer Center for Science and International Affairs
Attn: Fellowship Coordinator
79 John F. Kennedy Street, Mailbox 53
Cambridge, MA 02138
(617) 495-8806 Fax: (617) 495-8963
E-mail: bcsia_fellowships@hks.harvard.edu
Web: belfercenter.ksg.harvard.edu/fellowships

Summary To provide funding to professionals, postdoctorates, and doctoral students (particularly African Americans, other minorities, and women) who are interested in conducting research in areas of concern to the Belfer Center for Science and International Affairs at Harvard University in Cambridge, Massachusetts.

Eligibility The postdoctoral fellowship is open to recent recipients of the Ph.D. or equivalent degree, university faculty members, and employees of government, military, international, humanitarian, and private research institutions who have appropriate professional experience. Applicants for predoctoral fellowships must have passed their general examinations. Lawyers, economists, political scientists, those in the natural sciences, and others of diverse disciplinary backgrounds are also welcome to apply. The program especially encourages applications from women, minorities, and citizens of all countries. All applicants must be interested in conducting research in 1 of the 2 major program areas of the center: 1) the International Security Program (ISP), which addresses U.S. defense and foreign policy, security policy, nuclear proliferation, terrorism, internal and ethnic conflict, and related topics; and 2) the Science, Technology, and Public Policy Program (STPP), including technology and innovation, information and communications technology, water-energy nexus, managing the atom, energy technology innovation policy, China and environmental sustainability, geoengineering and climate policy, geopolitics of energy, and geospatial policy and management.

Financial data The stipend is $34,000 for postdoctoral research fellows or $20,000 for predoctoral research fellows. Health insurance is also provided.

Duration 10 months.

Number awarded A limited number each year.

Deadline January of each year.

[668] BENTON-MEIER NEUROPSYCHOLOGY SCHOLARSHIPS

American Psychological Foundation
750 First Street, N.E.
Washington, DC 20002-4242
(202) 336-5843 Fax: (202) 336-5812
E-mail: foundation@apa.org
Web: www.apa.org/apf/funding/benton-meier.aspx

Summary To provide research funding to graduate students (particularly African Americans and other students from diverse groups) who are completing a dissertation related to neuropsychology.

Eligibility This program is open to students who have been admitted to candidacy for a doctoral degree in the area of neuropsychology. Applicants must submit statements documenting their research competence and area commitment, a budget and justification, and how the scholarship money will be used. Selection is based on conformance with stated program goals and the applicant's demonstrated scholarship and research competence. The sponsor encourages applications from individuals who represent diversity in race, ethnicity, gender, age, disability, and sexual orientation.

Financial data The grant is $2,500.

Duration 1 year.

Additional information This program replaces the Henry Hécaen Scholarship, first awarded in 1994, and the Manfred Meier Scholarship, first awarded in 1997.

Number awarded 2 each year.

Deadline May of each year.

[669] BERNADINE JOHNSON-MARSHALL AND MARTHA BELL WILLIAMS SCHOLARSHIPS

Association of Black Women Lawyers of New Jersey, Inc.
Attn: Scholarship Committee
P.O. Box 22524
Trenton, NJ 08607
E-mail: abwlnj@yahoo.com
Web: www.abwlnj.org

Summary To provide financial assistance to African American women from New Jersey who are attending law school in any state.

Eligibility This program is open to African American women who are 1) residents of New Jersey and currently enrolled in their first, second, or third year at an accredited law school in any state; or 2) residents of other states enrolled at a law school in New Jersey. Selection is based on academic achievement, a brief writing sample or essay, demonstrated community service and civic involvement, and financial need.

Financial data The stipend is $1,000.

Duration 1 year.

Number awarded At least 3 each year.

Deadline March of each year.

[670] BETTY LEA STONE RESEARCH FELLOWSHIP

American Cancer Society-New England Division
30 Speen Street
Framingham, MA 01701
(508) 270-3109 Toll Free: (800) 952-7664, ext. 3109
Fax: (508) 270-4607 E-mail: koconnor@cancer.org
Web: www.cancer.org

Summary To provide funding for cancer research during the summer to medical students (particularly African American and other minority students) in New England.

Eligibility This program is open to first-year students at medical schools in New England. Applicants must be interested in working on a summer research project under the supervision of a faculty sponsor. Minority students and those with American Cancer Society volunteer experience are encouraged to apply.

Financial data The grant is $5,000.

Duration 10 weeks during the summer.

Number awarded 1 or more each year.

Deadline January of each year.

[671] BIG/FEEA SCHOLARSHIP

Blacks in Government
c/o Federal Employee Education and Assistance Fund
Attn: Scholarship Program
3333 South Wadsworth Boulevard, Suite 300
Lakewood, CO 80227
(303) 933-7580 Toll Free: (800) 323-4140
Fax: (303) 933-7587 E-mail: admin@feea.org
Web: www.feea.org

Summary To provide financial assistance for college or graduate school to dependents of members of Blacks in Government (BIG).

Eligibility This program is open to the children, stepchildren, and grandchildren of BIG members. The sponsoring BIG member must have at least 3 years of federal, state, or local government employment and 2 years of membership in BIG. Applicants must be entering or enrolled full time in an accredited 2- or 4-year postsecondary, graduate, or postgraduate program and have a GPA of 3.0 or higher. Along with their application, they must submit a 2-page essay on a topic related to a career in public service with the government, a letter of recommendation, a transcript, a list of extracurricular and community service activities, and verification of government employment; high school seniors must also submit a copy of their ACT, SAT, or other examination scores. Financial need is not considered in the selection process.

Financial data The stipend is $1,000 per year.

Duration 1 year; may be renewed.

Additional information This program, established in 2007, is jointly administered by BIG and the Federal Employee Education and Assistance Fund (FEEA).

Number awarded Up to 11 each year: 1 in each BIG region.

Deadline March of each year.

[672]
BILL BERNBACH DIVERSITY SCHOLARSHIPS

American Association of Advertising Agencies
Attn: AAAA Foundation
1065 Avenue of the Americas, 16th Floor
New York, NY 10018
(212) 262-2500 E-mail: bbscholarship@ddb.com
Web: www.aaaa.org

Summary To provide financial assistance to African American and other multicultural students who are interested in working on an undergraduate or graduate degree in advertising at designated schools.

Eligibility This program is open to African Americans, Asian Americans, Hispanic Americans, and Native Americans (including American Indians, Alaska Natives, Native Hawaiians, and other Pacific Islanders) who are interested in studying the advertising creative arts at designated institutions as a full-time student. Applicants must be working on or have already received an undergraduate degree and be able to demonstrate creative talent and promise. They must be U.S. citizens, nationals, or permanent residents. Along with their application, they must submit 10 samples of creative work in their respective field of expertise.

Financial data The stipend is $5,000.

Duration 1 year.

Additional information This program, which began in 1998, is currently sponsored by DDB Worldwide. The participating schools are the Art Center College of Design (Pasadena, California), Creative Circus (Atlanta, Georgia), Miami Ad School (Miami Beach, Florida), University of Texas at Austin, VCU Brandcenter (Richmond, Virginia), Savannah College of Art and Design (Savannah, Georgia), University of Oregon (Eugene), City College of New York, School of Visual Arts (New York, New York), Fashion Institute of Technology (New York, New York), and Brigham Young University (Provo, Utah).

Number awarded 3 each year.

Deadline October of each year.

[673]
BISHOP THOMAS HOYT, JR. FELLOWSHIP

St. John's University
Attn: Collegeville Institute for Ecumenical and Cultural Research
2475 Ecumenical Drive
P.O. Box 2000
Collegeville, MN 56321-2000
(320) 363-3366 Fax: (320) 363-3313
E-mail: staff@CollegevilleInstitute.org
Web: collegevilleinstitute.org

Summary To provide funding to African Americans and other students of color who wish to complete their doctoral dissertation while in residence at the Collegeville Institute for Ecumenical and Cultural Research of St. John's University in Collegeville, Minnesota.

Eligibility This program is open to people of color completing a doctoral dissertation in ecumenical and cultural research. Applicants must be interested in a residency at the Collegeville Institute for Ecumenical and Cultural Research of St. John's University. Along with their application, they must submit a 1,000-word description of the research project they plan to complete while in residence at the Institute.

Financial data The stipend covers the residency fee of $2,000, which includes housing and utilities.

Duration 1 year.

Additional information Residents at the Institute engage in research, publication, and education on the important intersections between faith and culture. They seek to discern and communicate the meaning of Christian identity and unity in a religiously and culturally diverse world.

Number awarded 1 each year.

Deadline October of each year.

[674]
BLACK ENTERTAINMENT AND SPORTS LAWYERS ASSOCIATION GENERAL SCHOLARSHIP FUND

Black Entertainment and Sports Lawyers Association
Attn: Scholarships
P.O. Box 230794
New York, NY 10023
E-mail: scholarship@besla.org
Web: www.besla.org/#!scholarship/cfvg

Summary To provide financial assistance to African American and other minority law students who are interested in the fields of entertainment and/or sports law.

Eligibility This program is open to minority students who have completed at least 1 year of full-time study at an accredited law school. Applicants must be able to demonstrate an interest in entertainment or sports law by 1 or more of the following: 1) completing an entertainment law or sports law related course; 2) internship or clerkship in the entertainment or sports law field; 3) current job in the field of entertainment or sports; 4) current membership in an entertainment or sports law society or association; or 5) attendance at an entertainment law or sports law seminar or conference since enrolling in law school. They must have a GPA of 2.5 or higher. Along with their application, they must submit a 5-page legal memorandum on an issue facing the entertainment or sports industry.

Financial data The stipend is at least $1,500.

Duration 1 year.

Additional information This program, established in 1989, includes the LeBaron and Yvonne M. Taylor Scholarship.

Number awarded 5 to 7 each year, including at least 1 at each Historically Black Law School (Howard University School of Law, North Carolina Central University School of Law, Southern University Law Center, Florida A&M University School of Law, and Texas Southern University Thurgood Marshall School of Law).

Deadline July of each year.

[675]
BLACK WOMEN IN ENTERTAINMENT LAW STUDENT SCHOLARSHIP

Black Women in Entertainment Law
Attn: Monica Andralliski
110 West 40th Street, Suite 900
New York, NY 10018
(212) 986-6262
Web: www.bwelfoundation.org/scholarships.html

Summary To provide financial assistance to African Americans and other women of color who are enrolled in law school and have an interest in entertainment law.

Eligibility This program is open to women of color who have completed at least 1 semester of law school as a full- or part-time student. Applicants must list the entertainment law courses they have taken and write a 1,500-word essay on a question related to entertainment law. They must have a GPA of 2.5 or higher. Financial need is considered in the selection process.

Financial data Stipends are $4,000 and $2,000.

Duration 1 year.

Number awarded 2 each year: 1 at $4,000 and 1 at $2,000.

Deadline April of each year.

[676]
BOARD OF CORPORATE AFFILIATES SCHOLARS AWARDS

National Society of Black Engineers
Attn: Programs Department
205 Daingerfield Road
Alexandria, VA 22314
(703) 549-2207 Fax: (703) 683-5312
E-mail: scholarships@nsbe.org
Web: www.nsbe.org/Programs/Scholarships.aspx

Summary To provide financial assistance to members of the National Society of Black Engineers (NSBE) who are working on a degree in engineering.

Eligibility This program is open to members of the society who are undergraduate or graduate engineering students. Applicants must have a GPA of 3.0 or higher. Selection is based on an essay; academic achievement; service to the society at the chapter, regional, and/or national level; and other professional, campus, and community activities. Applicants for the National Society of Black Engineers Fellows Scholarship Program who rank in the highest of 3 tiers receive these awards.

Financial data The stipend is $3,000. Travel, hotel accommodations, and registration to the national convention are also provided.

Duration 1 year.

Number awarded Varies each year; recently, 50 of these scholarships were awarded.

Deadline May of each year.

[677]
BROWN AND CALDWELL MINORITY SCHOLARSHIP

Brown and Caldwell
Attn: Scholarship Program
201 North Civic Drive, Suite 115
P.O. Box 8045
Walnut Creek, CA 94596
(925) 937-9010 Fax: (925) 937-9026
E-mail: scholarships@brwncald.com
Web: www.brownandcaldwell.com/scholarships.asp

Summary To provide financial assistance to African American and other minority students working on an undergraduate or graduate degree in an environmental or engineering field.

Eligibility This program is open to members of minority groups (African Americans, Hispanics, Asians, Pacific Islanders, Native Americans, or Alaska Natives) who are full-time juniors, seniors, or graduate students at an accredited 4-year college or university. Applicants must have a GPA of 3.0 or higher and a declared major in civil, chemical, or environmental engineering or an environmental science (e.g., biology, ecology, geology, hydrogeology). They must be U.S. citizens or permanent residents. Along with their application, they must submit an essay (up to 250 words) on their future career goals in environmental science. Financial need is not considered in the selection process.

Financial data The stipend is $5,000.

Duration 1 year.

Number awarded 4 each year.

Deadline April of each year.

[678]
BULLIVANT HOUSER BAILEY LAW STUDENT DIVERSITY FELLOWSHIP PROGRAM

Bullivant Houser Bailey PC
Attn: Manager of Professional Development, Recruitment and Diversity
888 S.W. Fifth Avenue, Suite 300
Portland, OR 97204-2017
(503) 228-6351 Toll Free: (800) 654-8972
Fax: (503) 295-0915 E-mail: jill.valentine@bullivant.com
Web: www.bullivant.com/diversity

Summary To provide financial aid and work experience to African American and other law students who come from a minority or disadvantaged background.

Eligibility This program is open to first-year law students who are members of a minority group (including any group underrepresented in the legal profession) and/or students coming from a disadvantaged educational or economic background. Applicants must have 1) a record of academic achievement and leadership in college and law school; 2) a willingness to complete a 12-week summer associateship at an office of the firm; and 3) a record of contributions to the community that promote diversity within society, the legal community, and/or law school.

Financial data The program provides a salaried associate position at an office of the firm during the summer following the first year of law school and a stipend of $7,500 for the second year.

Duration 1 year.

Number awarded 2 each year: 1 assigned to an associateship in the Sacramento office and 1 assigned to an associateship in the Portland office.

Deadline January of each year.

[679]
BUTLER RUBIN DIVERSITY SCHOLARSHIP

Butler Rubin Saltarelli & Boyd LLP
Attn: Diversity Partner
70 West Madison Street, Suite 1800
Chicago, IL 60602
(312) 242-4120 Fax: (312) 444-9294
E-mail: kborg@butlerrubin.com
Web: www.butlerrubin.com

Summary To provide financial aid and summer work experience to African American and other diverse law students who are interested in the area of business litigation.

Eligibility This program is open to law students of racial and ethnic backgrounds that will contribute to diversity in the legal profession. Applicants must be interested in the private practice of law in the area of business litigation and in a summer associateship in that field with Butler Rubin Saltarelli & Boyd in Chicago. Selection is based on academic performance and achievement, intention to remain in the Chicago area following graduation, and interpersonal and communication skills.

Financial data The stipend is $10,000 per year; funds are to be used for tuition and other expenses associated with law school. For the summer associateship, a stipend is paid.

Duration 1 year; may be renewed.

Additional information This program began in 2006.

Number awarded 1 each year.

Deadline Deadline not specified.

[680]
C. CLYDE FERGUSON LAW SCHOLARSHIP

New Jersey Commission on Higher Education
Attn: Educational Opportunity Fund
20 West State Street, Fourth Floor
P.O. Box 542
Trenton, NJ 08625-0542
(609) 984-2709 Fax: (609) 292-7225
E-mail: audrey.bennerson@njhe.state.nj.us
Web: www.state.nj.us/highereducation/EOF/index.html

Summary To provide financial assistance to African Americans and other disadvantaged or minority students from New Jersey who want to study law in the state.

Eligibility This program is open to students who 1) fall within specified income guidelines (currently, less than $21,660 for a family of 1 rising to $74,020 for a family of 8); 2) minority or disadvantaged students with financial need; or 3) former or current recipients of a New Jersey Educational Opportunity Fund undergraduate or graduate grant, or who would have been eligible to receive the grant as an undergraduate. Applicants must have been New Jersey residents for at least 12 months before receiving the award and must plan to enroll full time in the Minority Student Program at law schools in New Jersey (Rutgers University School of Law at Newark, Rutgers University School of Law at Camden, or Seton Hall Law School).

Financial data Awards are based on financial need. In no case, however, can awards exceed the maximum amount of tuition, fees, room, and board charged at Rutgers University School of Law at Newark.

Duration 1 year; may be renewed.

Number awarded 1 or more each year.

Deadline Deadline not specified.

[681]
CALIFORNIA BAR FOUNDATION DIVERSITY SCHOLARSHIPS

State Bar of California
Attn: California Bar Foundation
180 Howard Street
San Francisco, CA 94105-1639
(415) 856-0780 Fax: (415) 856-0788
E-mail: scholarships@calbarfoundation.org
Web: www.calbarfoundation.org/diversity-scholarship.html

Summary To provide financial assistance to African Americans and other underrepresented minorities from any state who are entering law school in California.

Eligibility This program to open to residents of any state who are entering their first year at a law school in California. Applicants must self-identify as being from a racial or ethnic group that historically has been underrepresented in the legal profession (Latino, African American, Asian and Pacific Islander, and Native American). They must be committed to making an impact in the community through leadership. Along with their application, they must submit a 500-word essay describing their commitment to serving the community and, if applicable, any significant obstacles or hurdles they have overcome to attend law school. Financial need is considered in the selection process.

Financial data The stipend is $7,500.

Duration 1 year.

Additional information This program began in 2008. Each year, the foundation grants awards named after sponsors that donate funding for the scholarships. Recipients are required to attend a reception in their honor in October of the year of their award and to submit a report on their progress at the end of that year.

Number awarded Varies each year; recently, 19 of these scholarships were awarded.

Deadline June of each year.

[682]
CALIFORNIA STATE UNIVERSITY CHANCELLOR'S DOCTORAL INCENTIVE PROGRAM

California State University
Office of the Chancellor
Attn: Human Resources
401 Golden Shore, Fourth Floor
Long Beach, CA 90802-4210
(562) 951-4425 Fax: (562) 951-4954
E-mail: forgivableloan@calstate.edu
Web: www.calstate.edu/hr/cdip

Summary To provide funding to African Americans and other graduate students who can help increase the diversity of persons qualified to compete for instructional faculty positions at campuses of the California State University (CSU) system.

Eligibility This program is open to new and continuing full-time students enrolled in a doctoral program anywhere in the United States, whether affiliated with a CSU campus or not. Applicants must present a plan of support from a full-time CSU faculty sponsor who has agreed to advise and support the candidate throughout doctoral study. Selection is based on the applicant's academic record; professional qualifications; and relevant background, experience, skills, and motivation to educate a diverse student body in the CSU system. The factors considered include experience working with persons with a wide range of backgrounds and perspectives, research interests related to educating an increasingly diverse student body, and experience in a variety of cultural environments. Primary consideration is given to candidates whose proposed area of study falls where CSU campuses anticipate the greatest difficulty in filling instructional faculty positions.

Financial data Participants receive up to $10,000 per year or a maximum of $30,000 over 5 years. The loans are converted to fellowships at the rate of 20% of the total loan amount for each postdoctoral year that the program participant teaches, for up to 5 years. Thus, the entire loan will be forgiven after the recipient has taught full time for 5 years on a CSU campus. Recipients who do not teach on a CSU campus or who discontinue full-time studies will be required to repay the total loan amount within a 15-year period at the rate established for other student loans.

Duration Up to 5 years.

Additional information This program began in 1987 as the California State University Forgivable Loan Program. It has loaned $46 million to 1,965 doctoral students enrolled in universities throughout the nation and abroad. Participants included 17.6% African American, 13.3% Asian, 26.2% Hispanic, 4.1% American Indian, and 32.1% White.

Number awarded Varies each year; recently, 60 new participants were admitted to the program.

Deadline The deadline varies at different CSU campuses but typically falls in February of each year.

[683]
CANFIT PROGRAM GRADUATE SCHOLARSHIPS

Communities-Adolescents-Nutrition-Fitness
Attn: Scholarship Program
2140 Shattuck Avenue, Suite 610
Berkeley, CA 94704
(510) 644-1533 Toll Free: (800) 200-3131
Fax: (510) 644-1535 E-mail: info@canfit.org
Web: www.canfit.org/scholarships

Summary To provide financial assistance to African American and other minority graduate students who are working on a degree in nutrition, physical education, or public health in California.

Eligibility This program is open to American Indians, Alaska Natives, African Americans, Asian Americans, Pacific Islanders, and Latinos/Hispanics from California who are enrolled in 1) an approved master's or doctoral program in nutrition, public health, or physical education in the state; or 2) a preprofessional practice program approved by the American Dietetic Association at an accredited university in the state. Applicants must have completed 12 to 15 units of graduate course work and have a cumulative GPA of 3.0 or higher. Along with their application, they must submit 1) documentation of financial need; 2) letters of recommendation from 2 individuals; 3) a 1- to 2-page letter describing their academic goals and involvement in community nutrition and/or physical education activities; and 4) an essay of 500 to 1,000 words on a topic related to healthy foods for youth from low-income communities of color.

Financial data A stipend is awarded (amount not specified).

Number awarded 1 or more each year.

Deadline March of each year.

[684]
CARMEN E. TURNER SCHOLARSHIPS

Conference of Minority Transportation Officials
Attn: National Scholarship Program
1875 I Street, N.W., Suite 500
Washington, DC 20006
(703) 234-4072 Fax: (202) 318-0364
Web: www.comto.org/?page=Scholarships

Summary To provide financial assistance for college or graduate school to African American and other members of the Conference of Minority Transportation Officials (COMTO).

Eligibility This program is open to undergraduate and graduate students who have been members of COMTO for at least 1 year. Applicants must be working on a degree in a field related to transportation and have a GPA of 2.5 or higher. They must be enrolled at least half time. Along with their application, they must submit a cover letter with a 500-word statement of career goals. Financial need is not considered in the selection process. U.S. citizenship or legal resident status is required.

Financial data The stipend is $3,500. Funds are paid directly to the recipient's college or university.

Duration 1 year.

Additional information COMTO was established in 1971 to promote, strengthen, and expand the roles of minorities in all aspects of transportation. Recipients are expected to attend the COMTO National Scholarship Luncheon.

Number awarded 1 each year.

Deadline May of each year.

[685]
CARTER G. WOODSON INSTITUTE PREDOCTORAL RESIDENTIAL RESEARCH FELLOWSHIP

University of Virginia
Carter G. Woodson Institute for African-American and African Studies
Attn: Director of the Fellowship Program
108 Minor Hall
P.O. Box 400162
Charlottesville, VA 22904-4162
(804) 924-8892 Fax: (804) 924-8820
E-mail: woodson@virginia.edu
Web: www.artsandsciences.virginia.edu

Summary To provide funding to doctoral candidates interested in conducting research at the University of Virginia's Woodson Institute in those disciplines of the humanities and social sciences concerned with African American and African studies.

Eligibility This program is open to doctoral candidates who have completed all requirements for the Ph.D. except the dissertation prior to August of the fellowship year. There are no citizenship or residence requirements. Applicants must be working in a field of the humanities or social sciences that focuses on Africa and/or the African Diaspora. Along with their application, they must submit a description of a research project to be conducted during the fellowship period at the Woodson Institute. Selection is based on the significance of the proposed work, the qualifications of the applicant, familiarity with existing relevant research literature, the research design of the project, and the promise of completion within the award period.

Financial data The stipend is $20,000 per year. Health insurance is also provided.

Duration 2 years; nonrenewable.

Additional information Fellows must be in residence at the University of Virginia for the duration of the award period. They are expected to contribute to the intellectual life of the university.

Number awarded 4 each year.

Deadline November of each year.

[686]
CATHY L. BROCK MEMORIAL SCHOLARSHIP

Institute for Diversity in Health Management
Attn: Education Specialist
155 North Wacker Avenue, Suite 400
Chicago, IL 60606
(312) 422-2658 Toll Free: (800) 233-0996
Fax: (312) 895-4511 E-mail: cbiddle@aha.org
Web: www.diversityconnection.org

Summary To provide financial assistance to African American and other minority graduate students in health care management, especially financial operations.

Eligibility This program is open to members of ethnic minority groups who are enrolled in the first or second year of an accredited graduate program in health care administration. Applicants must have a GPA of 3.0 or higher. They must demonstrate commitment to a career in health care finance. Along with their application, they must submit 1) a personal statement of 1 to 2 pages on their interest in health care management and their career goals; 2) an essay on what they see as the most challenging issue facing America's hospitals and health systems; and 3) a 500-word essay on their interest and background in health care finance. Selection is based on academic achievement, commitment to a career in health care finance, and financial need. U.S. citizenship is required.

Financial data The stipend is $1,000.

Duration 1 year.

Number awarded 1 each year.

Deadline January of each year.

[687]
CENIE "JOMO" WILLIAMS TUITION SCHOLARSHIP

National Association of Black Social Workers
Attn: NABSW Scholarships
2305 Martin Luther King Avenue, S.E.
Washington, DC 20020
(202) 678-4570 Fax: (202) 678-4572
E-mail: office-manager@nabsw.org
Web: www.nabsw.org/mserver/Forms.aspx

Summary To provide financial assistance for college or graduate school to members of the National Association of Black Social Workers (NABSW).

Eligibility This program is open to African American members of NABSW enrolled full time at an accredited social work or social welfare program with a GPA of 2.5 or higher. Applicants must be able to demonstrate community service and a research interest in the Black community. Along with their application, they must submit an essay of 2 to 3 pages on their professional interests, future social work aspirations, previous social work experiences (volunteer and professional), honors and achievements (academic and community service), and research interests within the Black community (for master's and doctoral students). Financial need is considered in the selection process.

Financial data The stipend is $2,000. Funds are sent directly to the recipient's school.

Duration 1 year.

Number awarded 2 each year.

Deadline January of each year.

[688]
CENTRAL FLORIDA CHAPTER NBMBAA SCHOLARSHIPS

National Black MBA Association-Central Florida Chapter
Attn: Scholarship Committee Chair
P.O. Box 692696
Orlando, FL 32869-2696
(321) 578-8305 E-mail: scholarships@cflblackmba.org
Web: www.cflblackmba.org

Summary To provide financial assistance to African Americans or members of another minority group who are residents of any state working on a degree in business at a university in Florida.

Eligibility This program is open to members of the following groups from any state: African American/Black, American Indian/Alaska Native, Asian American/Pacific Islander, or Hispanic/Latino. Applicants must be enrolled in a business program at an AACSB-accredited college or university in Florida. They must have a GPA of 3.0 or higher. Along with their application, they must submit a 2-page essay on a topic that changes annually but relates to minorities and business. Selection is based on that essay, transcripts, a resume, and extracurricular activities. The highest-ranked applicant receives a named scholarship sponsored by Darden Restaurants.

Financial data The Darden Named Scholarship is $5,000; a total of $10,000 in scholarships is awarded each year.

Duration 1 year.

Number awarded Varies each year.

Deadline October of each year.

[689]
CH2M HILL PARTNERSHIP SCHOLARSHIP

Women's Transportation Seminar
Attn: WTS Foundation
1701 K Street, N.W., Suite 800
Washington, DC 20006
(202) 955-5085 Fax: (202) 955-5088
E-mail: wts@wtsinternational.org
Web: www.wtsinternational.org/education/scholarships

Summary To provide financial assistance to women graduate students (particularly African American and other minority women) who are interested in preparing for a career in transportation.

Eligibility This program is open to women who are enrolled in a graduate degree program in a transportation-related field (e.g., transportation engineering, planning, finance, or logistics). Applicants must have at least a 3.0 GPA and be interested in a career in transportation. Along with their application, they must submit a 750-word statement about their career goals after graduation and why they think they should receive the scholarship award. Applications must be submitted first to a local chapter; the chapters forward selected applications for consideration on the national level. Minority women are particularly encouraged to apply. Selection is based on transportation involvement and goals, job skills, and academic record.

Financial data The stipend is $10,000.

Duration 1 year.

Additional information This program is sponsored by CH2M Hill. Local chapters may also award additional funding to winners in their area.

Number awarded 1 each year.

Deadline Applications must be submitted by November to a local WTS chapter.

[690]
CHARLES B. RANGEL GRADUATE FELLOWSHIP PROGRAM

Howard University
Attn: Ralph J. Bunche International Affairs Center
2281 Sixth Street, N.W.
Washington, DC 20059
(202) 806-4367 Toll Free: (877) 633-0002
Fax: (202) 806-5424 E-mail: pscroggs@howard.edu
Web: www.rangelprogram.org

Summary To provide financial assistance for graduate study in a field related to the work of the Foreign Service, especially to African Americans and members of other underrepresented minority groups.

Eligibility This program is open to U.S. citizens who are either graduating college seniors or recipients of an undergraduate degree. Applicants must be planning to enter graduate school to work on a master's degree in international affairs or other area of interest to the Foreign Service of the U.S. Department of State (e.g., public administration, public policy, business administration, foreign languages, economics, political science, or communications). They must have a GPA of 3.2 or higher. Strong preference is given to members of minority groups historically underrepresented in the Foreign Service and those who can demonstrate financial need.

Financial data The stipend is $35,000 per year.

Duration 2 years.

Additional information This program is offered jointly by Howard University and the U.S. Department of State. Fellows are provided an internship working on international issues for members of Congress during the summer after they are selected and before they begin graduate study. They are provided a second internship at a U.S. embassy overseas during the summer before their second year of graduate study. Fellows who complete the program and Foreign Service entry requirements receive appointments as Foreign Service Officers. Each fellow who obtains a master's degree is committed to at least 3 years of service as a Foreign Service Officer. If recipients do not complete the program successfully or do not fulfill the 3-year service obligation, they may be subject to a reimbursement obligation.

Number awarded 20 each year.

Deadline January of each year.

[691]
CHARLES S. BROWN SCHOLARSHIP IN PHYSICS

National Society of Black Physicists
Attn: Scholarship Committee Chair
1100 North Glebe Road, Suite 1010
Arlington, VA 22201
(703) 536-4207 Fax: (703) 536-4203
E-mail: scholarship@nsbp.org
Web: www.nsbp.org/scholarships

Summary To provide financial assistance to African American students working on an undergraduate or graduate degree in physics.

Eligibility This program is open to African American students who are working on an undergraduate or graduate degree in physics. Applicants must submit an essay on their academic and career objectives, information on their participation in extracurricular activities, a description of any awards and honors they have received, and 3 letters of recommendation. Financial need is not considered.

Financial data A stipend is awarded (amount not specified).

Duration 1 year; nonrenewable.

Number awarded 1 each year.

Deadline November of each year.

[692]
CIGNA HEALTHCARE GRADUATE SCHOLARSHIPS

National Forum for Black Public Administrators
Attn: Scholarship Program
777 North Capitol Street, N.E., Suite 807
Washington, DC 20002
(202) 408-9300 Fax: (202) 408-8558
E-mail: vharris@nfbpa.org
Web: www.nfbpa.org/i4a/pages/index.cfm?pageid=4047

Summary To provide financial assistance to African Americans working on a graduate degree in public administration or a related field at an Historically Black College or University (HBCU).

Eligibility This program is open to African American graduate students preparing for a career in public administration. Applicants must be working on a degree in public administration, political science, urban affairs, public policy, or a related field at an HBCU. They must have a GPA of 3.0 or higher, excellent interpersonal and analytical abilities, and strong oral and written communication skills. Along with their application, they must submit a 3-page essay on an assigned topic that relates to the public administration profession. Selection is based on academic record, leadership ability, participation in school activities, community service, and financial need.

Financial data The stipend is $5,000.

Duration 1 year.

Additional information This program is sponsored by CIGNA Healthcare. Recipients are required to attend the sponsor's annual conference to receive their scholarship; limited hotel and air accommodations are arranged and provided.

Number awarded 2 each year.

Deadline February of each year.

[693]
CLA SCHOLARSHIP FOR MINORITY STUDENTS IN MEMORY OF EDNA YELLAND

California Library Association
2471 Flores Street
San Mateo, CA 94403
(650) 376-0886 Fax: (650) 539-2341
E-mail: info@cla-net.org
Web: www.cla-net.org

Summary To provide financial assistance to African American and other minority students in California who are attending graduate school in any state to prepare for a career in library or information science.

Eligibility This program is open to California residents who are members of ethnic minority groups (American Indian/Alaska Native, African American/Black, Latino/Hispanic, Asian American, or Pacific Islander). Applicants must have completed at least 1 course in a master's program at an accredited graduate library school in any state. Evidence of financial need and U.S. citizenship or permanent resident status must be submitted. Finalists are interviewed.

Financial data The stipend is $2,500.

Duration 1 academic year.

Additional information This fellowship is named for the executive secretary of the California Library Association from 1947 to 1963 who worked to promote the goals of the California Library Association and the profession. Until 1985, it was named the Edna Yelland Memorial Scholarship.

Number awarded 3 each year.

Deadline July of each year.

[694]
CLINICAL RESEARCH PRE-DOCTORAL FELLOWSHIP PROGRAM

American Nurses Association
Attn: SAMHSA Minority Fellowship Programs
8515 Georgia Avenue, Suite 400
Silver Spring, MD 20910-3492
(301) 628-5247 Toll Free: (800) 274-4ANA
Fax: (301) 628-5339 E-mail: janet.jackson@ana.org
Web: www.emfp.org

Summary To provide financial assistance to African American and other minority nurses who are doctoral candidates interested in psychiatric, mental health, and substance abuse issues that impact the lives of ethnic minority people.

Eligibility This program is open to nurses who have a master's degree and are members of an ethnic or racial minority group, including but not limited to Blacks or African Americans, Hispanics or Latinos, American Indians and Alaska Natives, Asian Americans, and Native Hawaiians and other Pacific Islanders. Applicants must be able to demonstrate a commitment to a research career in nursing and psychiatric/mental health issues affecting ethnic minority populations. They must be interested in a program of full-time doctoral study, with a research focus on such issues of concern to minority populations as child abuse, violence in intimate relationships, mental health disorders, substance abuse, mental health service utilization, and stigma as a barrier to mental health care and personal resilience. U.S. citizenship or permanent resident status and membership in the American Nurses Association are required. Selection is based on research potential, scholarship, writing ability, knowledge of broad issues in mental health nursing, and professional commitment to ethnic minority concerns.

Financial data The program provides an annual stipend of $22,032 and tuition assistance.

Duration 3 to 5 years.

Additional information Funds for this program are provided by the Substance Abuse and Mental Health Services Administration (SAMHSA).

Number awarded 1 or more each year.

Deadline February of each year.

[695]
COMMITTEE ON ETHNIC MINORITY RECRUITMENT SCHOLARSHIP

United Methodist Church-California-Pacific Annual Conference
Attn: Board of Ordained Ministry
1720 East Linfield Street
Glendora, CA 91740
(626) 335-6629 Fax: (626) 335-5750
E-mail: cathy.adminbom@gmail.com
Web: www.calpacordainedministry.org/523451

Summary To provide financial assistance to African Americans and members of other ethnic minority groups in the California-Pacific Annual Conference of the United Methodist

Church (UMC) who are attending a seminary in any state to qualify for ordination as an elder or deacon.

Eligibility This program is open to members of ethnic minority groups in the UMC California-Pacific Annual Conference who are enrolled at a seminary in any state approved by the UMC University Senate. Applicants must have been approved as certified candidates by their district committee and be seeking Probationary Deacon or Elder's Orders. They may apply for 1 or more types of assistance: tuition scholarships, grants for books and school supplies (including computers), or emergency living expense grants.

Financial data Tuition stipends are $1,000 per year; books and supplies grants range up to $1,000 per year; emergency living expense grants depend on need and the availability of funds.

Duration 1 year; may be renewed up to 2 additional years.

Additional information The California-Pacific Annual Conference includes churches in southern California, Hawaii, Guam, and Saipan.

Number awarded Varies each year.

Deadline August of each year for fall term; December of each year for spring term.

[696] CONGRESSIONAL BLACK CAUCUS SPOUSES EDUCATION SCHOLARSHIP

Congressional Black Caucus Foundation, Inc.
Attn: Director, Educational Programs
1720 Massachusetts Avenue, N.W.
Washington, DC 20036
(202) 263-2800 Toll Free: (800) 784-2577
Fax: (202) 775-0773 E-mail: scholarships@cbcfinc.org
Web: www.cbcfinc.org/scholarships.html

Summary To provide financial assistance to African American and other undergraduate and graduate students, especially those who reside or attend college in a Congressional district represented by a member of the Congressional Black Caucus (CBC).

Eligibility This program is open to 1) African American and other graduating high school seniors planning to attend an accredited institution of higher education; and 2) currently-enrolled full-time undergraduate, graduate, and doctoral students in good academic standing with a GPA of 2.5 or higher. Preference is given to applicants who reside or attend school in a Congressional district represented by a member of the CBC. Along with their application, they must a personal statement of 500 to 1,000 words on 1) their future goals, major field of study, and how that field of study will help them to achieve their future career goals; 2) involvement in school activities, community and public service, hobbies, and sports; 3) how receiving this award will affect their current and future plans; and 4) other experiences, skills, or qualifications. They must also be able to demonstrate financial need, leadership ability, and participation in community service activities.

Financial data A stipend is awarded (amount not specified).

Duration 1 year.

Additional information The program began in 1988.

Number awarded Varies each year.

Deadline June of each year.

[697] CONSORTIUM FOR GRADUATE STUDY IN MANAGEMENT FELLOWSHIPS

Consortium for Graduate Study in Management
229 Chesterfield Business Parkway
Chesterfield, MO 63005
(636) 681-5553 Fax: (636) 681-5499
E-mail: recruiting@cgsm.org
Web: www.cgsm.org

Summary To provide college funding and work experience to African Americans and other underrepresented racial minorities who are interested in preparing for a management career in business.

Eligibility This program is open to African Americans, Hispanic Americans (Chicanos, Cubans, Dominicans, and Puerto Ricans), and Native Americans who have graduated from college and are interested in preparing for a career in business. Other U.S. citizens and permanent residents who can demonstrate a commitment to the sponsor's mission of enhancing diversity in business education are also eligible. An undergraduate degree in business or economics is not required. Applicants must be planning to work on an M.B.A. degree at 1 of the consortium's 18 schools.

Financial data The fellowship pays full tuition and required fees. Summer internships with the consortium's cooperative sponsors, providing paid practical experience, are also offered.

Duration Up to 4 semesters.

Additional information This program began in 1966. The participating schools are Carnegie Mellon University, Cornell University, Dartmouth College, Emory University, Georgetown University, Indiana University, University of Michigan, New York University, University of California at Berkeley, University of California at Los Angeles, University of North Carolina at Chapel Hill, University of Rochester, University of Southern California, University of Texas at Austin, University of Virginia, Washington University, University of Wisconsin at Madison, and Yale University. Fellowships are tenable at member schools only. Application fees are $150 for students applying to 1 or 2 schools, $200 for 3 schools, $240 for 4 schools, $275 for 5 schools, or $300 for 6 schools.

Number awarded Varies each year; recently, more than 380 of these fellowships were awarded.

Deadline March of each year.

[698] CONSTANGY, BROOKS & SMITH DIVERSITY SCHOLARS AWARD

Constangy, Brooks & Smith LLC
Attn: Chair, Diversity Council
200 West Forsyth Street, Suite 1700
Jacksonville, FL 32202-4317
(904) 356-8900 Fax: (904) 356-8200
E-mail: mzabijaka@constangy.com
Web: www.constangy.com/f-4.html

Summary To provide financial assistance to African Americans and other diverse students who are enrolled in law schools in selected states.

Eligibility This program is open to second-year students enrolled in accredited law schools located in 1 of 3 regions: South (Alabama, Florida, Georgia, South Carolina, Tennessee), Midwest/West Coast (California, Illinois, Kansas, Missouri, Texas, Wisconsin), or East (Massachusetts, New Jersey, North Carolina, Virginia/Washington D.C.). Applicants must submit a personal statement on why diversity is important to them personally and in the legal profession. They must have a GPA of 2.7 or higher. Selection is based on academic achievement, commitment to diversity, and personal achievement in overcoming obstacles.

Financial data The stipend is $3,000.

Duration 1 year.

Number awarded 3 each year: 1 in each region.

Deadline November of each year.

[699]
COOK/RUTLEDGE FELLOWSHIP

New Jersey Department of Health
Office of Minority and Multicultural Health
Attn: Executive Director
John Fitch Plaza, Room 501
P.O. Box 360
Trenton, NJ 08625-0360
(609) 292-6962 Fax: (609) 292-8713
Web: www.nj.gov/health/omh/professions.shtml

Summary To provide financial support to African American and other public health, law, and medical students in New Jersey who are interested in conducting research related to health disparities issues during the summer.

Eligibility This program is open to students in medical science, law, or master's of public health programs who are 1) residents of New Jersey attending school in the state or elsewhere; or 2) residents of other states attending a college or university in New Jersey. Applicants must be interested in working on a supervised project at the New Jersey Department of Health in Trenton on current and relevant health equity/health disparity issues impacting the racial or ethnic minority populations in New Jersey. Along with their application, they must submit letters of recommendation from 1) a college instructor indicating their commitment to an understanding of the issues facing the racial or ethnic minority populations; or 2) a community-based or faith-based organization or public health organization where they volunteered, worked, or assisted with a health care initiative that directly impacted a racial or ethnic minority group.

Financial data The stipend is $6,000.

Duration 8 to 10 weeks during the summer.

Number awarded 1 each year.

Deadline March of each year.

[700]
COOLEY LLP DIVERSITY FELLOWSHIP

Cooley LLP
Attn: Attorney Recruiting Manager
4401 Eastgate Mall
San Diego, CA 92121-1909
(858) 550-6474 E-mail: diversityfellowship@cooley.com
Web: www.cooley.com/diversityfellowship

Summary To provide financial aid and work experience to African American and other law students who are committed to promoting diversity in their community and are interested in summer associateships and employment at an office of Cooley LLP.

Eligibility This program is open to students enrolled full time at an ABA-accredited law school and planning to graduate 2 years after applying. Applicants must submit a 3-page personal statement describing their demonstrated commitment to promoting diversity (e.g., ethnicity, gender, physical disability, and/or sexual orientation) in their community. They must be interested in a summer associateship. Selection is based on undergraduate and law school academic performance, personal achievements, leadership abilities, community service, and demonstrated commitment to promoting diversity.

Financial data The award includes a stipend of $10,000 after completing a summer associateship after the first year of law school, another stipend of $10,000 after completing another summer associateship after the second year of law school, and another stipend of $10,000 after graduating from law school and joining the firm as a full-time associate.

Duration 3 years.

Additional information Summer associates may work in any of the firm's offices in California (Palo Alto, San Diego, or San Francisco), Colorado (Broomfield), Massachusetts (Boston), New York (New York), Virginia (Reston), Washington (Seattle), or Washington, D.C.

Number awarded 1 or more each year.

Deadline June of each year.

[701]
CORPORATE PARTNER SCHOLARSHIPS

National Association of Black Accountants
Attn: National Scholarship Program
7474 Greenway Center Drive, Suite 1120
Greenbelt, MD 20770
(301) 474-NABA Fax: (301) 474-3114
E-mail: scholarships@nabainc.org
Web: www.nabainc.org

Summary To provide financial assistance to student members of the National Association of Black Accountants (NABA) who are working on an undergraduate or graduate degree in a field related to accounting.

Eligibility This program is open to minorities who are NABA members and enrolled full time as 1) an undergraduate freshman, sophomore, junior, or first-semester senior majoring in accounting, business, or finance at a 4-year college or university; or 2) a graduate student working on a master's degree in accounting. High school seniors are not eligible. Applicants must have a GPA of 3.5 or higher in their major and 3.3 or higher overall. Along with their application, they must submit a 500-word personal statement on their involvement in NABA, career objectives, leadership abilities, and community activities. Financial need is not considered in the selection process.

Financial data Stipends range from $1,000 to $5,000.

Duration 1 year.

Number awarded Varies each year.

Deadline January of each year.

[702]
CORRIS BOYD SCHOLARSHIP

Association of University Programs in Health Administration
Attn: Prizes, Fellowships and Scholarships
2000 14th Street North, Suite 780
Arlington, VA 22201
(703) 894-0940, ext. 115 Fax: (703) 894-0941
E-mail: aupha@aupha.org
Web: www.aupha.org/i4a/pages/index.cfm?pageid=3541

Summary To provide financial assistance to African American and other minority students entering graduate schools affiliated with the Association of University Programs in Health Administration (AUPHA).

Eligibility This program is open to students of color (African Americans, American Indians, Alaska Natives, Asian Americans, Hispanic Americans, Native Hawaiians, and other Pacific Islanders) who have been accepted to a master's degree program in health care management at an AUPHA member institution. Applicants must be U.S. citizens or permanent residents and have a GPA of 3.0 or higher. Along with their application, they must submit a personal statement explaining why they are choosing to prepare for a career in health administration. Selection is based on leadership qualities, academic achievement, community involvement, and commitment to health care; financial need may be considered if all other factors are equal.

Financial data The stipend is $40,000.

Duration 1 year.

Additional information This program began in 2006.

Number awarded 2 each year.

Deadline May of each year.

[703]
CRCNA RACE RELATIONS MULTIRACIAL STUDENT SCHOLARSHIP

Christian Reformed Church
Attn: Office of Race Relations
2850 Kalamazoo Avenue, S.E.
Grand Rapids, MI 49560-0200
(616) 224-5883 Toll Free: (877) 279-9994
Fax: (616) 224-0834 E-mail: elugo@crcna.org
Web: www.crcna.org/race/scholarships

Summary To provide financial assistance to African American and other minority undergraduate and graduate students who are interested in attending colleges related to the Christian Reformed Church in North America (CRCNA).

Eligibility This program is open to students of color in the United States and Canada. Normally, applicants are expected to be members of CRCNA congregations who plan to pursue their educational goals at Calvin Theological Seminary or any of the colleges affiliated with the CRCNA. They must be interested in training for the ministry of racial reconciliation in church and/or in society. Students who have no prior history with the CRCNA must attend a CRCNA-related college or seminary for a full academic year before they are eligible to apply for this program. Students entering their sophomore year must have earned a GPA of 2.0 or higher as freshmen; students entering their junior year must have earned a GPA of 2.3 or higher as sophomores; students entering their senior year must have earned a GPA of 2.6 or higher as juniors.

Financial data First-year students receive $500 per semester. Other levels of students may receive up to $2,000 per academic year.

Duration 1 year.

Additional information This program was first established in 1971 and revised in 1991. Recipients are expected to train to engage actively in the ministry of racial reconciliation in church and in society. They must be able to work in the United States or Canada upon graduating and must consider working for 1 of the agencies of the CRCNA.

Number awarded Varies each year; recently, 31 students received a total of $21,000 in support.

Deadline March of each year.

[704]
CTA/MARTIN LUTHER KING, JR. MEMORIAL SCHOLARSHIP FUND

California Teachers Association
Attn: CTA Foundation for Teaching and Learning
1705 Murchison Drive
P.O. Box 921
Burlingame, CA 94011-0921
(650) 697-1400 E-mail: scholarships@cta.org
Web: www.cta.org

Summary To provide financial assistance for college or graduate school to African Americans and other racial and ethnic minorities who are members of the California Teachers Association (CTA), children of members, or members of the Student CTA.

Eligibility This program is open to members of racial or ethnic minority groups (African Americans, American Indians/Alaska Natives, Asians/Pacific Islanders, and Hispanics) who are 1) active CTA members; 2) dependent children of active, retired, or deceased CTA members; or 3) members of Student CTA. Applicants must be interested in preparing for a teaching career in public education or already engaged in such a career.

Financial data Stipends vary each year; recently, they ranged from $1,000 to $4,000.

Duration 1 year.

Number awarded Varies each year; recently, 25 of these scholarships were awarded: 5 to CTA members, 10 to children of CTA members, and 10 to Student CTA members.

Deadline February of each year.

[705]
CUMMINS SCHOLARSHIPS

Society of Women Engineers
Attn: Scholarship Selection Committee
203 North LaSalle Street, Suite 1675
Chicago, IL 60601-1269
(312) 596-5223 Toll Free: (877) SWE-INFO
Fax: (312) 644-8557 E-mail: scholarships@swe.org
Web: societyofwomenengineers.swe.org

Summary To provide financial assistance to minority and other women working on an undergraduate or graduate degree in computer science or designated engineering specialties.

Eligibility This program is open to women who are sophomores, juniors, seniors, or graduate students at 4-year ABET-accredited colleges and universities. Applicants must be working full time on a degree in computer science or automotive, chemical, computer, electrical, industrial, manufacturing, materials, or mechanical engineering and have a GPA of 3.5 or higher. Preference is given to members of groups underrepresented in engineering or computer science. Selection is based on merit. U.S. citizenship or permanent resident status is required.

Financial data The stipend is $1,000.

Duration 1 year.

Additional information This program is sponsored by Cummins, Inc.

Number awarded 2 each year.

Deadline February of each year.

[706]
CUTLER-DEKNIGHT NATIONAL GRADUATE FELLOWSHIP

American Association of Family and Consumer Sciences
Attn: Senior Manager, Awards and Governance
400 North Columbus Street, Suite 202
Alexandria, VA 22314
(703) 706-4608 Toll Free: (800) 424-8080, ext. 4608
Fax: (703) 706-4663 E-mail: staff@aafcs.org
Web: www.aafcs.org/Recognition/fellowshipseven.asp

Summary To provide financial assistance to African American graduate students who are working on a degree in family and consumer sciences, especially as related to communications or cooperative extension.

Eligibility This program is open to African American graduate students who are working full time on a degree in family and consumer sciences. Preference is given to qualified applicants who plan a career in family and consumer sciences communications or cooperative extension. Applicants must have completed at least 1 year of professional family and consumer sciences experience as a student assistant, trainee, or intern. Selection is based on ability to pursue graduate study (10 points); experience in relation to preparation for study in proposed field (15 points); special recognition and awards (5 points); voluntary participation in professional and community organizations and activities (10 points); evidence (or degree) of professional commitment and leadership (10 points); significance of proposed study or research interests to families and individuals (15 points); professional goals (15 points); written communication (10 points); and recommendations (10 points). Special consideration is given to applicants who have been members of the American Association of Family and Consumer Sciences (AAFCS) for up to 2 years (2 points) or for 2 or more years (5 points) or who have specialized AAFCS credentials (5 points). U.S. citizenship or permanent residence status is required.

Financial data The award provides a stipend of $5,000 and financial support of up to $1,000 for 1 year of AAFCS membership and participation in its annual conference and exposition.

Duration 1 year.

Additional information The Virginia F. Cutler Fellowship in Consumer Studies was first awarded for the 1976-77 academic year. The Freda A. DeKnight National Fellowship was established in 1975 in memory of the late food and home service editor of *Ebony* magazine, a creator of the "Ebony Fashion Fair" (an annual charitable event presented in over 100 American cities). Those 2 programs have been combined to produce this fellowship.

Number awarded 1 each year.

Deadline January of each year.

[707]
DAVID HILLIARD EATON SCHOLARSHIP

Unitarian Universalist Association
Attn: Ministerial Credentialing Office
25 Beacon Street
Boston, MA 02108-2800
(617) 948-6403 Fax: (617) 742-2875
E-mail: mcoadministrator@uua.org
Web: www.uua.org

Summary To provide financial assistance to African American and other minority women preparing for the Unitarian Universalist (UU) ministry.

Eligibility This program is open to women from historically marginalized groups who are currently enrolled or planning to enroll full or at least half time in a UU ministerial training program with aspirant or candidate status. Applicants must be citizens of the United States or Canada. Priority is given first to those who have demonstrated outstanding ministerial ability and secondarily to students with the greatest financial need (especially persons of color).

Financial data The stipend ranges from $1,000 to $15,000 per year.

Duration 1 year.

Number awarded 1 or 2 each year.

Deadline April of each year.

[708]
DAVID POHL SCHOLARSHIP

Unitarian Universalist Association
Attn: Ministerial Credentialing Office
25 Beacon Street
Boston, MA 02108-2800
(617) 948-6403 Fax: (617) 742-2875
E-mail: mcoadministrator@uua.org
Web: www.uua.org

Summary To provide financial assistance to seminary students (particularly African Americans and other persons of color) who are preparing for the Unitarian Universalist (UU) ministry.

Eligibility This program is open to seminary students who are enrolled full or at least half time in a UU ministerial training program with candidate status. Applicants must be citizens of the United States or Canada. Priority is given first to those who have demonstrated outstanding ministerial ability and secondarily to students with the greatest financial need (especially persons of color).

Financial data The stipend ranges from $1,000 to $15,000 per year.

Duration 1 year.

Number awarded 1 each year.

Deadline April of each year.

[709]
DAVIS WRIGHT TREMAINE 1L DIVERSITY SCHOLARSHIP PROGRAM

Davis Wright Tremaine LLP
Attn: Diversity Scholarship Program
1201 Third Avenue, Suite 2200
Seattle, WA 98101-3045
(206) 757-8761 Toll Free: (877) 398-8416
Fax: (206) 757-7700 E-mail: BrookDormaier@dwt.com
Web: www.dwt.com/1LDiversityScholarship

Summary To provide financial aid and summer work experience to African American and other law students of color.

Eligibility This program is open to first-year law students of color and others of diverse backgrounds. Applicants must have a record of academic achievement as an undergraduate and in the first year of law school that demonstrates promise for a successful career in law, a commitment to civic involvement that promotes diversity and will continue after entering the legal profession, and a commitment to practicing in the Northwest after law school. Although demonstrated need may be taken into account, applicants need not disclose their financial circumstances.

Financial data The award consists of a $7,500 stipend for second-year tuition and expenses and a paid summer clerkship.

Duration 1 academic year and summer.

Number awarded 2 each year: 1 in the Seattle office and 1 in the Portland office.

Deadline January of each year.

[710]
DELTA SIGMA THETA SORORITY GENERAL SCHOLARSHIPS

Delta Sigma Theta Sorority, Inc.
Attn: Scholarship and Standards Committee Chair
1707 New Hampshire Avenue, N.W.
Washington, DC 20009
(202) 986-2400 Fax: (202) 986-2513
E-mail: dstemail@deltasigmatheta.org
Web: www.deltasigmatheta.org

Summary To provide financial assistance to members of Delta Sigma Theta who are working on an undergraduate or graduate degree in any field.

Eligibility This program is open to active, dues-paying members of Delta Sigma Theta who are currently enrolled in college or graduate school. Applicants must submit an essay on their major goals and educational objectives, including realistic steps they foresee as necessary for the fulfillment of their plans. Financial need is considered in the selection process.

Financial data The stipends range from $1,000 to $2,000. The funds may be used to cover tuition, fees, and living expenses.

Duration 1 year; may be renewed for 1 additional year.

Additional information This sponsor is a traditionally-African American social sorority. The application fee is $20.

Number awarded Varies each year.

Deadline April of each year.

[711]
DEPARTMENT OF HOMELAND SECURITY SUMMER FACULTY AND STUDENT RESEARCH TEAM PROGRAM

Oak Ridge Institute for Science and Education
Attn: Science and Engineering Education
P.O. Box 117
Oak Ridge, TN 37831-0117
(865) 574-1447 Fax: (865) 241-5219
E-mail: Patti.Obenour@orau.gov
Web: see.orau.org

Summary To provide an opportunity for teams of students and faculty from minority-serving educational institutions to conduct research during the summer in areas of interest to the Department of Homeland Security (DHS).

Eligibility This program is open to teams of up to 2 students (undergraduate and/or graduate) and 1 faculty from Historically Black Colleges and Universities (HBCUs), Hispanic Serving Institutions (HSIs), Tribal Colleges and Universities (TCUs), Alaska Native Serving Institutions (ANSIs), and Native Hawaiian Serving Institutions (NHSIs). Applicants must be interested in conducting research at designated DHS Centers of Excellence in science, technology, engineering, or mathematics related to homeland security (HS-STEM), including explosives detection, mitigation, and response; social and behavioral sciences; risk, economics, and decision sciences; human factors; chemical threats and countermeasures; biological threats and countermeasures; community, commerce, and infrastructure resilience; food and agricultural security; transportation security; border security; immigration studies; maritime and port security; infrastructure protection; natural disasters and related geophysical studies; emergency preparedness and response; communications and interoperability; or advanced data analysis and visualization. Faculty must have a full-time appointment at an eligible institution and have received a Ph.D. in an HS-STEM discipline no more than 7 years previously; at least 2 years of full-time research and/or teaching experience is preferred. Students must have a GPA of 3.0 or higher and be enrolled full time. Undergraduates must be entering their junior or senior year. U.S. citizenship is required. Selection is based on relevance and intrinsic merit of the research (40%), faculty applicant qualifications (30%), academic benefit to the faculty applicant and his/her institution (10%), and student applicant qualifications (20%).

Financial data Stipends are $1,200 per week for faculty, $600 per week for graduate students, and $500 per week for undergraduates. Faculty members who live more than 50 miles from their assigned site may receive a housing allowance of $1,500 and travel expenses up to an additional $500. Limited travel expenses for 1 round trip are reimbursed for undergraduate and graduate students living more than 50 miles from their assigned site.

Duration 12 weeks during the summer.

Additional information This program is funded by DHS and administered by Oak Ridge Institute for Science and Education (ORISE). Recently, the available DHS Centers of Excellence were the Center for Advancing Microbial Risk Assessment (led by Michigan State University and Drexel University); the National Center for Risk and Economic Analysis of Terrorism Events (led by University of Southern California); the National Center for Food Protection and Defense (led by University of Minnesota); the Center of Excellence for

Zoonotic and Animal Disease Defense (led by Texas A&M University and Kansas State University); the National Consortium for the Study of Terrorism and Responses to Terrorism (led by University of Maryland); the Center of Excellence for Awareness and Localization of Explosives-Related Threats (led by Northeastern University and University of Rhode Island); the National Center for Border Security and Immigration (led by the University of Arizona and the University of Texas at El Paso); the Center for Maritime, Island and Remote and Extreme Environment Security (led by the University of Hawaii and Stevens Institute of Technology); the Coastal Hazards Center of Excellence (led by the University of North Carolina at Chapel Hill and Jackson State University); the National Transportation Security Center of Excellence (consisting of 7 institutions); and the Center of Excellence in Command, Control, and Interoperability (led by Purdue University and Rutgers University).

Number awarded Approximately 12 teams are selected each year.

Deadline January of each year.

[712]
DEPARTMENT OF TRANSPORTATION/ EISENHOWER GRADUATE TRANSPORTATION FELLOWSHIPS

Department of Transportation
Federal Highway Administration
Attn: Universities and Grants Programs
4600 North Fairfax Drive, Suite 800
Arlington, VA 22203-1553
(703) 235-0538 Toll Free: (877) 558-6873
Fax: (703) 235-0593 E-mail: transportationedu@dot.gov
Web: www.fhwa.dot.gov/tpp/ddetfp.htm

Summary To provide financial assistance to graduate students (particularly at Minority Serving Institutions) who are working on a master's or doctoral degree in transportation-related fields.

Eligibility This program is open to students enrolled or planning to enroll full time to work on a master's or doctoral degree in a field of study directly related to transportation. Applicants must be planning to enter the transportation profession after completing their higher level education. They must be U.S. citizens or have an I-20 (foreign student) or I-551 (permanent resident) identification card. Selection is based on the proposed plan of study, academic records (class standing, GPA, and official transcripts), transportation work experience (including employer's endorsement), and recommendations. Students at Historically Black Colleges and Universities (HBCUs), Hispanic Serving Institutions (HSIs), and Tribal Colleges and Universities (TCUs) are especially encouraged to apply.

Financial data Fellows receive tuition and fees (to a maximum of $10,000 per year), monthly stipends of $1,700 for master's degree students or $2,000 for doctoral students, and a 1-time allowance of up to $1,500 for travel to an annual meeting of the Transportation Research Board.

Duration For master's degree students, 24 months, and the degree must be completed within 3 years; for doctoral students, 36 months, and the degree must be completed within 5 years.

Number awarded Approximately 100 to 150 each year.

Deadline March of each year.

[713]
DEPARTMENT OF TRANSPORTATION/ EISENHOWER GRANTS FOR RESEARCH AND INTERN FELLOWSHIPS

Department of Transportation
Federal Highway Administration
Attn: Universities and Grants Programs
4600 North Fairfax Drive, Suite 800
Arlington, VA 22203-1553
(703) 235-0538 Toll Free: (877) 558-6873
Fax: (703) 235-0593 E-mail: transportationedu@dot.gov
Web: www.fhwa.dot.gov/tpp/ddetfp.htm

Summary To enable students (particularly those at Minority Serving Institutions) to participate in transportation-related research activities either at facilities of the U.S. Department of Transportation (DOT) Federal Highway Administration in the Washington, D.C. area or as interns for private or public organizations.

Eligibility This program is open to 1) students in their junior year of a baccalaureate program who will complete their junior year before being awarded a fellowship; 2) students in their senior year of a baccalaureate program; and 3) students who have completed their baccalaureate degree and are enrolled in a program leading to a master's, Ph.D., or equivalent degree. Applicants must be enrolled full time at an accredited U.S institution of higher education and planning to enter the transportation profession after completing their higher education. They must be U.S. citizens or have an I-20 (foreign student) or I-551 (permanent resident) identification card. For research fellowships, they select 1 or more projects from a current list of research activities underway at various DOT facilities; the research is conducted with academic supervision provided by a faculty adviser from their home university (which grants academic credit for the research project) and with technical direction provided by the DOT staff. Intern fellowships provide students with opportunities to perform transportation-related research, development, technology transfer, and other activities at public and private sector organizations. Specific requirements for the target projects vary; most require engineering backgrounds, but others involve transportation planning, information management, public administration, physics, materials science, statistical analysis, operations research, chemistry, economics, technology transfer, urban studies, geography, and urban and regional planning. The DOT encourages students at Historically Black Colleges and Universities (HBCUs), Hispanic Serving Institutions (HSIs), and Tribal Colleges and Universities (TCUs) to apply for these grants. Selection is based on match of the student's qualifications with the proposed research project (including the student's ability to accomplish the project in the available time), recommendation letters regarding the nominee's qualifications to conduct the research, academic records (including class standing, GPA, and transcripts), and transportation work experience (if any), including the employer's endorsement.

Financial data Fellows receive full tuition and fees that relate to the academic credits for the approved research project (to a maximum of $10,000) and a monthly stipend of $1,450 for undergraduates, $1,700 for master's students, or $2,000 for doctoral students. An allowance for travel to and from the DOT facility where the research is conducted is also provided, but selectees are responsible for their own housing accommodations. Recipients are also provided with a 1-time allowance of up to $1,500 to attend the annual Transportation Research Board (TRB) meeting.

Duration Projects normally range from 3 to 12 months.

Number awarded Varies each year; recently, 9 students participated in this program.

Deadline Applications remain open until each project is filled.

[714]
DICKSTEIN SHAPIRO DIVERSITY SCHOLARSHIP

Dickstein Shapiro LLP
Attn: Director of Professional Development and Attorney Recruiting
1825 Eye Street, N.W.
Washington, DC 20006-5403
(202) 420-4880 Fax: (202) 420-2201
E-mail: careers@dicksteinshapiro.com
Web: www.dicksteinshapiro.com/careers/diversity

Summary To provide financial aid and summer work experience at Dickstein Shapiro in Washington, D.C. or New York City to African American and other diverse law students from any state.

Eligibility This program is open to second-year diverse law students, including 1) members of the lesbian, gay, bisexual, and transgender (LGBT) community; 2) members of minority ethnic and racial groups (Blacks, Hispanics and Latinos, Asians, American Indians and Native Alaskans, and Native Hawaiians and Pacific Islanders); and 3) students with disabilities. Applicants must be interested in a summer associateship with Dickstein Shapiro in Washington, D.C. or New York City. Selection is based on academic and professional experience as well as the extent to which they reflect the core values of the firm: excellence, loyalty, respect, initiative, and integrity.

Financial data The stipend is $25,000, including $15,000 upon completion of the summer associate program and $10,000 upon acceptance of a full-time offer of employment following graduation.

Duration The associateship takes place during the summer following the second year of law school and the stipend covers the third year of law school.

Additional information This program began in 2006.

Number awarded 1 or more each year.

Deadline September of each year.

[715]
DINSMORE & SHOHL LLP DIVERSITY SCHOLARSHIP PROGRAM

Dinsmore & Shohl LLP
Attn: Manager of Legal Recruiting
255 East Fifth Street, Suite 1900
Cincinnati, OH 45202
(513) 977-8488 Fax: (513) 977-8141
E-mail: dinsmore.legalrecuiting@dinsmore.com
Web: www.dinsmorecareers.com

Summary To provide financial aid and summer work experience to African American and other law students from groups traditionally underrepresented in the legal profession.

Eligibility This program is open to first- and second-year law students who are members of groups traditionally underrepresented in the legal profession. Applicants must have a demonstrated record of academic or professional achievement and leadership qualities. They must also be interested in a summer associateship with Dinsmore & Shohl LLP. Along with their application, they must submit a 500-word personal statement explaining their interest in the scholarship program and how diversity has impacted their life.

Financial data The program provides an academic scholarship of $5,000 to $10,000 and a paid associateship at the firm.

Duration The academic scholarship is for 1 year. The summer associateship is for 12 weeks.

Additional information Associateships are available at firm offices in Charleston (West Virginia), Cincinnati (Ohio), or Morgantown (West Virginia). The program includes 1 associateship in which the student spends 6 weeks as a clerk in the legal department of the Procter & Gamble Company's worldwide headquarters in Cincinnati and 6 weeks at Dinsmore & Shohl's Cincinnati office. All associates are assigned to an attorney with the firm who serves as a mentor.

Number awarded Varies each year.

Deadline September of each year for second-year students; December of each year for first-year students.

[716]
DISSERTATION FELLOWSHIPS OF THE CONSORTIUM FOR FACULTY DIVERSITY

Consortium for Faculty Diversity at Liberal Arts Colleges
c/o Gettysburg College
Provost's Office
300 North Washington Street
Campus Box 410
Gettysburg, PA 17325
(717) 337-6796 E-mail: sgockows@gettysburg.edu
Web: www.gettysburg.edu/about/offices/provost/cfd

Summary To provide an opportunity for African Americans and other doctoral candidates who will promote diversity to work on their dissertation while in residence at selected liberal arts colleges.

Eligibility This program is open to U.S. citizens and permanent residents who have completed all the requirements for the Ph.D. or M.F.A. except the dissertation. Applicants must be interested in a residency at a member institution of the Consortium for Faculty Diversity at Liberal Arts Colleges during which they will complete their dissertation. They must be able to contribute to diversity at the institution.

Financial data Dissertation fellows receive a stipend based on the average salary paid to instructors at the participating college. Modest funds are made available to finance the fellow's proposed research, subject to the usual institutional procedures.

Duration 1 year.

Additional information The following schools are participating in the program: Allegheny College, Bard College, Bowdoin College, Bryn Mawr College, Carleton College, Centenary College of Louisiana, Centre College, College of Wooster, Colorado College, Denison University, DePauw University, Dickinson College, Gettysburg College, Goucher College, Grinnell College, Gustavus Adolphus College, Hamilton College, Haverford College, Hobart and William Smith Colleges, Lafayette College, Lawrence University, Luther College, Macalester College, Mount Holyoke College, Muhlenberg College, New College of Florida, Oberlin College, Pitzer College, Pomona College, Reed College, Rhodes College, University of Richmond, Ripon College, Scripps College, St. Olaf College, Skidmore College, Smith College, Southwestern University, Swarthmore College, Transylvania University, Trinity College, Vassar College, and Wellesley College. Fellows are expected to teach at least 1 course, participate in departmental seminars, and interact with students.

Number awarded Varies each year.

Deadline October of each year.

[717]
DISSERTATION FELLOWSHIPS OF THE FORD FOUNDATION DIVERSITY FELLOWSHIP PROGRAM

National Research Council
Attn: Fellowships Office, Keck 576
500 Fifth Street, N.W.
Washington, DC 20001
(202) 334-2872 Fax: (202) 334-3419
E-mail: infofell@nas.edu
Web: sites.nationalacademies.org

Summary To provide funding for dissertation research to African Americans and other graduate students whose success will increase the racial and ethnic diversity of U.S. colleges and universities.

Eligibility This program is open to citizens, permanent residents, and nationals of the United States who are Ph.D. or Sc.D. degree candidates committed to a career in teaching and research at the college or university level. Applicants must be completing a degree in fields of the arts, sciences, humanities, and social sciences, but not for most practice-oriented areas, terminal master's degrees, other doctoral degrees (e.g., Ed.D., D.F.A., Psy.D.), professional degrees (e.g., medicine, law, public health), or joint degrees (e.g., M.D./Ph.D., J.D./Ph.D., M.F.A./Ph.D.). The following are considered as positive factors in the selection process: evidence of superior academic achievement; promise of continuing achievement as scholars and teachers; membership in a group whose underrepresentation in the American professoriate has been severe and longstanding, including Black/African Americans, Puerto Ricans, Mexican Americans/Chicanos/Chicanas, Native American Indians, Alaska Natives (Eskimos, Aleuts, and other indigenous people of Alaska), and Native Pacific Islanders (Hawaiians, Micronesians, or Polynesians); capacity to respond in pedagogically productive ways to the learning needs of students from diverse backgrounds; sustained personal engagement with communities that are underrepresented in the academy and an ability to bring this asset to learning, teaching, and scholarship at the college and university level; and likelihood of using the diversity of human experience as an educational resource in teaching and scholarship.

Financial data The stipend is $21,000; stipend payments are made through fellowship institutions.

Duration 9 to 12 months.

Additional information The competition for this program is conducted by the National Research Council on behalf of the Ford Foundation. Fellows may not accept remuneration from another fellowship or similar external award while supported by this program; however, supplementation from institutional funds, educational benefits from the Department of Veterans Affairs, or educational incentive funds may be received concurrently with Ford Foundation support. Dissertation fellows are required to submit an interim progress report 6 months after the start of the fellowship and a final report at the end of the 12 month tenure.

Number awarded Approximately 35 each year.

Deadline November of each year.

[718]
DIVERSITY COMMITTEE SCHOLARSHIP

American Society of Safety Engineers
Attn: ASSE Foundation
Scholarship Award Program
1800 East Oakton Street
Des Plaines, IL 60018
(847) 699-2929 Fax: (847) 768-3434
E-mail: bzylstra@asse.org
Web: www.asse.org

Summary To provide financial assistance to African American and other diverse upper-division or graduate students who are working on a degree related to occupational safety.

Eligibility This program is open to students who are working on an undergraduate or graduate degree in occupational safety, health, environment, industrial hygiene, occupational health nursing, or a closely-related field (e.g., industrial or environmental engineering). Applicants must be full-time students who have completed at least 60 semester hours with a GPA of 3.0 or higher as undergraduates or at least 9 semester hours as graduate students. A goal of this program is to support individuals regardless of race, ethnicity, gender, religion, personal beliefs, age, sexual orientation, physical challenges, geographic location, university, or specific area of study. U.S. citizenship is not required. Membership in the American Society of Safety Engineers (ASSE) is not required, but preference is given to members.

Financial data The stipend is $1,000 per year.

Duration 1 year; recipients may reapply.

Number awarded 1 each year.

Deadline November of each year.

[719]
DIVERSITY IN PLANNING AWARD

American Planning Association-California Chapter
Attn: California Planning Foundation
c/o Paul Wack
California Polytechnic State University at San Luis Obispo
City and Regional Planning Department
San Luis Obispo, CA 93407-0283
(805) 756-6331 Fax: (805) 756-1340
E-mail: pwack@calpoly.edu
Web: www.californiaplanningfoundation.org

Summary To provide financial assistance to African American and other undergraduate and graduate students in accredited planning programs at California universities who will increase diversity in the profession.

Eligibility This program is open to students entering their final year for an undergraduate or master's degree in an accredited planning program at a university in California. Applicants must be students who will increase diversity in the planning profession. Selection is based on academic performance, professional promise, and financial need.

Financial data The stipend is $3,000. The award includes a 1-year student membership in the American Planning Association (APA) and payment of registration for the APA California Conference.

Duration 1 year.

Additional information The accredited planning programs are at 3 campuses of the California State University system (California State Polytechnic University at Pomona, California Polytechnic State University at San Luis Obispo, and San Jose State University), 3 campuses of the University of California (Berkeley, Irvine, and Los Angeles), and the University of Southern California.

Number awarded 1 each year.

Deadline March of each year.

[720]
DIVERSITY IN PSYCHOLOGY AND LAW RESEARCH AWARD

American Psychological Association
Attn: Division 41 (American Psychology-Law Society)
c/o Diane Sivasubramaniam, Minority Affairs Committee Chair
Swinburne University of Technology
Faculty of Life and Social Sciences
Mail H31
P.O. Box 218
Hawthorn, VIC 3122
Australia
61 3 9214 5858 E-mail: dsivasubramaniam@swin.edu.au
Web: www.ap-ls.org

Summary To provide funding to African American and other student members of the American Psychology-Law Society (AP-LS) who are interested in conducting a research project related to diversity.

Eligibility This program is open to undergraduate and graduate student members of AP-LS who are interested in conducting research on issues related to psychology, law, multiculturalism, and/or diversity (e.g., research pertaining to psycholegal issues on race, gender, culture, sexual orientation). Students from underrepresented groups are strongly encouraged to apply; underrepresented groups include, but are not limited to: racial and ethnic minorities; first-generation college students; lesbian, gay, bisexual, and transgender students; and physically disabled students. Applicants must submit a project description that includes a statement of the research problem, the project's likely impact on the field of psychology and law broadly, methodology, budget, and an overview of relevant literature. Selection is based on the impact of the project on diversity and multiculturalism and the expected completion within the allocated time.

Financial data The grant is $1,000.

Duration The project must be completed within 1 year.

Number awarded Up to 4 each year.

Deadline November of each year.

[721]
DOCTORAL DISSERTATION IMPROVEMENT GRANTS IN THE DIRECTORATE FOR BIOLOGICAL SCIENCES

National Science Foundation
Directorate for Biological Sciences
Attn: Division of Environmental Biology
4201 Wilson Boulevard
Arlington, VA 22230
(703) 292-8480 TDD: (800) 281-8749
E-mail: ddig-deb@nsf.gov
Web: www.nsf.gov/funding/pgm_summ.jsp?pims_id=5234

Summary To provide partial support to students (especially African Americans, other underrepresented minorities, women, and students with disabilities) for dissertation research in selected areas supported by the National Science Foundation (NSF) Directorate for Biological Sciences (DBS).

Eligibility Applications may be submitted through regular university channels by dissertation advisers on behalf of graduate students who have advanced to candidacy and have begun or are about to begin dissertation research. Students must be enrolled at U.S. institutions but need not be U.S. citizens. Proposals should focus on the ecology, ecosystems, systematics, or population biology programs in the DBS Division of Environmental Biology, or the animal behavior programs in the DBS Division of Integrative Organismal Systems. In the selection process, consideration is given to the achievement of societally relevant outcomes, including full participation of women, persons with disabilities, and underrepresented minorities.

Financial data Grants range up to $13,000; funds may be used for travel to specialized facilities or field research locations, specialized research equipment, purchase of supplies and services not otherwise available, fees for computerized or other forms of data, and rental of environmental chambers or other research facilities. Funding is not provided for stipends, tuition, textbooks, journals, allowances for dependents, travel to scientific meetings, publication costs, dissertation preparation or reproduction, or indirect costs.

Duration Normally 2 years.

Number awarded 100 to 120 each year; approximately $1,600,000 is available for this program each year.

Deadline October of each year.

[722]
DOCTORAL DIVERSITY FELLOWSHIPS IN SCIENCE, TECHNOLOGY, ENGINEERING, AND MATHEMATICS

State University of New York
Attn: Office of Diversity, Equity and Inclusion
State University Plaza
353 Broadway
Albany, NY 12246
(518) 320-1189
Web: www.suny.edu/provost/odee/programs.cfm

Summary To provide financial assistance to residents of any state (particularly African Americans and other underrepresented minorities) who are working on a doctoral degree in a field of science, technology, engineering, and mathematics (STEM) at campuses of the State University of New York (SUNY) and will contribute to the diversity of the student body.

Eligibility This program is open to U.S. citizens who are residents of any state and enrolled as doctoral students at any of the participating SUNY institutions. Applicants must be working on a degree in a field of STEM. They must be able to demonstrate how they will contribute to the diversity of the student body, primarily by having overcome a disadvantage or other impediment to success in higher education. Economic disadvantage, although not a requirement, may be the basis for eligibility. Membership in a racial or ethnic group that is underrepresented at the applicant's school or program may serve as a plus factor in making awards, but may not form the sole basis of selection.

Financial data The stipend is $20,000 per year.

Duration 3 years; may be renewed for up to 2 additional years.

Number awarded Up to 3 each year.

Deadline January of each year.

[723]
DOCTORAL/POST-DOCTORAL FELLOWSHIP PROGRAM IN LAW AND SOCIAL SCIENCE

American Bar Foundation
Attn: Administrative Assistant for Academic Affairs and Research Administration
750 North Lake Shore Drive
Chicago, IL 60611-4403
(312) 988-6517 Fax: (312) 988-6579
E-mail: aehrhardt@abfn.org
Web: www.americanbarfoundation.org

Summary To provide research funding to scholars (particularly African Americans and other minorities) who are completing or have completed doctoral degrees in fields related to law, the legal profession, and legal institutions.

Eligibility This program is open to Ph.D. candidates in the social sciences who have completed all doctoral requirements except the dissertation. Applicants who have completed the dissertation are also eligible. Doctoral and proposed research must be in the general area of sociolegal studies or in social scientific approaches to law, the legal profession, or legal institutions and legal processes. Applications must include 1) a dissertation abstract or proposal with an outline of the substance and methods of the research; 2) 2 letters of recommendation; and 3) a curriculum vitae. Minority candidates are especially encouraged to apply.

Financial data The stipend is $30,000. Fellows may request up to $1,500 to reimburse expenses associated with research, travel to meet with advisers, or travel to conferences at which papers are presented. Relocation expenses of up to $2,500 may be reimbursed on application.

Duration 12 months, beginning in September.

Additional information Fellows are offered access to the computing and word processing facilities of the American Bar Foundation and the libraries of Northwestern University and the University of Chicago. This program was established in 1996. Fellowships must be held in residence at the American Bar Foundation. Appointments to the fellowship are full time; fellows are not permitted to undertake other work.

Number awarded 1 or more each year.

Deadline December of each year.

[724]
DOLORES NYHUS GRADUATE FELLOWSHIP

California Dietetic Association
Attn: CDA Foundation
7740 Manchester Avenue, Suite 102
Playa del Rey, CA 90293-8499
(310) 822-0177 Fax: (310) 823-0264
E-mail: patsmith@dietitian.org
Web: www.dietitian.org/d_cdaf/cdaf_outreach.html

Summary To provide financial assistance to members (particularly African Americans or other minorities, men, and members with disabilities) of the Academy of Nutrition and Dietetics (AND) who live in California and are interested in working on a graduate degree in dietetics or a related field at a school in any state.

Eligibility This program is open to California residents who are AND members and have a bachelor's degree and 3 to 5 years of professional experience. Applicants must be a registered dietitian (R.D.), be a registered dietetic technician (D.T.R.), or have a credential earned at least 6 months previously. They must be enrolled in or admitted to a graduate school in any state in the areas of public health, gerontology, or a community-related program with the intention of practicing in the field of dietetics. Along with their application, they must submit a letter of application that includes a discussion of their career goals. Selection is based on that letter (15%), academic ability (25%), work or volunteer experience (15%), letters of recommendation (15%), extracurricular activities (5%), and financial need (25%). Applications are especially encouraged from ethnic minorities, men, and people with physical disabilities.

Financial data The stipend is normally $1,000.

Duration 1 year.

Additional information The California Dietetic Association is the California affiliate of the AND.

Number awarded 1 each year.

Deadline April of each year.

[725]
DONALD W. BANNER DIVERSITY SCHOLARSHIP

Banner & Witcoff, Ltd.
Attn: Christopher Hummel
1100 13th Street, N.W., Suite 1200
Washington, DC 20005-4051
(202) 824-3000 Fax: (202) 824-3001
E-mail: chummel@bannerwitcoff.com
Web: www.bannerwitcoff.com/about/diversity

Summary To provide financial assistance to African Americans and other law students who come from groups historically underrepresented in intellectual property law.

Eligibility This program is open to students enrolled in the first or second year of a J.D. program at an ABA-accredited law school in the United States. Applicants must come from a group historically underrepresented in intellectual property law; that underrepresentation may be the result of race, sex, ethnicity, sexual orientation, disability, education, culture, religion, age, or socioeconomic background. Selection is based on academic merit, commitment to the pursuit of a career in intellectual property law, written communication skills, oral communication skills (determined through an interview), leadership qualities, and community involvement.

Financial data The stipend is $5,000 per year.

Duration 1 year (the second or third year of law school); students who accept and successfully complete the firm's summer associate program may receive an additional $5,000 for a subsequent semester of law school.

Number awarded 2 each year.

Deadline October of each year.

[726]
DONNA HOKE SCHOLARSHIPS

New York Black Librarians Caucus, Inc.
Attn: Scholarships
Flatbush Station
P.O. Box 260605
Brooklyn, NY 11226
(718) 651-7116 E-mail: scholarship@nyblc.org
Web: www.nyblc.org/scholarship

Summary To provide financial assistance to African Americans in New York who wish to pursue a degree in librarianship.

Eligibility This program is open to residents of New York who are of African or African American descent. Applicants must be enrolled in or accepted to an accredited master's degree program in library science. Along with their application, they must submit an essay of 500 to 750 words on their personal philosophy in the field of librarianship, knowledge of the field, future goals in the field, and involvement in library-related organizations, conferences, and/or publications. Selection is based on that essay, transcripts, 2 letters of recommendation, and an interview.

Financial data The stipend is $1,000.

Duration 1 year.

Number awarded 2 each year.

Deadline August of each year.

[727]
DOROTHY ATKINSON LEGAL EDUCATION SCHOLARSHIP

National Association of Bench and Bar Spouses, Inc.
Attn: NABBS, Inc. Foundation
7422 Lonewolf Court
Fairview Heights, IL 62208
(618) 741-3589 E-mail: drwillmeanes@yahoo.com
Web: www.nabbsinc.org/Services.html

Summary To provide financial assistance to African American and other law students.

Eligibility This program is open to students enrolled full time in a legal education program at an ABA-accredited law school. Applicants must have a GPA of 2.0 or higher and be able to demonstrate financial need. They must be sponsored by a local chapter of the National Association of Bench and Bar Spouses (NABBS), an organization with historic roots in the African American legal community.

Financial data A stipend is awarded (amount not specified).

Duration 1 year; may be renewed if the recipient maintains a GPA of 2.0 or higher and continues to demonstrate financial need.

Additional information NABBS was founded in 1951 as the National Barristers' Wives, affiliated with the National Bar Association for African American attorneys. In 1987, it adopted its current name and in 1994 it organized the NABBS, Inc. Foundation.

Number awarded 1 or more each year.

Deadline July of each year.

[728]
DORSEY & WHITNEY DIVERSITY FELLOWSHIPS

Dorsey & Whitney LLP
Attn: Recruiting Manager
50 South Sixth Street, Suite 1500
Minneapolis, MN 55402-1498
(612) 340-2600 Toll Free: (800) 759-4929
Fax: (612) 340-2868 E-mail: forsmark.claire@dorsey.com
Web: www.dorsey.com/diversity_fellowship_12111

Summary To provide financial assistance for law school to African Americans and other students from diverse backgrounds who are interested in working during the summer at offices of the sponsoring law firm.

Eligibility This program is open to first-year students at ABA-accredited law schools who have accepted a summer associate position at an office of the sponsor in Denver, Minneapolis, or Seattle. Applicants must be able to demonstrate academic achievement and a commitment to promoting diversity in the legal community. Along with their application, they must submit a personal statement on the ways in which they have promoted and will continue to promote diversity in the legal community, what diversity means to them, and why they are interested in the sponsoring law firm.

Financial data Fellows receive a stipend of $7,500 for the second year of law school and, if they complete a summer associate position in the following summer, another stipend of $7,500 for the third year of law school. If they join the firm following graduation, they receive an additional $5,000.

Duration 1 year; may be renewed for 1 additional year.

Additional information This program began in 2006.

Number awarded 1 or more each year.

Deadline January of each year.

[729]
DR. BESSIE ELIZABETH DELANEY FELLOWSHIP

National Dental Association
Attn: National Dental Association Foundation, Inc.
3517 16th Street, N.W.
Washington, DC 20010
(202) 588-1697 Fax: (202) 588-1244
E-mail: admin@ndaonline.org
Web: www.ndafoundation.org/NDAF/Scholarships.html

Summary To provide financial assistance to dental master's and postdoctoral students who are female and either African American or a member of another minority group.

Eligibility This program is open to female members of minority groups who are working on a postdoctoral degree in subspecialty areas of dentistry, public health, administration, pediatrics, research, or law. Students working on a master's degree beyond their residency also may be considered. Applicants must be members of the National Dental Association (NDA) and U.S. citizens or permanent residents. Along with their application, they must submit a letter explaining why they should be considered for this scholarship, 2 letters of recommendation, a curriculum vitae, a description of the program, nomination by their program director, and documentation of financial need.

Financial data The stipend is $10,000.

Duration 1 year.

Additional information This program, established in 1990, is supported by the Colgate-Palmolive Company.

Number awarded 1 each year.

Deadline May of each year.

[730]
DR. CLIFTON O. DUMMETT AND LOIS DOYLE DUMMETT FELLOWSHIP

National Dental Association
Attn: National Dental Association Foundation, Inc.
3517 16th Street, N.W.
Washington, DC 20010
(202) 588-1697 Fax: (202) 588-1244
E-mail: admin@ndaonline.org
Web: www.ndafoundation.org/NDAF/Scholarships.html

Summary To provide financial assistance to African American and other minority dental master's and postdoctoral students.

Eligibility This program is open to members of minority groups who are working on a postdoctoral degree in subspecialty areas of dentistry, public health, administration, pediatrics, research, or law. Students working on a master's degree beyond their residency also may be considered. Applicants must be members of the National Dental Association (NDA) and U.S. citizens or permanent residents. Along with their application, they must submit a letter explaining why they should be considered for this scholarship, 2 letters of recommendation, a curriculum vitae, a description of the program, nomination by their program director, and documentation of financial need.

Financial data The stipend is $10,000.

Duration 1 year.

Additional information This program, established in 1990, is supported by the Colgate-Palmolive Company.

Number awarded 1 each year.

Deadline May of each year.

[731]
DR. DORRI PHIPPS FELLOWSHIPS

Alpha Kappa Alpha Sorority, Inc.
Attn: Educational Advancement Foundation
5656 South Stony Island Avenue
Chicago, IL 60637
(773) 947-0026 Toll Free: (800) 653-6528
Fax: (773) 947-0277 E-mail: akaeaf@akaeaf.net
Web: www.akaeaf.org/fellowships_endowments.htm

Summary To provide financial assistance to students (especially African American women) working on a degree in medicine or conducting research related to lupus.

Eligibility This program is open to students currently enrolled in a medical or related program in any state. Applicants must be working on a degree in medicine or conducting research related to lupus. Along with their application, they must submit 1) a list of honors, awards, and scholarships received; 2) a list of organizations in which they have memberships, especially minority organizations; 3) a description of the project or research on which they are currently working, or (if they are not involved in a project or research) the aspects of their field that interest them; and 4) a statement of their personal and career goals, including how this scholarship will enhance their ability to attain those goals. The sponsor is a traditionally African American women's sorority.

Financial data A stipend is awarded (amount not specified).

Duration 1 year.

Number awarded Varies each even-numbered year; recently, 5 of these fellowships were awarded.

Deadline April of each even-numbered year.

[732]
DR. JOSEPH L. HENRY SCHOLARSHIPS

National Dental Association
Attn: National Dental Association Foundation, Inc.
3517 16th Street, N.W.
Washington, DC 20010
(202) 588-1697 Fax: (202) 588-1244
E-mail: admin@ndaonline.org
Web: www.ndafoundation.org/NDAF/Scholarships.html

Summary To provide financial assistance to African Americans and other minorities entering their first year of dental school.

Eligibility This program is open to members of minority groups who are entering their first year of dental school as full-time students. Applicants must have an undergraduate GPA of 3.5 or higher. Along with their application, they must submit information on their community service, a letter from their school verifying that they are attending, a letter of recommendation from an undergraduate professor, college transcripts, and documentation of financial need. They must be U.S. citizens or permanent residents. Selection is based on academic performance in undergraduate school and service to community and/or country.

Financial data The stipend is $2,000 per year.

Duration 1 year; may be renewed up to 3 additional years.

Additional information This program, established in 1990, is supported by the Colgate-Palmolive Company.

Number awarded At least 5 each year.

Deadline May of each year.

[733]
DR. JOYCE BECKETT SCHOLARSHIP

National Association of Black Social Workers
Attn: NABSW Scholarships
2305 Martin Luther King Avenue, S.E.
Washington, DC 20020
(202) 678-4570 Fax: (202) 678-4572
E-mail: office-manager@nabsw.org
Web: www.nabsw.org/mserver/Forms.aspx

Summary To provide financial assistance to members of the National Association of Black Social Workers (NABSW) who are working on a master's degree.

Eligibility This program is open to African American members of NABSW working full time on a master's degree at an accredited U.S. social work or social welfare program with a GPA of 2.5 or higher. Applicants must be able to demonstrate community service and a research interest in the Black community. Along with their application, they must submit an essay of 2 to 3 pages on their professional interests, future social work aspirations, previous social work experiences (volunteer and professional), honors and achievements (academic and community service), and research interests within the Black community. Financial need is considered in the selection process.

Financial data The stipend is $1,000. Funds are sent directly to the recipient's school.

Duration 1 year.

Number awarded 1 each year.

Deadline January of each year.

[734]
DR. LENDON N. PRIDGEN GRADUATE FELLOWSHIP AWARD

National Organization for the Professional Advancement of Black Chemists and Chemical Engineers
Attn: Awards Committee Chair
P.O. Box 77040
Washington, DC 20013
Toll Free: (800) 776-1419 Fax: (202) 667-1705
E-mail: awards@nobcche.org
Web: www.nobcche.org

Summary To provide funding to African American doctoral students interested in conducting research in synthetic organic chemistry.

Eligibility This program is open to African American candidates in the third or fourth year of a Ph.D. program for synthetic organic chemistry. Applicants must submit 3 letters of recommendation, a resume, official transcripts for undergraduate and graduate study, a description of their proposed research, and a statement of their career objective. U.S. citizenship is required.

Financial data The grant is $25,000.

Duration 1 year.

Additional information This program is sponsored by GlaxoSmithKline.

Number awarded 1 each year.

Deadline June of each year.

[735]
DR. NANCY FOSTER SCHOLARSHIP PROGRAM

National Oceanic and Atmospheric Administration
Attn: Office of Education
1315 East-West Highway
SSMC3, Room 11146
Silver Spring, MD 20910
(301) 713-9437, ext. 150 Fax: (301) 713-9465
E-mail: fosterscholars@noaa.gov
Web: fosterscholars.noaa.gov

Summary To provide financial assistance to graduate students (especially African Americans, other minorities, and women) who are interested in working on a degree in fields related to marine sciences.

Eligibility This program is open to U.S. citizens, particularly women and members of minority groups, currently working on or intending to work on a master's or doctoral degree in oceanography, marine biology, or maritime archaeology, including all science, engineering, and resource management of ocean and coastal areas. Applicants must submit a description of their academic, research, and career goals, and how their proposed course of study or research will help them to achieve those goals. They must be enrolled full time and have a GPA of 3.0 or higher. As part of their program, they must be interested in participating in a summer research collaboration at a facility of the National Oceanic and Atmospheric Administration (NOAA). Selection is based on academic record and the statement of career goals and objectives (25%); quality of project and applicability to program priorities (35%); recommendations and/or endorsements (15%); additional relevant experience related to diversity of education, extracurricular activities, honors and awards, written and oral communication skills, and interpersonal skills (15%); and financial need (10%).

Financial data The program provides a stipend of $30,000 per academic year, a tuition allowance of up to $12,000 per academic year, and up to $10,000 of support for a 4- to 6-week research collaboration at a NOAA facility is provided.

Duration Master's degree students may receive up to 2 years of stipend and tuition support and 1 research collaboration (for a total of $94,000). Doctoral students may receive up to 4 years of stipend and tuition support and 2 research collaborations (for a total of $188,000).

Additional information This program began in 2001.

Number awarded Varies each year; recently, 3 of these fellowships were awarded.

Deadline February of each year.

[736]
DR. SPENCER G. SHAW SCHOLARSHIP

Black Caucus of the American Library Association-Connecticut Affiliate
Attn: Scholarship Committee
37 Grandview Avenue
Norwalk, CT 06850-3214
Web: www.bcala-ct.org/SCHOLARSHIPS.HTM

Summary To provide financial assistance to African American residents of Connecticut who are interested in working on a master's degree in librarianship at a school in any state.

Eligibility This program is open to residents of Connecticut who are of African American descent. Applicants must be entering, enrolled, or accepted at an ALA-accredited master's degree program in library and information studies. They must be members of the Connecticut Affiliate of the Black Caucus of the American Library Association (BCALA). Along with their application, they must submit a 1,000-word statement about their future goals, career interests, and commitment to library and information service.

Financial data The stipend is $2,000.

Duration 1 year; recipients may reapply.

Additional information This program began in 2009.

Number awarded 1 each year.

Deadline March of each year.

[737]
DRI LAW STUDENT DIVERSITY SCHOLARSHIP

DRI-The Voice of the Defense Bar
Attn: Deputy Executive Director
55 West Monroe Street, Suite 2000
Chicago, IL 60603
(312) 795-1101 Fax: (312) 795-0747
E-mail: dri@dri.org
Web: www.dri.org/About

Summary To provide financial assistance to African American, other minority, and female law students.

Eligibility This program is open to full-time students entering their second or third year of law school who are African American, Hispanic, Asian, Native American, or women. Applicants must submit an essay, up to 1,000 words, on a topic that changes annually but relates to the work of defense attorneys. Selection is based on that essay, demonstrated academic excellence, service to the profession, service to the community, and service to the cause of diversity. Students affiliated with the American Association for Justice as members, student members, or employees are not eligible. Finalists are invited to participate in personal interviews.

Financial data The stipend is $10,000.

Duration 1 year.

Additional information This program began in 2004.

Number awarded 2 each year.

Deadline May of each year.

[738]
DWIGHT DAVID EISENHOWER HISTORICALLY BLACK COLLEGES AND UNIVERSITIES TRANSPORTATION FELLOWSHIP PROGRAM

Department of Transportation
Federal Highway Administration
Attn: Universities and Grants Programs
4600 North Fairfax Drive, Suite 800
Arlington, VA 22203-1553
(703) 235-0538 Toll Free: (877) 558-6873
Fax: (703) 235-0593 E-mail: transportationedu@dot.gov
Web: www.fhwa.dot.gov/tpp/ddetfp.htm

Summary To provide financial assistance to undergraduate and graduate students working on a degree in a transportation-related field at a designated Historically Black College or University (HBCU).

Eligibility This program is open to students working on a bachelor's, master's, or doctoral degree at 1 of 18 federally-designated 4-year HBCUs. Applicants must be working on a degree in a transportation-related field (e.g., engineering, business, aviation, architecture, public policy and analysis, urban and regional planning). They must be U.S. citizens or have an I-20 (foreign student) or I-551 (permanent resident) identification card. Undergraduates must be entering at least their junior year and have a GPA of 3.0 or higher. Graduate students must have a GPA of at least 3.25. Selection is based on their proposed plan of study, academic achievement (based on class standing, GPA, and transcripts), transportation work experience, and letters of recommendation.

Financial data Fellows receive payment of full tuition and fees (to a maximum of $10,000) and a monthly stipend of $1,450 for undergraduates, $1,700 for master's students, or $2,000 for doctoral students. They are also provided with a 1-time allowance of up to $1,500 to attend the annual Transportation Research Board (TRB) meeting.

Duration 1 year.

Additional information This program is administered by the participating HBCUs. For a list, contact the sponsor.

Number awarded Varies each year.

Deadline January of each year.

[739]
EARL WARREN LEGAL TRAINING PROGRAM

NAACP Legal Defense and Educational Fund
Attn: Director of Scholarship Programs
99 Hudson Street, Suite 1600
New York, NY 10013-2897
(212) 965-2265 Fax: (212) 219-1595
E-mail: scholarships@naacpldf.org
Web: www.naacpldf.org/scholarships

Summary To provide financial assistance to African Americans and other students who are planning to enter law school.

Eligibility This program is open to students entering their first year of full-time study at an accredited law school. Applicants must be able to graduate within the normally prescribed time of 3 years. They must be dedicated to earning a law degree so they can protect and defend civil rights and liberties. Selection is based on academic achievement, leadership, commitment to public service (through volunteer or other activities), and financial need.

Financial data Stipends are normally $3,000 per year.

Duration 1 year; may be renewed for up to 2 additional years if satisfactory academic performance is maintained.

Additional information This program began in 1972 to enable African American law students to attend the newly desegregated colleges, public universities, and law schools of the South. It is currently open to all students, regardless of race, color, ethnicity, national origin, religion, creed, sex, age, marital status, parental status, physical disability, learning disability, political affiliation, veteran status, sexual orientation, or gender identity.

Number awarded 15 to 20 each year.

Deadline April of each year.

[740]
EDITH M. ALLEN SCHOLARSHIPS

United Methodist Church
Attn: General Board of Higher Education and Ministry
Office of Loans and Scholarships
1001 19th Avenue South
P.O. Box 340007
Nashville, TN 37203-0007
(615) 340-7344 Fax: (615) 340-7367
E-mail: umscholar@gbhem.org
Web: www.gbhem.org

Summary To provide financial assistance to Methodist students who are African American and working on an undergraduate or graduate degree in specified fields.

Eligibility This program is open to full-time undergraduate and graduate students at Methodist colleges and universities (preferably Historically Black United Methodist colleges) who have been active, full members of a United Methodist Church for at least 3 years prior to applying. Applicants must be African Americans working on a degree in education, social work, medicine, and/or other health professions. They must have at least a "B+" average and be recognized as a person whose academic and vocational contributions will help improve the quality of life for others.

Financial data Stipends average $1,000.

Duration 1 year; recipients may reapply.

Number awarded Varies each year.

Deadline February of each year.

[741]
EDWARD S. ROTH MANUFACTURING ENGINEERING SCHOLARSHIP

Society of Manufacturing Engineers
Attn: SME Education Foundation
One SME Drive
P.O. Box 930
Dearborn, MI 48121-0930
(313) 425-3300 Toll Free: (800) 733-4763, ext. 3300
Fax: (313) 425-3411 E-mail: foundation@sme.org
Web: www.smeef.org/scholarships

Summary To provide financial assistance to African Americans and other students enrolled or planning to work on a bachelor's or master's degree in manufacturing engineering at selected universities.

Eligibility This program is open to U.S. citizens who are graduating high school seniors or currently-enrolled undergraduate or graduate students. Applicants must be enrolled or planning to enroll as a full-time student at 1 of 13 selected 4-year universities to work on a bachelor's or master's degree in manufacturing engineering. They must have a GPA of 3.0 or higher. Preference is given to 1) students demonstrating financial need; 2) minority students; and 3) students participating in a co-op program. Some preference may also be given to graduating high school seniors and graduate students. Along with their application, they must submit a 300-word essay that covers their career and educational objectives, how this scholarship will help them attain those objectives, and why they want to enter this field.

Financial data Stipend amounts vary; recently, the value of all scholarships provided by this foundation averaged approximately $2,330.

Duration 1 year; may be renewed.

Additional information The eligible institutions are California Polytechnic State University at San Luis Obispo, California State Polytechnic State University at Pomona, University of Miami (Florida), Bradley University (Illinois), Central State University (Ohio), Miami University (Ohio), Boston University, Worcester Polytechnic Institute (Massachusetts), University of Massachusetts, St. Cloud State University (Minnesota), University of Texas-Pan American, Brigham Young University (Utah), and Utah State University.

Number awarded 2 each year.

Deadline January of each year.

[742]
E.J. JOSEY SCHOLARSHIP AWARD

Black Caucus of the American Library Association
c/o Sylvia Sprinkle Hamlin, Scholarship Committee Chair
Forsyth County Public Library
660 West Fifth Street
Winston-Salem, NC 27101
(336) 703-3016 Fax: (336) 727-2549
E-mail: hamlinss@forsythlibrary.org
Web: www.bcala.org/awards/joseyapps.htm

Summary To provide financial assistance to African Americans interested in working on a graduate degree in librarianship.

Eligibility This program is open to African American citizens of the United States or Canada who are enrolled as graduate students in an accredited library or information science program. Applicants must submit an essay of 1,000 to 1,200 words on a topic that changes annually; recently, applicants were asked to present their opinions on whether there is still a need for ethnic library associations. Selection is based on the essay's argument development, critical analysis, clear language, conciseness, and creativity.

Financial data The stipend is $2,000.

Duration 1 year.

Number awarded 2 each year.

Deadline December of each year.

[743]
ELIZABETH MUNSTERBERG KOPPITZ CHILD PSYCHOLOGY GRADUATE FELLOWSHIPS

American Psychological Foundation
750 First Street, N.E.
Washington, DC 20002-4242
(202) 336-5843 Fax: (202) 336-5812
E-mail: foundation@apa.org
Web: www.apa.org/apf/funding/koppitz.aspx

Summary To provide funding to doctoral students (particularly African Americans, other minorities, women, and students with disabilities) who are interested in conducting research in child psychology.

Eligibility This program is open to graduate students who have progressed academically through the qualifying examinations, usually after the third or fourth year of doctoral study. Applicants must be interested in conducting psychological research that promotes the advancement of knowledge and learning in the field of child psychology. Selection is based on conformance with stated program goals, magnitude of incremental contribution, quality of proposed work, and applicant's demonstrated scholarship and research competence. The sponsor encourages applications from individuals who represent diversity in race, ethnicity, gender, age, disability, and sexual orientation.

Financial data The grant is $25,000 for fellows or $5,000 for runners-up.

Duration 1 year.

Additional information This fellowship was first awarded in 2003.

Number awarded Varies each year; recently, 6 fellows and 2 runners-up were selected.

Deadline November of each year.

[744]
ELLA TACKWOOD FUND

United Methodist Higher Education Foundation
Attn: Scholarships Administrator
60 Music Square East, Suite 350
P.O. Box 340005
Nashville, TN 37203-0005
(615) 649-3990 Toll Free: (800) 811-8110
Fax: (615) 649-3980
E-mail: umhefscholarships@umhef.org
Web: www.umhef.org/scholarship-info

Summary To provide financial assistance to Methodist undergraduate and graduate students at Historically Black Colleges and Universities of the United Methodist Church.

Eligibility This program is open to students enrolling as full-time undergraduate and graduate students at the Historically Black Colleges and Universities of the United Methodist Church. Applicants must have been active, full members of a United Methodist Church for at least 1 year prior to applying. They must have a GPA of 2.5 or higher and be able to demonstrate financial need. U.S. citizenship or permanent resident status is required.

Financial data The stipend is at least $1,000 per year.

Duration 1 year; nonrenewable.

Additional information This program began in 1985. The qualifying schools are Bennett College for Women, Bethune-Cookman University, Claflin University, Clark Atlanta University, Dillard University, Huston-Tillotson College, Meharry Medical College, Paine College, Philander Smith College, Rust College, and Wiley College.

Number awarded Varies each year; recently, 2 of these scholarships were awarded.

Deadline February of each year.

[745]
ELLIOTT C. ROBERTS, SR. SCHOLARSHIP

Institute for Diversity in Health Management
Attn: Education Specialist
155 North Wacker Avenue, Suite 400
Chicago, IL 60606
(312) 422-2658 Toll Free: (800) 233-0996
Fax: (312) 895-4511 E-mail: cbiddle@aha.org
Web: www.diversityconnection.org

Summary To provide financial assistance to African American and other minority graduate students in health services management who have demonstrated outstanding community service.

Eligibility This program is open to members of ethnically diverse groups who are enrolled in the second year of a graduate program in health care administration. Applicants must have a GPA of 3.0 or higher. They must be able to demonstrate a commitment to community service. Along with their application, they must submit 1) a personal statement of 1 to 2 pages on their interest in health care management and their career goals; 2) an essay on what they see as the most challenging issue facing America's hospitals and health systems; and 3) a 500-word essay on how they currently serve their community beyond their academic career. Selection is based on academic achievement, commitment to community service, and financial need. U.S. citizenship is required.

Financial data The stipend is $1,000.

Duration 1 year.

Number awarded 1 each year.

Deadline January of each year.

[746]
ELLIS J. BONNER AWARD

National Association of Health Services Executives
Attn: Educational Assistance Program
1050 Connecticut Avenue, N.W., Tenth Floor
Washington, DC 20036
(202) 772-1030 Fax: (202) 772-1072
E-mail: nahsehg@nahse.org
Web: netforum.avectra.com

Summary To provide financial assistance to African American nontraditional students who are members of the National Association of Health Services Executives (NAHSE) and interested in preparing for a career in health care administration.

Eligibility This program is open to African Americans who are nontraditional students and either enrolled or accepted at an accredited college or university to work on a master's or doctoral degree in health care administration. Applicants must be members of NAHSE and able to demonstrate financial need. They must have a GPA of 2.5 or higher as undergraduates or 3.0 or higher as graduate students. Along with their application, they must submit a 3-page essay that describes themselves and their career goals, commitment and interest in health care management, and financial need.

Financial data The stipend is $2,500. Funds are sent to the recipient's institution.

Duration 1 year.

Number awarded 1 each year.

Deadline May of each year.

[747]
ELSIE MAE WHITE MEMORIAL SCHOLARSHIP FUND

Columbus Foundation
Attn: Scholarship Manager
1234 East Broad Street
Columbus, OH 43205-1453
(614) 251-4000 Fax: (614) 251-4009
E-mail: dhigginbotham@columbusfoundation.org
Web: tcfapp.org

Summary To provide financial assistance for college or graduate school to African American high school seniors and college students from any state.

Eligibility This program is open to African American high school seniors and college students. High school seniors must rank in the top third of their class; college students must have a GPA of 2.8 or higher. Applicants must be attending or planning to attend an accredited college or university in the United States as a full- or part-time undergraduate or graduate student. Preference is given to students at land grant colleges and universities. Along with their application, they must submit 300-word essays on 1) their educational and career plans and goals, why they have chosen their particular field, and why they think they will be a success; 2) why they feel they need this scholarship, especially as related to financial need; and 3) any other information that will assist the selection committee in making its decision.

Financial data The stipend is $1,000.

Duration 1 year.

Number awarded Varies each year.

Deadline May of each year.

[748]
ENDOCRINE SOCIETY SUMMER RESEARCH FELLOWSHIPS

Endocrine Society
Attn: Summer Research Fellowships
8401 Connecticut Avenue, Suite 900
Chevy Chase, MD 20815
(301) 951-2616 Toll Free: (888) 363-6274
Fax: (301) 576-7787 E-mail: awards@endo-society.org
Web: www.endo-society.org

Summary To provide funding to undergraduate, medical, and graduate students (particularly African Americans and other underrepresented minorities) who are interested in conducting a research project during the summer in endocrinology.

Eligibility This program is open to full-time students who are undergraduates in the third year of study or higher, medical students beyond their first year of study, and first-year graduate students. Applicants must be interested in participating in a research project under the supervision of a mentor. The mentor must be an active member of the Endocrine Society. Each member may sponsor only 1 student. Projects must be relevant to an aspect of endocrinology and are expected to have clearly defined research goals; students should not function as aides or general research assistants. Applications on behalf of underrepresented minority students are especially encouraged.

Financial data The grant of $4,000 provides funding for a stipend, fringe benefits, and indirect costs.

Duration 10 to 12 weeks during the summer.

Additional information At the conclusion of the fellowship period, students must submit a 1-page summary of their research project explaining how the fellowship affected their consideration of a career in endocrinology.

Number awarded 20 each year.

Deadline January of each year.

[749]
ESTELLE MASSEY OSBORNE SCHOLARSHIP

Nurses Educational Funds, Inc.
Attn: Scholarship Coordinator
304 Park Avenue South, 11th Floor
New York, NY 10010
(212) 590-2443 Fax: (212) 590-2446
E-mail: info@n-e-f.org
Web: www.n-e-f.org

Summary To provide financial assistance to African American nurses interested in earning a master's degree.

Eligibility This program is open to African American registered nurses who are members of a national professional nursing organization and enrolled full or part time in an accredited master's degree program in nursing. Applicants must have completed at least 12 credits and have a cumulative GPA of 3.6 or higher. They must be U.S. citizens or have declared their official intention of becoming a citizen. Along with their application, they must submit an 800-word essay on their professional goals and potential for making a contribution to the nursing profession. Selection is based on academic excellence and the essay's content and clarity.

Financial data Stipends range from $2,500 to $10,000, depending on the availability of funds.

Duration 1 year; nonrenewable.

Additional information There is a $20 application fee.

Number awarded 1 each year.

Deadline February of each year.

[750]
ESTHER KATZ ROSEN GRADUATE STUDENT FELLOWSHIPS

American Psychological Foundation
750 First Street, N.E.
Washington, DC 20002-4242
(202) 336-5843 Fax: (202) 336-5812
E-mail: foundation@apa.org
Web: www.apa.org/apf/funding/rosen.aspx

Summary To provide funding to graduate students (particularly African Americans, other minorities, and students with disabilities) who are interested in conducting research on psychological issues relevant to giftedness in children.

Eligibility This program is open to graduate students at universities in the United States and Canada who have advanced to candidacy. Applicants must be interested in conducting research on the psychological understanding of gifted and talented children and adolescents. Selection is based on conformance with stated program goals, magnitude of incremental contribution, quality of proposed work, and applicant's demonstrated scholarship and research competence. The sponsor encourages applications from individuals who represent diversity in race, ethnicity, gender, age, disability, and sexual orientation.

Financial data The grant is $20,000. The fellow's home institution is expected to provide a tuition waiver.

Duration 1 year.

Additional information This fund was established in 1974.

Number awarded 1 each year.

Deadline April of each year.

[751]
ESTHER MAYO SHERARD SCHOLARSHIP

American Health Information Management Association
Attn: AHIMA Foundation
233 North Michigan Avenue, 21st Floor
Chicago, IL 60601-5809
(312) 233-1175 Fax: (312) 233-1475
E-mail: info@ahimafoundation.org
Web: www.ahimafoundation.org

Summary To provide financial assistance to African American members of the American Health Information Management Association (AHIMA) who are interested in working on a graduate degree in a field related to health information management (HIM) or health information technology (HIT).

Eligibility This program is open to credentialed professionals in HIM or HIT who are African American members of AHIMA. Applicants must be working at least half time on a master's or doctoral degree in a program accredited by the Commission on Accreditation for Health Informatics and Information Management Education (CAHIM). They must have a GPA of 3.5 or higher and at least 1 full semester remaining after the date of the award. Selection is based on GPA and academic achievement, volunteer and work experience, commitment to the HIM profession, quality and relevance of references, and completeness and clarity of thought.

Financial data The stipend is $2,000 for master's degree students or $2,500 for doctoral students.

Duration 1 year.

Additional information This program began in 2000 by the Esther Mayo Sherard Foundation.

Number awarded 1 each year.

Deadline September of each year.

[752] ESTHER NGAN-LING CHOW AND MAREYJOYCE GREEN SCHOLARSHIP

Sociologists for Women in Society
Attn: Executive Officer
Southern Connecticut State University
Department of Sociology
501 Crescent Street
New Haven, CT 06515
(203) 392-7714 Fax: (203) 392-7715
E-mail: swseo@socwomen.org
Web: www.socwomen.org/awards.html

Summary To provide funding to African American and other women of color who are conducting dissertation research in sociology.

Eligibility This program is open to women from a racial/ethnic group that faces discrimination in the United States. Applicants must be in the early stages of writing a doctoral dissertation in sociology on a topic relating to the concerns that women of color face domestically and/or internationally. They must be able to demonstrate financial need. Both domestic and international students are eligible to apply. Along with their application, they must submit a personal statement that details their short- and long-term career and research goals; a resume or curriculum vitae; 2 letters of recommendation; and a 5-page dissertation proposal that includes the purpose of the research, the work to be accomplished through support from this scholarship, and a time line for completion.

Financial data The stipend is $15,000. An additional grant of $500 is provided to enable the recipient to attend the winter meeting of Sociologists for Women in Society (SWS), and travel expenses to attend the summer meeting are reimbursed.

Duration 1 year.

Additional information This program began in 2007 and originally named the Women of Color Dissertation Scholarship.

Number awarded 1 each year.

Deadline March of each year.

[753] ETS SUMMER RESEARCH INTERNSHIP PROGRAM FOR GRADUATE STUDENTS

Educational Testing Service
Attn: Fellowships
660 Rosedale Road
MS 19-T
Princeton, NJ 08541-0001
(609) 734-5543 Fax: (609) 734-5410
E-mail: internfellowships@ets.org
Web: www.ets.org/research/fellowships/summer

Summary To provide an opportunity for doctoral students (particularly African Americans and other underrepresented minorities) to conduct research during the summer under the guidance of senior staff at the Educational Testing Service (ETS).

Eligibility This program is open to doctoral students interested in working on a research project at ETS in 1 of the following areas: educational measurement and psychometrics, validity, natural language processing and speech technologies, cognitive psychology, learning theory, linguistics and computational linguistics, teaching and classroom research, statistics, or international large scale assessments. Applicants must have completed at least 2 years of full-time study for a Ph.D. or Ed.D. Selection is based on the scholarship of the applicant, match of applicant interests with participating ETS researchers, and the ETS affirmative action objectives. An explicit goal of the program is to increase the number of scholars and students from diverse backgrounds, especially such traditionally underrepresented groups as African Americans, Hispanic/Latino Americans, and American Indians, who are interested in conducting research in educational measurement and related fields.

Financial data The award includes a salary of $6,000 and a $3,000 relocation and housing allowance for interns residing outside a 50-mile radius of the ETS campus.

Duration 8 weeks in the summer.

Additional information Fellows work with senior staff at ETS in Princeton, New Jersey.

Number awarded 15 to 20 each year.

Deadline January of each year.

[754] EVERETT V. FOX STUDENT CASE COMPETITION

National Association of Health Services Executives
Attn: Case Competition
1050 Connecticut Avenue, N.W., Tenth Floor
Washington, DC 20036
(202) 772-1030 Fax: (202) 772-1072
E-mail: casecompetition@nahse.org
Web: netforum.avectra.com

Summary To recognize and reward teams of master's degree students, especially African Americans, who participate in a competition involving a case study in health administration.

Eligibility This competition is open to teams of 1 to 3 students enrolled in a master's degree program related to health administration (e.g., M.H.A., M.S.H.A., M.H.S.A., M.P.H.); students working on a master's degree in business administration or public administration may be eligible if they can document a strong emphasis on health issues. At least 1 member of the team must be African American. Applicants are presented with a case study modeled after real situations faced by actual organizations in the field of health care administration. They have 3 weeks in which to prepare their analysis and recommendations for a 20-minute oral presentation to a panel of judges, followed by a 10-minute question and answer period.

Financial data Awards are $4,000 per member for the first-place team, $3,000 per member for the second-place team, $2,000 per member for the third-place team, $1,000 per member for the fourth-place team, and $500 per member for the fifth-place team.

Duration The competition is held annually.

Additional information This competition was established in 1996. The registration fee is $250 per team member.

Number awarded 5 teams are selected as winners each year.

Deadline September of each year.

[755]
FACS GRADUATE FELLOWSHIPS

National Association of Teacher Educators for Family and Consumer Sciences
c/o Lela G. Goar, Fellowship Committee Chair
225 CR 207A
Burnet, TX 78611
(512) 715-8249 Fax: (512) 585-7606
E-mail: lkgoar@wildblue.net
Web: www.natefacs.org/scholarship.html

Summary To provide financial assistance to African American and other graduate students in family and consumer science education.

Eligibility This program is open to graduate students working on a master's or doctoral degree in family and consumer sciences education. Applicants must submit an autobiographical sketch (up to 3 pages in length) presenting their professional goals, including information on the institution where they are studying or planning to study, areas or emphases of study, possible research topic, and other pertinent information regarding their plans. Selection is based on likelihood of completing the degree, likelihood of contribution to family and consumer sciences education, previous academic work, professional association involvement, professional experience (including scholarly work), and references. At least 1 fellowship is reserved for a minority (African American, Hispanic American, Native American, or Asian American) candidate.

Financial data Stipends range from $2,000 to $4,000.

Duration 1 year.

Additional information The sponsor is an affiliate of the Family and Consumer Sciences (FACS) Division of the Association for Career and Technical Education.

Number awarded Varies each year.

Deadline October of each year.

[756]
FAEGRE BAKER DANIELS DIVERSITY AND INCLUSION FELLOWSHIPS

Faegre Baker Daniels
Attn: Diversity and Pro Bono Coordinator
300 North Meridian Street, Suite 2700
Indianapolis, IN 46204
(317) 237-8298 Fax: (317) 237-1000
E-mail: brita.horvath@faegrebd.com
Web: www.faegrebd.com/fellowship

Summary To provide financial aid and summer work experience to African Americans and other students from diverse backgrounds entering the second year of law school.

Eligibility This program is open to residents of any state who are entering their second year at an accredited law school. Applicants must reflect diversity, defined to mean that they come from varied ethnic, racial, cultural, and lifestyle backgrounds, as well as those with disabilities or unique viewpoints. They must also be interested in a place in the sponsor's associate program during the summer between their second and third year of law school. Along with their application, they must submit a 2-page personal statement describing how or why they will contribute meaningfully to diversity and inclusion at the sponsoring firm and/or in the legal profession.

Financial data The stipend is $10,000.

Duration 1 year.

Additional information This law firm was formerly Baker & Daniels LLP. Recipients of these fellowships may elect to conduct their associateship at offices in Boulder, Chicago, Denver, Des Moines, Fort Wayne, Indianapolis, Minneapolis, Silicon Valley (East Palo Alto), South Bend, and Washington, D.C.

Number awarded 4 each year.

Deadline September of each year.

[757]
FARM CREDIT EAST SCHOLARSHIPS

Farm Credit East
Attn: Scholarship Program
240 South Road
Enfield, CT 06082
(860) 741-4380 Toll Free: (800) 562-2235
Fax: (860) 741-4389
E-mail: specialoffers@famcrediteast.com
Web: www.farmcrediteast.com

Summary To provide financial assistance to African American and other residents of designated northeastern states who plan to attend school in any state to work on an undergraduate or graduate degree in a field related to agriculture, forestry, or fishing.

Eligibility This program is open to residents of Massachusetts, Connecticut, Rhode Island, New Jersey, and portions of New York and New Hampshire. Applicants must be working on or planning to work on an associate, bachelor's, or graduate degree in production agriculture, agribusiness, the forest products industry, or commercial fishing at a college or university in any state. They must submit a 200-word essay on why they wish to prepare for a career in agriculture, forestry, or fishing. Selection is based on the essay, extracurricular activities (especially farm work experience and activities indicative of an interest in preparing for a career in agriculture or agribusiness), and interest in agriculture. The program includes diversity scholarships reserved for members of minority groups (Black or African American, American Indian or Alaska Native, Asian, Native Hawaiian or other Pacific Islander, or Hispanic or Latino).

Financial data The stipend is $1,500. Funds are paid directly to the student to be used for tuition, room and board, books, and other academic charges.

Duration 1 year; nonrenewable.

Additional information Recipients are given priority for an internship with the sponsor in the summer following their junior year. Farm Credit East was formerly named First Pioneer Farm Credit.

Number awarded Up to 28 each year, including several diversity scholarships.

Deadline April of each year.

[758]
FDA GRADUATE STUDENT FELLOWSHIPS

National Science Foundation
Directorate for Engineering
Attn: Division of Chemical, Bioengineering, Environmental, and Transport Systems
4201 Wilson Boulevard, Room 565S
Arlington, VA 22230
(703) 292-7942 Fax: (703) 292-9098
TDD: (800) 281-8749 E-mail: lesterow@nsf.gov
Web: www.nsf.gov/funding/pgm_summ.jsp?pims_id=5605

Summary To provide an opportunity for graduate students (particularly African Americans, other underrepresented minorities, women, and students with disabilities) to conduct research at an intramural laboratory of the U.S. Food and Drug Administration (FDA).

Eligibility This program is open to graduate students (preferably Ph.D. students) in science, engineering, and mathematics fields of interest to the National Science Foundation (NSF). Applicants must be U.S. citizens, nationals, or permanent residents. They must be proposing a program of full- or part-time work at an FDA intramural laboratory in an area related to their research, conducted under the guidance of an academic adviser and an FDA mentor. The program encourages applications from all citizens, including women and men, underrepresented minorities, and persons with disabilities.

Financial data Graduate students may receive stipends $2,100 per month, plus transportation expenses. The faculty adviser may receive 10% of the total award for research-related expenses, excluding equipment. The academic institution receives an allowance of 15% of total direct costs for administrative expenses. The total award may be up to $35,000 for a fellowship for a single student. FDA provides office space, research facilities, research costs in the form of expendable and minor equipment purchases in the host laboratory, and the time of its research staff.

Duration 1 to 4 semesters.

Additional information This program is also offered by the NSF Directorate for Computer and Information Science and Engineering.

Number awarded A total of 3 to 10 grants for all FDA programs is awarded each year; total funding is approximately $500,000.

Deadline March of each year.

[759]
FEDERAL EMPLOYEE EDUCATION & ASSISTANCE (FEEA)-NABNA SCHOLARSHIP FUND

National Association of Black Narcotic Agents
c/o Federal Employee Education and Assistance Fund
Attn: Scholarship Program
3333 South Wadsworth Boulevard, Suite 300
Lakewood, CO 80227
(303) 933-7580 Toll Free: (800) 323-4140
Fax: (303) 933-7587 E-mail: admin@feea.org
Web: www.nabna.org/content/feea

Summary To provide financial assistance for college or graduate school to members of the National Association of Black Narcotic Agents (NABNA) and their dependents.

Eligibility This program is open to federal employees who are NABNA members and their dependent spouses and children entering or enrolled in an accredited 2- or 4-year undergraduate, graduate, or postgraduate program. Dependents must be full-time students; federal employees may be part-time students. Applicants or their sponsoring federal employee must have at least 3 years of civilian federal service. Along with their application, they must submit a 2-page essay on a topic related to a career in public service with the federal government, a letter of recommendation, a transcript with a GPA of 3.0 or higher, and a copy of their federal "Notice of Personnel Action;" high school seniors must also submit a copy of their ACT, SAT, or other examination scores. Financial need is not considered in the selection process.

Financial data The stipend is $1,000 per year.

Duration 1 year; may be renewed.

Additional information This program is jointly administered by NABNA and the Federal Employee Education and Assistance Fund (FEEA).

Number awarded 1 or more each year.

Deadline March of each year.

[760]
FELICIA C. BRADY SCHOLARSHIP FUND

Black Nurses' Association of Greater Washington, D.C. Area, Inc.
Attn: Scholarship Committee Chair
P.O. Box 55285
Washington, DC 20040
(202) 291-8866
Web: www.bnaofgwdca.org/scholarships.html

Summary To provide financial assistance to registered nurses from the Washington, D.C. area who are members of the National Black Nurses' Association and its local affiliate, and are interested in working on an advanced degree.

Eligibility This program is open to registered nurses who are currently enrolled in an associate, bachelor's, master's, or doctoral program and have a GPA of 3.0 or higher. Applicants must be residents of Washington, D.C. or adjoining counties in Maryland (Anne Arundel, Calvert, Charles, Howard, Montgomery, and Prince George's). They must be U.S. citizens, members of the National Black Nurses' Association, and members of the Black Nurses' Association of Greater Washington, D.C. Area. Along with their application, they must submit a copy of their nursing license, an official transcript from their nursing program, 2 letters of recommendation, and a written essay that describes their personal goals and objectives, financial need, and contributions to nursing and community service involvement in the greater Washington, D.C. area.

Financial data A stipend is awarded (amount not specified).

Duration 1 year.

Number awarded 1 each year.

Deadline January of each year.

[761]
FERMILAB PH.D. FELLOWSHIP PROGRAM FOR MINORITY STUDENTS

Fermi National Accelerator Laboratory
Attn: Equal Opportunity and Diversity Office
MS 117
P.O. Box 500
Batavia, IL 60510-0500
(630) 840-4574 Fax: (630) 840-5207
E-mail: scharles@fnal.gov
Web: www.fnal.gov/eeo/phd_fellowship.html

Summary To provide financial assistance for doctoral study in physics to African American and other underrepresented minority students at universities that are members of the Universities Research Association, Inc. (URA).

Eligibility This program is open to doctoral students who are members of minority groups historically underrepresented in physics (Hispanics, African Americans, and Native Americans). Applicants must be enrolled at 1 of the 82 universities in the United States that are URA members. They must be U.S. citizens or permanent residents. Along with their application, they must submit a statement on why they want to participate in this program, why they are considering physics as their course of study in graduate school, how they intend to use their physics training after they complete their education, and whether they plan to work or do postdoctoral study after completing their education. Selection is based on that statement, financial need, university transcripts, and a progress letter from the thesis adviser.

Financial data The stipend depends on the availability of funds and the needs of the student.

Duration 1 year; may be renewed up to 6 additional years.

Additional information Fermilab scientists are assigned to all recipients as advisers to aid their progress in graduate school. In addition, students are encouraged to work summers at Fermilab under the supervision of a staff physicist. Funding support for this program is provided by the U.S. Department of Energy.

Number awarded Varies each year.

Deadline July of each year.

[762]
FINNEGAN HENDERSON DIVERSITY SCHOLARSHIP

Finnegan, Henderson, Farabow, Garrett & Dunner, LLP
Attn: Attorney Recruitment Manager
901 New York Avenue, N.W.
Washington, DC 20001-4413
(202) 408-4034 Fax: (202) 408-4400
E-mail: diversityscholarship@finnegan.com
Web: www.finnegan.com/careers/summerprogram/overview

Summary To provide financial aid and work experience to African American and other law students from diverse groups who are interested in a career in intellectual property law.

Eligibility This program is open to law students who have demonstrated a commitment to a career in intellectual property law and are currently enrolled either as a first-year full-time student or second-year part-time student. Applicants must contribute to enhancing diversity; the sponsor defines diversity broadly, and has considered members of racial, ethnic, disabled, and sexual orientation groups that have been historically underrepresented in the legal profession. They must have earned an undergraduate degree in life sciences, engineering, or computer science, or have substantial prior trademark experience. Selection is based on academic performance at the undergraduate, graduate (if applicable), and law school level; relevant work experience; community service; leadership skills; and special accomplishments.

Financial data The stipend is $15,000 per year.

Duration 1 year; may be renewed 1 additional year as long as the recipient completes a summer associateship with the sponsor and maintains of GPA of 3.0 or higher.

Additional information The sponsor, the world's largest intellectual property law firm, established this scholarship in 2003. Summer associateships are available at its offices in Washington, D.C., Atlanta, Boston, Palo Alto, or Reston.

Number awarded 1 each year.

Deadline February of each year.

[763]
FISH & RICHARDSON DIVERSITY FELLOWSHIP PROGRAM

Fish & Richardson P.C.
Recruiting Department
Attn: Manager of Diversity
12390 El Camino Real
San Diego, CA 92130
(858) 678-5070 Fax: (858) 678-5099
E-mail: diversity@fr.com
Web: www.fr.com/diversity

Summary To provide financial assistance for law school to African Americans and other students who will contribute to diversity in the legal profession.

Eligibility This program is open to students enrolled in the first year at a law school anywhere in the country. Applicants must be African American/Black, American Indian/Alaskan, Hispanic/Latino, Native Hawaiian/Pacific Islander, Asian, 2 or more races, disabled, or openly GLBT. Along with their application, they must submit a 500-word essay describing their background, what led them to the legal field, their interest in the sponsoring law firm, and what they could contribute to its practice and the profession. They must also indicate their first

3 choices of an office of the firm where they are interested in a summer associate clerkship.

Financial data The stipend is $5,000.

Duration 1 year: the second year of law school.

Additional information Recipients are also offered a paid associate clerkship during the summer following their first year of law school at an office of the firm in the location of their choice in Atlanta, Austin, Boston, Dallas, Delaware, Houston, New York, San Diego, Silicon Valley, Twin Cities, or Washington, D.C. This program began in 2005.

Number awarded 1 or more each year.

Deadline January of each year.

[764]
FIVE COLLEGE FELLOWSHIP PROGRAM

Five Colleges, Incorporated
Attn: Five Colleges Fellowship Program Committee
97 Spring Street
Amherst, MA 01002-2324
(413) 542-4013 E-mail: ntherien@fivecolleges.edu
Web: www.fivecolleges.edu/faculty/fellowships

Summary To provide funding to African American and other graduate students from underrepresented groups who have completed all the requirements for the Ph.D. except the dissertation and are interested in teaching at selected colleges in Massachusetts.

Eligibility Fellows are chosen by the host department in each of the 4 participating liberal arts colleges (Amherst, Hampshire, Mount Holyoke, and Smith). Applicants must be graduate students at an accredited school who have completed all doctoral requirements except the dissertation and are interested in devoting full time to the completion of the dissertation. The chief goal of the program is to support scholars from underrepresented groups and/or scholars "with unique interests and histories whose engagement in the Academy will enrich scholarship and teaching."

Financial data The program provides a stipend of $30,000, a research grant, health benefits, office space, library privileges, and housing assistance.

Duration 1 academic year; nonrenewable.

Additional information Although the primary goal is completion of the dissertation, each fellow also has many opportunities to experience working with students and faculty colleagues on the host campus as well as with those at the other colleges. The fellows are also given an opportunity to teach (generally as a team teacher, in a section of a core course, or in a component within a course). Fellows meet monthly with each other to share their experiences. At Smith College, this program is named Mendenhall Fellowships. The fifth institution that belongs to this organization, the University of Massachusetts at Amherst, does not participate in this program.

Number awarded 4 each year; 1 at each of the participating colleges.

Deadline January of each year.

[765]
F.J. MCGUIGAN DISSERTATION AWARD

American Psychological Foundation
750 First Street, N.E.
Washington, DC 20002-4242
(202) 336-5843 Fax: (202) 336-5812
E-mail: foundation@apa.org
Web: www.apa.org/apf/funding/mcguigan-dissertation.aspx

Summary To provide funding to doctoral candidates (particularly African Americans, other minorities, women, and students with disabilities) who are interested in conducting research on the materialistic understanding of the human mind.

Eligibility This program is open to graduate students enrolled full time in a psychology program at an accredited college or university in the United States or Canada. Applicants must be interested in conducting dissertation research that addresses an aspect of mental function (e.g., cognition, affect, motivation) and should utilize behavioral and/or neuroscientific methods. Selection is based on conformance with stated program goals, quality of proposed work, and applicant's demonstrated scholarship and research competence. The sponsor encourages applications from individuals who represent diversity in race, ethnicity, gender, age, disability, and sexual orientation.

Financial data The grant is $2,000.

Duration 1 year.

Additional information This grant was first awarded in 2009.

Number awarded 1 each year.

Deadline May of each year.

[766]
FLETCHER MAE HOWELL SCHOLARSHIP

Woman's Missionary Union of Virginia
2828 Emerywood Parkway
Richmond, VA 23294
(804) 915-5000, ext. 8267
Toll Free: (800) 255-2428 (within VA)
Fax: (804) 672-8008 E-mail: wmuv@wmuv.org
Web: wmuv.org/developing-future-leaders/scholarships

Summary To provide financial assistance to African American women from Virginia who are working on a graduate degree in Christian education.

Eligibility This program is open to African American women from Virginia who are interested in full-time graduate study in Christian education. An interview is required.

Financial data The stipend is $1,000.

Duration 1 year.

Number awarded Up to 2 each year.

Deadline January of each year.

[767]
FLORENCE SMALL GAYNOR AWARD

National Association of Health Services Executives
Attn: Educational Assistance Program
1050 Connecticut Avenue, N.W., Tenth Floor
Washington, DC 20036
(202) 772-1030 Fax: (202) 772-1072
E-mail: nahsehg@nahse.org
Web: netforum.avectra.com

Summary To provide financial assistance to African American women who are members of the National Association of Health Services Executives (NAHSE) and interested in preparing for a career in health care administration.

Eligibility This program is open to African American women who are either enrolled or accepted at an accredited college or university to work on a master's or doctoral degree in health care administration. Applicants must be members of NAHSE and able to demonstrate financial need. They must have a GPA of 2.5 or higher as undergraduates or 3.0 or higher as graduate students. Along with their application, they must submit a 3-page essay that describes themselves and their career goals, commitment and interest in health care management, and financial need.

Financial data The stipend is $2,500. Funds are sent to the recipient's institution.

Duration 1 year.

Number awarded 1 each year.

Deadline May of each year.

[768]
FLORIDA LIBRARY ASSOCIATION MINORITY SCHOLARSHIPS

Florida Library Association
164 N.W. Madison Street, Suite 104
P.O. Box 1571
Lake City, FL 32056-1571
(386) 438-5795 Fax: (386) 438-5796
E-mail: fla.admin@comcast.net
Web: www.flalib.org/scholarships.php

Summary To provide financial assistance to African American and other minority students working on a graduate degree in library and information science in Florida.

Eligibility This program is open to residents of Florida who are working on a graduate degree in library and information science at schools in the state. Applicants must be members of a minority group: Black/African American, American Indian/Alaska Native, Asian/Pacific Islander, or Hispanic/Latino. They must have some experience in a Florida library, must be a member of the Florida Library Association, and must commit to working in a Florida library for at least 1 year after graduation. Along with their application, they must submit 1) a list of activities, honors, awards, and/or offices held during college and outside college; 2) an essay of 1 to 2 pages on why they are entering librarianship; and 3) an essay of 1 to 2 pages on their career goals with respect to Florida libraries. Financial need is considered in the selection process.

Financial data The stipend is $2,000.

Duration 1 year.

Number awarded 1 each year.

Deadline January of each year.

[769]
FOLEY & LARDNER DIVERSITY SCHOLARSHIP

Foley & Lardner LLP
Attn: Regional Legal Recruiting Coordinator
555 South Flower Street
Los Angeles, CA 90071-2411
(213) 972-4535 E-mail: enesbitt@foley.com
Web: www.foley.com/careers/lawstudents

Summary To provide financial aid and work experience to African American and other first-year law students who will contribute to diversity in the legal profession.

Eligibility This program is open to students completing the first year of full-time study at an ABA-accredited law school. Applicants must have demonstrated a commitment to promoting diversity and inclusion in the legal profession and the broader community. They must be interested in a summer associateship at an office of the sponsoring firm. Selection is based on involvement in diversity-related student organizations, involvement in community activities, undergraduate and law school academic achievement, and interest in employment with the sponsoring firm.

Financial data Upon completion of the associateship, participants receive a $20,000 fellowship.

Duration 1 summer and 1 academic year.

Additional information This program began in 1998. The sponsoring firm has offices in Boston, Chicago, Detroit, Jacksonville, Los Angeles, Madison, Miami, Milwaukee, New York, Orlando, Sacramento, San Diego, San Francisco, Silicon Valley, Tallahassee, Tampa, and Washington, D.C.

Number awarded 2 each year.

Deadline April of each year.

[770]
FOURTH DISTRICT MOSAIC SCHOLARSHIP

American Advertising Federation-District 4
c/o Maria Lucas, Governor
Farah & Farah
10 West Adams Street
Jacksonville, FL 32202
(904) 807-3113 Toll Free: (800) 533-5555
Fax: (904) 355-5599 E-mail: mlucas@farahandfarah.com
Web: 4aaf.com/education/scholarships

Summary To provide financial assistance to African American and other minority undergraduate and graduate students from any state who are enrolled at colleges and universities in Florida and interested in entering the field of advertising.

Eligibility This program is open to undergraduate and graduate students from any state enrolled at accredited colleges and universities in Florida who are U.S. citizens or permanent residents of African, African American, Hispanic, Hispanic American, Indian, Native American, Asian, Asian American, or Pacific Islander descent. Applicants must be working on a bachelor's or master's degree in advertising, marketing, communications, public relations, art, graphic arts, or a related field. They must have an overall GPA of 3.0 or higher. Along with their application, they must submit a 250-word essay on why multiculturalism, diversity, and inclusion are important in the advertising, marketing, and communications industry today. Preference is given to members of the American Advertising Federation.

Financial data The stipend is $1,000.

Duration 1 year.

Number awarded 1 or more each year.

Deadline February of each year.

[771]
FRAMELINE COMPLETION FUND

Frameline
Attn: Completion Fund
145 Ninth Street, Suite 300
San Francisco, CA 94103
(415) 703-8650 Fax: (415) 861-1404
E-mail: info@frameline.org
Web: www.frameline.org/filmmaker-support

Summary To provide funding to lesbian, gay, bisexual, and transgender (LGBT) film/video artists (particularly African Americans, other film/video artists of color, and women).

Eligibility This program is open to LGBT artists who are in the last stages of the production of documentary, educational, narrative, animated, or experimental projects about or of interest to LGBT people and their communities. Applicants may be independent artists, students, producers, or nonprofit corporations. They must be interested in completion work and must have 90% of the production completed; projects in development, script-development, pre-production, or production are not eligible. Student projects are eligible only if the student maintains artistic and financial control of the project. Women and people of color are especially encouraged to apply. Selection is based on financial need, the contribution the grant will make to completing the project, assurances that the project will be completed, and the statement the project makes about LGBT people and/or issues of concern to them and their communities.

Financial data Grants range from $1,000 to $5,000.

Duration These are 1-time grants.

Additional information This program began in 1990.

Number awarded Varies each year; recently, 5 of these grants were awarded. Since this program was established, it has provided $389,200 in support to 118 films.

Deadline October of each year.

[772]
FRANCHISE LAW DIVERSITY SCHOLARSHIP AWARD

International Franchise Association
Attn: President, Educational Foundation
1501 K Street, N.W., Suite 350
Washington, DC 20005
(202) 662-0764 Fax: (202) 628-0812
E-mail: jreynolds@franchise.org
Web: www.franchise.org/files/Scholarships.aspx

Summary To provide financial assistance to African American and other law students from diverse groups who are interested in taking courses related to franchise law.

Eligibility This program is open to second- and third-year students who are enrolled at ABA-accredited law schools and a member of a diverse group (defined as African Americans, American Indians, Hispanic Americans, Asian Americans, or gays/lesbians). Applicants must be enrolled in at least 1 course oriented toward franchise law (e.g., torts, unfair trade practices, trade secrets, antitrust, trademarks, contracts, agency, or securities). Along with their application, they must submit a current transcript, an essay explaining their interest in franchise law, and 2 letters of recommendation.

Financial data The stipend is $4,000. Funds are paid to the recipient's law school and are to be used for tuition.

Duration 1 year.

Additional information This award is cosponsored by the IFA Educational Foundation and DLA Piper US LLP. It may not be used by the recipient's law school to reduce the amount of any institutionally-awarded financial aid.

Number awarded 1 or more each year.

Deadline December of each year.

[773]
FRANCIS M. KEVILLE MEMORIAL SCHOLARSHIP

Construction Management Association of America
Attn: CMAA Foundation
7926 Jones Branch Drive, Suite 800
McLean, VA 22101-3303
(703) 356-2622 Fax: (703) 356-6388
E-mail: foundation@cmaanet.org
Web: www.cmaafoundation.org

Summary To provide financial assistance to minority and female undergraduate and graduate students working on a degree in construction management.

Eligibility This program is open to women and members of minority groups who are enrolled as full-time undergraduate or graduate students. Applicants must have completed at least 1 year of study and have at least 1 full year remaining for a bachelor's or master's degree in construction management or a related field. Along with their application, they must submit essays on why they are interested in a career in construction management and why they should be awarded this scholarship. Selection is based on that essay (20%), academic performance (40%), recommendation of the faculty adviser (15%), and extracurricular activities (25%); a bonus of 5% is given to student members of the Construction Management Association of America (CMAA).

Financial data The stipend is $3,000. Funds are disbursed directly to the student's university.

Duration 1 year.

Number awarded 1 each year.

Deadline June of each year.

[774]
FRANK/NORRELL SCHOLARSHIP PROGRAM

Southwestern Athletic Conference
Attn: Frank/Norrell Scholarship
2101 Sixth Avenue North, Suite 700
Birmingham, AL 35203
(205) 251-7573 Fax: (205) 297-9820
Web: www.swac.org

Summary To provide financial assistance to graduate students at Historically Black Colleges and Universities affiliated with the Southwestern Athletic Conference (SWAC) who are interested in working on a degree in a field related to physical education.

Eligibility This program is open to students who currently attend an Historically Black College or University that makes up the SWAC and plan to attend graduate school at a member institution of the conference. Applicants must be interested in working on a degree in health, physical education, recreation, sports administration and management, or a related field. They must have a GPA of 3.0 or higher, a commitment to working full time on a post-baccalaureate professional degree, and a record of participation in athletics that has been a positive influence on their personal and intellectual development.

Financial data The stipend is $3,000.

Duration 1 year.

Additional information This program began in 1998 with funding from Dr. Gwen Norrell, former professor and faculty athletics representative at Michigan State University, in honor of Dr. James Frank, long-time commissioner of the SWAC. The members of the SWAC include the following HBCUs: Alabama A&M University (Normal), Alabama State University (Montgomery), Alcorn State University (Alcorn State, Mississippi), University of Arkansas at Pine Bluff, Grambling State University (Grambling, Louisiana), Jackson State University (Jackson, Mississippi), Mississippi Valley State University (Itta Bena, Mississippi), Prairie View A&M University (Prairie View, Texas), Southern University and A&M College (Baton Rouge, Louisiana), and Texas Southern University (Houston).

Number awarded 1 each year.

Deadline June of each year.

[775]
FRANK T. MARTIN LEADERSHIP SCHOLARSHIP

Conference of Minority Transportation Officials
Attn: National Scholarship Program
1875 I Street, N.W., Suite 500
Washington, DC 20006
(703) 234-4072 Fax: (202) 318-0364
Web: www.comto.org/?page=Scholarships

Summary To provide financial assistance to African American and other minority undergraduate and graduate students working on a degree in transportation or a related field.

Eligibility This program is open to full-time undergraduate and graduate students who are working on a degree in transportation, engineering, planning, or a related discipline. They must be able to demonstrate leadership and active commitment to community service. Along with their application, they must submit a cover letter with a 500-word statement of career goals. Financial need is not considered in the selection process. U.S. citizenship or legal resident status is required.

Financial data The stipend is $3,000. Funds are paid directly to the recipient's college or university.

Duration 1 year.

Additional information The Conference of Minority Transportation Officials (COMTO) was established in 1971 to promote, strengthen, and expand the roles of minorities in all aspects of transportation. This program is sponsored by Atkins North America. Recipients are expected to attend the COMTO National Scholarship Luncheon.

Number awarded 1 each year.

Deadline May of each year.

[776]
FREDERICK DOUGLASS INSTITUTE FOR AFRICAN AND AFRICAN-AMERICAN STUDIES PREDOCTORAL DISSERTATION FELLOWSHIP

University of Rochester
Frederick Douglass Institute for African and African-American Studies
Attn: Director for Research Fellowships
302 Morey Hall
RC Box 270440
Rochester, NY 14627-0440
(585) 276-5744 Fax: (585) 256-2594
E-mail: FDI@mail.rochester.edu
Web: www.rochester.edu

Summary To provide funding to doctoral candidates interested in conducting research at the University of Rochester on Africa and its Diaspora.

Eligibility Graduate students at any university in the United States who are conducting dissertation research on aspects of the African or African American experience are invited to apply if they are interested in spending a year in residence, working on their research, at the University of Rochester. Applicants must have completed their preliminary course work, qualifying exams, and at least 1 chapter of their dissertation.

Financial data The stipend is $26,000.

Duration 1 academic year.

Additional information Fellows are given office space within the institute, full access to the facilities of the university, and opportunities for collaboration and discussion. Predoctoral fellows are expected to organize a colloquium, prepare a lecture, and make other contributions to the institute's program. They are expected to be in full-time residence at the institute during the tenure of their award.

Number awarded 1 each year.

Deadline December of each year.

[777]
FREDRIKSON & BYRON FOUNDATION MINORITY SCHOLARSHIP

Fredrikson & Byron Foundation
Attn: Attorney Recruiting Administrator
200 South Sixth Street, Suite 4000
Minneapolis, MN 55402-1425
(612) 492-7141 Fax: (612) 492-7077
E-mail: glarson@fredlaw.com
Web: www.fredlaw.com/firm/scholarship.htm

Summary To provide financial aid and summer work experience to African American and other minority law students from any state who are interested in practicing in the Twin Cities area of Minnesota.

Eligibility This program is open to African American, Asian American, Pacific Islander, Hispanic, Native American, and Alaska Native students enrolled in their first year of law school. Applicants must be interested in practicing law in the Minneapolis-St. Paul area. Along with their application, they must submit brief statement on their expectations and objectives in applying for this scholarship; the factors they will use to measure success in their legal career; what they see as potential issues, obstacles, and opportunities facing new lawyers in a large private practice firm; and their interest in a summer associate position in private practice, including their interest in practicing law in the Minneapolis-St. Paul area. Financial need is not considered.

Financial data The fellowship stipend is $10,000. The internship portion of the program provides a $1,000 weekly stipend.

Duration 1 year.

Additional information Fellows are also eligible to participate in an internship at the firm's offices in Minneapolis.

Number awarded 1 each year.

Deadline March of each year.

[778]
FULFILLING THE LEGACY SCHOLARSHIPS

National Society of Black Engineers
Attn: Programs Department
205 Daingerfield Road
Alexandria, VA 22314
(703) 549-2207 Fax: (703) 683-5312
E-mail: scholarships@nsbe.org
Web: www.nsbe.org/Programs/Scholarships.aspx

Summary To provide financial assistance to members of the National Society of Black Engineers (NSBE) who are or will be working on an undergraduate or graduate degree in engineering.

Eligibility This program is open to members of the society who are undergraduate or graduate engineering students. High school seniors are also eligible. Applicants must epitomize the society's mission of producing culturally responsible Black engineers who excel academically, succeed professionally, and positively impact the community. Selection is based on an essay; academic achievement; service to the society at the chapter, regional, and/or national level; and other professional, campus, and community activities.

Financial data The stipend is $1,000.

Duration 1 year; may be renewed.

Number awarded Varies each year, depending on the availability of funds. Recently, 10 of these scholarships were awarded to undergraduate and graduate students and 5 to high school seniors.

Deadline May of each year.

[779]
FUTURE ENGINEERING FACULTY FELLOWSHIP PROGRAM

Office of Naval Research
c/o North Carolina A&T State University
Department of Electrical and Computer Engineering
1601 East Market Street
Greensboro, NC 27411
(336) 334-7589, ext. 120 Fax: (336) 334-7540
E-mail: lrlittle@ncat.edu
Web: onrfellowship.ncat.edu

Summary To provide financial assistance for graduate school to students interested in becoming faculty members in engineering at Historically Black Engineering Colleges (HBECs).

Eligibility This program is open to U.S. citizens who intend to work on a Ph.D. in designated fields of engineering and, in return for the support, agree to join the engineering faculty of an HBEC. Applicants should be at or near the beginning of doctoral study. They must have a GPA of 3.3 or higher. The designated fields of study include the following specialties within engineering: aerospace, bio-environmental, chemical, civil, computer, electrical, environmental, industrial, manufacturing, mechanical, and ocean. Students of any gender or ethnicity are eligible. Selection is based on academic achievement, area of study, a personal statement, and letters of recommendation.

Financial data The program provides full payment of tuition and required fees and a competitive stipend that varies each year; recently, stipends were $32,400 for the first year, $33,600 for the second year, and $34,800 for the third year. Allowances of $1,300 for health insurance and $3,000 for travel to attend conferences or meetings are also provided.

Duration Up to 3 years.

Additional information This program is administered by North Carolina A&T State University on behalf of the Office of Naval Research (ONR). HBEC university members include Alabama A&M University, Florida A&M University, Hampton University, Howard University, Jackson State University, Morgan State University, North Carolina A&T State University, Prairie View University, Southern University, Tennessee State University, and Tuskegee University.

Number awarded Approximately 3 each year.

Deadline March of each year.

[780]
GAIUS CHARLES BOLIN DISSERTATION AND POST-MFA FELLOWSHIPS

Williams College
Attn: Dean of the Faculty
880 Main Street
Hopkins Hall, Third Floor
P.O. Box 141
Williamstown, MA 01267
(413) 597-4351 Fax: (413) 597-3553
E-mail: gburda@williams.edu
Web: dean-faculty.williams.edu

Summary To provide financial assistance to African Americans and members of other underrepresented groups who are interested in teaching courses at Williams College while working on their doctoral dissertation or building their post-M.F.A. professional portfolio.

Eligibility This program is open to members of underrepresented groups, including ethnic minorities, first-generation college students, women in predominantly male fields, and scholars with disabilities. Applicants must be 1) doctoral candidates in any field who have completed all work for a Ph.D. except for the dissertation; or 2) artists who completed an M.F.A. degree within the past 2 years and are building their professional portfolio. They must be willing to teach a course at Williams College. Along with their application, they must submit a full curriculum vitae, a graduate school transcript, 3 letters of recommendation, a copy of their dissertation prospectus or samples of their artistic work, and a description of their teaching interests within a department or program at Williams College. U.S. citizenship or permanent resident status is required.

Financial data Fellows receive $36,000 for the academic year, plus housing assistance, office space, computer and library privileges, and a research allowance of up to $4,000.

Duration 2 years.

Additional information Bolin fellows are assigned a faculty adviser in the appropriate department. This program was established in 1985. Fellows are expected to teach a 1-semester course each year. They must be in residence at Williams College for the duration of the fellowship.

Number awarded 3 each year.

Deadline November of each year.

[781]
GEM M.S. ENGINEERING FELLOWSHIP PROGRAM

National Consortium for Graduate Degrees for Minorities in Engineering and Science (GEM)
Attn: Manager, Fellowships Administration
1430 Duke Street
Alexandria, VA 22314
(703) 562-3646 Fax: (202) 207-3518
E-mail: info@gemfellowship.org
Web: www.gemfellowship.org/gem-fellowship

Summary To provide financial aid and summer work experience to African American and other underrepresented minority students interested in working on a master's degree in engineering or computer science.

Eligibility This program is open to U.S. citizens and permanent residents who are members of ethnic groups underrepresented in engineering: American Indians/Native Americans, Blacks/African Americans, or Latinos/Hispanic Americans. Applicants must be a senior or graduate of an ABET-accredited engineering or computer science program and have an academic record that indicates the ability to pursue graduate studies in engineering (including a GPA of 2.8 or higher). They must agree to apply to at least 3 of the 102 GEM member universities that offer a master's degree and to intern during summers with a sponsoring GEM employer.

Financial data Fellows receive 1) a stipend of $4,000 per semester; 2) full tuition and fees at the GEM member university; and 3) a salary during the summer work assignment as a GEM summer intern.

Duration Up to 4 semesters, plus summer work internships lasting 10 to 14 weeks for up to 2 summers.

Additional information During the summer internship, each fellow is assigned an engineering project in a research setting. Each project is based on the fellow's interest and background and is carried out under the supervision of an experienced engineer. At the conclusion of the internship, each fellow writes a project report. Recipients must work on a master's degree in the same engineering discipline as their baccalaureate degree.

Number awarded Approximately 300 each year.

Deadline November of each year.

[782]
GEM PH.D. ENGINEERING FELLOWSHIP PROGRAM

National Consortium for Graduate Degrees for Minorities in Engineering and Science (GEM)
Attn: Manager, Fellowships Administration
1430 Duke Street
Alexandria, VA 22314
(703) 562-3646 Fax: (202) 207-3518
E-mail: info@gemfellowship.org
Web: www.gemfellowship.org/gem-fellowship

Summary To provide financial aid and summer work experience to African American and other underrepresented minority students interested in obtaining a Ph.D. degree in engineering.

Eligibility This program is open to U.S. citizens and permanent residents who are members of ethnic groups underrepresented in engineering: American Indians/Native Americans, Blacks/African Americans, and Latinos/Hispanic Americans. Applicants must be college seniors, master's degree students, or graduates of an ABET-accredited program in engineering and have an academic record that indicates the ability to work on a doctoral degree in engineering (including a GPA of 3.0 or higher). They must agree to apply to at least 3 of the 102 GEM member universities that offer a doctoral degree in engineering and to intern during summer with a sponsoring GEM employer.

Financial data The stipend is $16,000 for the first year; in subsequent years, fellows receive full payment of tuition and fees plus a stipend and assistantship from their university that is equivalent to funding received by other doctoral students in their department.

Duration 3 to 5 years for the fellowship; 12 weeks during the summer immediately after sponsorship for the internship.

Additional information This program is valid only at 1 of the 102 participating GEM member universities; contact GEM for a list. The fellowship award is designed to support the student in the first year of the doctoral program without working. Subsequent years are subsidized by the respective universities and will usually include either a teaching or research assistantship. Recipients must participate in the GEM summer internship; failure to agree to accept the internship cancels the fellowship.

Number awarded Approximately 50 each year.

Deadline November of each year.

[783]
GEM PH.D. SCIENCE FELLOWSHIP PROGRAM

National Consortium for Graduate Degrees for Minorities in Engineering and Science (GEM)
Attn: Manager, Fellowships Administration
1430 Duke Street
Alexandria, VA 22314
(703) 562-3646 Fax: (202) 207-3518
E-mail: info@gemfellowship.org
Web: www.gemfellowship.org/gem-fellowship

Summary To provide financial aid and summer work experience to African American and other underrepresented minority students interested in working on a Ph.D. degree in the life sciences, mathematics, or physical sciences.

Eligibility This program is open to U.S. citizens and permanent residents who are members of ethnic groups underrepresented in the natural sciences: American Indians/Native Americans, Blacks/African Americans, and Latinos/Hispanic Americans. Applicants must be college seniors, master's degree students, or recent graduates in the biological sciences, mathematics, or physical sciences (chemistry, computer science, environmental sciences, and physics) with an academic record that indicates the ability to pursue doctoral studies (including a GPA of 3.0 or higher). They must agree to apply to at least 3 of the 102 GEM member universities that offer a doctoral degree in science and to intern during summer with a sponsoring GEM employer.

Financial data The stipend is $16,000 for the first year; in subsequent years, fellows receive full payment of tuition and fees plus a stipend and assistantship from their university that is equivalent to funding received by other doctoral students in their department.

Duration 3 to 5 years for the fellowship; 12 weeks during the summer immediately after sponsorship for the internship.

Additional information This program is valid only at 1 of 102 participating GEM member universities; contact GEM for a list. The fellowship award is designed to support the student in the first year of the doctoral program without working. Subsequent years are subsidized by the respective university and will usually include either a teaching or research assistantship. Recipients must participate in the GEM summer internship; failure to agree to accept the internship cancels the fellowship. Recipients must enroll in the same scientific discipline as their undergraduate major.

Number awarded Approximately 40 each year.

Deadline November of each year.

[784]
GENERAL MILLS HEALTH SCHOLARSHIP

Congressional Black Caucus Foundation, Inc.
Attn: Director, Educational Programs
1720 Massachusetts Avenue, N.W.
Washington, DC 20036
(202) 263-2800 Toll Free: (800) 784-2577
Fax: (202) 775-0773 E-mail: scholarships@cbcfinc.org
Web: www.cbcfinc.org/scholarships.html

Summary To provide financial assistance to undergraduate and graduate students who are interested in preparing for a health-related career, especially those who reside in a Congressional district represented by a member of the Congressional Black Caucus (CBC).

Eligibility This program is open to students attending or planning to attend an accredited institution of higher education as a full-time undergraduate or graduate student. Preference is given to those who reside or attend school in a Congressional district represented by a member of the CBC. Applicants must be interested in preparing for a career in a medical or other health-related field, including medicine, nursing, technology, nutrition, or engineering. They must have a GPA of 2.5 or higher. Along with their application, they must submit transcripts; a 1-page resume listing their extracurricular activities, honors, employment, community service, and special skills; and a personal statement of 500 to 1,000 words on themselves and their interests. They must also be able to demonstrate financial need, leadership ability, and participation in community service activities.

Financial data A stipend is awarded (amount not specified).

Duration 1 year.

Additional information The program was established in 1998 with support from General Mills, Inc.

Number awarded Varies each year.

Deadline February of each year.

[785]
GEOLOGICAL SOCIETY OF AMERICA GRADUATE STUDENT RESEARCH GRANTS

Geological Society of America
Attn: Program Officer-Grants, Awards and Recognition
3300 Penrose Place
P.O. Box 9140
Boulder, CO 80301-9140
(303) 357-1028 Toll Free: (800) 472-1988, ext. 1028
Fax: (303) 357-1070 E-mail: awards@geosociety.org
Web: www.geosociety.org/grants/gradgrants.htm

Summary To provide funding to graduate student members (particularly African Americans, other minorities, women, and students with disabilities) of the Geological Society of America (GSA) who are interested in conducting research at universities in the United States, Canada, Mexico, or Central America.

Eligibility This program is open to GSA members working on a master's or doctoral degree at a university in the United States, Canada, Mexico, or Central America. Applicants must be interested in conducting geological research. Minorities, women, and persons with disabilities are strongly encouraged to apply. Selection is based on the scientific merits of the proposal, the capability of the investigator, and the reasonableness of the budget.

Financial data Grants range up to $4,000 and recently averaged $1,829. Funds can be used for the cost of travel, room and board in the field, services of a technician or field assistant, funding of chemical and isotope analyses, or other expenses directly related to the fulfillment of the research contract. Support is not provided for the purchase of ordinary field equipment, for maintenance of the families of the grantees and their assistants, as reimbursement for work already accomplished, for institutional overhead, for adviser participation, or for tuition costs.

Duration 1 year.

Additional information In addition to general grants, GSA awards a number of specialized grants: the Gretchen L. Blechschmidt Award for women (especially in the fields of biostratigraphy and/or paleoceanography); the John T. Dillon Alaska Research Award for earth science problems particular to Alaska; the Robert K. Fahnestock Memorial Award for the field of sediment transport or related aspects of fluvial geomorphology; the Lipman Research Award for volcanology and petrology; the Bruce L. "Biff" Reed Award for studies in the tectonic and magmatic evolution of Alaska; the Alexander Sisson Award for studies in Alaska and the Caribbean; the Harold T. Stearns Fellowship Award for work on the geology of the Pacific Islands and the circum-Pacific region; the Parke D. Snavely, Jr. Cascadia Research Fund Award for studies of the Pacific Northwest convergent margin; the Alexander and Geraldine Wanek Fund Award for studies of coal and petroleum; the Charles A. and June R.P. Ross Research Fund Award for stratigraphy; and the John Montagne Fund Award for research in the field of quaternary geology or geomorphology.

Number awarded Varies each year; recently, the society awarded more than 300 grants worth more than $550,000 through this and all of its specialized programs.

Deadline January of each year.

[786]
GEOPHYSICAL FLUID DYNAMICS FELLOWSHIPS

Woods Hole Oceanographic Institution
Attn: Academic Programs Office
Clark Laboratory, MS 31
266 Woods Hole Road
Woods Hole, MA 02543-1541
(508) 289-2950 Fax: (508) 457-2188
E-mail: gfd@whoi.edu
Web: www.whoi.edu/gfd

Summary To provide summer research and study opportunities at Woods Hole Oceanographic Institution (WHOI) to pre- and postdoctoral scholars (particularly African Americans, other underrepresented minorities, and women) who are interested in geophysical fluid dynamics.

Eligibility This program is open to pre- and postdoctorates who are interested in pursuing research or study opportunities in a field that involves non-linear dynamics of rotating, stratified fluids. Fields of specialization include classical fluid dynamics, physical oceanography, meteorology, geophysical fluid dynamics, astrophysics, planetary atmospheres, hydromagnetics, physics, and applied mathematics. Applications from women and members of underrepresented groups are particularly encouraged.

Financial data Participants receive a stipend of $5,600 and an allowance for travel expenses within the United States.

Duration 10 weeks during the summer.

Additional information Each summer, the program at WHOI revolves around a central theme. A recent theme related to shear turbulence. The main components of the summer program are a series of principal lectures, a set of supplementary research seminars, and research projects conducted by the student fellows with the active support of the staff. Funding for this program, which began in 1959, is provided by the National Science Foundation and Office of Naval Research.

Number awarded Up to 10 graduate students are supported each year.

Deadline February of each year.

[787]
GEORGE A. LOTTIER GOLF FOUNDATION INTERNSHIP AND SCHOLARSHIP AWARD

Atlanta Tribune: The Magazine
Attn: Editor
875 Old Roswell Road, Suite C-100
Roswell, GA 30076-1660
(770) 587-0501, ext. 202 Fax: (770) 642-6501
E-mail: kmines@atlantatribune.com
Web: www.atlantatribune.com

Summary To provide financial aid and summer work experience at the *Atlanta Tribune: The Magazine* to African American and other minority upper-division and graduate students from any state interested in a career in print journalism.

Eligibility This program is open to minority college students from any state entering their junior or senior year of college or enrolled in a graduate program with a GPA of 3.0 or higher. Applicants must be majoring in a field related to print media, including communications, English, graphic design (with an emphasis on publication layout and design), journalism, marketing, or sales. Along with their application, they must submit a 500-word personal essay.

Financial data The program provides a paid internship and a scholarship stipend of $2,500.

Duration 1 year, including 10 weeks during the summer for the internship.

Number awarded Varies each year; recently, 4 of these scholarships and internships were awarded.

Deadline April of each year.

[788]
GEORGE A. STRAIT MINORITY SCHOLARSHIP ENDOWMENT

American Association of Law Libraries
Attn: Chair, Scholarships Committee
105 West Adams Street, Suite 3300
Chicago, IL 60603
(312) 939-4764 Fax: (312) 431-1097
E-mail: scholarships@aall.org
Web: www.aallnet.org

Summary To provide financial assistance to African American and other minority college seniors or college graduates who are interested in becoming law librarians.

Eligibility This program is open to college graduates with meaningful law library experience who are members of minority groups and intend to have a career in law librarianship. Applicants must be degree candidates at an ALA-accredited library school or an ABA-accredited law school. Along with their application, they must submit a personal statement that discusses their interest in law librarianship, reason for applying for this scholarship, career goals as a law librarian, and any other pertinent information.

Financial data The stipend is $3,500.

Duration 1 year.

Additional information This program, established in 1990, is currently supported by Thomson Reuters.

Number awarded Varies each year; recently, 5 of these scholarships were awarded.

Deadline March of each year.

[789]
GEORGE E. MEARES MEMORIAL SCHOLARSHIP

Omega Psi Phi Fraternity
Attn: Charles R. Drew Memorial Scholarship Commission
3951 Snapfinger Parkway
Decatur, GA 30035-3203
(404) 284-5533 Fax: (404) 284-0333
E-mail: scholarshipchairman@oppf.org
Web: www.oppf.org/scholarship

Summary To provide financial assistance to African American and other graduate students in selected social science fields.

Eligibility This program is open to all U.S. citizens who are interested in working on a graduate degree in social work, criminal justice, or social sciences. Applicants must include a statement of 200 to 250 words on their purpose for applying for this scholarship, how they believe funds from the fraternity can assist them in achieving their career goals, and other circumstances (including financial need) that make it important for them to receive financial assistance.

Financial data The stipend is $5,000.

Duration 1 year.

Additional information This program, established in 1977, is named for George E. Meares, who served as Grand Basileus of Omega Psi Phi (an historically Black fraternity) from 1964 to 1967. The winner is required to attend the Omega Psi Phi Grand Conclave or Leadership Conference. Up to $1,000 in travel expenses for attendance is provided.

Number awarded 1 each year.

Deadline April of each year.

[790]
GEORGE V. POWELL DIVERSITY SCHOLARSHIP

Lane Powell PC
Attn: Manager of Attorney Recruiting
1420 Fifth Avenue, Suite 4200
P.O. Box 91302
Seattle, WA 98111-9402
(206) 223-6123 Fax: (206) 223-7107
E-mail: rodenl@lanepowell.com
Web: www.lanepowell.com/422/diversity-scholarship

Summary To provide financial aid and work experience to African Americans and other law students who will contribute to the diversity of the legal community.

Eligibility This program is open to second-year students in good standing at an ABA-accredited law school. Applicants must be able to contribute meaningfully to the diversity of the legal community and have a demonstrated desire to work, live, and eventually practice law in Seattle or Portland. They must submit a cover letter that includes a statement indicating eligibility to participate in the program, a resume, a current copy of law school transcript, a legal writing sample, and a list of 2 or 3 professional or academic references. Selection is based on academic achievement and record of leadership abilities, community service, and involvement in community issues.

Financial data The program provides a stipend of $7,500 for the third year of law school and a paid summer associate clerkship.

Duration 1 year, including the summer.

Additional information This program began in 2005. Clerkships are provided at the offices of the sponsor in Seattle or Portland.

Number awarded 1 each year.

Deadline August of each year.

[791]
GEORGIA ASSOCIATION OF BLACK WOMEN ATTORNEYS SCHOLARSHIPS

Georgia Association of Black Women Attorneys
Attn: GABWA Foundation
P.O. Box 7381
Atlanta, GA 30309-9998
(678) 825-5675 E-mail: contact@gabwa.org
Web: www.gabwa.org/foundation.php

Summary To provide financial assistance to Black women from any state enrolled at law schools in Georgia.

Eligibility This program is open to Black women from any state enrolled in the second or third year at a law school in Georgia. Applicants must be able to demonstrate academic achievement, leadership, and commitment to the profession and their community. Along with their application, they must submit a 300-word personal statement that discusses their experience as a Black woman law student, how they expect their legal career to benefit the community at large, and how this scholarship will benefit their quest for a legal education and future career goals. Financial need is considered in the selection process but is not required.

Financial data Stipend amounts vary, depending on the availability of funds; recently, they averaged $5,000.

Duration 1 year.

Additional information This program began in 2002.

Number awarded Varies each year. Since the program was established, it has awarded nearly $200,000 to more than 50 African American women law students.

Deadline October of each year.

[792]
GOALI GRADUATE STUDENT INDUSTRIAL FELLOWSHIPS/TRAINEESHIPS

National Science Foundation
Directorate for Engineering
Attn: Division of Industrial Innovation and Partnerships
4201 Wilson Boulevard, Room 550S
Arlington, VA 22230
(703) 292-7082 Fax: (703) 292-9056
TDD: (800) 281-8749 E-mail: dsenich@nsf.gov
Web: www.nsf.gov

Summary To provide an opportunity for graduate students (particularly African Americans, other minorities, women, and students with disabilities) to work or conduct research in industry as part of the Grant Opportunities for Academic Liaison with Industry (GOALI) program of the National Science Foundation (NSF).

Eligibility This program is open to graduate students (preferably Ph.D. students) in science, engineering, and mathematics fields of interest to NSF. Applicants must be U.S. citizens, nationals, or permanent residents. They must be proposing a program of full- or part-time work in industry in an area related to their research under the guidance of an academic adviser and an industrial mentor. In the selection process, consideration is given to the achievement of societally relevant outcomes, including full participation of women, persons with disabilities, and underrepresented minorities.

Financial data Graduate students may receive stipends from $1,500 to $1,800 per month, plus transportation expenses. The faculty adviser may receive 10% of the total award for research-related expenses, excluding equipment. No indirect costs are allowed. The total award may be up to $30,000 for a fellowship for a single student.

Duration Up to 1 year.

Additional information This program is also offered by most other NSF directorates. Check the web site for a name and e-mail address of the contact person in each directorate.

Number awarded A total of 60 to 80 grants for all GOALI programs is awarded each year; total funding is approximately $5 million.

Deadline Applications may be submitted at any time.

[793]
GOLDMAN SACHS MBA FELLOWSHIP

Goldman Sachs
Attn: Human Capital Management
200 West Street, 25th Floor
New York, NY 10282
E-mail: Iris.Birungi@gs.com
Web: www.goldmansachs.com

Summary To provide financial aid and work experience to African American and other underrepresented minority students interested in working on an M.B.A. degree.

Eligibility This program is open to graduate students of Black, Latino, or Native American descent who are interested in working on an M.B.A. degree. Applicants must be preparing for a career in the financial services industry. Along with their application, they must submit 2 essays of 500 words or less on the following topics: 1) why they are preparing for a career in the financial services industry; and 2) their current involvement with a community-based organization. Selection is based on analytical skills and the ability to identify significant problems, gather facts, and analyze situations in depth; interpersonal skills, including, but not limited to, poise, confidence, and professionalism; academic record; evidence of hard work and commitment; ability to work well with others; and commitment to community involvement.

Financial data Fellows receive $15,000 toward payment of tuition and living expenses for the first year of business school; an internship at a domestic office of Goldman Sachs during the summer after the first year of business school; and (after successful completion of the summer internship and acceptance of an offer to return to the firm after graduation as a full-time regular employee) either payment of tuition costs for the second year of business school or an additional $15,000 toward tuition and living costs.

Duration Up to 2 years.

Additional information This program was initiated in 1997.

Number awarded 1 or more each year.

Deadline November of each year.

[794]
GRADUATE TRAINING IN DISPARITIES RESEARCH

Susan G. Komen Breast Cancer Foundation
Attn: Grants Department
5005 LBJ Freeway, Suite 250
Dallas, TX 75244
(972) 855-1616 Toll Free: (866) 921-9678
Fax: (972) 855-1640
E-mail: helpdesk@komengrantsaccess.org
Web: ww5.komen.org

Summary To provide funding for training to minority and other graduate students interested in conducting research related to disparities in breast cancer outcomes.

Eligibility This program provides support to students enrolled in a master's, combined master's/doctoral, or doctoral degree program. Applications must be submitted by a full-time faculty member at their institution who is currently conducting research on disparities in breast cancer outcomes. Neither the students nor the faculty mentors are required to be U.S. citizens or residents. The application must describe a training program that combines didactic course work and hands-on laboratory, clinical, and/or public health research. The training program must ensure that all students at all levels will develop the analytic, research, scientific, clinical, and public health skills critical for them to effectively explore the basis for differences in breast cancer outcomes and to develop and translate research discoveries into clinical and public health practice to eliminate those disparities. Strong preference is given to involving trainees from populations adversely affected by disparities in breast cancer outcomes.

Financial data The grant is $45,000 per student per year for direct costs only.

Duration 2 years; a third year may be approved, based on an assessment of first-year progress.

Additional information This program was formerly known as the Post-Baccalaureate Training in Disparities Research Grants.

Number awarded Varies each year; recently, 5 of these grants were awarded.

Deadline Pre-applications must be submitted by early September of each year; full applications are due in October.

[795]
GREAT LAKES SECTION IFT DIVERSITY SCHOLARSHIP

Institute of Food Technologists-Great Lakes Section
c/o Janice Harte, Scholarship Chair
Michigan State University
Department of Food Science and Human Nutrition
106 Malcolm Trout Building
East Lansing, MI 48824-1224
(517) 355-8474, ext. 105 Fax: (517) 353-8963
E-mail: harteja@msu.edu
Web: www.greatlakesift.org

Summary To provide financial assistance to African Americans and other minorities who are members of the Great Lakes Section of the Institute of Food Technologists (IFT) from any state and working on an undergraduate or graduate degree related to food technology at a college in Michigan.

Eligibility This program is open to minority residents of any state who are members of the IFT Great Lakes Section (GLS) and working full time on an undergraduate or graduate degree in food science, nutrition, food engineering, food packaging, or food service courses at a college or university in Michigan. Applicants must have a GPA of 3.0 or higher and plans for a career in the food industry. Along with their application, they must submit a 1-page personal statement that covers their academic program, future plans and career goals, extracurricular activities (including involvement in community, university, GLS, or national IFT activities), and work experience. Financial need is not considered in the selection process.

Financial data The stipend is $1,000.

Duration 1 year; nonrenewable.

Number awarded 1 each year.

Deadline January of each year.

[796] GREATER HARTFORD CHAPTER NBMBAA GRADUATE SCHOLARSHIP

National Black MBA Association-Greater Hartford Chapter
Attn: Scholarship Committee
P.O. Box 2438
Hartford, CT 06146
(860) 586-7002
Web: www.blackmbahartford.com

Summary To provide financial assistance to African Americans and other minorities from any state who are working on a master's degree in business or management at a school in Connecticut or the Springfield area of Massachusetts.

Eligibility This program is open to minority students who may be residents of any state but must be enrolled full or part time at a university in Connecticut or the greater Springfield, Massachusetts area. Applicants must have completed at least 1 semester of a master's degree program in business or management. They must have a GPA of 3.0 or higher. Along with their application, they must submit a 2-page essay on their choice of 4 topics that change annually but relate to African Americans and business. Selection is based on that essay, transcripts, a resume, and extracurricular activities.

Financial data Stipends range from $1,000 to $5,000.

Duration 1 year.

Number awarded 4 each year: 1 each at $5,000, $2,500, $2,000, and $1,000.

Deadline October of each year.

[797] GREENSPOON MARDER DIVERSITY SCHOLARSHIP

Community Foundation of Sarasota County
Attn: Grants and Scholarships Coordinator
2635 Fruitville Road
P.O. Box 49587
Sarasota, FL 34230-6587
(941) 556-7114 Fax: (941) 952-7115
E-mail: eyoung@cfsarasota.org
Web: www.cfsarasota.org/Default.aspx?tabid=263

Summary To provide financial assistance to African American and other minority students from any state attending designated law schools (most of which are in Florida).

Eligibility This program is open to racial and ethnic minority students from any state who are members of groups traditionally underrepresented in the legal profession. Applicants must be entering their second year of full-time study at the University of Florida Levin College of Law, Florida State University College of Law, Stetson University College of Law, Nova Southeastern University Shepard Broad Law Center, St. Thomas University School of Law, Florida A&M University College of Law, Howard University College of Law, Texas Southern University Thurgood Marshall School of Law, Florida Coastal School of Law, or Florida International University College of Law. They must have a GPA of 2.6 or higher. Along with their application, they must submit a 1,000-word personal statement that describes their personal strengths, their contributions through community service, any special or unusual circumstances that may have affected their academic performance, or their personal and family history of educational or socioeconomic disadvantage; it should include aspects of their minority racial or ethnic identity that are relevant to their application. Applicants may also include information about their financial circumstances if they wish to have those considered in the selection process. U.S. citizenship or permanent resident status is required.

Financial data The stipend is $2,500 per semester.

Duration 1 semester (the spring semester of the second year of law school); may be renewed 1 additional semester (the fall semester of the third year).

Additional information This program was established by the Florida law firm Ruden McClosky, which was acquired by the firm Greenspoon Marder in 2011. It is administered by the Community Foundation of Sarasota County, but the law firm selects the recipients.

Number awarded 1 or more each year.

Deadline July of each year.

[798] H. CARL MOULTRIE I LEGAL SCHOLAR AWARD

Omega Psi Phi Fraternity
Attn: Charles R. Drew Memorial Scholarship Commission
3951 Snapfinger Parkway
Decatur, GA 30035-3203
(404) 284-5533 Fax: (404) 284-0333
E-mail: scholarshipchairman@oppf.org
Web: www.oppf.org/scholarship

Summary To provide financial assistance for law school to members of Omega Psi Phi who have an outstanding academic record.

Eligibility This program is open to members of the fraternity who are currently enrolled full time at an accredited school of law and working on a J.D. or equivalent degree. Applicants must have demonstrated service to the fraternity during the year of application and be in good financial standing at all levels. Along with their application, they must submit a statement of 200 to 250 words on their purpose for applying for this scholarship, how they believe funds from the fraternity can assist them in achieving their career goals, and other circumstances (including financial need) that make it important for them to receive financial assistance. Selection is based on academic excellence.

Financial data The stipend is $5,000.

Duration 1 year.

Additional information The winner is required to attend the Omega Psi Phi Grand Conclave or Leadership Conference. Up to $1,000 in travel expenses for attendance is provided.

Number awarded 1 each year.

Deadline April of each year.

[799] HARRIETT G. JENKINS PREDOCTORAL FELLOWSHIP PROGRAM

United Negro College Fund Special Programs Corporation
6402 Arlington Boulevard, Suite 600
Falls Church, VA 22042
(703) 205-7625 Toll Free: (800) 530-6232
Fax: (703) 205-7645
E-mail: sheryl.karpowicz@uncfsp.org
Web: www.uncfsp.org

Summary To provide financial aid and work experience to African Americans, other minorities, women, and people with disabilities working on a graduate degree in a field of interest to the National Aeronautics and Space Administration (NASA).

Eligibility This program is open to members of groups underrepresented in science, technology, engineering, or mathematics (STEM), including women, minorities, and people with disabilities. Applicants must be full-time graduate students entering or in the first 3 years of a program leading to a master's or doctoral degree in a NASA-related discipline (aeronautics, aerospace engineering, astronomy, atmospheric science, bioengineering, biology, chemistry, computer science, earth sciences, engineering, environmental sciences, life sciences, materials sciences, mathematics, meteorology, neuroscience, physics, or robotics). They must be U.S. citizens and have a GPA of 3.0 or higher. Doctoral students who have advanced to candidacy are ineligible.

Financial data The stipend is $24,000 per year for doctoral fellows or $18,000 per year for master's degree students. The tuition offset is at least $8,500. Fellows who are also selected for a mini research award at a NASA Center or the Jet Propulsion Laboratory receive an additional grant of $8,000.

Duration 3 years.

Additional information This program, established in 2001, is funded by NASA and administered by the United Negro College Fund Special Programs Corporation. Fellows may also compete for a mini research award to engage in a NASA research experience that is closely aligned with the research conducted at the fellow's institution. The participating NASA facilities are Ames Research Center (Moffett Field, California), Jet Propulsion Laboratory (Pasadena, California), Dryden Flight Research Center (Edwards, California), Johnson Space Center (Houston, Texas), Stennis Space Center (Stennis Space Center, Mississippi), Marshall Space Flight Center (Marshall Space Flight Center, Alabama), Glenn Research Center (Cleveland, Ohio), Kennedy Space Center (Kennedy Space Center, Florida), Langley Research Center (Hampton, Virginia), and Goddard Space Flight Center (Greenbelt, Maryland).

Number awarded Approximately 20 each year.

Deadline April of each year.

[800] HARRY R. KENDALL LEADERSHIP DEVELOPMENT SCHOLARSHIPS

United Methodist Church
General Board of Global Ministries
Attn: United Methodist Committee on Relief
Health and Welfare Ministries
475 Riverside Drive, Room 330
New York, NY 10115
(212) 870-3871 Toll Free: (800) UMC-GBGM
E-mail: jyoung@gbgm-umc.org
Web: new.gbgm-umc.org/umcor/work/health/scholarships

Summary To provide financial assistance to African Americans who are Methodists or other Christians and preparing for a career in a health-related field.

Eligibility This program is open to undergraduate and graduate students who are U.S. citizens or permanent residents of African American descent. Applicants must be professed Christians, preferably United Methodists. They must be planning to enter a health care field or already be a practitioner in such a field. Financial need is considered in the selection process.

Financial data The stipend is $2,000.

Duration 1 year.

Additional information This program began in 1980.

Number awarded Varies each year.

Deadline June of each year.

[801] HAYNES/HETTING AWARD

Philanthrofund Foundation
Attn: Scholarship Committee
1409 Willow Street, Suite 109
Minneapolis, MN 55403-2241
(612) 870-1806 Toll Free: (800) 435-1402
Fax: (612) 871-6587 E-mail: info@PfundOnline.org
Web: www.pfundonline.org/scholarships.html

Summary To provide financial aid for college to African American and Native American undergraduate or graduate students in Minnesota who have supported gay, lesbian, bisexual, and transgender (GLBT) activities.

Eligibility This program is open to residents of Minnesota and students attending a Minnesota educational institution who are African American or Native American. Applicants must be self-identified as GLBT or from a GLBT family. They may be attending or planning to attend a trade school, technical college, college, or university (as an undergraduate or graduate student). Selection is based on the applicant's 1) affirmation of GLBT or allied identity; 2) evidence of experience and skills in service and leadership; and 3) evidence of service, leading, and working for change in GLBT communities, including serving as a role model, mentor, and/or adviser.

Financial data The stipend is $5,000. Funds must be used for tuition, books, fees, or dissertation expenses.

Duration 1 year.

Number awarded 1 each year.

Deadline January of each year.

[802]
HAYNES RICE AWARD

National Association of Health Services Executives
Attn: Educational Assistance Program
1050 Connecticut Avenue, N.W., Tenth Floor
Washington, DC 20036
(202) 772-1030 Fax: (202) 772-1072
E-mail: nahsehg@nahse.org
Web: netforum.avectra.com

Summary To provide financial assistance to African Americans who are members of the National Association of Health Services Executives (NAHSE) and interested in preparing for a career in health care administration.

Eligibility This program is open to African Americans who are either enrolled or accepted at an accredited college or university to work on a master's or doctoral degree in health care administration. Applicants must be members of NAHSE and able to demonstrate financial need. They must have a GPA of 2.5 or higher as undergraduates or 3.0 or higher as graduate students. Along with their application, they must submit a 3-page essay that describes themselves and their career goals, commitment and interest in health care management, and financial need.

Financial data The stipend is $2,500. Funds are sent to the recipient's institution.

Duration 1 year.

Number awarded 1 each year.

Deadline May of each year.

[803]
HEALTH RESEARCH AND EDUCATIONAL TRUST SCHOLARSHIPS

New Jersey Hospital Association
Attn: Health Research and Educational Trust
760 Alexander Road
P.O. Box 1
Princeton, NJ 08543-0001
(609) 275-4224 Fax: (609) 452-8097
Web: www.njha.com/education/scholarships

Summary To provide financial assistance to New Jersey residents (particularly African Americans, other minorities, and women) who are working on an undergraduate or graduate degree in a field related to health care administration at a school in any state.

Eligibility This program is open to residents of New Jersey enrolled in an upper-division or graduate program in hospital or health care administration, public administration, nursing, or other allied health profession at a school in any state. Graduate students working on an advanced degree to prepare to teach nursing are also eligible. Applicants must have a GPA of 3.0 or higher and be able to demonstrate financial need. Along with their application, they must submit a 2-page essay (on which 50% of the selection is based) describing their academic plans for the future. Minorities and women are especially encouraged to apply.

Financial data The stipend is $2,000.

Duration 1 year.

Additional information This program began in 1983.

Number awarded Varies each year; recently, 3 of these scholarships were awarded.

Deadline July of each year.

[804]
HEALTH SCIENCES STUDENT FELLOWSHIPS IN EPILEPSY

Epilepsy Foundation
Attn: Research Department
8301 Professional Place
Landover, MD 20785-2353
(301) 459-3700 Toll Free: (800) EFA-1000
Fax: (301) 577-2684 TDD: (800) 332-2070
E-mail: grants@efa.org
Web: www.epilepsyfoundation.org

Summary To provide financial assistance to medical and health science graduate students (particularly African Americans, other minorities, women, and students with disabilities) who are interested in working on an epilepsy project during the summer.

Eligibility This program is open to students enrolled, or accepted for enrollment, in a medical school, a doctoral program, or other graduate program. Applicants must have a defined epilepsy-related study or research plan to be carried out under the supervision of a qualified mentor. Because the program is designed as a training opportunity, the quality of the training plans and environment are considered in the selection process. Other selection criteria include the quality of the proposed project, the relevance of the proposed work to epilepsy, the applicant's interest in the field of epilepsy, the applicant's qualifications, the mentor's qualifications (including his or her commitment to the student and the project), and the quality of the training environment for research related to epilepsy. U.S. citizenship is not required, but the project must be conducted in the United States. Applications from women, members of minority groups, and people with disabilities are especially encouraged. The program is not intended for students working on a dissertation research project.

Financial data Stipends are $3,000.

Duration 3 months during the summer.

Additional information Support for this program is provided by many individuals, families, and corporations, especially the American Epilepsy Society, Abbott Laboratories, Ortho-McNeil Pharmaceutical, and Pfizer Inc.

Number awarded Varies each year; recently, 3 of these fellowships were awarded.

Deadline March of each year.

[805]
HELENE M. OVERLY MEMORIAL GRADUATE SCHOLARSHIP

Women's Transportation Seminar
Attn: WTS Foundation
1701 K Street, N.W., Suite 800
Washington, DC 20006
(202) 955-5085 Fax: (202) 955-5088
E-mail: wts@wtsinternational.org
Web: www.wtsinternational.org/education/scholarships

Summary To provide financial assistance to women graduate students (particularly African American and other minority women) who are interested in preparing for a career in transportation.

Eligibility This program is open to women who are enrolled in a graduate degree program in a transportation-related field (e.g., transportation engineering, planning, finance, or logistics). Applicants must have at least a 3.0 GPA and be interested in a career in transportation. Along with their application, they must submit a 750-word statement about their career goals after graduation and why they think they should receive the scholarship award. Applications must be submitted first to a local chapter; the chapters forward selected applications for consideration on the national level. Minority women are particularly encouraged to apply. Selection is based on transportation involvement and goals, job skills, and academic record.

Financial data The stipend is $10,000.

Duration 1 year.

Additional information This program began in 1981. Local chapters may also award additional funding to winners in their area.

Number awarded 1 each year.

Deadline Applications must be submitted by November to a local WTS chapter.

[806]
HENRY DAVID RESEARCH GRANT IN HUMAN REPRODUCTIVE BEHAVIOR AND POPULATION STUDIES

American Psychological Foundation
750 First Street, N.E.
Washington, DC 20002-4242
(202) 336-5843 Fax: (202) 336-5812
E-mail: foundation@apa.org
Web: www.apa.org/apf/funding/david.aspx

Summary To provide funding to young psychologists (particularly African Americans, other minorities, women, and individuals with disabilities) who are interested in conducting research on reproductive behavior.

Eligibility This program is open to doctoral students in psychology working on a dissertation and young psychologists who have no more than 7 years of postgraduate experience. Applicants must be interested in conducting research on human reproductive behavior or an area related to population concerns. Along with their application, they must submit a current curriculum vitae, 2 letters of recommendation, and an essay of 1 to 2 pages on their interest in human reproductive behavior or in population studies. The sponsor encourages applications from individuals who represent diversity in race, ethnicity, gender, age, disability, and sexual orientation.

Financial data The grant is $1,500.

Duration The grant is presented annually.

Number awarded 1 each year.

Deadline February of each year.

[807]
HERBERT W. NICKENS MEDICAL STUDENT SCHOLARSHIPS

Association of American Medical Colleges
Attn: Division of Diversity Policy and Programs
2450 N Street, N.W.
Washington, DC 20037-1126
(202) 862-6203 Fax: (202) 828-1125
E-mail: nickensawards@aamc.org
Web: www.aamc.org/initiatives/awards/nickens-student

Summary To provide financial assistance to African American and other medical students who have demonstrated efforts to address the health-care needs of minorities.

Eligibility This program is open to U.S. citizens and permanent residents entering their third year of study at a U.S. allopathic medical school. Each medical school may nominate 1 student for these awards. The letter must describe the nominee's 1) academic achievement through the first and second year, including special awards and honors, clerkships or special research projects, and extracurricular activities in which the student has shown leadership abilities; 2) leadership efforts to eliminate inequities in medical education and health care; 3) demonstrated leadership efforts in addressing the educational, societal, and health-care needs of minorities; and 4) awards and honors, special research projects, and extracurricular activities in which the student has shown leadership abilities. Nominees must submit a curriculum vitae and a 2-page essay that discusses their leadership efforts in eliminating inequities in medical education and health care for minorities.

Financial data The stipend is $5,000.

Duration 1 year.

Number awarded 5 each year.

Deadline April of each year.

[808]
HERMAN J. NEAL SCHOLARSHIP PROGRAM

Illinois CPA Society
Attn: CPA Endowment Fund of Illinois
550 West Jackson, Suite 900
Chicago, Il 60661-5716
(312) 993-0407 Toll Free: (800) 993-0407 (within IL)
Fax: (312) 993-9954
Web: www.icpas.org/hc-students.aspx?id=2724

Summary To provide financial assistance to African American residents of Illinois enrolled as upper-division or graduate students in accounting at a college or university in the state.

Eligibility This program is open to African American residents of Illinois enrolled as juniors, seniors, or graduate student at a college or university in the state. Applicants must be studying accounting and have a GPA of 3.0 or higher. They must be able to demonstrate a commitment to becoming a C.P.A. and financial need. U.S. citizenship or permanent resident status is required.

Financial data The maximum stipend is $4,000 for payment of tuition and fees. Awards include up to $500 in expenses for books and required classroom materials.

Duration 1 year.

Additional information The scholarship does not cover the cost of C.P.A. examination review courses. Recipients may not receive a full graduate assistantship, fellowship, or scholarship from a college or university, participate in a full-tuition reimbursement cooperative education or internship program, or participate in an employee full-tuition reimbursement program during the scholarship period.

Number awarded Varies each year; recently, 4 of these scholarships were awarded.

Deadline March of each year.

[809]
HILLIS CLARK MARTIN & PETERSON DIVERSITY FELLOWSHIP

Hillis Clark Martin & Peterson P.S.
Attn: Recruiting Coordinator
1221 Second Avenue, Suite 500
Seattle, WA 98101-2925
(206) 470-7647 Fax: (206) 623-7789
E-mail: Brenda@hcmp.com
Web: www.hcmp.com/index.php?p=1_144

Summary To provide financial aid and work experience to African American and other students whose background and life experiences will contribute to the diversity of the legal community.

Eligibility This program is open to students enrolled in the first year at an ABA-accredited law school. Applicants must have a background and life experiences that will contribute meaningfully to the diversity of the legal community. Along with their application, they must submit a resume, transcripts, a personal statement of 1 to 2 pages describing their background and addressing the selection criteria, a legal writing sample, and a list of 3 references. Selection is based on distinction in academic performance, accomplishments and activities, commitment to community service, leadership ability, and financial need.

Financial data The stipend is $7,500.

Duration 1 year.

Additional information The program includes a salaried summer associate position following the first year of law school.

Number awarded 1 or more each year.

Deadline January of each year.

[810]
HOLLY A. CORNELL SCHOLARSHIP

American Water Works Association
Attn: Scholarship Coordinator
6666 West Quincy Avenue
Denver, CO 80235-3098
(303) 794-7771 Toll Free: (800) 926-7337
Fax: (303) 347-0804 E-mail: lmoody@awwa.org
Web: www.awwa.org

Summary To provide financial assistance to outstanding minority and female students interested in working on an master's degree in the field of water supply and treatment.

Eligibility This program is open to minority and female students working on a master's degree in the field of water supply and treatment at a college or university in Canada, Guam, Mexico, Puerto Rico, or the United States. Students who have been accepted into graduate school but have not yet begun graduate study are encouraged to apply. Applicants must submit a 2-page resume, official transcripts, 3 letters of recommendation, a proposed curriculum of study, a 1-page statement of educational plans and career objectives demonstrating an interest in the drinking water field, and a 3-page proposed plan of research. Selection is based on academic record and potential to provide leadership in the field of water supply and treatment.

Financial data The stipend is $7,500.

Duration 1 year; nonrenewable.

Additional information Funding for this program comes from the consulting firm CH2M Hill.

Number awarded 1 each year.

Deadline January of each year.

[811]
HOWARD MAYER BROWN FELLOWSHIP

American Musicological Society
6010 College Station
Brunswick, ME 04011-8451
(207) 798-4243 Toll Free: (877) 679-7648
Fax: (207) 798-4254 E-mail: ams@ams-net.org
Web: www.ams-net.org/fellowships/hmb.php

Summary To provide financial assistance to African American and other minority students who are working on a doctoral degree in the field of musicology.

Eligibility This program is open to members of minority groups historically underrepresented in the field of musicology. In the United States, that includes African Americans, Native Americans, Hispanic Americans, and Asian Americans. In Canada, it refers to visible minorities. Applicants must have completed at least 1 year of full-time academic work at an institution with a graduate program in musicology and be planning to complete a Ph.D. degree in the field. There are no restrictions on research area, age, or sex. Candidates must submit a personal statement summarizing their musical and academic background and stating why they wish to work on an advanced degree in musicology, letters of support from 3 faculty members, a curriculum vitae, and samples of their work (such as term papers or published material). U.S. or Canadian citizenship or permanent resident status is required.

Financial data The stipend is $20,000.

Duration 1 year; nonrenewable.

Additional information This fellowship was first awarded in 1995.

Number awarded 1 each year.

Deadline November of each year.

[812]
HUBERTUS W.V. WILLEMS SCHOLARSHIP FOR MALE STUDENTS

National Association for the Advancement of Colored People
Attn: Education Department
4805 Mt. Hope Drive
Baltimore, MD 21215-3297
(410) 580-5760 Toll Free: (877) NAACP-98
E-mail: youth@naacpnet.org
Web: www.naacp.org/pages/naacp-scholarships

Summary To provide funding to males, particularly male members of the National Association for the Advancement of Colored People (NAACP), who are interested in undergraduate or graduate education in selected scientific fields.

Eligibility This program is open to males who are high school seniors, college students, or graduate students. Applicants must be majoring (or planning to major) in 1 of the following fields: engineering, chemistry, physics, or mathematics. Preference is given to members of the NAACP. The required minimum GPA is 2.5 for graduating high school seniors and undergraduate students or 3.0 for graduate students. Undergraduates must be enrolled full time but graduate students may be full- or part-time students. Applicants must be able to demonstrate financial need, defined as a family income of less than $16,245 for a family of 1 ranging to less than $49,905 for a family of 7. Along with their application, they must submit a 1-page essay on their interest in their major and a career, their life's ambition, what they hope to accomplish in their lifetime, and what position they hope to attain. Full-time enrollment is required for undergraduate students, although graduate students may be enrolled full or part time. U.S. citizenship is required.

Financial data The stipend is $2,000 per year for undergraduate students or $3,000 per year for graduate students.

Duration 1 year; may be renewed.

Number awarded Varies each year; recently, 7 of these scholarships were awarded.

Deadline March of each year.

[813] HUGGINS-QUARLES AWARD

Organization of American Historians
Attn: Award and Committee Coordinator
112 North Bryan Street
Bloomington, IN 47408-4141
(812) 855-7311 Fax: (812) 855-0696
E-mail: khamm@oah.org
Web: www.oah.org

Summary To provide funding to African American and other minority graduate students who are completing dissertations in American history.

Eligibility This program is open to graduate students of color at the dissertation research stage of their Ph.D. programs. Their dissertation must deal with a topic related to African American history.

Financial data The award is $1,500 (if 1 is presented) or $750 (if 2 are presented).

Additional information This award was established in honor of Benjamin Quarles and the late Nathan Huggins, both outstanding historians of the African American past.

Number awarded 1 or 2 each year.

Deadline November of each year.

[814] HUGH J. ANDERSEN MEMORIAL SCHOLARSHIPS

National Medical Fellowships, Inc.
Attn: Scholarship Program
347 Fifth Avenue, Suite 510
New York, NY 10016
(212) 483-8880 Toll Free: (877) NMF-1DOC
Fax: (212) 483-8897 E-mail: scholarships@nmfonline.org
Web: www.nmfonline.org

Summary To provide financial assistance to African American and other underrepresented minority medical students who reside or attend school in Minnesota.

Eligibility This program is open to African Americans, Hispanics/Latinos, Native Americans, Vietnamese, Cambodians, and Pacific Islanders who are entering the second or third year of medical school. Applicants must be Minnesota residents enrolled in an accredited U.S. medical school or residents of other states attending medical school in Minnesota. Selection is based on leadership, community service, and financial need.

Financial data The award is $2,500.

Duration 1 year.

Additional information This program began in 1982.

Number awarded Up to 5 each year.

Deadline September of each year.

[815] HURSTON/WRIGHT AWARD FOR COLLEGE WRITERS

Zora Neale Hurston/Richard Wright Foundation
Attn: Hurston/Wright Awards
12138 Central Avenue, Suite 953
Bowie, MD 20721
(301) 459-2108 E-mail: info@hurstonwright.org
Web: www.hurstonwright.org/#!college-awards/cs3d

Summary To recognize and reward the best fiction written by undergraduate or graduate students of African descent.

Eligibility This program is open to students of African descent who are enrolled full time as undergraduate or graduate students at a college or university in the United States. Applicants should submit a manuscript of a short story (up to 25 pages) or novel excerpt (up to 15 pages). They should indicate whether it is a short story or novel excerpt. Only 1 entry may be submitted per applicant. Writers who have already published a book (in any genre) are ineligible.

Financial data The first-place award is $1,000; finalist awards are $500.

Duration The prizes are awarded annually.

Additional information There is a $10 processing fee.

Number awarded 3 awards are presented each year: 1 first-place award and 2 finalist awards.

Deadline January of each year.

[816] IABA SCHOLARSHIPS

International Association of Black Actuaries
Attn: IABA Foundation Scholarship Committee
P.O. Box 369
Windsor, CT 06095
(860) 906-1286 Fax: (860) 906-1369
E-mail: iaba@blackactuaries.org
Web: www.blackactuaries.org/scholarships

Summary To provide financial assistance to Black upper-division and graduate students preparing for an actuarial career.

Eligibility This program is open to full-time juniors, seniors, and graduate students who are of African descent, originating from the United States, Canada, the Caribbean, or African nations. Applicants must have been admitted to a college or university offering either a program in actuarial science or courses that will prepare them for an actuarial career. They must be citizens or permanent residents of the United States or Canada or eligible to study in those countries under a U.S. student visa or Canadian student authorization. Other requirements include a GPA of 3.0 or higher, a mathematics SAT score of at least 600 or a mathematics ACT score of at least 28, completion of probability and calculus courses, attempting or passing an actuarial examination, completion of Validation by Educational Experience (VEE) requirements, and familiarity with actuarial profession demands. Selection is based on merit and financial need.

Financial data Stipends range from $3,500 to $5,000 per year.

Duration 1 year; may be renewed.

Additional information Support for this program is provided by Ernst & Young, Liberty Mutual, New York Life, Prudential, and Towers Watson.

Number awarded Varies each year; recently, 16 of these scholarships, with a total value of $59,000, were awarded.

Deadline May of each year.

[817]
IBM PHD FELLOWSHIP AWARDS PROGRAM

IBM Corporation
Attn: University Relations
1133 Westchester Avenue
White Plains, NY 10604
Toll Free: (800) IBM-4YOU TDD: (800) IBM-3383
E-mail: phdfellow@us.ibm.com
Web: www.research.ibm.com

Summary To provide funding and work experience to students (particularly minorities, women, and others who contribute to diversity) who are working on a Ph.D. in a research area of broad interest to IBM.

Eligibility Students nominated for this fellowship should be enrolled full time at an accredited college or university in any country and should have completed at least 1 year of graduate study in computer science or engineering, electrical or mechanical engineering, physical sciences (chemistry, material sciences, physics), mathematical sciences, public sector and business sciences, or service science, management, and engineering (SSME). Focus areas that receive special consideration include technology that creates new business or social value, innovative software, new types of computers, or interdisciplinary projects that create social and business value. Applicants should be planning a career in research. Nominations must be made by a faculty member and endorsed by the department head. The program values diversity, and encourages nominations of women, minorities, and others who contribute to that diversity. Selection is based on the applicants' potential for research excellence, the degree to which their technical interests align with those of IBM, and academic progress to date. Preference is given to students who have had an IBM internship or have closely collaborated with technical or services people from IBM.

Financial data Fellowships pay tuition, fees, and a stipend of $17,500 per year.

Duration 1 year; may be renewed up to 2 additional years, provided the recipient is renominated, interacts with IBM's technical community, and demonstrates continued progress and achievement.

Additional information Recipients are offered an internship at 1 of the IBM Research Division laboratories and are given an IBM computer.

Number awarded Varies each year; recently, 57 of these scholarships were awarded.

Deadline October of each year.

[818]
ILLINOIS NURSES FOUNDATION CENTENNIAL SCHOLARSHIP

Illinois Nurses Association
Attn: Illinois Nurses Foundation
105 West Adams Street, Suite 1420
Chicago, IL 60603
(312) 419-2900 Fax: (312) 419-2920
E-mail: inf@illinoisnurses.com
Web: www.illinoisnurses.com

Summary To provide financial assistance to nursing undergraduate and graduate students who are African American or members of other underrepresented groups.

Eligibility This program is open to students working on an associate, bachelor's, or master's degree at an accredited NLNAC or CCNE school of nursing. Applicants must be members of a group underrepresented in nursing (African Americans, Hispanics, American Indians, Asians, and males). Undergraduates must have earned a passing grade in all nursing courses taken to date and have a GPA of 2.85 or higher. Graduate students must have completed at least 12 semester hours of graduate work and have a GPA of 3.0 or higher. All applicants must be willing to 1) act as a spokesperson to other student groups on the value of the scholarship to continuing their nursing education; and 2) be profiled in any media or marketing materials developed by the Illinois Nurses Foundation. Along with their application, they must submit a narrative of 250 to 500 words on how they, as nurses, plan to affect policy at either the state or national level that impacts on nursing or health care generally, or how they believe they will impact the nursing profession in general.

Financial data A stipend is awarded (amount not specified).

Duration 1 year.

Number awarded 1 or more each year.

Deadline March of each year.

[819]
INDIANAPOLIS CHAPTER NBMBAA GRADUATE SCHOLARSHIP PROGRAM

National Black MBA Association-Indianapolis Chapter
Attn: Scholarship Program
P.O. Box 2325
Indianapolis, IN 46206-2325
(317) 308-6447 E-mail: scholarship@nbmbaa-indy.org
Web: www.nbmbaa-indy.org/nbmbaa_education.htm

Summary To provide financial assistance to African American students from Indiana working on an M.B.A. degree.

Eligibility This program is open to African American students enrolled full time in a graduate business or management program and working on an M.B.A. degree. Applicants must be Indiana residents or enrolled at an Indiana college or university and have a GPA of 2.0 or higher. They must submit essays on 3 topics that change annually but relate to African Americans and business. U.S. citizenship or permanent resident status is required.

Financial data The stipend is $2,000. A 1-year membership in the National Black MBA Association (NBMBAA) is also provided.

Duration 1 year.

Number awarded 2 each year.

Deadline October of each year.

[820]
INITIATIVE TO RECRUIT A DIVERSE WORKFORCE

Association of Research Libraries
Attn: Director of Diversity Programs
21 Dupont Circle, N.W., Suite 800
Washington, DC 20036
(202) 296-2296 Fax: (202) 872-0884
E-mail: mpuente@arl.org
Web: www.arl.org/diversity/init/index.shtml

Summary To provide financial assistance to African Americans and other minorities who are interested in preparing for a career as an academic or research librarian.

Eligibility This program is open to members of racial and ethnic minority groups that are underrepresented as professionals in academic and research libraries (American Indian or Alaska Native, Asian, Black or African American, Native Hawaiian or other Pacific Islander, or Hispanic or Latino). Preference is given to students who have an academic background in a discipline of science, technology, engineering, or mathematics (STEM). Applicants must be interested in working on an M.L.I.S. degree at an ALA-accredited program. They must be citizens or permanent residents of the United States (including Puerto Rico) or Canada. Along with their application, they must submit a 400-word essay on what attracts them to a career in a research library. The essays are judged on clarity and content of form, clear goals and benefits, enthusiasm, potential growth perceived, and professional goals.

Financial data The stipend is $5,000 per year.

Duration 2 years.

Additional information This program began in 2000. Funding is currently provided by the Institute of Museum and Library Services and by the contributions of 52 libraries that are members of the Association of Research Libraries (ARL). Recipients who do not have academic training in STEM disciplines must take additional course work to prepare them for a career in those fields.

Number awarded Varies each year; recently, 14 of these scholarships were awarded.

Deadline April of each year.

[821]
INSTITUTE FOR SUPPLY MANAGEMENT DOCTORAL DISSERTATION GRANT PROGRAM

Institute for Supply Management
Attn: Director, Education and Training
2055 East Centennial Circle
P.O. Box 22160
Tempe, AZ 85285-2160
(480) 752-6276, ext. 3092
Toll Free: (800) 888-6276, ext. 3092
Fax: (480) 752-7890 E-mail: cmendoza@ism.ws
Web: www.ism.ws

Summary To provide financial support to doctoral candidates (particularly African Americans, other minorities, women, and students with disabilities) who are conducting dissertation research in purchasing or related fields.

Eligibility This program is open to doctoral candidates who are working on a Ph.D. or D.B.A. in supply management, supply chain management, business, management, logistics, economics, industrial engineering, or a related field at an accredited university in the United States. International applicants are accepted. Examples of research projects that could be funded include: purchasing and supply management models, methodologies, measurement, supply networks, operations and logistics integration, produce/service innovation, supply relationships, supply's role in corporate success, or strategic development of supply. The research proposal (up to 25 pages) must discuss hypotheses, significance of the study, research methodology, and value of the research to the field of purchasing. The program encourages applications from a diverse population, regardless of gender, race, creed, age, ethnic or national origin, sexual orientation, or disability.

Financial data Grants range up to $6,000.

Duration 1 year.

Additional information The sponsoring organization was previously known as the National Association of Purchasing Management.

Number awarded Up to 4 each year.

Deadline January of each year.

[822]
INTEL CORPORATION SCHOLARSHIPS

Society of Women Engineers
Attn: Scholarship Selection Committee
203 North LaSalle Street, Suite 1675
Chicago, IL 60601-1269
(312) 596-5223 Toll Free: (877) SWE-INFO
Fax: (312) 644-8557 E-mail: scholarships@swe.org
Web: societyofwomenengineers.swe.org

Summary To provide financial assistance to women (particularly African American and other minority women) who are members of the Society of Women Engineers (SWE) and working on a graduate degree in computer science or specified fields of engineering.

Eligibility This program is open to SWE members working full time on a graduate degree in computer science or chemical, computer, electrical, industrial, manufacturing, materials, or mechanical engineering. Applicants must have a GPA of 3.5 or higher. Selection is based on merit and financial need. Preference is given to members of groups underrepresented in computer science and engineering and to residents of Arizona, California, Colorado, Massachusetts, New Mexico, Oregon, and Washington. U.S. citizenship or permanent residents status is required.

Financial data The stipend is $5,000.

Duration 1 year.

Additional information This program is sponsored by Intel Corporation.

Number awarded 2 each year.

Deadline February of each year.

[823]
INTELLECTUAL PROPERTY LAW SECTION WOMEN AND MINORITY SCHOLARSHIP

State Bar of Texas
Attn: Intellectual Property Law Section
c/o Syed K. Fareed, Scholarship Selection Committee
Vinson & Elkins LLP
2801 Via Fortuna, Suite 100
Austin, TX 78746
(512) 542-8400 Fax: (512) 542-8612
E-mail: sfareed@velaw.com
Web: texasbariplaw.org

Summary To provide financial assistance to African Americans, other minorities, and females who are enrolled at law schools in Texas and plan to practice intellectual property law.

Eligibility This program is open to women and members of minority groups (African Americans, Hispanics, Asian Americans, and Native Americans) from any state who are currently enrolled at an ABA-accredited law school in Texas. Applicants must be planning to practice intellectual property law in Texas. Along with their application, they must submit a 2-page essay explaining why they plan to prepare for a career in intellectual property law in Texas, any qualifications they believe are relevant for their consideration for this scholarship, and (optionally) any issues of financial need they wish to have considered.

Financial data The stipend is $2,500.

Duration 1 year.

Number awarded 2 each year: 1 to a women and 1 to a minority.

Deadline April of each year.

[824]
INTERFAITH SPIRITUALITY SCHOLARSHIP

Unitarian Universalist Association
Attn: Ministerial Credentialing Office
25 Beacon Street
Boston, MA 02108-2800
(617) 948-6403 Fax: (617) 742-2875
E-mail: mcoadministrator@uua.org
Web: www.uua.org

Summary To provide financial assistance to seminary students (particularly African Americans and other students of color) who are preparing for the Unitarian Universalist (UU) ministry and are interested in interfaith understanding.

Eligibility This program is open to seminary students who are enrolled full or at least half time in a UU ministerial training program with aspirant or candidate status. Applicants must have demonstrated 1) an interest in and desire to integrate interfaith understanding into their ministry; and 2) a commitment to guiding others on their own spiritual path. Priority is given first to those who have demonstrated outstanding ministerial ability and secondarily to students with the greatest financial need (especially persons of color).

Financial data The stipend ranges from $1,000 to $15,000 per year.

Duration 1 year.

Number awarded 1 each year.

Deadline April of each year.

[825]
INTERMOUNTAIN SECTION AWWA DIVERSITY SCHOLARSHIP

American Water Works Association-Intermountain Section
Attn: Member Services Coordinator
3430 East Danish Road
Sandy, UT 94093
(801) 712-1619, ext. 2 Fax: (801) 487-6699
E-mail: nicoleb@ims-awwa.org
Web: ims-awwa.site-ym.com/group/StudentPO

Summary To provide financial assistance to African Americans, other minorities, and women who are interested in working on an undergraduate or graduate degree in the field of water quality, supply, and treatment at a university in Idaho or Utah.

Eligibility This program is open to 1) women; and 2) students who identify as Hispanic or Latino, Black or African American, Native Hawaiian or other Pacific Islander, Asian, or American Indian or Alaska Native. Applicants must be entering or enrolled in an undergraduate or graduate program at a college or university in Idaho or Utah that relates to water quality, supply, or treatment. Along with their application, they must submit a 2-page essay on their academic interests and career goals and how those relate to water quality, supply, or treatment. Selection is based on that essay, letters of recommendation, and potential to contribute to the field of water quality, supply, and treatment in the Intermountain West.

Financial data The stipend is $1,000. The winner also receives a 1-year student membership in the Intermountain Section of the American Water Works Association (AWWA) and a 1-year subscription to *Journal AWWA.*

Duration 1 year; nonrenewable.

Number awarded 1 each year.

Deadline October of each year.

[826]
ISAAC J. "IKE" CRUMBLY MINORITIES IN ENERGY GRANT

American Association of Petroleum Geologists Foundation
Attn: Grants-in-Aid Program
1444 South Boulder Avenue
P.O. Box 979
Tulsa, OK 74101-0979
(918) 560-2644 Toll Free: (855) 302-2743
Fax: (918) 560-2642 E-mail: foundation@aapg.org
Web: foundation.aapg.org/gia/crumbly.cfm

Summary To provide funding to African Americans, other minorities, and women who are in graduate school and interested in conducting research related to earth science aspects of the petroleum industry.

Eligibility This program is open to women and ethnic minorities (Black, Hispanic, Asian, or Native American, including American Indian, Eskimo, Hawaiian, or Samoan) who are working on a master's or doctoral degree. Applicants must be interested in conducting research related to the search for and development of petroleum and energy-minerals resources and to related environmental geology issues. Selection is based on student's academic and employment history (10 points), scientific merit of proposal (30 points), suitability to program objectives (30 points), financial merit of proposal (20 points), and endorsement by faculty or department adviser (10 points).

Financial data Grants range from $500 to $3,000. Funds are to be applied to research-related expenses (e.g., a summer of field work). They may not be used to purchase capital equipment or to pay salaries, tuition, room, or board.

Duration 1 year. Doctoral candidates may receive a 1-year renewal.

Number awarded 1 each year.

Deadline February of each year.

[827]
JACK AND SADYE GIBSON SCHOLARSHIP FUND

Black Entertainment and Sports Lawyers Association
Attn: Scholarships
P.O. Box 230794
New York, NY 10023
E-mail: scholarship@besla.org
Web: www.besla.org/#!scholarship/cfvg

Summary To provide financial assistance to members of the National Black Law Students Association (NBLSA) who are interested in the fields of entertainment and/or sports law.

Eligibility This program is open to NBLSA members who have completed at least 1 year of full-time study at an accredited law school. Applicants must be able to demonstrate an interest in entertainment or sports law by 1 or more of the following: 1) completing an entertainment law or sports law related course; 2) internship or clerkship in the entertainment or sports law field; 3) current job in the field of entertainment or sports; 4) current membership in an entertainment or sports law society or association; or 5) attendance at an entertainment law or sports law seminar or conference since enrolling in law school. They must have a GPA of 2.5 or higher. Along with their application, they must submit a 5-page legal memorandum on an issue facing the entertainment or sports industry.

Financial data The stipend is at least $1,500.

Duration 1 year.

Number awarded 1 or more each year.

Deadline July of each year.

[828]
JAMES B. MORRIS SCHOLARSHIPS

James B. Morris Scholarship Fund
Attn: Scholarship Selection Committee
P.O. Box 12145
Des Moines, IA 50312
(515) 864-0922
Web: www.morrisscholarship.org

Summary To provide financial assistance to African American and other minority undergraduate, graduate, and law students from Iowa.

Eligibility This program is open to minority students (African Americans, Asian/Pacific Islanders, Hispanics, or Native Americans) who are interested in working on an undergraduate or graduate degree. Applicants must be either Iowa residents attending a college or university anywhere in the United States or non-Iowa residents who are attending a college or university in Iowa. Along with their application, they must submit an essay of 250 to 500 words on why they are applying for this scholarship, activities or organizations in which they are involved, and their future plans. Selection is based on the essay, academic achievement (GPA of 2.5 or higher), community service, and financial need. U.S. citizenship is required.

Financial data The stipend ranges from $1,000 to $2,500 per year.

Duration 1 year; may be renewed.

Additional information This fund was established in 1978 in honor of the J.B. Morris family, who founded the Iowa branch of the National Association for the Advancement of Colored People and published the *Iowa Bystander* newspaper. The program includes the Ann Chapman Scholarships, the Vincent Chapman, Sr. Scholarships, and the Brittany Hall Memorial Scholarships.

Number awarded Varies each year; recently, 19 of these scholarships were awarded.

Deadline March of each year.

[829]
JAMES CARLSON MEMORIAL SCHOLARSHIP

Oregon Student Access Commission
Attn: Grants and Scholarships Division
1500 Valley River Drive, Suite 100
Eugene, OR 97401-2146
(541) 687-7395 Toll Free: (800) 452-8807, ext. 7395
Fax: (541) 687-7414 TDD: (800) 735-2900
E-mail: awardinfo@osac.state.or.us
Web: www.oregonstudentaid.gov/scholarships.aspx

Summary To provide financial assistance to Oregon residents from diverse environments (including African Americans) who are majoring in education on the undergraduate or graduate school level at a school in any state.

Eligibility This program is open to residents of Oregon who are U.S. citizens or permanent residents and enrolled at a college or university in any state. Applicants must be either 1) college seniors or fifth-year students majoring in elementary or secondary education; or 2) graduate students working on an elementary or secondary certificate. Full-time enrollment and financial need are required. Priority is given to 1) students who come from diverse environments and submit an essay of 250 to 350 words on their experience living or working in diverse environments; 2) dependents of members of the Oregon Education Association; and 3) applicants committed to teaching autistic children.

Financial data Stipends for scholarships offered by the Oregon Student Access Commission (OSAC) range from $200 to $10,000 but recently averaged $2,300.

Duration 1 year.

Additional information This program is administered by the OSAC with funds provided by the Oregon Community Foundation.

Number awarded Varies each year; recently, 3 of these scholarships were awarded.

Deadline February of each year.

[830]
JAMES W. STOUDT SCHOLARSHIPS

Pennsylvania Bar Association
Attn: Foundation
100 South Street
P.O. Box 186
Harrisburg, PA 17108-0186
(717) 213-2501 Toll Free: (888) 238-3036
Fax: (717) 213-2548 E-mail: info@pabarfoundation.org
Web: www.pabarfoundation.org

Summary To provide financial assistance to African American and other residents of Pennsylvania who are attending law school in the state.

Eligibility This program is open to residents of Pennsylvania who are currently enrolled in the second year (or third year of a 4- or 5-year law school program) at a law school in the state. Applicants must be members of the Pennsylvania Bar Association student division. Some of the awards are reserved for students who are members of groups historically underrepresented in the legal profession (African Americans, Hispanic Americans, and Native Americans). Along with their application, they must submit a 500-word essay explaining how they plan to demonstrate their potential for making a contribution to society and the legal profession. Selection is based on that essay, academic achievement, and financial need.

Financial data The stipend is $3,000.

Duration 1 year.

Number awarded 4 each year, of which 2 are reserved for underrepresented minority students.

Deadline November of each year.

[831]
J.D. WILLIAMS SCHOLARSHIP

African Methodist Episcopal Church
Connectional Lay Organization
Attn: Scholarship Chair
P.O. Box 7682
Tallahassee, FL 32314
(850) 580-1400 Fax: (850) 224-3139
E-mail: hdbo12@yahoo.com
Web: www.connectionallay-amec.org

Summary To provide financial assistance to members of the African Methodist Episcopal (AME) Church who are interested in working on an undergraduate or graduate degree at a college or university affiliated with the denomination.

Eligibility This program is open to members of AME churches who are working on or planning to work on a bachelor's, M.Div., or D.Min. degree at an AME college or university. Applicants must submit a 500-word essay on the importance of a college education in the 21st century. Selection is based on academic record, qualities of leadership, extracurricular activities and accomplishments, reference letters, and financial need.

Financial data The stipend is $5,000. Funds are sent directly to the student.

Duration 1 year.

Number awarded 1 or more each year.

Deadline March of each year.

[832]
JDOS-INTERNATIONALE SCHOLARSHIP

National Forum for Black Public Administrators
Attn: Scholarship Program
777 North Capitol Street, N.E., Suite 807
Washington, DC 20002
(202) 408-9300 Fax: (202) 408-8558
E-mail: vharris@nfbpa.org
Web: www.nfbpa.org/i4a/pages/index.cfm?pageid=4047

Summary To provide financial assistance to African Americans working on a undergraduate or graduate degree in public administration or a related field.

Eligibility This program is open to African American undergraduate and graduate students preparing for a career in public service. Applicants must be working full time on a degree in public administration, political science, urban affairs, public policy, or a related field. They must have excellent interpersonal and analytical abilities and strong oral and written communication skills. Along with their application, they must submit a 3-page autobiographical essay that includes their academic and career goals and objectives. Selection is based on academic record, leadership ability, participation in school activities, community service, and financial need.

Financial data The stipend is $2,500.

Duration 1 year.

Additional information This program is sponsored by the construction management firm JDos-Internationalé of Washington, D.C. Recipients are required to attend the sponsor's annual conference to receive their scholarship; limited hotel and air accommodations are arranged and provided.

Number awarded 1 each year.

Deadline February of each year.

[833]
JEANNE SPURLOCK RESEARCH FELLOWSHIP IN SUBSTANCE ABUSE AND ADDICTION FOR MINORITY MEDICAL STUDENTS

American Academy of Child and Adolescent Psychiatry
Attn: Department of Research, Training, and Education
3615 Wisconsin Avenue, N.W.
Washington, DC 20016-3007
(202) 587-9663 Fax: (202) 966-5894
E-mail: training@aacap.org
Web: www.aacap.org

Summary To provide funding to African American and other minority medical students who are interested in working during the summer on the topics of drug abuse and addiction with a child and adolescent psychiatrist researcher-mentor.

Eligibility This program is open to African American, Asian American, Native American, Alaska Native, Mexican American, Hispanic, and Pacific Islander students in accredited U.S. medical schools. Applicants must present a plan for a program of research training in drug abuse and addiction that involves significant contact with a mentor who is an experienced child and adolescent psychiatrist researcher. The plan should include program planning discussions; instruction in research planning and implementation; regular meetings with the mentor, laboratory director, and research group; and assigned readings. The mentor must be a member of the American Academy of Child and Adolescent Psychiatry

(AACAP). Research assignments may include responsibility for part of the observation or evaluation, developing specific aspects of the research mechanisms, conducting interviews or tests, using rating scales, and psychological or cognitive testing of subjects. The training plan also should include discussion of ethical issues in research, such as protocol development, informed consent, collection and storage of raw data, safeguarding data, bias in analyzing data, plagiarism, protection of patients, and ethical treatment of animals. U.S. citizenship or permanent resident status is required.

Financial data The stipend is $4,000. Fellows also receive reimbursement of travel expenses to attend the annual meeting of the American Academy of Child and Adolescent Psychiatry.

Duration 12 weeks during the summer.

Additional information Upon completion of the training program, the student is required to submit a brief paper summarizing the research experience. The fellowship pays expenses for the fellow to attend the academy's annual meeting and present this paper. This program is co-sponsored by the National Institute on Drug Abuse.

Number awarded Up to 5 each year.

Deadline February of each year.

[834]
JERRY N. JOHNSON SCHOLARSHIP AWARD

National Forum for Black Public Administrators
Attn: Scholarship Program
777 North Capitol Street, N.E., Suite 807
Washington, DC 20002
(202) 408-9300 Fax: (202) 408-8558
E-mail: vharris@nfbpa.org
Web: www.nfbpa.org/i4a/pages/index.cfm?pageid=4047

Summary To provide financial assistance to African American graduate students from Washington, D.C. working on a degree in public administration.

Eligibility This program is open to African Americans who reside or attend school in Washington, D.C. Applicants must be working on a master's degree in public administration or a related field. They must have a GPA of 3.0 or higher, excellent interpersonal and analytical abilities, and strong oral and written communication skills. Along with their application, they must submit a 500-word essay on their prior or current public or community service involvement and how it has influenced their future aspirations in public administration. Selection is based on academic record, leadership ability, participation in school activities, community service, and financial need.

Financial data The stipend is $4,500.

Duration 1 year.

Additional information This program is sponsored by the Washington, D.C. Chapter of the National Forum for Black Public Administrators (NFBPA). Recipients are required to attend the sponsor's annual conference to receive their scholarship; limited hotel and air accommodations are arranged and provided.

Number awarded 1 each year.

Deadline February of each year.

[835]
JIM MCKAY SCHOLARSHIP PROGRAM

National Collegiate Athletic Association
Attn: Jim McKay Scholarship Program Staff Liaison
700 West Washington Street
P.O. Box 6222
Indianapolis, IN 46206-6222
(317) 917-6222 Fax: (317) 917-6888
E-mail: lthomas@ncaa.org
Web: www.ncaa.org

Summary To provide financial assistance to student-athletes (particularly African Americans, other minorities, and women) who are interested in attending graduate school to prepare for a career in sports communications.

Eligibility This program is open to college seniors planning to enroll full time in a graduate degree program and to students already enrolled full time in graduate study at an institution that is a member of the National Collegiate Athletic Association (NCAA). Applicants must have competed in intercollegiate athletics as a member of a varsity team at an NCAA member institution and have an overall undergraduate cumulative GPA of 3.5 or higher. They must be preparing for a career in the sports communications industry. Women and minorities are especially encouraged to apply. Neither financial need nor U.S. citizenship are required. Nominations must be submitted by the faculty athletics representative or chief academic officer at the institution in which the student is or was an undergraduate.

Financial data The stipend is $10,000.

Duration 1 year; nonrenewable.

Additional information This program began in 2008.

Number awarded 2 each year: 1 female and 1 male.

Deadline January of each year.

[836]
JNMA AWARDS FOR MEDICAL JOURNALISM

National Medical Fellowships, Inc.
Attn: Scholarship Program
347 Fifth Avenue, Suite 510
New York, NY 10016
(212) 483-8880 Toll Free: (877) NMF-1DOC
Fax: (212) 483-8897 E-mail: info@nmfonline.org
Web: www.nmfonline.org

Summary To provide financial assistance to African American medical students who are also interested in journalism.

Eligibility This program is open to African American medical students in their third or fourth year at accredited M.D. or D.O. degree-granting schools in the United States. Only nominations are accepted. Nominees must have published articles and photographs in (or been writers, editors, or photographers on the staffs of) medical school newspapers, medical student journals (e.g., *Journal of the Student National Medical Association* or the *New Physician* magazine), recognized professional journals (e.g., the *Journal of the National Medical Association,* the *Journal of the American Medical Association,* or the *New England Journal of Medicine*), or other respected scientific journals. Students who have written, produced, or directed health-related films, commercials, or videos are also eligible. Selection is based on academic achievement, demonstrated journalistic skill, leadership and community involvement, and potential for outstanding contributions to medicine.

Financial data The awards are $2,500.

Duration 1 year.

Additional information This program is sponsored by the Journal of the National Medical Association (JNMA).

Number awarded 2 each year.

Deadline April of each year.

[837] JOHN A. MAYES SCHOLARSHIP

National Athletic Trainers' Association
Attn: Ethnic Diversity Advisory Committee
2952 Stemmons Freeway, Suite 200
Dallas, TX 75247-6103
(214) 532-8802 Toll Free: (800) 879-6282
Fax: (214) 637-2206
Web: www.nata.org/edac/John-A-Mayes-Scholarship

Summary To provide financial aid to African American and other ethnically diverse graduate students who are preparing for a career as an athletic trainer.

Eligibility This program is open to members of ethnically diverse groups who have been accepted into an entry-level master's athletic training degree program or into a doctoral-level athletic training and/or sports medicine degree program. Applicants must be sponsored by a certified athletic trainer who is a member of the National Athletic Trainers' Association (NATA). They must have a cumulative GPA of 3.2 or higher. First priority is given to a student working on an entry-level athletic training master's degree; second priority is given to a student entering the second year of an athletic training master's degree program; third priority is given to a student working on a doctoral degree in athletic training or sports medicine. Special consideration is given to applicants who have been members of NATA for at least 2 years.

Financial data The stipend is $2,300.

Duration 1 year.

Additional information This program began in 2009.

Number awarded 1 each year.

Deadline February of each year.

[838] JOHN AND MURIEL LANDIS SCHOLARSHIPS

American Nuclear Society
Attn: Scholarship Coordinator
555 North Kensington Avenue
La Grange Park, IL 60526-5535
(708) 352-6611 Toll Free: (800) 323-3044
Fax: (708) 352-0499 E-mail: outreach@ans.org
Web: www.new.ans.org/honors/scholarships

Summary To provide financial assistance to undergraduate or graduate students (particularly African Americans, other minorities, and women) who are interested in preparing for a career in nuclear-related fields and can demonstrate financial need.

Eligibility This program is open to undergraduate and graduate students at colleges or universities located in the United States who are preparing for, or planning to prepare for, a career in nuclear science, nuclear engineering, or a nuclear-related field. Qualified high school seniors are also eligible. Applicants must have greater than average financial need and have experienced circumstances that render them disadvantaged. Along with their application, they must submit an essay on their academic and professional goals, experiences that have affected those goals, etc. Selection is based on that essay, academic achievement, letters of recommendation, and financial need. Women and members of minority groups are especially urged to apply. U.S. citizenship is not required.

Financial data The stipend is $5,000, to be used to cover tuition, books, fees, room, and board.

Duration 1 year; nonrenewable.

Number awarded Up to 9 each year.

Deadline January of each year.

[839] JOHN HOPE FRANKLIN DISSERTATION FELLOWSHIP

American Philosophical Society
Attn: Committee on Research
104 South Fifth Street
Philadelphia, PA 19106-3387
(215) 440-3429 Fax: (215) 440-3436
E-mail: LMusumeci@amphilsoc.org
Web: www.amphilsoc.org/grants/johnhopefranklin

Summary To provide funding to African American and other underrepresented minority graduate students conducting research for a doctoral dissertation.

Eligibility This program is open to African American, Hispanic American, and Native American graduate students working on a degree at a Ph.D. granting institution in the United States. Other talented students who have a demonstrated commitment to eradicating racial disparities and enlarging minority representation in academia are also eligible. Applicants must have completed all course work and examinations preliminary to the doctoral dissertation and be able to devote full-time effort, with no teaching obligations, to researching or writing their dissertation. The proposed research should relate to a topic in which the holdings of the Library of the American Philosophical Society (APS) are particularly strong: quantum mechanics, nuclear physics, computer development, the history of genetics and eugenics, the history of medicine, Early American political and cultural history, natural history in the 18th and 19th centuries, the development of cultural anthropology, or American Indian culture and linguistics.

Financial data The grant is $25,000; an additional grant of $5,000 is provided to support the cost of residency in Philadelphia.

Duration 12 months, to begin at the discretion of the grantee.

Additional information This program began in 2005. Recipients are expected to spend a significant amount of time in residence at the APS Library.

Number awarded 1 each year.

Deadline March of each year.

[840] JOHN MCLENDON MEMORIAL MINORITY POSTGRADUATE SCHOLARSHIP AWARD

National Association of Collegiate Directors of Athletics
Attn: NACDA Foundation
24651 Detroit Road
Westlake, OH 44145
(440) 788-7475 Fax: (440) 892-4007
E-mail: jbouyer@nacda.com
Web: www.nacda.com/mclendon/scholarship.html

Summary To provide financial assistance to African American and other minority college seniors who are interested in working on a graduate degree in athletics administration.

Eligibility This program is open to minority college students who are seniors, are attending school on a full-time basis, have a GPA of 3.2 or higher, intend to attend graduate school to earn a degree in athletics administration, and are involved in college or community activities. Also eligible are college graduates who have at least 2 years' experience in an athletics administration position. Candidates must be nominated by an official of a member institution of the National Association of Collegiate Directors of Athletics (NACDA) or (for college graduates) a supervisor.

Financial data The stipend is $10,000.

Duration 1 year.

Additional information Recipients must maintain full-time status during the senior year to retain their eligibility. They must attend NACDA-member institutions.

Number awarded 5 each year.

Deadline Nominations must be submitted by April of each year.

[841] JOHN S. SHROPSHIRE GRADUATE SCHOLARSHIP

Pennsylvania Black Conference on Higher Education
c/o Judith A.W. Thomas, Scholarship Committee Chair
Lincoln University, School of Social Sciences and Behavioral Studies
1570 Old Baltimore Pike
P.O. Box 179
Lincoln University, PA 19352
(484) 365-8159 E-mail: scholarships@pbcohe.org
Web: www.phcohe.org

Summary To provide financial assistance to African American residents of any state who are enrolled as graduate students at universities in Pennsylvania.

Eligibility This program is open to African Americans from any state who have earned at least 6 hours of graduate study at a college or university in Pennsylvania. Applicants must have a GPA of 3.0 or higher. Along with their application, they must submit an essay, up to 5 pages in length, on why they should receive this scholarship. Selection is based on that essay, academics, extracurricular activity participation, leadership qualities, and interpersonal qualities.

Financial data The stipend is $1,000.

Duration 1 year.

Number awarded 1 each year.

Deadline December of each year.

[842] JOHN STANFORD MEMORIAL WLMA SCHOLARSHIP

Washington Library Media Association
c/o Susan Kaphammer, Scholarship Chair
521 North 24th Avenue
Yakima, WA 98902
(509) 972-5999 E-mail: kaphammers@wvsd208.org
Web: www.wlma.org/scholarships

Summary To provide financial assistance to African Americans and other ethnic minorities in Washington who are interested in attending a school in any state to prepare for a library media career.

Eligibility This program is open to residents of Washington who are working toward a library media endorsement or graduate degree in the field at a school in any state. Applicants must be members of an ethnic minority group. They must be working or planning to work in a school library. Along with their application, they must submit a 3-page letter that includes a description of themselves and their achievements to date, their interest and work in the library field, their personal and professional activities, their goals and plans for further education and professional development, how they expect the studies funded by this award to impact their professional practice and contributions to the Washington school library community, and their financial need.

Financial data The stipend is $1,000.

Duration 1 year.

Number awarded 1 each year.

Deadline April of each year.

[843] JOHN W. WORK III MEMORIAL FOUNDATION SCHOLARSHIP

Community Foundation of Middle Tennessee
Attn: Scholarship Committee
3833 Cleghorn Avenue, Suite 400
Nashville, TN 37215-2519
(615) 321-4939 Toll Free: (888) 540-5200
Fax: (615) 327-2746 E-mail: grants@cfmt.org
Web: www.cfmt.org/request/scholarships/allscholarships

Summary To provide financial assistance to upper-division and graduate students from Tennessee, especially African Americans who are working on a degree in music at a school in any state.

Eligibility This program is open to residents of Tennessee, especially African Americans, enrolled as juniors, seniors, or graduate students at an accredited college, university, or institute in any state. Applicants must be working on a degree in music and have a GPA of 3.0 or higher. Selection is based on demonstrated potential for excellence in music, academic record, standardized test scores, extracurricular activities, work experience, community involvement, recommendations, and financial need.

Financial data Stipends range from $500 to $2,500 per year. Funds are paid to the recipient's school and must be used for tuition, fees, books, supplies, room, board, or miscellaneous expenses.

Duration 1 year.

Number awarded 1 or more each year.

Deadline March of each year.

[844]
JOHNNIE L. COCHRAN, JR./MWH SCHOLARSHIP

National Forum for Black Public Administrators
Attn: Scholarship Program
777 North Capitol Street, N.E., Suite 807
Washington, DC 20002
(202) 408-9300 Fax: (202) 408-8558
E-mail: vharris@nfbpa.org
Web: www.nfbpa.org/i4a/pages/index.cfm?pageid=4047

Summary To provide financial assistance to African Americans working on a undergraduate or graduate degree in public administration.

Eligibility This program is open to African American undergraduate and graduate students preparing for a career in public service. Applicants must be working full time on a degree in public administration, political science, urban affairs, public policy, or a related field. They must have a GPA of 3.0 or higher, excellent interpersonal and analytical abilities, and strong oral and written communication skills. Along with their application, they must submit a 3-page autobiographical essay that includes their academic and career goals and objectives. Selection is based on academic record, leadership ability, participation in school activities, community service, and financial need.

Financial data The stipend is $5,000.

Duration 1 year.

Additional information This program is sponsored by the engineering and financial consulting firm MWH. Recipients are required to attend the sponsor's annual conference to receive their scholarship; limited hotel and air accommodations are arranged and provided.

Number awarded 1 each year.

Deadline February of each year.

[845]
JOHNSON & JOHNSON-AMERICAN ASSOCIATION OF COLLEGES OF NURSING MINORITY NURSE FACULTY SCHOLARS PROGRAM

American Association of Colleges of Nursing
One Dupont Circle, N.W., Suite 530
Washington, DC 20036
(202) 463-6930 Fax: (202) 785-8320
E-mail: scholarship@aacn.nche.edu
Web: www.aacn.nche.edu/students/scholarships

Summary To provide funding to African American and other minority students who are working on a graduate degree in nursing to prepare for a career as a faculty member.

Eligibility This program is open to members of racial and ethnic minority groups (Alaska Native, American Indian, Black or African American, Native Hawaiian or other, Pacific Islander, Hispanic or Latino, or Asian American) who are enrolled full time at a school of nursing. Applicants must be working on 1) a doctoral nursing degree (e.g., Ph.D., D.N.P.); or 2) a clinically-focused master's degree in nursing (e.g., M.S.N., M.S.). They must commit to 1) serve in a teaching capacity at a nursing school for a minimum of 1 year for each year of support they receive; 2) provide 6-month progress reports to the American Association of Colleges of Nursing (AACN) throughout the entire funding process and during the payback period; 3) agree to work with an assigned mentor throughout the period of the scholarship grant; and 4) attend an annual leadership training conference to connect with their mentor, fellow scholars, and colleagues. Selection is based on ability to contribute to nursing education; leadership potential; development of goals reflecting education, research, and professional involvement; ability to work with a mentor/adviser throughout the award period; proposed research and/or practice projects that are significant and show commitment to improving nursing education and clinical nursing practice in the United States; proposed research and/or clinical education professional development plan that exhibits quality, feasibility, and innovativeness; and evidence of commitment to a career in nursing education and to recruiting, mentoring, and retaining future underrepresented minority nurses. Preference is given to students enrolled in doctoral nursing programs. Applicants must be U.S. citizens, permanent residents, refugees, or qualified immigrants.

Financial data The stipend is $18,000 per year. The award includes $1,500 that is held in escrow to cover the costs for the recipient to attend the leadership training conference. Recipients are required to sign a letter of commitment that they will provide 1 year of service in a teaching capacity at a nursing school in the United States for each year of support received; if they fail to complete that service requirement, they must repay all funds received.

Duration 1 year; may be renewed 1 additional year.

Additional information This program, established in 2007, is sponsored by the Johnson & Johnson Campaign for Nursing's Future.

Number awarded 5 each year.

Deadline April of each year.

[846]
JOSEPH B. GITTLER AWARD

American Psychological Foundation
750 First Street, N.E.
Washington, DC 20002-4242
(202) 336-5843 Fax: (202) 336-5812
E-mail: foundation@apa.org
Web: www.apa.org/apf/funding/gittler.aspx

Summary To recognize and reward scholars and graduate students in psychology (particularly African Americans, other minorities, women, and individuals with disabilities) whose work has transformed the philosophical foundations of the discipline.

Eligibility This award is available to scholars and graduate students whose body of work or whose individual work has transformed the philosophical foundations of psychological knowledge. Self-nominations are welcome. Selection is based on conformance with stated program goals and magnitude of contributions The sponsor encourages nominations of individuals who represent diversity in race, ethnicity, gender, age, disability, and sexual orientation.

Financial data The award is $10,000.

Duration The award is presented annually.

Additional information This award was first presented in 2008.

Number awarded 1 each year.

Deadline Nominations must be submitted by May of each year.

[847]
JOSEPH L. FISHER DOCTORAL DISSERTATION FELLOWSHIPS

Resources for the Future
Attn: Coordinator for Academic Programs
1616 P Street, N.W., Suite 600
Washington, DC 20036-1400
(202) 328-5020 Fax: (202) 939-3460
E-mail: fisher-award@rff.org
Web: www.rff.org

Summary To provide funding to doctoral candidates in economics (particularly African Americans, other minorities, and women) who are interested in conducting dissertation research on issues related to the environment, natural resources, or energy.

Eligibility This program is open to graduate students in their final year of research on a dissertation related to the environment, natural resources, or energy. Applicants must submit a brief letter of application and a curriculum vitae, a graduate transcript, a 1-page abstract of the dissertation, a technical summary of the dissertation (up to 2,500 words), a letter from their department chair, and 2 letters of recommendation from faculty members on the student's dissertation committee. The technical summary should describe clearly the aim of the dissertation, its significance in relation to the existing literature, and the research methods to be used. Women and minority candidates are strongly encouraged to apply. Non-citizens are eligible if they have proper work and residency documentation.

Financial data The stipend is $18,000.

Duration 1 academic year.

Additional information It is expected that recipients will not hold other employment during the fellowship period. Recipients must notify Resources for the Future of any financial assistance they receive from any other source for support of doctoral work.

Number awarded 1 to 3 each year.

Deadline February of each year.

[848]
JOSEPHINE FORMAN SCHOLARSHIP

Society of American Archivists
Attn: Chair, Awards Committee
17 North State Street, Suite 1425
Chicago, IL 60602-4061
(312) 606-0722 Toll Free: (866) 722-7858
Fax: (312) 606-0728 E-mail: info@archivists.org
Web: www.archivists.org/recognition

Summary To provide financial assistance to African American and other minority graduate students working on a degree in archival science.

Eligibility This program is open to members of minority groups (American Indian/Alaska Native, Asian, Black/African American, Hispanic/Latino, or Native Hawaiian/other Pacific Islander) currently enrolled in or accepted to a graduate program or a multi-course program in archival administration. The program must offer at least 3 courses in archival science and students may have completed no more than half of the credit requirements toward their graduate degree. Selection is based on potential for scholastic and personal achievement and commitment both to the archives profession and to advancing diversity concerns within it. U.S. citizenship or permanent resident status is required.

Financial data The stipend is $10,000.

Duration 1 year.

Additional information Funding for this program, established in 2011, is provided by the General Commission on Archives and History of the United Methodist Church.

Number awarded 1 each year.

Deadline February of each year.

[849]
JOSIAH MACY JR. FOUNDATION SCHOLARSHIPS

National Medical Fellowships, Inc.
Attn: Scholarship Program
347 Fifth Avenue, Suite 510
New York, NY 10016
(212) 483-8880 Toll Free: (877) NMF-1DOC
Fax: (212) 483-8897 E-mail: scholarships@nmfonline.org
Web: www.nmfonline.org

Summary To provide financial assistance to African Americans and other underrepresented minority medical students who demonstrate financial need.

Eligibility This program is open to African Americans, Hispanics/Latinos, Native Americans, Vietnamese, Cambodians, and Pacific Islanders who are entering their second or third year of medical school. Selection is based on academic achievement, leadership, community service, and financial need.

Financial data A stipend is awarded (amount not specified).

Duration 1 year.

Additional information This program is sponsored by the Josiah Macy Jr. Foundation.

Number awarded 4 each year.

Deadline September of each year.

[850]
J.P. MORGAN LAUNCHING LEADERS MBA SCHOLARSHIP

J.P. Morgan
Campus Recruiting
Attn: Launching Leaders
277 Park Avenue, Second Floor
New York, NY 10172
(212) 270-6000
E-mail: bronwen.x.baumgardner@jpmorgan.com
Web: careers.jpmorgan.com

Summary To provide financial aid and work experience to African American and other underrepresented minority students enrolled in the first year of an M.B.A. program.

Eligibility This program is open to Black, Hispanic, and Native American students enrolled in the first year of an M.B.A. program. Applicants must have a demonstrated commitment to working in financial services. Along with their application, they must submit essays on 1) a hypothetical proposal on how to use $50 million from a donor to their school to benefit all of its students; and 2) the special background and attributes they would contribute to the sponsor's diversity agenda and their motivation for applying to this scholarship program. They must be interested in a summer associate position in the sponsor's investment banking, sales and trading, or research divisions.

Financial data The stipend is $40,000 for the first year of study; a paid summer associate position is also provided.

Duration 1 year; may be renewed 1 additional year if the recipient successfully completes the 10-week summer associate program.

Number awarded Varies each year.

Deadline October of each year.

[851]
JULIA BUMRY JONES SCHOLARSHIP PROGRAM

Delta Sigma Theta Sorority, Inc.
Attn: Scholarship and Standards Committee Chair
1707 New Hampshire Avenue, N.W.
Washington, DC 20009
(202) 986-2400 Fax: (202) 986-2513
E-mail: dstemail@deltasigmatheta.org
Web: www.deltasigmatheta.org

Summary To provide financial assistance to members of Delta Sigma Theta who are interested in working on a graduate degree in journalism or another area of communications.

Eligibility This program is open to graduating college seniors and graduate students who are interested in preparing for a career in journalism or another area of communications. Applicants must be active, dues-paying members of Delta Sigma Theta. Selection is based on meritorious achievement.

Financial data The stipends range from $1,000 to $2,000. The funds may be used to cover tuition, fees, and living expenses.

Duration 1 year; may be renewed for 1 additional year.

Additional information This sponsor is a traditionally-African American social sorority. The application fee is $20.

Number awarded 1 or more each year.

Deadline April of each year.

[852]
JULIETTE DERRICOTTE SCHOLARSHIP

Delta Sigma Theta Sorority, Inc.
Attn: Scholarship and Standards Committee Chair
1707 New Hampshire Avenue, N.W.
Washington, DC 20009
(202) 986-2400 Fax: (202) 986-2513
E-mail: dstemail@deltasigmatheta.org
Web: www.deltasigmatheta.org

Summary To provide financial assistance to members of Delta Sigma Theta who are interested in preparing for a career in social work.

Eligibility This program is open to graduating college seniors or graduate students who are interested in preparing for a career in social work. Applicants must be active, dues-paying members of Delta Sigma Theta. Selection is based on meritorious achievement.

Financial data The stipends range from $1,000 to $2,000 per year. The funds may be used to cover tuition, school, and living expenses.

Duration 1 year; may be renewed for 1 additional year.

Additional information This sponsor is a traditionally-African American social sorority. The application fee is $20.

Number awarded 1 or more each year.

Deadline April of each year.

[853]
KAFI WILFORD CONSTANTINE FELLOWSHIP

Alpha Kappa Alpha Sorority, Inc.
Attn: Educational Advancement Foundation
5656 South Stony Island Avenue
Chicago, IL 60637
(773) 947-0026 Toll Free: (800) 653-6528
Fax: (773) 947-0277 E-mail: akaeaf@akaeaf.net
Web: www.akaeaf.org/fellowships_endowments.htm

Summary To provide financial assistance to undergraduates (especially African American women) who are working on a law degree.

Eligibility This program is open to full-time law students who are enrolled at a school in any state. Applicants must submit 1) a list of honors, awards, and scholarships received; 2) a list of organizations in which they have memberships, especially minority organizations; and 3) a statement of their personal and career goals, including how this scholarship will enhance their ability to attain those goals. The sponsor is a traditionally African American women's sorority.

Financial data A stipend is awarded (amount not specified).

Duration 1 year.

Number awarded 1 or more each even-numbered year.

Deadline April of each even-numbered year.

[854]
KALA SINGH MEMORIAL SCHOLARSHIP

American Speech-Language-Hearing Foundation
Attn: Programs Administrator
2200 Research Boulevard
Rockville, MD 20850-3289
(301) 296-8703 Fax: (301) 296-8567
E-mail: foundationprograms@asha.org
Web: www.ashfoundation.org/grants/GraduateScholarships

Summary To provide financial assistance to African Americans, other minorities, and international students who are interested in working on a graduate degree in communication sciences and disorders.

Eligibility This program is open to full-time international and minority graduate students who are enrolled in communication sciences and disorders programs. Applicants must submit an essay, up to 5 pages in length, on a topic that relates to the future of leadership in the discipline. Selection is based on academic promise and outstanding academic achievement.

Financial data The stipend is $5,000. Funds must be used for educational support (e.g., tuition, books, school living expenses), not for personal or conference travel.

Duration The award is granted annually.

Number awarded 1 each year.

Deadline June of each year.

[855] KATTEN MUCHIN ROSENMAN MINORITY SCHOLARSHIPS

Katten Muchin Rosenman LLP
Attn: Attorney Recruiting Manager
525 West Monroe Street
Chicago, IL 60661-3693
(312) 902-5200 Fax: (312) 902-1060
E-mail: nicole.morden@kattenlaw.com
Web: www.kattenlaw.com/minority-scholarship

Summary To provide financial aid and summer work experience in Chicago or New York City to African American and other minority law students from any state.

Eligibility This program is open to minority students from any state who have completed their first year of law school. Applicants must have applied for and been accepted as a summer associate at the sponsoring law firm's Chicago or New York office. Along with their application, they must submit 250-word statements on 1) their strongest qualifications for this award; 2) their reasons for preparing for law as a profession; and 3) their views on diversity and how their personal experience and philosophy will be an asset to the firm. Selection is based on academic achievement, leadership experience, and personal qualities that reflect the potential for outstanding contributions to the firm and the legal profession.

Financial data Participants receive the standard salary for the summer internship and a stipend of $15,000 for the academic year.

Duration 1 year.

Number awarded 2 each year; 1 for an internship in Chicago and 1 for an internship in New York City.

Deadline September of each year.

[856] KEGLER, BROWN, HILL & RITTER MINORITY MERIT SCHOLARSHIP

Kegler, Brown, Hill & Ritter
Attn: Human Resources Manager
Capitol Square, Suite 1800
65 East State Street
Columbus, OH 43215
(614) 462-5467 Toll Free: (800) 860-7885
Fax: (614) 464-2634
E-mail: ctammaro@keglerbrown.com
Web: www.keglerbrown.com

Summary To provide financial aid and summer work experience at Kegler, Brown, Hill & Ritter in Columbus, Ohio to African American and other minority students at law schools in any state.

Eligibility This program is open to first-year students of minority descent at law schools in any state. Applicants must be interested in a summer clerkship with the firm following their first year of law school. Along with their application, they must submit brief essays on 1) a major accomplishment that has shaped their life, how it influenced their decision to prepare for a career in law, and how it prepared them for a future as a lawyer; 2) what diversity means to them; 3) why they have applied for the scholarship; and 4) any training and/or experience they believe to be relevant to the clerkship. Selection is based on academic performance, accomplishments, activities, and potential contributions to the legal community.

Financial data The program provides a $5,000 stipend for law school tuition and a paid summer clerkship position.

Duration 1 year.

Additional information This program began in 2004.

Number awarded 2 each year.

Deadline January of each year.

[857] KENTUCKY LIBRARY ASSOCIATION SCHOLARSHIP FOR MINORITY STUDENTS

Kentucky Library Association
c/o Executive Secretary
1501 Twilight Trail
Frankfort, KY 40601
(502) 223-5322 Fax: (502) 223-4937
E-mail: info@kylibasn.org
Web: www.klaonline.org/scholarships965.cfm

Summary To provide financial assistance to African Americans and other minorities who are residents of Kentucky or attending school there and are working on an undergraduate or graduate degree in library science.

Eligibility This program is open to members of minority groups (defined as American Indian, Alaskan Native, Black, Hispanic, Pacific Islander, or other ethnic group) who are entering or continuing at a graduate library school accredited by the American Library Association (ALA) or an undergraduate library program accredited by the National Council of Teacher Education (NCATE). Applicants must be residents of Kentucky or a student in a library program in the state. Along with their application, they must submit a statement of their career objectives, why they have chosen librarianship as a career, and their reasons for applying for this scholarship. Selection is based on that statement, cumulative undergraduate and graduate GPA (if applicable), academic merit and potential, and letters of recommendation. U.S. citizenship or permanent resident status is required.

Financial data The stipend is $1,000.

Duration 1 year; nonrenewable.

Number awarded 1 or more each year.

Deadline June of each year.

[858] KENTUCKY MINORITY EDUCATOR RECRUITMENT AND RETENTION SCHOLARSHIPS

Kentucky Department of Education
Attn: Minority Educator Recruitment and Retention
500 Mero Street, 8th Floor
Frankfort, KY 40601
(502) 564-1479, ext. 4014 Fax: (502) 564-6952
TDD: (502) 564-4970
E-mail: monica.davis@education.ky.gov
Web: www.education.ky.gov

Summary To provide funding to African American and other minority undergraduate and graduate students enrolled in Kentucky public institutions who want to become teachers.

Eligibility This program is open to residents of Kentucky who are undergraduate or graduate students pursuing initial teacher certification at a public university or community college in the state. Applicants must have a GPA of 2.5 or higher and either maintain full-time enrollment or be a part-time student within 18 semester hours of receiving a teacher education degree. They must be U.S. citizens and meet the Kentucky definition of a minority student.

Financial data Stipends are $5,000 per year at the 8 state universities in Kentucky or $2,000 per year at community and technical colleges. Recipients are required to teach 1 semester in Kentucky for each semester or summer term the scholarship is received. If they fail to fulfill that requirement, the scholarship converts to a loan with severe penalties for nonpayment.

Duration 1 year; may be renewed up to 3 additional years.

Additional information The Kentucky General Assembly established this program in 1992.

Number awarded Varies each year.

Deadline Each state college of teacher education sets its own deadline.

[859] KING & SPALDING DIVERSITY FELLOWSHIP PROGRAM

King & Spalding
Attn: Diversity Fellowship Program
1180 Peachtree Street
Atlanta, GA 30309
(404) 572-4643 Fax: (404) 572-5100
E-mail: fellowship@kslaw.com
Web: www.kslaw.com/careers/Law-Students

Summary To provide financial aid and summer work experience at U.S. offices of King & Spalding to African American and other law students who will contribute to the diversity of the legal community.

Eligibility This program is open to second-year law students who 1) come from a minority ethnic or racial group (American Indian/Alaskan Native, Asian American/Pacific Islander, Black/African American, Hispanic, or multi-racial); 2) are a member of the gay, lesbian, bisexual, or transgender (GLBT) community; or 3) have a disability. Applicants must receive an offer of a clerkship at a U.S. office of King & Spalding during their second-year summer. Along with their application, they must submit a 500-word personal statement that describes their talents, qualities, and experiences and how they would contribute to the diversity of the firm.

Financial data Fellows receive a stipend of $10,000 for their second year of law school and a paid summer associate clerkship at a U.S. office of the firm during the following summer.

Duration 1 year.

Additional information The firm's U.S. offices are located in Atlanta, Austin, Charlotte, Houston, New York, San Francisco, Silicon Valley, and Washington.

Number awarded Up to 4 each year.

Deadline August of each year.

[860] KIRKLAND & ELLIS LLP DIVERSITY FELLOWSHIP PROGRAM

Kirkland & Ellis LLP
Attn: Attorney Recruiting Manager
333 South Hope Street
Los Angeles, CA 90071
(213) 680-8436 Fax: (213) 680-8500
E-mail: cherie.beffa@kirkland.com
Web: www.kirkland.com

Summary To provide financial assistance and summer work experience at an office of Kirkland & Ellis to African American and other minority law students from any state.

Eligibility This program is open to second-year students at ABA-accredited law schools who meet the racial and ethnic categories established by the Equal Employment Opportunity Commission. Applicants must have been accepted as summer associates at a domestic office of the sponsoring law firm (Chicago, Los Angeles, New York, Palo Alto, San Francisco, Washington, D.C.) and be likely to practice at 1 of those offices after graduation. Along with their application, they must submit a 1-page personal statement that describes ways in which they have promoted and will continue to promote diversity in the legal community, along with their interest in the firm. Selection is based on merit.

Financial data Fellows receive a salary during their summer associateship and a $25,000 stipend at the conclusion of the summer. Stipend funds are to be used for payment of educational expenses during the third year of law school.

Duration 1 year.

Additional information This program, which replaced the Kirkland & Ellis Minority Fellowship Program, was established at 14 law schools in 2004. In 2006, it began accepting applications from students at all ABA-accredited law schools.

Number awarded Varies each year; recently, 10 of these fellowships were awarded. Since the program began, it has awarded 121 fellowships worth more than $1.9 million.

Deadline August of each year.

[861] KPMG MINORITY ACCOUNTING DOCTORAL SCHOLARSHIPS

KPMG Foundation
Attn: Scholarship Administrator
Three Chestnut Ridge Road
Montvale, NJ 07645-0435
(201) 307-7161 Fax: (201) 624-7763
E-mail: us-kpmgfoundation@kpmg.com
Web: www.kpmgfoundation.org/foundinit.asp

Summary To provide funding to African American and other underrepresented minority students working on a doctoral degree in accounting.

Eligibility Applicants must be African Americans, Hispanic Americans, or Native Americans. They must be U.S. citizens or permanent residents and accepted or enrolled in a full-time accounting doctoral program. Along with their application, they must submit a brief letter explaining their reason for working on a Ph.D. in accounting.

Financial data The stipend is $10,000 per year.

Duration 1 year; may be renewed up to 4 additional years.

Additional information These funds are not intended to replace funds normally made available by the recipient's institution. The foundation recommends that the recipient's institution also award, to the recipient, a $5,000 annual stipend, a teaching or research assistantship, and a waiver of tuition and fees.

Number awarded 12 each year.

Deadline April of each year.

[862]
LAGRANT FOUNDATION GRADUATE SCHOLARSHIPS

Lagrant Foundation
Attn: Senior Programs and Outreach Manager
600 Wilshire Boulevard, Suite 1520
Los Angeles, CA 90017
(323) 469-8680, ext. 223 Fax: (323) 469-8683
E-mail: erickainiguez@lagrant.com
Web: www.lagrantfoundation.org

Summary To provide financial assistance to African American and other minority graduate students who are working on a degree in advertising, public relations, or marketing.

Eligibility This program is open to African Americans, Asian American/Pacific Islanders, Hispanics/Latinos, and Native Americans/American Indians who are full-time graduate students at an accredited institution. Applicants must have a GPA of 3.2 or higher and be working on a master's degree in advertising, marketing, or public relations. They must have at least 2 academic semesters remaining to complete their degree. Along with their application, they must submit 1) a 1- to 2-page essay outlining their career goals; why it is important to increase ethnic representation in the fields of advertising, marketing, and public relations; and the role of an advertising, marketing, or public relations practitioner; 2) a paragraph describing the graduate school and/or community activities in which they are involved; 3) a brief paragraph describing any honors and awards they have received; 4) a letter of reference; 5) a resume; and 6) an official transcript. U.S. citizenship or permanent resident status is required.

Financial data The stipend is $10,000 per year.

Duration 1 year.

Number awarded Varies each year; recently, 7 of these scholarships were awarded.

Deadline February of each year.

[863]
LARRY W. CARTER SCHOLARSHIP

Greater Des Moines Community Foundation
Finkbine Mansion
1915 Grand Avenue
Des Moines, IA 50309
(515) 883-2626 Fax: (515) 309-0704
E-mail: trettin@desmoinesfoundation.org
Web: www.desmoinesfoundation.org/article.aspx?id=82

Summary To provide financial assistance to African American undergraduate and graduate students in Iowa.

Eligibility Eligible to apply are African Americans who reside in Iowa and are enrolled in college or graduate school on a full- or part-time basis. Applicants must submit a personal statement that explains why they feel they should be selected to receive this scholarship and describes their personal and educational goals, motivations, and reasons for pursuing higher education. Financial need is considered in the selection process.

Financial data The stipend is $3,000.

Duration 1 year.

Number awarded Varies each year; recently, 3 of these scholarships were awarded.

Deadline May of each year.

[864]
LARRY WHITESIDE SCHOLARSHIP

National Association of Black Journalists
Attn: Communications Coordinator and Program Manager
University of Maryland
1100 Knight Hall, Suite 3100
College Park, MD 20742
(301) 405-2573 Fax: (301) 314-1714
E-mail: tjohnson@nabj.org
Web: www.nabj.org/?page=SEEDScholarships

Summary To provide financial assistance to undergraduate or graduate student members of the National Association of Black Journalists (NABJ) who are preparing for a career in sports journalism.

Eligibility This program is open to African American undergraduate or graduate student members of NABJ who are currently enrolled full time at an accredited 4-year college or university. Applicants must be studying journalism as preparing for a career in sports journalism and have a GPA of 2.5 or higher in their major and 2.0 overall. They must be able to demonstrate financial need. Along with their application, they must submit 5 samples of their work, an official college transcript, 3 letters of recommendation, a resume, and an essay of 1,000 to 2,000 words on a sports journalist (living or deceased) whom they admire and why that person has inspired them to prepare for a career in sports journalism.

Financial data The stipend is $2,500. Funds are paid directly to the recipient's college or university.

Duration 1 year; nonrenewable.

Number awarded 1 each year.

Deadline March of each year.

[865]
LATHAM & WATKINS DIVERSITY SCHOLARS PROGRAM

Latham & Watkins LLP
Attn: Diversity Committee Co-Chair
885 Third Avenue
New York, NY 10022-4834
(212) 906-1332 Fax: (212) 751-4864
E-mail: sharon.bowen@lw.com
Web: www.lw.com/AboutUs/Diversity

Summary To provide financial assistance to African American and other minority law students interested in working for a global law firm.

Eligibility Applicants must be second-year law students at an ABA-accredited law school and plan to practice law in a major city in the United States. Students who have received a similar scholarship from another sponsor are not eligible to apply. Applicants must submit a 500-word personal statement that describes their ability to contribute to the diversity objectives of global law firms; the life experiences that have shaped their values and that provide them with a unique perspective, including any obstacles or challenges they have overcome; their academic and/or leadership achievements; and their intent to practice in a global law firm environment.

Financial data The stipend is $10,000.

Duration 1 year; nonrenewable.

Additional information This program began in 2005. Recipients are not required to work for Latham & Watkins after graduation.

Number awarded 6 each year.

Deadline September of each year.

[866] LAUNCHING LEADERS MBA SCHOLARSHIP

JPMorgan Chase
Campus Recruiting
Attn: Launching Leaders
277 Park Avenue, Second Floor
New York, NY 10172
(212) 270-6000
E-mail: bronwen.x.baumgardner@jpmorgan.com
Web: careers.jpmorgan.com

Summary To provide financial assistance and work experience to African American and other underrepresented minority students enrolled in the first year of an M.B.A. program.

Eligibility This program is open to Black, Hispanic, and Native American students enrolled in the first year of an M.B.A. program. Applicants must have a demonstrated commitment to working in financial services. Along with their application, they must submit essays on 1) a hypothetical proposal on how to use $50 million from a donor to their school to benefit all of its students; and 2) the special background and attributes they would contribute to the sponsor's diversity agenda and their motivation for applying to this scholarship program. They must be interested in a summer associate position in the sponsor's investment banking, sales and trading, or research divisions.

Financial data The stipend is $40,000 for the first year of study; a paid summer associate position is also provided.

Duration 1 year; may be renewed 1 additional year if the recipient successfully completes the 10-week summer associate program.

Number awarded Varies each year.

Deadline October of each year.

[867] LAURENCE R. FOSTER MEMORIAL SCHOLARSHIPS

Oregon Student Access Commission
Attn: Grants and Scholarships Division
1500 Valley River Drive, Suite 100
Eugene, OR 97401-2146
(541) 687-7395 Toll Free: (800) 452-8807, ext. 7395
Fax: (541) 687-7414 TDD: (800) 735-2900
E-mail: awardinfo@osac.state.or.us
Web: www.oregonstudentaid.gov/scholarships.aspx

Summary To provide financial assistance to African Americans and other residents of Oregon who come from a diverse environment and are enrolled at a college or graduate school in any state to prepare for a public health career.

Eligibility This program is open to residents of Oregon who are enrolled at least half time at a 4-year college or university in any state to prepare for a career in public health (not private practice). Preference is given first to applicants from diverse environments; second to persons employed in, or graduate students working on a degree in, public health; and third to juniors and seniors majoring in a health program (e.g., nursing, medical technology, physician assistant). Applicants must be able to demonstrate financial need. Along with their application, they must submit essays of 250 to 350 words on 1) what public health means to them; 2) the public health aspect they intend to practice and the health and population issues impacted by that aspect; and 3) their experience living or working in diverse environments.

Financial data Stipends for scholarships offered by the Oregon Student Access Commission (OSAC) range from $200 to $10,000 but recently averaged $2,300.

Duration 1 year.

Additional information This program is administered by the OSAC with funds provided by the Oregon Community Foundation.

Number awarded Varies each year; recently, 6 of these scholarships were awarded.

Deadline February of each year.

[868] LEADERSHIP FOR DIVERSITY SCHOLARSHIP

California School Library Association
Attn: CSL Foundation
6444 East Spring Street, Number 237
Long Beach, CA 90815-1553
Toll Free: (888) 655-8480 Fax: (888) 655-8480
E-mail: info@csla.net
Web: www.csla.net

Summary To provide financial assistance to African American and other students who reflect the diversity of California's population and are interested in earning a credential as a library media teacher in the state.

Eligibility This program is open to students who are members of a traditionally underrepresented group enrolled in a college or university library media teacher credential program in California. Applicants must intend to work as a library media teacher in a California school library media center for a minimum of 3 years. Along with their application, they must submit a 250-word statement on their school library media career interests and goals, why they should be considered, what they can contribute, their commitment to serving the needs of multicultural and multilingual students, and their financial situation.

Financial data The stipend is $1,500.

Duration 1 year.

Number awarded 1 each year.

Deadline May of each year.

[869]
LEADERSHIP LEGACY SCHOLARSHIP FOR GRADUATES

Women's Transportation Seminar
Attn: WTS Foundation
1701 K Street, N.W., Suite 800
Washington, DC 20006
(202) 955-5085 Fax: (202) 955-5088
E-mail: wts@wtsinternational.org
Web: www.wtsinternational.org/education/scholarships

Summary To provide financial assistance to graduate women (particularly African Americans and other minorities) who are interested in a career in transportation.

Eligibility This program is open to women who are working on a graduate degree in transportation or a transportation-related field (e.g., transportation engineering, planning, business management, finance, or logistics). Applicants must have a GPA of 3.0 or higher and be interested in a career in transportation. Along with their application, they must submit a 1,000-word statement about their vision of how their education will give them the tools to better serve their community's needs and transportation issues. Applications must be submitted first to a local chapter; the chapters forward selected applications for consideration on the national level. Minority women are especially encouraged to apply. Selection is based on transportation involvement and goals, job skills, and academic record; financial need is not considered.

Financial data The stipend is $5,000.

Duration 1 year.

Additional information This program began in 2008. Each year, it focuses on women with a special interest; recently, it was reserved for women who have a specific interest in addressing the impact of transportation on sustainability, land use, environmental impact, security, and quality of life issues internationally.

Number awarded 1 each year.

Deadline Applications must be submitted by November to a local WTS chapter.

[870]
LEGAL WRITING COMPETITION

Black Entertainment and Sports Lawyers Association
Attn: Scholarships
P.O. Box 230794
New York, NY 10023
E-mail: scholarship@besla.org
Web: www.besla.org/#!scholarship/cfvg

Summary To recognize and reward law students who submit outstanding papers or digital responses to the Black Entertainment and Sports Lawyers Association on topics related to the fields of entertainment and/or sports law.

Eligibility This program is open to students who have completed at least 1 full year at a law school in the United States or its territories. Applicants must submit a written essay or a digital response (in the form of a video or slide show presentation) on a legal issue facing the entertainment or sports industry. Recently, students were asked to write on either 1) copyright assignment/transfer terminations and their impact on the entertainment industry; or 2) a pending class action lawsuit against the National Collegiate Athletic Association. Selection is based on focus, organization, critical legal analysis, conclusions and recommendations, originality, voice, and style and mechanics.

Financial data The award is a $1,000 scholarship.

Duration The competition is held annually.

Additional information This program began in 2004.

Number awarded 1 or more each year.

Deadline July of each year.

[871]
LEROY SCHMIDT MINORITY MASTER'S ACCOUNTING SCHOLARSHIP

Wisconsin Institute of Certified Public Accountants
Attn: WICPA Educational Foundation
235 North Executive Drive, Suite 200
Brookfield, WI 53005
(262) 785-0445, ext. 3025
Toll Free: (800) 772-6939 (within WI)
Fax: (262) 785-0838 E-mail: jessica@wicpa.org
Web: www.wicpa.org

Summary To provide financial assistance to African American and other underrepresented minority residents of Wisconsin who are working on a master's degree at a college or university in the state.

Eligibility This program is open to residents of Wisconsin who are African American, Native American/Alaskan Native, of Pacific Island races, or of Hispanic ethnic origin. Applicants must be working on a master's degree in accounting at a college or university in the state by completing the 150-hour accounting education requirement to sit for the C.P.A. examination. Along with their application, they must submit a 1-page personal statement on their career objectives, most significant accomplishment, and strongest personal attribute. Selection is based on that statement, honors and awards, academic achievement, extracurricular and volunteer activities, work experience, and letters of recommendation. U.S. citizenship is required.

Financial data The stipend is $5,000.

Duration 1 year.

Number awarded 1 or more each year.

Deadline February of each year.

[872]
LES PAYNE FOUNDER'S SCHOLARSHIP

National Association of Black Journalists
Attn: Communications Coordinator and Program Manager
University of Maryland
1100 Knight Hall, Suite 3100
College Park, MD 20742
(301) 405-2573 Fax: (301) 314-1714
E-mail: tjohnson@nabj.org
Web: www.nabj.org/?page=SEEDScholarships

Summary To provide financial assistance to undergraduate and graduate student members of the National Association of Black Journalists (NABJ) who are working on a degree in print journalism.

Eligibility This program is open to African American undergraduate or graduate student members of NABJ who are currently enrolled full time at an accredited 4-year college or university. Applicants must be working on a degree in print journalism and have a GPA of 3.0 or higher. They must be able to demonstrate financial need. Along with their application, they must submit 5 samples of their work, an official college transcript, 3 letters of recommendation, a resume, and an essay of 1,000 to 2,000 words describing 3 issues about which they are passionate and which they hope to cover as a professional journalist.

Financial data The stipend is $2,500.

Duration 1 year.

Number awarded 1 each year.

Deadline March of each year.

[873]
LIBRARY AND INFORMATION TECHNOLOGY ASSOCIATION MINORITY SCHOLARSHIPS

American Library Association
Attn: Library and Information Technology Association
50 East Huron Street
Chicago, IL 60611-2795
(312) 280-4270 Toll Free: (800) 545-2433, ext. 4270
Fax: (312) 280-3257 TDD: (888) 814-7692
E-mail: lita@ala.org
Web: www.ala.org/lita/awards

Summary To provide financial assistance to African American and other minority graduate students interested in preparing for a career in library automation.

Eligibility This program is open to U.S. or Canadian citizens who are interested in working on a master's degree in library/information science and preparing for a career in the field of library and automated systems. Applicants must be a member of 1 of the following ethnic groups: American Indian, Alaskan Native, Asian, Pacific Islander, African American, or Hispanic. They may not have completed more than 12 credit hours of course work for their degree. Selection is based on academic excellence, leadership potential, evidence of a commitment to a career in library automation and information technology, and prior activity and experience in those fields. Financial need is considered when all other factors are equal.

Financial data Stipends are $3,000 or $2,500. Funds are paid directly to the recipient.

Duration 1 year.

Additional information This program includes scholarships funded by Online Computer Library Center (OCLC) and by Library Systems & Services, Inc. (LSSI).

Number awarded 2 each year: 1 at $3,000 (funded by OCLC) and 1 at $2,500 (funded by LSSI).

Deadline February of each year.

[874]
LIONEL C. BARROW MINORITY DOCTORAL STUDENT SCHOLARSHIP

Association for Education in Journalism and Mass Communication
Attn: Communication Theory and Methodology Division
234 Outlet Pointe Boulevard, Suite A
Columbia, SC 29210-5667
(803) 798-0271 Fax: (803) 772-3509
E-mail: aejmc@aejmc.org
Web: aejmc.net

Summary To provide financial assistance to African Americans and other minorities who are interested in working on a doctorate in mass communication.

Eligibility This program is open to minority students enrolled in a Ph.D. program in journalism and/or mass communication. Applicants must submit 2 letters of recommendation, a resume, and a brief letter outlining their research interests and career plans. Membership in the association is not required, but applicants must be U.S. citizens or permanent residents. Selection is based on the likelihood that the applicant's work will contribute to communication theory and/or methodology.

Financial data The stipend is $1,400.

Duration 1 year.

Additional information This program began in 1972.

Number awarded 1 each year.

Deadline May of each year.

[875]
LIZETTE PETERSON-HOMER INJURY PREVENTION RESEARCH GRANT

American Psychological Foundation
750 First Street, N.E.
Washington, DC 20002-4242
(202) 336-5843 Fax: (202) 336-5812
E-mail: foundation@apa.org
Web: www.apa.org/apf/funding/peterson-homer.aspx

Summary To provide funding to graduate students and faculty (particularly African Americans, other minorities, women, and individuals with disabilities) who are interested in conducting research related to the prevention of injuries in children.

Eligibility This program is open to graduate students and faculty interested in conducting research that focuses on the prevention of physical injury in children and young adults through accidents, violence, abuse, or suicide. Applicants must submit a 100-word abstract, description of the project, detailed budget, curriculum vitae, and letter from the supporting faculty supervisor (if the applicant is a student). Selection is based on conformance with stated program goals, magnitude of incremental contribution, quality of proposed work, and applicant's demonstrated scholarship and research competence. The sponsor encourages applications from individuals who represent diversity in race, ethnicity, gender, age, disability, and sexual orientation.

Financial data Grants up to $5,000 are available.

Additional information This program began in 1999 as the Rebecca Routh Coon Injury Research Award. The current name was adopted in 2003. It is supported by Division 54 (Society of Pediatric Psychology) of the American Psychological Association and the American Psychological Foundation.

Number awarded 1 each year.

Deadline September of each year.

[876]
LLOYD M. JOHNSON, JR. SCHOLARSHIP PROGRAM

United Negro College Fund
Attn: Scholarships and Grants Department
8260 Willow Oaks Corporate Drive
P.O. Box 10444
Fairfax, VA 22031-8044
(703) 205-3466 Toll Free: (800) 331-2244
Fax: (703) 205-3574
Web: www.uncf.org

Summary To provide financial assistance to African Americans and other law students from disadvantaged backgrounds who are interested in corporate law and will contribute to diversity in the legal profession.

Eligibility Applicants must be U.S. citizens, have a strong academic record (an undergraduate GPA of 3.2 or higher), have been accepted to an ABA-accredited law school, be able to demonstrate community service and leadership qualities, have an interest in diversity, be financially disadvantaged, plan to study on a full-time basis, and have an interest in corporate law, including working in a corporate law department and/or law firm. Applicants must submit a current transcript, a resume, 2 letters of recommendation, a personal statement, and a diversity essay. All students are eligible, but the sponsor expects that most recipients will contribute to diversity in the legal profession.

Financial data The stipend is $10,000 for the first year and varying amounts for subsequent years.

Duration 1 year; may be renewed up to 2 additional years.

Additional information The Minority Corporate Counsel Association first began this program in 2005 and now cosponsors it with the United Negro College Fund. Mentoring and internship experiences are also offered to the winners.

Number awarded Approximately 10 each year.

Deadline May of each year.

[877]
LORRAINE HANSBERRY PLAYWRITING AWARD

John F. Kennedy Center for the Performing Arts
Education Department
Attn: Kennedy Center American College Theater Festival
2700 F Street, N.W.
Washington, DC 20566
(202) 416-8857 Fax: (202) 416-8860
E-mail: KCACTF@kennedy-center.org
Web: www.kcactf.org

Summary To recognize and reward student authors of plays on the African American experience in America.

Eligibility Students at any accredited junior or senior college in the United States are eligible to compete, provided their college agrees to participate in the Kennedy Center American College Theater Festival (KCACTF). Undergraduate students must be carrying at least 6 semester hours, graduate students must be enrolled in at least 3 semester hours, and continuing part-time students must be enrolled in a regular degree or certificate program. These awards are presented to the best plays written by students of African or Diasporan descent on the subject of the African American experience.

Financial data The first-place award is $1,000 and the second-place award is $500. In addition, grants of $750 and $500 are made to the theater departments of the colleges or universities producing the first- and second-place plays. The winning playwright also receives an all-expense paid professional development opportunity.

Duration The awards are presented annually.

Additional information This program is supported by the Kennedy Center and Dramatic Publishing Company. It honors the first African American playwright to win the New York Drama Critics Award who died in 1965 at the age of 34. First presented in 1977, it is part of the Michael Kanin Playwriting Awards Program. The sponsoring college or university must pay a registration fee of $275 for each production.

Number awarded 2 students and 2 sponsoring institutions receive awards each year.

Deadline November of each year.

[878]
LOUISE JANE MOSES/AGNES DAVIS MEMORIAL SCHOLARSHIP

California Librarians Black Caucus-Greater Los Angeles Chapter
Attn: Scholarship Committee
P.O. Box 882276
Los Angeles, CA 90009
E-mail: scholarship@clbc.org
Web: www.clbc.org/scholar.html

Summary To provide financial assistance to African Americans in California who are interested in becoming librarians or library paraprofessionals.

Eligibility This program is open to African American residents of California who are working on a degree from an accredited library/information science program or an accredited library/information science paraprofessional program in the state. Applicants must submit an essay of 300 to 500 words on their professional goals and their interest in a library or information-related career. Selection is based on demonstrated financial need, scholastic achievement, and commitment to the goals of encouraging and supporting African American library professionals and improving library service to the African American community. Interviews are required.

Financial data Stipends range from $750 to $1,500.

Duration 1 year.

Number awarded 2 to 3 each year.

Deadline October of each year.

[879]
LOUISIANA WMU SCHOLARSHIP FOR AFRICAN-AMERICAN MISSION PASTORS

Louisiana Baptist Convention
Attn: Woman's Missionary Union
1250 MacArthur Drive
P.O. Box 311
Alexandria, LA 71309-0311
(318) 448-3402 Toll Free: (800) 622-6549
E-mail: wmu@lbc.org
Web: www.lbc.org/Women/Interior.aspx?id=3400

Summary To provide financial assistance to African American Southern Baptists from Louisiana who are enrolled at a seminary in any state to prepare for a career as a missions pastor.

Eligibility This program is open to African Americans who are endorsed by the director of missions and the pastor of a sponsoring Southern Baptist church in Louisiana. Applicants must be enrolled full time at a seminary or a satellite campus to prepare for a career as a missions pastor and have a GPA of 2.5 or higher. They must be participating in a missions education organization of the church or on campus and must contribute to offerings of the church and other programs. Along with their application, they must submit evidence of their "devotion to the Lord and their call to ministry."

Financial data The stipend is $1,200 per year.

Duration Up to 3 years.

Number awarded 1 or more each year.

Deadline June of each year.

[880]
LTK SCHOLARSHIP

Conference of Minority Transportation Officials
Attn: National Scholarship Program
1875 I Street, N.W., Suite 500
Washington, DC 20006
(703) 234-4072 Fax: (202) 318-0364
Web: www.comto.org/?page=Scholarships

Summary To provide financial assistance to African American and other minority upper-division and graduate students in engineering or other fields related to transportation.

Eligibility This program is open to full-time minority juniors, seniors, and graduate students in engineering of other technical transportation-related disciplines. Applicants must have a GPA of 3.0 or higher. Along with their application, they must submit a cover letter with a 500-word statement of career goals. Financial need is not considered in the selection process. U.S. citizenship or legal resident status is required.

Financial data The stipend is $6,000. Funds are paid directly to the recipient's college or university.

Duration 1 year.

Additional information The Conference of Minority Transportation Officials (COMTO) was established in 1971 to promote, strengthen, and expand the roles of minorities in all aspects of transportation. This program is sponsored by LTK Engineering Services. Recipients are required to become members of COMTO if they are not already members and attend the COMTO National Scholarship Luncheon.

Number awarded 1 or more each year.

Deadline May of each year.

[881]
M. ELIZABETH CARNEGIE SCHOLARSHIP

Nurses Educational Funds, Inc.
Attn: Scholarship Coordinator
304 Park Avenue South, 11th Floor
New York, NY 10010
(212) 590-2443 Fax: (212) 590-2446
E-mail: info@n-e-f.org
Web: www.n-e-f.org

Summary To provide financial assistance to African American nurses who wish to work on a doctoral degree.

Eligibility This program is open to African American registered nurses who are members of a national professional nursing organization and enrolled in a nursing or nursing-related program at the doctoral level. Applicants must have a GPA of 3.6 or higher. They must be U.S. citizens or have declared their official intention of becoming a citizen. Along with their application, they must submit an 800-word essay on their professional goals and potential for making a contribution to the nursing profession. Selection is based on academic excellence and the essay's content and clarity.

Financial data Stipends range from $2,500 to $10,000, depending on the availability of funds.

Duration 1 year; nonrenewable.

Additional information There is a $20 application fee.

Number awarded 1 each year.

Deadline February of each year.

[882]
MABEL D. RUSSELL BLACK COLLEGE FUND

United Methodist Higher Education Foundation
Attn: Scholarships Administrator
60 Music Square East, Suite 350
P.O. Box 340005
Nashville, TN 37203-0005
(615) 649-3990 Toll Free: (800) 811-8110
Fax: (615) 649-3980
E-mail: umhefscholarships@umhef.org
Web: www.umhef.org/scholarship-info

Summary To provide financial assistance to Methodist undergraduate and graduate students at Historically Black Colleges and Universities of the United Methodist Church.

Eligibility This program is open to students enrolling as full-time undergraduate and graduate students at the Historically Black Colleges and Universities of the United Methodist Church. Applicants must have been active, full members of a United Methodist Church for at least 1 year prior to applying. They must have a GPA of 3.0 or higher and be able to demonstrate financial need. U.S. citizenship or permanent resident status is required.

Financial data The stipend is at least $1,000 per year.

Duration 1 year; nonrenewable.

Additional information This program began in 1978. The qualifying schools are Bennett College for Women, Bethune-Cookman University, Claflin University, Clark Atlanta University, Dillard University, Huston-Tillotson College, Meharry Medical College, Paine College, Philander Smith College, Rust College, and Wiley College.

Number awarded 1 each year.

Deadline February of each year.

[883]
MALENA RANCE SCHOLARSHIP FUND

Black Entertainment and Sports Lawyers Association
Attn: Scholarships
P.O. Box 230794
New York, NY 10023
E-mail: scholarship@besla.org
Web: www.besla.org/#!scholarship/cfvg

Summary To provide financial assistance to African American women who are interested in the fields of entertainment and/or sports law.

Eligibility This program is open to African American women who have completed at least 1 year of full-time study at an accredited law school. Applicants must be able to demonstrate an interest in entertainment or sports law by 1 or more of the following: 1) completing an entertainment law or sports law related course; 2) internship or clerkship in the entertainment or sports law field; 3) current job in the field of entertainment or sports; 4) current membership in an entertainment or sports law society or association; or 5) attendance at an entertainment law or sports law seminar or conference since enrolling in law school. They must have a GPA of 3.0 or higher. Along with their application, they must submit a 5-page legal memorandum on an issue facing the entertainment or sports industry.

Financial data The stipend is at least $1,500.

Duration 1 year.

Number awarded 1 or more each year.

Deadline July of each year.

[884]
MARATHON OIL CORPORATION COLLEGE SCHOLARSHIP PROGRAM OF THE HISPANIC SCHOLARSHIP FUND

Hispanic Scholarship Fund
Attn: Selection Committee
1411 West 190th Street, Suite 325
Gardena, CA 90248
Toll Free: (877) HSF-INFO E-mail: scholar1@hsf.net
Web: www.hsf.net/Scholarship-Programs.aspx

Summary To provide financial assistance to African American and other minority upper-division and graduate students working on a degree in a field related to the oil and gas industry.

Eligibility This program is open to U.S. citizens and permanent residents (must have a permanent resident card or a passport stamped I-551) who are of Hispanic American, African American, Asian Pacific Islander American, or American Indian/Alaskan Native heritage. Applicants must be currently enrolled full time at an accredited 4-year college or university in the United States, Puerto Rico, Guam, or the U.S. Virgin Islands with a GPA of 3.0 or higher. They must be 1) sophomores majoring in accounting, chemical engineering, computer engineering, computer science, electrical engineering, environmental engineering, geology, geosciences, information technology/management information systems, mechanical engineering, or petroleum engineering; or 2) seniors planning to work on a master's degree in geology, geosciences, or petroleum engineering. Selection is based on academic achievement, personal strengths, interest and commitment to a career in the oil and gas industry, leadership, and financial need.

Financial data The stipend is $15,000 per year.

Duration 2 years (the junior and senior undergraduate years or the first 2 years of a master's degree program).

Additional information This program is jointly sponsored by Marathon Oil Corporation and the Hispanic Scholarship Fund (HSF). Recipients may be offered a paid 8- to 10-week summer internship at various Marathon Oil Corporation locations.

Number awarded 1 or more each year.

Deadline November of each year.

[885]
MARATHON PETROLEUM CORPORATION COLLEGE SCHOLARSHIP PROGRAM OF THE HISPANIC SCHOLARSHIP FUND

Hispanic Scholarship Fund
Attn: Selection Committee
1411 West 190th Street, Suite 325
Gardena, CA 90248
Toll Free: (877) HSF-INFO E-mail: scholar1@hsf.net
Web: www.hsf.net/Scholarship-Programs.aspx

Summary To provide financial assistance to African American and other minority upper-division, graduate, or law students working on a degree in specified fields, especially at designated universities.

Eligibility This program is open to U.S. citizens and permanent residents (must have a permanent resident card or a passport stamped I-551) who are of Hispanic American, African American, Asian Pacific Islander American, or American Indian/Alaskan Native heritage. Applicants must be currently enrolled full time at an accredited 4-year college or university and have a GPA of 3.0 or higher. They must be 1) juniors, seniors, or fifth-year students majoring in accounting, chemical engineering, civil engineering, computer science, electrical engineering, environmental engineering, finance, industrial engineering, information technology/management information systems, marketing, or mechanical engineering; 2) first-year graduate students working on a degree in human resource management; or 3) first-year law students. Preference is given to students attending 1 of the following institutions: Bowling Green State University, Central Michigan University, Indiana University, Louisiana State University, Miami University of Ohio, Michigan State University, North Carolina A&T University, Ohio Northern University, Ohio State University, Purdue University, Tiffin University, University of Cincinnati, University of Dayton, University of Findlay, University of Illinois at Urbana-Champaign, University of Louisville, University of Michigan, University of Toledo, West Virginia University, or Western Michigan University. Selection is based on academic achievement, personal strengths, leadership, and financial need. Military veterans and ROTC students are especially encouraged to apply.

Financial data The stipend is $7,500.

Duration 1 year.

Additional information This program is jointly sponsored by Marathon Petroleum Corporation and the Hispanic Scholarship Fund (HSF). Recipients may be offered a paid 8- to 10-week summer internship at various Marathon Petroleum Corporation locations.

Number awarded 1 or more each year.

Deadline October of each year.

[886]
MARJORIE BOWENS-WHEATLEY SCHOLARSHIPS

Unitarian Universalist Association
Attn: UU Women's Federation
25 Beacon Street
Boston, MA 02108-2800
(617) 948-4692 Fax: (617) 742-2402
E-mail: uuwf@uua.org
Web: www.uuwf.org

Summary To provide financial assistance to African American and other women of color who are working on an undergraduate or graduate degree to prepare for Unitarian Universalist ministry or service.

Eligibility This program is open to women of color who are either 1) aspirants or candidates for the Unitarian Universalist ministry; or 2) candidates in the Unitarian Universalist Association's professional religious education or music leadership credentialing programs. Applicants must submit a 1- to 2-page narrative that covers their call to UU ministry, religious education, or music leadership; their passions; how their racial/ethnic/cultural background influences their goals for their calling; and how the work of the program's namesake relates to their dreams and plans for their UU service.

Financial data Stipends from $1,500 to $2,000.

Duration 1 year.

Additional information This program began in 2009.

Number awarded Varies each year; recently, 4 of these scholarships were awarded.

Deadline March of each year.

[887]
MARK MILLER AWARD

National Association of Black Accountants
Attn: National Scholarship Program
7474 Greenway Center Drive, Suite 1120
Greenbelt, MD 20770
(301) 474-NABA Fax: (301) 474-3114
E-mail: scholarships@nabainc.org
Web: www.nabainc.org

Summary To provide financial assistance to student members of the National Association of Black Accountants (NABA) who have overcome hardships and are working on an undergraduate or graduate degree in a field related to accounting.

Eligibility This program is open to NABA members who are ethnic minorities enrolled full time as 1) an undergraduate freshman, sophomore, junior, or first-semester senior majoring in accounting, business, or finance at a 4-year college or university; or 2) a graduate student working on a master's degree in accounting. High school seniors are not eligible. Applicants must have a GPA of 2.0 or higher in their major and 2.5 or higher overall. Along with their application, they must submit 1) a 500-word personal statement on their involvement in NABA, career objectives, leadership abilities, and community activities; and 2) a 500-word statement on how they overcame personal, family, or financial hardship to persevere in their pursuit of their degree.

Financial data The stipend is $2,500.

Duration 1 year.

Number awarded 1 each year.

Deadline January of each year.

[888]
MARK T. BANNER SCHOLARSHIP FOR LAW STUDENTS

Richard Linn American Inn of Court
c/o Matthew Walch, Scholarship Chair
Latham & Watkins LLP
233 South Wacker Drive, Suite 5800
Chicago, IL 60606
(312) 876-7603 E-mail: matthew.walch@lw.com
Web: www.linninn.org/marktbanner.htm

Summary To provide financial assistance to African American and other law students who are members of historically underrepresented groups and interested in specializing in intellectual property law.

Eligibility This program is open to students at ABA-accredited law schools in the United States who are members of groups historically underrepresented (by race, sex, ethnicity, sexual orientation, or disability) in intellectual property law. Applicants must submit a 3-page statement on how they have focused on ethics, civility, and professionalism have been their focus; how diversity has impacted them; and their commitment to a career in intellectual property law.

Financial data The stipend is $5,000.

Duration 1 year.

Number awarded 1 each year.

Deadline November of each year.

[889]
MARRIAGE AND FAMILY THERAPY MASTER'S STUDENT MINORITY SCHOLARSHIP

American Association for Marriage and Family Therapy
Attn: AAMFT Research and Education Foundation
112 South Alfred Street
Alexandria, VA 22314-3061
(703) 838-9808 Fax: (703) 838-9805
Web: www.aamft.org

Summary To provide financial assistance to African American and other minority students enrolled in master's and post-degree training programs in marriage and family therapy.

Eligibility This program is open to minority students (including African Americans, Hispanics, Native Americans, Asian Americans, and Pacific Islanders) enrolled in master's degree programs or post-degree institutes that provide training in marriage and family therapy. Applicants must be members of the American Association for Marriage and Family Therapy (AAMFT). They must be citizens or permanent residents of the United States or Canada and show promise in and commitment to a career in marital and family therapy education, research, or practice. Along with their application, they must submit a personal statement explaining how their racial or ethnic background has had an impact on them and their career decision; the statement should include their professional interests, goals, and commitment to the field of marriage and family therapy.

Financial data The stipend is $2,000. Awardees also receive a plaque and funding up to $750 to attend the association's annual conference.

Duration 1 year.

Additional information This program began in 1986.

Number awarded Up to 3 each year.

Deadline January of each year.

[890]
MARTHA AND ROBERT ATHERTON MINISTERIAL SCHOLARSHIP

Unitarian Universalist Association
Attn: Ministerial Credentialing Office
25 Beacon Street
Boston, MA 02108-2800
(617) 948-6403 Fax: (617) 742-2875
E-mail: mcoadministrator@uua.org
Web: www.uua.org

Summary To provide financial assistance minority and other seminary students preparing for the Unitarian Universalist (UU) ministry.

Eligibility This program is open to second- or third-year seminary students currently enrolled full or at least half time in a UU ministerial training program with aspirant or candidate status. Applicants must respect hard work as a foundation of a full life and appreciate the freedom, political system, and philosophical underpinnings of our country. They should be citizens of the United States or Canada. Priority is given first to those who have demonstrated outstanding ministerial ability and secondarily to students with the greatest financial need (especially persons of color).

Financial data The stipend ranges from $1,000 to $15,000 per year.

Duration 1 year.

Additional information This program began in 1997.

Number awarded 1 or 2 each year.

Deadline April of each year.

[891]
MASSACHUSETTS HISTORICAL SOCIETY AFRICAN AMERICAN STUDIES FELLOWSHIP

Massachusetts Historical Society
Attn: Short-Term Fellowships
1154 Boylston Street
Boston, MA 02215-3695
(617) 646-0568 Fax: (617) 859-0074
E-mail: fellowships@masshist.org
Web: www.masshist.org/research/fellowships/short-term

Summary To fund research visits to the Massachusetts Historical Society for graduate students postdoctorates, and independent scholars interested in African American history.

Eligibility This program is open to advanced graduate students, postdoctorates, and independent scholars who are conducting research in African American history and need to use the resources of the Massachusetts Historical Society. Applicants must be U.S. citizens or foreign nationals holding appropriate U.S. government documents. Along with their application, they must submit a curriculum vitae and a proposal describing the project and indicating collections at the society to be consulted. Graduate students must also arrange for a letter of recommendation from a faculty member familiar with their work and with the project being proposed. Preference is given to candidates who live 50 or more miles from Boston.

Financial data The grant is $1,500.

Duration 4 weeks.

Additional information This fellowship was first awarded in 1999.

Number awarded 1 each year.

Deadline February of each year.

[892]
MAYNARD H. JACKSON/FULL CIRCLE COMMUNICATIONS SCHOLARSHIP

National Forum for Black Public Administrators
Attn: Scholarship Program
777 North Capitol Street, N.E., Suite 807
Washington, DC 20002
(202) 408-9300 Fax: (202) 408-8558
E-mail: vharris@nfbpa.org
Web: www.nfbpa.org/i4a/pages/index.cfm?pageid=4047

Summary To provide financial assistance to African American undergraduate and graduate students preparing for a career in public service or a business field that supports the administration of public service.

Eligibility This program is open to African American undergraduate and graduate students preparing for a career in public service or a business field that supports the administration of public service. Applicants must be working full time on a degree in public administration, political science, urban affairs, public policy, business administration, or a related field. They must have a GPA of 3.0 or higher, a well-balanced focus of academic excellence and volunteerism/community involvement, and strong leadership and communication (oral and written) skills. Along with their application, they must submit a 3-page autobiographical essay that includes their academic and career goals and objectives. Selection is based on academic record, leadership ability, participation in school activities, community service, and financial need.

Financial data The stipend is $2,000.

Duration 1 year.

Additional information This program is sponsored by Full Circle Communications, a media management consulting firm based in Puerto Rico. Recipients are required to attend the sponsor's annual conference to receive their scholarship; limited hotel and air accommodations are arranged and provided.

Number awarded 1 each year.

Deadline February of each year.

[893]
MCANDREWS DIVERSITY IN PATENT LAW FELLOWSHIP

McAndrews, Held & Malloy, Ltd.
Attn: Diversity Fellowship
500 West Madison Street, Suite 3400
Chicago, IL 60661
(312) 775-8000 Fax: (312) 775-8100
E-mail: info@mcandrews-ip.com
Web: www.mcandrews-ip.com/diversity_fellowship.html

Summary To provide financial aid and work experience to African American and other law students who come from a diverse background and are interested in patent law.

Eligibility This program is open to first-year students at ABA-accredited law schools who come from a diverse background. Applicants must have a degree in science or engineering and be planning to practice patent law in the Chicago area. Along with their application, they must submit a 500-word personal statement on why they wish to prepare for a career in patent law, why they are interested in the sponsoring firm as a place to work, and how their background and/or life experiences would improve diversity in the field of intellectual property law. Selection is based on that statement, a resume (including their science or engineering educational credentials), a legal writing sample, undergraduate transcript, and at least 1 letter of recommendation.

Financial data The stipend is $5,000.

Duration 1 year (the second year of law school).

Additional information This fellowship was first awarded in 2008. It includes a paid clerkship position at McAndrews, Held & Malloy during the summer after the first year of law school and possibly another clerkship during the summer after the second year.

Number awarded 1 each year.

Deadline January of each year.

[894]
MCDERMOTT MINORITY SCHOLARSHIP

McDermott Will & Emery
Attn: Recruiting Coordinator
227 West Monroe Street
Chicago, IL 60606
(312) 984-6470 Fax: (312) 984-7700
E-mail: mcdermottscholarship@mwe.com
Web: www.mwe.com

Summary To provide financial aid and work experience to African American and other minority law students.

Eligibility This program is open to second-year minority (African American, Asian, Hispanic, Middle Eastern, Native American, LGBT) law students at ABA-accredited U.S. law schools. Applicants must be able to demonstrate leadership, community involvement, and a commitment to improving diversity in the legal community. They must be interested in participating in the sponsor's summer program and be able to meet its hiring criteria. Along with their application, they must submit an essay of 1 to 2 pages that provides ideas they have on how the number of minority students in law schools can be increased and how they have improved and intend to help improve diversity in the legal profession throughout their law school and legal career.

Financial data The stipend is $15,000.

Duration 1 year.

Additional information Recipients also participate in a summer program at the sponsor's offices in Boston, Chicago, Houston, Los Angeles, Miami, New York, Orange County, San Diego, Silicon Valley, or Washington, D.C.

Number awarded 2 each year.

Deadline October of each year.

[895]
MCKNIGHT DOCTORAL FELLOWSHIP PROGRAM

Florida Education Fund
201 East Kennedy Boulevard, Suite 1525
Tampa, FL 33602
(813) 272-2772 Fax: (813) 272-2784
E-mail: mdf@fefonline.org
Web: www.fefonline.org/mdf.html

Summary To provide financial assistance to African American and Hispanic doctoral students from any state who are working on a degree in designated fields at selected universities in Florida and preparing for an academic career in that state.

Eligibility This program is open to African Americans and Hispanics from any state who are working on a Ph.D. degree at 1 of 9 universities in Florida. Fellowships may be given in any discipline in the arts and sciences, business, engineering, health sciences, nursing, or the visual and performing arts; preference is given to the following fields of study: agriculture, biology, business administration, chemistry, computer science, engineering, marine biology, mathematics, physics, or psychology. Academic programs that lead to professional degrees (such as the M.D., D.B.A., D.D.S., J.D., or D.V.M.) are not covered by the fellowship. Graduate study in education, whether leading to an Ed.D. or a Ph.D., is generally not supported. Because this program is intended to increase African American and Hispanic graduate enrollment at the 9 participating universities, currently-enrolled doctoral students at those universities are not eligible to apply. U.S. citizenship is required.

Financial data Each award provides annual tuition up to $5,000 and an annual stipend of $12,000. Recipients are also eligible for the Fellows Travel Fund, which supports recipients who wish to attend and present papers at professional conferences.

Duration 3 years; an additional 2 years of support may be provided by the university if the recipient maintains satisfactory performance and normal progress toward the Ph.D. degree.

Additional information This program began in 1984. The participating universities are Florida Agricultural and Mechanical University, Florida Atlantic University, Florida Institute of Technology, Florida International University, Florida State University, University of Central Florida, University of Florida, University of Miami, and University of South Florida.

Number awarded Up to 50 each year.

Deadline January of each year.

[896]
MEDICAL LIBRARY ASSOCIATION SCHOLARSHIP FOR MINORITY STUDENTS

Medical Library Association
Attn: Grants and Scholarships
65 East Wacker Place, Suite 1900
Chicago, IL 60601-7246
(312) 419-9094, ext. 15 Fax: (312) 419-8950
E-mail: grants@mlahq.org
Web: www.mlanet.org/awards/grants

Summary To assist African American and other minority students interested in preparing for a career in medical librarianship.

Eligibility This program is open to racial minority students (Asians, Blacks or African Americans, Hispanics or Latinos, Aboriginals, North American Indians or Alaskan Natives, or Native Hawaiians or other Pacific Islanders) who are entering an ALA-accredited graduate program in librarianship or who have completed less than half of their academic requirements for a master's degree in library science. They must be interested in preparing for a career in medical librarianship. Selection is based on academic record, letters of reference, professional potential, and the applicant's statement of career objectives. U.S. or Canadian citizenship or permanent resident status is required.

Financial data The stipend is $5,000.

Duration 1 year.

Additional information This program began in 1973.

Number awarded 1 each year.

Deadline November of each year.

[897]
MELLON SCHOLARS PROGRAM DISSERTATION FELLOWSHIPS IN AFRICAN AMERICAN HISTORY

Library Company of Philadelphia
Attn: Program in African American History
1314 Locust Street
Philadelphia, PA 19107-5698
(215) 546-3181 Fax: (215) 546-5167
E-mail: era@udel.edu
Web: www.librarycompany.org/paah/fellowships.htm

Summary To provide funding to African Americans and other doctoral candidates from underrepresented backgrounds who are interested in conducting research on African American history at the Library Company of Philadelphia.

Eligibility This program is open to doctoral candidates from underrepresented backgrounds who are in the later stages of research or writing a dissertation and interested in conducting research in Philadelphia at the Library Company. The proposed research must relate to African American history prior to 1900.

Financial data The grant is $25,000 for an academic year or $12,500 for a semester.

Duration 1 academic year or 1 semester.

Additional information The Library Company of Philadelphia established its Program in African American History in 2013 with support from the Andrew W. Mellon Foundation.

Number awarded Either 1 fellowship for a year or 2 for a semester are supported each year.

Deadline February of each year.

[898]
MELLON SCHOLARS PROGRAM SHORT-TERM FELLOWSHIPS IN AFRICAN AMERICAN HISTORY

Library Company of Philadelphia
Attn: Program in African American History
1314 Locust Street
Philadelphia, PA 19107-5698
(215) 546-3181 Fax: (215) 546-5167
E-mail: era@udel.edu
Web: www.librarycompany.org/paah/fellowships.htm

Summary To provide funding to African American and other pre- and postdoctorates from underrepresented backgrounds who are interested in conducting short-term research on African American history at the Library Company of Philadelphia.

Eligibility This program is open to doctoral candidates and senior scholars from underrepresented backgrounds who are interested in conducting research in Philadelphia at the Library Company. The proposed research must relate to African American history prior to 1900.

Financial data The stipend is $2,500.

Duration 1 month.

Additional information The Library Company of Philadelphia established its Program in African American History in 2013 with support from the Andrew W. Mellon Foundation.

Number awarded Varies each year.

Deadline February of each year.

[899]
MENTAL HEALTH AND SUBSTANCE ABUSE FELLOWSHIP PROGRAM

Council on Social Work Education
Attn: Minority Fellowship Program
1701 Duke Street, Suite 200
Alexandria, VA 22314-3457
(703) 683-2050 Fax: (703) 683-8099
E-mail: cbrock@cswe.org
Web: www.cswe.org

Summary To provide financial assistance to African Americans and other minorities who are interested in preparing for a clinical career in the mental health fields.

Eligibility This program is open to U.S. citizens, noncitizen nationals, and permanent residents who have been underrepresented in the field of social work. These include but are not limited to the following groups: American Indians/Alaskan Natives, Asian/Pacific Islanders (e.g., Chinese, East Indians, South Asians, Filipinos, Hawaiians, Japanese, Koreans, and Samoans), Blacks, and Hispanics (e.g., Mexicans/Chicanos, Puerto Ricans, Cubans, Central or South Americans). Applicants must be interested in and committed to a career in mental health and/or substance abuse with specialization in the delivery of services of ethnic and racial minority groups. They must have a master's degree in social work and be accepted to or enrolled in a full-time doctoral degree program. Selection is based on potential for assuming leadership roles; potential for success in doctoral studies; and commitment to a career providing mental health and substance abuse services to ethnic, racial, social, and cultural minority individuals and communities.

Financial data Awards provide a stipend of $22,032 per year and tuition support to a maximum of $3,000.

Duration 1 academic year; renewable for 2 additional years if funds are available and the recipient makes satisfactory progress toward the degree objectives.

Additional information This program has been funded since 1978 by the Center for Mental Health Services (CMHS), the Center for Substance Abuse Prevention (CSAP), and the Center for Substance Abuse Treatment (CSAT) in the Substance Abuse and Mental Health Services Administration.

Number awarded Varies each year; recently, 8 new fellows and 16 returning fellows were appointed.

Deadline February of each year.

[900]
MENTAL HEALTH RESEARCH DISSERTATION GRANT TO INCREASE DIVERSITY

National Institute of Mental Health
Attn: Division of Extramural Activities
6001 Executive Boulevard, Room 6138
Bethesda, MD 20892-9609
(301) 443-3534 Fax: (301) 443-4720
TDD: (301) 451-0088 E-mail: armstrda@mail.nih.gov
Web: grants.nih.gov/grants/guide/pa-files/PAR-12-103.html

Summary To provide research funding to African American and other doctoral candidates from underrepresented groups planning to prepare for a research career in any area relevant to mental health and/or mental disorders.

Eligibility This program is open to doctoral candidates conducting dissertation research in a field related to mental health and/or mental disorders at a university, college, or professional school with an accredited doctoral degree granting program. Applicants must be 1) members of an ethnic or racial group that has been determined by the National Science Foundation to be underrepresented in health-related sciences (i.e., African Americans, Hispanic Americans, Alaska Natives, American Indians, Native Hawaiians, and other Pacific Islanders); 2) individuals with disabilities; or 3) individuals from socially, culturally, economically, or educationally disadvantaged backgrounds that have inhibited their ability to prepare for a career in health-related research. They must be U.S. citizens, nationals, or permanent residents.

Financial data The stipend is $22,032. An additional grant up to $15,000 is provided for additional research expenses, fringe benefits (including health insurance), travel to scientific meetings, and research costs of the dissertation. Facilities and administrative costs are limited to 8% of modified total direct costs.

Duration Up to 2 years; nonrenewable.

Number awarded Varies each year.

Deadline April, August, or December of each year.

[901]
MERCK GRADUATE SCIENCE RESEARCH DISSERTATION FELLOWSHIPS

United Negro College Fund
Attn: Merck Science Initiative
8260 Willow Oaks Corporate Drive, Suite 110
P.O. Box 10444
Fairfax, VA 22031-4511
(703) 205-3503 Fax: (703) 205-3574
E-mail: uncfmerck@uncf.org
Web: umsi.uncf.org

Summary To provide financial assistance to African American graduate students who are interested in pursuing biomedical study and research.

Eligibility This program is open to African American graduate students currently enrolled full time in a Ph.D. or equivalent doctoral program in the life or physical sciences or in engineering. Candidates for an M.D./Ph.D. degree are also eligible. Applicants must be U.S. citizens or permanent residents within 1 to 3 years of completing their dissertation. Selection is based on 1) the applicant's academic ability and record of accomplishment; and 2) the soundness of the proposed doctoral research.

Financial data The total award is $53,500, including up to $43,500 as a stipend for the student (the maximum stipend is $30,000 for any 12-month period) and a research grant up to $10,000. Funds must be used for completing course work, conducting research, and preparing the dissertation. Fringe benefits up to $5,350 are also allowed.

Duration 12 to 24 months.

Additional information This program, established in 1995, is funded by the Merck Company Foundation.

Number awarded At least 12 each year.

Deadline December of each year.

[902]
METRO DC CHAPTER NABA SCHOLARSHIP

National Association of Black Accountants-Metro Washington DC Chapter
Attn: Student Member Services Directors
P.O. Box 18602
Washington, DC 20036-8602
(202) 455-LIFT
E-mail: studentservices@nabametrodc.org
Web: www.nabametrodc.org

Summary To provide financial assistance to members of the Metro Washington DC chapter of the National Association of Black Accountants (NABA) who are working on an undergraduate or graduate degree in accounting, business, or finance.

Eligibility This program is open to NABA members who live or attend school in the Metropolitan Washington D.C. area (Maryland, northern Virginia, and the District of Columbia). Applicants must be 1) full-time freshmen, sophomores, juniors, or first-year seniors majoring in accounting, business, or finance; or 2) graduate students enrolled in a C.P.A. review program. They must have an overall GPA of 3.0 or higher. Along with their application, they must submit an essay of 500 to 750 words on a topic that changes annually but relates to minorities in finance. Financial need is not considered in the selection process.

Financial data A stipend is awarded (amount not specified).

Duration 1 year.

Number awarded 1 or more each year.

Deadline February of each year.

[903]
MIAMI CHAPTER BLACK NURSES' ASSOCIATION GRADUATE SCHOLARSHIP

Black Nurses' Association, Inc.-Miami Chapter
Attn: Scholarship Committee
P.O. Box 472826
Miami, FL 33147-2826
(305) 754-2280 E-mail: info@bna-miami.org
Web: bna-miami.org

Summary To provide financial assistance to members of the National Black Nurses' Association (NBNA) from Florida who are working on a graduate degree in nursing at a school in any state.

Eligibility This program is open to residents of Florida who have been NBNA members for at least 1 year and have completed at least 1 semester of a graduate program in nursing at a school in any state. Applicants must have a GPA of 3.0 or higher and be able to demonstrate financial need. Along with their application, they must submit a brief statement about themselves, their future goals in nursing, and their particular qualifications for this award. U.S. citizenship or permanent resident status is required.

Financial data The stipend is $2,000.

Duration 1 year.

Number awarded 1 each year.

Deadline April of each year.

[904]
MICHELLE JACKSON SCHOLARSHIP FUND

Christian Church (Disciples of Christ)
Attn: Disciples Home Missions
130 East Washington Street
P.O. Box 1986
Indianapolis, IN 46206-1986
(317) 713-2652 Toll Free: (888) DHM-2631
Fax: (317) 635-4426 E-mail: mail@dhm.disciples.org
Web: www.discipleshomemissions.org

Summary To provide financial assistance to African American women interested in preparing for a career in the ministry of the Christian Church (Disciples of Christ).

Eligibility This program is open to female African American ministerial students who are members of a Christian Church (Disciples of Christ) congregation in the United States or Canada. Applicants must plan to prepare for the ordained ministry, be working on an M.Div. or equivalent degree, provide evidence of financial need, be enrolled full time in an accredited school or seminary, provide a transcript of academic work, and be under the care of a regional Commission on the Ministry or in the process of coming under care.

Financial data A stipend is awarded (amount not specified).

Duration 1 year; recipients may reapply.

Number awarded 1 each year.

Deadline March of each year.

[905]
MIKE SHINN DISTINGUISHED MEMBER OF THE YEAR AWARDS

National Society of Black Engineers
Attn: Programs Department
205 Daingerfield Road
Alexandria, VA 22314
(703) 549-2207 Fax: (703) 683-5312
E-mail: scholarships@nsbe.org
Web: www.nsbe.org/Programs/Scholarships.aspx

Summary To provide financial assistance to male and female members of the National Society of Black Engineers (NSBE) who are working on a degree in engineering.

Eligibility This program is open to members of the society who are undergraduate or graduate engineering students. Applicants must have a GPA of 3.2 or higher. Selection is based on an essay; NSBE and university academic achievement; professional development; service to the society at the chapter, regional, and/or national level; and campus and community activities. The male and female applicants for the NSBE Fellows Scholarship Program who are judged most outstanding receive these awards.

Financial data The stipend is $7,500. Travel, hotel accommodations, and registration to the national convention are also provided.

Duration 1 year.

Number awarded 2 each year: 1 male and 1 female.

Deadline November of each year.

[906]
MILBANK DIVERSITY SCHOLARS PROGRAM

Milbank, Tweed, Hadley & McCloy LLP
Attn: Manager, Diversity and Inclusion
One Chase Manhattan Plaza
New York, NY 10005
(212) 530-5316 Fax: (212) 530-5219
E-mail: syohn@milbank.com
Web: www.milbank.com

Summary To provide financial aid and work experience to law students, especially those who are African Americans or members of other groups underrepresented at large law firms.

Eligibility This program is open to students who have completed their first year of a full-time J.D. program at an ABA-accredited law school. Joint degree candidates must have successfully completed 2 years of a J.D. program. Applications are particularly encouraged from members of groups traditionally underrepresented at large law firms. Applicants must submit a 500-word essay on 1) the challenges they have faced in pursuit of a legal career that have helped them understand the value of diversity and inclusion in the legal profession; and 2) the personal contributions they would make to furthering the diversity objectives of the sponsoring law firm. Selection is based on academic achievement, demonstrated leadership ability, writing and interpersonal skills, and interest in the firm's practice.

Financial data The stipend is $25,000. A paid associate position during the summer after the second year of law school is also provided. If the student is offered and accepts a permanent position with the firm after graduation, an additional $25,000 scholarship stipend is also awarded.

Duration 1 year (the third year of law school).

Additional information Scholars may be offered a permanent position with the firm, but there is no guarantee of such an offer.

Number awarded At least 2 each year.

Deadline August of each year.

[907]
MILDRED CATER BRADHAM SOCIAL WORK FELLOWSHIP

Zeta Phi Beta Sorority, Inc.
Attn: National Education Foundation
1734 New Hampshire Avenue, N.W.
Washington, DC 20009
(202) 387-3103 Fax: (202) 232-4593
E-mail: scholarship@ZPhiBNEF.org
Web: www.zphib1920.org/nef

Summary To provide financial assistance to members of Zeta Phi Beta Sorority who are interested in studying social work on the graduate level.

Eligibility This program is open to members of Zeta Phi Beta who are interested in working full time on a graduate or professional degree in social work. Applicants must have shown scholarly distinction or unusual ability in their chosen field. Along with their application, they must submit a 150-word essay on their educational goals and professional aspirations, how this award will help them to achieve those goals, and why they should receive the award. Financial need is not considered in the selection process.

Financial data The stipend ranges from $500 to $1,000 per year; funds are paid directly to the college or university.

Duration 1 academic year; may be renewed.

Number awarded 1 each year.

Deadline January of each year.

[908] MILLER JOHNSON WEST MICHIGAN DIVERSITY LAW SCHOOL SCHOLARSHIP

Grand Rapids Community Foundation
Attn: Education Program Officer
185 Oakes Street S.W.
Grand Rapids, MI 49503-4008
(616) 454-1751, ext. 103 Fax: (616) 454-6455
E-mail: rbishop@grfoundation.org
Web: www.grfoundation.org/scholarshipslist

Summary To provide financial assistance to African Americans and other minorities from Michigan who are attending law school in any state.

Eligibility This program is open to U.S. citizens who are students of color (African American, Asian, Hispanic, Native American, Pacific Islander) and residents of Michigan. Applicants must be attending an accredited law school in any state. They must have a GPA of 3.0 or higher and be able to demonstrate financial need.

Financial data The stipend is $5,000. Funds are paid directly to the recipient's institution.

Duration 1 year.

Number awarded 1 each year.

Deadline March of each year.

[909] MILLER NASH LAW STUDENT DIVERSITY FELLOWSHIP PROGRAM

Miller Nash LLP
Attn: Director of Recruiting and Professional Development
3400 U.S. Bancorp Tower
111 S.W. Fifth Avenue
Portland, OR 97204-3699
(503) 224-5858 Fax: (503) 224-0155
E-mail: MNrecruiting@millernash.com
Web: www.millernash.com

Summary To provide financial aid and work experience to African American and other law students who contribute to diversity and are interested in living and working in the Pacific Northwest following graduation from law school.

Eligibility This program is open to first- and second-year students at ABA-accredited law schools in any state. Applicants must be able to demonstrate academic excellence, interpersonal skills, leadership qualities, contributions to diversity, and meaningful contributions to the community. They must intend to work, live, and practice law in the Pacific Northwest. Along with their application, they must submit a personal statement of 2 to 4 pages that includes a description of organizations or projects in which they currently participate or have participated that address diversity issues or support diversity in their legal, business, or local communities.

Financial data Fellows receive a paid summer clerk position and a stipend of $7,500 for law school.

Duration 1 year (including 12 weeks for the summer clerk position); nonrenewable.

Additional information Summer clerk positions may be offered (depending on availability) at the sponsoring law firm's offices in Portland (Oregon), Seattle (Washington), or Vancouver (Washington).

Number awarded Up to 2 each year.

Deadline September of each year for second-year students; January of each year for first-year students.

[910] MINORITIES IN GOVERNMENT FINANCE SCHOLARSHIP

Government Finance Officers Association
Attn: Scholarship Committee
203 North LaSalle Street, Suite 2700
Chicago, IL 60601-1210
(312) 977-9700 Fax: (312) 977-4806
Web: www.gfoa.org

Summary To provide financial assistance to African American and other minority upper-division and graduate students who are preparing for a career in state and local government finance.

Eligibility This program is open to upper-division and graduate students who are preparing for a career in public finance by working on a degree in public administration, accounting, finance, political science, economics, or business administration (with a specific focus on government or nonprofit management). Applicants must be members of a minority group, citizens or permanent residents of the United States or Canada, and able to provide a letter of recommendation from a representative of their school. Selection is based on career plans, academic record, plan of study, letters of recommendation, and GPA. Financial need is not considered.

Financial data The stipend is $5,000.

Duration 1 year.

Additional information This program defines minorities as Blacks or African Americans, American Indians or Alaskan Natives, Hispanics or Latinos, Native Hawaiians or other Pacific Islanders, or Asians.

Number awarded 1 or more each year.

Deadline February of each year.

[911] MINORITY AND UNDERREPRESENTED ENVIRONMENTAL LITERACY PROGRAM

Missouri Department of Higher Education
Attn: Minority and Underrepresented Environmental Literacy Program
205 Jefferson Street
P.O. Box 1469
Jefferson City, MO 65102-1469
(573) 751-2361 Toll Free: (800) 473-6757
Fax: (573) 751-6635 E-mail: info@dhe.mo.gov
Web: dhe.mo.gov/ppc/grants/muelp_0310_final.php

Summary To provide financial assistance to African American and other underrepresented students from Missouri who are or will be working on a bachelor's or master's degree in an environmental field.

Eligibility This program is open to residents of Missouri who are high school seniors or current undergraduate or graduate students enrolled or planning to enroll full time at a college or university in the state. Priority is given to members of the following underrepresented minority ethnic groups: African Americans, Hispanic or Latino Americans, Native Americans and Alaska Natives, and Native Hawaiians and Pacific Islanders. Applicants must be working on or planning to work on a bachelor's or master's degree in 1) engineering (civil, chemical, environmental, mechanical, or agricultural); 2) environmental studies (geology, biology, wildlife management, natural resource planning, natural resources, or a closely-related course of study); 3) environmental chemistry; or 4) environmental law enforcement. They must be U.S. citizens or permanent residents or otherwise lawfully present in the United States. Graduating high school seniors must have a GPA of 3.0 or higher; students currently enrolled in college or graduate school must have a GPA of 2.5 or higher. Along with their application, they must submit a 1-page essay on their environmental education and career goals, 3 letters of recommendation, a resume of school and community activities, and transcripts that include SAT or ACT scores. Financial need is not considered in the selection process.

Financial data Stipends vary each year; recently, they averaged approximately $3,996 per year.

Duration 1 year; may be renewed if the recipient maintains a GPA of 2.5 or higher and full-time enrollment.

Additional information This program was established by the Missouri Department of Natural Resources but transferred to the Department of Higher Education in 2009.

Number awarded Varies each year.

Deadline May of each year.

[912] MINORITY FACULTY DEVELOPMENT SCHOLARSHIP AWARD IN PHYSICAL THERAPY

American Physical Therapy Association
Attn: Honors and Awards Program
1111 North Fairfax Street
Alexandria, VA 22314-1488
(703) 684-APTA Toll Free: (800) 999-APTA
Fax: (703) 684-7343 TDD: (703) 683-6748
E-mail: honorsandawards@apta.org
Web: www.apta.org

Summary To provide financial assistance to African American and other minority faculty members in physical therapy who are interested in working on a post-professional doctoral degree.

Eligibility This program is open to U.S. citizens and permanent residents who are members of the following minority groups: African American or Black, Asian, Native Hawaiian or other Pacific Islander, American Indian or Alaska Native, or Hispanic/Latino. Applicants must be full-time faculty members, teaching in an accredited or developing professional physical therapist education program, who will have completed the equivalent of 2 full semesters of post-professional doctoral course work. They must possess a license to practice physical therapy in a U.S. jurisdiction and be enrolled as a student in an accredited post-professional doctoral program whose content has a demonstrated relationship to physical therapy. Along with their application, they must submit a personal essay on their professional goals, including their plans to contribute to the profession and minority services. Selection is based on 1) commitment to minority affairs and services; 2) commitment to further the physical therapy profession through teaching and research; and 3) scholastic achievement.

Financial data A stipend is awarded (amount not specified).

Duration 1 year.

Additional information This program began in 1999.

Number awarded 1 or more each year.

Deadline November of each year.

[913] MINORITY FELLOWSHIPS IN EDUCATION RESEARCH

American Educational Research Association
1430 K Street, N.W., Suite 1200
Washington, DC 20005
(202) 238-3200 Fax: (202) 238-3250
E-mail: fellowships@aera.net
Web: www.aera.net

Summary To provide funding to African American and other minority doctoral students writing their dissertation on educational research.

Eligibility This program is open to U.S. citizens and permanent residents who have advanced to candidacy and successfully defended their Ph.D./Ed.D. dissertation research proposal. Applicants must plan to work full time on their dissertation in educational research. This program is targeted for members of groups historically underrepresented in higher education (African Americans, American Indians, Alaskan Natives, Asian Americans, Native Hawaiian or Pacific Islanders, and Hispanics or Latinos). Selection is based on scholarly achievements and publications, letters of recommendation, quality and significance of the proposed research, and commitment of the applicant's faculty mentor to the goals of the program.

Financial data The grant is $12,000. Up to $1,000 is provided to pay for travel to the sponsor's annual conference.

Duration 1 year; nonrenewable.

Additional information This program began in 1991.

Number awarded Up to 3 each year.

Deadline November of each year.

[914] MINORITY LEAP SCHOLARSHIPS

Missouri Society of Certified Public Accountants
Attn: LEAP Program
540 Maryville Centre Drive, Suite 200
P.O. Box 419042
St. Louis, MO 63141-9042
(314) 997-7966, ext. 125
Toll Free: (800) 264-7966, ext. 125 (within MO)
Fax: (314) 997-2592 E-mail: lsimpson@mocpa.org
Web: www.mocpa.org/students/scholarships

Summary To provide financial assistance to African American and other minority residents of Missouri who are working on an undergraduate or graduate degree in accounting at a university in the state.

Eligibility This program is open to members of minority groups underrepresented in the accounting profession (Black/African American, Hispanic/Latino, Native American, Asian American) who are currently working full time on an undergraduate or graduate degree in accounting at a college or university in Missouri. Applicants must either be residents of Missouri or the children of members of the Missouri Society of Certified Public Accountants (MSCPA). They must be U.S. citizens, have completed at least 30 semester hours of college work, have a GPA of 3.3 or higher, and be student members of the MSCPA. Selection is based on the GPA, involvement in MSCPA, educator recommendations, and leadership potential. Financial need is not considered.

Financial data The stipend is $1,250 per year.

Duration 1 year; may be renewed.

Additional information These scholarships are offered through the sponsor's Lead and Enhance the Accounting Profession (LEAP) program, established in 2001.

Number awarded Varies each year; recently, 2 of these scholarships were awarded.

Deadline February of each year.

[915]
MINORITY MEDICAL STUDENT AWARD PROGRAM OF THE AMERICAN SOCIETY OF HEMATOLOGY

American Society of Hematology
Attn: Awards Manager
2021 L Street, N.W., Suite 900
Washington, DC 20036
(202) 776-0544 Fax: (202) 776-0545
E-mail: awards@hematology.org
Web: www.hematology.org/Awards/MMSAP/2624.aspx

Summary To provide an opportunity for African American and other underrepresented minority medical students to conduct a research project in hematology.

Eligibility This program is open to medical students enrolled in D.O., M.D., or M.D./Ph.D. programs in the United States or Canada who are members of minority groups. For purposes of this program, minority is defined as a member of a racial or ethnic group that has been shown to be underrepresented in health-related sciences in the United States and Canada, including American Indians, Alaska Natives, Blacks or African Americans, Hispanics or Latinos, Native Hawaiians, other Pacific Islanders, African Canadians, Innuit, and First Nation Peoples. Applicants must be interested in conducting a research project in hematology at their home institution or at another institution that has agreed to host them. They must work with 2 mentors who are members of the American Society of Hematology (ASH): a research mentor who oversees the participant's work and progress and a career development mentor (who is from the same minority group as the student) who participates for the duration of the program. U.S. or Canadian citizenship or permanent resident status is required.

Financial data The grant includes $5,000 for research support, an additional $1,000 to support travel to the annual meeting of the ASH, and another $1,000 for making a short presentation about the research experience at a special reception at the ASH annual meeting. Research mentors receive an allowance of $2,000 for supplies and $1,000 for attendance at the ASH annual meeting. Career development mentors receives $1,000 as a travel allowance each time they accompany the student to an ASH annual meeting during their remaining years of medical school and residency.

Duration 8 to 12 weeks.

Additional information This program is supported by Amgen, Celgene Corporation, Cephalon Oncology, and Genentech BioOncology.

Number awarded Up to 10 each year.

Deadline March of each year.

[916]
MINORITY MEDICAL STUDENT ELECTIVE IN HIV PSYCHIATRY

American Psychiatric Association
Attn: Office of HIV Psychiatry
1000 Wilson Boulevard, Suite 1825
Arlington, VA 22209-3901
(703) 907-8668 Toll Free: (888) 357-7849
Fax: (703) 907-1087 E-mail: dpennessi@psych.org
Web: www.psychiatry.org

Summary To provide an opportunity for African American and other minority medical students to spend an elective residency learning about HIV psychiatry.

Eligibility This program is open to medical students entering their fourth year at an accredited M.D. or D.O. degree-granting institution. Preference is given to minority candidates and those who have primary interests in services related to HIV/AIDS and substance abuse and its relationship to the mental health or the psychological well-being of ethnic minorities. Applicants should be interested in a psychiatry, internal medicine, pediatrics, or research career. They must be interested in participating in a program that includes intense training in HIV mental health (including neuropsychiatry), a clinical and/or research experience working with a mentor, and participation in the Committee on AIDS of the American Psychiatric Association (APA). U.S. citizenship is required.

Financial data A stipend is provided (amount not specified).

Duration 1 year.

Additional information The heart of the program is in establishing a mentor relationship at 1 of 5 sites, becoming involved with a cohort of medical students interested in HIV medicine/psychiatry, participating in an interactive didactic/experimental learning program, and developing expertise in areas related to ethnic minority mental health research or psychiatric services. Students selected for the program who are not APA members automatically receive membership.

Number awarded Varies each year.

Deadline March of each year.

[917]
MINORITY MEDICAL STUDENT SUMMER EXTERNSHIP IN ADDICTION PSYCHIATRY

American Psychiatric Association
Attn: Department of Minority and National Affairs
1000 Wilson Boulevard, Suite 1825
Arlington, VA 22209-3901
(703) 907-8653 Toll Free: (888) 35-PSYCH
Fax: (703) 907-7852 E-mail: mking@psych.org
Web: www.psychiatry.org

Summary To provide funding to African American and other minority medical students who are interested in working on a research project during the summer with a mentor who specializes in addiction psychiatry.

Eligibility This program is open to minority medical students who have a specific interest in services related to substance abuse treatment and prevention. Minorities include American Indians, Alaska Natives, Native Hawaiians, Asian Americans, Hispanics/Latinos, and African Americans. Applicants must be interested in working with a mentor who specializes in addiction psychiatry. Work settings provide an emphasis on working clinically with or studying underserved minority populations and issues of co-occurring disorders, substance abuse treatment, and mental health disparity. Most of them are in inner-city or rural settings.

Financial data Externships provide $1,500 for travel expenses to go to the work setting of the mentor and up to another $1,500 for out-of-pocket expenses directly related to the conduct of the externship.

Duration 1 month during the summer.

Additional information Funding for this program is provided by the Substance Abuse and Mental Health Services Administration (SAMHSA).

Number awarded 10 each year.

Deadline February of each year.

[918]
MINORITY NURSE MAGAZINE SCHOLARSHIP PROGRAM

Minority Nurse Magazine
c/o Alloy Education
2 LAN Drive, Suite 100
Westford, MA 01886
Toll Free: (877) ASK-ALLO
E-mail: editor@minoritynurse.com
Web: www.minoritynurse.com

Summary To provide financial assistance to African Americans and members of other minority groups who are working on a bachelor's or master's degree in nursing.

Eligibility This program is open to racial and ethnic minority nursing students currently enrolled in 1) the third or fourth year of an accredited B.S.N. program; 2) an accelerated program leading to a B.S.N. degree (e.g., R.N. to B.S.N., B.A. to B.S.N.); or 3) an accelerated master's entry nursing program (e.g., B.A. to M.S.N.) for students with bachelor's degrees in fields other than nursing. Graduate students who already have a bachelor's degree in nursing are not eligible. Along with their application, they must submit a 250-word essay on their academic and personal accomplishments, community service, and goals for their future nursing career. Selection is based on academic excellence (GPA of 3.0 or higher), demonstrated commitment of service to the student's minority community, and financial need. U.S. citizenship of permanent resident status is required.

Financial data The stipends are $3,000 or $1,000.

Duration 1 year.

Additional information This program began in 2000. Winners are announced in the summer issue of *Minority Nurse* magazine.

Number awarded 3 each year: 1 at $3,000 and 2 at $1,000.

Deadline January of each year.

[919]
MINORITY PRE-DOCTORAL FELLOWSHIP IN CLINICAL PHARMACEUTICAL SCIENCE

American Foundation for Pharmaceutical Education
Attn: Grants Manager
2107 Wilson Boulevard, Suite 700
Arlington, VA 22201-3042
(703) 875-3095 Fax: (703) 875-3098
E-mail: info@afpenet.org
Web: www.afpenet.org/applicant.htm

Summary To provide funding for dissertation research to African American and Hispanic American graduate students working on a Ph.D. in clinical pharmaceutical science.

Eligibility This program is open to African American/Black and Hispanic/Latino students who have completed at least 3 semesters of graduate study and have no more than 3 and a half years remaining to complete a Ph.D. in clinical pharmaceutical science at a U.S. school or college of pharmacy. Students enrolled in joint Pharm.D./Ph.D. programs are eligible if they have completed 3 full semesters of graduate credit toward the Ph.D. and if the Ph.D. degree will be awarded within 3 additional years. Applicants must be U.S. citizens or permanent residents. Along with their application, they must submit 1) a brief statement on their objective in pursuing graduate study; 2) a brief statement on their future career plans; and 3) a description of their dissertation research project that includes its nature and scope, area of research, hypothesis to be tested, plan of investigation, and methodologies to be employed. Students with the following majors are encouraged to apply: clinical pharmaceutical sciences, medicinal/pharmaceutical chemistry, pharmaceutics, pharmacology/toxicology, pharmacognosy, pharmacoeconomics and health outcomes, pharmacokinetics/metabolism, pharmacotherapy and experimental therapeutics, or social and administrative science.

Financial data The grant is $6,500 per year. Funds must be used to enable the students to make progress on their Ph.D. (e.g., student stipend, laboratory supplies, books, materials, travel) but not for indirect costs for the institution.

Duration 1 year; may be renewed 1 additional year.

Number awarded Up to 5 each year.

Deadline February of each year.

[920]
MINORITY PRE-DOCTORAL FELLOWSHIP IN PHARMACEUTICAL SCIENCE

American Foundation for Pharmaceutical Education
Attn: Grants Manager
2107 Wilson Boulevard, Suite 700
Arlington, VA 22201-3042
(703) 875-3095 Fax: (703) 875-3098
E-mail: info@afpenet.org
Web: www.afpenet.org/applicant.htm

Summary To provide funding for dissertation research to African American and Hispanic graduate students working on a Ph.D. in pharmaceutical science.

Eligibility This program is open to African American/Black and Hispanic/Latino students who have completed at least 3 semesters of graduate study and have no more than 3 and a half years remaining to complete a Ph.D. in pharmaceutical science at a U.S. school or college of pharmacy. Students enrolled in joint Pharm.D./Ph.D. programs are eligible if they have completed 3 full semesters of graduate credit toward the Ph.D. and if the Ph.D. degree will be awarded within 3 additional years. Applicants must be U.S. citizens or permanent residents. Along with their application, they must submit 1) a brief statement on their objective in pursuing graduate study; 2) a brief statement on their future career plans; and 3) a description of their dissertation research project that includes its nature and scope, area of research, hypothesis to be tested, plan of investigation, and methodologies to be employed. Students with the following majors are encouraged to apply: pharmaceutical sciences, medicinal/pharmaceutical chemistry, pharmaceutics, pharmacology/toxicology, pharmacognosy, pharmacoeconomics and health outcomes, pharmacokinetics/metabolism, pharmacotherapy and experimental therapeutics, or social and administrative science.

Financial data The grant is $6,000 per year. Funds must be used to enable the students to make progress on their Ph.D. (e.g., student stipend, laboratory supplies, books, materials, travel) but not for indirect costs for the institution.

Duration 1 year; may be renewed 1 additional year.

Number awarded Up to 5 each year.

Deadline February of each year.

[921]
MINORITY TEACHERS OF ILLINOIS SCHOLARSHIP PROGRAM

Illinois Student Assistance Commission
Attn: Scholarship and Grant Services
1755 Lake Cook Road
Deerfield, IL 60015-5209
(847) 948-8550 Toll Free: (800) 899-ISAC
Fax: (847) 831-8549 TDD: (800) 526-0844
E-mail: isac.studentservices@isac.illinois.gov
Web: www.collegeillinois.org

Summary To provide funding to African American and other minority students in Illinois who plan to become teachers at the preschool, elementary, or secondary level.

Eligibility Applicants must be Illinois residents, U.S. citizens or eligible noncitizens, members of a minority group (African American/Black, Hispanic American, Asian American, or Native American), and high school graduates or holders of a General Educational Development (GED) certificate. They must be enrolled at least half time as an undergraduate or graduate student, have a GPA of 2.5 or higher, not be in default on any student loan, and be enrolled or accepted for enrollment in a teacher education program.

Financial data Grants up to $5,000 per year are awarded. Recipients must agree to teach full time 1 year for each year of support received. The teaching agreement may be fulfilled at a public, private, or parochial preschool, elementary school, or secondary school in Illinois; at least 30% of the student body at those schools must be minority. It must be fulfilled within the 5-year period following the completion of the undergraduate program for which the scholarship was awarded. The time period may be extended if the recipient serves in the U.S. armed forces, enrolls full time in a graduate program related to teaching, becomes temporarily disabled, is unable to find employment as a teacher at a qualifying school, or takes additional courses on at least a half-time basis to obtain certification as a teacher in Illinois. Recipients who fail to honor this work obligation must repay the award with 5% interest.

Duration 1 year; may be renewed for a total of 8 semesters or 12 quarters.

Number awarded Varies each year.

Deadline Priority consideration is given to applications received by February of each year.

[922]
MIRIAM WEINSTEIN PEACE AND JUSTICE EDUCATION AWARD

Philanthrofund Foundation
Attn: Scholarship Committee
1409 Willow Street, Suite 109
Minneapolis, MN 55403-2241
(612) 870-1806 Toll Free: (800) 435-1402
Fax: (612) 871-6587 E-mail: info@PfundOnline.org
Web: www.pfundonline.org/scholarships.html

Summary To provide financial assistance to African American and other minority students from Minnesota who have supported gay, lesbian, bisexual, and transgender (GLBT) activities and are interested in working on a degree in education.

Eligibility This program is open to residents of Minnesota and students attending a Minnesota educational institution who are members of a religious, racial, or ethnic minority. Applicants must be self-identified as GLBT or from a GLBT family and have demonstrated a commitment to peace and justice issues. They may be attending or planning to attend trade school, technical college, college, or university (as an undergraduate or graduate student). Preference is given to students who have completed at least 2 years of college and are working on a degree in education. Selection is based on the applicant's 1) affirmation of GLBT or allied identity; 2) evidence of experience and skills in service and leadership; and 3) evidence of service, leading, and working for change in GLBT communities, including serving as a role model, mentor, and/or adviser.

Financial data The stipend is $3,000. Funds must be used for tuition, books, fees, or dissertation expenses.

Duration 1 year.

Number awarded 1 each year.

Deadline January of each year.

[923]
MLA/NLM SPECTRUM SCHOLARSHIPS

Medical Library Association
Attn: Grants and Scholarships
65 East Wacker Place, Suite 1900
Chicago, IL 60601-7246
(312) 419-9094, ext. 15 Fax: (312) 419-8950
E-mail: grants@mlahq.org
Web: www.mlanet.org/awards/grants

Summary To provide financial assistance to African Americans and other minorities who are interested in preparing for a career as a medical librarian.

Eligibility This program is open to members of minority groups (African Americans, Hispanics, Asian, Native Americans, and Pacific Islanders) who are attending library schools accredited by the American Library Association (ALA). Applicants must be interested in preparing for a career as a health sciences information professional.

Financial data The stipend is $3,250.

Duration 1 year.

Additional information This program, established in 2001, is jointly sponsored by the Medical Library Association (MLA) and the National Library of Medicine (NLM) of the U.S. National Institutes of Health (NIH). It operates as a component of the Spectrum Initiative Scholarship program of the ALA.

Number awarded 2 each year.

Deadline February of each year.

[924]
MORGAN STANLEY MBA FELLOWSHIP

Morgan Stanley
Attn: Diversity Recruiting
1585 Broadway
New York, NY 10036
(212) 762-0211 Toll Free: (888) 454-3965
Fax: (212) 507-4972
E-mail: mbafellowship@morganstanley.com
Web: www.morganstanley.com

Summary To provide financial aid and work experience to African Americans and members of other underrepresented groups who are working on an M.B.A. degree.

Eligibility This program is open to full-time M.B.A. students who are women, African Americans, Hispanics, Native Americans, or lesbian/gay/bisexual/transgender. Selection is based on assigned essays, academic achievement, recommendations, extracurricular activities, leadership qualities, and on-site interviews.

Financial data The program provides full payment of tuition and fees and a paid summer internship.

Duration 1 year; may be renewed for a second year, providing the student remains enrolled full time in good academic standing and completes the summer internship following the first year.

Additional information The paid summer internship is offered within Morgan Stanley institutional securities (equity research, fixed income, institutional equity, investment banking), investment management, or private wealth management. This program was established in 1999.

Number awarded 1 or more each year.

Deadline December of each year.

[925]
MOSAIC SCHOLARSHIPS

Society of American Archivists
Attn: Chair, Awards Committee
17 North State Street, Suite 1425
Chicago, IL 60602-4061
(312) 606-0722 Toll Free: (866) 722-7858
Fax: (312) 606-0728 E-mail: info@archivists.org
Web: www.archivists.org/recognition

Summary To provide financial assistance to African American and other minority students who are working on a graduate degree in archival science.

Eligibility This program is open to minority graduate students, defined as those of American Indian/Alaska Native, Asian, Black/African American, Hispanic/Latino, or Native Hawaiian/other Pacific Islander descent. Applicants must be enrolled or planning to enroll full or part time in a graduate program or a multi-course program in archival administration. They may have completed no more than half of the credit requirements for a degree. Along with their application, they must submit a 500-word essay outlining their interests and future goals in the archives profession. U.S. or Canadian citizenship or permanent resident status is required.

Financial data The stipend is $5,000.

Duration 1 year.

Additional information This program began in 2009.

Number awarded 2 each year.

Deadline February of each year.

[926]
MOSS ADAMS FOUNDATION SCHOLARSHIP

Educational Foundation for Women in Accounting
Attn: Foundation Administrator
136 South Keowee Street
Dayton, OH 45402
(937) 424-3391 Fax: (937) 222-5749
E-mail: info@efwa.org
Web: www.efwa.org/scholarships_MossAdams.php

Summary To provide financial support to women (preference given to African American and other minority women) who are working on an accounting degree.

Eligibility This program is open to women who are enrolled in an accounting degree program at an accredited college or university. Applicants must meet 1 of the following criteria: 1) women pursuing a fifth-year requirement either through general studies or within a graduate program; 2) women returning to school as current or reentry juniors or seniors; or 3) minority women. Selection is based on aptitude for accounting and business, commitment to the goal of working on a degree in accounting (including evidence of continued commitment after receiving this award), clear evidence that the candidate has established goals and a plan for achieving those goals (both personal and professional), financial need, and a demonstration of how the scholarship will impact her life. U.S. citizenship is required.

Financial data The stipend is $1,000.

Duration 1 year.

Additional information This program was established by Rowling, Dold & Associates LLP, a woman-owned C.P.A. firm based in San Diego. It was renamed when that firm merged with Moss Adams LLP.

Number awarded 1 each year.

Deadline April of each year.

[927]
MSCPA/NABA SCHOLARSHIPS

Massachusetts Society of Certified Public Accountants
Attn: MSCPA Educational Foundation
105 Chauncy Street, Tenth Floor
Boston, MA 02111
(617) 556-4000 Toll Free: (800) 392-6145
Fax: (617) 556-4126 E-mail: info@mscpaonline.org
Web: www.cpatrack.com/scholarships

Summary To provide financial assistance to members of the National Association of Black Accountants (NABA) from Massachusetts who are working on an undergraduate or graduate degree in accounting at a college or university in the state.

Eligibility This program is open to African American students from any state who are members of the Boston Metropolitan Chapter of NABA and enrolled at a college or university in Massachusetts. Applicants must be undergraduates who have completed at least the first semester of their sophomore year or graduate students. They must be able to demonstrate financial need, academic excellence, and an intention to prepare for a career as a Certified Public Accountant (C.P.A.) at a firm in Massachusetts.

Financial data The stipend is $2,500.

Duration 1 year.

Additional information This program is sponsored by the Boston Metropolitan Chapter of NABA and the Massachusetts Society of Certified Public Accountants (MSCPA).

Number awarded 2 each year.

Deadline March of each year.

[928]
MYRA DAVIS HEMMINGS SCHOLARSHIP

Delta Sigma Theta Sorority, Inc.
Attn: Scholarship and Standards Committee Chair
1707 New Hampshire Avenue, N.W.
Washington, DC 20009
(202) 986-2400 Fax: (202) 986-2513
E-mail: dstemail@deltasigmatheta.org
Web: www.deltasigmatheta.org

Summary To provide financial assistance to members of Delta Sigma Theta who are interested in working on a graduate degree in the performing or creative arts.

Eligibility This program is open to graduating college seniors and graduate students who are interested in preparing for a career in the performing or creative arts. Applicants must be active, dues-paying members of Delta Sigma Theta. Selection is based on meritorious achievement.

Financial data The stipends range from $1,000 to $2,000 per year. The funds may be used to cover tuition and living expenses.

Duration 1 year; may be renewed for 1 additional year.

Additional information This sponsor is a traditionally-African American social sorority. The application fee is $20.

Number awarded 1 or more each year.

Deadline April of each year.

[929]
NABA 20 PEARLS SCHOLARSHIP

National Association of Black Accountants
Attn: National Scholarship Program
7474 Greenway Center Drive, Suite 1120
Greenbelt, MD 20770
(301) 474-NABA Fax: (301) 474-3114
E-mail: scholarships@nabainc.org
Web: www.nabainc.org

Summary To provide financial assistance to student members of the National Association of Black Accountants (NABA) who are also members of Alpha Kappa Alpha sorority and working on an undergraduate or graduate degree in a field related to accounting.

Eligibility This program is open to NABA members who are also Alpha Kappa Alpha members and enrolled full time as 1) an undergraduate freshman, sophomore, junior, or first-semester senior majoring in accounting, business, or finance at a 4-year college or university; or 2) a graduate student working on a master's degree in accounting. High school seniors are not eligible. Applicants must have a GPA of 3.5 or higher in their major and 3.3 or higher overall. Along with their application, they must submit a 500-word personal statement on their involvement in NABA, career objectives, leadership abilities, and community activities. Financial need is not considered in the selection process.

Financial data The stipend is $1,500.

Duration 1 year.

Number awarded 1 each year.

Deadline January of each year.

[930]
NABJ/CAROLE SIMPSON SCHOLARSHIP

National Association of Black Journalists
Attn: Communications Coordinator and Program Manager
University of Maryland
1100 Knight Hall, Suite 3100
College Park, MD 20742
(301) 405-2573 Fax: (301) 314-1714
E-mail: tjohnson@nabj.org
Web: www.nabj.org/?page=SEEDScholarships

Summary To provide financial assistance to undergraduate or graduate student members of the National Association of Black Journalists (NABJ) who are working on a degree in broadcast journalism.

Eligibility This program is open to African American undergraduate or graduate student members of NABJ who are currently enrolled full time at an accredited 4-year college or university. Applicants must be studying broadcast journalism as preparation for a career in television news and have a GPA of 2.5 or higher. They must be able to demonstrate financial need. Along with their application, they must submit 5 samples of their work, an official college transcript, 3 letters of recommendation, a resume, and an essay of 1,000 to 2,000 words on how the career of this program's namesake inspired them to prepare for a career in broadcast journalism and what they hope their legacy will be.

Financial data The stipend is $2,500. Funds are paid directly to the recipient's college or university.

Duration 1 year; nonrenewable.

Number awarded 1 each year.

Deadline March of each year.

[931]
NANCY B. WOOLRIDGE MCGEE GRADUATE FELLOWSHIP

Zeta Phi Beta Sorority, Inc.
Attn: National Education Foundation
1734 New Hampshire Avenue, N.W.
Washington, DC 20009
(202) 387-3103 Fax: (202) 232-4593
E-mail: scholarship@ZPhiBNEF.org
Web: www.zphib1920.org/nef

Summary To provide financial assistance for graduate school to members of Zeta Phi Beta Sorority.

Eligibility This program is open to members of Zeta Phi Beta Sorority who are working on or are interested in working full time on a graduate or professional degree. Applicants must have shown scholarly distinction or unusual ability in their chosen profession. Along with their application, they must submit a 150-word essay on their educational goals and professional aspirations, how this award will help them to achieve those goals, and why they should receive the award. Financial need is not considered in the selection process.

Financial data The stipend ranges from $500 to $1,000 per year; funds are paid to the college or university.

Duration 1 academic year; may be renewed.

Number awarded 1 each year.

Deadline January of each year.

[932]
NATIONAL ASSOCIATION OF BLACK ACCOUNTANTS MEMBER SCHOLARSHIP AWARDS

National Association of Black Accountants
Attn: National Scholarship Program
7474 Greenway Center Drive, Suite 1120
Greenbelt, MD 20770
(301) 474-NABA Fax: (301) 474-3114
E-mail: scholarships@nabainc.org
Web: www.nabainc.org

Summary To provide financial assistance to student members of the National Association of Black Accountants (NABA) who are working on an undergraduate or graduate degree in a field related to accounting.

Eligibility This program is open to minorities who are NABA members and enrolled full time as 1) an undergraduate freshman, sophomore, junior, or first-semester senior majoring in accounting, business, or finance at a 4-year college or university; or 2) a graduate student working on a master's degree in accounting. High school seniors are not eligible. Applicants must have a GPA of 3.5 or higher in their major and 3.3 or higher overall. Along with their application, they must submit a 500-word personal statement on their involvement in NABA, career objectives, leadership abilities, and community activities. Financial need is not considered in the selection process.

Financial data The stipend ranges from $1,000 to $3,000.

Duration 1 year.

Additional information This program includes named scholarships that vary from time to time. Recently, those included the Ralph and Valerie Thomas Scholarship, the Thomas S. Watson, Jr. Memorial Scholarship, the Travis C. Tomlin Memorial Scholarship, and the Walter and Victoria Smith Award.

Number awarded Varies each year.

Deadline January of each year.

[933]
NATIONAL ASSOCIATION OF BLACK ACCOUNTANTS NATIONAL SCHOLARSHIP

National Association of Black Accountants
Attn: National Scholarship Program
7474 Greenway Center Drive, Suite 1120
Greenbelt, MD 20770
(301) 474-NABA Fax: (301) 474-3114
E-mail: scholarships@nabainc.org
Web: www.nabainc.org

Summary To provide financial assistance to student members of the National Association of Black Accountants (NABA) who are working on an undergraduate or graduate degree in a field related to accounting.

Eligibility This program is open to minorities who are NABA members and enrolled full time as 1) an undergraduate freshman, sophomore, junior, or first-semester senior majoring in accounting, business, or finance at a 4-year college or university; or 2) a graduate student working on a master's degree in accounting. High school seniors are not eligible. Applicants must have a GPA of 3.5 or higher in their major and 3.3 or higher overall. Along with their application, they must submit a 500-word personal statement on their involvement in NABA, career objectives, leadership abilities, and community activities. Financial need is not considered in the selection process.

Financial data The stipend is $3,000.

Duration 1 year.

Number awarded 1 each year.

Deadline January of each year.

[934]
NATIONAL ASSOCIATION OF BLACK JOURNALISTS SCHOLARSHIP

National Association of Black Journalists
Attn: Communications Coordinator and Program Manager
University of Maryland
1100 Knight Hall, Suite 3100
College Park, MD 20742
(301) 405-2573 Fax: (301) 314-1714
E-mail: tjohnson@nabj.org
Web: www.nabj.org/?page=SEEDScholarships

Summary To provide financial assistance to undergraduate or graduate student members of the National Association of Black Journalists (NABJ) who are working on a degree in a field related to journalism.

Eligibility This program is open to African American undergraduate or graduate student members of NABJ who are currently enrolled full time at an accredited 4-year college or university. Applicants must be working on a degree in journalism or other communications-related field and have a GPA of 2.5 or higher. They must be able to demonstrate financial need. Along with their application, they must submit 5 samples of their work, an official college transcript, 3 letters of recommendation, a resume, and an essay of 1,000 to 2,000 words on how they see themselves as a journalist and what they would improve about the media business.

Financial data The stipend is $2,500. Funds are paid directly to the recipient's college or university.

Duration 1 year; nonrenewable.

Number awarded 1 each year.

Deadline March of each year.

[935]
NATIONAL ASSOCIATION OF NEGRO MUSICIANS SCHOLARSHIP CONTEST

National Association of Negro Musicians, Inc.
Attn: National Scholarship Chair
11551 South Laflin Street
P.O. Box 43053
Chicago, IL 60643
(773) 568-3818 Fax: (773) 785-5388
E-mail: nanm@nanm.org
Web: www.nanm.org/Scholarship

Summary To recognize and reward (with scholarships for additional study) young musicians who are sponsored by a branch of the National Association of Negro Musicians.

Eligibility This competition is open to musicians between 18 and 30 years of age. Contestants must be sponsored by a branch in good standing, although they do not need to be a member of a local branch or the national organization. For each category of the competition, they must select 2 compositions from assigned lists to perform, of which 1 list consists of works by African American composers. People ineligible to compete include former first-place winners of this competition; full-time public school teachers and college faculty (although graduate students holding teaching assistantships are still eligible if they receive less than 50% of their employment from that appointment); vocalists who have contracts as full-time solo performers in operatic, oratorio, or other types of professional singing organizations; instrumentalists with contractual full-time orchestral or ensemble jobs; and professional performers under management. Local branches nominate competitors for regional competitions. Regional winners advance to the national competition. Selection is based on musical accuracy (20 points), intonation (20 points), interpretation (20 points), tone quality (20 points), technical proficiency (10 points), and memorization (10 points). The category of the competition rotates on a 5-year schedule as follows: 2013: organ; 2014: winds and percussion; 2015: piano; 2016: voice; 2017: strings.

Financial data In the national competition, awards are at least $2,000 for first place, $1,500 for second, $1,000 for third, $750 for fourth, and $500 for fifth. All funds are paid directly to the winner's teacher/coach or institution.

Duration The competition is held annually.

Additional information The National Association of Negro Musicians was founded in 1919. Students must submit a $5 fee to enter a local branch competition. The branch must submit a $10 fee to enter the student in the regional competition. The region must submit a $15 fee to enter the student in the national competition.

Number awarded 5 each year.

Deadline Deadline not specified.

[936]
NATIONAL ASSOCIATION OF SCHOOL PSYCHOLOGISTS MINORITY SCHOLARSHIP

National Association of School Psychologists
Attn: Education and Research Trust
4340 East-West Highway, Suite 402
Bethesda, MD 20814
(301) 657-0270 Toll Free: (866) 331-NASP
Fax: (301) 657-0275 TDD: (301) 657-4155
E-mail: kbritton@naspweb.org
Web: www.nasponline.org

Summary To provide financial assistance to African American and other minority graduate students who are members of the National Association of School Psychologists (NASP) and enrolled in a school psychology program.

Eligibility This program is open to minority students who are NASP members enrolled in a regionally-accredited school psychology program in the United States. Applicants must have a GPA of 3.0 or higher. Doctoral candidates are not eligible. Applications must be accompanied by 1) a resume that includes undergraduate and/or graduate schools attended, awards and honors, student and professional activities, work and volunteer experiences, research and publications, workshops or other presentations, and any special skills, training, or experience, such as bilingualism, teaching experience, or mental health experience; 2) a statement, up to 1,000 words, of professional goals; 3) at least 2 letters of recommendation, including at least 1 from a faculty member from their undergraduate or graduate studies (if a first-year student) or at least 1 from a faculty member of their school psychology program (if a second- or third-year student); 4) a completed financial statement; 5) an official transcript of all graduate course work (first-year students may submit an official undergraduate transcript); 6) other personal accomplishments that the applicant wishes to be considered; and 7) a letter of acceptance from a school psychology program for first-year applicants. U.S. citizenship is required.

Financial data The stipend is $5,000 per year.

Duration 1 year; may be renewed up to 2 additional years.

Number awarded Varies each year; recently, 4 of these scholarships were awarded.

Deadline October of each year.

[937]
NATIONAL ASSOCIATION OF UNIVERSITY WOMEN FELLOWSHIPS

National Association of University Women
Attn: Fellowship Chair
1001 E Street, S.E.
Washington, DC 20003
(202) 547-3967 Fax: (202) 547-5226
E-mail: info@nauw1910.org
Web: www.nauw1910.org

Summary To provide financial assistance to members of the National Association of University Women (NAUW) and other women who are working on a doctoral degree.

Eligibility This program is open to women who already have a master's degree and are enrolled in a program leading to a doctoral degree. They should be close to completing their degree. Preference is given to members of NAUW, an organization that historically has served African American women.

Financial data The stipend is $3,000.

Duration 1 year; nonrenewable.

Number awarded 3 each year: 2 to members of NAUW and 1 to a non-member.

Deadline April of each year.

[938] NATIONAL BLACK ASSOCIATION FOR SPEECH-LANGUAGE AND HEARING STUDENT RESEARCH AWARD

National Black Association for Speech-Language and Hearing
Attn: Awards and Scholarship Committee
700 McKnight Park Drive, Suite 708
Pittsburgh, PA 15237
(855) 727-2836 Fax: (888) 729-3489
E-mail: nbaslh@nbaslh.org
Web: www.nbaslh.org/scholarships/scholarship-main.htm

Summary To recognize and reward outstanding research papers on communication sciences or disorders written by graduate student members of the National Black Association for Speech-Language and Hearing (NBASLH).

Eligibility This competition is open to African American students who are NBASLH members and enrolled full time in an ASHA-accredited master's degree program in speech-language pathology, audiology, or the speech-language-hearing sciences. Applicants must submit a paper of scientific or scholarly merit that deals with issues relevant to communication sciences and disorders. It is not required that the paper focus on African American populations or multicultural issues. It may address 1 of the following: 1) an empirical investigation that requires data gathering and analysis; 2) an issue paper that aims to redefine, evaluate, and synthesize existing knowledge in ways that offer a new conceptual framework or approach for conducting research or engaging in clinical practice; or 3) a description of a clinical case study that has implications for future research and/or clinical practice. The manuscript should not exceed 8 typed pages (2,000 words). Selection is based on completeness, appropriateness, manuscript quality, and significance.

Financial data The award is $1,000. In addition, the winner receives a $100 travel allowance to attend the association's convention (and read the paper there).

Duration The award is presented annually.

Number awarded 2 each year.

Deadline February of each year.

[939] NATIONAL BLACK MBA ASSOCIATION GRADUATE SCHOLARSHIP PROGRAM

National Black MBA Association
Attn: Scholarship Program
1 East Wacker Drive, Suite 3500
Chicago, IL 60601
(312) 236-BMBA Fax: (312) 580-8717
E-mail: Scholarship@nbmbaa.org
Web: www.nbmbaa.org

Summary To provide financial assistance to students interested in working on a master's degree in a field related to business and becoming involved in activities of the National Black MBA Association (NBMBAA).

Eligibility This program is open to minority students who entering or continuing in a full- or part-time master's degree program in business, management, or related field in the United States or Canada. Applicants must submit a 300-word essay on an assigned topic that relates to minorities in business. They must have a GPA of 3.0 or higher. Selection is based on the quality of the paper, academic excellence, leadership potential, communication skills, and involvement in local communities through service to others. U.S. citizenship is required.

Financial data Stipends range from $1,000 to $15,000. Membership in the NBMBAA is also included. Some recipients are provided with complimentary registration, round-trip airfare, housing, and special VIP access to receptions and events at the NBMBAA annual conference and exposition.

Duration 1 year.

Additional information Recipients must agree to become a member of the NBMBAA Scholarship Advisory Team and Scholarship Alumni Club, become an active member of their local NBMBAA chapter, and participate in limited public relations activities at the convention.

Number awarded Varies each year; recently, the sponsor awarded 18 undergraduate and graduate scholarships.

Deadline June of each year.

[940] NATIONAL DEFENSE SCIENCE AND ENGINEERING GRADUATE FELLOWSHIP PROGRAM

American Society for Engineering Education
Attn: NDSEG Fellowship Program
1818 N Street, N.W., Suite 600
Washington, DC 20036-2479
(202) 649-3831 Fax: (202) 265-8504
E-mail: ndseg@asee.org
Web: ndseg.asee.org

Summary To provide financial assistance to students (particularly African Americans, other minorities, women, and students with disabilities) who are working on a doctoral degree in areas of science and engineering that are of potential military importance.

Eligibility This program is open to U.S. citizens and nationals entering or enrolled in the early stages of a doctoral program in aeronautical and astronautical engineering; biosciences, including toxicology; chemical engineering; chemistry; civil engineering; cognitive, neural, and behavioral sciences; computer and computational sciences; electrical engineering; geosciences, including terrain, water, and air; materials science and engineering; mathematics; mechanical engineering; naval architecture and ocean engineering; oceanography; or physics, including optics. Applicants must be enrolled or planning to enroll as full-time students. Applications are particularly encouraged from women, members of ethnic minority groups (American Indians, African Americans, Hispanics or Latinos, Native Hawaiians, Alaska Natives, Asians, and Pacific Islanders), and persons with disabilities. Selection is based on all available evidence of ability, including academic records, letters of recommendation, and GRE scores.

Financial data The annual stipend is $30,500 for the first year, $31,000 for the second year; and $31,500 for the third year; the program also pays the recipient's institution full tuition and required fees (not to include room and board). Medical insurance is covered up to $1,000 per year.

Duration 3 years, as long as satisfactory academic progress is maintained.

Additional information This program is sponsored by the High Performance Computing Modernization Program within the Department of Defense, the Army Research Office, the Air Force Office of Scientific Research, and the Office of Naval Research. Recipients do not incur any military or other service obligation.

Number awarded Approximately 200 each year.

Deadline December of each year.

[941]
NATIONAL DENTAL ASSOCIATION FOUNDATION PRE-DOCTORAL SCHOLARSHIP PROGRAM

National Dental Association
Attn: National Dental Association Foundation, Inc.
3517 16th Street, N.W.
Washington, DC 20010
(202) 588-1697 Fax: (202) 588-1244
E-mail: admin@ndaonline.org
Web: www.ndafoundation.org/NDAF/Scholarships.html

Summary To provide financial assistance to African American and other minority dental students.

Eligibility This program is open to members of minority groups who are entering their second, third, or fourth year of dental school. Applicants must be members of the Student National Dental Association (SNDA) and U.S. citizens or permanent residents. Along with their application, they must submit a letter explaining why they should be considered for this scholarship, 2 letters of recommendation, and documentation of financial need. Selection is based on academic performance and service to community and/or country.

Financial data The stipend is $1,000 per year.

Duration 1 year. Recipients may reapply.

Additional information This program, established in 1990, is supported by the Colgate-Palmolive Company.

Number awarded Varies each year; recently, 65 of these scholarships were awarded.

Deadline May of each year.

[942]
NATIONAL DENTAL ASSOCIATION MEMORIAL AWARD

National Dental Association
Attn: National Dental Association Foundation, Inc.
3517 16th Street, N.W.
Washington, DC 20010
(202) 588-1697 Fax: (202) 588-1244
E-mail: admin@ndaonline.org
Web: www.ndafoundation.org/NDAF/Scholarships.html

Summary To provide financial assistance to African American and other minority dental postdoctoral or master's degree students.

Eligibility This program is open to members of minority groups who are working on a postdoctoral degree in subspecialty areas of dentistry, public health, administration, pediatrics, research, or law. Students working on a master's degree beyond their residency also may be considered. Applicants must be members of the National Dental Association (NDA) and U.S. citizens or permanent residents. Along with their application, they must submit a letter explaining why they should be considered for this scholarship, 2 letters of recommendation, a curriculum vitae, a description of the program, nomination by their program director, and documentation of financial need.

Financial data The stipend is $10,000.

Duration 1 year.

Additional information This program, established in 1990, is supported by the Colgate-Palmolive Company.

Number awarded 1 each year.

Deadline May of each year.

[943]
NATIONAL ESTUARINE RESEARCH RESERVE SYSTEM GRADUATE FELLOWSHIPS

National Oceanic and Atmospheric Administration
Attn: Estuarine Reserves Division
1305 East-West Highway
N/ORMS, SSMC4, Station 10503
Silver Spring, MD 20910
(301) 713-3155, ext. 105 Fax: (301) 713-4367
E-mail: Alison.Krepp@noaa.gov
Web: www.nerrs.noaa.gov/Fellowship.aspx

Summary To provide funding to graduate students (particularly African Americans and other minorities) who are interested in conducting research within the National Estuarine Research Reserve System (NERRS).

Eligibility This program is open to students admitted to or enrolled in a full-time master's or doctoral program at U.S. accredited universities. Applicants should have completed a majority of their course work at the beginning of their fellowship and have an approved thesis research program focused on improving coastal zone management while providing hands-on training in conducting ecological monitoring. Proposed research topics must address 1 of the following topics: 1) eutrophication, effects of non-point source pollution and/or nutrient dynamics; 2) habitat conservation and/or restoration; 3) biodiversity and/or the effects of invasive species; 4) mechanisms for sustaining resources within estuarine ecosystems; or 5) economic, sociological, and/or anthropological research applicable to estuarine ecosystem management. They must be willing to conduct their research within the NERRS. Minority students are specifically encouraged to apply. Selection is based on academic record and a statement of career goals and objectives (5%), quality of proposed research and its applicability to the NERRS research focus areas (70%), the research's applicability to specific reserve research and resource management goals (20%), and recommendations and endorsements (5%).

Financial data The stipend is $28,5720 per year, of which the federal government provides $20,000 and the recipient's institution provides $8,572 as matching funds. Grants may be used for any combination of research support, salary, tuition, supplies, or other costs as needed, including overhead.

Duration 1 to 3 years.

Additional information This program began in 1997. For a list of the National Estuarine Research Reserves, with the name and address of a coordinator at each, contact NERRS. Fellows are required to work with the research coordinator or manager at the host reserve to develop a plan to participate in the reserve's research and/or monitoring program for up to 15 hours per week.

Number awarded Varies each year; recently, 9 of these fellowships were available.

Deadline October of each year.

[944]
NATIONAL MEDICAL FELLOWSHIPS EMERGENCY SCHOLARSHIP FUND

National Medical Fellowships, Inc.
Attn: Scholarship Program
347 Fifth Avenue, Suite 510
New York, NY 10016
(212) 483-8880 Toll Free: (877) NMF-1DOC
Fax: (212) 483-8897 E-mail: info@nmfonline.org
Web: www.nmfonline.org

Summary To provide financial assistance to African American and other minority medical students who are facing financial emergencies.

Eligibility This program is open to U.S. citizens who are enrolled in the third or fourth year of an accredited M.D. or D.O. degree-granting program in the United States and are facing extreme financial difficulties because of unforeseen training-related expenses. Applicants must be African Americans, Latinos, Native Hawaiians, Alaska Natives, American Indians, Pacific Islanders, Vietnamese, or Cambodians who permanently reside in the United States. They must be interested in primary care practice in underserved communities.

Financial data Assistance ranges up to $10,000.

Duration 1 year; nonrenewable.

Additional information This program began in 2008, with support from the W.K. Kellogg Foundation.

Number awarded Varies each year; recently, 3 of these scholarships were awarded.

Deadline August of each year.

[945]
NATIONAL OCEANIC AND ATMOSPHERIC ADMINISTRATION EDUCATIONAL PARTNERSHIP PROGRAM WITH MINORITY SERVING INSTITUTIONS GRADUATE SCIENCES PROGRAM

National Oceanic and Atmospheric Administration
Attn: Office of Education
1315 East-West Highway
SSMC3, Room 10703
Silver Spring, MD 20910
(301) 713-9437, ext. 150 Fax: (301) 713-9465
E-mail: gsp@noaa.gov
Web: www.epp.noaa.gov/ssp_grad_sciences_page.html

Summary To provide financial aid and summer research experience to graduate students at Minority Serving Institutions who are majoring in scientific fields of interest to the National Oceanic and Atmospheric Administration (NOAA).

Eligibility This program is open to full-time graduate students working on master's or doctoral degrees at Minority Serving Institutions, including Alaska Native Serving Institutions (ANSIs), Hispanic Serving Institutions (HSIs), Historically Black Colleges and Universities (HBCUs), Native Hawaiian Serving Institutions (NHSIs), and Tribal Colleges and Universities (TCUs). Applicants must be working on a degree in biology, chemistry, computer science, economics, engineering, environmental law, geography, geology, mathematics, physical science, physics, or social science. They must have a GPA of 3.0 or higher. The program includes a training program during the summer at a NOAA research facility. Selection is based on academic records, a statement of career interests and goals, and compatibility of applicant's background with the interests of NOAA. U.S. citizenship is required.

Financial data During the school year, the program provides payment of tuition, laboratory fees, books, travel expenses, and a housing allowance at selected universities. During the summer, students receive a salary and benefits from NOAA.

Duration 1 year; may be renewed 1 additional year for master's candidates or 3 additional years for doctoral students, provided the recipient maintains a GPA of 3.0 or higher.

Number awarded Varies each year; recently, 2 of these fellowships were awarded.

Deadline January of each year.

[946]
NATIONAL PHYSICAL SCIENCE CONSORTIUM GRADUATE FELLOWSHIPS

National Physical Science Consortium
c/o University of Southern California
3716 South Hope Street, Suite 348
Los Angeles, CA 90007-4344
(213) 821-2409 Toll Free: (800) 854-NPSC
Fax: (213) 821-2407 E-mail: npschq@npsc.org
Web: www.npsc.org

Summary To provide financial assistance and summer work experience to African Americans, other underrepresented minorities and women interested in working on a Ph.D. in designated science and engineering fields.

Eligibility This program is open to U.S. citizens who are seniors graduating from college with a GPA of 3.0 or higher, enrolled in the first year of a doctoral program, completing a terminal master's degree, or returning from the workforce and holding no more than a master's degree. Students currently in the third or subsequent year of a Ph.D. program or who already have a doctoral degree in any field (Ph.D., M.D., J.D., Ed.D.) are ineligible. Applicants must be interested in working on a Ph.D. in fields that vary but emphasize astronomy, chemistry, computer science, engineering (chemical, computer, electrical, environmental, or mechanical), geology, materials science, mathematical sciences, or physics. The program welcomes applications from all qualified students and continues to emphasize the recruitment of underrepresented minority (African American, Hispanic, Native American Indian, Eskimo, Aleut, and Pacific Islander) and women physical science and engineering students. Fellowships are provided to students at more than 100 universities that are members of the consortium. Selection is based on academic standing (GPA), course work taken in preparation for graduate school, university and/or industry research experience, letters of recommendation, and GRE scores.

Financial data The fellowship pays tuition and fees plus an annual stipend of $20,000. It also provides on-site paid summer employment to enhance technical experience. The exact value of the fellowship depends on academic standing, summer employment, and graduate school attended; the total amount generally exceeds $200,000.

Duration Support is initially provided for 2 or 3 years, depending on the employer-sponsor. If the fellow makes satisfactory progress and continues to meet the conditions of the award, support may continue for a total of up to 6 years or completion of the Ph.D., whichever comes first.

Additional information This program began in 1989. Tuition and fees are provided by the participating universities. Stipends and summer internships are provided by sponsoring organizations. Students must submit separate applications for internships, which may have additional eligibility requirements. Internships are currently available at Lawrence Livermore National Laboratory in Livermore, California (astronomy, chemistry, computer science, geology, materials science, mathematics, and physics); National Institute of Standards and Technology in Gaithersburg, Maryland (various fields of STEM); National Security Agency in Fort Meade, Maryland (astronomy, chemistry, computer science, geology, materials science, mathematics, and physics); Sandia National Laboratory in Livermore, California (biology, chemistry, computer science, environmental science, geology, materials science, mathematics, and physics); and Sandia National Laboratory in Albuquerque, New Mexico (chemical engineering, chemistry, computer science, materials science, mathematics, mechanical engineering, and physics). Fellows must submit a separate application for dissertation support in the year prior to the beginning of their dissertation research program, but not until they can describe their intended research in general terms.

Number awarded Varies each year; recently, 11 of these fellowships were awarded.

Deadline November of each year.

[947] NATIONAL SOCIETY OF BLACK ENGINEERS MAJOR SPONSORS SCHOLARS AWARDS

National Society of Black Engineers
Attn: Programs Department
205 Daingerfield Road
Alexandria, VA 22314
(703) 549-2207 Fax: (703) 683-5312
E-mail: scholarships@nsbe.org
Web: www.nsbe.org/Programs/Scholarships.aspx

Summary To provide financial assistance to members of the National Society of Black Engineers (NSBE) who are working on a degree in engineering.

Eligibility This program is open to members of the society who are undergraduate or graduate engineering students. Applicants must have a GPA of 3.0 or higher. Selection is based on an essay; academic achievement; service to the society at the chapter, regional, and/or national level; and other professional, campus, and community activities. Applicants for the National Society of Black Engineers Fellows Scholarship Program who rank in the second of 3 tiers receive these awards.

Financial data The stipend is $1,500. Travel, hotel accommodations, and registration to the national convention are also provided.

Duration 1 year.

Number awarded Varies each year; recently, 17 of these scholarships were awarded.

Deadline May of each year.

[948] NATIONAL SPACE GRANT COLLEGE AND FELLOWSHIP PROGRAM

National Aeronautics and Space Administration
Attn: Office of Education
300 E Street, S.W.
Mail Suite 6M35
Washington, DC 20546-0001
(202) 358-1069 Fax: (202) 358-7097
E-mail: Diane.D.DeTroye@nasa.gov
Web: www.nasa.gov

Summary To provide financial assistance to undergraduate and graduate students (particularly African Americans, other underrepresented minorities, and women) who are interested in preparing for a career in a space-related field.

Eligibility This program is open to undergraduate and graduate students at colleges and universities that participate in the National Space Grant program of the U.S. National Aeronautics and Space Administration (NASA) through their state consortium. Applicants must be interested in a program of study and/or research in a field of science, technology, engineering, or mathematics (STEM) related to space. A specific goal of the program is to recruit and train U.S. citizens, especially underrepresented minorities, women, and persons with disabilities, for careers in aerospace science and technology. Financial need is not considered in the selection process.

Financial data Each consortium establishes the terms of the fellowship program in its state.

Additional information NASA established the Space Grant program in 1989. It operates through 52 consortia in each state, the District of Columbia, and Puerto Rico. Each consortium includes selected colleges and universities in that state as well as other affiliates from industry, museums, science centers, and state and local agencies.

Number awarded Varies each year.

Deadline Each consortium sets its own deadlines.

[949] NATIONAL URBAN FELLOWS PROGRAM

National Urban Fellows, Inc.
Attn: Program Director
989 Avenue of the Americas, Suite 400
New York, NY 10018
(212) 730-1700 Fax: (212) 730-1823
E-mail: info@nuf.org
Web: www.nuf.org/fellows-overview

Summary To offer financial assistance to mid-career public sector professionals (especially African Americans, other minorities, and women) who are interested in working on a master's degree program coupled with a mentorship.

Eligibility This program is open to U.S. citizens who have a bachelor's degree, have at least 3 years of administrative or managerial experience, have demonstrated exceptional ability and leadership potential, meet academic admission requirements, have a high standard of integrity and work ethic, and are committed to the solution of urban problems.

Applicants must a 1,000-word autobiographical statement and a 1,000-word statement on their career goals. They may be of any racial or ethnic background, but the program's goal is to increase the number of competent administrators from underrepresented ethnic and cultural groups at all levels of public and private urban management organizations. Semifinalists are interviewed.

Financial data The stipend is $25,000. The program also provides full payment of tuition, a relocation allowance of $500, a book allowance of $500, and reimbursement for program-related travel.

Duration 14 months.

Additional information The program begins with a summer semester of study at Bernard M. Baruch College of the City University of New York. Following this, fellows spend 9 months in mentorship assignments with a senior administrator in a government agency, a major nonprofit, or a foundation. The final summer is spent in another semester of study at Baruch College. Fellows who successfully complete all requirements are granted a master's of public administration from that college. A $75 processing fee must accompany each application.

Number awarded Varies; approximately 40 each year.

Deadline February of each year.

[950]
NCAA ETHNIC MINORITY ENHANCEMENT SCHOLARSHIP PROGRAM

National Collegiate Athletic Association
Attn: Office for Diversity and Inclusion
700 West Washington Street
P.O. Box 6222
Indianapolis, IN 46206-6222
(317) 917-6222 Fax: (317) 917-6888
E-mail: tstrum@ncaa.org
Web: www.ncaa.org

Summary To provide funding to African American and other ethnic minority graduate students who are interested in preparing for a career in intercollegiate athletics.

Eligibility This program is open to members of minority groups who have been accepted into a program at a National Collegiate Athletic Association (NCAA) member institution that will prepare them for a career in intercollegiate athletics (athletics administrator, coach, athletic trainer, or other career that provides a direct service to intercollegiate athletics). Applicants must be U.S. citizens, have performed with distinction as a student body member at their respective undergraduate institution, and be entering the first semester or term of full-time postgraduate study. Selection is based on the applicant's involvement in extracurricular activities, course work, commitment to preparing for a career in intercollegiate athletics, and promise for success in that career. Financial need is not considered.

Financial data The stipend is $6,000; funds are paid to the college or university of the recipient's choice.

Duration 1 year; nonrenewable.

Number awarded 13 each year.

Deadline November of each year.

[951]
NELLIE STONE JOHNSON SCHOLARSHIP

Nellie Stone Johnson Scholarship Program
P.O. Box 40309
St. Paul, MN 55104
(651) 738-1404 Toll Free: (866) 738-5238
E-mail: info@nelliestone.org
Web: www.nelliestone.org

Summary To provide financial assistance to African American and other minority union members or their families who are interested in working on an undergraduate or graduate degree in any field at a Minnesota state college or university.

Eligibility This program is open to students in undergraduate and graduate programs at a 2- or 4-year institution that is a component of Minnesota State Colleges and Universities (MnSCU). Applicants must be a minority (Asian, American Indian, Alaska Native, Black/African American, Hispanic/Latino, Native Hawaiian, or Pacific Islander) union member or the child, grandchild, or spouse of a minority union member. They must submit a 2-page essay about their background, educational goals, career goals, and other activities that may impact the cause of human or civil rights. Undergraduates must have a GPA of 2.0 or higher; graduate students must have a GPA of 3.0 or higher. Preference is given to Minnesota residents. Selection is based on the essay, commitment to human or civil rights, extracurricular activities, volunteer activities, community involvement, academic standing, and financial need.

Financial data Stipends range from $500 to $2,000 per year.

Duration 1 year; may be renewed up to 3 additional years for students working on a bachelor's degree, 1 additional year for students working on a master's degree, or 1 additional year for students in a community or technical college program.

Number awarded Varies each year; recently, 18 of these scholarships were awarded.

Deadline April of each year.

[952]
NEW MEXICO MINORITY DOCTORAL LOAN-FOR-SERVICE PROGRAM

New Mexico Higher Education Department
Attn: Financial Aid Division
2048 Galisteo Street
Santa Fe, NM 87505-2100
(505) 476-8411 Toll Free: (800) 279-9777
Fax: (505) 476-8454 E-mail: feliz.romero1@state.nm.us
Web: hed.state.nm.us/MinDoc.aspx

Summary To provide funding to African Americans, other underrepresented minorities, and women who reside in New Mexico and are interested in working on a doctoral degree in selected fields.

Eligibility This program is open to ethnic minorities and women who are residents of New Mexico and have received a baccalaureate degree from a public 4-year college or university in the state in mathematics, engineering, the physical or life sciences, or any other academic discipline in which ethnic minorities and women are demonstrably underrepresented in New Mexico academic institutions. Applicants must have been admitted as a full-time doctoral student at an approved university in any state. They must be sponsored by a New Mexico institution of higher education which has agreed to employ them in a tenure-track faculty position after they obtain their degree. U.S. citizenship is required.

Financial data Loans average $15,000. This is a loan-for-service program; for every year of service as a college faculty member in New Mexico, a portion of the loan is forgiven. If the entire service agreement is fulfilled, 100% of the loan is eligible for forgiveness. Penalties may be assessed if the service agreement is not satisfied.

Duration 1 year; may be renewed up to 3 additional years.

Number awarded Up to 12 each year.

Deadline March of each year.

[953] NEXSEN PRUET DIVERSITY SCHOLARSHIPS

Nexsen Pruet
Attn: Diversity Scholarship
1230 Main Street, Suite 700
P.O. Drawer 2426
Columbia, SC 29202-2426
(803) 771-8900 Fax: (803) 727-1469
E-mail: diversity@nexsenpruet.com
Web: www.nexsenpruet.com/firm-diversity.html

Summary To provide financial assistance to African Americans and members of other minority groups attending designated law schools in North and South Carolina.

Eligibility This program is open to minority students currently enrolled in the first year at the University of North Carolina School of Law, University of South Carolina School of Law, Wake Forest University School of Law, North Carolina Central University School of Law, Charleston School of Law, or Charlotte School of Law. Applicants must be interested in practicing law in North or South Carolina after graduation. Along with their application, they must submit information on their academic achievements; their contributions to promoting diversity in their community, school, or work environment; and their ability to overcome challenges in the pursuit of their goals. They must also submit essays of 250 words each on 1) their reasons for preparing for a legal career; 2) their interest in the private practice of law in North Carolina and/or South Carolina; 3) any obstacles, including but not limited to financial obstacles, that the scholarship will help them overcome; and 4) what they see as potential obstacles, issues, and opportunities facing new minority lawyers.

Financial data The stipend is $3,000 per year.

Duration 1 year; recipients may reapply.

Additional information Recipients are considered for summer employment in an office of the firm after completion of their first year of law school.

Number awarded Varies each year; recently, 3 of these scholarships were awarded.

Deadline October of each year.

[954] NLGJA/KAY LONGCOPE SCHOLARSHIP AWARD

National Lesbian & Gay Journalists Association
2120 L Street, N.W., Suite 850
Washington, DC 20037
(202) 588-9888 Fax: (202) 588-1818
E-mail: info@nlgfa.org
Web: www.nlgja.org/students/longcope

Summary To provide financial assistance to African American and other lesbian, gay, bisexual, and transgender (LGBT) undergraduate and graduate students of color who are interested in preparing for a career in journalism.

Eligibility This program is open to LGBT students of color who are 1) high school seniors accepted to a U.S. community college or 4-year university and planning to enroll full time; 2) full-time undergraduate students at U.S. community colleges and 4-year universities; or 3) undergraduate students who have been accepted for their first year at a U.S. graduate school. Applicants must be planning a career in journalism and be committed to furthering the sponsoring organization's mission of fair and accurate coverage of the LGBT community. They must demonstrate an awareness of the issues facing the LGBT community and the importance of fair and accurate news coverage. For undergraduates, a declared major in journalism and/or communications is desirable but not required; non-journalism majors may demonstrate their commitment to a journalism career through work samples, internships, and work on a school news publication, online news service, or broadcast affiliate. Graduate students must be enrolled in a journalism program. Along with their application, they must submit a 1-page resume, 5 work samples, official transcripts, 3 letters of recommendation, and a 750-word news story on a designated subject involving the LGBT community. U.S. citizenship or permanent resident status is required. Selection is based on journalistic and scholastic ability.

Financial data The stipend is $3,000.

Duration 1 year.

Additional information This program began in 2008.

Number awarded 1 each year.

Deadline June of each year.

[955] NMA EMERGING SCHOLARS AWARDS

National Medical Fellowships, Inc.
Attn: Scholarship Program
347 Fifth Avenue, Suite 510
New York, NY 10016
(212) 483-8880 Toll Free: (877) NMF-1DOC
Fax: (212) 483-8897 E-mail: info@nmfonline.org
Web: www.nmfonline.org

Summary To provide financial assistance to African American medical students.

Eligibility This program is open to African American medical students who are U.S. citizens in their first, second, or third year at an accredited M.D. or D.O. degree-granting school in the United States. Only nominations are accepted. All nominees must submit a personal essay on their motivation for a career in medicine and career plans over the next 10 years. Selection is based on financial need, community involvement, academic achievement, and potential for a responsible role in medicine.

Financial data The stipend is $2,250.

Duration 1 year.

Additional information This program is sponsored by the National Medical Association (NMA).

Number awarded Varies each year; recently, 6 of these awards were granted.

Deadline April of each year.

[956]
NORMAN'S ORCHIDS MASTERS SCHOLARSHIP

American Orchid Society
c/o Fairchild Tropical Botanic Garden
10901 Old Cutler Road
Coral Gables, FL 33156
(305) 740-2010 Fax: (305) 740-2011
E-mail: TheAOS@aos.org
Web: www.aos.org/Default.aspx?id=545

Summary To provide funding for research to students (particularly African Americans, other underrepresented minorities, women, and individuals with disabilities) who are working on a master's degree in a field related to orchids.

Eligibility This program is open to students working on a master's degree at an accredited institution. Applicants must have a thesis project that deals with an aspect of orchid education, applied science, or orchid biology in the disciplines of physiology, molecular biology, structure, systematics, cytology, ecology, or evolution. They must submit a current curriculum vitae, transcripts of all college course work, a synopsis of the proposed project or research, a 1-page statement of the value of their project and importance to the future of orchid education or orchidology, and a letter of recommendation from their chairperson. Women, minorities, and persons with disabilities are especially encouraged to apply.

Financial data The grant is $5,000 per year. Funds are paid through the recipient's college or university, but institutional overhead is not allowed.

Duration 2 years.

Additional information This program, established in 2005, is supported by Norman's Orchids of Montclair, California.

Number awarded 1 each year.

Deadline March of each year.

[957]
NORTH CAROLINA CPA FOUNDATION OUTSTANDING MINORITY ACCOUNTING STUDENT SCHOLARSHIPS

North Carolina Association of Certified Public Accountants
Attn: North Carolina CPA Foundation, Inc.
3100 Gateway Centre Boulevard
P.O. Box 80188
Raleigh, NC 27623-0188
(919) 469-1040, ext. 130 Toll Free: (800) 722-2836
Fax: (919) 378-2000 E-mail: jtahler@ncacpa.org
Web: ncacpa.org

Summary To provide financial assistance to African American and other minority undergraduate and graduate students working on a degree in accounting at colleges and universities in North Carolina.

Eligibility This program is open to North Carolina residents who have completed at least 36 semester hours, including at least 4 accounting courses, at a college or university in the state. Applicants must be members of a minority group, defined as Black, Native American/Alaskan Native, Middle-Eastern, Asian or Pacific Islander, or Hispanic. They must be enrolled full time in an academic program leading to a degree in accounting or its equivalent and have a GPA of 3.0 or higher. Along with their application, they must submit a 500-word essay on 1 of the following questions: 1) what the profession can do to educate minorities about understanding the impact of and ways to survive the national financial crisis; 2) how they will impact minority communities by becoming a C.P.A.; or 3) the challenges that minority C.P.A.s face in the profession. Selection is based on GPA (30%), extracurricular activities (20%), essay content (25%), and essay grammar (25%).

Financial data Stipends are $2,000 or $1,000.

Duration 1 year; may be renewed up to 2 additional years.

Number awarded 2 each year: 1 at $2,000 and 1 at $1,000.

Deadline March of each year.

[958]
NOTRE DAME INSTITUTE FOR ADVANCED STUDY GRADUATE STUDENT FELLOWSHIPS

University of Notre Dame
Institute for Advanced Study
Attn: Programs Administrator
1124 Flanner Hall
Notre Dame, IN 46556
(574) 631-6240 E-mail: csherman@nd.edu
Web: ndias.nd.edu/fellowships/graduate-student

Summary To provide funding to graduate students (particularly African Americans and members of other traditionally underrepresented groups) who are interested in conducting research on topics of interest to the Notre Dame Institute for Advanced Study (NDIAS) while in residence at the institute.

Eligibility This program is open to graduate students in all disciplines, including the arts, engineering, the humanities, law, and the natural, social, and physical sciences. Applicants must be interested in conducting research that furthers the work of the NDIAS, defined as cultivating "the contemplative ideal that is an essential factor in the Catholic intellectual tradition and vital for the progression of scholarship." They must be able to demonstrate excellent records of scholarly, artistic, or research accomplishment in their field; ability to interact with other fellows and to engage in collegial discussions of research presentations; a willingness to contribute to a cooperative community of scholars; and projects that touch on normative, integrative, or ultimate questions, especially as the involve the Catholic intellectual tradition. Applications are especially encouraged from traditionally underrepresented groups. There are no citizenship requirements; non-U.S. nationals are welcome to apply.

Financial data The grant is $25,000, including a $1,000 research account, office facilities, a computer and printer, access to libraries and other facilities, and weekly institute seminars and events.

Duration 1 academic year.

Number awarded 1 or more each year.
Deadline October of each year.

[959]
NSBE FELLOWS SCHOLARSHIP PROGRAM

National Society of Black Engineers
Attn: Programs Department
205 Daingerfield Road
Alexandria, VA 22314
(703) 549-2207 Fax: (703) 683-5312
E-mail: scholarships@nsbe.org
Web: www.nsbe.org/Programs/Scholarships.aspx

Summary To provide financial assistance to members of the National Society of Black Engineers (NSBE) who are working on a degree in engineering.

Eligibility This program is open to members of the society who are undergraduate or graduate engineering students. Applicants must have a GPA of 2.7 or higher. Selection is based on an essay; academic achievement; service to the society at the chapter, regional, and/or national level; and other professional, campus, and community activities. Applicants for this program who rank in the third of 3 tiers receive these awards.

Financial data The stipend is $1,000.

Duration 1 year.

Number awarded Varies each year; recently, 9 of these scholarships were awarded.

Deadline May of each year.

[960]
NSCA MINORITY SCHOLARSHIPS

National Strength and Conditioning Association
Attn: Grants and Scholarships Program
1885 Bob Johnson Drive
Colorado Springs, CO 80906-4000
(719) 632-6722, ext. 152 Toll Free: (800) 815-6826
Fax: (719) 632-6367 E-mail: foundation@nsca-lift.org
Web: www.nsca-lift.org/Foundation/grants-and-scholarships

Summary To provide financial assistance to African Americans and other minorities who are interested in working on an undergraduate or graduate degree in strength training and conditioning.

Eligibility This program is open to Blacks, Hispanics, Asian Americans, and Native Americans who are 17 years of age and older. Applicants must have been accepted into an accredited postsecondary institution to work on an undergraduate or graduate degree in the strength and conditioning field. Along with their application, they must submit a 500-word essay on their personal and professional goals and how receiving this scholarship will assist them in achieving those goals. Selection is based on that essay, academic achievement, strength and conditioning experience, honors and awards, community involvement, letters of recommendation, and involvement in the National Strength and Conditioning Association (NSCA).

Financial data The stipend is $1,500.

Duration 1 year.

Additional information The NSCA is a nonprofit organization of strength and conditioning professionals, including coaches, athletic trainers, physical therapists, educators, researchers, and physicians. This program was first offered in 2003.

Number awarded Varies each year; recently, 9 of these scholarships were awarded.

Deadline March of each year.

[961]
NSF GRADUATE RESEARCH FELLOWSHIP PROGRAM

National Science Foundation
Directorate for Education and Human Resources
Attn: Division of Graduate Education
4201 Wilson Boulevard, Room 875S
Arlington, VA 22230
(703) 292-8694 Toll Free: (866) NSF-GRFP
Fax: (703) 292-9048 E-mail: info@nsfgrfp.org
Web: www.nsf.gov/funding/pgm_summ.jsp?pims_id=6201

Summary To provide financial assistance to graduate students (particularly African Americans, other minorities, women, veterans, and students with disabilities) who are interested in working on a master's or doctoral degree in fields supported by the National Science Foundation (NSF).

Eligibility This program is open to U.S. citizens, nationals, and permanent residents who wish to work on research-based master's or doctoral degrees in a field of science, technology, engineering, or mathematics (STEM) supported by NSF (including astronomy, chemistry, computer and information sciences and engineering, geosciences, engineering, life sciences, materials research, mathematical sciences, physics, psychology, social sciences, or STEM education and learning). Other work in medical, dental, law, public health, or practice-oriented professional degree programs, or in joint science-professional degree programs, such as M.D./Ph.D. and J.D./Ph.D. programs, is not eligible. Applications normally should be submitted during the senior year in college or in the first year of graduate study; eligibility is limited to those who have completed no more than 12 months of graduate study since completion of a baccalaureate degree. Applicants who have already earned an advanced degree in science, engineering, or medicine (including an M.D., D.D.S., or D.V.M.) are ineligible. Selection is based on 1) intellectual merit of the proposed activity: strength of the academic record, proposed plan of research, previous research experience, references, appropriateness of the choice of institution; and 2) broader impacts of the proposed activity: how well does the activity advance discovery and understanding, how well does it broaden the participation of underrepresented groups (e.g., women, minorities, persons with disabilities, veterans), to what extent will it enhance the infrastructure for research and education, will the results be disseminated broadly to enhance scientific and technological understanding, what may be the benefits of the proposed activity to society).

Financial data The stipend is $30,000 per year; an additional $12,000 cost-of-education allowance is provided to the recipient's institution.

Duration Up to 3 years, usable over a 5-year period.

Number awarded Approximately 2,000 each year.

Deadline November of each year.

[962]
NSNA/BREAKTHROUGH TO NURSING SCHOLARSHIPS

National Student Nurses' Association
Attn: Foundation
45 Main Street, Suite 606
Brooklyn, NY 11201
(718) 210-0705 Fax: (718) 797-1186
E-mail: nsna@nsna.org
Web: www.nsna.org

Summary To provide financial assistance to African American and other minority undergraduate and graduate students who wish to prepare for careers in nursing.

Eligibility This program is open to students currently enrolled in state-approved schools of nursing or pre-nursing associate degree, baccalaureate, diploma, generic master's, generic doctoral, R.N. to B.S.N., R.N. to M.S.N., or L.P.N./L.V.N. to R.N. programs. Graduating high school seniors are not eligible. Support for graduate education is provided only for a first degree in nursing. Applicants must be members of a racial or ethnic minority underrepresented among registered nurses (American Indian or Alaska Native, Hispanic or Latino, Native Hawaiian or other Pacific Islander, Black or African American, or Asian). They must be committed to providing quality health care services to underserved populations. Along with their application, they must submit a 200-word description of their professional and educational goals and how this scholarship will help them achieve those goals. Selection is based on academic achievement, financial need, and involvement in student nursing organizations and community health activities. U.S. citizenship or permanent resident status is required.

Financial data Stipends range from $1,000 to $2,500.

Duration 1 year.

Additional information Applications must be accompanied by a $10 processing fee.

Number awarded Varies each year; recently, 13 of these scholarships were awarded: 10 sponsored by the American Association of Critical-Care Nurses and 3 sponsored by the Mayo Clinic.

Deadline January of each year.

[963]
NUCLEAR REGULATORY COMMISSION HISTORICALLY BLACK COLLEGES AND UNIVERSITIES STUDENT RESEARCH PARTICIPATION PROGRAM

Oak Ridge Institute for Science and Education
Attn: Science and Engineering Education
P.O. Box 117
Oak Ridge, TN 37831-0117
(865) 576-3937 Fax: (865) 241-5220
E-mail: michael.hubbard@orau.gov
Web: see.orau.org

Summary To provide funding to students at Historically Black Colleges and Universities (HBCUs) who wish to participate in research at various facilities of the U.S. Nuclear Regulatory Commission (NRC).

Eligibility This program is open to undergraduate and graduate students at HBCUs who are U.S. citizens or permanent residents. Applicants must be studying computer science, engineering, earth or geosciences, health physics, materials science, mathematics, molecular/radiation biology, performance and risk assessments, physical sciences, or statistics-related nuclear material control and accounting. They must be interested in participating in a research project at a laboratory where NRC research is being conducted, on an HBCU campus, or at a host university under the guidance of a principal investigator who has an NRC research grants.

Financial data The stipend is $700 per week for graduate students or $600 per week for undergraduates. Also provided is limited travel reimbursement for round-trip transportation between the facility and home or campus.

Duration 10 to 12 weeks during the summer. Some 1-year appointments at participating facilities or on campus are also available.

Additional information This program is funded by the NRC and administered by Oak Ridge Institute for Science and Education (ORISE).

Number awarded Varies each year.

Deadline Applications may be submitted at any time.

[964]
NWA/DAVID SANKEY MINORITY SCHOLARSHIP IN METEOROLOGY

National Weather Association
Attn: Executive Director
228 West Millbrook Road
Raleigh, NC 27609-4304
(919) 845-1546 Fax: (919) 845-2956
E-mail: exdir@nwas.org
Web: www.nwas.org

Summary To provide financial assistance to African Americans and other members of minority groups who are working on an undergraduate or graduate degree in meteorology.

Eligibility This program is open to members of minority ethnic groups who are either entering their sophomore or higher year of undergraduate study or enrolled as graduate students. Applicants must be working on a degree in meteorology. Along with their application, they must submit a 1-page statement explaining why they are applying for this scholarship. Selection is based on that statement, academic achievement, and 2 letters of recommendation.

Financial data The stipend is $1,000.

Duration 1 year.

Additional information This program began in 2002.

Number awarded 1 each year.

Deadline April of each year.

[965]
OFFICE OF STUDENT AFFAIRS COMMUNITY LEADERSHIP TUITION SCHOLARSHIP

National Association of Black Social Workers
Attn: NABSW Scholarships
2305 Martin Luther King Avenue, S.E.
Washington, DC 20020
(202) 678-4570 Fax: (202) 678-4572
E-mail: office-manager@nabsw.org
Web: www.nabsw.org/mserver/Forms.aspx

Summary To provide financial assistance to members of the National Association of Black Social Workers (NABSW) who have provided outstanding community service and are working on an undergraduate or graduate degree.

Eligibility This program is open to African American members of NABSW who are enrolled at least half time at an accredited U.S. institution. Applicants must be working on an associate, bachelor's, master's, or Ph.D. degree in social work, sociology, or other field of human services. They must have a GPA of 3.0 or higher and a record of volunteer service to the African American community. Along with their application, they must submit a letter of recommendation from a prestigious community leader that highlights their volunteer work and leadership efforts within the African American community. Financial need is considered in the selection process.

Financial data The stipend is $1,000. Funds are sent directly to the recipient's school.

Duration 1 year.

Number awarded 1 each year.

Deadline January of each year.

[966]
OLIVER GOLDSMITH, M.D. SCHOLARSHIP

Kaiser Permanente Southern California
Attn: Residency Administration and Recruitment
393 East Walnut Street, Fifth Floor
Pasadena, CA 91188
Toll Free: (877) 574-0002 Fax: (626) 405-6581
E-mail: socal.residency@kp.org
Web: residency.kp.org

Summary To provide financial assistance to African American and other medical students who will help bring diversity to the profession.

Eligibility This program is open to students entering their third or fourth year of allopathic or osteopathic medical school. Members of all ethnic and racial groups are encouraged to apply, but applicants must have demonstrated their commitment to diversity through community service, clinical volunteering, or research. They may be attending medical school in any state, but they must intend to practice in southern California and they must be available to participate in a mentoring program and a clerkship at a Kaiser Permanente facility in that region.

Financial data The stipend is $5,000.

Duration 1 year.

Additional information This program began in 2004.

Number awarded 14 each year.

Deadline February of each year.

[967]
OLIVER W. HILL SCHOLARSHIP

LeClairRyan
Attn: Recruiting Manager
Riverfront Plaza, East Tower
951 East Byrd Street, Eighth Floor
Richmond, VA 23219
(804) 783-7597 Fax: (804) 783-2294
E-mail: droberts@leclairryan.com
Web: www.leclairryan.com

Summary To provide financial assistance to African Americans and other students of color at law schools in designated states.

Eligibility This program is open to students who have completed at least 1 semester at a law school in a state in which the sponsoring firm has an office (currently, California, Connecticut, Massachusetts, Michigan, New Jersey, New York, Pennsylvania, Virginia, and Washington, D.C.). Applicants must identify as a member of a minority racial ethnic group or as LGBT. They must have a GPA of 3.0 or higher. Along with their application, they must submit a 2,000-word essay presenting their ideas of pursuing social justice through the law.

Financial data The stipend is $5,000.

Duration 1 year.

Additional information This program began in 2009.

Number awarded 1 each year.

Deadline April of each year.

[968]
OLYMPIA BROWN AND MAX KAPP AWARD

Unitarian Universalist Association
Attn: Ministerial Credentialing Office
25 Beacon Street
Boston, MA 02108-2800
(617) 948-6403 Fax: (617) 742-2875
E-mail: mcoadministrator@uua.org
Web: www.uua.org

Summary To provide financial assistance to Unitarian Universalist (UU) candidates for the ministry (especially African Americans and other students of color) who submit a project on an aspect of Universalism.

Eligibility This program is open to students currently enrolled full or at least half time in a UU ministerial training program with candidate status. Applicants are primarily citizens of the United States or Canada. Along with their application, they may submit a paper, sermon, or a special project on an aspect of Unitarian Universalism. Priority is given first to those who have demonstrated outstanding ministerial ability and secondarily to students with the greatest financial need (especially persons of color).

Financial data The stipend is $2,500.

Duration 1 year.

Number awarded 1 each year.

Deadline April of each year.

[969]
OMEGA PSI PHI FOUNDERS' MEMORIAL SCHOLARSHIPS

Omega Psi Phi Fraternity
Attn: Charles R. Drew Memorial Scholarship Commission
3951 Snapfinger Parkway
Decatur, GA 30035-3203
(404) 284-5533 Fax: (404) 284-0333
E-mail: scholarshipchairman@oppf.org
Web: www.oppf.org/scholarship

Summary To provide financial assistance to outstanding undergraduate and graduate members of Omega Psi Phi fraternity.

Eligibility This program is open to members of the fraternity who are enrolled full time as sophomores, juniors, or graduate students and have a GPA of 3.0 or higher. Each chapter may nominate 1 undergraduate and 1 graduate member to the district. Candidates must submit a statement of 200 to 250 words on their purpose for applying for this scholarship, how they believe funds from the fraternity can assist them in achieving their career goals, and other circumstances (including financial need) that make it important for them to receive financial assistance. Selection is based on academic achievement, extracurricular activities, and community and campus involvement.

Financial data The stipend is $5,000.

Duration The scholarships are offered annually.

Additional information The winners are required to attend the Omega Psi Phi Grand Conclave or Leadership Conference. Up to $1,000 in travel expenses for attendance is provided.

Number awarded 4 each year: 3 to undergraduates and 1 to a graduate student.

Deadline Applications must be submitted to the district scholarship committee chair by January of each year.

[970]
OMEGA PSI PHI GRAND BASILEUS AWARD

Omega Psi Phi Fraternity
Attn: Charles R. Drew Memorial Scholarship Commission
3951 Snapfinger Parkway
Decatur, GA 30035-3203
(404) 284-5533 Fax: (404) 284-0333
E-mail: scholarshipchairman@oppf.org
Web: www.oppf.org/scholarship

Summary To provide financial assistance for graduate or professional education to members of Omega Psi Phi who have an outstanding academic record.

Eligibility This program is open to members of the fraternity who are graduating college seniors planning to continue on to graduate or professional school. Applicants must be enrolled full time at a 4-year college or university and have a GPA of 3.3 or higher. Along with their application, they must submit a statement of 200 to 250 words on their purpose for applying for this scholarship, how they believe funds from the fraternity can assist them in achieving their career goals, and other circumstances (including financial need) that make it important for them to receive financial assistance.

Financial data The stipend is $5,000.

Duration 1 year.

Additional information The winner is required to attend the Omega Psi Phi Grand Conclave or Leadership Conference. Up to $1,000 in travel expenses for attendance is provided.

Number awarded 1 each year.

Deadline April of each year.

[971]
OMEGA PSI PHI UNDERGRADUATE AND GRADUATE SCHOLARSHIPS

Omega Psi Phi Fraternity
Attn: Charles R. Drew Memorial Scholarship Commission
3951 Snapfinger Parkway
Decatur, GA 30035-3203
(404) 284-5533 Fax: (404) 284-0333
E-mail: scholarshipchairman@oppf.org
Web: www.oppf.org/scholarship

Summary To provide financial assistance for undergraduate, graduate, or professional education to members of Omega Psi Phi who have an outstanding academic record.

Eligibility This program is open to members of the fraternity who are either 1) a sophomore, junior, or senior planning to continue on to graduate or professional school; or 2) currently attending graduate or professional school. Applicants must be enrolled full time at a 4-year college or university and have a GPA of 3.0 or higher. Along with their application, they must submit a statement of 200 to 250 words on their purpose for applying for this scholarship, how they believe funds from the fraternity can assist them in achieving their career goals, and other circumstances (including financial need) that make it important for them to receive financial assistance.

Financial data The stipend is $4,000.

Duration 1 year.

Additional information The winners are required to attend the Omega Psi Phi Grand Conclave or Leadership Conference. Up to $1,000 in travel expenses for attendance is provided.

Number awarded 2 each year: 1 to an undergraduate and 1 to a graduate student.

Deadline April of each year.

[972]
OPERATION JUMP START III SCHOLARSHIPS

American Association of Advertising Agencies
Attn: AAAA Foundation
1065 Avenue of the Americas, 16th Floor
New York, NY 10018
(212) 262-2500 E-mail: ameadows@aaaa.org
Web: www.aaaa.org

Summary To provide financial assistance to African American and other multicultural art directors and copywriters interested in working on an undergraduate or graduate degree in advertising.

Eligibility This program is open to African Americans, Asian Americans, Hispanic Americans, and Native Americans who are U.S. citizens or permanent residents. Applicants must be incoming graduate students at 1 of 6 designated portfolio schools or full-time juniors at 1 of 2 designated colleges. They must be able to demonstrate extreme financial need, creative talent, and promise. Along with their application, they must submit 10 samples of creative work in their respective field of expertise.

Financial data The stipend is $5,000 per year.

Duration Most awards are for 2 years.

Additional information Operation Jump Start began in 1997 and was followed by Operation Jump Start II in 2002. The current program began in 2006. The 6 designated portfolio schools are the AdCenter at Virginia Commonwealth University, the Creative Circus in Atlanta, the Portfolio Center in Atlanta, the Miami Ad School, the University of Texas at Austin, and Pratt Institute. The 2 designated colleges are the Minneapolis College of Art and Design and the Art Center College of Design at Pasadena, California.

Number awarded 20 each year.

Deadline Deadline not specified.

[973]
OREGON STATE BAR SCHOLARSHIPS

Oregon State Bar
Attn: Diversity and Inclusion Department
16037 S.W. Upper Boones Ferry Road
P.O. Box 231935
Tigard, OR 97281-1935
(503) 431-6338
Toll Free: (800) 452-8260, ext. 338 (within OR)
Fax: (503) 598-6938 E-mail: tkelich@osbar.org
Web: www.osbar.org/diversity

Summary To provide financial assistance to entering and continuing students from any state enrolled at law schools in Oregon, especially those who will help the Oregon State Bar achieve its diversity objectives.

Eligibility This program is open to students entering or continuing at 1 of the law schools in Oregon (Willamette, University of Oregon, and Lewis and Clark). Preference is given to students who will contribute to the Oregon State Bar's diversity program to "increase the diversity of the Oregon bench and bar to reflect the diversity of the people of Oregon." Applicants must submit 1) a personal statement on their history of disadvantage or barriers to educational advancement, personal experiences of discrimination, extraordinary financial obligations, composition of immediate family, extraordinary health or medical needs, and languages in which they are fluent as well as barriers they have experienced because English is a second language; and 2) a state bar statement on why they chose to attend an Oregon law school; if they are not committed but are considering practicing in Oregon, what would help them to decide to practice in the state; and how they will improve the quality of legal service or increase access to justice in Oregon. Selection is based on financial need (30%), the personal statement (25%), the state bar statement (25%), community activities (10%), and employment history (10%).

Financial data The stipend is $2,000 per year. Funds are credited to the recipient's law school tuition account.

Duration 1 year; recipients may reapply.

Number awarded 8 each year.

Deadline March of each year.

[974]
PATRICIA G. ARCHBOLD PREDOCTORAL SCHOLAR AWARD

Gerontological Society of America
Attn: National Hartford Centers of Gerontological Nursing Excellence
1220 L Street, N.W., Suite 901
Washington, DC 20005-4001
(202) 842-1275 Fax: (202) 842-1150
E-mail: nhcgne@geron.org
Web: www.geriatricnursing.org

Summary To provide funding to African American and other nurses from underrepresented minority groups who are interested in working on a doctoral degree in gerontological nursing.

Eligibility This program is open to registered nurses who are members of underrepresented minority groups (American Indians, Alaska Natives, Asians, Blacks or African Americans, Hispanics or Latinos/Latinas, Native Hawaiians or other Pacific Islanders) and have been admitted to a doctoral program as a full-time student. Applicants must plan an academic research career in geriatric nursing. They must identify a mentor/adviser with whom they will work and whose program of research in geriatric nursing is a good match with their own research interest area. Selection is based on potential for substantial long-term contributions to the knowledge base in geriatric nursing; leadership potential; evidence of commitment to a career in academic geriatric nursing; and evidence of involvement in educational, research, and professional activities. U.S. citizenship or permanent resident status is required.

Financial data The stipend is $50,000 per year. An additional stipend of $5,000 is available to fellows whose research includes the study of pain in the elderly.

Duration 2 years.

Additional information This program began in 2001 with funding from the John A. Hartford Foundation. In 2004, the Mayday Fund added support to scholars who focus on the study of pain in the elderly. Until 2013 it was known as the Building Academic Geriatric Nursing Capacity Program.

Number awarded Varies each year; recently, 12 of these scholarships were awarded.

Deadline January of each year.

[975]
PATRICK D. MCJULIEN MINORITY GRADUATE SCHOLARSHIP

Association for Educational Communications and Technology
Attn: ECT Foundation
1800 North Stonelake Drive, Suite 2
P.O. Box 2447
Bloomington, IN 47402-2447
(812) 335-7675 Toll Free: (877) 677-AECT
Fax: (812) 335-7678 E-mail: aect@aect.org
Web: www.aect.org/newsite

Summary To provide financial assistance to African American and other minority members of the Association for Educational Communications and Technology (AECT) who are working on a graduate degree in the field of educational communications and technology.

Eligibility This program is open to AECT members who are members of minority groups. Applicants must be full-time graduate students enrolled in a degree-granting program in educational technology at the master's (M.S.), specialist (Ed.S.), or doctoral (Ph.D., Ed.D.) levels. They must have a GPA of 3.0 or higher.

Financial data A stipend is awarded (amount not specified).

Duration 1 year.

Number awarded 1 each year.

Deadline July of each year.

[976]
PATTI LABELLE MEDICAL STUDENT SCHOLARSHIP

National Medical Fellowships, Inc.
Attn: Scholarship Program
347 Fifth Avenue, Suite 510
New York, NY 10016
(212) 483-8880 Toll Free: (877) NMF-1DOC
Fax: (212) 483-8897 E-mail: info@nmfonline.org
Web: www.nmfonline.org

Summary To provide financial assistance to African American medical students.

Eligibility This program is open to African American medical students who are U.S. citizens in their first, second, or third year at an accredited M.D. or D.O. degree-granting school in the United States. Only nominations are accepted. All nominees must submit a personal essay on their motivation for a career in medicine and career plans over the next 10 years. Selection is based on financial need, community involvement, academic achievement, and potential for a responsible role in medicine.

Financial data The stipend is $5,000.

Duration 1 year.

Additional information This program is sponsored by the National Medical Association (NMA).

Number awarded 1 each year.

Deadline April of each year.

[977]
PAUL D. WHITE SCHOLARSHIP

BakerHostetler LLP
Attn: Attorney Recruitment and Development Manager
PNC Center
1900 East Ninth Street, Suite 3200
Cleveland, OH 44114-3482
(216) 621-0200 Fax: (216) 696-0740
E-mail: ddriscole@bakerlaw.com
Web: www.bakerlaw.com/firmdiversity/scholarship

Summary To provide financial aid and summer work experience to African American and other minority law school students.

Eligibility This program is open to first- and second-year law students of Black/African American, Hispanic/Latino, Asian, Native Hawaiian/Pacific Islander or American Indian/Alaska Native descent. Selection is based on law school performance, demonstrated leadership abilities (as evidenced by community and collegiate involvement), collegiate academic record, extracurricular activities, work experience, and a written personal statement.

Financial data The program provides a stipend of $7,500 for the scholarship and a paid summer clerkship with the sponsoring firm. To date, the firm has expended more than $2.0 million in scholarships and clerkships.

Duration 1 year, including the following summer.

Additional information This program began in 1997. Clerkships may be performed at any of the firm's offices in Cincinnati, Cleveland, or Orlando.

Number awarded 1 or more each year.

Deadline January of each year.

[978]
PAULA J. CARTER GRADUATE SCHOLARSHIP

Missouri Legislative Black Caucus Foundation
c/o Senator Shalonn "Kiki" Curls
4609 Paseo Boulevard, Suite 102
Kansas City, MO 64110
Toll Free: (877) 63-MLBCF E-mail: mlbcf@aol.com
Web: www.mlbcf.com

Summary To provide financial assistance to African American and other residents of Missouri who come from a disadvantaged background and are interested in working on a graduate degree in any field at a school in any state.

Eligibility This program is open to graduate students from Missouri who come from a disadvantaged background. Applicants may be attending or planning to attend a college or university in any state. They must have a GPA of 3.0 or higher. Along with their application, they must submit a 250-word personal statement on how their education will assist them in achieving their goals. Selection is based on academic excellence, community service, leadership skills, and financial need.

Financial data A stipend is awarded (amount not specified).

Duration 1 year; recipients may reapply for up to 2 years of support.

Number awarded 1 or more each year.

Deadline May of each year.

[979]
PERKINS COIE DIVERSITY STUDENT FELLOWSHIPS

Perkins Coie LLP
Attn: Chief Diversity Officer
131 South Dearborn Street, Suite 1700
Chicago, IL 60603-5559
(312) 324-8593 Fax: (312) 324-9400
E-mail: diversity@perkinscoie.com
Web: www.perkinscoie.com/diversity/Diversity.aspx

Summary To provide financial assistance to African American and other law students who reflect the diversity of communities in the country.

Eligibility This program is open to students enrolled in the first year of a J.D. program at an ABA-accredited law school. Applicants must contribute meaningfully to the diversity of the law school student body and the legal profession. Diversity is defined broadly to include members of racial, ethnic, disabled, and sexual orientation minority groups, as well as those who may be the first person in their family to pursue higher education. Applicants must submit a 1-page personal statement that describes their unique personal history, a legal writing sample, a current resume, and undergraduate and law school transcripts. They are not required to disclose their financial circumstances, but a demonstrated need for financial assistance may be taken into consideration.

Financial data The stipend is $7,500.

Duration 1 year.

Additional information Fellows are also offered a summer associateship at their choice of the firm's offices in Anchorage, Bellevue, Boise, Chicago, Dallas, Los Angeles, Madison, Palo Alto, Phoenix, Portland, San Diego, San Francisco, Seattle, or Washington, D.C.

Number awarded Varies each year; recently, 7 of these fellowships were awarded.
Deadline January of each year.

[980]
PFATS-NFL CHARITIES MINORITY SCHOLARSHIPS

Professional Football Athletic Trainers Society
c/o Britt Brown, ATC, Associate Athletic Trainer
Dallas Cowboys
One Cowboys Parkway
Irving, TX 75063
(972) 497-4992 E-mail: bbrown@dallascowboys.net
Web: www.pfats.com/about/scholarships

Summary To provide financial assistance to African American and other minority undergraduate and graduate students working on a degree in athletic training.
Eligibility This program is open to ethnic minority students who are working on an undergraduate or graduate degree in athletic training. Applicants must have a GPA of 2.5 or higher. Along with their application, they must submit a cover letter, a curriculum vitae, and a letter of recommendation from their supervising athletic trainer.
Financial data A stipend is awarded (amount not specified).
Duration 1 year.
Additional information Recipients also have an opportunity to work at summer training camp of a National Football League (NFL) team. Support for this program, which began in 1993, is provided by NFL Charities.
Number awarded 1 or more each year.
Deadline March of each year.

[981]
PHIL B. CURLS, SR. SCHOLARSHIP

Missouri Legislative Black Caucus Foundation
c/o Senator Shalonn "Kiki" Curls
4609 Paseo Boulevard, Suite 102
Kansas City, MO 64110
Toll Free: (877) 63-MLBCF E-mail: mlbcf@aol.com
Web: www.mlbcf.com

Summary To provide financial assistance to African Americans and other residents of Missouri who come from a disadvantaged background and are interested in working on an undergraduate or graduate degree in a health-related field at a school in any state.
Eligibility This program is open to undergraduate and graduate students from Missouri who are preparing for a career as a physician, nurse, dentist, health researcher, hospital administrator, or other health-related professional. Applicants must come from a disadvantaged background and have a GPA of 2.0 or higher. They may be attending a college or university in any state. Along with their application, they must submit a 250-word personal statement on how their education will assist them in achieving their goals. Selection is based on academic excellence, community service, leadership skills, and financial need.
Financial data A stipend is awarded (amount not specified).
Duration 1 year; recipients may reapply for up to 6 years of support.
Additional information This foundation was established in 1989 to provide scholarships and other assistance to disadvantaged youths in Missouri. Its motto is, "Building a Brighter Future for African American families."
Number awarded 1 or more each year.
Deadline May of each year.

[982]
PHYSICAL AND LIFE SCIENCES DIRECTORATE INTERNSHIPS

Lawrence Livermore National Laboratory
Physical and Life Sciences Directorate
Attn: Education Coordinator
7000 East Avenue, L-418
Livermore, CA 94550
(925) 422-0455 E-mail: hutcheon3@llnl.gov
Web: www-pls.llnl.gov

Summary To provide an opportunity for undergraduate and graduate students (particularly African Americans, other minorities, and women) to work on summer research projects within the Physical and Life Sciences Directorate (PLS) of Lawrence Livermore National Laboratory (LLNL).
Eligibility This program is open to full-time undergraduate and graduate students who are interested in working on research projects within the PLS Directorate of LLNL. Openings are currently available in chemistry (organic, inorganic, synthetic, analytical, computational, nuclear, and environmental) and materials science (theory, simulation and modeling, synthesis and processing, materials under extreme conditions, dynamic materials science, metallurgy, nuclear fuels, optical materials, and surface science). Applicants must have a GPA of 3.0 or higher. Selection is based on academic record, aptitude, research interests, and recommendations of instructors. Women and minorities are encouraged to apply.
Financial data The stipend is $14 to $20 per hour for undergraduates or $4,100 to $4,900 per month for graduate students. Living accommodations and arrangements are the responsibility of the intern.
Duration 2 or 3 months, during the summer.
Number awarded Varies each year.
Deadline February of each year.

[983]
PORTER PHYSIOLOGY DEVELOPMENT AWARDS

American Physiological Society
Attn: Education Office
9650 Rockville Pike, Room 3111
Bethesda, MD 20814-3991
(301) 634-7132 Fax: (301) 634-7098
E-mail: education@the-aps.org
Web: www.the-aps.org

Summary To provide financial assistance to African Americans and other minorities who are members of the American Physiological Society (APS) and interested in working on a doctoral degree in physiology.
Eligibility This program is open to U.S. citizens and permanent residents who are members of racial or ethnic minority groups (Hispanic or Latino, American Indian or Alaska Native, Asian, Black or African American, or Native Hawaiian or other Pacific Islander). Applicants must be currently enrolled in or accepted to a doctoral program in physiology at

a university as full-time students. They must be APS members and have actively participated in its work. Selection is based on the applicant's potential for success (academic record, statement of interest, previous awards and experiences, letters of recommendation); applicant's proposed training environment (including quality of preceptor); and applicant's research and training plan (clarity and quality).

Financial data The stipend is $23,500 per year. No provision is made for a dependency allowance or tuition and fees.

Duration 1 year; may be renewed for 1 additional year and, in exceptional cases, for a third year.

Additional information This program is supported by the William Townsend Porter Foundation (formerly the Harvard Apparatus Foundation). The first Porter Fellowship was awarded in 1920. In 1966 and 1967, the American Physiological Society established the Porter Physiology Development Committee to award fellowships to minority students engaged in graduate study in physiology. The highest ranked applicant for these fellowships is designated the Eleanor Ison Franklin Fellow.

Number awarded Varies each year; recently, 8 of these fellowships were awarded.

Deadline January of each year.

[984] PREDOCTORAL FELLOWSHIPS IN BEHAVIORAL NEUROSCIENCE

Texas Consortium in Behavioral Neuroscience
c/o University of Texas at Austin
Department of Psychology
1 University Station A8000
Austin, TX 78712
(512) 471-1068 Fax: (512) 471-1073
E-mail: lima@mail.utexas.edu
Web: homepage.psy.utexas.edu

Summary To provide an opportunity for African American and other doctoral candidates from underrepresented groups to obtain research training in neuroscience at selected universities in Texas.

Eligibility This program is open to members of populations underrepresented in health-related sciences, including specified racial and ethnic groups (Blacks, Hispanics, and Native Americans), individuals with disabilities, and individuals from disadvantaged backgrounds. Applicants must have a bachelor's degree and plan to work on a doctoral degree in neuroscience. They must be interested in a program of research training at the University of Texas at Austin, the University of Texas at San Antonio, the University of Texas Health Science Center at San Antonio, Texas A&M University, or Texas A&M University System Health Science Center. U.S. citizenship or permanent resident status is required.

Financial data The stipend is $22,032 per year.

Duration 3 years.

Additional information This program is sponsored by 3 components of the NIH: the National Institute of Mental Health, the National Institute on Drug Abuse, and the National Institute of Neurological Disorders and Stroke. The training program covers brain metabolic mapping of behavioral functions, neuropharmacology, neuroimaging, and electrophysiology. Trainees are required to complete courses covering the brain and behavior, scientific ethics, experimental design, and statistical analysis.

Number awarded 10 each year.

Deadline Applications may be submitted at any time.

[985] PREDOCTORAL FELLOWSHIPS OF THE FORD FOUNDATION DIVERSITY FELLOWSHIP PROGRAM

National Research Council
Attn: Fellowships Office, Keck 576
500 Fifth Street, N.W.
Washington, DC 20001
(202) 334-2872 Fax: (202) 334-3419
E-mail: infofell@nas.edu
Web: sites.nationalacademies.org

Summary To provide financial assistance for graduate school to African Americans and other students whose success will increase the racial and ethnic diversity of U.S. colleges and universities.

Eligibility This program is open to citizens, permanent residents, and nationals of the United States who are enrolled or planning to enroll full time in a Ph.D. or Sc.D. degree program and are committed to a career in teaching and research at the college or university level. Applicants may be undergraduates in their senior year, individuals who have completed undergraduate study or some graduate study, or current Ph.D. or Sc.D. students who can demonstrate that they can fully utilize a 3-year fellowship award. They must be working on or planning to work on a degree in most areas of the arts, sciences, humanities, and social sciences or in interdisciplinary ethnic or area studies. Support is not provided to students working on a degree in most practice-oriented areas, terminal master's degrees, other doctoral degrees (e.g., Ed.D., D.F.A., Psy.D.), professional degrees (e.g., medicine, law, public health), or joint degrees (e.g., M.D./Ph.D., J.D./Ph.D., M.F.A./Ph.D.). The following are considered as positive factors in the selection process: evidence of superior academic achievement; promise of continuing achievement as scholars and teachers; membership in a group whose underrepresentation in the American professoriate has been severe and longstanding, including Black/African Americans, Puerto Ricans, Mexican Americans/Chicanos/Chicanas, Native American Indians, Alaska Natives (Eskimos, Aleuts, and other indigenous people of Alaska), and Native Pacific Islanders (Hawaiians, Micronesians, or Polynesians); capacity to respond in pedagogically productive ways to the learning needs of students from diverse backgrounds; sustained personal engagement with communities that are underrepresented in the academy and an ability to bring this asset to learning, teaching, and scholarship at the college and university level; and likelihood of using the diversity of human experience as an educational resource in teaching and scholarship.

Financial data The program provides a stipend to the student of $20,000 per year and an award to the host institution of $2,000 per year in lieu of tuition and fees.

Duration 3 years of support is provided, to be used within a 5-year period.

Additional information The competition for this program is conducted by the National Research Council on behalf of the Ford Foundation. Applicants who merit receiving the fellowship but to whom awards cannot be made because of insufficient funds are given Honorable Mentions; this recognition does not carry with it a monetary award but honors applicants who have demonstrated substantial academic achievement. The National Research Council publishes a list of those Honorable Mentions who wish their names publicized. Fellows may not accept remuneration from another fellowship or similar external award while on this program; however, supplementation from institutional funds, educational benefits from the Department of Veterans Affairs, or educational incentive funds may be received concurrently with Ford Foundation support. Predoctoral fellows are required to submit an interim progress report 6 months after the start of the fellowship and a final report at the end of the 12 month tenure.

Number awarded Approximately 60 each year.

Deadline November of each year.

[986] PREDOCTORAL RESEARCH TRAINING FELLOWSHIPS IN EPILEPSY

Epilepsy Foundation
Attn: Research Department
8301 Professional Place
Landover, MD 20785-2353
(301) 459-3700 Toll Free: (800) EFA-1000
Fax: (301) 577-2684 TDD: (800) 332-2070
E-mail: grants@efa.org
Web: www.epilepsyfoundation.org

Summary To provide funding to doctoral candidates (particularly African Americans, other minorities, women, and individuals with disabilities) who are enrolled in designated fields and interested in conducting dissertation research on a topic related to epilepsy.

Eligibility This program is open to full-time graduate students working on a Ph.D. in biochemistry, genetics, neuroscience, nursing, pharmacology, pharmacy, physiology, or psychology. Applicants must be conducting dissertation research on a topic relevant to epilepsy under the guidance of a mentor with expertise in the area of epilepsy investigation. Applications from women, members of minority groups, and people with disabilities are especially encouraged. U.S. citizenship is not required, but the project must be conducted in the United States. Selection is based on the relevance of the proposed work to epilepsy, the applicant's qualifications, the mentor's qualifications, the scientific quality of the proposed dissertation research, the quality of the training environment for research related to epilepsy, and the adequacy of the facility.

Financial data The grant is $20,000, consisting of $19,000 for a stipend and $1,000 to support travel to attend the annual meeting of the American Epilepsy Society.

Duration 1 year.

Additional information Support for this program, which began in 1998, is provided by many individuals, families, and corporations, especially the American Epilepsy Society, Abbott Laboratories, Ortho-McNeil Pharmaceutical, and Pfizer Inc.

Number awarded Varies each year.

Deadline August of each year.

[987] PUBLIC INTEREST FELLOWSHIPS FOR LAW STUDENTS OF COLOR

Goodwin Procter LLP
Attn: Recruiting Manager
53 State Street
Boston, MA 02109
(617) 570-8156 Fax: (617) 523-1231
E-mail: fellowships@goodwinprocter.com
Web: www.goodwinprocter.com

Summary To provide financial aid and work experience to African American and other minority students who are interested in public interest law.

Eligibility This program is open to students of color entering their second year at a law school in any state. Applicants must actively express an interest in working in the sponsoring firm's summer program in public interest law. If they are applying for the Goodwin MassMutual Diversity Fellowship, they must express an interest in working with MassMutual's legal department in Springfield, Massachusetts for 2 weeks as part of the summer program and specializing in the investment or insurance business or in a legal focus to advance business objectives. Selection is based on academic performance, leadership abilities, involvement in minority student organizations, commitment to community service, interpersonal skills, other special achievements and honors, and interest in working with the firm during the summer.

Financial data The stipend is $7,500.

Duration 1 year; nonrenewable.

Additional information This program began in 2005. In 2007, it added the Goodwin MassMutual Diversity Fellowship, created in conjunction with its long-standing client, Massachusetts Mutual Life Insurance Company (MassMutual). Summer positions are available at the firm's offices in Boston, Los Angeles, New York, Palo Alto, San Diego, San Francisco, and Washington, D.C.

Number awarded 4 each year, including 1 Goodwin MassMutual Diversity Fellowship.

Deadline October of each year.

[988] RA CONSULTING SERVICES/MARIA RILEY SCHOLARSHIP

National Forum for Black Public Administrators
Attn: Scholarship Program
777 North Capitol Street, N.E., Suite 807
Washington, DC 20002
(202) 408-9300 Fax: (202) 408-8558
E-mail: vharris@nfbpa.org
Web: www.nfbpa.org/i4a/pages/index.cfm?pageid=4047

Summary To provide financial assistance to African Americans working on an undergraduate or graduate degree in engineering or information technology.

Eligibility This program is open to African American undergraduate and graduate students preparing for a career as a public administrator serving the engineering and information technology fields. Applicants must be working full time on a degree in engineering or information technology. They must have a GPA of 3.0 or higher, excellent interpersonal and analytical abilities, and strong oral and written communication skills. Along with their application, they must submit a 3-page autobiographical essay that includes their academic and career goals and objectives. Selection is based on academic record, leadership ability, participation in school activities, community service, and financial need.

Financial data The stipend is $2,500.

Duration 1 year.

Additional information This program is sponsored by RA Consulting Services. Recipients are required to attend the sponsor's annual conference to receive their scholarship; limited hotel and air accommodations are arranged and provided.

Number awarded 1 each year.

Deadline February of each year.

[989]
RACIAL ETHNIC PASTORAL LEADERSHIP PROGRAM

Synod of Southern California and Hawaii
Attn: Racial Ethnic Pastoral Leadership Work Group
3325 Wilshire Boulevard, Suite 850
Los Angeles, CA 90010-1761
(213) 483-3840, ext. 103 Fax: (213) 483-4275
E-mail: LeonFanniel@synod.org
Web: www.synod.org/repl/index.html

Summary To provide financial assistance to African Americans and members of other racial minority groups in the Presbyterian Church (USA) Synod of Southern California and Hawaii who are preparing for a career as a pastor or other church vocation.

Eligibility Applicants must be under care of their church's Session and enrolled with a Presbytery within the Synod of Southern California and Hawaii. They must be members of racial ethnic groups interested in becoming a Presbyterian pastor or other church worker (e.g., commissioned ruling elder, certified Christian educator) and serving in a racial ethnic ministry within the PCUSA. Racial ethnic persons who already have an M.Div. degree, are from another denomination in correspondence with the PCUSA, and are seeking to meet PCUSA requirements for ordination or transfer may also be eligible if they plan to serve in a racial ethnic congregation or an approved specialized ministry. Applicants must submit documentation of financial need, recommendations from the appropriate presbytery committee or session, a current transcript, and essays on their goals and objectives. They must be enrolled full or part time in a PCUSA seminary or other seminary approved by the Committee on Preparation for Ministry of their Presbytery.

Financial data The stipend is $2,000 per year.

Duration 1 year; may be renewed.

Additional information This program began in 1984.

Number awarded Varies each year.

Deadline April of each year.

[990]
RACIAL ETHNIC SUPPLEMENTAL GRANTS

Presbyterian Church (USA)
Attn: Office of Financial Aid for Studies
100 Witherspoon Street, Room M-052
Louisville, KY 40202-1396
(502) 569-5224 Toll Free: (800) 728-7228, ext. 5224
Fax: (502) 569-8766 TDD: (800) 833-5955
E-mail: finaid@pcusa.org
Web: gamc.pcusa.org

Summary To provide financial assistance to African American and other minority graduate students who are Presbyterian Church (USA) members interested in preparing for church occupations.

Eligibility This program is open to racial/ethnic graduate students (Asian American, African American, Hispanic American, Native American, or Alaska Native) who are enrolled full time at a PCUSA seminary or accredited theological institution approved by their Committee on Preparation for Ministry. Applicants must be working on 1) an M.Div. degree and enrolled as an inquirer or candidate by a PCUSA presbytery; or 2) an M.A.C.E. degree and preparing for a church occupation. They must be PCUSA members, U.S. citizens or permanent residents, able to demonstrate financial need, and recommended by the financial aid officer at their theological institution. Along with their application, they must submit a 1,000-word essay on what they believe God is calling them to do in ministry.

Financial data Stipends range from $500 to $1,000 per year. Funds are intended as supplements to students who have been awarded a Presbyterian Study Grant but still demonstrate remaining financial need.

Duration 1 year; may be renewed up to 2 additional years.

Number awarded Varies each year.

Deadline June of each year.

[991]
RALPH W. SHRADER DIVERSITY SCHOLARSHIPS

Armed Forces Communications and Electronics Association
Attn: AFCEA Educational Foundation
4400 Fair Lakes Court
Fairfax, VA 22033-3899
(703) 631-6138 Toll Free: (800) 336-4583, ext. 6138
Fax: (703) 631-4693 E-mail: scholarshipsinfo@afcea.org
Web: www.afcea.org

Summary To provide financial assistance to African American and other master's degree students in fields related to communications and electronics.

Eligibility This program is open to U.S. citizens working on a master's degree at an accredited college or university in the United States. Applicants must be enrolled full time and studying computer science, computer technology, engineering (chemical, electrical, electronic, communications, or systems), mathematics, physics, management information systems, or a field directly related to the support of U.S. national security or intelligence enterprises. At least 1 of these scholarships is set aside for a woman or a minority. Selection is based primarily on academic excellence.

Financial data The stipend is $3,000. Funds are paid directly to the recipient.

Duration 1 year.

Additional information This program is sponsored by Booz Allen Hamilton.

Number awarded Up to 5 each year, at least 1 of which is for a woman or minority candidate.

Deadline February of each year.

[992] RANDY GERSON MEMORIAL GRANT

American Psychological Foundation
750 First Street, N.E.
Washington, DC 20002-4242
(202) 336-5843 Fax: (202) 336-5812
E-mail: foundation@apa.org
Web: www.apa.org/apf/funding/gerson.aspx

Summary To provide funding to graduate students (particularly African Americans, other minorities, women, and students with disabilities) who are interested in conducting research in the psychology of couple and/or family dynamics and/or multi-generational processes.

Eligibility This program is open to full-time graduate students in psychology. Applicants must be proposing a project that advances the systemic understanding of couple and/or family dynamics and/or multi-generational processes. Work that advances theory, assessment, or clinical practice in those areas is eligible. Preference is given to projects that use or contribute to the development of Bowen family systems. Selection is based on conformance with stated program goals, magnitude of incremental contribution, quality of proposed work, and applicant's demonstrated scholarship and research competence. The sponsor encourages applications from individuals who represent diversity in race, ethnicity, gender, age, disability, and sexual orientation.

Financial data The grant is $6,000.

Duration The grant is presented annually.

Additional information This grant was first awarded in 1998.

Number awarded 1 each year.

Deadline January of each year.

[993] RDW GROUP, INC. MINORITY SCHOLARSHIP FOR COMMUNICATIONS

Rhode Island Foundation
Attn: Funds Administrator
One Union Station
Providence, RI 02903
(401) 427-4017 Fax: (401) 331-8085
E-mail: lmonahan@rifoundation.org
Web: www.rifoundation.org

Summary To provide financial assistance to African Americans and other residents of color from Rhode Island who are working on a undergraduate or graduate degree in communications in any state.

Eligibility This program is open to undergraduate and graduate students at colleges and universities in any state who are Rhode Island residents of color. Applicants must intend to work on a degree in communications (including computer graphics, art, cinematography, or other fields that would prepare them for a career in advertising). They must be able to demonstrate financial need and a commitment to a career in communications. Along with their application, they must submit an essay (up to 300 words) on the impact they would like to have on the communications field.

Financial data The stipend is approximately $2,000 per year.

Duration 1 year; recipients may reapply.

Additional information This program is sponsored by the RDW Group, Inc.

Number awarded 1 each year.

Deadline April of each year.

[994] REED SMITH DIVERSE SCHOLARS PROGRAM

Reed Smith LLP
Attn: U.S. Director of Legal Recruiting
2500 One Liberty Place
1650 Market Street
Philadelphia, PA 19103
(215) 851-8100 E-mail: dlevin@reedsmith.com
Web: www.reedsmith.com/Diverse_Scholars_Program

Summary To provide financial aid and summer work experience to African American and other law students who are will contribute to diversity in the field.

Eligibility This program is open to students completing their first year of law school. Applicants must be able to demonstrate a record of academic excellence and a commitment to diversity, inclusion, and community. Along with their application, they must submit a 750-word personal statement on how they believe they can contribute to the sponsoring law firm's goals of diversity and inclusion, including 1) how their life experiences have impacted their commitment to diversity; 2) their community involvement; and 3) their academic or leadership achievements.

Financial data The stipend is $15,000. Recipients are also offered a summer associate position at their choice of the firm's 9 U.S. offices after completion of their second year of law school (in Chicago, Houston, Los Angeles, New York, Philadelphia, Pittsburgh, Richmond, San Francisco, or Washington, D.C.).

Duration 1 year (the second year of law school).

Additional information The firm established this program in 2008 as part of its commitment to promote diversity in the legal profession.

Number awarded 2 each year.

Deadline August of each year.

[995] RICHARD AND HELEN BROWN COREM SCHOLARSHIPS

United Church of Christ
Parish Life and Leadership Ministry Team
Attn: COREM Administrator
700 Prospect Avenue East
Cleveland, OH 44115-1100
(216) 736-2113 Toll Free: (866) 822-8224, ext. 2113
Fax: (216) 736-3783
Web: www.ucc.org/seminarians/ucc-scholarships-for.html

Summary To provide financial assistance to African American and other minority seminary students who are interested in becoming a pastor in the United Church of Christ (UCC).

Eligibility This program is open to students at accredited seminaries who have been members of a UCC congregation for at least 1 year. Applicants must work through 1 of the member bodies of the Council for Racial and Ethnic Ministries (COREM): United Black Christians (UBC), Ministers for Racial, Social and Economic Justice (MRSEJ), Council for Hispanic Ministries (CHM), Pacific Islander and Asian American Ministries (PAAM), or Council for American Indian Ministries (CAIM). They must 1) have a GPA of 3.0 or higher; 2) be enrolled in a course of study leading to ordained ministry; 3) be in care of an association or conference at the time of application; and 4) demonstrate leadership ability through participation in their local church, association, conference, or academic environment.

Financial data Stipends are approximately $10,000 per year.

Duration 1 year.

Number awarded Varies each year; recently, 7 scholarships were awarded by UBC, 2 by MRSEJ, 1 by PAAM, and 2 by CHM.

Deadline Deadline not specified.

[996]
RICHARD D. HAILEY AAJ LAW STUDENT SCHOLARSHIPS

American Association for Justice
Attn: Scholarships
777 Sixth Street, N.W., Suite 200
Washington, DC 20001
(202) 965-3500, ext. 2834
Toll Free: (800) 424-2725, ext. 2834
Fax: (202) 965-0355
E-mail: catherine.rodman@justice.org
Web: www.justice.org/cps/rde/xchg/justice/hs.xsl/648.htm

Summary To provide financial assistance for law school to African American and other minority student members of the American Association for Justice (AAJ).

Eligibility This program is open to African American, Hispanic, Asian American, Native American, and biracial members of the association who are entering the first, second, or third year of law school. Applicants must submit a 500-word essay on how they meet the selection criteria: commitment to the association, involvement in student chapter and minority caucus activities, desire to represent victims, interest and proficiency of skills in trial advocacy, and financial need.

Financial data The stipend is $1,000.

Duration 1 year.

Additional information The American Association for Justice was formerly the Association of Trial Lawyers of America.

Number awarded Up to 6 each year.

Deadline May of each year.

[997]
ROBERT A. CATLIN/DAVID W. LONG MEMORIAL SCHOLARSHIP

American Planning Association
Attn: Planning and the Black Community Division
205 North Michigan Avenue, Suite 1200
Chicago, IL 60601
(312) 431-9100 Fax: (312) 786-6700
E-mail: pbcd.policy@gmail.com
Web: www.planning.org

Summary To provide financial assistance to African Americans interested in working on a graduate degree in planning or a related field.

Eligibility This program is open to African Americans who are 1) undergraduate students applying to or accepted into an urban planning program for graduate students; or 2) graduate students already working on a degree in urban planning or a related field (e.g., geography, environmental studies, urban studies, urban policy). Applicants must submit 1) a 1-page personal statement on what interests them about the field of planning and their professional goals; and 2) a 3-page essay explaining the positive role that planning could play in developing and supporting Black communities. Financial need is not considered in the selection process.

Financial data The stipend is $1,500.

Duration 1 year; nonrenewable.

Number awarded 1 each year.

Deadline February of each year.

[998]
ROBERT D. WATKINS GRADUATE RESEARCH FELLOWSHIP

American Society for Microbiology
Attn: Education Board
1752 N Street, N.W.
Washington, DC 20036-2904
(202) 942-9283 Fax: (202) 942-9329
E-mail: fellowships@asmusa.org
Web: www.asm.org/index.php/fellowships-2

Summary To provide funding for research in microbiology to African American and other underrepresented minority doctoral students who are members of the American Society for Microbiology (ASM).

Eligibility This program is open to African Americans, Hispanics, Native Americans, Alaskan Natives, and Pacific Islanders enrolled as full-time graduate students who have completed their first year of doctoral study and who are members of the society. Applicants must propose a joint research plan in collaboration with a society member scientist. They must have completed all graduate course work requirements for the doctoral degree by the date of the activation of the fellowship. U.S. citizenship or permanent resident status is required. Selection is based on academic achievement, evidence of a successful research plan developed in collaboration with a research adviser/mentor, relevant career goals in the microbiological sciences, and involvement in activities that serve the needs of underrepresented groups.

Financial data Students receive $21,000 per year as a stipend; funds may not be used for tuition or fees.

Duration 3 years.

Number awarded Varies each year.
Deadline April of each year.

[999]
ROBERT TOIGO FOUNDATION FELLOWSHIPS

Robert Toigo Foundation
Attn: Fellowship Program Administrator
180 Grand Avenue, Suite 900
Oakland, CA 94612
(510) 763-5771 Fax: (510) 763-5778
E-mail: info@toigofoundation.org
Web: www.toigofoundation.org

Summary To provide financial assistance to African American and other minority students working on a master's degree in business administration or a related field.

Eligibility This program is open to members of minority groups (African American, Hispanic/Latino, Native American/Alaskan Native, South Asian American, or Asian American/Pacific Islander) who are entering or enrolled in a program for an M.B.A., J.D./M.B.A., master's in real estate, or master's in finance. Applicants must be preparing for a career in finance, including (but not limited to) investment management, investment banking, corporate finance, real estate, private equity, venture capital, business development, pension fund investment, or financial services consulting. U.S. citizenship or permanent resident status is required.

Financial data The stipend is $2,500 per year.

Duration Up to 2 years.

Additional information The application fee is $40.

Number awarded Approximately 50 to 60 each year.

Deadline March of each year.

[1000]
ROBIN GAINES MEMORIAL SCHOLARSHIP

New England Regional Black Nurses Association, Inc.
P.O. Box 190690
Boston, MA 02119
(617) 524-1951
Web: www.nerbna.org/org/scholarships.html

Summary To provide financial assistance to registered nurses (R.N.s) from New England who are working on a master's degree and have contributed to the African American community.

Eligibility The program is open to residents of the New England states who are R.N.s and currently working on a master's degree (nursing, advanced nursing practice, or public health) at a school in any state. Applicants must have at least 1 full year of school remaining. Along with their application, they must submit a 3-page essay that covers their career aspirations in the nursing profession; how they have contributed to the African American or other communities of color in such areas as work, volunteering, church, or community outreach; an experience that has enhanced their personal and/or professional growth; and any financial hardships that may hinder them from completing their education.

Financial data A stipend is awarded (amount not specified).

Duration 1 year.

Number awarded 1 or more each year.

Deadline March of each year.

[1001]
RONALD M. DAVIS SCHOLARSHIP

American Medical Association
Attn: AMA Foundation
515 North State Street
Chicago, IL 60610
(312) 464-4193 Fax: (312) 464-4142
E-mail: amafoundation@ama-assn.org
Web: www.ama-assn.org

Summary To provide financial assistance to medical school students who are African Americans or members of other underrepresented minority groups and planning to become a primary care physician.

Eligibility This program is open to first- and second-year medical students who are members of the following minority groups: African American/Black, American Indian, Native Hawaiian, Alaska Native, or Hispanic/Latino. Candidates must have an interest in becoming a primary care physician. Only nominations are accepted. Each medical school is invited to submit 2 nominees. U.S. citizenship or permanent resident status is required.

Financial data The stipend is $10,000.

Duration 1 year.

Additional information This program is offered by the AMA Foundation of the American Medical Association in collaboration with the National Business Group on Health.

Number awarded 1 each year.

Deadline April of each year.

[1002]
ROSA L. PARKS SCHOLARSHIPS

Conference of Minority Transportation Officials
Attn: National Scholarship Program
1875 I Street, N.W., Suite 500
Washington, DC 20006
(703) 234-4072 Fax: (202) 318-0364
Web: www.comto.org/?page=Scholarships

Summary To provide financial assistance for college to children of members of the Conference of Minority Transportation Officials (COMTO) and to other students interested in working on a bachelor's or master's degree in transportation.

Eligibility This program is open to 1) college-bound high school seniors whose parent has been a COMTO member for at least 1 year; 2) undergraduates who have completed at least 60 semester credit hours in a transportation discipline; and 3) students working on a master's degree in transportation who have completed at least 15 credits. Applicants must have a GPA of 3.0 or higher. Along with their application, they must submit a cover letter with a 500-word statement of career goals. Financial need is not considered in the selection process. U.S. citizenship or legal resident status is required.

Financial data The stipend is $4,500. Funds are paid directly to the recipient's college or university.

Duration 1 year.

Additional information COMTO was established in 1971 to promote, strengthen, and expand the roles of minorities in all aspects of transportation. Recipients are expected to attend the COMTO National Scholarship Luncheon.

Number awarded 1 each year.

Deadline May of each year.

[1003]
ROY H. POLLACK SCHOLARSHIP

Unitarian Universalist Association
Attn: Ministerial Credentialing Office
25 Beacon Street
Boston, MA 02108-2800
(617) 948-6403 Fax: (617) 742-2875
E-mail: mcoadministrator@uua.org
Web: www.uua.org

Summary To provide financial assistance to seminary students (especially African Americans and other students of color) preparing for the Unitarian Universalist (UU) ministry.

Eligibility This program is open to seminary students who are enrolled full or at least half time in their second or third year in a UU ministerial training program with candidate status. Applicants must be citizens of the United States or Canada. Priority is given first to those who have demonstrated outstanding ministerial ability and secondarily to students with the greatest financial need (especially persons of color).

Financial data The stipend ranges from $1,000 to $15,000 per year.

Duration 1 year.

Number awarded Varies each year; recently, 2 of these scholarships were awarded.

Deadline April of each year.

[1004]
ROY SCRIVNER MEMORIAL RESEARCH GRANTS

American Psychological Foundation
750 First Street, N.E.
Washington, DC 20002-4242
(202) 336-5843 Fax: (202) 336-5812
E-mail: foundation@apa.org
Web: www.apa.org/apf/funding/scrivner.aspx

Summary To provide funding to graduate students (particularly African Americans and other students from diverse backgrounds) who are interested in conducting dissertation research on lesbian, gay, bisexual, and transgender (LGBT) family psychology and therapy.

Eligibility This program is open to doctoral candidates who are interested in conducting empirical research in all fields of the behavioral and social sciences that focus on LGBT family psychology and LGBT family therapy. Proposals are especially encouraged for empirical studies that address the following: problems faced by LGBT families such as those associated with cultural, racial, socioeconomic, and family structure diversity; successful coping mechanisms such as sources of support and resilience for family members; and clinical issues and interventions in the domain of LGBT. Selection is based on conformance with stated program goals, magnitude of incremental contribution, quality of proposed work, and applicant's demonstrated scholarship and research competence. The sponsor encourages applications from individuals who represent diversity in race, ethnicity, gender, age, disability, and sexual orientation.

Financial data The grant is $12,000.

Duration 1 year.

Number awarded 1 each year.

Deadline October of each year.

[1005]
RUTH L. KIRSCHSTEIN NATIONAL RESEARCH SERVICE AWARDS FOR INDIVIDUAL PREDOCTORAL FELLOWSHIPS TO PROMOTE DIVERSITY IN HEALTH-RELATED RESEARCH

National Institutes of Health
Office of Extramural Research
Attn: Grants Information
6705 Rockledge Drive, Suite 4090
Bethesda, MD 20892-7983
(301) 435-0714 Fax: (301) 480-0525
TDD: (301) 451-5936 E-mail: grantsinfo@od.nih.gov
Web: grants.nih.gov/grants/guide/pa-files/PA-11-112.html

Summary To provide financial assistance to African Americans and other students from underrepresented groups who are interested in working on a doctoral degree and preparing for a career in biomedical and behavioral research.

Eligibility This program is open to students enrolled or accepted for enrollment in a Ph.D. or equivalent research degree program; a formally combined M.D./Ph.D. program; or other combined professional doctoral/research Ph.D. program in the biomedical, behavioral, health, or clinical sciences. Students in health professional degree programs (e.g., M.D., D.O., D.D.S., D.V.M.) are not eligible. Applicants must be 1) members of an ethnic or racial group underrepresented in biomedical or behavioral research; 2) individuals with disabilities; or 3) individuals from socially, culturally, economically, or educationally disadvantaged backgrounds that have inhibited their ability to prepare for a career in health-related research. They must be U.S. citizens, nationals, or permanent residents.

Financial data The fellowship provides an annual stipend of $22,032, a tuition and fee allowance (60% of costs up to $16,000 or 60% of costs up to $21,000 for dual degrees), and an institutional allowance of $4,200 ($3,100 at for-profit and federal institutions) for travel to scientific meetings, health insurance, and laboratory and other training expenses.

Duration Up to 5 years.

Additional information These fellowships are offered by most components of the National Institutes of Health (NIH). Contact the NIH for a list of names and telephone numbers of responsible officers at each component.

Number awarded Varies each year.

Deadline April, August, or December of each year.

[1006]
RUTH WHITEHEAD WHALEY SCHOLARSHIP

Association of Black Women Attorneys, Inc.
Attn: Scholarship Committee Chair
255 West 36th Street, Suite 800
New York, NY 10018
Web: abwanewyork.org/scholarships

Summary To provide financial assistance to African American and other minority students at law schools in Connecticut, New Jersey, and New York who are interested in public interest or civil rights law.

Eligibility This program is open to minority students from any state who are currently enrolled at accredited law schools in Connecticut, New Jersey, or New York. Applicants must be able to demonstrate financial need and an interest in public interest or civil rights law. Along with their application, they must submit a 200-word essay on their professional goals, especially community service activities or events in areas where they have been employed or volunteered. In the selection process, academic performance is not the deciding factor.

Financial data A stipend is awarded (amount not specified).

Duration 1 year.

Additional information This program began in 1995 to honor the first African American woman admitted to the North Carolina Bar.

Number awarded Varies each year; since the program was established, it has awarded more than $30,000 in scholarships.

Deadline April of each year.

[1007] SADIE T.M. ALEXANDER SCHOLARSHIP

Delta Sigma Theta Sorority, Inc.
Attn: Scholarship and Standards Committee Chair
1707 New Hampshire Avenue, N.W.
Washington, DC 20009
(202) 986-2400 Fax: (202) 986-2513
E-mail: dstemail@deltasigmatheta.org
Web: www.deltasigmatheta.org

Summary To provide financial assistance to members of Delta Sigma Theta who are interested in preparing for a career in law.

Eligibility This program is open to graduating college seniors and students who are currently enrolled in law school. Applicants must be active, dues-paying members of Delta Sigma Theta. Selection is based on meritorious achievement.

Financial data The stipends range from $1,000 to $2,000 per year. The funds may be used to cover tuition and living expenses.

Duration 1 year; may be renewed for 1 additional year.

Additional information This sponsor is a traditionally African American social sorority. The application fee is $20.

Number awarded 1 or more each year.

Deadline April of each year.

[1008] SBE DOCTORAL DISSERTATION RESEARCH IMPROVEMENT GRANTS

National Science Foundation
Attn: Directorate for Social, Behavioral, and Economic Sciences
4201 Wilson Boulevard, Room 905N
Arlington, VA 22230
(703) 292-8700 Fax: (703) 292-9083
TDD: (800) 281-8749
Web: www.nsf.gov/funding/pgm_summ.jsp?pims_id=13453

Summary To provide partial support to doctoral candidates (particularly African Americans, other minorities, women, and students with disabilities) who are conducting dissertation research in areas of interest to the Directorate for Social, Behavioral, and Economic Sciences (SBE) of the National Science Foundation (NSF).

Eligibility Applications may be submitted through regular university channels by dissertation advisers on behalf of graduate students who have advanced to candidacy and have begun or are about to begin dissertation research. Students must be enrolled at U.S. institutions, but they need not be U.S. citizens. The proposed research must relate to SBE's Division of Behavioral and Cognitive Sciences (archaeology, cultural anthropology, documenting endangered languages, geography and spatial sciences, linguistics, or biological anthropology); Division of Social and Economic Sciences (decision, risk, and management science; economics; law and social science; methodology, measurement, and statistics; political science; sociology; or science, technology, and society); National Center for Science and Engineering Statistics (science and technology surveys and statistics); or Office of Multidisciplinary Activities (science and innovation policy). Women, minorities, and persons with disabilities are strongly encouraged to apply.

Financial data Grants have the limited purpose of providing funds to enhance the quality of dissertation research. They are to be used exclusively for necessary expenses incurred in the actual conduct of the dissertation research, including (but not limited to) conducting field research in settings away from campus that would not otherwise be possible, data collection and sample survey costs, payments to subjects or informants, specialized research equipment, analysis and services not otherwise available, supplies, travel to archives, travel to specialized facilities or field research locations, and partial living expenses for conducting necessary research away from the student's U.S. academic institution. Funding is not provided for stipends, tuition, textbooks, journals, allowances for dependents, travel to scientific meetings, publication costs, dissertation preparation or reproduction, or indirect costs.

Duration Up to 2 years.

Number awarded 200 to 300 each year. Approximately $2.5 million is available for this program annually.

Deadline Deadline dates for the submission of dissertation improvement grant proposals differ by program within the divisions of the SBE Directorate; applicants should obtain information regarding target dates for proposals from the relevant program.

[1009] SCHOLARSHIPS FOR MINORITY ACCOUNTING STUDENTS

American Institute of Certified Public Accountants
Attn: Academic and Career Development Division
220 Leigh Farm Road
Durham, NC 27707-8110
(919) 402-4931 Fax: (919) 419-4705
E-mail: scholarships@aicpa.org
Web: www.aicpa.org

Summary To provide financial assistance to African Americans and other minorities interested in studying accounting at the undergraduate or graduate school level.

Eligibility This program is open to minority undergraduate and graduate students, enrolled full time, who have a GPA of 3.3 or higher (both cumulatively and in their major) and intend to pursue a C.P.A. credential. The program defines minority students as those whose heritage is Black or African American, Hispanic or Latino, Native American, or Asian American. Undergraduates must have completed at least 30 semester hours, including at least 6 semester hours of a major in accounting. Graduate students must be working on a master's degree in accounting, finance, taxation, or a related program. Applicants must be U.S. citizens or permanent residents and student affiliate members of the American Institute of Certified Public Accountants (AICPA). Along with their application, they must submit 500-word essays on 1) why they want to become a C.P.A. and how attaining that licensure will contribute to their goals; and 2) how they would spread the message about accounting and the C.P.A. profession in their community and school. In the selection process, some consideration is given to financial need.

Financial data Stipends range from $1,500 to $3,000 per year. Funds are disbursed directly to the recipient's school.

Duration 1 year; may be renewed up to 3 additional years or until completion of a bachelor's or master's degree, whichever is earlier.

Additional information This program began in 1969.

Number awarded Varies each year; recently, 78 students received funding through this program.

Deadline March of each year.

[1010] SCHOLARSHIPS SUPPORTING POST-SECONDARY EDUCATION FOR A CAREER IN THE AUDIOVISUAL INDUSTRY

InfoComm International
International Communications Industries Foundation
11242 Waples Mill Road, Suite 200
Fairfax, VA 22030
(703) 273-7200 Toll Free: (800) 659-7469
Fax: (703) 278-8082 E-mail: jhardwick@infocomm.org
Web: www.infocomm.org

Summary To provide financial assistance to undergraduate and graduate students (particularly African Americans, other minorities, and women) who are interested in preparing for a career in the audiovisual (AV) industry.

Eligibility This program is open to second-year students at 2-year colleges, juniors and seniors at 4-year institutions, and graduate students. Applicants must have a GPA of 2.75 or higher and be majoring or planning to major in audiovisual subjects or related fields, including audio, video, audiovisual, radio/television/film, or other field related to a career in the audiovisual industry. Students in other programs, such as journalism, may be eligible if they can demonstrate a relationship to career goals in the AV industry. Along with their application, they must submit 1) an essay of 150 to 200 words on the career path they plan to pursue in the audiovisual industry in the next 5 years; and 2) an essay of 250 to 300 words on the experience or person influencing them the most in selecting the audiovisual industry as their career of choice. Minority and women candidates are especially encouraged to apply. Selection is based on the essays, presentation of the application, GPA, AV-related experience, work experience, and letters of recommendation.

Financial data The stipend is $4,000. Funds are sent directly to the school.

Duration 1 year.

Additional information InfoComm International, formerly the International Communications Industries Association, established the International Communications Industries Foundation (ICIF) to manage its charitable and educational activities.

Number awarded Varies each year.

Deadline April of each year.

[1011] SCHWABE, WILLIAMSON & WYATT SUMMER ASSOCIATE DIVERSITY SCHOLARSHIP

Schwabe, Williamson & Wyatt, Attorneys at Law
Attn: Attorney Recruiting Administrator
1211 S.W. Fifth Avenue, Suite 1500-2000
Portland, OR 97204
(503) 796-2889 Fax: (503) 796-2900
E-mail: dcphillips@schwabe.com
Web: www.schwabe.com/recruitdiversity.aspx

Summary To provide financial aid and summer work experience in Portland, Oregon or Seattle, Washington to African American and other law students who will contribute to the diversity of the legal profession.

Eligibility This program is open to first-year students working on a J.D. degree at an ABA-accredited law school. Applicants must 1) contribute to the diversity of the law school student body and the legal community; 2) possess a record of academic achievement, capacity, and leadership as an undergraduate and in law school that indicates promise for a successful career in the legal profession; and 3) demonstrate a commitment to practice law in the Pacific Northwest upon completion of law school. They must be interested in a paid summer associateship at the sponsoring law firm's office in Portland, Oregon or Seattle, Washington. Along with their application, they must submit a resume, undergraduate and law school transcripts, a legal writing sample, and a 1- to 2-page personal statement explaining their interest in the scholarship and how they will contribute to diversity in the legal community.

Financial data The program provides a paid summer associateship during the summer following completion of the first year of law school and an academic scholarship of $7,500 to help pay tuition and other expenses during the recipient's second year of law school.

Duration 1 year.

Number awarded 1 each year.

Deadline January of each year.

[1012] SCOTT AND PAUL PEARSALL SCHOLARSHIP

American Psychological Foundation
750 First Street, N.E.
Washington, DC 20002-4242
(202) 336-5843 Fax: (202) 336-5812
E-mail: foundation@apa.org
Web: www.apa.org/apf/funding/pearsall.aspx

Summary To provide funding to graduate students (particularly African Americans, other minorities, and students with disabilities) who are interested in conducting research on the psychological effect of stigma on people with disabilities.

Eligibility This program is open to full-time graduate students at accredited universities in the United States and Canada. Applicants must be interested in conducting research that seeks to increase the public's understanding of the psychological pain and stigma experiences by adults living with physical disabilities, such as cerebral palsy. Selection is based on conformance with stated program goals and the quality of proposed work. The sponsor encourages applications from individuals who represent diversity in race, ethnicity, gender, age, disability, and sexual orientation.

Financial data The grant is $10,000.

Duration 1 year.

Additional information This program began in 2013.

Number awarded 1 each year.

Deadline September of each year.

[1013] SCOVEL RICHARDSON SCHOLARSHIP

Mound City Bar Association
Attn: Scholarship Committee
P.O. Box 1543
St. Louis, MO 63188
E-mail: president@moundcitybar.com
Web: www.moundcitybar.com/scholarship.html

Summary To provide financial assistance to African American and other minority law students who have limited financial resources.

Eligibility This program is open to minority students entering the second or third year of law school. Applicants must be able to demonstrate financial need and a record of community service and leadership. Along with their application, they must submit a short autobiographical sketch, including the individuals and/or events that have helped to shape their life, their short- and long-term career goals, and the contributions they would like to make to create a better community. Special consideration is given to students who plan to live and work in the greater St. Louis metropolitan area.

Financial data The stipend ranges up to $7,000.

Duration 1 year.

Additional information The Mound City Bar Association was established in 1922 as the St. Louis Negro Bar Association. It established this program is help create a judiciary that is more responsive and accountable to African Americans and other minorities.

Number awarded 1 or more each year.

Deadline April of each year.

[1014] SELECTED PROFESSIONS FELLOWSHIPS FOR WOMEN OF COLOR

American Association of University Women
Attn: AAUW Educational Foundation
301 ACT Drive, Department 60
P.O. Box 4030
Iowa City, IA 52243-4030
(319) 337-1716, ext. 60 Fax: (319) 337-1204
E-mail: aauw@act.org
Web: www.aauw.org

Summary To provide financial assistance to African American and other women of color who are in their final year of graduate training in the fields of business administration, law, or medicine.

Eligibility This program is open to women who are working full time on a degree in fields in which women of color have been historically underrepresented: business administration (M.B.A.), law (J.D.), or medicine (M.D., D.O.). They must be African Americans, Mexican Americans, Puerto Ricans and other Hispanics, Native Americans, Alaska Natives, Asian Americans, or Pacific Islanders. U.S. citizenship or permanent resident status is required. Applicants in business administration must be entering their second year of study; applicants in law must be entering their third year of study; applicants in medicine may be entering their third or fourth year of study. Special consideration is given to applicants who 1) demonstrate their intent to enter professional practice in disciplines in which women are underrepresented, to serve underserved populations and communities, or to pursue public interest areas; and 2) are nontraditional students. Selection is based on professional promise and personal attributes (50%), academic excellence and related academic success indicators (40%), and financial need (10%).

Financial data Stipends range from $5,000 to $18,000.

Duration 1 academic year, beginning in September.

Additional information The filing fee is $35.

Number awarded Varies each year; recently, a total of 25 Selected Professions Fellowships were awarded.

Deadline January of each year.

[1015] SEMICONDUCTOR RESEARCH CORPORATION MASTER'S SCHOLARSHIP PROGRAM

Semiconductor Research Corporation
Attn: Global Research Collaboration
1101 Slater Road, Suite 120
P.O. Box 12053
Research Triangle Park, NC 27709-2053
(919) 941-9400 Fax: (919) 941-9450
E-mail: students@src.org
Web: www.src.org/student-center/fellowship

Summary To provide financial assistance to African Americans, other minorities, and women who are interested in working on a master's degree in a field of microelectronics relevant to the interests of the Semiconductor Research Corporation (SRC).

Eligibility This program is open to women and members of underrepresented minority groups (African Americans, Hispanics, and Native Americans). Applicants must be U.S. citizens or have permanent resident, refugee, or political asylum status in the United States. They must be admitted to an SRC participating university to work on a master's degree in a field relevant to microelectronics under the guidance of an SRC-sponsored faculty member and under an SRC-funded contract. Selection is based on academic achievement.

Financial data The fellowship provides full tuition and fee support, a competitive stipend (recently, $2,186 per month), an annual grant of $2,000 to the university department with which the student recipient is associated, and travel expenses to the Graduate Fellowship Program Annual Conference.

Duration Up to 2 years.

Additional information This program began in 1997 for underrepresented minorities and expanded to include women in 1999.

Number awarded Approximately 12 each year.

Deadline February of each year.

[1016]
SHERRY R. ARNSTEIN MINORITY STUDENT SCHOLARSHIP

American Association of Colleges of Osteopathic Medicine
Attn: Scholarships
5550 Friendship Boulevard, Suite 310
Chevy Chase, MD 20815-7231
(301) 968-4142 Fax: (301) 968-4101
Web: www.aacom.org

Summary To provide financial assistance to African American and other underrepresented minority students already enrolled in osteopathic medical school.

Eligibility This program is open to African American, mainland Puerto Rican, Hispanic, Native American, Native Hawaiian, and Alaska Native students currently enrolled in good standing in their first, second, or third year of osteopathic medical school. Applicants must submit a 750-word essay on what osteopathic medical schools can do to recruit and retain more underrepresented minority students, what they personally plan to do as a student and as a future D.O. to help increase minority student enrollment at a college of osteopathic medicine, and how and why they were drawn to osteopathic medicine.

Financial data The stipend is $2,500.

Duration 1 year; nonrenewable.

Number awarded 1 each year.

Deadline March of each year.

[1017]
SHERRY R. ARNSTEIN NEW STUDENT MINORITY STUDENT SCHOLARSHIP

American Association of Colleges of Osteopathic Medicine
Attn: Scholarships
5550 Friendship Boulevard, Suite 310
Chevy Chase, MD 20815-7231
(301) 968-4142 Fax: (301) 968-4101
Web: www.aacom.org

Summary To provide financial assistance to African American and other underrepresented minority students planning to enroll at an osteopathic medical school.

Eligibility This program is open to African American, mainland Puerto Rican, Hispanic, Native American, Native Hawaiian, and Alaska Native students who have been accepted and are planning to enroll as a first-time student at any of the colleges of osteopathic medicine that are members of the American Association of Colleges of Osteopathic Medicine (AACOM). Applicants must submit a 750-word essay on what osteopathic medical schools can do to recruit and retain more underrepresented minority students, what they personally plan to do as a student and as a future D.O. to help increase minority student enrollment at a college of osteopathic medicine, and how and why they were drawn to osteopathic medicine.

Financial data The stipend is $2,500.

Duration 1 year; nonrenewable.

Number awarded 1 each year.

Deadline March of each year.

[1018]
SHIRLEY DELIBERO SCHOLARSHIP

American Public Transportation Association
Attn: American Public Transportation Foundation
1666 K Street, N.W., Suite 1100
Washington, DC 20006
(202) 496-4803 Fax: (202) 496-4323
E-mail: yconley@apta.com
Web: www.aptfd.org/work/scholarship.htm

Summary To provide financial assistance to African American undergraduate and graduate students who are preparing for a career in the public transportation industry.

Eligibility This program is open to African American sophomores, juniors, seniors, and graduate students who are preparing for a career in the transit industry. Any member organization of the American Public Transportation Association (APTA) can nominate and sponsor candidates for this scholarship. Nominees must be enrolled in a fully-accredited institution, have and maintain at least a 3.0 GPA, and be either employed by or demonstrate a strong interest in entering the business administration or management area of the public transportation industry. They must submit a 1,000-word essay on the topic, "In what segment of the public transportation industry will you make a career and why?" Selection is based on demonstrated interest in the transit field as a career, need for financial assistance, academic achievement, essay content and quality, and involvement in extracurricular citizenship and leadership activities.

Financial data The stipend is $2,500.

Duration 1 year; may be renewed.

Number awarded 1 each year.

Deadline May of each year.

[1019]
SIDLEY DIVERSITY AND INCLUSION SCHOLARSHIP

Sidley Austin LLP
Attn: Scholarships
One South Dearborn Street
Chicago, IL 60603
(312) 853-7000 Fax: (312) 853-7036
E-mail: scholarship@sidley.com
Web: www.sidley.com

Summary To provide financial aid and work experience to African American and other law students who come from a diverse background.

Eligibility The program is open to students entering their second year of law school; preference is given to students at schools where the sponsor conducts on-campus interviews or participates in a resume collection. Applicants must have a demonstrated ability to contribute meaningfully to the diversity of the law school and/or legal profession. Along with their application, they must submit a 500-word essay that includes their thoughts on and efforts to improve diversity, how they might contribute to the sponsor's commitment to improving diversity, and their interest in practicing law at a global firm (specifically the sponsor). Selection is based on academic achievement and leadership qualities.

Financial data The stipend is $15,000.

Duration 1 year.

Additional information These scholarships were first offered in 2011. Recipients are expected to participate in the sponsor's summer associate program following their second year of law school. They must apply separately for the associate position. The firm has offices in Chicago, Dallas, Los Angeles, New York, Palo Alto, San Francisco, and Washington, D.C.

Number awarded A limited number are awarded each year.

Deadline August of each year.

[1020]
SIDNEY B. WILLIAMS, JR. INTELLECTUAL PROPERTY LAW SCHOOL SCHOLARSHIPS

Thurgood Marshall College Fund
4801 Woodway, Suite 300 E
Houston, TX 77056
(713) 574-4923 Fax: (480) 287-9632
E-mail: misha.lesley@tmcfund.org
Web: www.thurgoodmarshallcollegefund.org

Summary To provide financial assistance to African American and other underrepresented minority law school students who are interested in preparing for a career in intellectual property law.

Eligibility This program is open to members of underrepresented minority groups currently enrolled in or accepted to an ABA-accredited law school. Applicants must be U.S. citizens with a demonstrated intent to engage in the full-time practice of intellectual property law. Along with their application, they must submit a 250-word essay on how this scholarship will make a difference to them in meeting their goal of engaging in the full-time practice of intellectual property law and why they intend to do so. Selection is based on 1) demonstrated commitment to developing a career in intellectual property law; 2) academic performance at the undergraduate, graduate, and law school levels (as applicable); 3) general factors, such as leadership skills, community activities, or special accomplishments; and 4) financial need.

Financial data The stipend is $10,000 per year. Funds may be used for tuition, fees, books, supplies, room, board, and a patent bar review course.

Duration 1 year; may be renewed if the recipient maintains a GPA of 2.0 or higher.

Additional information This program, which began in 2002, is administered by the Thurgood Marshall College Fund with support from the American Intellectual Property Law Education Foundation.

Number awarded Varies each year; recently, 12 of these scholarships were awarded.

Deadline March of each year.

[1021]
SIGMA GAMMA RHO SCHOLARSHIPS/ FELLOWSHIPS

Sigma Gamma Rho Sorority, Inc.
Attn: National Education Fund
1000 Southhill Drive, Suite 200
Cary, NC 27513
(919) 678-9720 Toll Free: (888) SGR-1922
Fax: (919) 678-9721 E-mail: info@sgrho1922.org
Web: www.sgrho1922.org/nef

Summary To provide financial assistance for undergraduate or graduate study to African American and other applicants who can demonstrate financial need.

Eligibility This program is open to high school seniors, undergraduates, and graduate students who can demonstrate financial need. The sponsor is a traditionally African American sorority, but support is available to males and females of all races. Applicants must have a GPA of "C" or higher.

Financial data A stipend is awarded (amount not specified).

Duration 1 year.

Additional information This program includes the following named awards: the Lorraine A. Williams Scholarship, the Philo Sallie A. Williams Scholarship, the Cleo W. Higgins Scholarship (limited to doctoral students), the Angela E. Randall Scholarship, the Inez Colson Memorial Scholarship (limited to students majoring in education or mathematics at Savannah State University), and the Philo Geneva Young Scholarship. A processing fee of $20 is required.

Number awarded Varies each year.

Deadline April of each year.

[1022]
SMITHSONIAN MINORITY AWARDS PROGRAM

Smithsonian Institution
Attn: Office of Fellowships and Internships
470 L'Enfant Plaza, Suite 7102
P.O. Box 37012, MRC 902
Washington, DC 20013-7012
(202) 633-7070 Fax: (202) 633-7069
E-mail: siofi@si.edu
Web: www.smithsonianofi.com

Summary To provide funding to African American and other minority undergraduate and graduate students who are interested in conducting research at the Smithsonian Institution.

Eligibility This program is open to members of U.S. minority groups underrepresented in the Smithsonian's scholarly programs. Applicants must be undergraduates or beginning graduate students interested in conducting research in the Institution's disciplines and in the museum field. They must be U.S. citizens or permanent residents and have a GPA of 3.0 or higher.

Financial data Students receive a grant of $600 per week.

Duration Up to 10 weeks.

Additional information Recipients must carry out independent research projects in association with the Smithsonian's research staff. Eligible fields of study currently include animal behavior, ecology, and environmental science (including an emphasis on the tropics); anthropology (including archaeology); astrophysics and astronomy; earth sciences and paleobiology; evolutionary and systematic biology; history of science and technology; history of art (especially American, contemporary, African, Asian, and 20th-century art); American crafts and decorative arts; social and cultural history of the United States; and folk life. Students are required to be in residence at the Smithsonian for the duration of the fellowship.

Number awarded Varies each year; recently, 25 of these awards were granted: 2 for fall, 19 for summer, and 4 for spring.

Deadline January of each year for summer and fall residency; September of each year for spring residency.

[1023]
SOCIETY OF PEDIATRIC PSYCHOLOGY DIVERSITY RESEARCH GRANT

American Psychological Association
Attn: Division 54 (Society of Pediatric Psychology)
c/o Anna Maria Patino-Fernandez
University of Miami School of Medicine
Mailman Center for Child Development
Division of Clinical Psychology
1601 N.W. 12th Avenue, 4018B
Miami, FL 33136-1005
(305) 243-6837 Fax: (305) 243-8470
E-mail: Apatino-fernandez@med.miami.edu
Web: www.apadivisions.org

Summary To provide funding to graduate student and post-doctoral members of the Society of Pediatric Psychology (particularly African Americans and others who come from diverse backgrounds) who are interested in conducting research on diversity aspects of pediatric psychology.

Eligibility This program is open to current members of the society who are graduate students, fellows, or early-career (within 3 years of appointment) faculty. Applicants must be interested in conducting pediatric psychology research that features diversity-related variables, such as race or ethnicity, gender, culture, sexual orientation, language differences, socioeconomic status, and/or religiosity. Along with their application, they must submit a 2,000-word description of the project, including its purpose, methodology, predictions, and implications; a detailed budget; a current curriculum vitae, and (for students) a curriculum vitae of the faculty research mentor and a letter of support from that mentor. Selection is based on relevance to diversity in child health (5 points), significance of the study (5 points), study methods and procedures (10 points), and investigator qualifications (10 points).

Financial data Grants up to $1,000 are available. Funds may not be used for convention or meeting travel, indirect costs, stipends of principal investigators, or costs associated with manuscript preparation.

Duration The grant is presented annually.

Additional information The Society of Pediatric Psychology is Division 54 of the American Psychological Association (APA). This grant was first presented in 2008.

Number awarded 1 each year.

Deadline September of each year.

[1024]
SOUTH CAROLINA GRADUATE INCENTIVE SCHOLARSHIP PROGRAM

South Carolina Commission on Higher Education
Attn: Student Services
1122 Lady Street, Suite 300
Columbia, SC 29201
(803) 737-2262 Toll Free: (877) 349-7183
Fax: (803) 737-2297 E-mail: ecaulder@che.sc.gov
Web: www.che.sc.gov/AccessEquity/GISInfoCtr.htm

Summary To provide funding to African American and other graduate students who are preparing for careers as college teachers in South Carolina.

Eligibility This program is open to historically underrepresented students, defined as African Americans at traditionally white public institutions in South Carolina and whites at traditionally Black public institutions in the state. Applicants must be U.S. citizens and accepted for admission or enrolled in a doctoral program, a terminal degree program in the fine or applied arts, a first professional level degree program, or a master's degree program. Students in master's and professional degree programs must also be South Carolina residents; students in doctoral and terminal arts degree programs may be residents of any state, but preference is given to South Carolina residents. All applicants must be studying or planning to study in designated academic or professional areas in which overall shortages exist in South Carolina or areas in which Black residents are underrepresented.

Financial data The stipend is $7,500 per year for full-time master's degree students or $15,000 per year for full-time doctoral and certain first-year professional students. Stipends for part-time students are prorated accordingly. This is a forgivable loan program; for each year of full-time employment in South Carolina in the designated shortage area following graduation, up to $5,000 of the total amount borrowed will be forgiven. Requests for forgiveness must be submitted to the respective institution within 6 months following the recipient's graduation. Otherwise, the full amount of the loan must be repaid within 5 years at 8% interest.

Duration 1 year; may be renewed if the recipient maintains satisfactory academic standing and continued enrollment in an eligible program.

Additional information The participating institutions are Clemson University, Medical University of South Carolina, University of South Carolina, University of South Carolina School of Medicine, College of Charleston, The Citadel, Winthrop University, South Carolina State University, and Francis Marion University. Information on the program and applications are available from the financial aid office of the institution.

Number awarded Varies each year.

Deadline Each participating institution sets its own deadline.

[1025]
SOUTHERN REGIONAL EDUCATION BOARD DISSERTATION AWARDS

Southern Regional Education Board
Attn: Coordinator, Program and Scholar Services
592 Tenth Street N.W.
Atlanta, GA 30318-5776
(404) 879-5569 Fax: (404) 872-1477
E-mail: doctoral.scholars@sreb.org
Web: www.sreb.org/page/1113/types_of_awards.html

Summary To provide funding to African American and other minority students who wish to complete a Ph.D. dissertation, especially in the fields of science, technology, engineering, or mathematics (STEM), while in residence at a university in the southern states.

Eligibility This program is open to U.S. citizens and permanent residents who are members of racial/ethnic minority groups (Native Americans, Hispanic Americans, Asian Americans, and African Americans) and have completed all requirements for a Ph.D. except the dissertation. Applicants must be enrolled at a designated college or university in the following 10 states: Alabama, Arkansas, Georgia, Kentucky, Louisiana, Mississippi, South Carolina, Tennessee, Virginia, West Virginia. Enrollment at a graduate school in 5 of those states (Georgia, Mississippi, South Carolina, Tennessee, and Virginia) is available only to residents of those states. Residents of any state in the country may attend a university in the other 5 states. Preference is given to students in STEM disciplines with particularly low minority representation, although all academic fields are eligible. Applicants must be in a position to write full time and must expect to complete their dissertation within the year of the fellowship. Eligibility is limited to individuals who plan to become full-time faculty members at a college or university upon completion of their doctoral degree. The program is not open to students working on other doctoral degrees (e.g., M.D., D.B.A., D.D.S., J.D., D.V.M., Ed.D., Pharm.D., D.N.P., D.P.T.).

Financial data Fellows receive waiver of tuition and fees (in or out of state), a stipend of $20,000, a $500 research allowance, and reimbursement of expenses for attending the Compact for Faculty Diversity's annual Institute on Teaching and Mentoring.

Duration 1 year; nonrenewable.

Additional information This program began in 1993 as part of the Compact for Faculty Diversity, supported by the Pew Charitable Trusts and the Ford Foundation. It currently operates at universities in 10 of the member states of the Southern Regional Education Board (SREB): Alabama, Arkansas, Georgia, Kentucky, Louisiana, Mississippi, South Carolina, Tennessee, Virginia, and West Virginia; the other 6 member states (Delaware, Florida, Maryland, North Carolina, Oklahoma, and Texas) do not participate.

Number awarded Varies each year.

Deadline March of each year.

[1026]
SPIE SCHOLARSHIP PROGRAM

SPIE-The International Society for Optical Engineering
Attn: Scholarship Committee
1000 20th Street
P.O. Box 10
Bellingham, WA 98227-0010
(360) 676-3290 Toll Free: (888) 504-8171
Fax: (360) 647-1445 E-mail: scholarships@spie.org
Web: spie.org/x7236.xml

Summary To provide financial assistance to entering or continuing undergraduate and graduate student members of SPIE-The International Society for Optical Engineering (particularly African Americans, other minorities, women, and veterans) who are preparing for a career in optical science or engineering.

Eligibility This program is open to high school seniors planning to attend college, current undergraduate students, and current graduate students. Applicants must be society members majoring or planning to enroll full or part time and major in optics, optoelectronics, photonics, imaging, or a related discipline (e.g., physics, electrical engineering) at a college or university anywhere in the world. Along with their application, they must submit a 500-word essay on their academic work, career objectives, how this scholarship would help them attain their goals, and what they have achieved and learned through their studies and activities. Financial need is not considered in the selection process. Women, minorities, and veterans are encouraged to apply.

Financial data Stipends range from $2,000 to $11,000. Special awards include the D.J. Lovell Scholarship at $11,000; the John Kiel Scholarship at $10,000; the Laser Technology, Engineering, and Applications Scholarship at $5,000; the Optical Design and Engineering Scholarship at $5,000, and the BACUS Scholarship at $5,000.

Duration 1 year.

Additional information The International Society for Optical Engineering was founded in 1955 as the Society of Photo-Optical Instrumentation Engineers (SPIE). This program includes the following special named scholarships: the D.J. Lovell Scholarship, sponsored by SPIE (the most prestigious of the scholarships); the John Kiel Scholarship, awarded for a student's potential for long-term contribution to the field of optics and optical engineering; the Optical Design and Engineering Scholarship in Optical Engineering, established to honor Bill Price and Warren Smith and awarded to a full-time graduate or undergraduate student in the field of optical design and engineering; the Laser Technology, Engineering, and Applications Scholarship (formerly the F-MADE Scholarship), sponsored by the Forum for Military Applications of Directed Energy (F-MADE) in recognition of a student's scholarly achievement in laser technology, engineering, or applications; and the BACUS Scholarship, awarded to a full-time undergraduate or graduate student in the field of microlithography with an emphasis on optical tooling and/or semiconductor manufacturing technologies, sponsored by BACUS (SPIE's photomask international technical group).

Number awarded Varies each year; recently, this program awarded 140 scholarships with a value of $353,000. Since the program was established, it has awarded more than $3.8 million to nearly 2,000 students in 86 countries.

Deadline February of each year.

[1027]
SREB DOCTORAL AWARDS

Southern Regional Education Board
Attn: Coordinator, Program and Scholar Services
592 Tenth Street N.W.
Atlanta, GA 30318-5776
(404) 879-5569 Fax: (404) 872-1477
E-mail: doctoral.scholars@sreb.org
Web: www.sreb.org/page/1113/types_of_awards.html

Summary To provide financial assistance to African American and other minority students who wish to work on a doctoral degree, especially in fields of science, technology, engineering, or mathematics (STEM), at designated universities in the southern states.

Eligibility This program is open to U.S. citizens and permanent residents who are members of racial/ethnic minority groups (Native Americans, Hispanic Americans, Asian Americans, and African Americans) and have or will receive a bachelor's or master's degree. Applicants must be entering or enrolled in the first year of a Ph.D. program at a designated college or university in the following 10 states: Alabama, Arkansas, Georgia, Kentucky, Louisiana, Mississippi, South Carolina, Tennessee, Virginia, West Virginia. Enrollment at a graduate school in 5 of those states (Georgia, Mississippi,

South Carolina, Tennessee, and Virginia) is available only to residents of those states. Residents of any state in the country may attend a university in the other 5 states. Applicants must indicate an interest in becoming a full-time college or university professor. The program does not support students working on other doctoral degrees (e.g., M.D., D.B.A., D.D.S., J.D., D.V.M., Ed.D., Pharm.D., D.N.P., D.P.T.). Preference is given to applicants in STEM disciplines with particularly low minority representation, although all academic fields are eligible.

Financial data Scholars receive a waiver of tuition and fees (in or out of state) for up to 5 years, an annual stipend of $20,000 for 3 years, an annual allowance of $500 for research and professional development activities, and reimbursement of travel expenses to attend the Compact for Faculty Diversity's annual Institute on Teaching and Mentoring.

Duration Up to 5 years.

Additional information This program began in 1993 as part of the Compact for Faculty Diversity, supported by the Pew Charitable Trusts and the Ford Foundation.

Number awarded Varies each year; recently, the program was supporting more than 300 scholars.

Deadline March year.

[1028]
SSSP RACIAL/ETHNIC MINORITY GRADUATE SCHOLARSHIP

Society for the Study of Social Problems
Attn: Executive Officer
University of Tennessee
901 McClung Tower
Knoxville, TN 37996-0490
(865) 689-1531 Fax: (865) 689-1534
E-mail: sssp@utk.edu
Web: www.sssp1.org

Summary To provide funding to African American and other minority members of the Society for the Study of Social Problems (SSSP) who are interested in conducting research for their doctoral dissertation.

Eligibility This program is open to SSSP members who are Black or African American, Hispanic or Latino, Asian or Asian American, Native Hawaiian or other Pacific Islander, or American Indian or Alaska Native. Applicants must have completed all requirements for a Ph.D. (course work, examinations, and approval of a dissertation prospectus) except the dissertation. They must have a GPA of 3.25 or higher and be able to demonstrate financial need. Their field of study may be any of the social and/or behavioral sciences that will enable them to expand their perspectives in the investigation into social problems. U.S. citizenship or permanent resident status is required.

Financial data The stipend is $12,000. Additional grants provide $500 for the recipient to 1) attend the SSSP annual meeting prior to the year of the work to receive the award; and 2) attend the meeting after the year of the award to present a report on the work completed.

Duration 1 year.

Number awarded 1 each year.

Deadline January of each year.

[1029]
ST. PHILIP'S EPISCOPAL CHURCH/ABSALOM JONES SCHOLARSHIP FUND

St. Philip's Episcopal Church
Attn: Absalom Jones Scholarship Selection Committee
522 Main Street
Laurel, MD 20707-4118
(301) 776-5151 Fax: (301) 776-6337
E-mail: absalomjonesfund@stphilipslaurel.org
Web: www.stphilipslaurel.org/about/ministries

Summary To provide financial assistance to African American and other undergraduate and graduate students at schools in any state who have a tie to the Episcopal Diocese of Washington, D.C.

Eligibility This program is open to students who reside, work, attend school, or are members of a parish in the Episcopal Diocese of Washington. Applicants must be attending or planning to attend a college, seminary, or vocational/technical institute in any state as an undergraduate or graduate student. They must be able to demonstrate the qualities for which Absalom Jones, the first African American priest in the Episcopal Church, was noted: compassion, service, leadership, and an emphasis on education. Financial need is considered in the selection process.

Financial data The stipend is $1,000.

Duration 1 year.

Additional information The Episcopal Diocese of Washington serves the District of Columbia and the Maryland counties of Charles, St. Mary's, Prince George's, and Montgomery.

Number awarded 2 each year.

Deadline April of each year.

[1030]
STAN BECK FELLOWSHIP

Entomological Society of America
Attn: Entomological Foundation
9332 Annapolis Road, Suite 210
Lanham, MD 20706-3150
(301) 459-9082 Fax: (301) 459-9084
E-mail: melodie@entfdn.org
Web: www.entfdn.org/awards_education.php

Summary To assist minority and other "needy" students working on an undergraduate or graduate degree in entomology who are nominated by members of the Entomological Society of America (ESA).

Eligibility This program is open to students working on an undergraduate or graduate degree in entomology at a college or university in Canada, Mexico, or the United States. Candidates must be nominated by members of the society. They must be "needy" students; for the purposes of this program, need may be based on physical limitations, or economic, minority, or environmental conditions.

Financial data The stipend is $2,000 per year.

Duration 1 year; may be renewed up to 3 additional years.

Additional information This fellowship was first awarded in 1996. Recipients are expected to be present at the society's annual meeting, where the award will be presented.

Number awarded 1 each year.

Deadline June of each year.

[1031]
STANLEY J. TARVER MEMORIAL SCHOLARSHIP FUND

Community Foundations of the Hudson Valley
Attn: Scholarship Committee
80 Washington Street, Suite 201
Poughkeepsie, NY 12601
(845) 452-3077 Fax: (845) 452-3083
E-mail: cfhv@cfhvny.org
Web: www.cfdcny.org/page31379.cfm

Summary To provide financial assistance to students of African descent who are working on a graduate degree in African history and/or culture.

Eligibility This program is open to graduate students of African descent, including African Americans and Black people of other nationalities. Applicants must be working on a master's or doctorate degree in African history and/or culture and have completed at least 1 year of graduate study at a college or university in the United States. Along with their application, they must submit a 500-word essay on their interest, project, and activities in African history and/or culture.

Financial data The stipend is $2,000.

Duration 1 year; nonrenewable.

Additional information This program began in 1994.

Number awarded 1 each year.

Deadline March of each year.

[1032]
STAR FELLOWSHIPS FOR GRADUATE ENVIRONMENTAL STUDY

Environmental Protection Agency
Attn: National Center for Environmental Research
Ariel Rios Building
1200 Pennsylvania Avenue, N.W.
Washington, DC 20460
(202) 343-9850 Toll Free: (800) 490-9194
E-mail: jones.brandon@epa.gov
Web: www.epa.gov/careers/fellowships

Summary To provide financial support to graduate students (particularly African Americans, other minorities, women, and students with disabilities) who are planning to obtain advanced degrees and prepare for a career in environmentally-related fields.

Eligibility Applicants must be U.S. citizens or permanent residents enrolled or accepted for enrollment at an accredited U.S. college or university. They must be interested in working on a master's or doctoral degree, in the United States or abroad, in an environmentally-related field of specialization. Relevant fields of study include ecology, economics, engineering, modeling, the health sciences, physical sciences, earth sciences, exposure sciences, social sciences, informational sciences, mathematical and computer sciences, and environmental sciences; applications are also welcome from students who have not participated in traditional environmental conversations or research, especially those that attend Minority Academic Institutions. Selection is based on demonstrated commitment to an environmental career, potential for success in the proposed area of inquiry, and potential for their proposal to have broader societal impacts. The program strongly encourages women, minorities, and persons with disabilities to apply. At least 10% of the awards are reserved for students at Minority Academic Institutions, defined as Historically Black Colleges and Universities, Tribal Colleges and Universities, Hispanic Serving Institutions, and Asian American and Native Pacific Islander-Serving Institutions.

Financial data The total award is $42,000 per year, including a student stipend of $25,000 (paid at the rate of $2,083 per month for 12 months), an expense allowance of $5,000, and an allowance of up to $12,000 for tuition and fees paid directly to the institution.

Duration Up to 2 years for master's students; up to 3 years for doctoral students, usable over a period of 5 years.

Additional information This program, which began in 1995, is the graduate student component of the Science to Achieve Results (STAR) program of the Environmental Protection Agency. Fellows may conduct research outside the United States, but no additional funding is provided for foreign travel or other expenses.

Number awarded Approximately 80 each year, of which 8 are reserved for students at Minority Academic Institutions.

Deadline November of each year.

[1033]
STAR SUPPORTER SCHOLARSHIP/LOAN

Christian Church (Disciples of Christ)
Attn: Disciples Home Missions
130 East Washington Street
P.O. Box 1986
Indianapolis, IN 46206-1986
(317) 713-2652 Toll Free: (888) DHM-2631
Fax: (317) 635-4426 E-mail: mail@dhm.disciples.org
Web: www.discipleshomemissions.org

Summary To provide funding to African Americans interested in preparing for a career in the ministry of the Christian Church (Disciples of Christ).

Eligibility This program is open to African American seminary students who are members of a Christian Church (Disciples of Christ) congregation in the United States or Canada. Applicants must plan to prepare for the ordained ministry, be working on an M.Div. or equivalent degree, provide evidence of financial need, be enrolled full time in an accredited school or seminary, provide a transcript of academic work, and be under the care of a regional Commission on the Ministry or in the process of coming under care.

Financial data Recipients are awarded these funds with 2 methods of repayment: 1) the amount of the scholarship/loan must be repaid in cash (with 6% interest, beginning 3 months after leaving school) if the recipient does not enter the ministry; or 2) the amount of the scholarship/loan is reduced by one-third for each year of full-time professional ministry performed by the recipient, so that 3 years of service cancels the entire amount.

Duration 1 year; may be renewed.

Additional information Recipients must sign a promissory note.

Number awarded Varies each year.

Deadline March of each year.

[1034]
STOEL RIVES FIRST-YEAR DIVERSITY FELLOWSHIPS

Stoel Rives LLP
Attn: Lawyer Recruiting Manager
900 S.W. Fifth Avenue, Suite 2600
Portland, OR 97204
(503) 224-3380 Fax: (503) 220-2480
E-mail: portlandfellowship@stoel.com
Web: www.stoel.com/diversity.aspx?Show=2805

Summary To provide financial aid for law school and work experience to law students who bring diversity to the profession and are interested in a summer associate position with Stoel Rives.

Eligibility This program is open to first-year law students who contribute to the diversity of the student body at their law school and who will contribute to the diversity of the legal community. Diverse students include those who are American Indian or Alaskan Native, Asian, Black or African American, Hispanic or Latino, Native Hawaiian or other Pacific Islander, disabled, or LGBT. Applicants must be willing to accept a summer associate position at Stoel Rives offices in designated communities. Selection is based on academic excellence, leadership, community service, interest in practicing in the Pacific Northwest, and financial need.

Financial data The program provides a stipend of $7,500 to help defray expenses of law school and a salaried summer associate position.

Duration 1 year.

Additional information This program began in 2004. The firm has offices in Anchorage, Boise, Lake Tahoe, Minneapolis, Portland, Sacramento, Salt Lake City, San Diego, San Francisco, Seattle, and Vancouver.

Number awarded At least 2 each year.

Deadline January of each year.

[1035]
STUDENT AFFILIATES IN SCHOOL PSYCHOLOGY DIVERSITY SCHOLARSHIPS

American Psychological Association
Attn: Division 16 (School Psychology)
750 First Street, N.E.
Washington, DC 20002-4242
(202) 336-6165 Fax: (202) 218-3599
TDD: (202) 336-6123 E-mail: cchambers@apa.org
Web: www.apadivisions.org/division-16/awards/index.aspx

Summary To provide financial assistance to graduate student members of the Student Affiliates in School Psychology (SASP) of Division 16 (School Psychology) of the American Psychological Association (APA) who are African Americans or from other underrepresented cultural backgrounds.

Eligibility This program is open to SASP members who come from underrepresented cultural backgrounds. Applicants must be working on a graduate degree to prepare for a career as a school psychologist. Awards are available to both incoming students (entering their first or second year of graduate study) and advanced students (entering their third, fourth, or fifth year of graduate study).

Financial data The stipend is $1,000.

Duration 1 year; nonrenewable.

Number awarded 2 each year: 1 to an incoming student and 1 to an advanced student.

Deadline Deadline not specified.

[1036]
SUMMER RESEARCH OPPORTUNITY PROGRAM IN PATHOLOGY

American Society for Investigative Pathology
Attn: Executive Officer
9650 Rockville Pike, Suite E133
Bethesda, MD 20814-3993
(301) 634-7130 Fax: (301) 634-7990
E-mail: asip@asip.org
Web: www.asip.org/awards/sropp.cfm

Summary To provide an opportunity for African Americans and members of other underrepresented minority groups to participate in a summer research program in pathology.

Eligibility This program is open to students who are members of underrepresented minority groups. Applicants must be interested in visiting prominent research laboratories and institutions during the summer to learn and participate in new research in the mechanisms of disease. To qualify for additional funding, they must select a pathology mentor.

Financial data The program provides 1) a travel and living allowance to cover airfare, ground transportation, meals, housing, and related expenses incurred during the summer research program; 2) a grant up to $1,650 to provide travel support to submit and present an abstract at the Experimental Biology meeting; and 3) for students who select a pathology mentor, a supplemental grant of $2,500 to cover travel and subsistence.

Additional information This program operates as a component of the Minority Access to Research Careers (MARC) program of the Federation of American Societies for Experimental Biology (FASEB), funded by the National Institute of General Medical Sciences of the National Institutes of Health. Additional support is provided by the Intersociety Council for Pathology Information, Inc.

Number awarded Varies each year; recently, 6 of these grants were awarded.

Deadline Deadline not specified.

[1037]
SUNY GRADUATE DIVERSITY FELLOWSHIP PROGRAM

State University of New York
Attn: Office of Diversity, Equity and Inclusion
State University Plaza
353 Broadway
Albany, NY 12246
(518) 320-1189
Web: www.suny.edu/provost/odee/programs.cfm

Summary To provide financial assistance to African Americans and other graduate students at campuses of the State University of New York (SUNY) who will contribute to the diversity of the student body.

Eligibility This program is open to U.S. citizens and permanent residents who are entering or enrolled full-time graduate or professional students at any of the participating SUNY colleges. Applicants must be able to demonstrate how they will contribute to the diversity of the student body for the program for which they are applying, including having overcome a disadvantage or other impediment to success in higher education. Economic disadvantage, although not a requirement, may be the basis for eligibility. Membership in a racial or ethnic group that is underrepresented in the graduate or professional program involved may serve as a plus factor in making awards, but may not form the sole basis of selection. Awards are granted in the following priority order: 1) new graduate students who are being recruited but have not yet accepted admission to a graduate program; 2) Graduate Opportunity Waiver Program students who can be awarded a stipend to supplement their waiver to tuition; 3) currently-enrolled doctoral candidates who have completed all degree requirements except the dissertation; and 4) graduate assistants and teaching assistants who can receive a supplement to their current stipends to enhance their retention in graduate studies.

Financial data Stipends range from $7,500 to $10,000.

Duration 1 year; renewable.

Number awarded Varies each year; recently, this program awarded nearly $6 million in fellowships to 551 graduate students on 24 SUNY campuses. Of the recipients 38% were Latinos, 35% African Americans, 12% Whites, 6% Asians, and 6% Native Americans.

Deadline Deadline not specified.

[1038]
SUSAN M. JACKSON MINISTERIAL SCHOLARS FUND

Unitarian Universalist Association
Attn: Ministerial Credentialing Office
25 Beacon Street
Boston, MA 02108-2800
(617) 948-6403 Fax: (617) 742-2875
E-mail: mcoadministrator@uua.org
Web: www.uua.org

Summary To provide financial assistance to seminary students (particularly African Americans and other students of color) who are preparing for the Unitarian Universalist (UU) ministry and demonstrate enthusiasm about their faith.

Eligibility This program is open to seminary students who are enrolled full or at least half time in a UU ministerial training program with candidate status. Applicants must be citizens of the United States or Canada. They must be able to demonstrate their enthusiasm about Unitarian Universalist ideas and conclusions, drawn from their faith, that influence their lives. Priority is given first to those who have demonstrated outstanding ministerial ability and secondarily to students with the greatest financial need (especially persons of color).

Financial data The stipend ranges from $1,000 to $15,000 per year.

Duration 1 year.

Number awarded 1 each year.

Deadline April of each year.

[1039]
SYNOD OF LAKES AND PRAIRIES RACIAL ETHNIC SCHOLARSHIPS

Synod of Lakes and Prairies
Attn: Committee on Racial Ethnic Ministry
2115 Cliff Drive
Eagen, MN 55122-3327
(651) 357-1140 Toll Free: (800) 328-1880, ext. 202
Fax: (651) 357-1141 E-mail: mkes@lakesandprairies.org
Web: www.lakesandprairies.org

Summary To provide financial assistance to African American and other minority residents of the Presbyterian Church (USA) Synod of Lakes and Prairies who are working on an undergraduate or graduate degree at a college or seminary in any state in preparation for service to the church.

Eligibility This program is open to members of Presbyterian churches who reside within the Synod of Lakes and Prairies (Iowa, Minnesota, Nebraska, North Dakota, South Dakota, and Wisconsin). Applicants must be members of ethnic minority groups studying at least half time for service in the Presbyterian Church (USA) as a teaching elder, ordained minister, commissioned ruling elder, lay professional, or volunteer. They must be in good academic standing, making progress toward an undergraduate or graduate degree, and able to demonstrate financial need. Along with their application, they must submit essays of 200 to 500 words on 1) what the church needs to do to be faithful to its mission in the world today; and 2) the people, practices, or events that influence their commitment to Christ in ways that renew their fair and strengthen their service.

Financial data Stipends range from $850 to $3,500.

Duration 1 year.

Number awarded Varies each year; recently, 9 of these scholarships were awarded.

Deadline September of each year.

[1040]
SYNOD OF THE COVENANT ETHNIC THEOLOGICAL SCHOLARSHIPS

Synod of the Covenant
Attn: Ministries in Higher Education
1911 Indianwood Circle, Suite B
Maumee, OH 43537-4063
(419) 754-4050
Toll Free: (800) 848-1030 (within MI and OH)
Fax: (419) 754-4051
E-mail: SOC@synodofthecovenant.org
Web: www.synodofthecovenant.org

Summary To provide financial assistance to African American and other ethnic students working on a master's degree at an approved Presbyterian theological institution (with priority given to Presbyterian applicants from Ohio and Michigan).

Eligibility This program is open to ethnic individuals enrolled full time in church vocations programs at approved Presbyterian theological institutions. Priority is given to Presbyterian applicants from the states of Michigan and Ohio. Financial need is considered in the selection process.

Financial data Students may be awarded a maximum of $1,500 on initial application. They may receive up to $2,000 on subsequent applications, with evidence of continuing progress. Funds are made payable to the session for distribution.

Duration Students are eligible to receive scholarships 1 time per year, up to a maximum of 5 years.

Number awarded Varies each year.

Deadline August of each year.

[1041]
TDC SCHOLARSHIP

National Association of Black Accountants
Attn: National Scholarship Program
7474 Greenway Center Drive, Suite 1120
Greenbelt, MD 20770
(301) 474-NABA Fax: (301) 474-3114
E-mail: scholarships@nabainc.org
Web: www.nabainc.org

Summary To provide financial assistance to student members of the National Association of Black Accountants (NABA) who are working on an undergraduate or graduate degree in a field related to accounting.

Eligibility This program is open to minorities who are NABA members and enrolled full time as 1) an undergraduate freshman, sophomore, junior, or first-semester senior majoring in accounting, business, or finance at a 4-year college or university; or 2) a graduate student working on a master's degree in accounting. High school seniors are not eligible. Applicants must have a GPA of 2.0 or higher in their major and 2.5 or higher overall. Along with their application, they must submit a 500-word personal statement on their involvement in NABA, career objectives, leadership abilities, and community activities. Financial need is not considered in the selection process.

Financial data The stipend is $1,000.

Duration 1 year.

Number awarded 1 each year.

Deadline January of each year.

[1042]
TECHNICAL RESEARCH EXHIBITION AWARDS

National Society of Black Engineers
Attn: Programs Department
205 Daingerfield Road
Alexandria, VA 22314
(703) 549-2207 Fax: (703) 683-5312
E-mail: programs@nsbe.org
Web: www.nsbe.org

Summary To recognize and reward outstanding technical papers by undergraduate and graduate student members of the National Society of Black Engineers (NSBE).

Eligibility This competition is open to undergraduate and graduate student members of the society. Candidates must submit technical papers that are between 10 and 20 pages in length and that follow a standard style for such work. All papers must include an abstract and a high degree of technical content. International members who are unable to attend the national convention may also apply through an online procedure. Undergraduate students (both domestic and international) are encouraged to submit results from hands-on project based research as well as theoretical research with an academic or project-based focus. Graduate students (both domestic and international) are encouraged to submit topics demonstrating theoretical research with an academic focus. Domestic applicants must specify whether they wish to participate in a poster session, oral presentation (10 minutes, followed by a 10-minute question and answer session), or both at the NSBE national convention. Based on the abstracts, 50 members are selected to present their research at the convention. Winners are selected, either from presentations at the convention or from posts on the web site. Selection is based on format (15 points), organization (10 points), technical content (40 points), clarity (10 points), grammar (15 points), and use of visual aids (10 points).

Financial data In the oral presentations category, first prize is $2,000, second $1,000, and third $500. In the posters category, first prize is $1,600, second $800, and third $400.

Duration The competition is held annually.

Number awarded 6 cash awards (3 for oral presentations and 3 for posters) are presented each year.

Deadline January of each year.

[1043]
TEXAS MEDICAL ASSOCIATION MINORITY SCHOLARSHIP PROGRAM

Texas Medical Association
Attn: Educational Loans Department
401 West 15th Street
Austin, TX 78701-1680
(512) 370-1300 Toll Free: (800) 880-2828
Fax: (512) 370-1693 E-mail: info@tmaloanfunds.com
Web: www.tmaloanfunds.com/Content/Template.aspx?id=9

Summary To provide financial assistance to African Americans and members of other underrepresented minority groups from any state who are entering medical school in Texas.

Eligibility This program is open to members of minority groups that are underrepresented in the medical profession (African American, Mexican American, Native American). Applicants must have been accepted at a medical school in Texas; students currently enrolled are not eligible. Along with their application, they must submit a 750-word essay on how they, as a physician, would improve the health of all Texans.

Financial data The stipend is $5,000.

Duration 1 year; renewable.

Additional information This program began in 1999.

Number awarded 1 to 8 each year.

Deadline February of each year.

[1044]
THE REV. DR. JOSEPH H. EVANS PASTORAL SCHOLARSHIP

United Church of Christ
United Black Christians
Attn: Grants, Scholarships, and Resources
700 Prospect Avenue East
Cleveland, OH 44115-1100
(216) 736-3839 Toll Free: (866) 822-8224, ext. 3839
Fax: (216) 736-3783 E-mail: jeffersv@ucc.org
Web: www.ucc.org

Summary To provide financial assistance to African American members of United Church of Christ (UCC) congregations who are currently enrolled at a seminary.

Eligibility This program is open to African Americans who have been members of a UCC congregation for at least 1 year. Applicants must be enrolled in the second or third year of an ATS-accredited seminary and have a GPPA of 3.0 or higher.

Financial data A stipend is awarded (amount not specified).

Duration 1 year.

Additional information This scholarship was established in 2009 and first awarded in 2014.

Number awarded 1 or more each year.

Deadline February of each year.

[1045] THOMARA LATIMER CANCER FOUNDATION SCHOLARSHIPS

Thomara Latimer Cancer Foundation
Attn: Scholarship Committee
Franklin Plaza Center
29193 Northwestern Highway, Suite 528
Southfield, MI 48034
(248) 557-2346 Fax: (248) 557-9230
E-mail: info@thomlatimercares.org
Web: www.thomlatimercares.org

Summary To provide financial assistance to African American residents of Michigan (especially those who have had cancer) who are interested in studying a medically-related field at a college in any state.

Eligibility This program is open to African American residents of Michigan between 17 and 30 years of age. Applicants must be 1) a high school senior accepted at an accredited college or university in any state in a medically-related program (e.g., medical technician, physician assistant); or 2) a student admitted to a medically-related professional program (e.g., nursing, medicine, physical or occupational therapy) at a college or university in any state. They must have a GPA of 3.0 or higher. Along with their application, they must submit a brief essay on why they should be awarded this scholarship. Financial need is not considered in the selection process. Special consideration is given to students who are cancer survivors.

Financial data The stipend is $1,000.

Duration 1 year; may be renewed 1 additional year.

Number awarded 10 each year.

Deadline December of each year.

[1046] THOMAS G. NEUSOM SCHOLARSHIPS

Conference of Minority Transportation Officials
Attn: National Scholarship Program
1875 I Street, N.W., Suite 500
Washington, DC 20006
(703) 234-4072 Fax: (202) 318-0364
Web: www.comto.org/?page=Scholarships

Summary To provide financial assistance for college or graduate school to African American and other members of the Conference of Minority Transportation Officials (COMTO).

Eligibility This program is open to undergraduate and graduate students who have been members of COMTO for at least 1 year. Applicants must be working (either full or part time) on a degree in a field related to transportation and have a GPA of 2.5 or higher. Along with their application, they must submit a cover letter with a 500-word statement of career goals. Financial need is not considered in the selection process. U.S. citizenship or legal resident status is required.

Financial data The stipend is $5,500. Funds are paid directly to the recipient's college or university.

Duration 1 year.

Additional information COMTO was established in 1971 to promote, strengthen, and expand the roles of minorities in all aspects of transportation. Recipients are expected to attend the COMTO National Scholarship Luncheon.

Number awarded 1 each year.

Deadline May of each year.

[1047] THURGOOD MARSHALL DISSERTATION FELLOWSHIP FOR AFRICAN-AMERICAN SCHOLARS

Dartmouth College
Attn: Office of Graduate Studies
6062 Wentworth Hall, Room 304
Hanover, NH 03755-3526
(603) 646-2106 Fax: (603) 646-8762
Web: graduate.dartmouth.edu/funding/fellowships/cem.html

Summary To provide funding to African American and other doctoral students who are interested in working on their dissertation at Dartmouth College.

Eligibility This program is open to doctoral candidates who have completed all requirements for the Ph.D. except the dissertation and are planning a career in higher education. Applicants must be African Americans or other graduate students with a demonstrated commitment and ability to advance educational diversity. They must be interested in working on their dissertation at Dartmouth College. All academic fields that are taught in the Dartmouth undergraduate Arts and Sciences curriculum are eligible. Selection is based on academic achievement and promise; demonstrated commitment to increasing opportunities for underrepresented minorities and increasing cross-racial understanding; and potential for serving as an advocate and mentor for minority undergraduate and graduate students.

Financial data The stipend is $25,000. In addition, fellows receive office space, library privileges, and a $2,500 research allowance.

Duration 1 year, beginning in September.

Additional information The fellows are affiliated with a department or program at Dartmouth College. Fellows are expected to be in residence at Dartmouth College for the duration of the program and to complete their dissertation during that time. They are also expected to teach a course, either as the primary instructor or as part of a team.

Number awarded 1 each year.

Deadline January of each year.

[1048]
TRAILBLAZER SCHOLARSHIP

Conference of Minority Transportation Officials
Attn: National Scholarship Program
1875 I Street, N.W., Suite 500
Washington, DC 20006
(703) 234-4072 Fax: (202) 318-0364
Web: www.comto.org/?page=Scholarships

Summary To provide financial assistance to African American and other minority undergraduate and graduate students working on a degree in a field related to transportation.

Eligibility This program is open to minority undergraduate and graduate students who are working (either full or part time) on a degree in a field related to transportation and have a GPA of 2.5 or higher. Along with their application, they must submit a cover letter with a 500-word statement of career goals. Financial need is not considered in the selection process. U.S. citizenship or legal resident status is required.

Financial data The stipend is $2,500. Funds are paid directly to the recipient's college or university.

Duration 1 year.

Additional information The Conference of Minority Transportation Officials (COMTO) was established in 1971 to promote, strengthen, and expand the roles of minorities in all aspects of transportation. Recipients are expected to attend the COMTO National Scholarship Luncheon.

Number awarded 1 each year.

Deadline May of each year.

[1049]
TYLA MINORITY SCHOLARSHIP PROGRAM

Texas Young Lawyers Association
Attn: Minority Involvement Committee
1414 Colorado, Suite 502
P.O. Box 12487
Austin, TX 78711-2487
(512) 427-1529 Toll Free: (800) 204-2222, ext. 1529
Fax: (512) 427-4117 E-mail: btrevino@texasbar.com
Web: www.tyla.org

Summary To provide financial assistance to African Americans, other minorities, and women from any state who are attending law school in Texas.

Eligibility This program is open to members of recognized minority groups, including students of varying gender, national origin, racial and ethnic backgrounds, sexual orientation and gender identity, and of disability status. Applicants must be attending an ABA-accredited law school in Texas. Along with their application, they must submit a 2-page essay on either 1) the role the minority attorney should play in the community and profession; or 2) how attorneys, specifically minority attorneys, can improve the image of the legal profession. Selection is based on academic performance, merit, participation in extracurricular activities inside and outside law school, and financial need.

Financial data The stipend is $1,000.

Duration 1 year.

Number awarded 9 each year: 1 at each accredited law school in Texas.

Deadline October of each year.

[1050]
UNCF CORPORATE SCHOLARS PROGRAMS

United Negro College Fund
Attn: Corporate Scholars Program
P.O. Box 1435
Alexandria, VA 22313-9998
Toll Free: (866) 671-7237 E-mail: internship@uncf.org
Web: www.uncf.org

Summary To provide financial aid and work experience to African Americans and other minority students working on a degree in designated fields of business, science, and engineering.

Eligibility A number of corporate sponsors provides funding for this program; each establishes its own specifications. All are open to undergraduates; some are also available to graduate students. Some allow students to be enrolled at the college or university of their choice, others are limited to students at Historically Black Colleges and Universities (HBCUs), and others are restricted to UNCF member institutions. Some are open to minority (African American, Alaskan Native, American Indian, Asian Pacific Islander American, Hispanic) students in general, but others are more restrictive. Fields of study vary, but most focus on areas of business, science, and engineering of interest to the corporate sponsor. All include summer internships at the corporate sponsor's facilities. GPA requirements vary; some are as high as 3.0.

Financial data The students selected for this program receive paid internships and need-based scholarships that range up to $15,000 per year.

Duration 8 to 10 weeks for the internships; 1 year for the scholarships, which may be renewed.

Number awarded Varies each year.

Deadline Each sponsor sets its own deadline.

[1051]
UNDERREPRESENTED MINORITY DENTAL STUDENT SCHOLARSHIP

American Dental Association
Attn: ADA Foundation
211 East Chicago Avenue
Chicago, IL 60611
(312) 440-2547 Fax: (312) 440-3526
E-mail: adaf@ada.org

Summary To provide financial assistance to African American and other underrepresented minorities who wish to enter the field of dentistry.

Eligibility This program is open to U.S. citizens from a minority group that is currently underrepresented in the dental profession: Native American, African American, or Hispanic. Applicants must have a GPA of 3.0 or higher and be entering their second year of study at a dental school in the United States accredited by the Commission on Dental Accreditation. Selection is based upon academic achievement, a written summary of personal and professional goals, letters of reference, and demonstrated financial need.

Financial data The maximum stipend is $2,500. Funds are sent directly to the student's financial aid office to be used to cover tuition, fees, books, supplies, and living expenses.

Duration 1 year.

Additional information This program, established in 1991, is supported by the Harry J. Bosworth Company, Colgate-Palmolive, Sunstar Americas, and Procter & Gamble Company. Students receiving a full scholarship from any other source are ineligible to receive this scholarship.

Number awarded Approximately 25 each year.

Deadline October of each year.

[1052]
UNITED HEALTH FOUNDATION/NMF DIVERSE MEDICAL SCHOLARS PROGRAM

National Medical Fellowships, Inc.
Attn: Scholarship Program
347 Fifth Avenue, Suite 510
New York, NY 10016
(212) 483-8880 Toll Free: (877) NMF-1DOC
Fax: (212) 483-8897 E-mail: scholarships@nmfonline.org
Web: www.nmfonline.org/uhf

Summary To provide financial assistance to African American and other underrepresented minority students at medical schools in designated areas who are interested in conducting a community health project.

Eligibility This program is open to African Americans, Hispanics/Latinos, Native Americans, Vietnamese, Cambodians, and Pacific Islanders who are currently enrolled at an accredited medical school in the greater New York City metropolitan area (including Connecticut, New Jersey, New York, and Pennsylvania), Florida (greater Miami area), Louisiana (Baton Rouge, New Orleans, or Shreveport), or Georgia (Atlanta). Applicants must have demonstrated leadership and a commitment to servicing medically underserved communities. They must be interested in conducting a self-directed health project of 200 hours at a site of choice in an underserved community in the same area as their medical school. U.S. citizenship is required.

Financial data The stipend is $7,000.

Duration 1 year; recipients may apply for a second year of funding.

Additional information This program, sponsored by United Health Foundation, began in 2007.

Number awarded 22 each year.

Deadline October of each year.

[1053]
UNITED METHODIST WOMEN OF COLOR SCHOLARS PROGRAM

United Methodist Church
Attn: General Board of Higher Education and Ministry
Office of Loans and Scholarships
1001 19th Avenue South
P.O. Box 340007
Nashville, TN 37203-0007
(615) 340-7344 Fax: (615) 340-7367
E-mail: umscholar@gbhem.org
Web: www.gbhem.org

Summary To provide financial assistance to African American and other Methodist women of color who are working on a doctoral degree to prepare for a career as an educator at a United Methodist seminary.

Eligibility This program is open to women of color (have at least 1 parent who is African American, African, Hispanic, Asian, Native American, Alaska Native, or Pacific Islander) who have an M.Div. degree. Applicants must have been active, full members of a United Methodist Church for at least 3 years prior to applying. They must be enrolled full time in a degree program at the Ph.D. or Th.D. level to prepare for a career teaching at a United Methodist seminary.

Financial data The maximum stipend is $10,000 per year.

Duration 1 year; may be renewed up to 3 additional years.

Number awarded Varies each year; recently, 10 of these scholarships were awarded.

Deadline January of each year.

[1054]
VALERIE RUSSELL SCHOLARSHIP

United Church of Christ
Justice and Witness Ministries
Attn: Grants, Scholarships, and Resources
700 Prospect Avenue East
Cleveland, OH 44115-1100
(216) 736-3839 Toll Free: (866) 822-8224, ext. 3839
Fax: (216) 736-3783 E-mail: jeffersv@ucc.org
Web: www.ucc.org/women/the-valerie-russell.html

Summary To provide financial assistance to African American laywomen who are members of a United Church of Christ (UCC) congregation and working on an undergraduate or graduate degree to advance the justice ministries of the denomination.

Eligibility This program is open to African American laywomen who have a strong theologically-grounded commitment to the justice ministries of the UCC but are not a member in discernment, licensed, commissioned, or ordained. Applicants must be 1) working on an undergraduate or graduate degree in a field that will affirm the values of the UCC and promote its justice commitments; or 2) already professionally engaged in justice work either in the church or in a secular organization and seeking funds for continuing education activities (e.g., classes, workshops, travel) that will assist in personal skill building.

Financial data Stipends range from $1,500 to $2,000 per year. Funds may be used for tuition for undergraduate or graduate study or for continuing education activities.

Duration 1 year; may be renewed.

Number awarded 1 or more each year.

Deadline April of each year.

[1055]
VARNUM DIVERSITY AND INCLUSION FELLOWSHIPS

Varnum LLP
Attn: Human Resources
333 Bridge Street N.W.
P.O. Box 352
Grand Rapids, MI 49501-0352
(616) 336-6620 Fax: (616) 336-7000
E-mail: 2Lfellowship@varnumlaw.com
Web: www.varnumlaw.com

Summary To provide financial assistance to African Americans and other law students who will contribute to diversity in the legal profession and are interested in a summer associateship in Grand Rapids, Michigan.

Eligibility This program is open to students currently enrolled at an accredited law school in any state who have a GPA of 3.3 or higher. Applicants must be members of an ethnic or racial minority or demonstrate a significant commitment to issues of diversity and inclusion. They must have a GPA of 3.0 or higher and have accepted an offer to participate in the sponsoring firm's summer associate program. Along with their application, they must submit a 750-word statement on their efforts to promote greater ethnic or racial diversity and inclusion within the legal profession and/or their community.

Financial data The stipend is $7,500.

Duration 1 year.

Number awarded 2 each year.

Deadline October of each year.

[1056]
VASHTI TURLEY MURPHY SCHOLARSHIP PROGRAM

Delta Sigma Theta Sorority, Inc.
Attn: Scholarship and Standards Committee Chair
1707 New Hampshire Avenue, N.W.
Washington, DC 20009
(202) 986-2400 Fax: (202) 986-2513
E-mail: dstemail@deltasigmatheta.org
Web: www.deltasigmatheta.org

Summary To provide financial assistance to members of Delta Sigma Theta who are interested in working on a graduate degree to prepare for a career in ministry.

Eligibility This program is open to graduating college seniors and graduate students who are interested in working on a master's or doctoral degree to prepare for a career in ministry. Applicants must be active, dues-paying members of Delta Sigma Theta. Selection is based on meritorious achievement.

Financial data The stipends range from $1,000 to $2,000. The funds may be used to cover tuition, fees, and living expenses.

Duration 1 year; may be renewed for 1 additional year.

Additional information This sponsor is a traditionally-African American social sorority. The application fee is $20.

Number awarded 1 or more each year.

Deadline April of each year.

[1057]
VERIZON NSBE CORPORATE SCHOLARSHIPS

National Society of Black Engineers
Attn: Programs Department
205 Daingerfield Road
Alexandria, VA 22314
(703) 549-2207 Fax: (703) 683-5312
E-mail: scholarships@nsbe.org
Web: www.nsbe.org/Programs/Scholarships.aspx

Summary To provide financial assistance to members of the National Society of Black Engineers (NSBE) who are working on an undergraduate or graduate degree in specified fields of science, engineering, or business.

Eligibility This program is open to members of the society who are undergraduate or graduate students working on a degree in computer engineering, computer science, electric engineering, wireless communication, or business (M.B.A. degree only). Applicants must have a GPA of 3.0 or higher and a demonstrated interest in employment with Verizon and its affiliated companies in the fields of wireless, business, or telecommunications.

Financial data Stipends are $6,500 or $5,000.

Duration 1 year.

Additional information This program is supported by Verizon.

Number awarded 3 each year: 1 at $6,500 and 2 at $5,000.

Deadline May of each year.

[1058]
VERNE LAMARR LYONS MEMORIAL SCHOLARSHIP

National Association of Social Workers
Attn: NASW Foundation
750 First Street, N.E., Suite 700
Washington, DC 20002-4241
(202) 408-8600, ext. 298 Fax: (202) 336-8292
E-mail: naswfoundation@naswdc.org
Web: www.naswfoundation.org/fellowships.asp

Summary To provide financial assistance to African American and other students interested in working on a master's degree in social work.

Eligibility This program is open to members of the National Association of Social Workers (NASW) who have applied to or been accepted into an accredited M.S.W. program. Applicants must have demonstrated a commitment to working with African American communities and have an interest and/or demonstrated ability in health/mental health practice. They must have the potential for completing an M.S.W. program and have a GPA of 3.0 or higher.

Financial data The stipend is $2,000.

Duration 1 year.

Number awarded 2 each year.

Deadline March of each year.

[1059]
VICTORIA NAMAN GRADUATE SCHOOL SCHOLARSHIP

Delta Sigma Theta Sorority, Inc.-Denver Alumnae Chapter
Attn: Scholarship Committee
P.O. Box 7432
Denver, CO 80207
(303) 858-9972 E-mail: info@milehighdst.org
Web: denverdeltas.org/programs/scholarship

Summary To provide financial assistance to female African American residents of Colorado who are interested in attending graduate school in any state.

Eligibility This program is open to African American women who are residents of Colorado and enrolled or planning to enroll at a graduate school in any state. Applicants must have a GPA of 3.0 or higher. They must submit an essay of at least 200 words on their personal goals, academic achievements, and plans for making a difference in their community. Selection is based on the essay, financial need, scholastic record, 2 letters of recommendation, and an interview.

Financial data Stipends range from $1,000 to $3,000.

Duration 1 year.

Number awarded 1 or more each year.

Deadline March of each year.

[1060]
VINSON & ELKINS DIVERSITY FELLOWSHIPS

Vinson & Elkins L.L.P.
Attn: Talent Management
1001 Fannin Street, Suite 2500
Houston, TX 77002-6760
(713) 758-2222 Fax: (713) 758-2346
Web: www.velaw.com/careers/law_students.aspx?id=602

Summary To provide financial assistance to African American and other minority law students who are interested in working in a law firm setting.

Eligibility This program is open to students who are entering the second year at an ABA-accredited law school and are members of a racial or ethnic group that has been historically underrepresented in the legal profession (Asian, American Indian/Alaskan Native, Black/African American, Hispanic/Latino, multiracial, or Native Hawaiian or other Pacific Islander). Applicants must be able to demonstrate a strong undergraduate and law school record, excellent writing skills, and an interest in working in a law firm setting.

Financial data The stipend is $3,500 per year.

Duration 2 years (the second and third year of law school).

Additional information Fellows are also considered for summer associate positions at the sponsor's offices in Austin, Dallas, or Houston following their first year of law school.

Number awarded 4 each year.

Deadline January of each year.

[1061]
VIOLET AND CYRIL FRANKS SCHOLARSHIP

American Psychological Foundation
750 First Street, N.E.
Washington, DC 20002-4242
(202) 336-5843 Fax: (202) 336-5812
E-mail: foundation@apa.org
Web: www.apa.org/apf/funding/franks.aspx

Summary To provide funding to doctoral students (particularly African Americans and others from diverse backgrounds) who are interested in conducting research related to mental illness.

Eligibility This program is open to full-time graduate students who are interested in conducting a research project that uses a psychological perspective to help understand and reduce stigma associated with mental illness. Applicants must identify the project's goal, the prior research that has been conducted in the area, whom the project will serve, the in intended outcomes and how the project will achieve those, and the total cost of the project. Selection is based on conformance with stated program goals and quality of proposed work. The sponsor encourages applications from individuals who represent diversity in race, ethnicity, gender, age, disability, and sexual orientation.

Financial data The grant is $5,000.

Duration 1 year.

Additional information This grant was first awarded in 2007.

Number awarded 1 each year.

Deadline May of each year.

[1062]
VIRGINIA NURSE PRACTITIONER/NURSE MIDWIFE SCHOLARSHIP PROGRAM

Virginia Department of Health
Attn: Office of Minority Health and Public Health Policy
109 Governor Street, Suite 1016 East
Richmond, VA 23219
(804) 864-7435 Fax: (804) 864-7440
E-mail: IncentivePrograms@vdh.virginia.gov
Web: www.vdh.virginia.gov

Summary To provide funding to nursing students in Virginia (particularly African Americans and other minorities) who are willing to work as nurse practitioners and/or midwives in the state following graduation.

Eligibility This program is open to residents of Virginia who are enrolled or accepted for enrollment full or part time at a nurse practitioner program in the state or a nurse midwifery program in Virginia or a nearby state. Applicants must have a cumulative GPA of at least 3.0 in undergraduate and/or graduate courses. Preference is given to 1) residents of designated medically underserved areas of Virginia; 2) students enrolled in family practice, obstetrics and gynecology, pediatric, adult health, and geriatric nurse practitioner programs; and 3) minority students. Selection is based on scholastic achievement, character, and stated commitment to postgraduate employment in a medically underserved area of Virginia.

Financial data The stipend is $5,000 per year. Recipients must agree to serve in a designated medically underserved area of Virginia for a period of years equal to the number of years of scholarship support received. The required service must begin within 2 years of the recipient's graduation and must be in a facility that provides services to persons who are unable to pay for the service and that participates in all government-sponsored insurance programs designed to assure full access to medical care service for covered persons. If the recipient fails to complete the course of study, or pass the licensing examination, or provide the required service, all scholarship funds received must be repaid with interest and a penalty.

Duration 1 year; may be renewed for 1 additional year.

Number awarded Up to 5 each year.

Deadline June of each year.

[1063]
VISITING RESEARCH INTERNSHIP PROGRAM

Harvard Medical School
Office for Diversity Inclusion and Community Partnership
Attn: Minority Faculty Development Program
164 Longwood Avenue, Second Floor
Boston, MA 02115-5818
(617) 432-1892 Fax: (617) 432-3834
E-mail: rachel_milliron@hms.harvard.edu
Web: www.mfdp.med.harvard.edu

Summary To provide an opportunity for medical students, especially African Americans and other underrepresented minorities, to conduct a mentored research project at Harvard Medical School during the summer.

Eligibility This program is open to first- and second-year medical students, particularly underrepresented minority and/or disadvantaged individuals, in good standing at accredited U.S. medical schools. Applicants must be interested in conducting a summer research project at Harvard Medical

School under the mentorship of a faculty advisor. They must be interested in a research and health-related career, especially in clinical or translational research or research that transforms scientific discoveries arising from laboratory, clinical, or population studies into clinical or population-based applications to improve health. U.S. citizenship, nationality, or permanent resident status is required.

Financial data Participants receive a stipend (amount not specified), housing, and limited reimbursement of transportation costs to Boston.

Duration 8 weeks during the summer.

Additional information This program, established in 2008, is funded by the National Center for Research Resources of the National Institutes of Health NIH). It is a joint enterprise of Harvard University, its 10 schools, its 17 Academic Healthcare Centers, Boston College School of Nursing, MIT, the Cambridge Health Alliance, and other community partners. Interns attend weekly seminars with Harvard faculty focusing on such topics as research methodology, health disparities, ethics, and career paths. They also have the opportunity to participate in offerings of other Harvard Medical School programs, such a career development seminars and networking dinners.

Number awarded Varies each year; recently, 6 medical students were admitted to this program.

Deadline February of each year.

[1064]
VISUAL TASK FORCE SCHOLARSHIPS

National Association of Black Journalists
Attn: Communications Coordinator and Program Manager
University of Maryland
1100 Knight Hall, Suite 3100
College Park, MD 20742
(301) 405-2573 Fax: (301) 314-1714
E-mail: tjohnson@nabj.org
Web: www.nabj.org/?page=SEEDScholarships

Summary To provide financial assistance to high school seniors and undergraduate or graduate student members of the National Association of Black Journalists (NABJ) who are interested in a career in visual journalism.

Eligibility This program is open to African American high school seniors and undergraduate and graduate student members of NABJ who are currently enrolled or planning to enroll full time at an accredited 4-year college or university. Applicants must be interested in working on a degree in a field related to visual journalism (e.g., photojournalism, design and informational graphics, broadcast photojournalism) to prepare for a career in newspaper, magazine, broadcast, or online journalism. They must have a GPA of 2.75 or higher and be able to demonstrate financial need. Along with their application, they must submit samples of their work, an official college transcript, 3 letters of recommendation, a resume, and an essay of 1,000 to 2,000 words on the reasons they wish to prepare for a career in visual journalism and how they use their visual skills to tell a story effectively and creatively.

Financial data The stipend is $1,500. Funds are paid directly to the recipient's college or university.

Duration 1 year; nonrenewable.

Number awarded 2 each year.

Deadline March of each year.

[1065]
W. MONTAGUE COBB MEDICAL SCHOLAR AWARD

Omega Psi Phi Fraternity
Attn: Charles R. Drew Memorial Scholarship Commission
3951 Snapfinger Parkway
Decatur, GA 30035-3203
(404) 284-5533 Fax: (404) 284-0333
E-mail: scholarshipchairman@oppf.org
Web: www.oppf.org/scholarship

Summary To provide financial assistance for medical school to members of Omega Psi Phi who have an outstanding academic record.

Eligibility This program is open to members of the fraternity who are currently enrolled full time at an accredited school of medicine and working on a doctoral degree (not a residency. Applicants must have demonstrated service to the fraternity during the year of application and be in good financial standing at all levels. Along with their application, they must submit a statement of 200 to 250 words on their purpose for applying for this scholarship, how they believe funds from the fraternity can assist them in achieving their career goals, and other circumstances (including financial need) that make it important for them to receive financial assistance. Selection is based on academic excellence.

Financial data The stipend is $5,000.

Duration 1 year.

Additional information The winner is required to attend the Omega Psi Phi Grand Conclave or Leadership Conference. Up to $1,000 in travel expenses for attendance is provided.

Number awarded 1 each year.

Deadline April of each year.

[1066]
WAKE FOREST UNIVERSITY SCHOOL OF MEDICINE EXCELLENCE IN CARDIOVASCULAR SCIENCES SUMMER RESEARCH PROGRAM

Wake Forest University School of Medicine
Attn: Hypertension and Vascular Research Center
Medical Center Boulevard
Winston-Salem, NC 27157-1032
(336) 716-1080 Fax: (336) 716-2456
E-mail: nsarver@wakehealth.edu
Web: www.wakehealth.edu

Summary To provide African American and other underrepresented or disadvantaged students with an opportunity to engage in a summer research project in cardiovascular science at Wake Forest University in Winston-Salem, North Carolina.

Eligibility This program is open to undergraduates and master's degree students who are members of underrepresented minority groups (African Americans, Alaskan Natives, Asian Americans, Native Americans, Pacific Islanders, and Hispanics) or who come from disadvantaged backgrounds (e.g., rural areas, first-generation college students). Applicants must be interested in participating in a program of summer research in the cardiovascular sciences that includes "hands-on" laboratory research, a lecture series by faculty and guest speakers, and a research symposium at which students present their research findings. U.S. citizenship or permanent resident status is required.

Financial data The stipend is $1,731 per month, housing in a university dormitory, and round-trip transportation expense.

Duration 2 months during the summer.

Additional information This program is sponsored by the National Heart, Lung, and Blood Institute (NHLBI) of the National Institutes of Health (NIH).

Number awarded Approximately 12 each year.

Deadline February of each year.

[1067]
WALTER VAUGHN EXCELLENCE IN HUMAN RESOURCES SCHOLARSHIP

National Forum for Black Public Administrators
Attn: Scholarship Program
777 North Capitol Street, N.E., Suite 807
Washington, DC 20002
(202) 408-9300 Fax: (202) 408-8558
E-mail: vharris@nfbpa.org
Web: www.nfbpa.org/i4a/pages/index.cfm?pageid=4047

Summary To provide financial assistance to African Americans working on an undergraduate or graduate degree in public administration with an emphasis on human resource management.

Eligibility This program is open to African American undergraduate and graduate students preparing for a career in public service. Applicants must be working full time on a degree in public administration, human resource management, or a related field. They must have a GPA of 3.0 or higher, a record of involvement in extracurricular activities (excluding athletics), excellent interpersonal and leadership abilities, and strong oral and written communication skills. Along with their application, they must submit a 3-page autobiographical essay that includes their academic and career goals and objectives. Selection is based on academic record, leadership ability, participation in school activities, community service, and financial need.

Financial data The stipend is $2,500.

Duration 1 year.

Additional information This program is sponsored by CPS Human Resource Services. Recipients are required to attend the sponsor's annual conference to receive their scholarship; limited hotel and air accommodations are arranged and provided.

Number awarded 1 each year.

Deadline February of each year.

[1068]
WARNER NORCROSS & JUDD LAW SCHOOL SCHOLARSHIP

Grand Rapids Community Foundation
Attn: Education Program Officer
185 Oakes Street S.W.
Grand Rapids, MI 49503-4008
(616) 454-1751, ext. 103 Fax: (616) 454-6455
E-mail: rbishop@grfoundation.org
Web: www.grfoundation.org/scholarshipslist

Summary To provide financial assistance to African Americans and other minorities from Michigan who are attending law school.

Eligibility This program is open to students of color who are attending or planning to attend an accredited law school. Applicants must be residents of Michigan or attending law school in the state. They must be U.S. citizens or permanent residents and have a GPA of 2.5 or higher. Financial need is considered in the selection process.

Financial data The stipend is $5,000. Funds are paid directly to the recipient's institution.

Duration 1 year.

Additional information Funding for this program is provided by the law firm Warner Norcross & Judd LLP.

Number awarded 1 each year.

Deadline March of each year.

[1069]
WASHINGTON, DC CHAPTER GRADUATE SCHOLARSHIP PROGRAM

National Black MBA Association-Washington, DC Chapter
Attn: Scholarship Program
P.O. Box 14042
Washington, DC 20044
(202) 628-0138 E-mail: outreach@dcbmbaa.org
Web: www.dcbmbaa.org/zpindex.zpl

Summary To provide financial assistance to African American and other minority students from Washington, D.C., Maryland, or Virginia who are working on a master's degree in business or management at a school in any state.

Eligibility This program is open to minority students who are enrolled full or part time in a graduate business or management program in any state and working on an M.B.A. degree. Applicants must currently reside in Washington, D.C., Maryland, or Virginia, either permanently or as a student. Along with their application, they must submit an essay (from 800 to 1,000 words) on a topic that changes annually but focuses on minorities in business. Selection is based on the essay, GPA, extracurricular activity, and community involvement.

Financial data The stipend is $2,500.

Duration 1 year.

Additional information This program began in 2000.

Number awarded 1 each year.

Deadline June of each year.

[1070]
WASHINGTON HEADQUARTERS REGION NBCFAE SCHOLARSHIP

National Black Coalition of Federal Aviation Employees-Washington Headquarters Region
c/o Deames Bynum, President
4905 Cranford Terrace
Upper Marlboro, MD 20772
(301) 627-5277
Web: www.nbcfaehq.org/indexs.html

Summary To provide financial assistance to residents of Washington, D.C., especially those with a tie to the National Black Coalition of Federal Aviation Employees (NBCFAE), who are interested in attending college or graduate school in any state to work on a degree in any field.

Eligibility This program is open to graduating high school seniors, current undergraduates, college seniors entering graduate school, and first-year graduate students. Applicants must meet 1 of the following requirements: 1) reside in Washington, D.C.; 2) work for or be a family member of an employee of the Department of Transportation within the District of Columbia; 3) be a member or a family member of the Washington Headquarters Region of NBCFAE; or 4) be referred by a member of the Washington Headquarters Region of NBCFAE. They must be working on or planning to work on an associate, bachelor's, or master's degree in any field at a school in any state and have a GPA of 2.5 or higher. Along with their application, they must submit an essay of 300 to 500 words describing 1 or more of the following: career goals, personal goals, overcoming the odds, or someone they admire. Financial need is not considered in the selection process.

Financial data A stipend is awarded (amount not specified).

Duration 1 year.

Number awarded 1 or more each year.

Deadline May of each year.

[1071]
WATSON MIDWIVES OF COLOR SCHOLARSHIP

American College of Nurse-Midwives
Attn: ACNM Foundation, Inc.
8403 Colesville Road, Suite 1550
Silver Spring, MD 20910-6374
(240) 485-1850 Fax: (240) 485-1818
E-mail: fdn@acnm.org
Web: www.midwife.org

Summary To provide financial assistance for midwifery education to African Americans and other students of color who belong to the American College of Nurse-Midwives (ACNM).

Eligibility This program is open to ACNM members of color who are currently enrolled in an accredited basic midwife education program and have successfully completed 1 academic or clinical semester/quarter or clinical module. Applicants must submit a 150-word essay on their 5-year midwifery career plans and a 100-word essay on their intended future participation in the local, regional, and/or national activities of the ACNM. Selection is based on leadership potential, financial need, academic history, and potential for future professional contribution to the organization.

Financial data The stipend is $3,000.

Duration 1 year.

Number awarded Varies each year; recently, 3 of these scholarships were awarded.

Deadline March of each year.

[1072]
WAYNE F. PLACEK GRANTS

American Psychological Foundation
750 First Street, N.E.
Washington, DC 20002-4242
(202) 336-5843 Fax: (202) 336-5812
E-mail: foundation@apa.org
Web: www.apa.org/apf/funding/placek.aspx

Summary To provide funding to pre- and postdoctoral scholars (particularly African Americans, other minorities, women, and individuals with disabilities) who are interested in conducting research that will increase the general public's understanding of homosexuality and alleviate the stress experienced by gay men and lesbians.

Eligibility This program is open to scholars who have a doctoral degree (e.g., Ph.D., Psy.D., M.D.) and to graduate students in all fields of the behavioral and social sciences. Applicants must be interested in conducting empirical studies that address the following topics: prejudice, discrimination, and violence based on sexual orientation, including heterosexuals' attitudes and behaviors toward lesbian, gay, bisexual, and transgender (LGBT) people; family and workplace issues relevant to LGBT people; and subgroups of the LGBT population that have been historically underrepresented in scientific research. Selection is based on conformance with stated program goals, magnitude of incremental contribution, quality of proposed work, and applicant's demonstrated scholarship and research competence. The sponsor encourages applications from individuals who represent diversity in race, ethnicity, gender, age, disability, and sexual orientation.

Financial data The grant is $15,000.

Duration 1 year.

Additional information This program began in 1995.

Number awarded 1 or 2 each year.

Deadline February of each year.

[1073]
WESTCHESTER/GREATER CONNECTICUT CHAPTER NBMBAA GRADUATE SCHOLARSHIP

National Black MBA Association-Westchester/Greater Connecticut Chapter
Attn: Scholarship Chair
P.O. Box 3586
Stamford, CT 06905
Toll Free: (866) 966-9942 E-mail: info@nbmbaa-wgc.org
Web: www.nbmbaa-wgc.org/education/scholarship.html

Summary To provide financial assistance to African Americans and other underrepresented minority residents of Connecticut and Westchester County, New York who are working on a business-related graduate degree at a college in any state.

Eligibility This program is open to residents of Connecticut or Westchester County, New York who are members of underrepresented minority groups. Applicants must be enrolled full time at an accredited college or university in any state and working on a graduate degree in accounting, business, economics, entrepreneurship, management, marketing, or a related area. They must be U.S. citizens (or in possession of a current student visa) and have a GPA of 3.0 or higher. Selection is based on an essay on an assigned topic, academic ability, demonstrated leadership ability, and participation in college and community activities.

Financial data The stipend is $2,000.

Duration 1 year.

Number awarded 1 or more each year.

Deadline December of each year.

[1074] WILLIAM G. ANDERSON, D.O. MINORITY SCHOLARSHIP

American Osteopathic Foundation
Attn: Director of Programs
142 East Ontario Street
Chicago, IL 60611-2864
(312) 202-8232 Toll Free: (866) 455-9383
Fax: (312) 202-8216 E-mail: vheck@aof-foundation.org
Web: www.aof-foundation.org

Summary To provide financial assistance to African American and other minority students enrolled in colleges of osteopathic medicine.

Eligibility This program is open to minority (African American, Native American, Asian American, Pacific Islander, or Hispanic) students entering their second, third, or fourth year at an accredited college of osteopathic medicine. Applicants must demonstrate 1) interest in osteopathic medicine, its philosophy, and its principles; 2) academic achievement; 3) leadership efforts in addressing the educational, societal, and health needs of minorities; 4) leadership efforts in addressing inequities in medical education and health care; 5) accomplishments, awards and honors, clerkships or special projects; and extracurricular activities in which the student has shown leadership abilities; and 6) financial need.

Financial data The stipend is $5,000.

Duration 1 year.

Additional information This program began in 1998.

Number awarded 1 each year.

Deadline April of each year.

[1075] WILLIAM K. SCHUBERT M.D. MINORITY NURSING SCHOLARSHIP PROGRAM

Cincinnati Children's Hospital Medical Center
Attn: Office of Diversity and Inclusion, MLC 9008
3333 Burnet Avenue
Cincinnati, OH 45229-3039
(513) 803-6416 Toll Free: (800) 344-2462
Fax: (513) 636-5643 TDD: (513) 636-4900
E-mail: diversity@cchmc.org
Web: www.cincinnatichildrens.org

Summary To provide financial assistance to African Americans and members of other underrepresented groups who are interested in working on a bachelor's or master's degree in nursing to prepare for licensure in Ohio.

Eligibility This program is open to members of groups underrepresented in the nursing profession (males, American Indians or Alaska Natives, Blacks or African Americans, Hawaiian Natives or other Pacific Islanders, Hispanics or Latinos, or Asians). Applicants must be enrolled or accepted in a professional bachelor's or master's registered nurse program at an accredited school of nursing to prepare for initial licensure in Ohio. They must have a GPA of 2.75 or higher. Along with their application, they must submit a 750-word essay that covers 1) their long-range personal, educational, and professional goals; 2) why they chose nursing as a profession; 3) how their experience as a member of an underrepresented group has influenced a major professional and/or personal decision in their life; 4) any unique qualifications, experiences, or special talents that demonstrate their creativity; and 5) how their work experience has contributed to their personal development.

Financial data The stipend is $2,750 per year.

Duration 1 year. May be renewed up to 3 additional years for students working on a bachelor's degree or 1 additional year for students working on a master's degree; renewal requires that students maintain a GPA of 2.75 or higher.

Number awarded 1 or more each year.

Deadline April of each year.

[1076] WILLIAM TOWNSEND PORTER FELLOWSHIP FOR MINORITY INVESTIGATORS

Marine Biological Laboratory
Attn: Chief Academic and Scientific Officer
7 MBL Street
Woods Hole, MA 02543-1015
(508) 289-7173 Fax: (508) 457-1924
E-mail: casoofice@mbl.edu
Web: hermes.mbl.edu

Summary To support African Americans and other underrepresented minorities who wish to conduct research during the summer at the Marine Biological Laboratory (MBL) in Woods Hole, Massachusetts.

Eligibility This program is open to young scientists (undergraduates, senior graduate students, and postdoctoral trainees) who are from an underrepresented minority group (African American, Hispanic American, or Native American), are U.S. citizens or permanent residents, and are interested in conducting research with senior investigators at MBL. Applicants must submit a statement of the potential impact of this award on their career development. Fields of study include, but are not limited to, cell biology, developmental biology, ecology, evolution, microbiology, neurobiology, physiology, regenerative biology, and tissue engineering.

Financial data Grants range from $5,000 to $25,000, typically to cover laboratory rental and/or housing costs. Awardees are responsible for other costs, such as supplies, shared resource usage, affiliated staff who accompany them, or travel.

Duration 8 to 10 weeks during the summer.

Additional information This fellowship was first awarded in 1921. Funding is provided by the Harvard Apparatus Foundation.

Number awarded 1 or more each year.

Deadline December of each year.

[1077] WILLIE T. LOUD-CH2M HILL SCHOLARSHIP

National Forum for Black Public Administrators
Attn: Scholarship Program
777 North Capitol Street, N.E., Suite 807
Washington, DC 20002
(202) 408-9300 Fax: (202) 408-8558
E-mail: vharris@nfbpa.org
Web: www.nfbpa.org/i4a/pages/index.cfm?pageid=4047

Summary To provide financial assistance to African Americans working on a bachelor's or master's degree in public administration.

Eligibility This program is open to African American graduate students preparing for a career in public service. Applicants must be working full time on a bachelor's or master's degree in public administration, urban affairs, or a related field. They must have a GPA of 3.0 or higher, strong interpersonal skills, and excellent writing, analytical, and oral communication abilities. Along with their application, they must submit a 3-page autobiographical essay that includes their academic and career goals and objectives. Selection is based on academic record, leadership ability, participation in school activities, community service, and financial need.

Financial data The stipend is $5,000.

Duration 1 year.

Additional information This program, established in 1997, is sponsored by CH2M Hill. Recipients are required to attend the sponsor's annual conference to receive their scholarship; limited hotel and air accommodations are arranged and provided.

Number awarded 1 each year.

Deadline February of each year.

[1078]
WINSTON & STRAWN DIVERSITY SCHOLARSHIP PROGRAM

Winston & Strawn LLP
Attn: Amanda Sommerfeld
333 South Grand Avenue
Los Angeles, CA 90071-1543
(213) 615-1724 Fax: (213) 615-1750
E-mail: asommerfeld@winston.com
Web: www.winston.com

Summary To provide financial assistance to African American and other diverse law students who are interested in practicing in a city in which Winston & Strawn LLP has an office.

Eligibility This program is open to second-year law students who self-identify as a member of 1 of the following groups: American Indian or Alaska Native, Asian or Pacific Islander, Black or African American, or Hispanic or Latino. Applicants must submit a resume, law school transcript, and 500-word personal statement. Selection is based on 1) interest in practicing law after graduation in a large law firm in a city in which Winston & Strawn has an office (currently, Charlotte, Chicago, Houston, Los Angeles, New York, San Francisco, and Washington, D.C.); 2) law school and undergraduate record, including academic achievements and involvement in extracurricular activities; 3) demonstrated leadership skills; 4) and interpersonal skills.

Financial data The stipend is $10,000.

Duration 1 year (the third year of law school).

Additional information This program began in 2004.

Number awarded 3 each year.

Deadline September of each year.

[1079]
WISCONSIN MINORITY TEACHER LOANS

Wisconsin Higher Educational Aids Board
131 West Wilson Street, Suite 902
P.O. Box 7885
Madison, WI 53707-7885
(608) 267-2212 Fax: (608) 267-2808
E-mail: deanna.schulz@wisconsin.gov
Web: heab.state.wi.us/programs.html

Summary To provide funding to African Americans and other minorities in Wisconsin who are interested in teaching in Wisconsin school districts with large minority enrollments.

Eligibility This program is open to residents of Wisconsin who are African Americans, Hispanic Americans, American Indians, or southeast Asians (students who were admitted to the United States after December 31, 1975 and who are a former citizen of Laos, Vietnam, or Cambodia or whose ancestor was a citizen of 1 of those countries). Applicants must be enrolled at least half time as juniors, seniors, or graduate students at an independent or public institution in the state in a program leading to teaching licensure and have a GPA of 2.5 or higher. They must agree to teach in a Wisconsin school district in which minority students constitute at least 29% of total enrollment or in a school district participating in the interdistrict pupil transfer program. Financial need is not considered in the selection process.

Financial data Loans are provided up to $2,500 per year. For each year the student teaches in an eligible school district, 25% of the loan is forgiven; if the student does not teach in an eligible district, the loan must be repaid at an interest rate of 5%.

Duration 1 year; may be renewed 1 additional year.

Additional information Eligible students should apply through their school's financial aid office.

Number awarded Varies each year.

Deadline Deadline dates vary by institution; check with your school's financial aid office.

[1080]
WOMBLE CARLYLE SCHOLARS PROGRAM

Womble Carlyle Sandridge & Rice, PLLC
Attn: Director of Entry-Level Recruiting and Development
301 South College Street, Suite 3500
Charlotte, NC 28202-6037
(704) 331-4900 Fax: (704) 331-4955
E-mail: wcsrscholars@wcsr.com
Web: www.wcsr.com

Summary To provide financial aid and summer work experience to African Americans and other diverse students at designated law schools.

Eligibility This program is open to students at designated law schools who are members of underrepresented groups. Applicants must be able to demonstrate solid academic credentials, personal or professional achievement outside the classroom, and significant participation in community service. Along with their application, they must submit a 300-word essay on their choice of 2 topics that change annually but relate to the legal profession. They must also submit a brief statement explaining how they would contribute to the goal of creating a more diverse legal community.

Financial data The stipend is $4,000 per year. Recipients are also offered summer employment at 1 of the 14 offices of the sponsoring law firm. Salaries are the same as the firm's other summer associates in each office.

Duration 1 year (the second year of law school); may be renewed 1 additional year.

Additional information This program began in 2004. The eligible law schools are North Carolina Central University School of Law (Durham, North Carolina), University of North Carolina at Chapel Hill School of Law (Chapel Hill, North Carolina), Duke University School of Law (Durham, North Carolina), Wake Forest University School of Law (Winston-Salem, North Carolina), University of South Carolina School of Law (Columbia, South Carolina), Howard University School of Law (Washington, D.C.), University of Virginia School of Law (Charlottesville, Virginia), University of Georgia School of Law (Athens, Georgia), Georgia Washington University Law School (Washington, D.C.), Emory University School of Law (Atlanta, Georgia), and University of Maryland School of Law (Baltimore, Maryland). The sponsoring law firm has offices in Atlanta (Georgia), Baltimore (Maryland), Charleston (South Carolina), Charlotte (North Carolina), Columbia (South Carolina), Greensboro (North Carolina), Greenville (South Carolina), Raleigh (North Carolina), Research Triangle Park (North Carolina), Silicon Valley (Cupertino, California), Tysons Corner (Virginia), Washington (D.C.), Wilmington (Delaware), and Winston-Salem (North Carolina).

Number awarded Varies each year; recently, 9 of these scholarships were awarded.

Deadline May of each year.

[1081] WORLD COMMUNION NATIONAL SCHOLARSHIPS

United Methodist Church
General Board of Global Ministries
Attn: Scholarship/Leadership Development Office
475 Riverside Drive, Room 333
New York, NY 10115
(212) 870-3787 Toll Free: (800) UMC-GBGM
E-mail: scholars@umcmission.org
Web: www.umcmission.org/Explore-Our-Work/Scholarships

Summary To provide financial assistance to African Americans and other students of color who are interested in attending graduate school to prepare for leadership in promoting the mission goals of the United Methodist Church.

Eligibility This program is open to U.S. citizens and permanent residents who are members of a community of color. Applicants must have applied to or been admitted to a master's, doctoral, or professional program at an institution of higher education in the United States. They must indicate a willingness to provide 5 years of Christian service after graduation in the areas of elimination of poverty, expansion of global health, leadership development, or congregational development. High priority is given to members of the United Methodist Church. Financial need is considered in the selection process.

Financial data The stipend ranges from $1,000 to $12,500, depending on the recipient's related needs and school expenses.

Duration 1 year.

Additional information These awards are funded by the World Communion Offering received in United Methodist Churches on the first Sunday in October.

Number awarded 5 to 10 each year.

Deadline November of each year.

[1082] XEROX TECHNICAL MINORITY SCHOLARSHIP PROGRAM

Xerox Corporation
Attn: Technical Minority Scholarship Program
150 State Street, Fourth Floor
Rochester, NY 14614
(585) 422-7689 E-mail: GlobalCareers@xerox.com
Web: www.xerox.com/jobs/minority-scholarships/enus.html

Summary To provide financial assistance to African Americans and other minorities interested in undergraduate or graduate education in the sciences and/or engineering.

Eligibility This program is open to minorities (people of African American, Asian, Pacific Islander, Native American, Native Alaskan, or Hispanic descent) working full time on a bachelor's, master's, or doctoral degree in chemistry, computing and software systems, engineering (chemical, computer, electrical, imaging, manufacturing, mechanical, optical, or software), information management, laser optics, materials science, physics, or printing management science. Applicants must be U.S. citizens or permanent residents with a GPA of 3.0 or higher and attending a 4-year college or university.

Financial data Stipends range from $1,000 to $10,000.

Duration 1 year.

Number awarded Varies each year, recently, 130 of these scholarships were awarded.

Deadline September of each year.

[1083] YEAR-LONG MEDICAL RESEARCH FELLOWS PROGRAM AT AN ACADEMIC OR NONPROFIT RESEARCH INSTITUTION

Howard Hughes Medical Institute
Attn: Department of Science Education
4000 Jones Bridge Road
Chevy Chase, MD 20815-6789
(301) 951-6708 Toll Free: (800) 448-4882, ext. 8889
Fax: (301) 215-8888 E-mail: medfellows@hhmi.org
Web: www.hhmi.org

Summary To provide financial assistance to medical, dental, and veterinary students (particularly African Americans, other underrepresented minorities, and women) who are interested in pursuing research training.

Eligibility Applicants must be enrolled in a medical, dental, or veterinary school in the United States, although they may be citizens of any country with a visa authorizing them to work in this country. They must describe a proposed research project to be conducted at an academic or nonprofit research institution in the United States (other than a facility of the National Institutes of Health in Bethesda, Maryland) or abroad. Research proposals should reflect the interests of the Howard Hughes Medical Institute (HHMI), especially in biochemistry, bioinformatics, biomedical engineering, biophysics, biostatistics, cell biology, developmental biology, epidemiology, genetics, immunology, mathematical and computational biology, microbiology, molecular biology, neuroscience, pharmacology, physiology, structural biology, or virology. Applications from women and minorities underrepresented in the sciences (Blacks or African Americans, Hispanics, American Indians, Native Alaskans, and Native Pacific Islanders) are especially encouraged. Students enrolled in M.D./Ph.D., Ph.D., or Sc.D. programs and those who have completed a Ph.D. or Sc.D. in a laboratory-based science are not eligible. Selection is based on the applicant's ability and promise for a research career as a physician-scientist and the quality of training that will be provided.

Financial data Fellows receive a stipend of $29,000 per year. Indirect costs are not covered, but the institution receives an institutional allowance of $5,500 and a research allowance of $5,500. If fellows are conducting research at an institution other than their own, a travel and moving allowance of $1,500 is provided.

Duration 12 months, beginning any time between June and August.

Additional information This program complements the HHMI-NIH Research Scholars Program; students may not apply to both programs in the same year. HHMI has entered into partnership agreements with designated sponsors to support fellows in certain areas; those include the Burroughs Wellcome Fund for veterinary students, the Foundation Fighting Blindness for ophthalmology research (particularly in the area of inherited retinal degenerative diseases), the GM Trust for research in a field related to Duchenne Muscular Dystrophy, and the Society of Interventional Radiology Foundation for preclinical research in interventional radiology.

Number awarded Up to 66 each year.

Deadline January of each year.

Professionals/ Postdoctorates

Listed alphabetically by program title and described in detail here are 251 grants, awards, educational support programs, residencies, and other sources of "free money" available to African American professionals and postdoctorates. This funding is available to support research, creative activities, professional projects, training courses, and/or residencies in the United States.

[1084]
A. PHILLIP RANDOLPH MESSENGER AWARDS

National Newspaper Publishers Association
Attn: NNPA Foundation
3200 13th Street, N.W.
Washington, DC 20010-2410
(202) 588-8764 Fax: (202) 588-5302
E-mail: nnpafoundation@nnpa.org
Web: nnpa.org/nnpa-foundation

Summary To recognize and reward journalists at newspapers that are members of the National Newspaper Publishers Association (NNPA) who submit outstanding articles in designated categories.

Eligibility This program is open to journalists at newspapers that are members of NNPA. Applicants must submit articles (news stories, editorials, or commentary) in the following categories: 1) breaking news; 2) economic empowerment (workforce development and jobs); 3) sustainability and environment (green stories); 4) feature; or 5) commentary. Entries may be submitted by a single reporter or a team; they must be factual coverage of current events and should have local, regional, national, or international significance.

Financial data The awards are $5,000 for the winner and $500 for each finalist.

Duration The awards are presented annually.

Additional information The NNPA, also known as the Black Press of America, is a federation of more than 200 Black community newspapers from across the United States. It offers these awards in cooperation with MillerCoors (formerly Miller Brewing Company).

Number awarded 15 each year: 1 winner and 2 finalists in each category.

Deadline May of each year.

[1085]
AAOGF FOUNDATION SCHOLARSHIPS

American Association of Obstetricians and Gynecologists Foundation
2105 Laurel Bush Road, Suite 201
Bel Air, MD 21015
(443) 640-1051 Fax: (443) 640-1031
E-mail: info@aaogf.org
Web: www.aaogf.org/scholarship.asp

Summary To provide funding to physicians (particularly African Americans, other minorities, and women) who are interested in a program of research training in obstetrics and gynecology.

Eligibility Applicants must have an M.D. degree and be eligible for the certification process of the American Board of Obstetrics and Gynecology (ABOG). They must be interested in participating in research training conducted by 1 or more faculty mentors at an academic department of obstetrics and gynecology in the United States or Canada. The research training may be either laboratory-based or clinical, and should focus on fundamental biology, disease mechanisms, interventions or diagnostics, epidemiology, or translational research. Applicants for the scholarship co-sponsored by the Society for Maternal-Fetal Medicine (SMFM) must also be members or associate members of the SMFM. Women and minority candidates are strongly encouraged to apply. Selection is based on the scholarly, clinical, and research qualifications of the candidate; evidence of the candidate's commitment to an investigative career in academic obstetrics and gynecology in the United States or Canada; qualifications of the sponsoring department and mentor; overall quality of the mentoring plan; and quality of the research project.

Financial data The grant is $120,000 per year. Sufficient funds to support travel to the annual fellows' retreat must be set aside. The balance of the funds may be used for salary, technical support, and supplies.

Duration 1 year; may be renewed for 2 additional years, based on satisfactory progress of the scholar.

Additional information Scholars must devote at least 75% of their effort to the program of research training.

Number awarded 2 each year: 1 co-sponsored by ABOG and 1 co-sponsored by SMFM.

Deadline June of each year.

[1086]
ADVANCED POSTDOCTORAL CAREER TRANSITION AWARD TO PROMOTE DIVERSITY IN NEUROSCIENCE RESEARCH

National Institute of Neurological Disorders and Stroke
Attn: Office of Training, Career Development and Workforce Diversity
6001 Executive Boulevard, Suite 2149
Bethesda, MD 20892-9535
(301) 451-7966 Fax: (301) 594-5929
TDD: (301) 451-0088 E-mail: jonesmiche@ninds.nih.gov
Web: grants.nih.gov/grants/guide/pa-files/PAR-12-163.html

Summary To provide funding to postdoctoral fellows who are African Americans or members of other underrepresented groups and are interested in preparing for a career as an independent investigator in neuroscience.

Eligibility This program is open to U.S. citizens, nationals, and permanent residents who have a doctoral degree in a field of neuroscience and have completed 2 to 5 years of postdoctoral research training. Applicants must be interested in participating in a program of training that will help them transition to a stable and productive independent research position. They must qualify as 1) a member of an ethnic or racial group shown to be underrepresented in health-related sciences on a national basis; or 2) an individual with a disability. Selection is based on scientific merit and programmatic considerations. The program expects fellows to devote the first phase to advanced postdoctoral training, after which they should obtain a faculty position.

Financial data During the first phase of advanced postdoctoral training, grants range from $44,340 for fellows with 2 years of postdoctoral training to $49,884 for those with 5 years of training. During a subsequent phase as a faculty member, grants provide an annual award of up to $85,000 for salary and fringe benefits. The program also provides an annual research allowance of up to $25,000 during the first phase and up to $100,000 per year during the second phase for direct research and career development costs. The institution may apply for up to 8% of direct costs for facilities and administrative costs.

Duration Up to 5 years, including the first phase of up to 3 years of support for the advanced postdoctoral training period and a second phase of up to 3 years for a subsequent first faculty position.

Additional information Recipients must devote 75% of full-time professional effort to conducting health-related research.

Number awarded Varies each year.

Deadline February, June, or October of each year.

[1087]
ADVANCED POSTDOCTORAL FELLOWSHIPS IN DIABETES RESEARCH

Juvenile Diabetes Research Foundation International
Attn: Grant Administrator
26 Broadway, 14th Floor
New York, NY 10004
(212) 479-7572 Toll Free: (800) 533-CURE
Fax: (212) 785-9595 E-mail: info@jdrf.org
Web: jdrf.org

Summary To provide advanced research training to scientists (particularly African Americans, other underrepresented minorities, women, and individuals with disabilities) who are beginning their professional careers and are interested in conducting research on the causes, treatment, prevention, or cure of diabetes or its complications.

Eligibility This program is open to postdoctorates who show extraordinary promise for a career in diabetes research. Applicants must have received their first doctoral degree (M.D., Ph.D., D.M.D., or D.V.M.) within the past 5 years and should have completed 1 to 3 years of postdoctoral training. They may not have a faculty appointment. There are no citizenship requirements. Applications are encouraged from women, members of minority groups underrepresented in the sciences, and people with disabilities. The proposed research training may be conducted at foreign or domestic, for-profit or nonprofit, or public or private institutions, including universities, colleges, hospitals, laboratories, units of state or local government, or eligible agencies of the federal government. Selection is based on the applicant's previous experience and academic record; the caliber of the proposed research; the quality of the mentor, training program, and environment; and the applicant's potential to obtain an independent research position in the future. Fellows who obtain a faculty position at any time during the term of the fellowship may apply for a transition award for support during their first year as a faculty member.

Financial data The total grant is $90,000 per year, including salary that depends on number of years of experience, ranging from $39,264 for zero up to $54,180 for 7 or more years of experience. In the first year only, funds in excess of the grant may be used for travel to scientific meetings (up to $2,000), journal subscriptions, books, training courses, laboratory supplies, equipment, or purchase of a personal computer (up to $2,000). Indirect costs are not allowed. Fellows who receive a faculty position are granted a transition award of up to $110,000 for 1 year, including up to 10% in indirect costs.

Duration Up to 3 years.

Number awarded Varies each year.

Deadline August of each year.

[1088]
AERA-AIR FELLOWS PROGRAM

American Educational Research Association
1430 K Street, N.W., Suite 1200
Washington, DC 20005
(202) 238-3200 Fax: (202) 238-3250
E-mail: fellowships@aera.net
Web: www.aera.net

Summary To provide an opportunity for junior scholars in the field of education (particularly African Americans and other underrepresented minorities) to engage in a program of research and advanced training while in residence in Washington, D.C.

Eligibility This program is open to early scholars who received a Ph.D. or Ed.D. degree within the past 3 years in a field related to education and educational processes. Applicants must be proposing a program of intensive research and training in Washington, D.C. Selection is based on past academic record, writing sample, goal statement, range and quality of research experiences, other relevant work or professional experiences, potential contributions to education research, and references. A particular goal of the program is to increase the number of underrepresented minority professionals conducting advanced research or providing technical assistance. U.S. citizenship or permanent resident status is required.

Financial data Stipends range from $55,000 to $65,000 per year.

Duration Up to 2 years.

Additional information This program, jointly sponsored by the American Educational Research Association (AERA) and the American Institutes for Research (AIR), was first offered for 2006. Fellows rotate between the 2 organizations and receive mentoring from recognized researchers and practitioners in a variety of substantive areas in education.

Number awarded Up to 3 each year.

Deadline November of each year.

[1089]
AFRL/DAGSI OHIO STUDENT-FACULTY RESEARCH FELLOWSHIP PROGRAM

Dayton Area Graduate Studies Institute
3155 Research Boulevard, Suite 205
Kettering, OH 45420
(937) 781-4001 Fax: (937) 781-4005
E-mail: kelam@dagsi.org
Web: www.dagsi.org/pages/osrfp_proinforeq.html

Summary To provide funding to faculty and graduate students (particularly African Americans and other minorities, women, and individuals with disabilities) at designated universities in Ohio who are from any state and interested in conducting research in aerospace technologies of interest to the U.S. Air Force.

Eligibility This program is open to research teams of full-time graduate students and faculty at 18 designated Ohio universities. Applicants must be interested in conducting research that will utilize the facilities of the Air Force Research Laboratory (AFRL) at Wright-Patterson Air Force Base. All 6 directorates at the AFRL (air vehicles, propulsion, sensors, materials and manufacturing, human effectiveness, and information) participate in this program. Applications from Ph.D. candidates must be developed and written largely by the student, with support, guidance, and input as necessary from the faculty partner. For master's projects, the proposal can be developed and written jointly by the faculty member and the student. All participants (faculty and student) must be U.S. citizens. Underrepresented minorities, women, and persons with disabilities are strongly urged to apply.

Financial data Grants provide stipends of $23,500 for students who have a master's degree and are working on a Ph.D. or $18,500 for students who have a bachelor's degree and are working on a master's; student's tuition for 1 academic year; a faculty stipend of $11,000; student and faculty allowances of $3,000 each for program-related travel or other approved expenses; and overhead at a maximum off-campus rate of 26% of student and faculty stipends and miscellaneous allowances.

Duration 1 year; may be renewed for 1 additional year by master's students and for 2 additional years by Ph.D. candidates. Students are expected to spend 8 consecutive weeks conducting research at AFRL and faculty members are expected to spend at least 1 month conducting research at AFRL.

Additional information DAGSI was established in 1994 as a consortium of graduate engineering schools at the University of Dayton, Wright State University, and the Air Force Institute of Technology. The Ohio State University and the University of Cincinnati joined as affiliated members in 1996 and Miami University and Ohio University joined as associate members in 2001. Students from the following universities are also eligible to participate in this program: University of Akron, Bowling Green State University, Central State University, Cleveland State University, Kent State University, Shawnee State University, University of Toledo, Youngstown State University, Medical College of Ohio, Northeastern Ohio Universities College of Medicine, and Case Western Reserve University.

Number awarded At least 20 each year.

Deadline January of each year.

[1090]
AGA RESEARCH SCHOLAR AWARDS

American Gastroenterological Association
Attn: AGA Research Foundation
Research Awards Manager
4930 Del Ray Avenue
Bethesda, MD 20814-2512
(301) 222-4012 Fax: (301) 654-5920
E-mail: awards@gastro.org
Web: www.gastro.org/aga-foundation/grants

Summary To provide research funding to young investigators (particularly African Americans, other minorities, and women) who are developing an independent career in an area of gastroenterology, hepatology, or related fields.

Eligibility Applicants must hold full-time faculty positions at North American universities or professional institutes at the time of application. They should be early in their careers (fellows and established investigators are not appropriate candidates). Candidates with an M.D. degree must have completed clinical training within the past 5 years and those with a Ph.D. must have completed their degree within the past 5 years. Membership in the American Gastroenterological Association (AGA) is required. Selection is based on significance, investigator, innovation, approach, environment, relevance to AGA mission, and evidence of institutional commitment. Women, minorities, and physician/scientist investigators are strongly encouraged to apply.

Financial data The grant is $90,000 per year. Funds are to be used for project costs, including salary, supplies, and equipment but excluding travel. Indirect costs are not allowed.

Duration 2 years.

Additional information At least 70% of the recipient's research effort should relate to the gastrointestinal tract or liver.

Number awarded 4 each year.

Deadline October of each year.

[1091]
AHRQ INDIVIDUAL AWARDS FOR POSTDOCTORAL FELLOWS

Agency for Healthcare Research and Quality
Attn: Office of Extramural Research, Education, and Priority Populations
540 Gaither Road
Rockville, MD 20850
(301) 427-1528 Fax: (301) 427-1562
TDD: (301) 451-0088
E-mail: Shelley.Benjamin@ahrq.hhs.gov
Web: grants.nih.gov/grants/guide/pa-files/PA-12-261.html

Summary To provide funding to postdoctoral scholars (particularly African Americans, other underrepresented minorities, and individuals with disabilities) who are interested in academic training and supervised experience in applying quantitative research methods to the systematic analysis and evaluation of health services.

Eligibility Applicants must be U.S. citizens, nationals, or permanent residents who have received a Ph.D., M.D., D.O., D.C., D.D.S., D.V.M., O.D., Sc.D., Eng.D., D.P.M., D.N.Sc., N.D., Dr.P.H., Pharm.D., D.S.W., Psych.D., or equivalent doctoral degree from an accredited domestic or foreign institution. They must be proposing to pursue postdoctoral training at an appropriate institution under the guidance of a sponsor who is an established investigator active in health services research. The proposed training should help promote the sponsoring agency's strategic research goals of 1) reducing the risk of harm from health care services by promoting the delivery of appropriate care that achieves the best quality outcomes; 2) achieving wider access to effective health care services and reducing health care costs; and 3) assuring that providers and consumers/patients use beneficial and timely health care information to make informed decisions. Preference is given to proposals that address health services research issues critical to such priority populations as individuals living in inner city and rural (including frontier) areas; low-income and minority groups; women, children, and the elderly; and individuals with special health care needs, including those with disabilities and those who need chronic or end-of-life health care. Members of underrepresented ethnic and racial groups, individuals from disadvantaged backgrounds, and individuals with disabilities are especially encouraged to apply.

Financial data The award provides an annual stipend based on the number of years of postdoctoral experience, ranging from $41,364 for less than 1 year to $54,180 for 7 or more years. For fellows sponsored by domestic non-federal institutions, the stipend is paid through the sponsoring institution; for fellows sponsored by federal or foreign institutions, the monthly stipend is paid directly to the fellow. Institutions also receive an allowance to help defray such awardee expenses as self-only health insurance, research supplies, equipment, travel to scientific meetings, and related items; the allowance is $7,850 per 12-month period for fellows at non-federal, nonprofit, and foreign institutions and $6,750 per 12-month period at federal laboratories and for-profit institutions. In addition, tuition and fees are reimbursed at a rate of 60%, up to $16,000 for an additional degree.

Duration 1 to 3 years.

Number awarded Varies each year.

Deadline April, August, or December of each year.

[1092]
AHRQ SMALL RESEARCH GRANT PROGRAM

Agency for Healthcare Research and Quality
Attn: Office of Extramural Research, Education, and Priority Populations
540 Gaither Road
Rockville, MD 20850
(301) 427-1556 Fax: (301) 427-1562
TDD: (301) 451-0088
E-mail: Kishena.Wadhwani@ahrq.hhs.gov
Web: grants.nih.gov/grants/guide/pa-files/PA-10-168.html

Summary To provide funding (especially to African Americans, other minorities, individuals with disabilities, and new investigators) for small research projects designed to improve the quality, appropriateness, and effectiveness of health care services and access to those services.

Eligibility This program is open to investigators at domestic, nonprofit, public and private organizations, including universities, clinics, units of state and local governments, nonprofit firms, and nonprofit foundations. Applicants must be proposing projects in 1 of the research portfolio areas of the Agency for Healthcare Research and Quality (AHRQ): 1) the value portfolio, for research that can be used to reduce unnecessary health care costs (waste) while maintaining or improving health care quality; 2) the health information technology portfolio, for the use of information and communication technology in health care to support the delivery of patient or population care; 3) the comparative effectiveness portfolio, for research focusing on comparative effectiveness of different clinical treatments and services; 4) the prevention/care management portfolio, to improve the quality, safety, efficiency, and effectiveness of preventive services and chronic care management in ambulatory care settings; 5) the patient safety portfolio, for research projects to identify the risks and hazards encountered by patients as a result of health care; or 6) the innovations and emerging areas portfolio, for research on ideas that have the potential for high impact. Members of underrepresented ethnic and racial groups, individuals with disabilities, and new investigators are especially encouraged to apply. U.S. citizenship or permanent resident status is required.

Financial data Total costs (including direct costs and facilities and administrative costs) may not exceed $100,000.

Duration Up to 2 years.

Additional information Funding from this program may not be used for dissertation research.

Number awarded Varies each year.

Deadline February, June, or October of each year.

[1093]
AIR FORCE SUMMER FACULTY FELLOWSHIP PROGRAM

American Society for Engineering Education
Attn: AFSFF Program
1818 N Street, N.W., Suite 600
Washington, DC 20036-2479
(202) 649-3834 Fax: (202) 265-8504
E-mail: sffp@asee.org
Web: sffp.asee.org

Summary To provide funding to science and engineering faculty and graduate students (particularly African Americans and other underrepresented minorities) who are interested in conducting research during the summer at Air Force facilities.

Eligibility This program is open to U.S. citizens and permanent residents who have a full-time faculty appointment at a U.S. college or university in a field of engineering or science of interest to the Air Force. Applicants must be interested in conducting a research project, under the direction of an Air Force research adviser, at an Air Force Research Laboratory, the U.S. Air Force Academy, or the Air Force Institute of Technology. A graduate student may accompany the faculty member. Faculty and students at Historically Black Colleges and Universities ((HBCUs), Minority Institutions (MIs), American Indian Tribal Colleges and Universities (TCUs), and Hispanic Serving Institutions (HSIs) are especially encouraged to apply.

Financial data Stipends are $1,700 per week for full professors, $1,500 per week for associate professors, $1,300 per week for assistant professors, $884 per week for graduate students working on a master's degree, or $1,037 per week for graduate students working on a doctoral degree. Relocation reimbursement and a daily expense allowance of $50 (for fellows with a commute distance greater than 50 miles) are also available.

Duration 8 to 12 weeks during the summer. May be renewed for a second and third summer, but recipients may not reapply for 2 years after completing a third summer.

Additional information This program began operating in 2005. Research must be conducted in residence at an Air Force facility.

Number awarded Approximately 100 each year.

Deadline December of each year.

[1094]
ALEXANDER GRALNICK RESEARCH INVESTIGATOR PRIZE

American Psychological Foundation
750 First Street, N.E.
Washington, DC 20002-4242
(202) 336-5843 Fax: (202) 336-5812
E-mail: foundation@apa.org
Web: www.apa.org/apf/funding/gralnick.aspx

Summary To recognize and reward psychologists (particularly African Americans and members of other groups representing diversity) who have conducted exceptional research on serious mental illness.

Eligibility This program is open to psychologists who have a doctoral degree, have a record of significant research productivity, and are able to demonstrate evidence on continuing creativity in the area of research on serious mental illness (including, but not limited to, schizophrenia, bipolar disorder, and paranoia). Nominees must also have significant involvement in training and development of younger investigators. They must have an affiliation with an accredited college, university, or other treatment or research institution. The sponsor encourages nominations of individuals who represent diversity in race, ethnicity, gender, age, disability, and sexual orientation.

Financial data The award is $20,000.

Duration The award is presented biennially, in even-numbered years.

Additional information This award was first presented in 2002.

Number awarded 1 each even-numbered year.

Deadline April of each even-numbered year.

[1095]
ALFRED P. SLOAN FOUNDATION RESEARCH FELLOWSHIPS

Alfred P. Sloan Foundation
630 Fifth Avenue, Suite 2550
New York, NY 10111-0242
(212) 649-1649 Fax: (212) 757-5117
E-mail: researchfellows@sloan.org
Web: www.sloan.org/sloan-research-fellowships

Summary To provide funding for research in selected fields of science to recent doctorates (particularly African Americans, other underrepresented minorities, and women).

Eligibility This program is open to scholars who are no more than 6 years from completion of the most recent Ph.D. or equivalent in computational and evolutionary molecular biology, chemistry, computer science, economics, mathematics, ocean sciences (including marine biology), neuroscience, physics, or a related interdisciplinary field. Applicants must have a tenure track position at a college or university in the United States or Canada. Direct applications are not accepted; candidates must be nominated by department heads or other senior scholars. Although fellows must be at an early stage of their research careers, they should give strong evidence of independent research accomplishments and creativity. The sponsor strongly encourages the participation of women and members of underrepresented minority groups.

Financial data The stipend is $25,000 per year. Funds are paid directly to the fellow's institution to be used by the fellow for equipment, technical assistance, professional travel, trainee support, or any other research-related expense; they may not be used to augment an existing full-time salary.

Duration 2 years; may be extended if unexpended funds still remain.

Additional information This program began in 1955, when it awarded $235,000 to 22 chemists, physicists, and pure mathematicians. Neuroscience was added in 1972, economics and applied mathematics in 1980, computer science in 1993, computational and evolutionary molecular biology in 2002, and ocean sciences in 2012. Currently, the program awards more than $5.5 million in grants annually.

Number awarded 126 each year: 23 in chemistry, 12 in computational and evolutionary molecular biology, 16 in computer science, 8 in economics, 20 in mathematics, 16 in neuroscience, 8 in ocean sciences, and 23 in physics.

Deadline September of each year.

[1096]
ALZHEIMER'S ASSOCIATION INVESTIGATOR-INITIATED RESEARCH GRANTS

Alzheimer's Association
Attn: Medical and Scientific Affairs
225 North Michigan Avenue, 17th Floor
Chicago, IL 60601-7633
(312) 335-5747 Toll Free: (800) 272-3900
Fax: (866) 699-1246 TDD: (312) 335-5886
E-mail: grantsapp@alz.org
Web: www.alz.org

Summary To provide funding to scientists (particularly African Americans and members of other underrepresented groups) who are interested in conducting research on Alzheimer's Disease.

Eligibility This program is open to postdoctoral investigators at public, private, domestic, and foreign research laboratories, medical centers, hospitals, and universities. Applicants must be proposing to conduct research with focus areas that change annually but are related to Alzheimer's Disease. They must have a full-time staff or faculty appointment. Scientists from underrepresented groups are especially encouraged to apply.

Financial data Grants up to $100,000 per year, including direct expenses and up to 10% for overhead costs, are available. The total award for the life of the grant may not exceed $240,000.

Duration Up to 3 years.

Number awarded Up to 20 each year.

Deadline Letters of intent must be submitted by the end of January of each year. Final applications are due in March.

[1097]
ALZHEIMER'S ASSOCIATION NEW INVESTIGATOR RESEARCH GRANTS

Alzheimer's Association
Attn: Medical and Scientific Affairs
225 North Michigan Avenue, 17th Floor
Chicago, IL 60601-7633
(312) 335-5747 Toll Free: (800) 272-3900
Fax: (866) 699-1246 TDD: (312) 335-5886
E-mail: grantsapp@alz.org
Web: www.alz.org

Summary To provide funding for research on Alzheimer's Disease to junior and postdoctoral investigators (particularly African Americans and members of other underrepresented groups).

Eligibility This program is open to investigators, including postdoctoral fellows, at public, private, domestic, and foreign research laboratories, medical centers, hospitals, and universities. Applicants must be proposing to conduct research with focus areas that change annually but are related to Alzheimer's Disease. Eligibility is restricted to investigators who have less than 10 years of research experience, including postdoctoral fellowships or residencies. Scientists from underrepresented groups are especially encouraged to apply.

Financial data Grants up to $60,000 per year, including direct expenses and up to 10% for overhead costs, are available. The total award for the life of the grant may not exceed $100,000.

Duration Up to 2 years.

Number awarded Up to 25 each year.

Deadline Letters of intent must be submitted by the end of January or September of each year. Final applications are due in March or October.

[1098]
AMERICAN ASSOCIATION FOR THE ADVANCEMENT OF SCIENCE CONGRESSIONAL FELLOWSHIPS

American Association for the Advancement of Science
Attn: Science and Technology Policy Fellowships
1200 New York Avenue, N.W.
Washington, DC 20005-3920
(202) 326-6700 Fax: (202) 289-4950
E-mail: fellowships@aaas.org
Web: www.fellowships.aaas.org

Summary To provide a fellowship to postdoctoral scientists and engineers (particularly African Americans, other minorities, and individuals with disabilities) so they can work as special legislative assistants on the staffs of members of Congress or Congressional committees.

Eligibility This program is open to doctoral-level scientists (Ph.D., M.D., D.V.M., D.Sc., and other terminal degrees) in any field of science (behavioral, biological, computational, earth, health, medical, physical, or social), engineering, or mathematics. Engineers with a master's degree and at least 3 years of professional experience are also eligible. Applicants must demonstrate solid scientific and technical credentials; a commitment to serve society; good communication skills; the ability to engage with non-scientific audiences; and an interest in working as special legislative assistants for Congress. U.S. citizenship is required; federal employees are not eligible. The sponsor seeks candidates from a broad array of backgrounds and a diversity of geographic, disciplinary, gender, and ethnic perspectives, as well as disability status.

Financial data The stipend is $74,872. Also provided are a $4,000 relocation allowance for fellows from outside the Washington, D.C. area, reimbursement for health insurance, and a $4,000 travel allowance.

Duration 1 year, beginning in September.

Additional information The program includes an orientation on Congressional and executive branch operations and a year-long seminar program on issues involving science and public policy. Approximately 30 other national science and engineering societies sponsor fellows in collaboration with this program; for a list of all of those, contact the sponsor.

Number awarded 2 each year.

Deadline October of each year.

[1099]
AMERICAN EDUCATIONAL RESEARCH ASSOCIATION RESEARCH GRANTS PROGRAM

American Educational Research Association
1430 K Street, N.W., Suite 1200
Washington, DC 20005
(202) 238-3200 Fax: (202) 238-3250
E-mail: fellowships@aera.net
Web: www.aera.net

Summary To provide funding to faculty members and other postdoctorates (particularly African Americans and other underrepresented minorities) who are interested in conducting research on educational policy.

Eligibility This program is open to scholars who have completed a doctoral degree in such disciplines as (but not limited to) education, sociology, economics, psychology, demography, statistics, or psychometrics. Applicants may be U.S. citizens, U.S. permanent residents, or non-U.S. citizens working at a U.S. institution. Underrepresented minority researchers are strongly encouraged to apply. Research topics may cover a wide range of policy-related issues, but priority is given to proposals that 1) develop or benefit from new quantitative measures or methodological approaches for addressing education issues; 2) include interdisciplinary teams with subject matter expertise, especially when studying science, technology, engineering, or mathematics (STEM) learning; 3) analyze TIMSS, PISA, or other international data resources; or 4) include the integration and analysis of more than 1 data set. Research projects must include the analysis of data from at least 1 of the large-scale, nationally or internationally representative data sets, such as those of the National Science Foundation (NSF), National Center for Education Statistics (NCES), or National Institutes of Health (NIH). Selection is based on the importance of the proposed policy issue, the strength of the methodological model and proposed statistical analysis of the study, and relevant experience or research record.

Financial data Grants up to $20,000 for 1 year or $35,000 for 2 years are available. Funding is linked to the approval of the recipient's progress report and final report. Grantees receive one-third of the total award at the beginning of the grant period, one-third upon acceptance of the progress report, and one-third upon acceptance of the final report.

Duration 1 or 2 years.

Additional information Funding for this program is provided by the NSF and the NCES. Grantees must submit a brief (3 to 6 pages) progress report midway through the grant period. A final report must be submitted at the end of the grant period.

Number awarded Approximately 15 each year.

Deadline January, March, or August of each year.

[1100]
AMERICAN SOCIETY FOR THEATRE RESEARCH GRANTS FOR RESEARCHERS WITH HEAVY TEACHING LOADS

American Society for Theatre Research
P.O. Box 1798
Boulder, CO 80306-1798
(303) 530-1838 Toll Free: (888) 530-1838
Fax: (303) 530-1839 E-mail: info@astr.org
Web: www.astr.org/awards

Summary To provide funding for research in theater history to scholars (particularly African Americans and other minorities) at institutions with heavy teaching loads and limited support for scholarship.

Eligibility This program is open to full-time faculty in the field of theater history whose teaching load is at least 4 courses per semester. Applicants must be seeking research support, which may include contributing towards course release, funding of a research assistant, or travel to research materials. Minority faculty and/or faculty teaching at Historically Black Colleges and Universities (HBCUs) or other institutions that historically have provided educational opportunities to large minority communities are especially encouraged to apply.

Financial data The grant is $1,000. The program also provides a year's membership in the American Society for Theatre Research (ASTR) and registration and travel to its annual conference.

Duration The grant is presented annually.

Number awarded 1 or more each year.

Deadline March of each year.

[1101]
AMERICAN SOCIETY OF TRANSPLANTATION BASIC SCIENCE FELLOWSHIP GRANT

American Society of Transplantation
Attn: Chair, Awards and Grants Committee
15000 Commerce Parkway, Suite C
Mt. Laurel, NJ 08054
(856) 439-9986 Fax: (856) 439-9982
E-mail: info@a-s-t.org
Web: www.a-s-t.org/research-funding/research-funding

Summary To provide funding to recent postdoctorates (particularly African Americans, other minorities, and women) who are interested in a program of research training related to the basic science of transplantation under the mentorship of a member of the American Society of Transplantation (AST).

Eligibility This program is open to scientists who have an M.D., D.O., Ph.D., D.V.M. or equivalent graduate degree and have spent 2 years or less performing research in basic transplantation science since obtaining their last degree. Applicants must be sponsored by an AST member at a North American institution who will serve as their mentor. They must be citizens, permanent residents, or lawfully-admitted foreign nationals with appropriate visas in Canada, Mexico, or the United States. Their proposed research training must involve support work in transplantation biology, ranging from pertinent basic immunology to animal studies; all types of organ, tissue, and cell transplants are considered. Research topics that involve underrepresented areas (minorities, women, and pediatrics) are strongly encouraged. The AST also encourages applications from women and underrepresented minority investigators. Selection is based on the quality of the applicant, scientific project, sponsor, and institution, with an emphasis on preparing the applicant for a career as an independent investigator.

Financial data The grant is $40,000 per year. Funds are to support the fellow's salary and cannot be used for indirect costs.

Duration 2 years.

Additional information The American Society of Transplantation also sponsors a number of other similar grants, including the American Society of Transplantation Basic Science Faculty Development Grant, American Society of Transplantation Branch-Out Grants, American Society of Transplantation Clinical Science Faculty Development Grant, and American Society of Transplantation Clinical Science (applicants can receive only 1 of these awards at a time). Fellowship Grants.

Number awarded 1 or more each year.

Deadline December of each year.

[1102]
ANISFIELD-WOLF BOOK AWARDS

Cleveland Foundation
1422 Euclid Avenue, Suite 1300
Cleveland, OH 44115-2001
(216) 861-3810 Fax: (216) 861-1729
E-mail: Hello@anisfield-wolf.org
Web: www.anisfield-wolf.org

Summary To recognize and reward recent books that have contributed to an understanding of racism or appreciation of the rich diversity of human cultures.

Eligibility Works published in English during the preceding year that "contribute to our understanding of racism or our appreciation of the rich diversity of human cultures" are eligible to be considered. Entries may be either scholarly or imaginative (fiction, poetry, memoir). Plays and screenplays are not eligible, nor are works in progress. Manuscripts and self-published works are not eligible, and no grants are made for completing or publishing manuscripts.

Financial data The prize is $10,000. If more than 1 author is chosen in a given year, the prize is divided equally among the winning books.

Duration The award is presented annually.

Additional information This program began in 1936.

Number awarded 5 each year: 2 for fiction, 1 for poetry, 1 for nonfiction, and 1 for lifetime achievement.

Deadline December of each year.

[1103]
APA/SAMHSA MINORITY FELLOWSHIP PROGRAM

American Psychiatric Association
Attn: Department of Minority and National Affairs
1000 Wilson Boulevard, Suite 1825
Arlington, VA 22209-3901
(703) 907-8653 Toll Free: (888) 35-PSYCH
Fax: (703) 907-7852 E-mail: mking@psych.org
Web: www.psychiatry.org

Summary To provide educational enrichment to psychiatrists-in-training (particularly African Americans and other minorities) who are interested in providing quality and effective services to minorities and the underserved.

Eligibility This program is open to residents who are in at least their second year of psychiatric training, members of the American Psychiatric Association (APA), and U.S. citizens or permanent residents. A goal of the program is to develop leadership to improve the quality of mental health care for members of ethnic minority groups (American Indians, Native Alaskans, Asian Americans, Native Hawaiians, Native Pacific

Islanders, African Americans, and Hispanics/Latinos). Applicants must be interested in working with a component of the APA that is of interest to them and relevant to their career goals. Along with their application, they must submit a 2-page essay on how the fellowship would be utilized to alter their present training and ultimately assist them in achieving their career goals. Selection is based on commitment to serve ethnic minority populations, demonstrated leadership abilities, awareness of the importance of culture in mental health, and interest in the interrelationship between mental health/illness and transcultural factors.

Financial data Fellows receive a monthly stipend (amount not specified) and reimbursement of transportation, lodging, meals, and incidentals in connection with attendance at program-related activities. They are expected to use the funds to enhance their own professional development, improve training in cultural competence at their training institution, improve awareness of culturally relevant issues in psychiatry at their institution, expand research in areas relevant to minorities and underserved populations, enhance the current treatment modalities for minority patients and underserved individuals at their institution, and improve awareness in the surrounding community about mental health issues (particularly with regard to minority populations).

Duration 1 year; may be renewed 1 additional year.

Additional information Funding for this program is provided by the Substance Abuse and Mental Health Services Administration (SAMHSA). As part of their assignment to an APA component, fellows must attend the fall component meetings in September and the APA annual meeting in May. At those meeting, they can share their experiences as residents and minorities and discuss issues that impact on minority populations. This program is an outgrowth of the fellowships that were established in 1974 under a grant from the National Institute of Mental Health in answer to concerns about the underrepresentation of minorities in psychiatry.

Number awarded Varies each year; recently, 21 of these fellowships were awarded.

Deadline January of each year.

[1104]
APA SUBSTANCE ABUSE FELLOWSHIP PROGRAM

American Psychiatric Association
Attn: Department of Minority and National Affairs
1000 Wilson Boulevard, Suite 1825
Arlington, VA 22209-3901
(703) 907-8653 Toll Free: (888) 35-PSYCH
Fax: (703) 907-7852 E-mail: mking@psych.org
Web: www.psychiatry.org

Summary To provide educational enrichment to African American and other minority psychiatrists-in-training and stimulate their interest in providing quality and effective services related to substance abuse to minorities and the underserved.

Eligibility This program is open to psychiatric residents who are members of the American Psychiatric Association (APA) and U.S. citizens or permanent residents. A goal of the program is to develop leadership to improve the quality of mental health care for members of ethnic minority groups (American Indians, Native Alaskans, Asian Americans, Native Hawaiians, Native Pacific Islanders, African Americans, and Hispanics/Latinos). Applicants must be in at least their fifth year of a substance abuse training program approved by an affiliated medical school or agency where a significant number of substance abuse patients are from minority and underserved groups. They must also be interested in working with a component of the APA that is of interest to them and relevant to their career goals. Along with their application, they must submit a 2-page essay on how the fellowship would be utilized to alter their present training and ultimately assist them in achieving their career goals. Selection is based on commitment to serve ethnic minority populations, demonstrated leadership abilities, awareness of the importance of culture in mental health, and interest in the interrelationship between mental health/illness and transcultural factors.

Financial data Fellows receive a monthly stipend (amount not specified) and reimbursement of transportation, lodging, meals, and incidentals in connection with attendance at program-related activities. They are expected to use the funds to enhance their own professional development, improve training in cultural competence at their training institution, improve awareness of culturally relevant issues in psychiatry at their institution, expand research in areas relevant to minorities and underserved populations, enhance the current treatment modalities for minority patients and underserved individuals at their institution, and improve awareness in the surrounding community about mental health issues (particularly with regard to minority populations).

Duration 1 year; may be renewed 1 additional year.

Additional information Funding for this program is provided by the Substance Abuse and Mental Health Services Administration (SAMHSA). As part of their assignment to an APA component, fellows must attend the fall component meetings in September and the APA annual meeting in May. At those meeting, they can share their experiences as residents and minorities and discuss issues that impact minority populations. This program is an outgrowth of the fellowships that were established in 1974 under a grant from the National Institute of Mental Health in answer to concerns about the underrepresentation of minorities in psychiatry.

Number awarded Varies each year; recently, 3 of these fellowships were awarded.

Deadline January of each year.

[1105]
ARL BROAD AGENCY ANNOUNCEMENT

Army Research Office
Attn: Army Contracting Command-Aberdeen Proving Ground
4300 South Miami Boulevard
P.O. Box 12211
Research Triangle Park, NC 27709-2211
(919) 549-4375 Fax: (919) 549-4388
Web: www.arl.army.mil/www/default.cfm?Page=8

Summary To provide funding to investigators (particularly those at Historically Black Colleges and Universities) who are interested in conducting scientific research of interest to the U.S. Army.

Eligibility This program is open to investigators qualified to perform research in designated scientific and technical areas of interest to the Army Research Laboratory (ARL) and the Army Research Office (ARO). Those areas include ballistics and aeromechanics sciences, chemistry, computing and network sciences, electronics, environmental sciences, human sciences, information sciences, life sciences, materials sciences, mathematics, mechanical sciences, physics and survivability, lethality, and vulnerability analysis and assessment. Applications are especially encouraged from Historically Black Colleges and Universities (HBCUs) and Minority Institutions (MIs).

Financial data The amounts of the awards depend on the nature of the proposal and the availability of funds.

Duration 3 years.

Additional information Although the Army Research Office intends to award a fair proportion of its acquisitions to HBCUs and MIs, it does not set aside a specified percentage.

Number awarded Varies each year.

Deadline Applications may be submitted at any time.

[1106]
ARTIST ENRICHMENT GRANT PROGRAM

Kentucky Foundation for Women
Heyburn Building
332 West Broadway, Suite 1215-A
Louisville, KY 40202-2184
(502) 562-0045 Toll Free: (866) 654-7564
Fax: (502) 561-0420 E-mail: team@kfw.org
Web: www.kfw.org/artenr.html

Summary To support women (particularly African American women) in Kentucky who wish to promote positive social change through feminist expression in the arts.

Eligibility This program is open to women who have resided in Kentucky for at least 1 year and are artists at any stage in their career able to demonstrate potential in terms of quality of work and an understanding of the power of art for social change. Applicants must be seeking funding for a range of activities, including artistic development, artist residencies, the exploration of new areas or techniques, or building a body of work. In the selection process, the following criteria are considered: artwork in the sample is strong, highly original, and reflects feminism and social change; the proposed activities will further the applicant's development as a feminist social change artist; application and work sample demonstrate applicant's understanding and practice of feminism; application and work sample demonstrate a clear understanding of the relationship between art and social change; work plan, timeline, and budget are clear, detailed, and realistic; and applicant's ability to complete the proposed activities in clearly shown. If applications are of equal artistic merit, priority is given to first-time applicants and those from underrepresented demographic populations (such as lesbians, African Americans, and women with disabilities).

Financial data Grants may range from $1,000 to $7,500, but most average between $2,000 and $4,000.

Duration Up to 1 year.

Additional information The foundation was established in 1985. Funding is not provided for general operating costs for organizations; for-profit organizations; tuition costs or living expenses while working toward a degree; endowment or capital campaigns; projects that do not focus on changing the lives of women in Kentucky; the promotion of religious doctrines; non-art related expenses, such as overdue bills or taxes; or work conducted by artists or organizations that have not resided in Kentucky for at least 1 year.

Number awarded Varies each year; recently, 35 of these grants were awarded. A total of $100,000 is available annually.

Deadline September of each year.

[1107]
ASH-AMFDP AWARDS

American Society of Hematology
Attn: Awards Manager
2021 L Street, N.W., Suite 900
Washington, DC 20036
(202) 776-0544 Fax: (202) 776-0545
E-mail: awards@hematology.org
Web: www.hematology.org

Summary To provide an opportunity for African Americans and other historically disadvantaged postdoctoral physicians to conduct a research project in hematology.

Eligibility This program is open to postdoctoral physicians who are members of historically disadvantaged groups, defined as individuals who face challenges because of their race, ethnicity, socioeconomic status, or other similar factors. Applicants must be committed to a career in academic medicine in hematology and to serving as a role model for students and faculty of similar backgrounds. They must identify a mentor at their institution to work with them and give them research and career guidance. Selection is based on excellence in educational career; willingness to devote 4 consecutive years to research; and commitment to an academic career, improving the health status of the underserved, and decreasing health disparities. U.S. citizenship or permanent resident status is required.

Financial data The grant includes a stipend of up to $75,000 per year, a grant of $30,000 per year for support of research activities, complimentary membership in the American Society of Hematology (ASH), and travel support to attend the ASH annual meeting.

Duration 4 years.

Additional information This program, first offered in 2006, is a partnership between the ASH and the Robert Wood Johnson Foundation, whose Minority Medical Faculty Development Program (MMFDP) was renamed the Harold Amos Medical Faculty Development Program (AMFDP) in honor of the first African American to chair a department at the Harvard Medical School. Scholars must spend at least 70% of their time in research activities.

Number awarded At least 1 each year.

Deadline March of each year.

[1108]
ASTRONOMY AND ASTROPHYSICS POSTDOCTORAL FELLOWSHIPS

National Science Foundation
Directorate for Mathematical and Physical Sciences
Attn: Division of Astronomical Sciences
4201 Wilson Boulevard, Room 1030S
Arlington, VA 22230
(703) 292-5039 Fax: (703) 292-9034
TDD: (800) 281-8749 E-mail: eajhar@nsf.gov
Web: www.nsf.gov/funding/pgm_summ.jsp?pims_id=5291

Summary To provide funding to recent doctoral recipients in astronomy or astrophysics (particularly African Americans, other underrepresented minorities, women, and individuals with disabilities) who are interested in pursuing a program of research and education.

Eligibility This program is open to U.S. citizens, nationals, and permanent residents who completed a Ph.D. in astronomy or astrophysics during the previous 5 years. Applicants must be interested in a program of research of an observational, instrumental, or theoretical nature, especially research that is facilitated or enabled by new ground-based capability in radio, optical/IR, or solar astrophysics. Research may be conducted at a U.S. institution of higher education; a national center, facility, or institute funded by the National Science Foundation (NSF), such as the Kavli Institute for Theoretical Physics; a U.S. nonprofit organization with research and educational missions; and/or an international site operated by a U.S. organization eligible for NSF funding, such as Cerro Tololo InterAmerican Observatory. The proposal must include a coherent program of educational activities, such as teaching a course each year at the host institution or an academic institution with ties to the host institution, developing educational materials, or engaging in a significant program of outreach or general education. In the selection process, consideration is given to the achievement of societally relevant outcomes, including full participation of women, persons with disabilities, and underrepresented minorities.

Financial data Grants up to $89,000 per year are available, including a stipend of $62,000 per year paid directly to the fellow and an allowance of $27,000 per year to cover expenses directly related to the research, facilities and other institutional resources, and fringe benefits.

Duration Up to 3 years.

Number awarded 8 to 9 each year.

Deadline October of each year.

[1109]
ATMOSPHERIC AND GEOSPACE SCIENCES POSTDOCTORAL RESEARCH FELLOWSHIPS

National Science Foundation
Directorate for Geosciences
Attn: Division of Atmospheric and Geospace Sciences
4201 Wilson Boulevard, Room 775S
Arlington, VA 22230
(703) 292-4708 Fax: (703) 292-9022
TDD: (800) 281-8749 E-mail: lgeorge@nsf.gov
Web: www.nsf.gov/funding/pgm_summ.jsp?pims_id=12779

Summary To provide funding to postdoctoral scientists (particularly African Americans, other underrepresented minorities, women, and individuals with disabilities) who are interested in conducting research related to activities of the National Science Foundation (NSF) Division of Atmospheric and Geospace Sciences.

Eligibility This program is open to U.S. citizens, nationals, and permanent residents who received a Ph.D. within the past 3 years. Applicants must be interested in conducting a research project that is relevant to the activities of NSF Division of Atmospheric and Geospace Sciences: studies of the physics, chemistry, and dynamics of Earth's upper and lower atmosphere and its space environment; research on climate processes and variations; or studies to understand the natural global cycles of gases and particles in Earth's atmosphere. The project should be conducted at an institution (college or university, private nonprofit institute or museum, government installation, or laboratory) in the United States or abroad other than the applicant's Ph.D.-granting institution. In the selection process, consideration is given to the achievement of societally relevant outcomes, including full participation of women, persons with disabilities, and underrepresented minorities.

Financial data Grants are $86,000 per year, including a stipend of $58,000 per year, a research allowance of $19,000 per year, and a fringe benefit allowance of $9,000 per year.

Duration 2 years.

Number awarded 10 each year.

Deadline January of each year.

[1110]
BEHAVIORAL SCIENCES POSTDOCTORAL FELLOWSHIPS IN EPILEPSY

Epilepsy Foundation
Attn: Research Department
8301 Professional Place
Landover, MD 20785-2353
(301) 459-3700 Toll Free: (800) EFA-1000
Fax: (301) 577-2684 TDD: (800) 332-2070
E-mail: grants@efa.org
Web: www.epilepsyfoundation.org

Summary To provide funding to postdoctorates in the behavioral sciences (particularly African Americans, other minorities, women, and individuals with disabilities) who wish to pursue research training in an area related to epilepsy.

Eligibility Applicants must have received a Ph.D. or equivalent degree in a field of social science, including (but not limited to) sociology, social work, anthropology, nursing, or economics. They must be interested in receiving additional research training to prepare for a career in clinical behavioral aspects of epilepsy. Academic faculty holding the rank of instructor or above are not eligible, nor are graduate or medical students, medical residents, permanent government employees, or employees in private industry. Because these fellowships are designed as training opportunities, the quality of the training plans and environment are considered in the selection process. Other selection criteria include the scientific quality of the proposed research, a statement regarding the relevance of the research to epilepsy, the applicant's qualifications, the preceptor's qualifications, adequacy of the facility, and related epilepsy programs at the institution. Applications from women, members of minority groups, and people with disabilities are especially encouraged. U.S. citizenship is not required, but the research must be conducted in the United States.

Financial data Grants up to $40,000 are available.

Duration 1 year.

Number awarded Varies each year.

Deadline March of each year.

[1111]
BELFER CENTER FOR SCIENCE AND INTERNATIONAL AFFAIRS FELLOWSHIPS

Harvard University
John F. Kennedy School of Government
Belfer Center for Science and International Affairs
Attn: Fellowship Coordinator
79 John F. Kennedy Street, Mailbox 53
Cambridge, MA 02138
(617) 495-8806 Fax: (617) 495-8963
E-mail: bcsia_fellowships@hks.harvard.edu
Web: belfercenter.ksg.harvard.edu/fellowships

Summary To provide funding to professionals, postdoctorates, and doctoral students (particularly African Americans, other minorities, and women) who are interested in conducting research in areas of concern to the Belfer Center for Science and International Affairs at Harvard University in Cambridge, Massachusetts.

Eligibility The postdoctoral fellowship is open to recent recipients of the Ph.D. or equivalent degree, university faculty members, and employees of government, military, international, humanitarian, and private research institutions who have appropriate professional experience. Applicants for predoctoral fellowships must have passed their general examinations. Lawyers, economists, political scientists, those in the natural sciences, and others of diverse disciplinary backgrounds are also welcome to apply. The program especially encourages applications from women, minorities, and citizens of all countries. All applicants must be interested in conducting research in 1 of the 2 major program areas of the center: 1) the International Security Program (ISP), which addresses U.S. defense and foreign policy, security policy, nuclear proliferation, terrorism, internal and ethnic conflict, and related topics; and 2) the Science, Technology, and Public Policy Program (STPP), including technology and innovation, information and communications technology, water-energy nexus, managing the atom, energy technology innovation policy, China and environmental sustainability, geoengineering and climate policy, geopolitics of energy, and geospatial policy and management.

Financial data The stipend is $34,000 for postdoctoral research fellows or $20,000 for predoctoral research fellows. Health insurance is also provided.

Duration 10 months.

Number awarded A limited number each year.

Deadline January of each year.

[1112]
BIG DATA AND ANALYTICS FELLOWSHIPS

American Association for the Advancement of Science
Attn: Science and Technology Policy Fellowships
1200 New York Avenue, N.W.
Washington, DC 20005-3920
(202) 326-6700 Fax: (202) 289-4950
E-mail: fellowships@aaas.org
Web: www.fellowships.aaas.org

Summary To provide postdoctoral scientists and engineers (particularly African Americans, other minorities, women, and individuals with disabilities) at all career stages with an opportunity to work at a federal agency on data and trend analysis issues.

Eligibility This program is open to doctoral-level scientists (Ph.D., M.D., D.V.M., D.Sc., and other terminal degrees) in any field of science (behavioral, biological, computational, earth, health, medical, physical, or social), engineering, or mathematics. Engineers with a master's degree and at least 3 years of professional experience are also eligible. Applicants should be able to apply their analytical skills to data and trend analysis issues from infrastructure, technology, quality control, and presentation to security, integrity, and ethics. They must demonstrate solid scientific and technical credentials; a commitment to serve society; good communication skills; the ability to engage with non-scientific audiences; and an interest in working as special assistants for any federal agency in Washington, D.C. that partners with the sponsoring organization. U.S. citizenship is required; federal employees are not eligible. The sponsor seeks candidates from a broad array of backgrounds and a diversity of geographic, disciplinary, gender, and ethnic perspectives, as well as disability status.

Financial data The stipend for fellows with 0 to 7 years of postdoctoral experience is $74,872 in the first year and $77,368 in the second year. For fellows with 7 to 15 years of experience, the stipend is $84,855 in the first year and $87,350 in the second year. Fellows who have 15 or more years of postdoctoral experience receive $97,333 in the first year and $99,829 in the second year. Also provided are a $4,000 relocation allowance for fellows from outside the Washington, D.C. area, reimbursement for health insurance, and a $4,000 travel allowance.

Duration 1 year, beginning in September; may be renewed for 1 additional year.

Additional information This program began in 2014.

Number awarded 5 to 15 each year.

Deadline October of each year.

[1113]
BIOMEDICAL RESEARCH TRAINING PROGRAM FOR UNDERREPRESENTED GROUPS

National Heart, Lung, and Blood Institute
Attn: Office of Training and Minority Health
6701 Rockledge Drive, Suite 9180
Bethesda, MD 20892-7913
(301) 451-5081 Toll Free: (301) 451-0088
Fax: (301) 480-0862 E-mail: mishoeh@nhlbi.nih.gov
Web: www.nhlbi.nih.gov

Summary To provide training in fundamental biomedical sciences and clinical research disciplines to postbaccalaureate students from underrepresented groups (particularly African Americans, other underrepresented minorities, and individuals with disabilities).

Eligibility This program is open to members of underrepresented groups who are interested in receiving training in fundamental biomedical sciences and clinical research disciplines of interest to the National Heart, Lung, and Blood Institute (NHLBI) of the National Institutes of Health (NIH). Underrepresented individuals include African Americans, Hispanic Americans, American Indians, Alaskan Natives, Native Hawaiians and Pacific Islanders, individuals with disabilities, and individuals from disadvantaged backgrounds. Applicants must be U.S. citizens or permanent residents who have recently completed or will complete a bachelor's degree by the summer of selection with course work relevant to biomedical, behavioral, or statistical research. They must have a

GPA of 3.3 or higher. Research experiences are available in the NHLBI Division of Intramural Research and its Division of Cardiovascular Sciences.

Financial data Stipends in the first year of work are $27,200 for participants with 0 to 1 year of experience or $29,100 for those with 1 to 2 years of experience. In the second year of work, stipends are $29,100 for those who begin with 0 to 1 year of experience or $30,400 for those with 1 to 2 years of experience.

Duration 1 to 2 years, beginning from June to September of the selection year.

Additional information Training is conducted in the laboratories of the NHLBI in Bethesda, Maryland. Activities in the Division of Intramural Research include clinical research training in the hematology branch and the cardio-pulmonary branch; basic science research training is provided by its centers for genetics and developmental biology, immunology, molecular medicine, systems biology, cell biology and physiology, and biochemistry and biophysics. The Division of Cardiovascular Sciences provides training in the basic principles of design, implementation, and analysis of epidemiology studies and clinical trials. Upon completion of this training, participants are expected to apply to graduate or professional school.

Number awarded Varies each year.

Deadline January of each year.

[1114]
BROADENING PARTICIPATION RESEARCH INITIATION GRANTS IN ENGINEERING (BRIGE)

National Science Foundation
Directorate for Engineering
Attn: Engineering Education and Centers
4201 Wilson Boulevard, Room 585N
Arlington, VA 22230
(703) 292-8071 Fax: (703) 292-9085
TDD: (800) 281-8749 E-mail: rnsmith@nsf.gov
Web: www.nsf.gov

Summary To provide funding to African Americans and members of other underrepresented groups who are junior faculty members interested in conducting research in engineering.

Eligibility This program is open to U.S. citizens or permanent residents who are members of groups underrepresented in engineering: women, persons with disabilities, African Americans, Hispanics, Native Americans, Alaska Natives, and Pacific Islanders. Applicants must have held a full-time tenure-track faculty position for no more than 3 years. They must be interested in conducting engineering research that is innovative and potentially transformative. Faculty at Minority Serving Institutions (Historically Black Colleges and Universities, Hispanic Serving Institutions, Tribal Colleges and Universities, and Predominantly Black Institutions) are also encouraged to apply.

Financial data The maximum grant is $175,000 in direct and indirect costs for up to 24 months.

Duration Up to 2 years.

Number awarded 25 to 30 each year.

Deadline April of each year.

[1115]
BURROUGHS WELLCOME FUND CAREER AWARDS FOR MEDICAL SCIENTISTS

Burroughs Wellcome Fund
21 T.W. Alexander Drive, Suite 100
P.O. Box 13901
Research Triangle Park, NC 27709-3901
(919) 991-5100 Fax: (919) 991-5160
E-mail: info@bwfund.org
Web: www.bwfund.org

Summary To provide funding to biomedical scientists in the United States and Canada (particularly African Americans, other underrepresented minorities, and women) who require assistance to make the transition from postdoctoral training to faculty appointment.

Eligibility This program is open to citizens and permanent residents of the United States and Canada who have an M.D., D.D.S., or D.V.M. degree and from 2 to 10 years of postdoctoral research experience. Candidates who work in reproductive science are encouraged to apply. Applicants must be interested in a program of research training in the area of basic biomedical, disease-oriented, or translational research. Training must take place at a degree-granting medical school, graduate school, hospital, or research institute in the United States or Canada. Each U.S. and Canadian institution may nominate up to 5 candidates. The sponsor encourages institutions to nominate women and underrepresented minorities (African Americans, Hispanics, or Native Americans); if a woman or underrepresented minority is among the initial 5 candidates, the institution may nominate a sixth candidate who is a woman or underrepresented minority.

Financial data The stipend is $140,000 per year.

Duration 5 years.

Additional information This program began in 1995 as Career Awards in the Biomedical Sciences (CABS). It was revised to its current format in 2006 as a result of the NIH K99/R00 Pathway to Independence program. As the CABS, the program provided more than $100 million in support to 241 U.S. and Canadian scientists. Awardees are required to devote at least 75% of their time to research-related activities.

Number awarded Varies each year: recently, 10 of these awards were granted.

Deadline September of each year.

[1116]
BYRD POSTDOCTORAL FELLOWSHIP PROGRAM

Ohio State University
Byrd Polar Research Center
Attn: Fellowship Committee
Scott Hall Room 108
1090 Carmack Road
Columbus, OH 43210-1002
(614) 292-6531 Fax: (614) 292-4697
Web: bprc.osu.edu/byrdfellow

Summary To provide funding to postdoctorates (particularly African Americans, other minorities, women, individuals with disabilities, and those with ties to the military) who are interested in conducting research on the Arctic or Antarctic areas at Ohio State University.

Eligibility This program is open to postdoctorates of superior academic background who are interested in conducting advanced research on either Arctic or Antarctic problems at the Byrd Polar Research Center at Ohio State University. Applicants must have received their doctorates within the past 5 years. Along with their application, they must submit a description of the specific research to be conducted during the fellowship and a curriculum vitae. Women, minorities, Vietnam-era veterans, disabled veterans, and individuals with disabilities are particularly encouraged to apply.

Financial data The stipend is $42,000 per year; an allowance of $5,000 for research and travel is also provided.

Duration 18 months.

Additional information This program was established by a major gift from the Byrd Foundation in memory of Rear Admiral Richard Evelyn Byrd and Marie Ames Byrd, his wife. Except for field work or other research activities requiring absence from campus, fellows are expected to be in residence at the university for the duration of the program.

Deadline March of each year.

[1117]
CAREER DEVELOPMENT AWARDS IN DIABETES RESEARCH

Juvenile Diabetes Research Foundation International
Attn: Grant Administrator
26 Broadway, 14th Floor
New York, NY 10004
(212) 479-7572 Toll Free: (800) 533-CURE
Fax: (212) 785-9595 E-mail: info@jdrf.org
Web: jdrf.org

Summary To assist young scientists (particularly African Americans, other underrepresented minorities, individuals with disabilities, and women) to develop into independent investigators in diabetes-related research.

Eligibility This program is open to postdoctorates early in their faculty careers who show promise as diabetes researchers. Applicants must have received their first doctoral (M.D., Ph.D., D.M.D., D.V.M., or equivalent) degree at least 3 but not more than 7 years previously. They may not have an academic position at the associate professor, professor, or equivalent level, but they must be a faculty member (instructor or assistant professor) at a university, health science center, or comparable institution with strong, well-established research and training programs. The proposed research must relate to Type 1 diabetes, but it may be basic or clinical. There are no citizenship requirements. Applications are encouraged from women, members of minority groups underrepresented in the sciences, and people with disabilities. The proposed research may be conducted at foreign or domestic, for-profit or non-profit, or public or private institutions, including universities, colleges, hospitals, laboratories, units of state or local government, or eligible agencies of the federal government. Selection is based on the applicant's perceived ability and potential for a career in Type 1 diabetes research, the caliber of the proposed research, and the quality and commitment of the host institution.

Financial data The total award may be up to $150,000 each year. Indirect costs cannot exceed 10%.

Duration Up to 5 years.

Additional information Fellows must spend up to 75% of their time in research.

Number awarded Varies each year.

Deadline August of each year.

[1118]
CAROLINE CRAIG AUGUSTYN AND DAMIAN AUGUSTYN AWARD IN DIGESTIVE CANCER

American Gastroenterological Association
Attn: AGA Research Foundation
Research Awards Manager
4930 Del Ray Avenue
Bethesda, MD 20814-2512
(301) 222-4012 Fax: (301) 654-5920
E-mail: awards@gastro.org
Web: www.gastro.org/aga-foundation/grants

Summary To provide funding to junior investigators (particularly African Americans, other minorities, and individuals with disabilities) who are interested in conducting research related to digestive cancer.

Eligibility Applicants must have an M.D., Ph.D., or equivalent degree and a full-time faculty position at an accredited North American institution. They must have received an NIH K series or other federal or non-federal career development award of at least 4 years duration, but may not have received an R01 or equivalent award. For M.D. applicants, no more than 7 years may have elapsed following the completion of clinical training, and for Ph.D. applicants no more than 7 years may have elapsed since the completion of their degree. Individual membership in the American Gastroenterology Association (AGA) is required. The proposal must relate to the pathogenesis, prevention, diagnosis, or treatment of digestive cancer. Women and minority investigators are strongly encouraged to apply. Selection is based on the qualifications of the candidate and the novelty, feasibility, and significance of their research.

Financial data The grant is $40,000. Funds may be used for salary, supplies, or equipment. Indirect costs are not allowed.

Duration 1 year.

Number awarded 1 each year.

Deadline January of each year.

[1119]
CARTER G. WOODSON INSTITUTE POSTDOCTORAL RESIDENTIAL RESEARCH AND TEACHING FELLOWSHIP

University of Virginia
Carter G. Woodson Institute for African-American and African Studies
Attn: Director of the Fellowship Program
108 Minor Hall
P.O. Box 400162
Charlottesville, VA 22904-4162
(804) 924-8892 Fax: (804) 924-8820
E-mail: woodson@virginia.edu
Web: www.artsandsciences.virginia.edu

Summary To support postdoctoral research at the University of Virginia's Woodson Institute in those disciplines of the humanities and social sciences concerned with African American and African studies.

Eligibility Applicants for postdoctoral fellowships must have completed their Ph.D. by the time of application or furnish proof of its receipt before July of the fellowship year. They must be interested in conducting research in the fields of African American studies, African studies, or Afro-Caribbean studies, and in those disciplines within the humanities and social sciences traditionally related to those fields. Preference is given to applicants whose work 1) advances theories on the construction of race and race in relation to other social identities (class, gender, sexuality, nationality, disability) as well as that which focuses on refining methods of interdisciplinary scholarship on race; 2) engages the professions (law, medicine, social work, public policy, education, architecture, planning) in innovative ways; or 3) can be readily adapted for the creation of courses and pedagogies directly related to the institute's curriculum in African American and Diasporic Studies. Selection is based on the significance of the proposed work, the qualifications of the applicant, familiarity with existing relevant research literature, the research design of the project, and the promise of completion within the award period. Awards are granted without restriction on citizenship or current residence.

Financial data The grant is $45,000 per year.

Duration 2 years.

Additional information Fellows must be in residence at the University of Virginia for the duration of the award period. They are expected to contribute to the intellectual life of the university.

Number awarded 1 or 2 each year.

Deadline November of each year.

[1120]
CENTER FOR ADVANCED STUDY IN THE BEHAVIORAL SCIENCES RESIDENTIAL POSTDOCTORAL FELLOWSHIPS

Center for Advanced Study in the Behavioral Sciences
Attn: Secretary and Program Coordinator
75 Alta Road
Stanford, CA 94305-8090
(650) 736-0100 Fax: (650) 736-0221
E-mail: casbs-secretary@casbs.org
Web: www.casbs.org

Summary To provide funding to behavioral scientists (particularly African Americans, other minorities, women, and younger scholars) who are interested in conducting research at the Center for Advanced Study in the Behavioral Sciences in Stanford, California.

Eligibility Eligible to be nominated for this fellowship are scientists and scholars from this country or abroad who show exceptional accomplishment or promise in the core social and behavioral disciplines: anthropology, economics, political science, psychology, or sociology; applications are also accepted from scholars in a wide range of humanistic disciplines, education, linguistics, and the biological sciences. Selection is based on standing in the field rather than on the merit of a particular project under way at a given time. A special effort is made to promote diversity among the scholars by encouraging participation from groups that often have been overlooked in academia: younger scholars, women, minorities, international scholars, and scholars whose home universities are not research-oriented.

Financial data The stipend is based on the fellow's regular salary for the preceding year, with a cap of $65,000. In most cases, the fellow contributes to the cost of the stipend with support from sabbatical or other funding source.

Duration From 9 to 11 months.

Additional information Fellows must be in residence in a community within 10 miles of the center for the duration of the program (that requirement excludes San Francisco, Berkeley, and San Jose, for example).

Number awarded Approximately 45 each year.

Deadline September of each year.

[1121]
CHARLES L. BREWER DISTINGUISHED TEACHING OF PSYCHOLOGY AWARD

American Psychological Foundation
750 First Street, N.E.
Washington, DC 20002-4242
(202) 336-5843 Fax: (202) 336-5812
E-mail: foundation@apa.org
Web: www.apa.org/apf/funding/brewer.aspx

Summary To recognize and reward the distinguished career contributions of outstanding psychology professors, particularly those who are African Americans, other minorities, women, or individuals with disabilities.

Eligibility This award is available to psychologists who demonstrate outstanding teaching. Selection is based on evidence of influence as a teacher of students who become psychologists, research on teaching, development of effective teaching methods and/or materials, development of innovation curricula and courses, performance as a classroom teacher, demonstrated training of teachers of psychology, teaching of advanced research methods and practice in psychology, and/or administrative facilitation of teaching. Nominators must complete an application form, write a letter of support, and submit the nominee's current vitae and bibliography. The sponsor encourages nominations of individuals who represent diversity in race, ethnicity, gender, age, disability, and sexual orientation.

Financial data Awardees receive a plaque, a $2,000 honorarium, and an all-expense paid trip to the annual convention where the award is presented.

Duration The award is presented annually.

Additional information This award, originally named the Distinguished Teaching in Psychology Award, was first presented in 1970.

Number awarded 1 each year.

Deadline Nominations must be submitted by November of each year.

[1122]
CLINICAL RESEARCH POST-DOCTORAL FELLOWSHIP PROGRAM

American Nurses Association
Attn: SAMHSA Minority Fellowship Programs
8515 Georgia Avenue, Suite 400
Silver Spring, MD 20910-3492
(301) 628-5247 Toll Free: (800) 274-4ANA
Fax: (301) 628-5339 E-mail: janet.jackson@ana.org
Web: www.emfp.org

Summary To provide funding to African American and other minority postdoctoral nurses who are interested in a program of research and study on psychiatric, mental health, and substance abuse issues that impact the lives of ethnic minority people.

Eligibility This program is open to doctoral-prepared nurses who are members of an ethnic or racial minority group, including but not limited to Blacks or African Americans, Hispanics or Latinos, American Indians and Alaska Natives, Asian Americans, and Native Hawaiians and other Pacific Islanders. Applicants must be able to demonstrate a commitment to a research career in nursing and psychiatric/mental health issues affecting ethnic minority populations. They must be interested in a program of full-time postdoctoral study, with a research focus on such issues of concern to minority populations as substance abuse treatment capacity, mental health system transformation, prevention, co-occurring disorders, seclusion and restraint, children and families, disaster readiness and response, homelessness, older adults, HIV/AIDS and hepatitis, and criminal and juvenile justice. U.S. citizenship or permanent resident status and membership in the American Nurses Association are required.

Financial data The stipend depends on the number of years of postdoctoral experience, ranging from $39,264 for less than 1 year to $54,180 for 7 or more years.

Duration 1 to 2 years.

Additional information Funds for this program are provided by the Substance Abuse and Mental Health Services Administration (SAMHSA).

Number awarded 1 or more each year.

Deadline February of each year.

[1123]
CMS HISTORICALLY BLACK COLLEGES AND UNIVERSITIES HEALTH SERVICES RESEARCH GRANT PROGRAM

Centers for Medicare & Medicaid Services
Attn: Center for Medicare and Medicaid Innovation
Mail Stop WB-06-05
7500 Security Boulevard
Baltimore, MD 21244-1850
(410) 786-7250 Toll Free: (877) 267-2323
TDD: (877) 486-2048
E-mail: Richard.Bragg@cms.hhs.gov
Web: www.cms.gov

Summary To provide funding to faculty at Historically Black Colleges and Universities (HBCUs) interested in carrying out health services research activities.

Eligibility This program is open to faculty at HBCUs that meet 1 of the following requirements: 1) offers a Ph.D. or master's degree in 1 or more of the following disciplines: allied health, gerontology, health care administration, nursing, pharmacology, public health, or social work; 2) has a school of medicine; or 3) is a member of the National HBCU Network for Health Services and Health Disparities. Applicants must be interested in conducting small research projects that relate to health care deliver and health financing issues affecting African American communities, including issues of access to health care, utilization of health care services, health outcomes, quality of services, cost of care, health disparities, socio-economic differences, cultural barriers, managed care systems, and activities related to health screening, prevention, outreach, and education.

Financial data Grants range up to $100,000 per year.

Duration Up to 2 years.

Additional information This program began in 1997. Until 2001, the Centers for Medicare & Medicaid Services was known as the Health Care Financing Administration.

Number awarded Varies each year; recently, 1 of these grants was available.

Deadline Letters of intent must be submitted in June of each year. Final applications are due in July.

[1124]
CONGRESSIONAL FELLOWS PROGRAM

Congressional Black Caucus Foundation, Inc.
Attn: Leadership Institute for Public Service
1720 Massachusetts Avenue, N.W.
Washington, DC 20036
(202) 263-2800 Toll Free: (800) 784-2577
Fax: (202) 775-0773 E-mail: internships@cbcfinc.org
Web: www.cbcfinc.org/lips.html

Summary To provide African Americans with a fellowship so they can work directly with members of Congress on committees or as personal staff.

Eligibility This program is open to African Americans who have a master's or professional degree and familiarity with the federal legislative process, Congress, the Congressional Black Caucus (CBC), and its members. Applicants must be interested in working in Washington, D.C. on the staff or committee of a member of the CBC. They must be able to demonstrate an interest in public policy, a record of academic and professional achievement, evidence of leadership skills, potential for further growth, and U.S. citizenship or permit to work in the United States. Preference is given to applicants with expertise in areas that support policy agendas of CBC members.

Financial data The stipend is $40,000; fellows are responsible for their own travel, housing, and other expenses.

Duration 20 months, beginning in September.

Additional information This program began in 1976 as a graduate intern program and was expanded to its present form in 1982.

Number awarded 6 to 9 each year.

Deadline March of each year.

[1125]
CORETTA SCOTT KING BOOK AWARD

American Library Association
Attn: Ethnic and Multicultural Material Information Exchange Round Table
c/o Office for Literacy and Outreach Services
50 East Huron Street
Chicago, IL 60611-2795
(312) 280-4294 Toll Free: (800) 545-2433, ext. 4294
Fax: (312) 280-3256 TDD: (888) 814-7692
E-mail: olos@ala.org
Web: www.ala.org/emiert/cskbookawards

Summary To recognize and reward African American authors and illustrators of published works for youth on the African American experience.

Eligibility This award is available to African American authors and illustrators who have written or illustrated work for a young audience. Entries must be original work that portrays an aspect of the African American experience, including biographical, social, historical, and social history treatments.

Work by authors must meet established standards of quality writing for youth, including clear plot, well-drawn characters that portray growth and development during the course of the story, writing style that is consistent with and suitable to the audience, and accuracy. Work by illustrators should lead to an appreciation of beauty, be neither coy nor condescending, enlarge upon the story elements that were suggested in the text, and include details that will awaken and strengthen the imagination of readers and permit them to interpret the words and pictures in a manner unique to them. Particular attention is given to titles that seek to motivate readers to develop their own attitudes and behaviors as well as comprehend their personal duty and responsibility as citizens in a pluralistic society. Authors and illustrators must live in the United States or maintain dual residency/citizenship.

Financial data The awards, presented at the annual conference of the American Library Association, consist of a plaque and $1,000.

Duration The award is presented annually.

Additional information These awards have been presented since 1969.

Number awarded 2 each year: 1 to an author and 1 to an illustrator.

Deadline November of each year.

[1126] DANIEL H. EFRON RESEARCH AWARD

American College of Neuropsychopharmacology
Attn: Executive Office
5034-A Thoroughbred Lane
Brentwood, TN 37027
(615) 324-2360 Fax: (615) 523-1715
E-mail: acnp@acnp.org
Web: www.acnp.org/programs/awards.aspx

Summary To recognize and reward young scientists (particularly African Americans, other minorities, and women) who have completed outstanding basic or translational research to neuropsychopharmacology.

Eligibility This award is available to scientists who are younger than 50 years of age. Nominees must have made an outstanding basic or translational contribution to neuropsychopharmacology. The contribution may be preclinical or work that emphasizes the relationship between basic and clinical research. Selection is based on the quality of the contribution and its impact on advancing neuropsychopharmacology. Membership in the American College of Neuropsychopharmacology (ACNP) is not required. Nomination of women and minorities is highly encouraged.

Financial data The award consists of an expense-paid trip to the ACNP annual meeting, a monetary honorarium, and a plaque.

Duration The award is presented annually.

Additional information This award was first presented in 1974.

Number awarded 1 each year.

Deadline Nominations must be submitted by June of each year.

[1127] DARLENE CLARK HINE AWARD

Organization of American Historians
Attn: Award and Committee Coordinator
112 North Bryan Street
Bloomington, IN 47408-4141
(812) 855-7311 Fax: (812) 855-0696
E-mail: khamm@oah.org
Web: www.oah.org/awards/awards.hine.index.html

Summary To recognize and reward authors of outstanding books dealing with African American women's and gender history.

Eligibility This award is presented to the author of the outstanding book in African American women's and gender history. Entries must have been published during the current calendar year.

Financial data The award is $1,000.

Duration The award is presented annually.

Additional information This award was first presented in 2010.

Number awarded 1 each year.

Deadline September of each year.

[1128] DEPARTMENT OF DEFENSE SMALL BUSINESS INNOVATION RESEARCH GRANTS

Department of Defense
Attn: Office of Small Business Programs
4800 Mark Center Drive, Suite 15G13
Alexandria, VA 22530
Toll Free: (866) SBIR-HLP
E-mail: administrator.dodsbir@osd.mil
Web: www.acq.osd.mil/osbp/sbir

Summary To support small businesses (especially those owned by African Americans, other minorities, or women) that have the technological expertise to contribute to the research and development mission of various agencies within the Department of Defense.

Eligibility For the purposes of this program, a "small business" is defined as a firm that is organized for profit with a location in the United States; is in the legal form of an individual proprietorship, partnership, limited liability company, corporation, joint venture, association, trust, or cooperative; is at least 51% owned and controlled by 1 or more individuals who are citizens or permanent residents of the United States; and has (including its affiliates) fewer than 500 employees. The primary employment of the principal investigator must be with the firm at the time of award and during the conduct of the proposed project. Applications are encouraged from 1) women-owned small business concerns, defined as those that are at least 51% owned by a woman or women who also control and operate them; and 2) socially and economically disadvantaged small business concerns that are at least 51% owned by an Indian tribe, a Native Hawaiian organization, or 1 or more socially and economically disadvantaged individuals (African Americans, Hispanic Americans, Native Americans, Asian Pacific Americans, or subcontinent Asian Americans). Agencies that offer Department of Defense Small Business Innovation Research (SBIR) programs are the Department of the Army, Department of the Navy, Department of the Air Force, Defense Advanced Research Projects

Agency (DARPA), Defense Threat Reduction Agency (DTRA), Chemical and Biological Defense (CBD), Defense Health Program (DHP), Defense Logistics Agency (DLA), Special Operations Command (SOCOM), Missile Defense Agency (MDA), National Geospatial-Intelligence Agency (NGA), Defense Microelectronics Activity (DMEA), and Office of Secretary of Defense (OSD). Selection is based on the soundness, technical merit, and innovation of the proposed approach and its incremental progress toward topic or subtopic solution; the qualifications of the principal investigator, supporting staff, and consultants; and the potential for commercial application and the benefits expected to accrue from this commercialization.

Financial data Grants are offered in 2 phases. In phase 1, awards normally range from $70,000 to $150,000 (for both direct and indirect costs); in phase 2, awards normally range from $500,000 to $1,000,000 (including both direct and indirect costs).

Duration Phase 1 awards may extend up to 6 months; phase 2 awards may extend up to 2 years.

Number awarded Varies each year; recently, 1,816 Phase 1 awards were granted: 582 for Department of the Navy, 295 for Department of the Army, 480 for Department of the Air Force, 68 for DARPA, 17 for DTRA, 16 for CBD, 16 for SOCOM, 122 for MDA, 7 for DLA, 40 for DHP, 4 for NGA, and 160 for OSD. The number of Phase 2 awards was 938, including 321 for Department of the Navy, 190 for Department of the Army, 207 for Department of the Air Force, 60 for DARPA, 4 for DTRA, 12 for CBD, 8 for SOCOM, 67 for MDA, 2 for DLA, 1 for DMEA, 27 for DHP, and 39 for OSD. Total funding was approximately $1.04 billion.

Deadline September of each year.

[1129]
DEPARTMENT OF DEFENSE SMALL BUSINESS TECHNOLOGY TRANSFER GRANTS

Department of Defense
Attn: Office of Small Business Programs
4800 Mark Center Drive, Suite 15G13
Alexandria, VA 22530
Toll Free: (866) SBIR-HLP
E-mail: administrator.dodsbir@osd.mil
Web: www.acq.osd.mil/osbp/sbir

Summary To provide financial support to cooperative research and development projects carried out between small business concerns (particularly those owned by African Americans, other minorities, or women) and research institutions in areas of interest to various agencies within the Department of Defense.

Eligibility For the purposes of this program, a "small business" is defined as a firm that is organized for profit with a location in the United States; is in the legal form of an individual proprietorship, partnership, limited liability company, corporation, joint venture, association, trust, or cooperative; is at least 51% owned and controlled by 1 or more individuals who are citizens or permanent residents of the United States; and has (including its affiliates) fewer than 500 employees. Unlike the Department of Defense Small Business Innovation Research Grants, the primary employment of the principal investigator does not need to be with the business concern. This program, however, requires that the small business apply in collaboration with a nonprofit research institution for conduct of a project that has potential for commercialization. At least 40% of the work must be performed by the small business and at least 30% of the work must be performed by the research institution. Principal investigators from the nonprofit research institution must commit at least 10% of their effort to the project. Applications are encouraged from 1) women-owned small business concerns, defined as those that are at least 51% owned by a woman or women who also control and operate them; and 2) socially and economically disadvantaged small business concerns that are at least 51% owned by an Indian tribe, a Native Hawaiian organization, or 1 or more socially and economically disadvantaged individuals (African Americans, Hispanic Americans, Native Americans, Asian Pacific Americans, or subcontinent Asian Americans). Partnerships between small businesses and Historically Black Colleges and Universities (HBCUs) and Minority Institutions (MIs) are especially encouraged. Agencies of the Department of Defense currently participating in this program are the Department of the Army, Department of the Navy, Department of the Air Force, Defense Advanced Research Projects Agency (DARPA), Missile Defense Agency (MDA), and Office of Secretary of Defense (OSD). Selection is based on the soundness, technical merit, and innovation of the proposed approach and its incremental progress toward topic or subtopic solution; the qualifications of the proposed principal investigators, supporting staff, and consultants; and the potential for commercial application and the benefits expected to accrue from this commercialization.

Financial data In the first phase, annual awards range from $70,000 to $150,000 for direct costs, indirect costs, and negotiated fixed fees. In the second phase, awards from $500,000 to $1,000,000 for the full period are available.

Duration Generally 1 year for the first phase and 2 years for the second phase.

Additional information Grants in the first phase are to determine the scientific, technical, and commercial merit and feasibility of the proposed cooperative effort and the quality of performance of the small business concern. In the second phase, the research and development efforts continue, depending on the results of the first phase.

Number awarded Varies each year; recently, 309 Phase 1 awards were granted: 63 for Department of the Army, 117 for Department of the Navy, 87 for Department of the Air Force, 23 for OSD, and 19 for MDA. The number of Phase 2 awards was 127, including 31 for Department of the Army, 54 for Department of the Navy, 28 for Department of the Air Force, 5 for DARPA, 3 for OSD, and 6 for MDA. Total funding was approximately $117 million.

Deadline April of each year.

[1130]
DEPARTMENT OF EDUCATION SMALL BUSINESS INNOVATION RESEARCH GRANTS

Department of Education
Attn: Institute of Education Sciences
555 New Jersey Avenue, N.W., Room 608D
Washington, DC 20208-5544
(202) 208-1983 Fax: (202) 219-2030
E-mail: Edward.metz@ed.gov
Web: www2.ed.gov/programs/sbir/index.html

Summary To support small businesses (especially those owned by African Americans, other minorities, or women) that have the technological expertise to contribute to the research and development mission of the Department of Education.

Eligibility For the purposes of this program, a "small business" is defined as a firm that is organized for profit with a location in the United States; is in the legal form of an individual proprietorship, partnership, limited liability company, corporation, joint venture, association, trust, or cooperative; is at least 51% owned and controlled by 1 or more individuals who are citizens or permanent residents of the United States; and has (including its affiliates) fewer than 500 employees. The primary employment of the principal investigator must be with the firm at the time of award and during the conduct of the proposed project. Applications are encouraged from 1) women-owned small business concerns, defined as those that are at least 51% owned by a woman or women who also control and operate them; and 2) socially and economically disadvantaged small business concerns that are at least 51% owned by an Indian tribe, a Native Hawaiian organization, or 1 or more socially and economically disadvantaged individuals (African Americans, Hispanic Americans, Native Americans, Asian Pacific Americans, or subcontinent Asian Americans). Firms with strong research capabilities in science, engineering, or educational technology in any of the topic areas are encouraged to participate. Recently, the program operated in 2 branches of the Department of Education: 1) the National Institute on Disability and Rehabilitations Research (NIDRR) within the Office of Special Education and Rehabilitative Services (OSERS); and 2) the Institute of Education Sciences (IES), formerly the Office of Educational Research and Improvement (OERI). Selection is based on quality of project design (45 points), significance (25 points), quality of project personnel (20 points), and adequacy of resources (10 points).

Financial data Grants are offered in 2 phases. Phase 1 awards normally do not exceed $150,000; phase 2 awards normally do not exceed $750,000 for IES programs or $500,000 for OSERS/NIDRR programs.

Duration Phase 1 awards may extend up to 6 months; phase 2 awards may extend up to 2 years.

Additional information Information on the NIDRR program is available from the Office of Special Education and Rehabilitative Services, Potomac Center Plaza, 550 12th Street, Room 5140, Washington, DC 20202-2700, (202) 245-7338, E-mail: Lynn.Medley@ed.gov.

Number awarded Varies each year; recently, 25 Phase 1 awards (9 for IES and 16 for NIDRR) and 21 Phase 1 awards (16 for IES and 5 for NIDRR) were granted.

Deadline February of each year for IES proposals; June of each year for NIDRR proposals.

[1131]
DEPARTMENT OF HOMELAND SECURITY SMALL BUSINESS INNOVATION RESEARCH GRANTS

Department of Homeland Security
Homeland Security Advanced Research Projects Agency
Attn: SBIR Program Manager
Washington, DC 20528
(202) 254-6768 Toll Free: (800) 754-3043
Fax: (202) 254-7170 E-mail: elissa.sobolewski@dhs.gov
Web: www.dhs.gov/files/grants/gc_1247254058883.shtm

Summary To support small businesses (especially those owned by African Americans, other minorities, disabled veterans, or women) that have the technological expertise to contribute to the research and development mission of the Department of Homeland Security (DHS).

Eligibility For the purposes of this program, a "small business" is defined as a firm that is organized for profit with a location in the United States; is in the legal form of an individual proprietorship, partnership, limited liability company, corporation, joint venture, association, trust, or cooperative; is at least 51% owned and controlled by 1 or more individuals who are citizens or permanent residents of the United States; and has (including its affiliates) fewer than 500 employees. The primary employment of the principal investigator must be with the firm at the time of award and during the conduct of the proposed project. Applications are encouraged from 1) women-owned small business concerns, defined as those that are at least 51% owned by a woman or women who also control and operate them; 2) socially and economically disadvantaged small business concerns that are at least 51% owned by an Indian tribe, a Native Hawaiian organization, or 1 or more socially and economically disadvantaged individuals (African Americans, Hispanic Americans, Native Americans, Asian Pacific Americans, or subcontinent Asian Americans); and 3) service-disabled veteran small business concerns that are at least 51% owned by a service-disabled veteran and controlled by such a veteran or (for veterans with permanent and severe disability) the spouse or permanent caregiver of such a veteran. Each year, DHS identifies specialized topics for investigation. Selection is based on the soundness, technical merit, and innovation of the proposed approach and its incremental progress toward topic or subtopic solution; the qualifications of the proposed principal investigators, supporting staff, and consultants; the potential for commercial application and the benefits expected to accrue from this commercialization; and the realism and reasonableness of the cost proposal.

Financial data Grants are offered in 2 phases. In phase 1, awards normally range up to $100,000; in phase 2, awards normally range up to $750,000.

Duration Phase 1 awards may extend up to 6 months; phase 2 awards may extend up to 2 years.

Number awarded Varies each year; recently, 61 Phase 1 awards were granted.

Deadline January and July of each year.

[1132]
DEPARTMENT OF HOMELAND SECURITY SUMMER FACULTY AND STUDENT RESEARCH TEAM PROGRAM

Oak Ridge Institute for Science and Education
Attn: Science and Engineering Education
P.O. Box 117
Oak Ridge, TN 37831-0117
(865) 574-1447 Fax: (865) 241-5219
E-mail: Patti.Obenour@orau.gov
Web: see.orau.org

Summary To provide an opportunity for teams of students and faculty from minority-serving educational institutions to conduct research during the summer in areas of interest to the Department of Homeland Security (DHS).

Eligibility This program is open to teams of up to 2 students (undergraduate and/or graduate) and 1 faculty from Historically Black Colleges and Universities (HBCUs), Hispanic Serving Institutions (HSIs), Tribal Colleges and Universities (TCUs), Alaska Native Serving Institutions (ANSIs), and Native Hawaiian Serving Institutions (NHSIs). Applicants must be interested in conducting research at designated DHS Centers of Excellence in science, technology, engineering, or mathematics related to homeland security (HS-STEM), including explosives detection, mitigation, and response; social and behavioral sciences; risk, economics, and decision sciences; human factors; chemical threats and countermeasures; biological threats and countermeasures; community, commerce, and infrastructure resilience; food and agricultural security; transportation security; border security; immigration studies; maritime and port security; infrastructure protection; natural disasters and related geophysical studies; emergency preparedness and response; communications and interoperability; or advanced data analysis and visualization. Faculty must have a full-time appointment at an eligible institution and have received a Ph.D. in an HS-STEM discipline no more than 7 years previously; at least 2 years of full-time research and/or teaching experience is preferred. Students must have a GPA of 3.0 or higher and be enrolled full time. Undergraduates must be entering their junior or senior year. U.S. citizenship is required. Selection is based on relevance and intrinsic merit of the research (40%), faculty applicant qualifications (30%), academic benefit to the faculty applicant and his/her institution (10%), and student applicant qualifications (20%).

Financial data Stipends are $1,200 per week for faculty, $600 per week for graduate students, and $500 per week for undergraduates. Faculty members who live more than 50 miles from their assigned site may receive a housing allowance of $1,500 and travel expenses up to an additional $500. Limited travel expenses for 1 round trip are reimbursed for undergraduate and graduate students living more than 50 miles from their assigned site.

Duration 12 weeks during the summer.

Additional information This program is funded by DHS and administered by Oak Ridge Institute for Science and Education (ORISE). Recently, the available DHS Centers of Excellence were the Center for Advancing Microbial Risk Assessment (led by Michigan State University and Drexel University); the National Center for Risk and Economic Analysis of Terrorism Events (led by University of Southern California); the National Center for Food Protection and Defense (led by University of Minnesota); the Center of Excellence for Zoonotic and Animal Disease Defense (led by Texas A&M University and Kansas State University); the National Consortium for the Study of Terrorism and Responses to Terrorism (led by University of Maryland); the Center of Excellence for Awareness and Localization of Explosives-Related Threats (led by Northeastern University and University of Rhode Island); the National Center for Border Security and Immigration (led by the University of Arizona and the University of Texas at El Paso); the Center for Maritime, Island and Remote and Extreme Environment Security (led by the University of Hawaii and Stevens Institute of Technology); the Coastal Hazards Center of Excellence (led by the University of North Carolina at Chapel Hill and Jackson State University); the National Transportation Security Center of Excellence (consisting of 7 institutions); and the Center of Excellence in Command, Control, and Interoperability (led by Purdue University and Rutgers University).

Number awarded Approximately 12 teams are selected each year.

Deadline January of each year.

[1133] DIANE J. WILLIS EARLY CAREER AWARD

American Psychological Foundation
750 First Street, N.E.
Washington, DC 20002-4242
(202) 336-5843 Fax: (202) 336-5812
E-mail: foundation@apa.org
Web: www.apa.org/apf/funding/div-37-willis.aspx

Summary To provide funding to young psychologists (particularly African Americans, other underrepresented minorities, women, and individuals with disabilities) who are interested in conducting research or other projects related to children and families.

Eligibility This program is open to young psychologists who completed a doctoral degree (Ed.D., Psy.D., Ph.D.) within the past 7 years. Applicants must be interested in conducting research or other projects that inform, advocate for, and improve the mental health and well-being of children and families, particularly through public policy. The sponsor encourages applications from individuals who represent diversity in race, ethnicity, gender, age, disability, and sexual orientation.

Financial data The grant is $2,000.

Duration 1 year.

Additional information This program, sponsored by Division 37 (Child and Family Policy and Practice) of the American Psychological Association (APA), began in 2013.

Number awarded 1 each year.

Deadline January of each year.

[1134] DIPLOMACY, SECURITY, AND DEVELOPMENT FELLOWSHIPS

American Association for the Advancement of Science
Attn: Science and Technology Policy Fellowships
1200 New York Avenue, N.W.
Washington, DC 20005-3920
(202) 326-6700 Fax: (202) 289-4950
E-mail: fellowships@aaas.org
Web: www.fellowships.aaas.org

Summary To provide postdoctoral scientists and engineers (particularly African Americans, other minorities, women, and individuals with disabilities) with an opportunity to work at designated federal agencies on scientific and engineering issues related to diplomacy, security, and development.

Eligibility This program is open to doctoral-level scientists (Ph.D., M.D., D.V.M., D.Sc., and other terminal degrees) in any field of science (behavioral, biological, computational, earth, health, medical, physical, or social), engineering, or mathematics. Engineers with a master's degree and at least 3 years of professional experience are also eligible. Applicants should be able to contribute scientific and technical expertise into policy development, program planning, implementation, and evaluation in the areas of 1) foreign policy, international trade, treaty engagement, and multilateral cooperation; 2) disaster preparedness and response; 3) infrastructure, environmental, cyber and health security; terrorism and warfare prevention; and non-proliferation; or 4) international aid, capacity building, and development assistance. They must demonstrate solid scientific and technical credentials; a commitment to serve society; good communication skills; the ability to engage with non-scientific audiences; and an interest in working as special assistants for designated federal agencies (Department of Homeland Security (DHS), Agency for International Development (AID), Fogarty International Center of the National Institutes of Health (NIH), Foreign Agriculture Service of the U.S. Department of Agriculture (USDA), Department of Defense, or Department of State). U.S. citizenship is required; federal employees are not eligible. The sponsor seeks candidates from a broad array of backgrounds and a diversity of geographic, disciplinary, gender, and ethnic perspectives, as well as disability status.

Financial data The stipend for fellows with 0 to 7 years of postdoctoral experience is $74,872 in the first year and $77,368 in the second year. For fellows with 7 to 15 years of experience, the stipend is $84,855 in the first year and $87,350 in the second year. Fellows who have 15 or more years of postdoctoral experience receive $97,333 in the first year and $99,829 in the second year. Also provided are a $4,000 relocation allowance for fellows from outside the Washington, D.C. area, reimbursement for health insurance, and a $4,000 travel allowance.

Duration 1 year, beginning in September; may be renewed for 1 additional year.

Number awarded 35 to 45 each year.

Deadline October of each year.

[1135]
DIRECTOR'S AWARD FOR DISTINGUISHED TEACHING SCHOLARS

National Science Foundation
Directorate for Education and Human Resources
Attn: Division of Undergraduate Education
4201 Wilson Boulevard, Room 835N
Arlington, VA 22230
(703) 292-4627 Fax: (703) 292-9015
TDD: (800) 281-8749 E-mail: npruitt@nsf.gov
Web: www.nsf.gov/funding/pgm_summ.jsp?pims_id=8170

Summary To recognize and reward African American and other scholars affiliated with institutions of higher education who have contributed to the teaching of science, technology, engineering, or mathematics (STEM) at the K-12 and undergraduate level.

Eligibility This program is open to teaching-scholars affiliated with institutions of higher education who are nominated by their president, chief academic officer, or other independent researcher. Nominees should have integrated research and education and approached both education and research in a scholarly manner. They should have demonstrated leadership in their respective fields as well as innovativeness and effectiveness in facilitating K-12 and undergraduate student learning in STEM disciplines. Consideration is given to faculty who have a history of substantial impact on 1) research in a STEM discipline or on STEM educational research; or 2) the STEM education of K-16 students who have diverse interests and aspirations, including future K-12 teachers of science and mathematics, students who plan to pursue STEM careers, and those who need to understand science and mathematics in a society increasingly dependent on science and technology. Based on letters of nomination, selected scholars are invited to submit applications for support of their continuing efforts to integrate education and research. Nominations of all citizens, including women and men, underrepresented minorities, and persons with disabilities are especially encouraged.

Financial data The maximum grant is $300,000 for the life of the project.

Duration 4 years.

Number awarded Approximately 6 each year.

Deadline Letters of intent are due in September of each year; full applications must be submitted in October.

[1136]
DIVISION 17 COUNSELING PSYCHOLOGY GRANTS

American Psychological Foundation
750 First Street, N.E.
Washington, DC 20002-4242
(202) 336-5843 Fax: (202) 336-5812
E-mail: foundation@apa.org
Web: www.apa.org/apf/funding/counseling.aspx

Summary To provide funding to psychologists (particularly African Americans, other underrepresented minorities, women, and individuals with disabilities) who wish to conduct a project related to counseling psychology.

Eligibility This program is open to psychologists who wish to conduct a project to enhance the science and practice of counseling psychology, including basic and applied research, literary, and educational activities. Applicants must be members of Division 17 (Society of Counseling Psychotherapy) of the American Psychological Association, members of an educational institution or nonprofit organization, or affiliate of an educational institution or nonprofit organization. Selection is based on conformance with stated program goals, magnitude of incremental contribution in specified activity area, quality of proposed work, and applicant's demonstrated competence and capability to execute the proposed work. The sponsor encourages applications from individuals who represent diversity in race, ethnicity, gender, age, disability, and sexual orientation.

Financial data Grants range up to $5,000.

Duration 1 year.

Additional information These grants were first awarded in 2007.

Number awarded Varies each year; recently, 2 of these grants were awarded.

Deadline March of each year.

[1137]
DIVISION 29 EARLY CAREER AWARD

American Psychological Foundation
750 First Street, N.E.
Washington, DC 20002-4242
(202) 336-5843 Fax: (202) 336-5812
E-mail: foundation@apa.org
Web: www.apa.org/apf/funding/div-29.aspx

Summary To recognize and reward young psychologists (particularly African Americans, other underrepresented minorities, women, and individuals with disabilities) who have made outstanding contributions to psychotherapy.

Eligibility This award is available to psychologists who are no more than 7 years past completion of their doctoral degree. Nominees must have demonstrated promising professional achievement related to psychotherapy theory, practice, research, or training. They must be members of Division 29 (Psychotherapy) of the American Psychological Association. Self-nominations are not accepted. Selection is based on conformance with stated program goals and qualifications and applicant's demonstrated accomplishments and promise. The sponsor encourages nominations of individuals who represent diversity in race, ethnicity, gender, age, disability, and sexual orientation.

Financial data The award is $2,500.

Duration The award is presented annually.

Additional information This award was established in 1981 and named the Jack D. Krasner Memorial Award. It was renamed in 2007.

Number awarded 1 each year.

Deadline Nominations must be submitted by December of each year.

[1138]
DOCTORAL/POST-DOCTORAL FELLOWSHIP PROGRAM IN LAW AND SOCIAL SCIENCE

American Bar Foundation
Attn: Administrative Assistant for Academic Affairs and Research Administration
750 North Lake Shore Drive
Chicago, IL 60611-4403
(312) 988-6517 Fax: (312) 988-6579
E-mail: aehrhardt@abfn.org
Web: www.americanbarfoundation.org

Summary To provide research funding to scholars (particularly African Americans and other minorities) who are completing or have completed doctoral degrees in fields related to law, the legal profession, and legal institutions.

Eligibility This program is open to Ph.D. candidates in the social sciences who have completed all doctoral requirements except the dissertation. Applicants who have completed the dissertation are also eligible. Doctoral and proposed research must be in the general area of sociolegal studies or in social scientific approaches to law, the legal profession, or legal institutions and legal processes. Applications must include 1) a dissertation abstract or proposal with an outline of the substance and methods of the research; 2) 2 letters of recommendation; and 3) a curriculum vitae. Minority candidates are especially encouraged to apply.

Financial data The stipend is $30,000. Fellows may request up to $1,500 to reimburse expenses associated with research, travel to meet with advisers, or travel to conferences at which papers are presented. Relocation expenses of up to $2,500 may be reimbursed on application.

Duration 12 months, beginning in September.

Additional information Fellows are offered access to the computing and word processing facilities of the American Bar Foundation and the libraries of Northwestern University and the University of Chicago. This program was established in 1996. Fellowships must be held in residence at the American Bar Foundation. Appointments to the fellowship are full time; fellows are not permitted to undertake other work.

Number awarded 1 or more each year.

Deadline December of each year.

[1139]
DOE SMALL BUSINESS INNOVATION RESEARCH GRANTS

Department of Energy
Attn: SBIR/STTR Program, SC-29
Germantown Building
1000 Independence Avenue, S.W.
Washington, DC 20585-1290
(301) 903-5707 Fax: (301) 903-5488
E-mail: sbir-sttr@science.doe.gov
Web: science.energy.gov/sbir

Summary To support small businesses (especially those owned by African Americans, other minorities, or women) that have the technological expertise to contribute to the research and development mission of the Department of Energy (DOE).

Eligibility For the purposes of this program, a "small business" is defined as a firm that is organized for profit with a location in the United States; is in the legal form of an individual proprietorship, partnership, limited liability company, corporation, joint venture, association, trust, or cooperative; is at least 51% owned and controlled by 1 or more individuals who are citizens or permanent residents of the United States; and has (including its affiliates) fewer than 500 employees. The primary employment of the principal investigator must be with the firm at the time of award and during the conduct of the proposed project. Applications are encouraged from 1) women-owned small business concerns, defined as those that are at least 51% owned by a woman or women who also control and operate them; and 2) socially and economically disadvantaged small business concerns that are at least 51% owned by an Indian tribe, a Native Hawaiian organization, or 1 or more socially and economically disadvantaged individuals (African Americans, Hispanic Americans, Native Americans, Asian Pacific Americans, or subcontinent Asian Americans). Each office within DOE defines technical topics eligible for research.

Financial data Support is offered in 2 phases: in phase 1, awards normally do not exceed $150,000 (for both direct and indirect costs); in phase 2, awards normally do not exceed $1,000,000 (including both direct and indirect costs).

Duration Phase 1: up to 9 months; phase 2: up to 2 years.

Additional information The objectives of this program include increasing private sector commercialization of technology developed through research and development supported by the Department of Energy, stimulating technological innovation in the private sector, strengthening the role of small business in meeting federal research and development needs, and improving the return on investment from federally-funded research for economic and social benefits to the nation.

Number awarded Varies each year; recently 279 Phase 1 and 113 Phase 2 grants were awarded.

Deadline November of each year.

[1140]
DOE SMALL BUSINESS TECHNOLOGY TRANSFER GRANTS

Department of Energy
Attn: SBIR/STTR Program, SC-29
Germantown Building
1000 Independence Avenue, S.W.
Washington, DC 20585-1290
(301) 903-5707 Fax: (301) 903-5488
E-mail: sbir-sttr@science.doe.gov
Web: science.energy.gov/sbir

Summary To provide financial support to cooperative research and development projects carried out between small business concerns (particularly those owned by African Americans, other minorities, or women) and research institutions in areas of interest to the Department of Energy (DOE).

Eligibility For the purposes of this program, a "small business" is defined as a firm that is organized for profit with a location in the United States; is in the legal form of an individual proprietorship, partnership, limited liability company, corporation, joint venture, association, trust, or cooperative; is at least 51% owned and controlled by 1 or more individuals who are citizens or permanent residents of the United States; and has (including its affiliates) fewer than 500 employees. Unlike the Department of Energy Small Business Innovation Research Grants, the primary employment of the principal investigator does not need to be with the business concern. This program, however, requires that the small business apply in collaboration with a nonprofit research institution for conduct of a project that has potential for commercialization. At least 40% of the work must be performed by the small business and at least 30% of the work must be performed by the research institution. Principal investigators from the nonprofit research institution must commit at least 10% of their effort to the project. Applications are encouraged from 1) women-owned small business concerns, defined as those that are at least 51% owned by a woman or women who also control and operate them; and 2) socially and economically disadvantaged small business concerns that are at least 51% owned by an Indian tribe, a Native Hawaiian organization, or 1 or more socially and economically disadvantaged individuals (African Americans, Hispanic Americans, Native Americans, Asian Pacific Americans, or subcontinent Asian Americans). Each office within DOE defines technical topics eligible for research.

Financial data In the first phase, annual awards do not exceed $150,000 for direct costs, indirect costs, and negotiated fixed fees. In the second phase, awards up to $1,000,000 are available.

Duration Generally 9 months for the first phase and 2 years for the second phase.

Additional information Grants in the first phase are to determine the scientific, technical, and commercial merit and feasibility of the proposed cooperative effort and the quality of performance of the small business concern. In the second phase, the research and development efforts continue, depending on the results of the first phase.

Number awarded Varies each year; recently 39 Phase 1 and 15 Phase 2 grants were awarded.

Deadline January of each year.

[1141]
DONALD M. PAYNE FOREIGN POLICY FELLOWS PROGRAM

Congressional Black Caucus Foundation, Inc.
Attn: Leadership Institute for Public Service
1720 Massachusetts Avenue, N.W.
Washington, DC 20036
(202) 263-2800 Toll Free: (800) 784-2577
Fax: (202) 775-0773 E-mail: internships@cbcfinc.org
Web: www.cbcfinc.org/lips.html

Summary To provide an opportunity for young professionals to work on a program of training in foreign policy issues in collaboration with the Congressional Black Caucus (CBC).

Eligibility This program is open to professionals who have a graduate or professional degree in a foreign policy-related field and familiarity with the federal legislative process, Congress, and the CBC. Applicants must be interested in working in Washington, D.C. on foreign policy-related issues, especially how those policies affect African Americans and other minorities, as a member of the staff or committee of a member of the CBC. They must be able to demonstrate an interest in public policy, commitment to creating and implementing policy to improve the living conditions for underserved and underrepresented individuals, a record of academic and professional achievement, evidence of leadership skills, the potential for further growth, and U.S. citizenship or permit to work in the United States.

Financial data Fellows receive a stipend of $40,000 per year and benefits.

Duration 20 months, beginning in September.

Additional information This program began in 2012. Fellows are assigned to Congressional offices or committees and work on issues related to foreign policy.

Number awarded 1 or more each year.

Deadline March of each year.

[1142]
DR. BESSIE ELIZABETH DELANEY FELLOWSHIP

National Dental Association
Attn: National Dental Association Foundation, Inc.
3517 16th Street, N.W.
Washington, DC 20010
(202) 588-1697 Fax: (202) 588-1244
E-mail: admin@ndaonline.org
Web: www.ndafoundation.org/NDAF/Scholarships.html

Summary To provide financial assistance to dental master's and postdoctoral students who are female and either African American or a member of another minority group.

Eligibility This program is open to female members of minority groups who are working on a postdoctoral degree in subspecialty areas of dentistry, public health, administration, pediatrics, research, or law. Students working on a master's degree beyond their residency also may be considered. Applicants must be members of the National Dental Association (NDA) and U.S. citizens or permanent residents. Along with their application, they must submit a letter explaining why they should be considered for this scholarship, 2 letters of recommendation, a curriculum vitae, a description of the program, nomination by their program director, and documentation of financial need.

Financial data The stipend is $10,000.

Duration 1 year.

Additional information This program, established in 1990, is supported by the Colgate-Palmolive Company.

Number awarded 1 each year.

Deadline May of each year.

[1143]
DR. CLIFTON O. DUMMETT AND LOIS DOYLE DUMMETT FELLOWSHIP

National Dental Association
Attn: National Dental Association Foundation, Inc.
3517 16th Street, N.W.
Washington, DC 20010
(202) 588-1697 Fax: (202) 588-1244
E-mail: admin@ndaonline.org
Web: www.ndafoundation.org/NDAF/Scholarships.html

Summary To provide financial assistance to African American and other minority dental master's and postdoctoral students.

Eligibility This program is open to members of minority groups who are working on a postdoctoral degree in subspecialty areas of dentistry, public health, administration, pediatrics, research, or law. Students working on a master's degree beyond their residency also may be considered. Applicants must be members of the National Dental Association (NDA) and U.S. citizens or permanent residents. Along with their application, they must submit a letter explaining why they should be considered for this scholarship, 2 letters of recommendation, a curriculum vitae, a description of the program, nomination by their program director, and documentation of financial need.

Financial data The stipend is $10,000.

Duration 1 year.

Additional information This program, established in 1990, is supported by the Colgate-Palmolive Company.

Number awarded 1 each year.

Deadline May of each year.

[1144]
DR. DANIEL D. SAVAGE MEMORIAL SERVICE AWARD

Association of Black Cardiologists, Inc.
2400 N Street, N.W., Suite 616
Washington, DC 20037
(202) 375-6618 Toll Free: (800) 753-9222
Fax: (202) 373-6801
E-mail: membershipservices@abcardio.org
Web: www.abcardio.org

Summary To recognize and reward scientific achievement in the areas of cardiovascular disease and research by members of the Association of Black Cardiologists.

Eligibility This award is available to scientists and researchers who have made major contributions to the advancement of scientific knowledge in the field of cardiovascular medicine. Nominees must be members of the Association of Black Cardiologists. Self-nominations are accepted.

Financial data The award is $2,000.

Duration The award is presented annually.

Additional information This award was first presented in 1990.

Number awarded 1 each year.

Deadline Nominations must be submitted by May of each year.

[1145]
DR. JAY BROWN BEST ABSTRACT AWARD

Association of Black Cardiologists, Inc.
2400 N Street, N.W., Suite 616
Washington, DC 20037
(202) 375-6618 Toll Free: (800) 753-9222
Fax: (202) 373-6801
E-mail: membershipservices@abcardio.org
Web: www.abcardio.org

Summary To recognize and reward cardiology residents and fellows who are members of the Association of Black Cardiologists (ABC) and submit outstanding abstracts.

Eligibility This award is available to ABC members who are currently in a residency or cardiology fellowship training program. Applicants must submit an abstract for presentation at the ABC Annual Scientific Sessions that relates to cardiovascular disease; the research may be clinical, basic, or population science. They must also submit a 3-page essay that including their research interests and experiences, publications, career goals, and involvement in ABC.

Financial data The winner receives an award of $1,000. The winner and honorable mentions receive up to $1,500 to attend the ABC Annual Scientific Sessions, where the winner presents the research paper.

Duration The award is presented annually.

Number awarded 1 winner and 3 honorable mentions are selected each year.

Deadline March of each year.

[1146]
DRS. ROSALEE G. AND RAYMOND A. WEISS RESEARCH AND PROGRAM INNOVATION GRANT

American Psychological Foundation
750 First Street, N.E.
Washington, DC 20002-4242
(202) 336-5843 Fax: (202) 336-5812
E-mail: foundation@apa.org
Web: www.apa.org/apf/funding/vision-weiss.aspx

Summary To provide funding to professionals (particularly African Americans, other minorities, women, and individuals with disabilities) who are interested in conducting projects that use psychology to solve social problems related to the priorities of the American Psychological Foundation (APF).

Eligibility This program is open to professionals at nonprofit organizations engaged in research, education, and intervention projects and programs. Applicants must be interested in conducting an activity that uses psychology to solve social problems in the following priority areas: understanding and fostering the connection between mental and physical health; reducing stigma and prejudice; understanding and preventing violence to create a safer, more humane world; or addressing the long-term psychological needs of individuals and communities in the aftermath of disaster. Selection is based on the criticality of the proposed funding for the proposed work; conformance with stated program goals and requirements; innovative and potential impact qualities; quality, viability, and promise of proposed work, and competence and capability of project leaders. The sponsor encourages applications from individuals who represent diversity in race, ethnicity, gender, age, disability, and sexual orientation.

Financial data The grant is $2,500.

Duration 1 year; nonrenewable.

Additional information This program began in 2003.

Number awarded 1 each year.

Deadline March of each year.

[1147]
DUBOIS-MANDELA-RODNEY FELLOWSHIP PROGRAM

University of Michigan
Attn: Department of Afroamerican and African Studies
4700 Haven Hall
505 South State Street
Ann Arbor, MI 48109-1045
(734) 764-5513 Fax: (734) 763-0543
E-mail: gricer@umich.edu
Web: www.lsa.umich.edu

Summary To provide funding to scholars who are interested in conducting research on African American, African, and Caribbean experiences at the University of Michigan's Department of Afroamerican and African Studies.

Eligibility Applicants must have a Ph.D. in hand but be no more than 5 years beyond completion of their degree. They should be interested in conducting research on Africa or the African Diaspora at the center. Consideration is given to all disciplines, including, but not limited to, the humanities, social sciences, physical sciences, and professional schools. Scholars from or who study the Gullah speaking Sea islands, Cape Verde islands, the Anglophone Caribbean, the Canary islands, Madagascar, and/or other less studied areas are especially encouraged to apply.

Financial data The stipend is $42,000. Health insurance plus $1,000 for research and up to $2,000 for travel expenses are also included.

Duration 1 academic year, beginning in September of each even-numbered year.

Additional information Fellows must spend their fellowship year at the University of Michigan's Center for Afroamerican and African Studies. They must conduct at least 1 seminar.

Number awarded 1 each even-numbered year.

Deadline November of each odd-numbered year.

[1148]
DUPONT MINORITIES IN ENGINEERING AWARD

American Society for Engineering Education
Attn: Awards Administration
1818 N Street, N.W., Suite 600
Washington, DC 20036-2479
(202) 331-3550 Fax: (202) 265-8504
E-mail: board@asee.org
Web: www.asee.org/member-resources/awards

Summary To recognize and reward outstanding achievements by African American and other engineering educators who have worked to increase diversity by ethnicity and gender in science, engineering, and technology.

Eligibility Eligible for nomination are engineering or engineering technology educators who, as part of their educational activity, either assume or are charged with the responsibility of motivating underrepresented students to enter and continue in engineering or engineering technology curricula at the college or university level, graduate or undergraduate. Nominees must demonstrate leadership in the conception, organization, and operation of pre-college and college activities designed to increase participation by underrepresented students in engineering and engineering technology.

Financial data The award consists of $1,500, a certificate, and a grant of $500 for travel expenses to the ASEE annual conference.

Duration The award is granted annually.

Additional information Funding for this award is provided by DuPont. It was originally established in 1956 as the Vincent Bendix Minorities in Engineering Award.

Number awarded 1 each year.

Deadline January of each year.

[1149]
EARLY CAREER PATIENT-ORIENTED DIABETES RESEARCH AWARD

Juvenile Diabetes Research Foundation International
Attn: Grant Administrator
26 Broadway, 14th Floor
New York, NY 10004
(212) 479-7572 Toll Free: (800) 533-CURE
Fax: (212) 785-9595 E-mail: info@jdrf.org
Web: jdrf.org

Summary To provide funding to physician scientists (particularly African Americans, other minorities, women, and persons with disabilities) who are interested in pursuing a program of clinical diabetes-related research training.

Eligibility This program is open to investigators in diabetes-related research who have an M.D. or M.D./Ph.D. degree and a faculty appointment at the late training or assistant professor level. Applicants must be sponsored by an investigator who is affiliated full time with an accredited institution, who pursues patient-oriented clinical research, and who agrees to supervise the applicant's training. There are no citizenship requirements. Applications are encouraged from women, members of minority groups underrepresented in the sciences, and people with disabilities. Areas of relevant research can include: mechanisms of human disease, therapeutic interventions, clinical trials, and the development of new technologies. The proposed research may be conducted at foreign or domestic, for-profit or nonprofit, or public or private institutions, including universities, colleges, hospitals, laboratories, units of state or local government, or eligible agencies of the federal government.

Financial data The total award may be up to $150,000 each year, up to $75,000 of which may be requested for research (including a technician, supplies, equipment, and travel). The salary request must be consistent with the established salary structure of the applicant's institution. Equipment purchases in years other than the first must be strongly justified. Indirect costs may not exceed 10%.

Duration The award is for 5 years and is generally nonrenewable.

Number awarded Varies each year.
Deadline August of each year.

[1150]
EARTH SCIENCES POSTDOCTORAL FELLOWSHIPS

National Science Foundation
Directorate for Geosciences
Attn: Division of Earth Sciences
4201 Wilson Boulevard, Room 785S
Arlington, VA 22230
(703) 292-5047 Fax: (703) 292-9025
TDD: (800) 281-8749 E-mail: lpatino@nsf.gov
Web: www.nsf.gov

Summary To provide funding to postdoctoral scientists (particularly African Americans, other underrepresented minorities, women, and individuals with disabilities) who are interested in participating in a program of research training and education, in the United States or abroad, in a field relevant to the work of the Division of Earth Sciences of the National Science Foundation (NSF).

Eligibility This program is open to U.S. citizens, nationals, and permanent residents who received a Ph.D. within the past 18 months. Applicants must be interested in a program of research training in any of the disciplines supported by the NSF Division of Earth Sciences: geobiology and low temperature geochemistry, geomorphology and land use dynamics, geophysics, hydrologic sciences, petrology and geochemistry, sedimentary geology and paleobiology, and tectonics. The project should be conducted at an institution in the United States or abroad other than the applicant's Ph.D.-granting institution. The application must include a plan to broaden the participation of groups underrepresented in earth sciences (women, persons with disabilities, African Americans, Hispanics, Native Americans, Alaska Natives, and Pacific Islanders).

Financial data Grants are $87,000 per year, including a stipend of $62,000 per year and an annual fellowship allowance of $25,000 that is intended to cover direct research expenses, facilities and other institutional resources, and fringe benefits.

Duration 2 years.

Number awarded 10 each year.

Deadline July of each year.

[1151]
ECOLOGY OF INFECTIOUS DISEASES INITIATIVE

Fogarty International Center
Attn: Division of International Training and Research
31 Center Drive, Room B2C39
Bethesda, MD 20892-2220
(301) 496-1653 Fax: (301) 402-0779
TDD: (301) 451-0088 E-mail: Christine.Jessup@nih.gov
Web: www.fic.nih.gov

Summary To provide funding to U.S. scientists (particularly African Americans, other underrepresented minorities, and individuals with disabilities) who are interested in conducting research on the underlying ecological and biological mechanisms that govern relationships between human-induced environmental changes and the emergence and transmission of infectious diseases.

Eligibility This program is open to investigators at domestic and foreign for-profit and nonprofit organizations, both public and private, such as universities, colleges, hospitals, laboratories, units of state and local governments, and eligible agencies of the federal government. Applicants should be proposing to conduct research on the ecological and socio-ecological determinants of transmission by vectors or abiotic agents, the population dynamics of reservoir species, the transmission to humans or other hosts, or the cultural, social, behavioral, and economic dimensions of disease communication. Proposals for research on disease systems of public health concern to developing countries are strongly encouraged. Applicants are also encouraged to include links to the public health research community in the United States and developing countries, including participation by epidemiologists, physicians, veterinarians, medical social scientists, medical entomologists, virologists, or parasitologists. The program encourages applications from all citizens, including underrepresented minorities and persons with disabilities.

Financial data Grants provide up to $500,000 per year.

Duration Up to 5 years.

Additional information This program, established in 2000, is jointly funded by 3 components of the National Science Foundation (NSF): the Directorate for Biological Sciences, the Directorate for Geosciences, and the Directorate for Social, Behavioral, and Economic Sciences, and 3 components of the National Institutes of Health (NIH): the Fogarty International Center, the National Institute of Allergy and Infectious Diseases, and the National Institute of General Medical Sciences.

Number awarded Approximately 8 each year.

Deadline December of each year.

[1152]
EDWARD A. BOUCHET AWARD

American Physical Society
Attn: Honors Program
One Physics Ellipse
College Park, MD 20740-3844
(301) 209-3268 Fax: (301) 209-0865
E-mail: honors@aps.org
Web: www.aps.org/programs/honors/awards/bouchet.cfm

Summary To recognize and reward outstanding research in physics by African Americans and members of other underrepresented minority groups.

Eligibility Nominees for this award must be African Americans, Hispanic Americans, or Native Americans who have made significant contributions to physics research and are effective communicators.

Financial data The award consists of a grant of $3,500 to the recipient, a travel allowance for the recipient to visit 3 academic institutions to deliver lectures, and an allowance for travel expenses to the meeting of the American Physical Society (APS) at which the prize is presented.

Duration The award is presented annually.

Additional information This award was established in 1994 and is currently funded by a grant from the Research Corporation. As part of the award, the recipient visits 3 academic institutions where the impact of the visit on minority students will be significant. The purpose of those visits is to deliver technical lectures on the recipient's field of specialization, to visit classrooms where appropriate, to assist the institution with precollege outreach efforts where appropriate, and to talk informally with faculty and students about research and teaching careers in physics.

Number awarded 1 each year.

Deadline June of each year.

[1153] E.E. JUST ENDOWED RESEARCH FELLOWSHIP FUND

Marine Biological Laboratory
Attn: Chief Academic and Scientific Officer
7 MBL Street
Woods Hole, MA 02543-1015
(508) 289-7173 Fax: (508) 457-1924
E-mail: casoofice@mbl.edu
Web: hermes.mbl.edu

Summary To provide funding to African American and other minority scientists who wish to conduct research during the summer at the Marine Biological Laboratory (MBL) in Woods Hole, Massachusetts.

Eligibility This program is open to minority faculty members who are interested in conducting summer research at the MBL. Applicants must submit a statement of the potential impact of this award on their career development. Fields of study include, but are not limited to, cell biology, developmental biology, ecology, evolution, microbiology, neurobiology, physiology, regenerative biology, and tissue engineering.

Financial data Grants range from $5,000 to $25,000, typically to cover laboratory rental and/or housing costs. Awardees are responsible for other costs, such as supplies, shared resource usage, affiliated staff who accompany them, or travel.

Duration 8 to 10 weeks during the summer.

Number awarded 1 each year.

Deadline December of each year.

[1154] EINSTEIN POSTDOCTORAL FELLOWSHIP PROGRAM

Smithsonian Astrophysical Observatory
Attn: Chandra X-Ray Center
Einstein Fellowship Program Office
60 Garden Street, MS4
Cambridge, MA 02138
(617) 496-7941 Fax: (617) 495-7356
E-mail: fellows@head.cfa.harvard.edu
Web: cxc.harvard.edu/fellows

Summary To provide funding to recent postdoctoral scientists (particularly African Americans, other minorities, and women) who are interested in conducting research related to high energy astrophysics missions of the National Aeronautics and Space Administration (NASA).

Eligibility This program is open to postdoctoral scientists who completed their Ph.D., Sc.D., or equivalent doctoral degree within the past 3 years in astronomy, physics, or related disciplines. Applicants must be interested in conducting research related to NASA Physics of the Cosmos program missions: Chandra, Fermi, XMM-Newton and International X-Ray Observatory, cosmological investigations relevant to the Planck and JDEM missions, and gravitational astrophysics relevant to the LISA mission. They must be citizens of the United States or English-speaking citizens of other countries who have valid visas. Women and minorities are strongly encouraged to apply.

Financial data Stipends are approximately $66,500 per year. Fellows may also receive health insurance, relocation costs, and moderate support (up to $16,000 per year) for research-related travel, computing services, publications, and other direct costs.

Duration 3 years (depending on a review of scientific activity).

Additional information This program, which began in 2009 with funding from NASA, incorporates the former Chandra and GLAST Fellowship programs.

Number awarded Up to 10 each year.

Deadline November of each year.

[1155] ELSEVIER PILOT RESEARCH AWARDS

American Gastroenterological Association
Attn: AGA Research Foundation
Research Awards Manager
4930 Del Ray Avenue
Bethesda, MD 20814-2512
(301) 222-4012 Fax: (301) 654-5920
E-mail: awards@gastro.org
Web: www.gastro.org/aga-foundation/grants

Summary To provide funding to new or established investigators (particularly African Americans, other minorities, and women) for pilot research projects in areas related to gastroenterology or hepatology.

Eligibility Applicants must have an M.D., Ph.D., or equivalent degree and a full-time faculty position at an accredited North American institution. They may not hold grants for projects on a similar topic from other agencies. Individual membership in the American Gastroenterology Association (AGA) is required. The proposal must involve obtaining new data that can ultimately provide the basis for subsequent grant applications for more substantial funding and duration in gastroenterology- or hepatology-related areas. Women and minority investigators are strongly encouraged to apply. Selection is based on novelty, importance, feasibility, environment, commitment of the institution, and overall likelihood that the project will lead to more substantial grant applications.

Financial data The grant is $25,000. Funds may be used for salary, supplies, or equipment. Indirect costs are not allowed.

Duration 1 year.

Additional information This award is sponsored by Elsevier Science.

Number awarded 3 each year.

Deadline January of each year.

[1156]
ENERGY, ENVIRONMENT, AND AGRICULTURE FELLOWSHIPS

American Association for the Advancement of Science
Attn: Science and Technology Policy Fellowships
1200 New York Avenue, N.W.
Washington, DC 20005-3920
(202) 326-6700 Fax: (202) 289-4950
E-mail: fellowships@aaas.org
Web: www.fellowships.aaas.org

Summary To provide a fellowship to postdoctoral scientists and engineers (particularly African Americans, other minorities, women, and individuals with disabilities) who are interested in participating on projects relating to energy, environment, or agriculture at specified federal agencies.

Eligibility This program is open to doctoral-level scientists (Ph.D., M.D., D.V.M., D.Sc., and other terminal degrees) in any field of science (behavioral, biological, computational, earth, health, medical, physical, or social), engineering, or mathematics. Engineers with a master's degree and at least 3 years of professional experience are also eligible. Applicants should be able to engage in projects, policies, risk assessment, evaluation, and outreach initiatives to 1) protect animal, plant, and environmental health; 2) address ecosystem degradation, pollution, and biological threats; 3) tackle challenges and opportunities in agriculture, fisheries, climate change, and energy; or 4) safeguard air, water, land, wildlife, and natural resources. They must demonstrate solid scientific and technical credentials; a commitment to serve society; good communication skills; the ability to engage with non-scientific audiences; and an interest in working as special assistants for designated federal agencies (the U.S. Department of Agriculture (USDA), the Department of Energy (DOE), the National Oceanic and Atmospheric Administration (NOAA), the National Science Foundation (NSF), the Environmental Protection Agency (EPA), the National Aeronautics and Space Administration (NASA), the U.S. Geological Survey (USGS), or the Forest Service). U.S. citizenship is required; federal employees are not eligible. The sponsor seeks candidates from a broad array of backgrounds and a diversity of geographic, disciplinary, gender, and ethnic perspectives, as well as disability status.

Financial data The stipend for fellows with 0 to 7 years of postdoctoral experience is $74,872 in the first year and $77,368 in the second year. For fellows with 7 to 15 years of experience, the stipend is $84,855 in the first year and $87,350 in the second year. Fellows who have 15 or more years of postdoctoral experience receive $97,333 in the first year and $99,420 in the second year. Also provided are a $4,000 relocation allowance for fellows from outside the Washington, D.C. area, reimbursement for health insurance, and a $4,000 travel allowance.

Duration 1 year, beginning in September; may be renewed 1 additional year.

Number awarded 35 to 45 each year.

Deadline October of each year.

[1157]
EPILEPSY FOUNDATION RESEARCH GRANTS PROGRAM

Epilepsy Foundation
Attn: Research Department
8301 Professional Place
Landover, MD 20785-2353
(301) 459-3700 Toll Free: (800) EFA-1000
Fax: (301) 577-2684 TDD: (800) 332-2070
E-mail: grants@efa.org
Web: www.epilepsyfoundation.org

Summary To provide funding to junior investigators (particularly African Americans, other minorities, women, and individuals with disabilities) who are interested in conducting research that will advance the understanding, treatment, and prevention of epilepsy.

Eligibility Applicants must have a doctoral degree and an academic appointment at the level of assistant professor in a university or medical school (or equivalent standing at a research institution or medical center). They must be interested in conducting basic or clinical research to advance understanding of the behavioral and psychosocial aspects of having epilepsy. Faculty with appointments at the level of associate professor or higher are not eligible. Applications from women, members of minority groups, and people with disabilities are especially encouraged. U.S. citizenship is not required, but the research must be conducted in the United States. Selection is based on the scientific quality of the research plan, the relevance of the proposed research to epilepsy, the applicant's qualifications, and the adequacy of the institution and facility where research will be conducted.

Financial data The grant is $50,000 per year.

Duration 1 year; recipients may reapply for 1 additional year of funding.

Additional information Support for this program is provided by many individuals, families, and corporations, especially the American Epilepsy Society, Abbott Laboratories, Ortho-McNeil Pharmaceutical, and Pfizer Inc.

Number awarded Varies each year.

Deadline August of each year.

[1158]
EPILEPSY RESEARCH RECOGNITION AWARDS PROGRAM

American Epilepsy Society
342 North Main Street
West Hartford, CT 06117-2507
(860) 586-7505 Fax: (860) 586-7550
E-mail: ctubby@aesnet.org
Web: www.aesnet.org/research/research-awards

Summary To provide funding to investigators (particularly African Americans, other minorities, and women) who are interested in conducting research related to epilepsy.

Eligibility This program is open to active scientists and clinicians working in any aspect of epilepsy. Candidates must be nominated by their home institution and be at the level of associate professor or professor. There are no geographic restrictions; nominations from outside the United States and North America are welcome. Nominations of women and members of minority groups are especially encouraged. Selection is based on pioneering research, originality of research, quality of publications, research productivity, relationship of the candidate's work to problems in epilepsy, training activities, other contributions in epilepsy, and productivity over the next decade; all criteria are weighted equally.

Financial data The grant is $10,000. No institutional overhead is allowed.

Additional information This program began in 1991.

Number awarded 2 each year.

Deadline August of each year.

[1159]
ETAC GRANTS

Alzheimer's Association
Attn: Medical and Scientific Affairs
225 North Michigan Avenue, 17th Floor
Chicago, IL 60601-7633
(312) 335-5747 Toll Free: (800) 272-3900
Fax: (866) 699-1246 TDD: (312) 335-5886
E-mail: grantsapp@alz.org
Web: www.alz.org

Summary To provide funding to investigators (particularly African Americans and members of other underrepresented groups) who are interested in developing technology for uses related to Alzheimer's Disease.

Eligibility This program is open to investigators who are full-time staff or faculty at public, private, domestic, and foreign research laboratories, medical centers, hospitals, and universities. Applicants must be interested in conducting research on personalized diagnostics, preventive tools, and interventions for adults coping with the spectrum of cognitive aging and neurodegenerative disease, particularly Alzheimer's Disease. Priority is given to groundbreaking studies on emerging information and communication technologies as well as their clinical and social implications. Research topics may include, but are not limited to, behavioral assessment for early detection, prevention, safety monitoring and support for caregivers, supporting independent function in daily life, social support through face or audio recognition, detecting moments and patterns of lucidity, and privacy and security concerns of Alzheimer's families. Scientists from underrepresented groups are especially encouraged to apply.

Financial data Grants up to $90,000 per year, including direct expenses and up to 10% for overhead costs, are available. The total award for the life of the grant may not exceed $200,000.

Duration Up to 3 years.

Additional information This program is jointly supported by the Alzheimer's Association and Intel Corporation.

Number awarded Up to 2 each year.

Deadline Letters of intent must be submitted by the end of January of each year. Final applications are due in March.

[1160]
ETS POSTDOCTORAL FELLOWSHIP AWARD PROGRAM

Educational Testing Service
Attn: Fellowships
660 Rosedale Road
MS 19-T
Princeton, NJ 08541-0001
(609) 734-5543 Fax: (609) 734-5410
E-mail: internfellowships@ets.org
Web: www.ets.org/research/fellowships

Summary To provide funding to postdoctorates (particularly African Americans and members of other underrepresented groups) who wish to conduct independent research at the Educational Testing Service (ETS).

Eligibility Applicants must have a doctorate in a relevant discipline and be able to provide evidence of prior research. They must be interested in conducting research at ETS in 1 of the following areas: measurement theory, validity, natural language processing and computational linguistics, cognitive psychology, learning theory, linguistics, speech recognition and processing, teaching and classroom research, or statistics. Selection is based on the scholarly and technical strength of the proposed research, the relationship between the objective of the research and ETS goals and priorities, and the ETS affirmative action objectives. An explicit goal of the program is to increase the number of scholars and students from diverse backgrounds, especially such traditionally underrepresented groups as African Americans, Hispanic/ Latino Americans, and American Indians, who are conducting research in educational measurement and related fields.

Financial data The stipend is $55,000 per year; fellows and their families also receive limited reimbursement for relocation expenses.

Duration Up to 2 years.

Additional information Fellows work with senior staff at ETS in Princeton, New Jersey.

Number awarded Up to 3 each year.

Deadline Preliminary application materials must be submitted by December of each year; final application materials are due by the end of February.

[1161]
EVA KING KILLAM RESEARCH AWARD

American College of Neuropsychopharmacology
Attn: Executive Office
5034-A Thoroughbred Lane
Brentwood, TN 37027
(615) 324-2360 Fax: (615) 523-1715
E-mail: acnp@acnp.org
Web: www.acnp.org/programs/awards.aspx

Summary To recognize and reward young scientists (particularly African Americans, other minorities, and individuals with disabilities) who have made outstanding translational research contributions to neuropsychopharmacology.

Eligibility This award is available to scientists who are younger than 50 years of age. Nominees must have made an outstanding translational research contribution to neuropsychopharmacology. The contributions should focus on translating advances from basic science to human investigations. Selection is based on the quality of the contribution and its impact in advancing neuropsychopharmacology. Neither membership in the American College of Neuropsychopharmacology (ACNP) nor U.S. citizenship are required. Nomination of women and minorities is highly encouraged.

Financial data The award consists of an expense-paid trip to the ACNP annual meeting, a monetary honorarium, and a plaque.

Duration The award is presented annually.

Additional information This award was first presented in 2011.

Number awarded 1 each year.

Deadline Nominations must be submitted by June of each year.

[1162]
FACULTY AT FDA GRANTS

National Science Foundation
Directorate for Engineering
Attn: Division of Chemical, Bioengineering, Environmental, and Transport Systems
4201 Wilson Boulevard, Room 565S
Arlington, VA 22230
(703) 292-7942 Fax: (703) 292-9098
TDD: (800) 281-8749 E-mail: lesterow@nsf.gov
Web: www.nsf.gov/funding/pgm_summ.jsp?pims_id=5605

Summary To provide an opportunity for faculty members (particularly African Americans, other minorities, and individuals with disabilities) to conduct research at an intramural laboratory of the U.S. Food and Drug Administration (FDA).

Eligibility This program is open to full-time faculty members at U.S. colleges and universities in science, engineering, and mathematics fields of interest to the National Science Foundation (NSF). Applicants must be U.S. citizens, nationals, or permanent residents. They must present a plan for collaboration between their institution and the FDA, with a description of the facilities and resources that will be available at an FDA laboratory to support the proposed research. The program encourages applications from all citizens, including women and men, underrepresented minorities, and persons with disabilities.

Financial data Grants range from $25,000 to $150,000, including 85% of the faculty member's salary and fringe benefits during the industrial residency period. Up to 20% of the total requested amount may be used for travel and research expenses for the faculty and his/her students, including materials but excluding equipment. In lieu of indirect costs, up to 15% of the total cost may be allocated for administrative expenses. The fellow's home institution must commit to support the other 15% of the faculty salary and fringe benefits. FDA provides office space, research facilities, research costs in the form of expendable and minor equipment purchases in the host laboratory, and the time of its research staff.

Duration 3 to 12 months.

Additional information This program is also offered by the NSF Directorate for Computer and Information Science and Engineering.

Number awarded A total of 3 to 10 grants for all FDA programs is awarded each year; total funding is approximately $500,000.

Deadline March of each year.

[1163]
FACULTY DEVELOPMENT AWARD TO PROMOTE DIVERSITY IN NEUROSCIENCE RESEARCH

National Institute of Neurological Disorders and Stroke
Attn: Office of Training, Career Development and Workforce Diversity
6001 Executive Boulevard, Suite 2149
Bethesda, MD 20892-9535
(301) 451-7966 Fax: (301) 594-5929
TDD: (301) 451-0088 E-mail: jonesmiche@ninds.nih.gov
Web: grants.nih.gov/grants/guide/pa-files/PAR-12-152.html

Summary To provide funding to neurological research scientists who are African Americans or members of other underrepresented groups and interested in preparing for a career as an independent investigator.

Eligibility This program is open to U.S. citizens, nationals, and permanent residents who have a doctoral degree in a field of neuroscience and are in the first 3 years of a faculty appointment. Applicants must be interested in participating in an intensive, supervised career development experience in neuroscience research. They must qualify as 1) a member of an ethnic or racial group shown to be underrepresented in health-related sciences on a national basis; 2) an individual with a disability; or 3) an individual from a disadvantaged background. Selection is based on scientific merit and programmatic considerations.

Financial data Grants provide an annual award of up to $85,000 for salary and fringe benefits and an annual research allowance of up to $100,000 per year for direct research costs. The institution may apply for up to 8% of direct costs for facilities and administrative costs.

Duration Up to 3 years; nonrenewable.

Additional information Recipients must devote 75% of full-time professional effort to conducting health-related research.

Number awarded Varies each year.

Deadline February, June, or October of each year.

[1164]
FACULTY EARLY CAREER DEVELOPMENT PROGRAM

National Science Foundation
Directorate for Education and Human Resources
Senior Staff Associate for Cross Directorate Programs
4201 Wilson Boulevard, Room 805
Arlington, VA 22230
(703) 292-8600 TDD: (800) 281-8749
E-mail: info@nsf.gov
Web: www.nsf.gov

Summary To provide funding to outstanding new faculty (particularly African Americans, other underrepresented minorities, and individuals with disabilities) who are working in science and engineering fields of interest to the National Science Foundation (NSF) and intend to develop academic careers involving both research and education.

Eligibility This program, identified as the CAREER program, is open to faculty members who meet all of the following requirements: 1) be employed in a tenure-track (or equivalent) position at an institution in the United States, its territories or possessions, or the Commonwealth of Puerto Rico that awards degrees in a field supported by NSF or that is a nonprofit, non-degree granting organization, such as a museum, observatory, or research laboratory; 2) have a doctoral degree in a field of science or engineering supported by NSF: 3) not have competed more than 3 times in this program; 4) be untenured; and 5) not be a current or former recipient of a Presidential Early Career Award for Scientists and Engineers (PECASE) or CAREER award. Applicants are not required to be U.S. citizens or permanent residents. They must submit a career development plan that indicates a description of the proposed research project, including preliminary supporting data (if appropriate), specific objectives, methods, procedures to be used, and expected significance of the results; a description of the proposed educational activities, including plans to evaluate their impact; a description of how the research and educational activities are integrated with each other; and results of prior NSF support (if applicable). Proposals from women, underrepresented minorities, and persons with disabilities are especially encouraged.

Financial data The grant is at least $80,000 per year (or $100,000 per year for the Directorate of Biological Sciences or the Office of Polar Programs), including indirect costs or overhead.

Duration 5 years.

Additional information This program is operated by various disciplinary divisions within the NSF; for a list of the participating divisions and their telephone numbers, contact the sponsor. Outstanding recipients of these grants are nominated for the NSF component of the PECASE awards, which are awarded to 20 recipients of these grants as an honorary award.

Number awarded Approximately 600 each year.

Deadline July of each year.

[1165] FELLOWSHIP PROGRAM IN MEASUREMENT

American Educational Research Association
1430 K Street, N.W., Suite 1200
Washington, DC 20005
(202) 238-3200 Fax: (202) 238-3250
E-mail: fellowships@aera.net
Web: www.aera.net

Summary To provide an opportunity for junior scholars in the field of education (particularly African Americans, other underrepresented minorities, and women) to engage in a program of research and advanced training while in residence at Educational Testing Service (ETS) in Princeton, New Jersey.

Eligibility This program is open to junior scholars and early career research scientists in fields and disciplines related to education research. Applicants must have completed their Ph.D. or Ed.D. degree within the past 3 years. They must be proposing a program of intensive research and training at the ETS campus in Princeton, New Jersey in such areas as educational measurement, assessment design, psychometrics, statistical analyses, large-scale evaluations, and other studies directed to explaining student progress and achievement. A particular goal of the program is to increase the involvement of women and underrepresented minority professionals in measurement, psychometrics, assessment, and related fields. U.S. citizenship or permanent resident status is required.

Financial data The stipend is $55,000 per year. Fellows also receive relocation expenses and ETS employee benefits.

Duration Up to 2 years.

Additional information This program is jointly sponsored by the American Educational Research Association (AERA) and ETS.

Number awarded Up to 2 each year.

Deadline November of each year.

[1166] FELLOWSHIPS FOR TRANSFORMATIVE COMPUTATIONAL SCIENCE USING CYBERINFRASTRUCTURE

National Science Foundation
Attn: Office of Cyberinfrastructure
4201 Wilson Boulevard, Room 1145S
Arlington, VA 22230
(703) 292-8061 Fax: (703) 292-9060
TDD: (800) 281-8749 E-mail: citracs@nsf.gov
Web: www.nsf.gov

Summary To provide funding for research training to postdoctoral scientists (particularly African Americans, other underrepresented minorities, and individuals with disabilities) who plan to work in areas of interest to the Office of Cyberinfrastructure of the National Science Foundation (NSF).

Eligibility This program is open to citizens, nationals, and permanent residents of the United States who are graduate students completing a Ph.D. or have earned the degree no earlier than 2 years preceding the deadline date. Applicants must be interested in a program of research and training in the use of computational concepts, methodologies, and technologies in all sciences (including physical, biological, geological, mathematical, social, behavioral, economic, computer, information, and data). They must identify a host research organization (college, university, privately-sponsored nonprofit institute, government agency, or laboratory) that has agreed to support the applicant's proposed research and educational activities and has identified a mentor to work with the applicant. Selection is based on the applicant's ability to contribute to computational research and educational efforts that integrate distinct theoretical models and computational methodologies to achieve overall goals and lead to a new generation of applications and technologies for solving important real-world problems using cyberinfrastructure (CI). The program encourages applications from all citizens, including women and men, underrepresented minorities, and persons with disabilities.

Financial data Stipends are $60,000 for the first year, $65,000 for the second year, and $70,000 for the third year. Also provided are a research allowance supplement of $10,000 per year and an institutional allowance of $5,000 per year. Fellows who complete this program and move on to a tenure-track faculty position may apply for a research starter supplement of up to $50,000 to support the setup of their research environment.

Duration Up to 3 years.

Number awarded 6 to 8 each year. Approximately $2.0 million is available for this program annually.

Deadline January of each year.

[1167]
FIRST BOOK GRANT PROGRAM FOR MINORITY SCHOLARS

Louisville Institute
Attn: Executive Director
1044 Alta Vista Road
Louisville, KY 40205-1798
(502) 992-5432 Fax: (502) 894-2286
E-mail: info@louisville-institute.org
Web: www.louisville-institute.org/Grants/programs.aspx

Summary To provide funding to African Americans and other scholars of color who are interested in completing a major research and book project that focuses on an aspect of Christianity in North America.

Eligibility This program is open to members of racial/ethnic minority groups (African Americans, Hispanics, Native Americans, Asian Americans, Arab Americans, and Pacific Islanders) who have an earned doctoral degree (normally the Ph.D. or Th.D.). Applicants must be a pre-tenured faculty member in a full-time, tenure-track position at an accredited institution of higher education (college, university, or seminary) in North America. They must be able to negotiate a full academic year free from teaching and committee responsibilities in order to engage in a scholarly research project leading to the publication of their first (or second) book focusing on an aspect of Christianity in North America. Selection is based on the intellectual quality of the research and writing project, its potential to contribute to scholarship in religion, and the potential contribution of the research to the vitality of North American Christianity.

Financial data The grant is $40,000. Awards are intended to make possible a full academic year of sabbatical research and writing by providing up to half of the grantee's salary and benefits for that year. Funds are paid directly to the grantee's institution, but no indirect costs are allowed.

Duration 1 academic year; nonrenewable.

Additional information The Louisville Institute is located at Louisville Presbyterian Theological Seminary and is supported by the Lilly Endowment. These grants were first awarded in 2003. Grantees may not accept other awards that provide a stipend during the tenure of this award, and they must be released from all teaching and committee responsibilities during the award year.

Number awarded Varies each year; recently, 2 of these grants were awarded.

Deadline January of each year.

[1168]
F.J. MCGUIGAN EARLY CAREER INVESTIGATOR RESEARCH PRIZE

American Psychological Foundation
750 First Street, N.E.
Washington, DC 20002-4242
(202) 336-5843 Fax: (202) 336-5812
E-mail: foundation@apa.org
Web: www.apa.org/apf/funding/mcguigan-prize.aspx

Summary To provide funding to young psychologists (particularly African Americans, other minorities, women, and individuals with disabilities) who are interested in conducting research related to the human mind.

Eligibility This program is open to investigators who have earned a doctoral degree in psychology or in a related field within the past 9 years. Nominees must have an affiliation with an accredited college, university, or other research institution. They must be engaged in research that seeks to explicate the concept of the human mind. The approach must be materialistic and should be primarily psychophysiological, but physiological and behavioral research may also qualify. Self-nominations are not accepted; candidates must be nominated by a senior colleague. The sponsor encourages nominations of individuals who represent diversity in race, ethnicity, gender, age, disability, and sexual orientation.

Financial data The grant is $25,000.

Duration These grants are awarded biennially, in even-numbered years.

Additional information The first grant under this program was awarded in 2002.

Number awarded 1 every other year.

Deadline February of even-numbered years.

[1169]
FRAMELINE COMPLETION FUND

Frameline
Attn: Completion Fund
145 Ninth Street, Suite 300
San Francisco, CA 94103
(415) 703-8650 Fax: (415) 861-1404
E-mail: info@frameline.org
Web: www.frameline.org/filmmaker-support

Summary To provide funding to lesbian, gay, bisexual, and transgender (LGBT) film/video artists (particularly African Americans, other film/video artists of color, and women).

Eligibility This program is open to LGBT artists who are in the last stages of the production of documentary, educational, narrative, animated, or experimental projects about or of interest to LGBT people and their communities. Applicants may be independent artists, students, producers, or nonprofit corporations. They must be interested in completion work and must have 90% of the production completed; projects in development, script-development, pre-production, or production are not eligible. Student projects are eligible only if the student maintains artistic and financial control of the project. Women and people of color are especially encouraged to apply. Selection is based on financial need, the contribution the grant will make to completing the project, assurances that the project will be completed, and the statement the project makes about LGBT people and/or issues of concern to them and their communities.

Financial data Grants range from $1,000 to $5,000.

Duration These are 1-time grants.

Additional information This program began in 1990.

Number awarded Varies each year; recently, 5 of these grants were awarded. Since this program was established, it has provided $389,200 in support to 118 films.

Deadline October of each year.

[1170]
FREDERICK DOUGLASS INSTITUTE FOR AFRICAN AND AFRICAN-AMERICAN STUDIES POSTDOCTORAL FELLOWSHIP

University of Rochester
Frederick Douglass Institute for African and African-American Studies
Attn: Director for Research Fellowships
302 Morey Hall
RC Box 270440
Rochester, NY 14627-0440
(585) 276-5744 Fax: (585) 256-2594
E-mail: FDI@mail.rochester.edu
Web: www.rochester.edu

Summary To support postdoctoral research on African and African American studies at the University of Rochester.

Eligibility This program is open to scholars who have a Ph.D. degree in a field related to the African and African American experience. Applicants must be interested in completing a research project at the Frederick Douglass Institute at the University of Rochester. Along with their application, they must submit a curriculum vitae, a 3- to 5-page description of the project, a sample of published or unpublished writing on a topic related to the proposal, and 3 letters of recommendation.

Financial data The program provides a stipend of $40,000 and a $3,000 fund for research-related activities.

Duration 1 year; nonrenewable.

Additional information This is a residential fellowship. All fellows are given office space within the institute, full access to the facilities of the university, and opportunities for collaboration and discussion there. Fellows are expected to teach 2 courses (1 each semester) during the fellowship year. Fellows must be in full-time residence at the institution during the tenure of the award.

Number awarded 1 each year.

Deadline December of each year.

[1171]
GAIUS CHARLES BOLIN DISSERTATION AND POST-MFA FELLOWSHIPS

Williams College
Attn: Dean of the Faculty
880 Main Street
Hopkins Hall, Third Floor
P.O. Box 141
Williamstown, MA 01267
(413) 597-4351 Fax: (413) 597-3553
E-mail: gburda@williams.edu
Web: dean-faculty.williams.edu

Summary To provide financial assistance to African Americans and members of other underrepresented groups who are interested in teaching courses at Williams College while working on their doctoral dissertation or building their post-M.F.A. professional portfolio.

Eligibility This program is open to members of underrepresented groups, including ethnic minorities, first-generation college students, women in predominantly male fields, and scholars with disabilities. Applicants must be 1) doctoral candidates in any field who have completed all work for a Ph.D. except for the dissertation; or 2) artists who completed an M.F.A. degree within the past 2 years and are building their professional portfolio. They must be willing to teach a course at Williams College. Along with their application, they must submit a full curriculum vitae, a graduate school transcript, 3 letters of recommendation, a copy of their dissertation prospectus or samples of their artistic work, and a description of their teaching interests within a department or program at Williams College. U.S. citizenship or permanent resident status is required.

Financial data Fellows receive $36,000 for the academic year, plus housing assistance, office space, computer and library privileges, and a research allowance of up to $4,000.

Duration 2 years.

Additional information Bolin fellows are assigned a faculty adviser in the appropriate department. This program was established in 1985. Fellows are expected to teach a 1-semester course each year. They must be in residence at Williams College for the duration of the fellowship.

Number awarded 3 each year.

Deadline November of each year.

[1172]
GEOPHYSICAL FLUID DYNAMICS FELLOWSHIPS

Woods Hole Oceanographic Institution
Attn: Academic Programs Office
Clark Laboratory, MS 31
266 Woods Hole Road
Woods Hole, MA 02543-1541
(508) 289-2950 Fax: (508) 457-2188
E-mail: gfd@whoi.edu
Web: www.whoi.edu/gfd

Summary To provide summer research and study opportunities at Woods Hole Oceanographic Institution (WHOI) to pre- and postdoctoral scholars (particularly African Americans, other underrepresented minorities, and women) who are interested in geophysical fluid dynamics.

Eligibility This program is open to pre- and postdoctorates who are interested in pursuing research or study opportunities in a field that involves non-linear dynamics of rotating, stratified fluids. Fields of specialization include classical fluid dynamics, physical oceanography, meteorology, geophysical fluid dynamics, astrophysics, planetary atmospheres, hydromagnetics, physics, and applied mathematics. Applications from women and members of underrepresented groups are particularly encouraged.

Financial data Participants receive a stipend of $5,600 and an allowance for travel expenses within the United States.

Duration 10 weeks during the summer.

Additional information Each summer, the program at WHOI revolves around a central theme. A recent theme related to shear turbulence. The main components of the summer program are a series of principal lectures, a set of supplementary research seminars, and research projects conducted by the student fellows with the active support of the staff. Funding for this program, which began in 1959, is provided by the National Science Foundation and Office of Naval Research.

Number awarded Up to 10 graduate students are supported each year.

Deadline February of each year.

[1173]
GERALD OSHITA MEMORIAL FELLOWSHIP

Djerassi Resident Artists Program
Attn: Admissions
2325 Bear Gulch Road
Woodside, CA 94062-4405
(650) 747-1250 Fax: (650) 747-0105
E-mail: drap@djerassi.org
Web: www.djerassi.org/artistresidencies.html

Summary To provide an opportunity for African Americans and other composers of color to participate in the Djerassi Resident Artists Program.

Eligibility This program is open to composers of Asian, African, Latino, or Native American ethnic background. Applicants must be interested in utilizing a residency to compose, study, rehearse, and otherwise advance their own creative projects.

Financial data The fellow is offered housing, meals, studio space, and a stipend of $2,500.

Duration 1 month, from late March through mid-November.

Additional information This fellowship was established in 1994. The program is located in northern California, 45 miles south of San Francisco, on 600 acres of rangeland, redwood forests, and hiking trails. There is a $45 non-refundable application fee.

Number awarded 1 each year.

Deadline February of each year.

[1174]
GERTRUDE AND MAURICE GOLDHABER DISTINGUISHED FELLOWSHIPS

Brookhaven National Laboratory
Attn: Bill Bookless
Building 460
40 Brookhaven Avenue
Upton, NY 11973
(631) 344-5734 E-mail: wbookless@bnl.gov
Web: www.bnl.gov/hr/goldhaber.asp

Summary To provide funding to postdoctoral scientists (particularly African Americans, other minorities, and women) who are interested in conducting research at Brookhaven National Laboratory (BNL).

Eligibility This program is open to scholars who are no more than 3 years past receipt of the Ph.D. and are interested in working at BNL. Candidates must be interested in working in close collaboration with a member of the BNL scientific staff and qualifying for a scientific staff position at BNL upon completion of the appointment. The sponsoring scientist must have an opening and be able to support the candidate at the standard starting salary for postdoctoral research associates. The program especially encourages applications from minorities and women.

Financial data The program provides additional funds to bring the salary to $75,000 per year.

Duration 3 years.

Additional information This program is funded by Battelle Memorial Institute and the State University of New York at Stony Brook.

Number awarded Up to 2 each year.

Deadline June of each year.

[1175]
GILBERT F. WHITE POSTDOCTORAL FELLOWSHIP PROGRAM

Resources for the Future
Attn: Coordinator for Academic Programs
1616 P Street, N.W., Suite 600
Washington, DC 20036-1400
(202) 328-5020 Fax: (202) 939-3460
E-mail: white-award@rff.org
Web: www.rff.org

Summary To provide funding to postdoctoral researchers (particularly African Americans, other minorities, and women) who wish to devote a year to scholarly work at Resources for the Future (RFF) in Washington, D.C.

Eligibility This program is open to individuals in any discipline who have completed their doctoral requirements and are interested in conducting scholarly research at RFF in social or policy science areas that relate to natural resources, energy, or the environment. Teaching and/or research experience at the postdoctoral level is preferred but not essential. Individuals holding positions in government as well as at academic institutions are eligible. Women and minority candidates are strongly encouraged to apply. Non-citizens are eligible if they have proper work and residency documentation.

Financial data Fellows receive an annual stipend (based on their academic salary) plus research support, office facilities at RFF, and an allowance of up to $1,000 for moving or living expenses. Fellowships do not provide medical insurance or other RFF fringe benefits.

Duration 11 months.

Additional information Fellows are assigned to an RFF research division: the Energy and Natural Resources division, the Quality of the Environment division, or the Center for Risk, Resource, and Environmental Management. Fellows are expected to be in residence at Resources for the Future for the duration of the program.

Number awarded 1 each year.

Deadline February of each year.

[1176]
GLORIA E. ANZALDUA BOOK PRIZE

National Women's Studies Association
Attn: Book Prizes
11 East Mount Royal Avenue, Suite 100
Baltimore, MD 21202
(410) 528-0355 Fax: (410) 528-0357
E-mail: awards@nwsa.org
Web: www.nwsa.org/content.asp?pl=16&contentid=16

Summary To recognize and reward members of the National Women's Studies Association (NWSA) who have written outstanding books on women of color and transnational issues.

Eligibility This award is available to NWSA members who submit a book that was published during the preceding year. Entries must present groundbreaking scholarship in women's studies and make a significant multicultural feminist contribution to women of color and/or transnational studies.

Financial data The award provides an honorarium of $1,000 and lifetime membership in NWSA.

Duration The award is presented annually.

Additional information This award was first presented in 2008.

Number awarded 1 each year.

Deadline April of each year.

[1177]
GOALI FACULTY IN INDUSTRY AWARDS

National Science Foundation
Directorate for Engineering
Attn: Division of Industrial Innovation and Partnerships
4201 Wilson Boulevard, Room 550S
Arlington, VA 22230
(703) 292-7082 Fax: (703) 292-9056
TDD: (800) 281-8749 E-mail: dsenich@nsf.gov
Web: www.nsf.gov

Summary To provide funding to science, engineering, and mathematics faculty (particularly African Americans, other underrepresented minorities, women, and individuals with disabilities) who wish to conduct research in an industrial setting as part of the Grant Opportunities for Academic Liaison with Industry (GOALI) program of the National Science Foundation (NSF).

Eligibility This program is open to full-time faculty members at U.S. colleges and universities in science, engineering, and mathematics fields of interest to NSF. Applicants must be U.S. citizens, nationals, or permanent residents. They must present a plan for collaboration between their institution and industry, with a description of the facilities and resources that will be available at the industrial site to support the proposed research. In the selection process, consideration is given to the achievement of societally relevant outcomes, including full participation of women, persons with disabilities, and underrepresented minorities.

Financial data Grants range from $30,000 to $75,000, including 50% of the faculty member's salary and fringe benefits during the industrial residency period. Up to 20% of the total requested amount may be used for travel and research expenses for the faculty and his/her students, including materials but excluding equipment. The industrial partner must commit to support the other 50% of the faculty salary and fringe benefits.

Duration 3 to 12 months.

Additional information This program is also offered by most other NSF directorates. Check the web site for a name and e-mail address of the contact person in each directorate.

Number awarded A total of 60 to 80 grants for all GOALI programs is awarded each year; total funding is approximately $5 million.

Deadline Applications may be submitted at any time.

[1178]
GOALI POSTDOCTORAL INDUSTRIAL FELLOWSHIPS

National Science Foundation
Directorate for Engineering
Attn: Division of Industrial Innovation and Partnerships
4201 Wilson Boulevard, Room 550S
Arlington, VA 22230
(703) 292-7082 Fax: (703) 292-9056
TDD: (800) 281-8749 E-mail: dsenich@nsf.gov
Web: www.nsf.gov

Summary To provide an opportunity for recent postdoctorates (particularly African Americans, other minorities, women, and Individuals with disabilities) to work in industry as part of the Grant Opportunities for Academic Liaison with Industry (GOALI) program of the National Science Foundation (NSF).

Eligibility Applicants for these fellowships must have held a Ph.D. degree in a science, engineering, or mathematics field of interest to NSF for no more than 3 years. They must be U.S. citizens, nationals, or permanent residents. Along with their application, they must submit a plan for full-time work in industry under the guidance of an academic adviser and an industrial mentor. In the selection process, consideration is given to the achievement of societally relevant outcomes, including full participation of women, persons with disabilities, and underrepresented minorities.

Financial data Grants range up to $75,000 per year. Funding, up to $4,000, may also be provided for transportation and moving expenses. Indirect costs are not allowed, but an institutional allowance of $5,000 is provided.

Duration 1 or 2 years.

Additional information This program is also offered by most other NSF directorates. Check the web site for a name and e-mail address of the contact person in each directorate.

Number awarded A total of 60 to 80 grants for all GOALI programs is awarded each year; total funding is approximately $5 million.

Deadline Applications may be submitted at any time.

[1179]
HARRY AND MIRIAM LEVINSON AWARD FOR EXCEPTIONAL CONTRIBUTIONS TO CONSULTING ORGANIZATIONAL PSYCHOLOGY

American Psychological Association
Attn: Office of Division Services
750 First Street, N.E.
Washington, DC 20002-4242
(202) 336-6022 E-mail: divisions@apa.org
Web: www.apa.org/about/awards/div-13-levinson.aspx

Summary To recognize and reward outstanding consulting psychologists, particularly African Americans and others who represent diversity in race, gender, age, etc.

Eligibility This award is presented to a member of the American Psychological Association (APA) who is a consulting psychologist. Nominees must have shown evidence of ability to convert psychological theory and concepts into applications through which managers and leaders can create effective, healthy, and humane organizations. The sponsor encourages nominations of individuals who represent diversity in race, ethnicity, gender, age, disability, and sexual orientation.

Financial data The award is $5,000.

Duration The award is presented annually.

Additional information This award, first presented in 1992, is sponsored by Division 13 (Consulting Psychology) in conjunction with Division 12 (Society of Clinical Psychology), Division 14 (Industrial/Organizational Psychology), and Division 39 (Psychoanalysis) of the APA.

Number awarded 1 each year.

Deadline Nominations must be submitted by March of each year.

[1180]
HARVARD MEDICAL SCHOOL DEAN'S POSTDOCTORAL FELLOWSHIP

Harvard Medical School
Office for Diversity Inclusion and Community Partnership
Attn: Program Manager, Dean's Postdoctoral Fellowship
164 Longwood Avenue, Second Floor
Boston, MA 02115-5818
(617) 432-1083 Fax: (617) 432-3834
E-mail: brian_anderson@hms.harvard.edu
Web: www.hms.harvard.edu/dcp/deanspdfellowship

Summary To provide an opportunity for postdoctoral scholars (particularly African Americans or other minorities) with an advanced degree in the social and basic sciences who are interested in a postdoctoral fellowship to obtain research training at Harvard Medical School.

Eligibility This program is open to U.S. citizens and permanent residents who have completed an M.D., Ph.D., Sc.D., or equivalent degree in the basic or social sciences and have less than 5 years of relevant postdoctoral research experience. Applicants must be interested in a program of research training under the mentorship of a professor in 1 of the departments of Harvard Medical School: biological chemistry and molecular pharmacology, cell biology, genetics, global health and social medicine, health care policy, microbiology and immunobiology, neurobiology, stem cell and regenerative biology, or systems biology. Scientists from minority and disadvantaged backgrounds are especially encouraged to apply. Selection is based on academic achievement, scholarly promise, potential to add to the diversity of the Harvard Medical School community, and the likelihood that the application will become an independent scientist and societal leader.

Financial data Fellows receive a professional development allowance of $1,250 per year and a stipend that depends on the years of postdoctoral experience, ranging from $40,992 for zero to $47,820 for 4 years.

Duration 2 years.

Number awarded 2 each year.

Deadline Applications may be submitted at any time.

[1181]
HARVARD–NEWCOMEN POSTDOCTORAL FELLOWSHIP IN BUSINESS HISTORY

Harvard Business School
Attn: Fellowships
Rock Center 104
Boston, MA 02163
(617) 495-1003 Fax: (617) 495-0594
E-mail: wfriedman@hbs.edu
Web: www.hbs.edu/businesshistory/fellowships.html

Summary To provide residencies for study and research at Harvard Business School to scholars (particularly African Americans, other minorities, and women) in the fields of history, economics, or a related field.

Eligibility This program is open to scholars who, within the last 10 years, have received a Ph.D. degree in history, economics, or a related field. Applicants must be proposing to engage in research that would benefit from the resources at the Harvard Business School and the larger Boston scholarly community. In addition, they must be interested in participating in the school's business history courses, seminars, and case development activities. Along with their application, they must submit concise statements and descriptions of academic research undertaken in the past and a detailed description of the research they wish to undertake at Harvard. Women and minorities are especially encouraged to apply.

Financial data The stipend is $46,000. In addition, a travel fund, a book fund, and administrative support are provided.

Duration 12 months, beginning in July.

Additional information This program began in 1949. Fellows spend approximately two-thirds of their time conducting research of their own choosing. The remainder of their time is devoted to participating in activities of the school, including attendance at the business history seminar and working with faculty teaching the business history courses offered in the M.B.A. program. Fellows are strongly encouraged to submit an article to *Business History Review* during their year at the school. Support for this fellowship is provided by the Newcomen Society of the United States.

Deadline October of each year.

[1182]
HEALTH AND AGING POLICY FELLOWSHIPS

Columbia University College of Physicians and Surgeons
Attn: Department of Psychiatry
Director, Health and Aging Policy Fellows
1051 Riverside Drive, Unit 9
New York, NY 10032
(212) 543-5401 Fax: (212) 543-6063
E-mail: pincush@nyspi.columbia.edu
Web: www.healthandagingpolicy.org

Summary To provide an opportunity for health professionals (particularly African Americans and members of other underrepresented groups) who have an interest in aging and policy issues to work as legislative assistants in Congress or at other sites.

Eligibility This program is open to physicians, nurses, and social workers who have a demonstrated commitment to health and aging issues and a desire to be involved in health policy at the federal, state, or local levels. Other professionals with clinical backgrounds (e.g., dentists, dieticians, economists, epidemiologists, health care administrators, psychologists) working in the field of health and aging are also eligible. Preference is given to professionals early or midway through their careers. Applicants must be interested serving as residential fellows by participating in the policymaking process on either the federal or state level as legislative assistants in Congress or as professional staff members in executive agencies or policy organizations. A non-residential track is also available to applicants who wish to work on a policy project throughout the year at relevant sites. Candidates from underrepresented groups are strongly encouraged to apply. Selection is based on commitment to health and aging issues and improving the health and well-being of older Americans, potential for leadership in health policy, professional qualifications and achievements, impact of the fellowship experience on the applicant's career, and interpersonal and communication skills. U.S. citizenship or permanent resident status is required.

Financial data For residential fellows, the stipend depends on their current base salary, to a maximum of $120,000 per year; other benefits include a travel allowance for pre-fellowship arrangements and to fellowship-related meetings, a relocation grant of up to $3,500, and up to $400 per month for health insurance. For non-residential fellows, grants provide up to $30,000 to cover related fellowship and travel costs.

Duration 9 to 12 months; fellows may apply for a second year of participation.

Additional information This program, which began in 2009, operates in collaboration with the American Political Science Association Congressional Fellowship Program. Funding is provided by The Atlantic Philanthropies. The John Heinz/Health and Aging Policy Fellowship, an activity of the Teresa and H. John Heinz III Foundation, supports 1 fellow to work in the Senate. Support is also provided by the Centers for Disease Control and Prevention, the John A. Hartford Foundation, and the Gerontological Society of America.

Number awarded Varies each year; recently, 4 residential and 6 non-residential fellowships were awarded.

Deadline May of each year.

[1183]
HEALTH, EDUCATION, AND HUMAN SERVICES FELLOWSHIPS

American Association for the Advancement of Science
Attn: Science and Technology Policy Fellowships
1200 New York Avenue, N.W.
Washington, DC 20005-3920
(202) 326-6700 Fax: (202) 289-4950
E-mail: fellowships@aaas.org
Web: www.fellowships.aaas.org

Summary To provide postdoctoral scientists and engineers (particularly African Americans, other minorities, and individuals with disabilities) with an opportunity to work at designated federal agencies on issues of health, education, and human services.

Eligibility This program is open to doctoral-level scientists (Ph.D., M.D., D.V.M., D.Sc., and other terminal degrees) in any field of science (behavioral, biological, computational, earth, health, medical, physical, or social), engineering, or mathematics. Engineers with a master's degree and at least 3 years of professional experience are also eligible. Applicants should be able to support improved programs, policies, planning, risk analysis, regulation, monitoring, and evaluation for a broad range of initiatives in 1) preventive and community health, disease identification and response, and medical research; 2) individual, family, and community social services, systems, and support; 3) food processing and distribution safety; and 4) science education, research, and innovation. They must demonstrate solid scientific and technical credentials; a commitment to serve society; good communication skills; the ability to engage with non-scientific audiences; and an interest in working as special assistants for designated federal agencies (the Food Safety Inspection Service (FSIS) of the U.S. Department of Agriculture (USDA), National Science Foundation (NSF), National Institutes of Health (NIH), Department of Health and Human Services (DHHS), or Department of Veterans Affairs). U.S. citizenship is required; federal employees are not eligible. The sponsor seeks candidates from a broad array of backgrounds and a diversity of geographic, disciplinary, gender, and ethnic perspectives, as well as disability status.

Financial data The stipend for fellows with 0 to 7 years of postdoctoral experience is $74,872 in the first year and $77,368 in the second year. For fellows with 7 to 15 years of experience, the stipend is $84,855 in the first year and $87,350 in the second year. Fellows who have 15 or more years of postdoctoral experience receive $97,333 in the first year and $99,420 in the second year. Also provided are a $4,000 relocation allowance for fellows from outside the Washington, D.C. area, reimbursement for health insurance, and a $4,000 travel allowance.

Duration 1 year, beginning in September.

Number awarded 30 to 40 each year.

Deadline October of each year.

[1184]
HEALTH SERVICES RESEARCH PROJECTS

Agency for Healthcare Research and Quality
Attn: Office of Extramural Research, Education, and Priority Populations
540 Gaither Road
Rockville, MD 20850
(301) 427-1556 Fax: (301) 427-1562
TDD: (301) 451-0088
E-mail: Kishena.Wadhwani@ahrq.hhs.gov
Web: grants.nih.gov/grants/guide/pa-files/PA-13-045.html

Summary To provide funding to scholars (particularly African Americans, other underrepresented minorities, and individuals with disabilities) who are interested in conducting research that is designed to improve the outcomes, quality, cost, and utilization of health care services.

Eligibility This program is open to investigators at domestic and foreign, nonprofit, public and private organizations, including universities, clinics, units of state and local governments, nonprofit firms, and nonprofit foundations. Applicants must be proposing projects in 1 of the research portfolio areas of the Agency for Healthcare Research and Quality (AHRQ): 1) the value portfolio, for research that can be used to reduce unnecessary health care costs (waste) while maintaining or improving health care quality; 2) the health information technology portfolio, for the use of information and communication technology in health care to support the delivery of patient or population care; 3) the comparative effectiveness portfolio, for research focusing on comparative effectiveness of different clinical treatments and services; 4) the prevention/care management portfolio, to improve the quality, safety, efficiency, and effectiveness of preventive services and chronic care management in ambulatory care settings; 5) the patient safety portfolio, for research projects to identify the risks and hazards encountered by patients as a result of health care; or 6) the innovations and emerging areas portfolio, for research on ideas that have the potential for high impact. Members of underrepresented ethnic and racial groups and individuals with disabilities are especially encouraged to apply as principal investigators.

Financial data The maximum grant is $250,000 per year, including both direct costs and facilities and administrative costs.

Duration 1 year; may be renewed up to 4 additional years.

Number awarded Varies each year.

Deadline March, July, or November of each year.

[1185]
HENRY DAVID RESEARCH GRANT IN HUMAN REPRODUCTIVE BEHAVIOR AND POPULATION STUDIES

American Psychological Foundation
750 First Street, N.E.
Washington, DC 20002-4242
(202) 336-5843 Fax: (202) 336-5812
E-mail: foundation@apa.org
Web: www.apa.org/apf/funding/david.aspx

Summary To provide funding to young psychologists (particularly African Americans, other minorities, women, and individuals with disabilities) who are interested in conducting research on reproductive behavior.

Eligibility This program is open to doctoral students in psychology working on a dissertation and young psychologists who have no more than 7 years of postgraduate experience. Applicants must be interested in conducting research on human reproductive behavior or an area related to population concerns. Along with their application, they must submit a current curriculum vitae, 2 letters of recommendation, and an essay of 1 to 2 pages on their interest in human reproductive behavior or in population studies. The sponsor encourages applications from individuals who represent diversity in race, ethnicity, gender, age, disability, and sexual orientation.

Financial data The grant is $1,500.

Duration The grant is presented annually.

Number awarded 1 each year.

Deadline February of each year.

[1186]
HIGH PRIORITY, SHORT-TERM BRIDGE AWARDS IN DIABETES RESEARCH

Juvenile Diabetes Research Foundation International
Attn: Grant Administrator
26 Broadway, 14th Floor
New York, NY 10004
(212) 479-7572 Toll Free: (800) 533-CURE
Fax: (212) 785-9595 E-mail: info@jdrf.org
Web: jdrf.org

Summary To provide funding to scientists (particularly African Americans, other underrepresented minorities, women, and individuals with disabilities) who are interested in conducting diabetes-related research but have not yet received any support.

Eligibility Applicants must have an M.D., D.M.D., D.V.M., Ph.D., or equivalent degree and have a full-time faculty position or equivalent at a college, university, medical school, or other research facility. They must have applied for grants previously and scored within 10% of the funding payline of a research funding agency but failed to receive support. Awards must be used to obtain new data to support the feasibility or validity of the research, address reviewers' concerns, or revise approaches to the research. There are no citizenship requirements. Applications are encouraged from women, members of minority groups underrepresented in the sciences, and people with disabilities. The proposed research may be conducted at foreign or domestic, for-profit or nonprofit, or public or private institutions, including universities, colleges, hospitals, laboratories, units of state or local government, or eligible agencies of the federal government.

Financial data Awards are limited to $55,000 plus 10% indirect costs.

Duration 1 year; generally nonrenewable.

Number awarded Varies each year.

Deadline February, May, or October of each year.

[1187]
HIGH-RISK RESEARCH IN BIOLOGICAL ANTHROPOLOGY AND ARCHAEOLOGY GRANTS

National Science Foundation
Social, Behavioral, and Economic Sciences
Attn: Division of Behavioral and Cognitive Sciences
4201 Wilson Boulevard, Room 995 N
Arlington, VA 22230
(703) 292-8759 Fax: (703) 292-9068
TDD: (800) 281-8749 E-mail: jyellen@nsf.gov
Web: www.nsf.gov/funding/pgm_summ.jsp?pims_id=5319

Summary To provide funding to scholars (particularly African Americans, other underrepresented minorities, and individuals with disabilities) who are interested in conducting high-risk research in anthropology or archaeology.

Eligibility This program is open to scholars interested in conducting research projects in cultural anthropology, archaeology, or physical anthropology that might be considered too risky for normal review procedures. A project is considered risky if the data may not be obtainable in spite of all reasonable preparation on the researcher's part. Proposals for extremely urgent research where access to the data may not be available in the normal review schedule, even with all reasonable preparation by the researcher, are also appropriate for this program. Graduate students are not eligible. Applications are encouraged from all citizens, including women and men, underrepresented minorities, and persons with disabilities.

Financial data Grants up to $35,000, including indirect costs, are available.

Duration 1 year.

Number awarded Generally, 5 of these grants are awarded each year.

Deadline Applications may be submitted at any time.

[1188]
HIVMA MINORITY CLINICAL FELLOWSHIPS

Infectious Diseases Society of America
Attn: HIV Medicine Association
1300 Wilson Boulevard, Suite 300
Arlington, VA 22209
(703) 299-1215 Toll Free: (888) 844-4372
Fax: (703) 299-8766 E-mail: info@hivma.org
Web: www.hivma.org/Minority_Clinical_Fellowship.aspx

Summary To provide an opportunity for African American and Latino physicians to participate in a clinical training program related to HIV.

Eligibility This program is open to physicians (M.D. or D.O.) who are of African American or Latino descent and have a demonstrated interest in HIV medicine. Applicants must be legal residents of the United States and have an intent to establish their practice in areas of the country with large minority populations. They must have completed their residencies (or be within the first 5 years of clinical practice) and be board eligible. Their proposed clinical training program must have a link to an academic institution where the majority of their time will be spent engaged in HIV clinical care and where they will have the opportunity to manage continuously at least 30 HIV patients in both inpatient and outpatient settings. Clinical settings with large minority patient populations are required. Applicants must identify a mentor to oversee their clinical experience; mentors must be members of the HIV Medicine Association (HIVMA).

Financial data The stipend is $60,000. Fellows also receive fringe benefits equivalent to those enjoyed by staff of similar rank at the sponsoring institution, 1 year membership in HIVMA, and free registration and travel support for the annual meeting of the Infectious Diseases Society of America (IDSA). An additional $10,000 is paid to the institution to offset administrative costs.

Duration 1 year.

Additional information Fellows may elect to spend up to 2 months of their fellowship at another approved institution, clinic, or practice to supplement their clinical experience. Support for this program is provided by Pfizer, Gilead Sciences, Bristol-Myers Squibb, Janssen Therapeutics, and Genentech. Fellows currently in clinical practice are expected to spend at least 50% of their time on clinical care and clinical education associated with the fellowship.

Number awarded 2 each year: 1 African American and 1 Latino.

Deadline March of each year.

[1189]
HUBBLE FELLOWSHIPS

Space Telescope Science Institute
Attn: Hubble Fellowship Program Office
3700 San Martin Drive
Baltimore, MD 21218
(410) 338-5079 Fax: (410) 338-4211
E-mail: hfinquiry@stsci.edu
Web: www.stsci.edu/institute/smo/fellowships/hubble

Summary To provide funding to recent postdoctoral scientists (particularly African Americans, other minorities, and women) who are interested in conducting research related to the Hubble Space Telescope or related missions of the National Aeronautics and Space Administration (NASA).

Eligibility This program is open to postdoctoral scientists who completed their doctoral degree within the past 3 years in astronomy, physics, or related disciplines. Applicants must be interested in conducting research related to NASA Cosmic Origins missions: the Hubble Space Telescope, Herschel Space Observatory, James Webb Space Telescope, Stratospheric Observatory for Infrared Astronomy, or the Spitzer Space Telescope. They may U.S. citizens or English-speaking citizens of other countries with valid visas. Research may be theoretical, observational, or instrumental. Women and members of minority groups are strongly encouraged to apply.

Financial data Stipends are approximately $66,500 per year. Other benefits may include health insurance, relocation costs, and support for travel, equipment, and other direct costs of research.

Duration 3 years: an initial 1-year appointment and 2 annual renewals, contingent on satisfactory performance and availability of funds.

Additional information This program, funded by NASA, began in 1990 and was limited to work with the Hubble Space Telescope. A parallel program, called the Spitzer Fellowship, began in 2002 and was limited to work with the Spitzer Space Telescope. In 2009, those programs were combined into this single program, which was also broadened to include the other NASA Cosmic Origins missions. Fellows are required to be in residence at their host institution engaged in full-time research for the duration of the grant.

Number awarded Varies each year; recently, 17 of these fellowships were awarded.

Deadline October of each year.

[1190]
HURSTON/WRIGHT LEGACY AWARD

Zora Neale Hurston/Richard Wright Foundation
Attn: Hurston/Wright Awards
12138 Central Avenue, Suite 953
Bowie, MD 20721
(301) 459-2108 E-mail: info@hurstonwright.org
Web: www.hurstonwright.org/#!legacy-awards/cwp3

Summary To recognize and reward the best fiction, nonfiction, and poetry written by authors of African descent.

Eligibility This award is available to writers of African descent from any area of the Diaspora. Publishers may submit (with permission of the author) full-length books of fiction and nonfiction, collections of short stories, or collections of essays in 3 categories: fiction (novel, novella, or short story collection); nonfiction (autobiography, memoir, biography, history, social issues, or literary criticism); or poetry (books in verse, prose poetry, formal verse, experimental verse). Paperback originals, self-published authors, and English translations of books originally written in another language are eligible, but reprints of a book published in a previous year, poetry books with less than 50 pages, and books written by more than 1 author are not considered. Entries must have been published in the preceding calendar year in the United States or be U.S. editions of foreign books published for the first time in the United States.

Financial data Cash prizes are awarded.

Duration The prizes are awarded annually.

Additional information This program began in 2002. There is a $30 entry fee for each title.

Number awarded 9 awards are presented each year: 1 first-place award and 2 finalist awards in each of the 3 categories.

Deadline November of each year.

[1191]
INDEPENDENT SCIENTIST AWARD

Agency for Healthcare Research and Quality
Attn: Office of Extramural Research, Education, and Priority Populations
540 Gaither Road
Rockville, MD 20850
(301) 427-1555 Fax: (301) 427-1562
TDD: (301) 451-0088
E-mail: Kay.Anderson@ahrq.hhs.gov
Web: grants.nih.gov/grants/guide/pa-files/PA-09-086.html

Summary To provide funding to newly independent scientists (particularly African Americans, other underrepresented minorities, and individuals with disabilities) who are interested in conducting research to improve the outcomes, effectiveness, quality, cost, and utilization of health care services.

Eligibility This program is open to U.S. citizens or permanent residents who have a clinical (e.g., M.D., D.O., D.D.S., D.M.D., D.C., O.D., D.N.S., Pharm.D.) or research (e.g., Ph.D., Sc.D., Dr.P.H.) doctoral degree and are no more than 7 years beyond their latest research training experience. Applicants must be proposing projects in 1 of the research portfolio areas of the Agency for Healthcare Research and Quality (AHRQ): 1) the value portfolio, for research that can be used to reduce unnecessary health care costs (waste) while maintaining or improving health care quality; 2) the health information technology portfolio, for the use of information and communication technology in health care to support the delivery of patient or population care; 3) the comparative effectiveness portfolio, for research focusing on comparative effectiveness of different clinical treatments and services; 4) the prevention/care management portfolio, to improve the quality, safety, efficiency, and effectiveness of preventive services and chronic care management in ambulatory care settings; 5) the patient safety portfolio, for research projects to identify the risks and hazards encountered by patients as a result of health care; or 6) the innovations and emerging areas portfolio, for research on ideas that have the potential for high impact. Members of underrepresented ethnic and racial groups, individuals with disabilities, and individuals from disadvantaged backgrounds are especially encouraged to apply.

Financial data Grants provide salary up to $90,000 annually, plus associated fringe benefits. Also available are up to $25,000 per year for research development support (tuition, fees, and books related to career development; research expenses such as supplies, equipment, and technical personnel; travel to research meetings or training; and statistical services, including personnel and computer time). Facilities and administrative costs are reimbursed at 8% of modified total direct costs.

Duration 3 to 5 years; nonrenewable.

Additional information At least 75% of the recipient's full-time professional effort must be devoted to the program and the remainder devoted to other research-related and/or teaching pursuits consistent with the objectives of the award.

Number awarded Varies each year.

Deadline February, June, or October of each year.

[1192]
INSTITUTIONAL RESEARCH AND ACADEMIC CAREER DEVELOPMENT AWARDS

National Institute of General Medical Sciences
Attn: MORE Special Initiatives Branch
45 Center Drive, Suite 2AS37
Bethesda, MD 20892-6200
(301) 594-3900 Fax: (301) 480-2753
TDD: (301) 451-0088 E-mail: singhs@nigms.nih.gov
Web: grants.nih.gov/grants/guide/pa-files/PAR-11-255

Summary To provide an opportunity for African American and other underrepresented postdoctoral biomedical scientists to gain experience at a research-intensive institution (RII) while they complete a teaching assignment at a Minority Serving Institution (MSI).

Eligibility This program is open to members of minority groups underrepresented in the biomedical and behavioral sciences, defined as individuals with disabilities and African Americans, Hispanic Americans, Native Americans (including Alaska Natives), and natives of the U.S. Pacific Islands. Candidates must have a Ph.D., M.D., or comparable doctoral degree, be committed to research, and have the potential to develop as independent investigators. They must be interested in a mentored research experience at an RII, typical of other competitive postdoctoral opportunities, combined with a mentored teaching experience at a partner MSI.

Financial data Grants up to $500,000 per year are available. Funding includes salary support for the scholar at a rate consistent with the established salary structure at the sponsoring institution, research development support (e.g., tuition and fees related to career development, supplies and other modest research expenses, travel to a scientific meeting, statistical services such as personnel and computer time), academic development support, and program administration. Facilities and administrative costs are reimbursed at 8% of modified total direct costs.

Duration 2 to 4 years.

Additional information The National Institute of General Medical Sciences, a component of the National Institutes of Health (NIH), operates this program as part of its Minority Opportunities for Research (MORE) Division. Funds are issued through a principal investigator at an RII, which submits the application to NIH and which then partners with 1 or more MSI. Scientists interested in participating in the program apply through the MSI. Scholars are expected to devote approximately 25% of their time to their teaching experience at the partner MSI.

Number awarded 1 or 2 each year.

Deadline September of each year.

[1193]
INTERNATIONAL COLLABORATION IN CHEMISTRY BETWEEN U.S. INVESTIGATORS AND THEIR COUNTERPARTS ABROAD

National Science Foundation
Directorate for Mathematical and Physical Sciences
Attn: Division of Chemistry
4201 Wilson Boulevard, Room 1055 S
Arlington, VA 22230
(703) 292-7719 Fax: (703) 292-9037
TDD: (800) 281-8749 E-mail: zrosenzw@nsf.gov
Web: www.nsf.gov/funding/pgm_summ.jsp?pims_id=13627

Summary To provide funding to chemists in the United States (particularly African Americans, other underrepresented minorities, women, and individuals with disabilities) who are interested in conducting collaborative research with counterparts in designated foreign countries.

Eligibility This program is open to chemists at colleges and universities in the United States. Applicants must be interested in conducting a research project in collaboration with a scientist in Austria, Brazil, France, Israel, Japan, Luxembourg, Russia, or Taiwan. Preference is given to proposals where the efforts on the U.S. and foreign sides are balanced and complementary. Applications are encouraged from all citizens, including women and men, underrepresented minorities, and persons with disabilities.

Financial data Awards average $140,000 per year.

Duration 3 years.

Additional information This program operates in conjunction with Austrian Science Fund, the State of São Paulo Research Foundation, the French National Research Agency, the United States-Israel Binational Science Foundation, the National Research Fund of Luxembourg, the Russian Foundation for Basic Research, and the National Science Council of Taiwan.

Number awarded 10 to 40 each year. A total of $10 million is available for this program annually.

Deadline Preliminary proposals must be submitted by July of each year; full proposals are due in October.

[1194]
INVESTIGATOR AWARDS IN HEALTH POLICY RESEARCH

Robert Wood Johnson Foundation
College Road East and U.S. Route 1
P.O. Box 2316
Princeton, NJ 08543-2316
(609) 932-8701 Toll Free: (877) 843-RWJF
E-mail: mail@rwjf.org
Web: www.rwjf.org

Summary To provide funding to African Americans and other investigators from diverse fields who are interested in conducting research on health policy.

Eligibility This program is open to investigators in the health, social, and behavioral sciences. Members of minority groups, researchers early in their careers, and individuals in non-academic settings, such as research firms and policy organizations, are especially encouraged to apply. The proposed research should help develop, interpret, or substantially advance ideas or knowledge that can improve health or health care policy in the United States. Selection is based on the relevance of the research to national policy and its potential to inform and improve policy-making; the contribution and potential significance of the project to the theoretical underpinnings and knowledge base of health care, health policy, or other disciplines; the extent to which the work represents an innovative perspective on health, health care, or health policy; the soundness of the project's conceptual framework and methodology; the feasibility of the work; the likelihood that the findings can be useful to policy-makers and other leaders; capability of the investigator to undertake and complete the project on schedule; and investigator's research record.

Financial data Grants up to $335,000 are provided. Funds are to be used primarily for project salary support for the principal investigator(s) and for indirect costs at a rate of up to 12%.

Duration 24 to 36 months.

Number awarded Approximately 8 each year.

Deadline Letters of intent must be submitted by January of each year. Completed applications are due in June.

[1195]
INVESTIGATORS IN PATHOGENESIS OF INFECTIOUS DISEASE

Burroughs Wellcome Fund
21 T.W. Alexander Drive, Suite 100
P.O. Box 13901
Research Triangle Park, NC 27709-3901
(919) 991-5112 Fax: (919) 991-5160
E-mail: info@bwfund.org
Web: www.bwfund.org

Summary To provide funding to physician/scientists in the United States and Canada (particularly African Americans, other minorities, and women) who wish to conduct research on pathogenesis, with a focus on the intersection of human and pathogen biology.

Eligibility This program is open to established independent physician/scientists who are citizens or permanent residents of the United States or Canada and affiliated with accredited degree-granting U.S. or Canadian medical schools. Applicants must be interested in conducting research projects related to the fungal, metazoan, and protozoan pathogens. Candidates must have an M.D., D.V.M., or Ph.D. degree and be tenure-track investigators as an assistant professor or equivalent at a degree-granting institution. Each institution (including its medical school, graduate schools, and all affiliated hospitals and research institutes) may nominate up to 2 candidates. Institutions that nominate a researcher who has a D.V.M. are allowed 3 nominations. The sponsor also encourages institutions to nominate underrepresented minorities and women. Selection is based on qualifications of the candidate and potential to conduct innovative research; demonstration of an established record of independent research; and quality and originality of the proposed research and its potential to advance understanding of fundamental issues of how infectious agents and human hosts interact.

Financial data The grant provides $100,000 per year. No more than $20,000 of the grant may be used for salary support, but institutions may supplement the award to a level consistent with its own scale.

Duration 5 years.

Additional information This program began in 2001 as a replacement for several former programs: New Investigator and Scholar Awards in Molecular Pathogenic Mycology, New Investigator and Scholar Awards in Molecular Parasitology, and New Initiatives in Malaria Awards. Awardees are required to devote at least 75% of their time to research-related activities.

Number awarded Varies each year; recently, 9 of these grants were awarded.

Deadline October of each year.

[1196]
J. ROBERT GLADDEN ORTHOPAEDIC SOCIETY BASIC RESEARCH GRANTS

J. Robert Gladden Orthopaedic Society
Attn: Scientific Committee
6300 North River Road, Suite 727
Rosemont, IL 60018-4226
(847) 698-1633 Fax: (847) 823-4921
E-mail: jrgos@aaos.org
Web: www.gladdensociety.org

Summary To provide funding to members of the J. Robert Gladden Orthopaedic Society (JRGOS) who are African American or from another underrepresented group and interested in conducting a basic research project.

Eligibility This program is open to members of underrepresented minority groups who are JRGOS members and interested in conducting a basic research project. Applicants must be affiliated with a research institution that provides laboratory space and basic facilities. They must be able to demonstrate the compatibility of their project's clinical relevance with the mission and goals of the society. Preference is given to applicants planning to work with a senior JRGOS member.

Financial data The grant is $25,000.

Duration 1 year.

Additional information This program is sponsored by DePuy/Johnson & Johnson.

Number awarded 1 or more each year.

Deadline September of each year.

[1197]
JAMES A. RAWLEY PRIZE

Organization of American Historians
Attn: Award and Committee Coordinator
112 North Bryan Street
Bloomington, IN 47408-4141
(812) 855-7311 Fax: (812) 855-0696
E-mail: khamm@oah.org
Web: www.oah.org/awards/awards.rawley.index.html

Summary To recognize and reward authors of outstanding books dealing with race relations in the United States.

Eligibility This award is presented to the author of the outstanding book on the history of race relations in America. Entries must have been published during the current calendar year.

Financial data The award is $1,000 and a certificate.

Duration The award is presented annually.

Additional information This award was established in 1990.

Number awarded 1 each year.

Deadline September of each year.

[1198]
JAMES WELDON JOHNSON INSTITUTE VISITING FELLOWS PROGRAM

Emory University
Attn: James Weldon Johnson Institute
1599 Clifton Road N.E., Room 6-223
Atlanta, GA 30322
(404) 727-2515 Fax: (404) 727-2539
E-mail: jwji@emory.edu
Web: www.jamesweldonjohnson.emory.edu

Summary To provide funding to African American and other scholars interested in conducting research related to the modern civil rights movement while in residence at the James Weldon Johnson Institute of Emory University.

Eligibility This program is open to scholars interested in conducting research on the origins, evolution, impact, and legacy of the civil rights movement or the rise of the Niagara Movement from 1905 to the present. Applicants must be U.S. citizens or permanent residents who have a Ph.D. Special consideration is given to research proposals that examine the civil right movement and its points of intersection with other social justice movements, such as the women's movement, the lesbian, gay, bisexual, transgendered movement, or the human rights movement. Applications are welcomed from scholars in American studies, African American studies, English, ethnic studies, gay and lesbian studies, history, law, music, and women's studies.

Financial data Grants are $60,000 for full professors, $40,000 for associate professors, or $30,000 for assistant professors.

Duration 1 academic year.

Additional information This program began in 2008 with support from the Andrew W. Mellon Foundation. Scholars teach 1 undergraduate or graduate course during the period of their residency in the Emory University sponsoring departments (African American studies, English, history, music, and the Graduate Institute of the Liberal Arts) or its school of law.

Number awarded 5 each year.

Deadline March of each year.

[1199]
JOEL ELKES RESEARCH AWARD

American College of Neuropsychopharmacology
Attn: Executive Office
5034-A Thoroughbred Lane
Brentwood, TN 37027
(615) 324-2360 Fax: (615) 523-1715
E-mail: acnp@acnp.org
Web: www.acnp.org/programs/awards.aspx

Summary To recognize and reward young scientists (particularly African Americans, other minorities, and women) who have contributed outstanding clinical or translational research to neuropsychopharmacology.

Eligibility This award is available to scientists who are younger than 50 years of age. Nominees must have made an outstanding clinical or translational contribution to neuropsychopharmacology. The contribution may be based on a single discovery or a cumulative body of work. Emphasis is placed on contributions that further understanding of self-regulatory processes as they affect mental function and behavior in disease and well-being. Membership in the American College of

Neuropsychopharmacology (ACNP) is not required. Nomination of women and minorities is highly encouraged.

Financial data The award consists of an expense-paid trip to the ACNP annual meeting, a monetary honorarium, and a plaque.

Duration The award is presented annually.

Additional information This award was first presented in 1986.

Number awarded 1 each year.

Deadline Nominations must be submitted by June of each year.

[1200]
JOHN AND POLLY SPARKS EARLY CAREER GRANT

American Psychological Foundation
750 First Street, N.E.
Washington, DC 20002-4242
(202) 336-5843 Fax: (202) 336-5812
E-mail: foundation@apa.org
Web: www.apa.org/apf/funding/sparks-early-career.aspx

Summary To provide funding to young psychologists (particularly African Americans, other minorities, women, and individuals with disabilities) who are interested in conducting research on serious emotional disturbance in children.

Eligibility This program is open to young psychologists who completed a doctoral degree (Ed.D., Psy.D., Ph.D.) within the past 7 years. Applicants must be interested in conducting research in the area of early intervention and treatment for serious emotional disturbance in children. The sponsor encourages applications from individuals who represent diversity in race, ethnicity, gender, age, disability, and sexual orientation.

Financial data The grant is $10,000.

Duration 1 year.

Additional information This program began in 2013.

Number awarded 1 each year.

Deadline May of each year.

[1201]
JOHN V. KRUTILLA RESEARCH STIPEND

Resources for the Future
Attn: Coordinator for Academic Programs
1616 P Street, N.W., Suite 600
Washington, DC 20036-1400
(202) 328-5020 Fax: (202) 939-3460
E-mail: krutilla-award@rff.org
Web: www.rff.org

Summary To provide funding for research related to environmental and resource economics to young scholars (particularly African Americans, other minorities, and women).

Eligibility This program is open to scholars who received their doctoral degree within the past 5 years. Applicants must be interested in conducting research related to environmental and resource economics. They must submit a short description of the proposed research, a curriculum vitae, and a letter of recommendation. Women and minority candidates are strongly encouraged to apply. Non-citizens are eligible if they have proper work and residency documentation.

Financial data The grant is $5,500.

Duration 1 year.

Additional information This award was first presented in 2006.

Number awarded 1 each year.

Deadline February of each year.

[1202]
JOHN W. BLASSINGAME AWARD

Southern Historical Association
c/o John C. Inscoe, Secretary-Treasurer
University of Georgia
Department of History
LeConte Hall, Room 111
Athens, GA 30602-1602
(706) 542-8848 E-mail: jinscoe@uga.edu
Web: sha.uga.edu/awards/blassingame.htm

Summary To recognize and reward African American and other faculty members who have a record of outstanding scholarship and mentorship in African American studies.

Eligibility This award is available to members of all areas of the academic community, including community and junior colleges, Historically Black Colleges and Universities, and large research universities. Nominations may be submitted by members of the Southern Historical Association, based on distinguished careers as mentors of African American students, personal scholarly accomplishments, or some combination of both. For nominations involving a primary role of mentoring African American students, letters from students (undergraduate or graduate) are particularly welcome.

Financial data The award is $1,000.

Duration The award is presented triennially (2015, 2018, etc.).

Additional information This award was first presented in 2004.

Number awarded 1 every third year.

Deadline May of the year of the award.

[1203]
JONATHAN REICHERT AND BARBARA WOLFF-REICHERT AWARD FOR EXCELLENCE IN ADVANCED LABORATORY INSTRUCTION

American Physical Society
Attn: Honors Program
One Physics Ellipse
College Park, MD 20740-3844
(301) 209-3268 Fax: (301) 209-0865
E-mail: honors@aps.org
Web: www.aps.org/programs/honors/awards/lab.cfm

Summary To recognize and reward physicists (particularly African Americans, other underrepresented minorities, and women) who have developed and taught outstanding undergraduate laboratory courses.

Eligibility This award is available to individuals or teams of individuals who have taught, developed, and sustained advanced undergraduate physics laboratory courses for at least 4 years at an institution in the United States. Nominations should present evidence of the dissemination of the laboratory work to the broader physics community. Nominations of qualified women and members of underrepresented minority groups are especially encouraged.

Financial data The award consists of $5,000 as an honorarium, a certificate citing the accomplishments of the recipient, and an allowance up to $2,000 for travel expenses to the meeting where the award is presented.

Duration The award is presented annually.

Additional information This award was established in 2012.

Number awarded 1 each year.

Deadline June of each year.

[1204]
JOSEPH B. GITTLER AWARD

American Psychological Foundation
750 First Street, N.E.
Washington, DC 20002-4242
(202) 336-5843 Fax: (202) 336-5812
E-mail: foundation@apa.org
Web: www.apa.org/apf/funding/gittler.aspx

Summary To recognize and reward scholars and graduate students in psychology (particularly African Americans, other minorities, women, and individuals with disabilities) whose work has transformed the philosophical foundations of the discipline.

Eligibility This award is available to scholars and graduate students whose body of work or whose individual work has transformed the philosophical foundations of psychological knowledge. Self-nominations are welcome. Selection is based on conformance with stated program goals and magnitude of contributions The sponsor encourages nominations of individuals who represent diversity in race, ethnicity, gender, age, disability, and sexual orientation.

Financial data The award is $10,000.

Duration The award is presented annually.

Additional information This award was first presented in 2008.

Number awarded 1 each year.

Deadline Nominations must be submitted by May of each year.

[1205]
JRGOS CLINICAL RESEARCH GRANTS

J. Robert Gladden Orthopaedic Society
Attn: Scientific Committee
6300 North River Road, Suite 727
Rosemont, IL 60018-4226
(847) 698-1633 Fax: (847) 823-4921
E-mail: jrgos@aaos.org
Web: www.gladdensociety.org

Summary To provide funding to members of the J. Robert Gladden Orthopaedic Society (JRGOS) who are African American or from another underrepresented minority group and interested in conducting a clinical research project in areas where funding is difficult to obtain.

Eligibility This program is open to members of underrepresented minority groups who are new or experienced JRGOS members and interested in conducting a research project in clinical areas where funding is difficult to obtain. Applicants must be seeking seed money to initiate studies to obtain background data with the goal of obtaining future funding from other sources. They must be able to demonstrate the compatibility of their project's clinical problems with the mission and goals of the society. Preference is given to applicants planning to work with a senior JRGOS member.

Financial data The grant is $30,000 per year.

Duration 1 year; may be renewed 1 additional year.

Additional information This program is sponsored by DePuy/Johnson & Johnson.

Number awarded 1 or more each year.

Deadline September of each year.

[1206]
JUDICIAL BRANCH FELLOWSHIPS

American Association for the Advancement of Science
Attn: Science and Technology Policy Fellowships
1200 New York Avenue, N.W.
Washington, DC 20005-3920
(202) 326-6700 Fax: (202) 289-4950
E-mail: fellowships@aaas.org
Web: www.fellowships.aaas.org

Summary To provide postdoctoral scientists and engineers (particularly African Americans, other minorities, women, and individuals with disabilities) with an opportunity to work with the federal judiciary.

Eligibility This program is open to doctoral-level scientists (Ph.D., M.D., D.V.M., D.Sc., and other terminal degrees) in any field of science (behavioral, biological, computational, earth, health, medical, physical, or social), engineering, or mathematics who have at least 3 years of professional postdoctoral experience. Preference is given to scientists and engineers who also have a J.D. degree or legal experience. Applicants should be able to contribute scientific and technical expertise to judicial administration, operations, education programs, protocol and discovery, or courtroom technology while learning first-hand about contemporary policy issues facing the judiciary. They must demonstrate solid scientific and technical credentials; a commitment to serve society; good communication skills; the ability to engage with non-scientific audiences; and an interest in working as special assistants for the Federal Judicial Center or the Federal Judicial Court of Washington, D.C. U.S. citizenship is required; federal employees are not eligible. The sponsor seeks candidates from a broad array of backgrounds and a diversity of geographic, disciplinary, gender, and ethnic perspectives, as well as disability status.

Financial data The stipend for fellows with 0 to 7 years of postdoctoral experience is $74,872 in the first year and $77,368 in the second year. For fellows with 7 to 15 years of experience, the stipend is $84,855 in the first year and $87,350 in the second year. Fellows who have 15 or more years of postdoctoral experience receive $97,333 in the first year and $99,829 in the second year. Also provided are a $4,000 relocation allowance for fellows from outside the Washington, D.C. area, reimbursement for health insurance, and a $4,000 travel allowance.

Duration 1 year, beginning in September; may be renewed for 1 additional year.

Additional information This program began in 2014.

Number awarded 5 to 15 each year.

Deadline October of each year.

[1207]
JULIUS AXELROD MENTORSHIP AWARD

American College of Neuropsychopharmacology
Attn: Executive Office
5034-A Thoroughbred Lane
Brentwood, TN 37027
(615) 324-2360 Fax: (615) 523-1715
E-mail: acnp@acnp.org
Web: www.acnp.org/programs/awards.aspx

Summary To recognize and reward professionals and postdoctorates (particularly African Americans, other minorities, and women) who are members of the American College of Neuropsychopharmacology (ACNP) and have demonstrated outstanding mentoring of young scientists.

Eligibility This award is available to ACNP members who have made an outstanding contribution to neuropsychopharmacology by mentoring and developing young scientists into leaders in the field. Nominations must be accompanied by letters of support from up to 3 people who have been mentored by the candidate. Nomination of women and minorities is highly encouraged.

Financial data The award consists of a monetary honorarium and a plaque.

Duration The award is presented annually.

Additional information This award was first presented in 2004.

Number awarded 1 each year.

Deadline Nominations must be submitted by June of each year.

[1208]
JUVENILE DIABETES RESEARCH FOUNDATION INNOVATIVE GRANTS

Juvenile Diabetes Research Foundation International
Attn: Grant Administrator
26 Broadway, 14th Floor
New York, NY 10004
(212) 479-7572 Toll Free: (800) 533-CURE
Fax: (212) 785-9595 E-mail: info@jdrf.org
Web: jdrf.org

Summary To provide funding to scientists (particularly African Americans, other underrepresented minorities, women, and individuals with disabilities) who are interested in conducting innovative diabetes-related research.

Eligibility Applicants must have an M.D., D.M.D., D.V.M., Ph.D., or equivalent degree and have a full-time faculty position or equivalent at a college, university, medical school, or other research facility. They must be seeking "seed" money for investigative work based on a sound hypothesis for which preliminary data are insufficient for a regular research grant but that are likely to lead to important results for the treatment of diabetes and its complications. Applicants must specifically explain how the proposal is innovative. Selection is based on whether 1) the proposed research is innovative; 2) the underlying premise, goal, or hypothesis is plausible; 3) the proposed research can be completed in 1 year; and 4) the proposed research is relevant to the mission of the Juvenile Diabetes Research Foundation and its potential impact. There are no citizenship requirements. Applications are encouraged from women, members of minority groups underrepresented in the sciences, and people with disabilities. The proposed research may be conducted at foreign or domestic, for-profit or nonprofit, or public or private institutions, including universities, colleges, hospitals, laboratories, units of state or local government, or eligible agencies of the federal government.

Financial data Awards are limited to $110,000 plus 10% indirect costs.

Duration 1 year; nonrenewable.

Number awarded Varies each year.

Deadline August of each year.

[1209]
LEO GOLDBERG FELLOWSHIPS

National Optical Astronomy Observatories
Attn: Human Resources Office
950 North Cherry Avenue
P.O. Box 26732
Tucson, AZ 85726-6732
(520) 318-8000 Fax: (520) 318-8494
E-mail: hrnoao@noao.edu
Web: ast.noao.edu/opportunities/post-doc-programs

Summary To provide an opportunity for postdoctorates in astronomy (particularly African Americans, other underrepresented minorities, and women) to conduct research at the facilities of the National Optical Astronomy Observatories (NOAO) in Arizona or Chile.

Eligibility This program is open to recent Ph.D. recipients in observational astronomy, astronomical instrumentation, or theoretical astrophysics. Applicants must be interested in conducting a research program of their own choosing or participating in a current NOAO initiative at Kitt Peak National Observatory (KPNO) near Tucson, Arizona or Cerro Tololo Inter-American Observatory (CTIO) in La Serena, Chile. Women and candidates from underrepresented minorities are particularly encouraged to apply. Preference is given to Native Americans living on or near the Tohono O'Odham Reservation in Arizona. Selection is based on the applicant's promise for an outstanding career in astronomy, their proposed use of KPNO or CTIO facilities, the relationship of their research to a proposed interaction with NOAO programs to develop community facilities, and the relationship of their research to programs conducted by NOAO staff.

Financial data A competitive salary is paid. Additional support is provided to fellows and their families in Chile.

Duration 5 years. The first 4 years are spent either at Kitt Peak or in La Serena; the final year is spent at an U.S. university or astronomical institute willing to host the fellow.

Additional information NOAO is supported under a contract between the National Science Foundation and the Association of Universities for Research in Astronomy, Inc. This program, which began in 2002, was formerly known as the NOAO 5-Year Science Fellowship.

Number awarded 1 each year.

Deadline November of each year.

[1210]
LIZETTE PETERSON-HOMER INJURY PREVENTION RESEARCH GRANT

American Psychological Foundation
750 First Street, N.E.
Washington, DC 20002-4242
(202) 336-5843 Fax: (202) 336-5812
E-mail: foundation@apa.org
Web: www.apa.org/apf/funding/peterson-homer.aspx

Summary To provide funding to graduate students and faculty (particularly African Americans, other minorities, women, and individuals with disabilities) who are interested in conducting research related to the prevention of injuries in children.

Eligibility This program is open to graduate students and faculty interested in conducting research that focuses on the prevention of physical injury in children and young adults through accidents, violence, abuse, or suicide. Applicants must submit a 100-word abstract, description of the project, detailed budget, curriculum vitae, and letter from the supporting faculty supervisor (if the applicant is a student). Selection is based on conformance with stated program goals, magnitude of incremental contribution, quality of proposed work, and applicant's demonstrated scholarship and research competence. The sponsor encourages applications from individuals who represent diversity in race, ethnicity, gender, age, disability, and sexual orientation.

Financial data Grants up to $5,000 are available.

Additional information This program began in 1999 as the Rebecca Routh Coon Injury Research Award. The current name was adopted in 2003. It is supported by Division 54 (Society of Pediatric Psychology) of the American Psychological Association and the American Psychological Foundation.

Number awarded 1 each year.

Deadline September of each year.

[1211]
LONG RANGE BROAD AGENCY ANNOUNCEMENT FOR NAVY AND MARINE CORPS SCIENCE AND TECHNOLOGY

Office of Naval Research
Attn: Acquisition Department, Code BD25
875 North Randolph Street
Arlington, VA 22203-1995
(703) 696-1474 E-mail: Ganesh.Krish@navy.mil
Web: www.onr.navy.mil

Summary To provide financial support to investigators (particularly African Americans and other minorities) who are interested in conducting long-range science and technology research on topics of interest to the U.S. Navy and Marine Corps.

Eligibility This program is open to researchers from academia (colleges and universities) and industry. Applicants must be interested in conducting long-range projects in fields of science and technology that offer potential for advancement and improvement of Navy and Marine Corps operations. The proposed research must relate to 1 of the following topic areas: 1) expeditionary maneuver warfare and combating terrorism; 2) command, control communications, computers, intelligence, surveillance, and reconnaissance; 3) ocean battlespace sensing; 4) sea warfare and weapons; 5) warfighter performance; and 6) naval air warfare and weapons. Researchers at Historically Black Colleges and Universities (HBCUs) and Minority Institutions (MIs) are encouraged to submit proposals and join others in submitting proposals, but no portion of funds is set aside for HBCU and MI participation.

Financial data Grant amounts depend on the nature of the proposal.

Duration Applicants may specify the length of time they wish to devote to the project.

Number awarded Varies each year.

Deadline September of each year.

[1212]
LOUIS STOKES URBAN HEALTH PUBLIC POLICY FELLOWS PROGRAM

Congressional Black Caucus Foundation, Inc.
Attn: Leadership Institute for Public Service
1720 Massachusetts Avenue, N.W.
Washington, DC 20036
(202) 263-2800 Toll Free: (800) 784-2577
Fax: (202) 775-0773 E-mail: internships@cbcfinc.org
Web: www.cbcfinc.org/lips.html

Summary To provide an opportunity for health policy professionals (particularly African Americans) to work on a program of original research, advanced legislative training, and health policy analysis in collaboration with the Congressional Black Caucus (CBC).

Eligibility This program is open to professionals who have a graduate or professional degree in a health-related field (behavioral sciences, social sciences, biological sciences, and health professions) and familiarity with the federal legislative process, Congress, and the CBC. Applicants must be interested in working in Washington, D.C. on health-related issues, especially how health policies affect African Americans and other minorities, as a member of the staff or committee of a member of the CBC. They must be able to demonstrate an interest in public health policy, a record of academic and professional achievement, evidence of leadership skills, the potential for further growth, and U.S. citizenship or permit to work in the United States.

Financial data Fellows receive a stipend of $40,000 per year and benefits.

Duration 20 months, beginning in September.

Additional information This program began in 2003. Fellows are assigned to Congressional offices or committees and work on issues related to minority health.

Number awarded 2 each year.

Deadline March of each year.

[1213]
LYMAN T. JOHNSON POSTDOCTORAL FELLOWSHIP

University of Kentucky
Attn: Vice President for Research
311 Main Building
Lexington, KY 40506-0032
(859) 257-5090 Fax: (859) 323-2800
E-mail: vprgrants@uky.edu
Web: www.research.uky.edu

Summary To provide an opportunity for recent postdoctorates, especially African Americans and other minorities, to conduct research at the University of Kentucky (U.K.).

Eligibility This program is open to U.S. citizens and permanent residents who have completed a doctoral degree within the past 2 years. Applicants must be interested in conducting an individualized research program under the mentorship of a U.K. professor. They should indicate, in their letter of application, how their participation in this program would contribute to the compelling interest of diversity at U.K. Race, ethnicity, and national origin are among the factors that contribute to diversity. Selection is based on evidence of scholarship with competitive potential for a tenure-track faculty appointment at a research university, compatibility of specific research interests with those in doctorate-granting units at U.K., quality of the research proposal, support from mentor and references, and effect of the appointment on the educational benefit of diversity within the research or professional area.

Financial data The fellowship provides a stipend of $35,000 plus $5,000 for support of research activities.

Duration Up to 2 years.

Additional information In addition to conducting an individualized research program under the mentorship of a U.K. professor, fellows actively participate in research, teaching, and service to the university, their profession, and the community. This program began in 1992.

Number awarded 2 each year.

Deadline October of each year.

[1214]
MANY VOICES FELLOWSHIPS

Playwrights' Center
2301 Franklin Avenue East
Minneapolis, MN 55406-1099
(612) 332-7481 Fax: (612) 332-6037
E-mail: info@pwcenter.org
Web: www.pwcenter.org/fellows_voices.php

Summary To provide funding to African Americans and other playwrights of color so they can spend a year in residence at the Playwrights' Center in Minneapolis.

Eligibility This program is open to playwrights of color who are citizens or permanent residents of the United States; both residents of Minnesota and of any state are eligible. Applicants must be interested in playwriting and creating theater in a supportive artist community at the Playwrights' Center.

Financial data The stipend is $10,000, plus an addition $2,500 for living expenses and $1,500 in play development funds.

Duration 9 months, beginning in October.

Additional information This program, which began in 1994, is funded by the Jerome Foundation. Fellows must be in residence at the Playwrights' Center for the duration of the program.

Number awarded 2 each year: 1 to a resident of Minnesota and 1 to a resident of any state.

Deadline February of each year.

[1215]
MASSACHUSETTS HISTORICAL SOCIETY AFRICAN AMERICAN STUDIES FELLOWSHIP

Massachusetts Historical Society
Attn: Short-Term Fellowships
1154 Boylston Street
Boston, MA 02215-3695
(617) 646-0568 Fax: (617) 859-0074
E-mail: fellowships@masshist.org
Web: www.masshist.org/research/fellowships/short-term

Summary To fund research visits to the Massachusetts Historical Society for graduate students postdoctorates, and independent scholars interested in African American history.

Eligibility This program is open to advanced graduate students, postdoctorates, and independent scholars who are conducting research in African American history and need to use the resources of the Massachusetts Historical Society. Applicants must be U.S. citizens or foreign nationals holding appropriate U.S. government documents. Along with their application, they must submit a curriculum vitae and a proposal describing the project and indicating collections at the society to be consulted. Graduate students must also arrange for a letter of recommendation from a faculty member familiar with their work and with the project being proposed. Preference is given to candidates who live 50 or more miles from Boston.

Financial data The grant is $1,500.

Duration 4 weeks.

Additional information This fellowship was first awarded in 1999.

Number awarded 1 each year.

Deadline February of each year.

[1216]
MATHEMATICAL SCIENCES POSTDOCTORAL RESEARCH FELLOWSHIPS

National Science Foundation
Directorate for Mathematical and Physical Sciences
Attn: Division of Mathematical Sciences
4201 Wilson Boulevard, Room 1025N
Arlington, VA 22230
(703) 292-4488 Fax: (703) 292-9032
TDD: (800) 281-8749 E-mail: jwang@nsf.gov
Web: www.nsf.gov/funding/pgm_summ.jsp?pims_id=5301

Summary To provide financial assistance to postdoctorates (particularly African Americans, other minorities, women, and individuals with disabilities) who are interested in pursuing research training in mathematics.

Eligibility Applicants for these fellowships must 1) be U.S. citizens, nationals, or permanent residents; 2) have earned a Ph.D. in a mathematical science or have had equivalent research training and experience; 3) have held the Ph.D. for no more than 2 years; and 4) have not previously held any other postdoctoral fellowship from the National Science Foundation (NSF) or been offered an award from this program. They must be proposing to conduct a program of postdoctoral research training at an appropriate nonprofit U.S. institution, including government laboratories, national laboratories, and privately sponsored nonprofit institutes, as well as institutions of higher education in any country. A senior scientist at the institution must indicate availability for consultation and agreement to work with the fellow. In the selection process, consideration is given to the achievement of societally relevant outcomes, including full participation of women, persons with disabilities, and underrepresented minorities.

Financial data The total grant is $150,000, consisting of 3 components: 1) a monthly stipend of $5,000 for full-time support or $2,500 for half-time support, paid directly to the fellow; 2) a research allowance of $12,000, also paid directly to the fellow; and 3) an institutional allowance of $9,000, paid to the host institution for fringe benefits (including health insurance payments for the fellow) and expenses incurred in support of the fellow, such as space, equipment, and general purpose supplies. Fellows who wish to conduct their training at an international host institution may apply for an additional allowance of up to $20,000.

Duration Fellows may select either of 2 options: the research fellowship option provides full-time support for any 18 academic-year months in a 3-year period, in intervals not shorter than 3 consecutive months; the research instructorship option provides a combination of full-time and half-time support over a period of 3 academic years. Both options include 6 summer months.

Number awarded 30 to 33 each year. A total of $5.0 million is available for this program annually.

Deadline October of each year.

[1217]
MELLON SCHOLARS PROGRAM POSTDOCTORAL FELLOWSHIPS IN AFRICAN AMERICAN HISTORY

Library Company of Philadelphia
Attn: Program in African American History
1314 Locust Street
Philadelphia, PA 19107-5698
(215) 546-3181 Fax: (215) 546-5167
E-mail: era@udel.edu
Web: www.librarycompany.org/paah/fellowships.htm

Summary To provide funding to African American and other postdoctorates from underrepresented backgrounds who are interested in conducting research on African American history at the Library Company of Philadelphia.

Eligibility This program is open to scholars from underrepresented backgrounds who have completed a Ph.D. and are interested in conducting research in Philadelphia at the Library Company. The proposed research must relate to African American history prior to 1900.

Financial data The grant is $50,000 for an academic year or $25,000 for a semester.

Duration 1 academic year or 1 semester.

Additional information The Library Company of Philadelphia established its Program in African American History in 2013 with support from the Andrew W. Mellon Foundation.

Number awarded Either 1 fellowship for a year or 2 for a semester are supported each year.

Deadline February of each year.

[1218]
MELLON SCHOLARS PROGRAM SHORT-TERM FELLOWSHIPS IN AFRICAN AMERICAN HISTORY

Library Company of Philadelphia
Attn: Program in African American History
1314 Locust Street
Philadelphia, PA 19107-5698
(215) 546-3181 Fax: (215) 546-5167
E-mail: era@udel.edu
Web: www.librarycompany.org/paah/fellowships.htm

Summary To provide funding to African American and other pre- and postdoctorates from underrepresented backgrounds who are interested in conducting short-term research on African American history at the Library Company of Philadelphia.

Eligibility This program is open to doctoral candidates and senior scholars from underrepresented backgrounds who are interested in conducting research in Philadelphia at the Library Company. The proposed research must relate to African American history prior to 1900.

Financial data The stipend is $2,500.

Duration 1 month.

Additional information The Library Company of Philadelphia established its Program in African American History in 2013 with support from the Andrew W. Mellon Foundation.

Number awarded Varies each year.

Deadline February of each year.

[1219]
MENTOR-BASED MINORITY POSTDOCTORAL FELLOWSHIPS IN DIABETES

American Diabetes Association
Attn: Research Programs
1701 North Beauregard Street
Alexandria, VA 22311
(703) 549-1500, ext. 2362 Toll Free: (800) DIABETES
Fax: (703) 549-1715
E-mail: grantquestions@diabetes.org
Web: professional.diabetes.org

Summary To provide financial assistance to African American and other minority postdoctoral fellows working with established diabetes investigators.

Eligibility Applications for these fellowships may be submitted by established and active investigators in diabetes research who wish to supervise the work of a postdoctoral fellow, whom they will select. They must currently hold a grant from the American Diabetes Association. The fellow selected by the investigator must be a member of an underrepresented minority group (African American; Spanish, Hispanic, or Latino; American Indian or Alaskan Native; Native Hawaiian or Pacific Islander); must have an M.D., Ph.D., D.O., D.P.M., or Pharm.D. degree; must not be serving an internship or residency during the fellowship period; and must not have more than 3 years of postdoctoral research experience in the field of diabetes/endocrinology. Applicant investigators and fellows must be U.S. citizens or permanent residents. The applicant investigator must also hold an appointment at a U.S. research institution and have sufficient research support to provide an appropriate training environment for the fellow. The applicant investigator must be a member of the Professional Section of the American Diabetes Association; the fellow must also be, or agree to become, a member. Selection is based on the quality and activity of the applicant investigator's diabetes research program, the likelihood that the fellow trained by the mentor will actively pursue a career in diabetes research, the applicant investigator's past training record, and evidence of sufficient research support and adequate facilities to provide an appropriate training environment for a postdoctoral fellow.

Financial data The grant is $45,000 per year. Within that total, the applicant investigator may determine the salary of the fellow; up to $3,000 per year of the total may be used for laboratory supply costs, up to $1,000 for travel by the fellow to attend diabetes-related scientific meetings, and up to $500 for book purchases.

Duration 2 to 3 years.

Number awarded Varies each year.

Deadline January of each year.

[1220] MENTORED CAREER DEVELOPMENT AWARD TO PROMOTE FACULTY DIVERSITY/RE-ENTRY IN BIOMEDICAL RESEARCH

National Heart, Lung, and Blood Institute
Attn: Division of Cardiovascular Sciences
6701 Rockledge Drive
Bethesda, MD 20892-7940
(301) 435-0535 Fax: (301) 480-1455
E-mail: scottj2@nhlbi.nih.gov
Web: grants.nih.gov

Summary To provide funding to African Americans and members of other underrepresented groups who are interested in developing into independent biomedical investigators in research areas relevant to the mission of the National Heart, Lung, and Blood Institute (NHLBI).

Eligibility This program is open to U.S. citizens, nationals, and permanent residents who are full-time non-tenured faculty members at U.S. domestic institutions of higher education and eligible agencies of the federal government; applications are especially encouraged from faculty at Historically Black Colleges and Universities (HBCUs), Tribally Controlled Colleges and Universities (TCCUs), Hispanic Serving Institutions (HSIs), and Alaska Native and Native Hawaiian Serving Institutions. Candidates must have received, at least 2 years previously, a doctoral degree or equivalent in a basic or clinical area related to cardiovascular, pulmonary, or hematologic diseases. Applications are especially encouraged from members of a group that will promote greater diversity in scientific research, including 1) members of underrepresented racial and ethnic groups (African Americans, Hispanic Americans, Alaska Natives, American Indians, Native Hawaiians, non-Asian Pacific Islanders); 2) individuals with disabilities; and 3) individuals from disadvantaged backgrounds. Candidates who have experienced an interruption in their research careers for a period of at least 3 but no more than 8 years (e.g., starting and/or raising a family, an incapacitating illness or injury, caring for an ill immediate family member, performing military service) are also eligible. The proposed research development plan, under the guidance of an experienced mentor or supervisor, must enable the candidate to become an independent investigator in cardiovascular, pulmonary, hematologic, and sleep disorders research with either a clinical or basic science emphasis.

Financial data The grant provides salary support of up to $75,000 per year plus fringe benefits. In addition, up to $30,000 per year may be provided for research project requirements and related support (e.g., technical personnel costs, supplies, equipment, candidate travel, telephone charges, publication costs, and tuition for necessary courses). Facilities and administrative costs may be reimbursed at the rate of 8% of total direct costs.

Duration 3 to 5 years.

Additional information At least 75% of the awardee's effort must be devoted to the research program. The remainder may be devoted to other clinical and teaching pursuits that are consistent with the program goals of developing the awardee into an independent biomedical scientist or the maintenance of the teaching and/or clinical skills needed for an academic research career.

Number awarded Varies each year; recently, 8 to 10 awards were available through this program; total funding was approximately $1,200,000.

Deadline Letters of intent must be submitted by January of each year; completed applications are due in February.

[1221] MENTORED CLINICAL SCIENTIST RESEARCH CAREER DEVELOPMENT AWARD

Agency for Healthcare Research and Quality
Attn: Office of Extramural Research, Education, and Priority Populations
540 Gaither Road
Rockville, MD 20850
(301) 427-1555 Fax: (301) 427-1562
TDD: (301) 451-0088
E-mail: Kay.Anderson@ahrq.hhs.gov
Web: grants.nih.gov/grants/guide/pa-files/PA-13-039.html

Summary To provide funding to clinicians (particularly African Americans, other underrepresented minorities, and individuals with disabilities) who are interested in obtaining additional research training to enable them to become independent investigators in health services research.

Eligibility This program is open to U.S. citizens, nationals, or permanent residents who have received a clinical doctoral degree (e.g., M.D., D.O., D.C., O.D., N.D., D.D.S., D.M.D., Pharm.D.); scientists who have a Ph.D. or other doctoral degree in clinical disciplines such as clinical psychology, nursing, speech-language pathology, audiology, or rehabilitation are also eligible. Applicants must have identified a mentor with extensive research experience and be willing to spend at least 75% of full-time professional effort conducting research and developing a research career to promote improvements in clinical and health systems practices. They must be proposing projects related to the strategic goals of the Agency for Healthcare Research and Quality (AHRQ): safety and quality, effectiveness, and efficiency. Members of underrepresented ethnic and racial groups, individuals from disadvantaged backgrounds, and individuals with disabilities are especially encouraged to apply.

Financial data Grants provide salary up to $90,000 annually, plus associated fringe benefits. Also available are up to $25,000 per year for research development support (tuition, fees, and books related to career development; research expenses, such as supplies, equipment, and technical personnel; travel to research meetings or training; and statistical services, including personnel and computer time). Facilities and administrative costs are reimbursed at 8% of modified total direct costs.

Duration 3 to 5 years.

Number awarded Varies each year.

Deadline February, June, or October of each year.

[1222] MENTORED NEW INVESTIGATOR RESEARCH GRANTS TO PROMOTE DIVERSITY OF THE ALZHEIMER'S ASSOCIATION

Alzheimer's Association
Attn: Medical and Scientific Affairs
225 North Michigan Avenue, 17th Floor
Chicago, IL 60601-7633
(312) 335-5747 Toll Free: (800) 272-3900
Fax: (866) 699-1246 TDD: (312) 335-5886
E-mail: grantsapp@alz.org
Web: www.alz.org

Summary To provide funding for mentored research on Alzheimer's Disease to African Americans and other junior investigators who will contribute to diversity in the field.

Eligibility This program is open to investigators who have less than 10 years of research experience after receipt of their terminal degree. Applicants must be proposing to conduct research with focus areas that change annually but are related to Alzheimer's Disease. They must identify a mentor who is experienced in conducting Alzheimer's and related dementia research and in mentoring investigators. Eligibility is restricted to investigators who will contribute to diversity in the field of biomedical research, including members of underrepresented racial and ethnic minority groups (African Americans, Hispanic Americans, American Indians/Alaska Natives, Native Hawaiians, and Pacific Islanders) and individuals with disabilities.

Financial data Grants up to $60,000 per year, including direct expenses and up to 10% for overhead costs, are available. The total award for the life of the grant may not exceed $170,000, including $150,000 for costs related to the proposed research, $10,000 to the fellow upon successful completion of the program, and $10,000 to the mentor upon successful completion of the program.

Duration Up to 3 years.

Number awarded 1 or 2 each year.

Deadline Letters of intent must be submitted by the end of January or September of each year. Final applications are due in March or October.

[1223] MENTORED RESEARCH SCIENTIST RESEARCH CAREER DEVELOPMENT AWARD

Agency for Healthcare Research and Quality
Attn: Office of Extramural Research, Education, and Priority Populations
540 Gaither Road
Rockville, MD 20850
(301) 427-1555 Fax: (301) 427-1562
TDD: (301) 451-0088
E-mail: Kay.Anderson@ahrq.hhs.gov
Web: grants.nih.gov/grants/guide/pa-files/PA-09-087.html

Summary To provide funding to scientists (particularly African Americans, other underrepresented minorities, and individuals with disabilities) who are interested in obtaining additional research training to enable them to become independent investigators in health services research.

Eligibility This program is open to U.S. citizens, nationals, or permanent residents who have received a research doctoral degree (e.g., Ph.D., Sc.D., Dr.P.H.). Applicants must have identified a mentor with extensive research experience and be willing to spend at least 75% of full-time professional effort conducting research and developing a research career to promote improvements in clinical and health systems practices. They must be proposing projects in 1 of the research portfolio areas of the Agency for Healthcare Research and Quality (AHRQ): 1) the value portfolio, for research that can be used to reduce unnecessary health care costs (waste) while maintaining or improving health care quality; 2) the health information technology portfolio, for the use of information and communication technology in health care to support the delivery of patient or population care; 3) the comparative effectiveness portfolio, for research focusing on comparative effectiveness of different clinical treatments and services; 4) the prevention/care management portfolio, to improve the quality, safety, efficiency, and effectiveness of preventive services and chronic care management in ambulatory care settings; 5) the patient safety portfolio, for research projects to identify the risks and hazards encountered by patients as a result of health care; or 6) the innovations and emerging areas portfolio, for research on ideas that have the potential for high impact. Members of underrepresented ethnic and racial groups, individuals from disadvantaged backgrounds, and individuals with disabilities are especially encouraged to apply.

Financial data Grants provide salary up to $90,000 annually, plus associated fringe benefits. Also available are up to $25,000 per year for research development support (tuition, fees, and books related to career development; research expenses, such as supplies, equipment, and technical personnel; travel to research meetings or training; and statistical services, including personnel and computer time). Facilities and administrative costs are reimbursed at 8% of modified total direct costs.

Duration 3 to 5 years.

Number awarded Varies each year.

Deadline February, June, or October of each year.

[1224]
MERCK POSTDOCTORAL SCIENCE RESEARCH FELLOWSHIPS

United Negro College Fund
Attn: Merck Science Initiative
8260 Willow Oaks Corporate Drive, Suite 110
P.O. Box 10444
Fairfax, VA 22031-4511
(703) 205-3503 Fax: (703) 205-3574
E-mail: uncfmerck@uncf.org
Web: umsi.uncf.org

Summary To provide financial assistance to African American postdoctoral fellows who are interested in pursuing research in the life or physical sciences.

Eligibility This program is open to African Americans who have been appointed as a postdoctoral fellow at an academic or non-academic research institution (private industrial laboratories are excluded). Applicants must be U.S. citizens or permanent residents interested in preparing for a career in the life or physical sciences. Selection is based on the record of accomplishments and soundness of the proposed postdoctoral research.

Financial data The total award is $92,000, including up to $77,000 as a stipend for the fellow (the maximum stipend is $55,000 for any 12-month period) and a research grant up to $15,000. Fringe benefits up to $9,200 are also allowed, but no provision is made for indirect costs.

Duration 12 to 24 months.

Additional information This program, established in 1995, is funded by the Merck Company Foundation.

Number awarded At least 10 each year.

Deadline December of each year.

[1225]
MICROBIOLOGY OF THE BUILT ENVIRONMENT PROGRAM FELLOWSHIPS

Alfred P. Sloan Foundation
630 Fifth Avenue, Suite 2550
New York, NY 10111-0242
(212) 649-1649 Fax: (212) 757-5117
E-mail: olsiewski@sloan.org
Web: www.sloan.org

Summary To provide funding to recent doctorates (particularly African Americans and members of other underrepresented groups) who are interested in conducting research on the microbiology of the build environment.

Eligibility This program is open to early stage Ph.D. scientists and engineers in laboratories engaged in research on the microbiology of the build environment in the United States or Canada. Cross-disciplinary studies in microbial biology and engineering are encouraged. Applications may be submitted by graduate students if accompanied by a letter of commitment from a potential postdoctoral adviser. Members of underrepresented groups in science and engineering are especially encouraged to apply. Selection is based on an assessment of the proposed research, the arrangements for the interdisciplinary educational broadening of the fellow, and the previous research records of the potential fellow and adviser.

Financial data The grant is $60,000 per year, including $48,000 as a stipend (may be supplemented by institutional or other sources), $2,000 for travel or research expenses, and $10,000 for fringe benefits.

Duration 2 years.

Additional information This program began in 2013.

Number awarded 8 each year.

Deadline September of each year.

[1226]
MILDRED BARRY GARVIN PRIZE

New Jersey Historical Commission
Attn: Grants and Prizes
225 West State Street
P.O. Box 305
Trenton, NJ 08625-0305
(609) 292-6062 Fax: (609) 633-8168
E-mail: Feedback@sos.state.nj.us
Web: www.state.nj.us/state/historical/dos_his_grants.html

Summary To recognize and reward outstanding New Jersey educators who are teaching Black American history.

Eligibility This program is open to teachers, guidance counselors, and school librarians in New Jersey. Nominees must have demonstrated outstanding teaching of Black American history in kindergarten through high school or outstanding performance in a related activity, such as developing curriculum materials. Self-nominations are accepted.

Financial data The award is $1,500.

Duration The award is presented annually.

Number awarded 1 each year.

Deadline October of each year.

[1227]
MINORITIES AFFAIRS COMMITTEE VISITING PROFESSOR AWARDS

American Society for Cell Biology
Attn: Minority Affairs Committee
8120 Woodmont Avenue, Suite 750
Bethesda, MD 20814-2762
(301) 347-9323 Fax: (301) 347-9310
E-mail: dmccall@ascb.org
Web: www.ascb.org

Summary To provide funding for research during the summer to faculty members (particularly African Americans and other minorities) who are at primarily teaching institutions that serve minority students and scientists.

Eligibility Eligible to apply for this support are professors at primarily teaching institutions. They must be interested in working in the laboratories of members of the American Society for Cell Biology during the summer. Hosts and visitor scientists are asked to submit their applications together as a proposed team. Minority professors and professors at Minority Serving Institutions are especially encouraged to apply for this award. Minorities are defined as U.S. citizens of Black, Native American, Chicano/Hispanic, or Pacific Islands background.

Financial data The stipend for the summer is $13,500 plus $700 for travel expenses and $4,000 to the host institution for supplies.

Duration From 8 to 10 weeks during the summer.

Additional information Funds for this program, established in 1997, are provided by the Minorities Access to

Research Careers (MARC) program of the National Institutes of Health.

Number awarded Varies each year; recently, 3 of these grants were awarded.

Deadline March of each year.

[1228]
MINORITIES IN CANCER RESEARCH JANE COOK WRIGHT LECTURESHIP

American Association for Cancer Research
Attn: Scientific Awards
615 Chestnut Street, 17th Floor
Philadelphia, PA 19106-4404
(215) 440-9300 Toll Free: (866) 423-3965
Fax: (215) 440-9372 E-mail: awards@aacr.org
Web: www.aacr.org

Summary To recognize and reward investigators who, through leadership or by example, have furthered the advancement of minorities in cancer research.

Eligibility This award is available to investigators affiliated with institutions in any country involved in cancer research, cancer medicine, or cancer-related biomedical science. Nominees must have made meritorious contributions to the field of cancer research and, through leadership or by example, have furthered the advancement of minority investigators in cancer research. Selection is based on the nominee's contributions to cancer research and to the advancement of minorities; no consideration is given to age, race, gender, nationality, geographic location, or religious or political views.

Financial data The award consists of an honorarium (amount not specified), a commemorative item, and support for the winner and a guest to attend the sponsor's annual meeting where the winner delivers a major lecture.

Duration The award is presented annually.

Additional information This award was established in 2006.

Number awarded 1 each year.

Deadline October of each year.

[1229]
MINORITY FACULTY DEVELOPMENT SCHOLARSHIP AWARD IN PHYSICAL THERAPY

American Physical Therapy Association
Attn: Honors and Awards Program
1111 North Fairfax Street
Alexandria, VA 22314-1488
(703) 684-APTA Toll Free: (800) 999-APTA
Fax: (703) 684-7343 TDD: (703) 683-6748
E-mail: honorsandawards@apta.org
Web: www.apta.org

Summary To provide financial assistance to African American and other minority faculty members in physical therapy who are interested in working on a post-professional doctoral degree.

Eligibility This program is open to U.S. citizens and permanent residents who are members of the following minority groups: African American or Black, Asian, Native Hawaiian or other Pacific Islander, American Indian or Alaska Native, or Hispanic/Latino. Applicants must be full-time faculty members, teaching in an accredited or developing professional physical therapist education program, who will have completed the equivalent of 2 full semesters of post-professional doctoral course work. They must possess a license to practice physical therapy in a U.S. jurisdiction and be enrolled as a student in an accredited post-professional doctoral program whose content has a demonstrated relationship to physical therapy. Along with their application, they must submit a personal essay on their professional goals, including their plans to contribute to the profession and minority services. Selection is based on 1) commitment to minority affairs and services; 2) commitment to further the physical therapy profession through teaching and research; and 3) scholastic achievement.

Financial data A stipend is awarded (amount not specified).

Duration 1 year.

Additional information This program began in 1999.

Number awarded 1 or more each year.

Deadline November of each year.

[1230]
MOREHOUSE PHYSICS PRIZE

National Society of Black Physicists
1100 North Glebe Road, Suite 1010
Arlington, VA 22201
(703) 536-4207 Fax: (703) 536-4203
E-mail: headquarters@nsbp.org
Web: www.nsbp.org/morehouse_prize

Summary To recognize and reward graduates of Historically Black Colleges and Universities (HBCUs) who demonstrate promise as a physics researcher.

Eligibility This award is available to anyone who has 1) received an earned degree from an HBCU; 2) earned a doctorate in physics; and 3) demonstrated promise as a physics researcher. Applicants must submit a full curriculum vitae, representative publications, a research plan, a teaching plan, and 3 letters of reference.

Financial data The awardee receives a cash award and a travel stipend to give a colloquium at Morehouse College.

Duration The prize is awarded annually.

Additional information This prize was first awarded in 2007.

Number awarded 1 each year.

Deadline November of each year.

[1231]
MULTIDISCIPLINARY RESEARCH PROGRAM OF THE UNIVERSITY RESEARCH INITIATIVE

Office of Naval Research
One Liberty Center
875 North Randolph Street, Suite 1425
Arlington, VA 22203-1995
(703) 696-4111 E-mail: paula.barden.ctr@navy.mil
Web: www.onr.navy.mil

Summary To provide funding for research (particularly research conducted by African American and other minority researchers) on subjects of interest to the Department of Defense (DoD) that intersect several traditional science and engineering disciplines.

Eligibility This program is open to research teams at U.S. institutions of higher education with degree-granting programs in science and/or engineering or by consortia led by such institutions. Applications must be for research on topics that may change annually but are specified by the participating DoD agencies: the Office of Naval Research, the Army Research Office, and the Air Force Office of Scientific Research. Researchers at Historically Black Colleges and Universities (HBCUs) and other Minority Institutions (MIs) are encouraged to submit proposals and join others in submitting proposals, but no portion of funds is set aside for HBCU and MI participation.

Financial data Grants normally range up to $1,500,000 per year, depending on the topic, technical goals, and availability of funds.

Duration Varies; recent grants have been for 3 years with 2 additional years possible as options.

Number awarded Varies each year; recently, 17 grants worth $25.5 million over 3 years were awarded.

Deadline White papers must be submitted by October of each year; full proposals are due by mid-December.

[1232]
NASA ASTROBIOLOGY PROGRAM MINORITY INSTITUTION RESEARCH SUPPORT

United Negro College Fund Special Programs Corporation
Attn: NASA Astrobiology Program
6402 Arlington Boulevard, Suite 600
Falls Church, VA 22042
(703) 205-6581 Toll Free: (800) 530-6232
Fax: (703) 205-7645 E-mail: malik.hopkins@uncfsp.org
Web: www.uncfsp.org

Summary To provide an opportunity for faculty at Minority Serving Institutions (MSIs) to work on a summer research project in partnership with an established astrobiology investigator.

Eligibility This program is open to full-time tenured or tenure-track faculty members at MSIs who have a Ph.D., Sc.D., or equivalent degree in a field of STEM (science, technology, engineering, or mathematics). Applicants must be interested in conducting a summer research project on a topic related to astrobiology. They must identify an established investigator of the National Aeronautics and Space Administration (NASA) Astrobiology Program who has agreed to serve as host researcher. Eligible fields of study include biology, microbiology, astronomy, planetary science, astrochemistry, astrophysics, geology, geochemistry, or geobiochemistry. U.S. citizenship or permanent resident status is required.

Financial data Fellows receive a stipend of $10,000 and an additional grant of $5,000 to cover travel, lodging, and living expenses.

Duration 10 weeks during the summer.

Additional information This program is funded by the NASA Astrobiology Institute and administered by the United Negro College Fund Special Programs Corporation.

Number awarded Varies each year.

Deadline March of each year.

[1233]
NATIONAL CANCER INSTITUTE MENTORED CLINICAL SCIENTIST RESEARCH CAREER DEVELOPMENT AWARD TO PROMOTE DIVERSITY

National Cancer Institute
Attn: Center to Reduce Cancer Health Disparities
9609 Medical Center Drive
Sixth Floor, West Tower
Bethesda, MD 20892-9746
(240) 276-6186 TDD: (301) 451-0088
E-mail: ojeifojo@mail.nih.gov
Web: grants.nih.gov/grants/guide/pa-files/PAR-12-051.html

Summary To provide funding to African Americans and members of other underrepresented groups who are interested in a program of training in clinical cancer research under the supervision of an experienced mentor.

Eligibility This program is open to U.S. citizens, nationals, and permanent residents who have a clinical doctoral degree; individuals with a Ph.D. or other doctoral degree in clinical disciplines such as clinical psychology, nursing, clinical genetics, speech-language pathology, audiology, or rehabilitation are also eligible. Candidates must be nominated by an eligible institution on the basis of their intent to conduct a research project highly relevant to cancer biology, cancer health disparities, etiology, pathogenesis, prevention, diagnosis, and/or treatment that has the potential for establishing an independent research program. They must qualify as 1) members of an ethnic or racial group shown to be underrepresented in health-related sciences on a national basis; 2) individuals with a disability; or 3) individuals from a disadvantaged background, including those from a low-income family and those from a social, cultural, and/or educational environment that has inhibited them from preparation for a research career. The mentor must be a senior or mid-level faculty member with research competence and an appreciation of the cultural, socioeconomic, and research background of the individual candidate. Selection is based on the applicant's qualifications, interests, accomplishments, motivation, and potential for a career in laboratory or field-based cancer research.

Financial data The award provides salary up to $100,000 per year plus related fringe benefits. In addition, up to $30,000 per year is provided for research development support. Facilities and administrative costs are reimbursed at 8% of modified total direct costs.

Duration Up to 5 years.

Additional information This program was originally established in 2002 as the successor of a program designated the Minorities in Clinical Oncology Program Grants. Recipients must devote at least 75% of their full-time professional effort to cancer-related research and training activities.

Number awarded Varies each year, depending on the availability of funds.

Deadline February, June, or October of each year.

[1234]
NATIONAL CANCER INSTITUTE TRANSITION CAREER DEVELOPMENT AWARD TO PROMOTE DIVERSITY

National Cancer Institute
Attn: Center to Reduce Cancer Health Disparities
9609 Medical Center Drive
Sixth Floor, West Tower
Bethesda, MD 20892-9746
(240) 276-6183 TDD: (301) 451-0088
E-mail: walia@mail.nih.gov
Web: grants.nih.gov/grants/guide/pa-files/PAR-12-062.html

Summary To provide funding to African Americans and other underrepresented scientists who are establishing an independent research and academic career in cancer research.

Eligibility This program is open to U.S. citizens, nationals, and permanent residents who have earned a terminal clinical or research doctorate and intend to conduct a research project highly relevant to cancer biology, cancer health disparities, etiology, pathogenesis, prevention, diagnosis, and treatment that has the potential for establishing an independent research program. Candidates must be sponsored by an eligible institution that can demonstrate a commitment to the promotion of diversity in their student and faculty populations. They must qualify as 1) members of an ethnic or racial group shown to be underrepresented in health-related sciences on a national basis; 2) individuals with a disability; or 3) individuals from a disadvantaged background, including those from a low-income family and those from a social, cultural, and/or educational environment that has inhibited them from preparation for a research career.

Financial data The award provides salary up to $100,000 per year plus related fringe benefits. In addition, up to $50,000 per year is provided for research support costs. Facilities and administrative costs are reimbursed at 8% of modified total direct costs.

Duration Up to 3 years.

Additional information Recipients must devote at least 75% of their full-time professional effort to cancer-related research and peer review activities. The remaining 25% can be divided among other activities only if they are consistent with the program goals, i.e., the candidate's development into an independent investigator.

Number awarded Approximately 10 each year.

Deadline February, June, or October of each year.

[1235]
NATIONAL CENTER FOR ATMOSPHERIC RESEARCH POSTDOCTORAL APPOINTMENTS

National Center for Atmospheric Research
Attn: Advanced Study Program
3090 Center Green Drive
P.O. Box 3000
Boulder, CO 80307-3000
(303) 497-1601 Fax: (303) 497-1646
E-mail: apply@asp.ucar.edu
Web: www.asp.ucar.edu/pdfp/pd_announcement.jsp

Summary To provide funding to recent Ph.D.s (particularly African Americans, other minorities, and women) who wish to conduct research at the National Center for Atmospheric Research (NCAR) in Boulder, Colorado.

Eligibility This program is open to recent Ph.D.s and Sc.D.s in applied mathematics, chemistry, engineering, and physics as well as specialists in atmospheric sciences from such disciplines as biology, economics, geography, geology, and science education. Applicants must be interested in conducting research at the center in atmospheric sciences and global change. Selection is based on the applicant's scientific capability and potential, originality and independence, and the match between their interests and the research opportunities at the center. Applications from women and minorities are encouraged.

Financial data The stipend is $57,500 in the first year and $60,000 in the second year. Fellows also receive life and health insurance, a relocation allowance (up to $1,000 for travel within the United States or up to $2,500 for travel from abroad), an allowance of $750 for moving and storing personal belongings, and At least $3,500 per year for scientific travel and registration fees.

Duration 2 years.

Additional information NCAR is operated by the University Corporation for Atmospheric Research (a consortium of 70 universities and research institutes) and sponsored by the National Science Foundation.

Number awarded Varies; currently, up to 9 each year.

Deadline January of each year.

[1236]
NATIONAL DENTAL ASSOCIATION MEMORIAL AWARD

National Dental Association
Attn: National Dental Association Foundation, Inc.
3517 16th Street, N.W.
Washington, DC 20010
(202) 588-1697 Fax: (202) 588-1244
E-mail: admin@ndaonline.org
Web: www.ndafoundation.org/NDAF/Scholarships.html

Summary To provide financial assistance to African American and other minority dental postdoctoral or master's degree students.

Eligibility This program is open to members of minority groups who are working on a postdoctoral degree in subspecialty areas of dentistry, public health, administration, pediatrics, research, or law. Students working on a master's degree beyond their residency also may be considered. Applicants must be members of the National Dental Association (NDA) and U.S. citizens or permanent residents. Along with their application, they must submit a letter explaining why they should be considered for this scholarship, 2 letters of recommendation, a curriculum vitae, a description of the program, nomination by their program director, and documentation of financial need.

Financial data The stipend is $10,000.

Duration 1 year.

Additional information This program, established in 1990, is supported by the Colgate-Palmolive Company.

Number awarded 1 each year.

Deadline May of each year.

[1237]
NATIONAL ENDOWMENT FOR THE HUMANITIES FELLOWSHIPS

National Endowment for the Humanities
Attn: Division of Research Programs
1100 Pennsylvania Avenue, N.W., Room 318
Washington, DC 20506
(202) 606-8200 Toll Free: (800) NEH-1121
Fax: (202) 606-8204 TDD: (866) 372-2930
E-mail: fellowships@neh.gov
Web: www.neh.gov/grants/research/fellowships

Summary To provide funding to scholars and faculty members (particularly those at Historically Black Colleges and Universities, Hispanic Serving Institutions, and Tribal Colleges and Universities) who wish to conduct research in the humanities.

Eligibility This program is open to faculty and staff of colleges, universities, primary schools, and secondary schools, as well as independent scholars and writers. Applicants must be U.S. citizens or foreign nationals who have resided in the United States or its jurisdictions for at least 3 years. The proposed project should contribute to scholarly knowledge or to the public's understanding of the humanities, usually in the form of scholarly articles, monographs on specialized subjects, books on broad topics, archaeological site reports, translations, editions, or other scholarly tools. Applicants do not need to have advanced degrees, but students currently enrolled in a degree-granting program are ineligible. Grants are not provided for curriculum development; empirical social science research, unless part of a larger humanities project; specific policy studies; the development of pedagogical tools; educational or technical impact assessments; the creation or enhancement of databases, unless part of a larger interpretive project; inventories of collections; the writing of autobiographies or memoirs; the writing of guide books, how-to books, or self-help books; preparation or revision of textbooks; works in the creative or performing arts; projects that seek to promote a particular political, philosophical, religious, or ideological point of view; projects that advocate a particular program of social action; works in the creative or performing arts; or doctoral dissertations or theses. Selection is based on 1) the intellectual significance of the project to the humanities, including its value to scholars and general audiences in the humanities; 2) the quality or promise of quality of the applicant's work as an interpreter of the humanities; 3) the quality of the conception, definition, organization, and description of the project; 4) the feasibility of the proposed plan of work; and 5) the likelihood that the applicant will complete the project. The program encourages submission of applications from faculty at Historically Black Colleges and Universities, Hispanic Serving Institutions, and Tribal Colleges and Universities.

Financial data The grant is $4,200 per month, to a maximum of $50,400 for 12 months.

Duration 6 to 12 months.

Additional information Fellows may hold other fellowships or grants in support of the same project during their tenure, including sabbaticals and grants from their own institutions.

Number awarded Approximately 90 each year.

Deadline April of each year.

[1238]
NATIONAL INSTITUTES OF HEALTH INDIVIDUAL RESEARCH PROJECT GRANTS

National Institutes of Health
Office of Extramural Research
Attn: Grants Information
6705 Rockledge Drive, Suite 4090
Bethesda, MD 20892-7983
(301) 435-0714 Fax: (301) 480-0525
TDD: (301) 451-5936 E-mail: grantsinfo@od.nih.gov
Web: grants.nih.gov/grants/guide/pa-files/PA-11-260.html

Summary To support professionals and postdoctorates (particularly African Americans, other minorities, and individuals with disabilities) who are conducting research in biomedical and behavioral areas that will improve human health in areas of interest to the National Institutes of Health (NIH).

Eligibility This program is open to investigators at 1) public and private institutions of higher education (especially Hispanic Serving institutions, Historically Black Colleges and Universities, Tribal Colleges and Universities, and Alaska Native and Native Hawaiian Serving Institutions); 2) nonprofit institutions; 3) for profit organizations; 4) units of state and local governments and eligible agencies of the federal government; 5) other organizations such as school districts, public housing authorities, Native American tribal organizations, and faith-based organizations; and 6) foreign institutions and foreign components of U.S. organizations. Applications are accepted for health-related research and development in all areas within the scope of the institutes' mission and by all component institutes and centers. Specific subjects of research are announced periodically either as Program Announcements (PAs) for ongoing research or as Requests for Applications (RFAs) for specific 1-time research projects. Usually, the research is to be conducted within the United States, but research projects conducted at foreign sites may be proposed if the project presents special opportunities for furthering research programs through the use of unusual talent, resources, populations, or environmental conditions that exist in other countries and either are not available in the United States or augment existing U.S. resources. For all projects, members of underrepresented racial or ethnic groups and individuals with disabilities are particularly encouraged to apply as principal investigators.

Financial data The level of funding depends on the scope of the proposed research. Funds may be used for supplies, equipment, personnel, and travel. Foreign institutions do not receive support for administrative costs associated with the research.

Duration 1 year or longer.

Additional information These grants are offered by 23 of NIH's component institutes. The most meritorious first-time recipients of these awards who are new investigators (with no more than five years of research experience since completion of postdoctoral training) are also nominated to receive Presidential Early Career Awards for Scientists and Engineers.

Number awarded Varies each year; recently, 8,765 of these grants were awarded.

Deadline February, June, or October of each year.

[1239]
NATIONAL SCIENCE FOUNDATION ANTARCTIC RESEARCH PROGRAM

National Science Foundation
Office of Polar Programs
Attn: Division of Antarctic Sciences
4201 Wilson Boulevard, Room 755S
Arlington, VA 22230
(703) 292-7425 Fax: (703) 292-9079
TDD: (800) 281-8749 E-mail: vpapita@nsf.gov
Web: www.nsf.gov/funding/pgm_summ.jsp?pims_id=5519

Summary To provide funding to scientists (particularly African Americans, other underrepresented minorities, women, and individuals with disabilities) who are interested in conducting research related to Antarctica.

Eligibility This program is open to investigators at U.S. institutions, primarily universities and, to a lesser extent, federal agencies and other organizations. Applicants must be proposing to conduct Antarctic-related research in the following major areas: astrophysics and geospace sciences, earth sciences, glaciology, organisms and ecosystems, instrumentation and technology development, integrated system science, and ocean and atmospheric sciences. In the selection process, consideration is given to the achievement of societally relevant outcomes, including full participation of women, persons with disabilities, and underrepresented minorities.

Financial data The amounts of the awards depend on the nature of the proposal and the availability of funds.

Additional information The NSF operates 3 year-round research stations in Antarctica, additional research facilities and camps, airplanes, helicopters, various types of surface vehicles, and ships.

Number awarded Varies each year; recently, the program planned to make 50 awards with a total budget of $55 million for standard and continuing awards, including $9 million for astrophysics and geospace science, $8 million for earth science, $6 million for glaciology, $12 million for instrumentation and technology development, $6 million for integrated system science, $6 million for ocean and atmospheric science, and $8 million for organisms and ecosystems.

Deadline April of each year.

[1240]
NATIONAL SCIENCE FOUNDATION ARCTIC RESEARCH OPPORTUNITIES

National Science Foundation
Office of Polar Programs
Attn: Division of Arctic Sciences
4201 Wilson Boulevard, Suite 755S
Arlington, VA 22230
(703) 292-4482 Fax: (703) 292-9082
TDD: (800) 281-8749 E-mail: rcrain@nsf.gov
Web: www.nsf.gov/funding/pgm_summ.jsp?pims_id=5521

Summary To provide funding to experienced researchers (particularly African Americans, other underrepresented minorities, women, and individuals with disabilities) who are interested in conducting research related to the Arctic.

Eligibility This program is open to investigators affiliated with U.S. universities, research institutions, or other organizations, including local or state governments. Applicants must be proposing to conduct research in the 4 program areas of Arctic science: 1) Arctic Natural Sciences, with areas of special interest in marine and terrestrial ecosystems, Arctic atmospheric and oceanic dynamics and climatology, Arctic geological and glaciological processes, and their connectivity to lower latitudes; 2) Arctic Social Sciences, including (but not limited to) anthropology, archaeology, economics, geography, linguistics, political science, psychology, science and technology studies, sociology, traditional knowledge, and related subjects; 3) Arctic System Science, for research focused on a system understanding of the Arctic, understanding the behavior of the Arctic system (past, present, and future), understanding the role of the Arctic as a component of the global system, and society as an integral part of the Arctic system; 4) Arctic Observing Networks, for work related to a pan-Arctic, science-driven, observing system; or 5) Polar Cyberinfrastructure, for projects using high-performance computing for direct and sustainable advances in current Arctic research. In the selection process, consideration is given to the achievement of societally relevant outcomes, including full participation of women, persons with disabilities, and underrepresented minorities.

Financial data The amounts of the awards depend on the nature of the proposal and the availability of funds.

Number awarded Approximately 75 each year; recently, this program awarded approximately $25 million in grants.

Deadline October of each year.

[1241]
NCI MENTORED PATIENT-ORIENTED RESEARCH CAREER DEVELOPMENT AWARD TO PROMOTE DIVERSITY

National Cancer Institute
Attn: Comprehensive Minority Biomedical Branch
9609 Medical Center Drive
Sixth Floor, West Tower
Bethesda, MD 20892-9746
(240) 276-6186 TDD: (301) 451-0088
E-mail: ojeifojo@mail.nih.gov
Web: grants.nih.gov/grants/guide/pa-files/PAR-12-052.html

Summary To provide funding to African Americans and members of other underrepresented groups who are interested in a program of research training in patient-oriented oncology under the supervision of an experienced mentor.

Eligibility This program is open to U.S. citizens, nationals, and permanent residents who have a health professional doctoral degree or a doctoral degree in nursing research or practice; individuals with a Ph.D. degree in clinical disciplines such as clinical psychology, clinical genetics, speech-language pathology, audiology, or rehabilitation are also eligible. Candidates must be nominated by a domestic nonprofit or for-profit organization, public or private (such as a university, college, hospital, laboratory, unit of state or local government, or eligible agency of the federal government) that can demonstrate a commitment to diversification of their student and faculty populations. Institutions must certify that the candidate qualifies as 1) a member of an ethnic or racial group shown to be underrepresented in health-related sciences on a national basis; 2) an individual with a disability; or 3) an individual from a disadvantaged background, including those from a low-income family and those from a social, cultural, and/or educational environment that have inhibited them from preparation for a research career. At least 2 mentors are required: 1 who is recognized as an accomplished clinical investigator and at least 1 additional mentor or adviser who is recognized as an accomplished independent basic science investigator in the proposed research area.

Financial data The award provides salary up to $100,000 per year plus related fringe benefits. In addition, up to $30,000 per year is provided for research development support. Facilities and administrative costs are reimbursed at 8% of modified total direct costs.

Duration 3 to 5 years.

Additional information Recipients must devote at least 75% of their full-time professional effort to cancer-related research and training activities.

Number awarded Varies each year.

Deadline February, June, or October of each year.

[1242]
NCI MENTORED RESEARCH SCIENTIST DEVELOPMENT AWARD TO PROMOTE DIVERSITY

National Cancer Institute
Attn: Center to Reduce Cancer Health Disparities
9609 Medical Center Drive
Sixth Floor, West Tower
Bethesda, MD 20892-9746
(240) 276-6186 TDD: (301) 451-0088
E-mail: ojeifojo@mail.nih.gov
Web: grants.nih.gov/grants/guide/pa-files/PAR-12-050.html

Summary To provide funding to African Americans and members of other underrepresented groups who need a period of "protected time" for intensive cancer research career development leading to research independence.

Eligibility This program is open to U.S. citizens, nationals, and permanent residents who have a research or health professional doctorate and have completed a mentored research training experience. Candidates must be proposing to conduct a research project to prepare for an independent research career related to cancer biology, cancer health disparities, etiology, pathogenesis, prevention, diagnosis, and/or treatment. They must be nominated by an eligible institution that can demonstrate a commitment to the promotion of diversity of their student and faculty populations. Institutions must certify that the candidate qualifies as 1) a member of an ethnic or racial group shown to be underrepresented in health-related sciences on a national basis; 2) an individual with a disability; or 3) an individual from a disadvantaged background, including those from a low-income family and those from a social, cultural, and/or educational environment that have inhibited them from preparation for a research career.

Financial data The award provides salary up to $100,000 per year plus related fringe benefits. In addition, up to $30,000 per year is provided for research development support. Facilities and administrative costs are reimbursed at 8% of modified total direct costs.

Duration 3, 4, or 5 years.

Additional information Recipients must devote at least 75% of their full-time professional effort to cancer-related research and training activities.

Number awarded Varies each year.

Deadline February, June, or October of each year.

[1243]
NEH AWARDS FOR FACULTY AT HISTORICALLY BLACK COLLEGES AND UNIVERSITIES

National Endowment for the Humanities
Attn: Division of Research Programs
1100 Pennsylvania Avenue, N.W., Room 318
Washington, DC 20506
(202) 606-8200 Toll Free: (800) NEH-1121
Fax: (202) 606-8204 TDD: (866) 372-2930
E-mail: FacultyAwards@neh.gov
Web: www.neh.gov

Summary To provide funding for research to faculty at Historically Black Colleges and Universities (HBCUs).

Eligibility This program is open to faculty members at HBCUs who are interested in conducting research of value to humanities scholars, students, or general audiences. Eligible projects include conducting research in primary and secondary sources; producing articles, monographs, books, digital materials, archaeological site reports, translations, editions, or other scholarly resources; or conducting basic research leading to the improvement of an existing undergraduate course or the achievement or institutional or community research goals. Applicants must be U.S. citizens or foreign nationals who have lived in the United States for at least 3 years. They are not required to have advanced degrees, but individuals enrolled in a degree-granting program are ineligible.

Financial data The grant is $4,200 per month, to a maximum of $50,400 for 12 months.

Duration 2 to 12 months.

Number awarded Approximately 2 each year.

Deadline April of each year.

[1244]
NEH COLLABORATIVE RESEARCH GRANTS

National Endowment for the Humanities
Attn: Division of Research Programs
1100 Pennsylvania Avenue, N.W., Room 318
Washington, DC 20506
(202) 606-8200 Toll Free: (800) NEH-1121
Fax: (202) 606-8204 TDD: (866) 372-2930
E-mail: collaborative@neh.gov
Web: www.neh.gov

Summary To provide funding to teams of scholars (particularly those at Historically Black Colleges and Universities, Hispanic Serving Institutions, or Tribal Colleges and Universities) who wish to conduct research in the humanities.

Eligibility This program is open to 1) U.S. citizens and foreign nationals who have been living in the United States or its jurisdictions for at least 3 years; 2) state and local governmental agencies; and 3) nonprofit, tax-exempt institutions and organizations in the United States. It supports original research undertaken by a team of 2 or more scholars or research coordinated by an individual scholar that, because of its scope or complexity, requires additional staff or resources beyond the individual's salary. Eligible projects include research that significantly adds to knowledge and understanding in the humanities; archaeology projects that interpret and communicate the results of archaeological field work; research that uses the knowledge, methods, and perspectives of the humanities to enhance understanding of science, technology, medicine, and the social sciences; translations into English of works that provide insight into the history, literature, philosophy, and artistic achievements of other cultures; and conferences on topics of major importance in the humanities that will benefit ongoing research. Selection is based on 1) the intellectual significance of the project, including its potential contribution to scholarship in the humanities, the likelihood that it will stimulate new research, its relationship to larger themes in the humanities, and the significance of the material on which the project is based; 2) the pertinence of the research questions being posed, the appropriateness of research methods or conference design, the feasibility of the work plan, the quality of samples, and the appropriateness of the field work, the archival or source materials, and the research site; 3) the qualifications, expertise, and levels of commitment to the project of the project director and key project staff or contributors, and the appropriateness of the staff to the goals of the project; 4) soundness of the dissemination and access plans; and 5) the potential for success, including the likelihood that the project will be successfully completed within the projected time frame. The program encourages submission of applications from faculty at Historically Black Colleges and Universities, Hispanic Serving Institutions, and Tribal Colleges and Universities.

Financial data Grants range from $25,000 to $100,000 per year. The use of federal matching funds in encouraged. Normally, support does not exceed 80% of total costs.

Duration 1 to 3 years.

Additional information All grantees are expected to publish or in other ways to disseminate the results of their work.

Number awarded Approximately 17 each year.

Deadline December of each year.

[1245] NEH SUMMER STIPENDS

National Endowment for the Humanities
Attn: Division of Research Programs
1100 Pennsylvania Avenue, N.W., Room 318
Washington, DC 20506
(202) 606-8200 Toll Free: (800) NEH-1121
Fax: (202) 606-8204 TDD: (866) 372-2930
E-mail: stipends@neh.gov
Web: www.neh.gov/grants/research/summer-stipends

Summary To provide funding to scholars and other professionals (particularly those at Historically Black Colleges and Universities, Hispanic Serving Institutions, and Tribal Colleges and Universities) who are interested in conducting research in the humanities during the summer.

Eligibility Faculty members teaching full time in U.S. colleges and universities may be nominated by their schools for these awards. Each school may nominate 2 candidates. Also eligible are independent scholars not affiliated with a college or university, non-faculty college and university staff members who will not be teaching during the academic year preceding the grant tenure, and adjunct and part-time faculty with academic appointments that terminate by the summer of the grant tenure; such applicants do not require nomination. All applicants must be U.S. citizens or foreign nationals who have lived in the United States or its territories for 3 years prior to the application deadline. They must be proposing to pursue research in the humanities that contributes to scholarly knowledge or to the public's understanding of the humanities, normally through scholarly articles, a monograph on a specialized subject, a book on a broad topic, an archaeological site report, a translation, an edition, a database, or other scholarly tools. Support is not provided for research for doctoral dissertations or theses by students enrolled in a degree program; specific policy studies or educational or technical impact assessments; preparation or publication of textbooks; studying teaching methods or theories, surveys of courses and programs, or curriculum development; works in the creative or performing arts; projects that seek to promote a particular political, philosophical, religious, or ideological point of view; projects that advocate a particular program of social action; or creating inventories of collections. Persons who have held a major fellowship or research grant or its equivalent during any of the preceding 3 academic years are ineligible. Selection is based on the intellectual significance of the proposed project, including its value to humanities scholars, general audiences, or both; the quality or promise of quality of the applicant's work as an interpreter of the humanities; the quality of the conception, definition, organization, and description of the proposed project; the feasibility of the proposed plan of work; and the likelihood that the applicant will complete the project. The program encourages submission of applications from faculty at Historically Black Colleges and Universities, Hispanic Serving Institutions, and Tribal Colleges and Universities.

Financial data The stipend is $6,000.

Duration 2 months during the summer.

Additional information Previous recipients may reapply after 5 years. Recipients may hold other research grants during the tenure of their awards, and they must devote full time to their projects for the 2 months of their tenure.

Number awarded Approximately 74 each year.

Deadline September of each year.

[1246] NEW INVESTIGATOR RESEARCH GRANTS TO PROMOTE DIVERSITY OF THE ALZHEIMER'S ASSOCIATION

Alzheimer's Association
Attn: Medical and Scientific Affairs
225 North Michigan Avenue, 17th Floor
Chicago, IL 60601-7633
(312) 335-5747 Toll Free: (800) 272-3900
Fax: (866) 699-1246 TDD: (312) 335-5886
E-mail: grantsapp@alz.org
Web: www.alz.org

Summary To provide funding for research on Alzheimer's Disease to junior investigators (particularly African Americans, other underrepresented minorities, and individuals with disabilities) who will contribute to diversity in the field.

Eligibility This program is open to investigators who have less than 10 years of research experience after receipt of their terminal degree. Applicants must be proposing to conduct research with focus areas that change annually but are related to Alzheimer's Disease. Eligibility is restricted to investigators who will contribute to diversity in the field of biomedical research, including members of underrepresented racial and ethnic minority groups (African Americans, Hispanic Americans, American Indians/Alaska Natives, Native Hawaiians, and Pacific Islanders) and individuals with disabilities.

Financial data Grants up to $60,000 per year, including direct expenses and up to 10% for overhead costs, are available. The total award for the life of the grant may not exceed $100,000.

Duration Up to 2 years.

Number awarded 1 or 2 each year.

Deadline Letters of intent must be submitted by the end of January or September of each year. Final applications are due in March or October.

[1247] NEW VISIONS AWARD

Lee & Low Books
95 Madison Avenue, Suite 1205
New York, NY 10016
(212) 779-4400 Fax: (212) 683-1894
E-mail: general@leeandlow.com
Web: www.leeandlow.com/p/new_visions_award.mhtml

Summary To recognize and reward outstanding unpublished fantasy or mystery books for young readers by African Americans and other writers of color.

Eligibility The contest is open to writers of color who are residents of the United States. Applicants must submit a manuscript of a fantasy, science fiction, or mystery book directed to readers at the middle grade or young adult level.

Financial data The award is a $1,000 cash grant plus the standard publication contract, including the standard advance and royalties. The Honor Award winner receives a cash grant of $500.

Duration The competition is held annually.

Additional information This program began in 2012. Manuscripts may not be sent to any other publishers while under consideration for this award.

Number awarded 2 each year.

Deadline October of each year.

[1248] NEW VOICES AWARD

Lee & Low Books
95 Madison Avenue, Suite 1205
New York, NY 10016
(212) 779-4400 Fax: (212) 683-1894
E-mail: general@leeandlow.com
Web: www.leeandlow.com/p/new_voices_award.mhtml

Summary To recognize and reward outstanding unpublished children's picture books by African Americans and other writers of color.

Eligibility The contest is open to writers of color who are residents of the United States and who have not previously published a children's picture book. Writers who have published in other venues, (e.g., children's magazines, young adult fiction and nonfiction) are eligible. Manuscripts previously submitted to the sponsor are not eligible. Submissions should be no more than 1,500 words and must address the needs of children of color by providing stories with which they can identify and relate and that promote a greater understanding of each other. Submissions may be fiction or nonfiction for children between the ages of 5 and 12. Folklore and animal stories are not considered. Up to 2 submissions may be submitted per entrant.

Financial data The award is a $1,000 cash grant plus the standard publication contract, including the standard advance and royalties. The Honor Award winner receives a cash grant of $500.

Duration The competition is held annually.

Additional information This program began in 2000. Manuscripts may not be sent to any other publishers while under consideration for this award.

Number awarded 2 each year.

Deadline October of each year.

[1249] NHLBI MENTORED CAREER AWARD FOR FACULTY AT INSTITUTIONS THAT PROMOTE DIVERSITY

National Heart, Lung, and Blood Institute
Attn: Division of Blood Diseases and Resources
6701 Rockledge Drive, Room 9176
Bethesda, MD 20892-7950
(301) 435-0067 Fax: (301) 480-1060
TDD: (301) 451-0088 E-mail: changh@nhlbi.nih.gov
Web: grants.nih.gov

Summary To provide funding to African American and other faculty investigators at institutions that promote diversity who are interested in receiving further research training in areas relevant to the mission of the National Heart, Lung, and Blood Institute (NHLBI) of the National Institutes of Health (NIH).

Eligibility This program is open to full-time faculty members at colleges and universities that promote diversity, especially Hispanic Serving Institutions, Historically Black Colleges and Universities, Tribally Controlled Colleges and Universities, and Alaska Native and Native Hawaiian Serving Institutions. Candidates must have received a doctoral degree at least 2 years previously and be able to demonstrate a commitment to develop into an independent biomedical investigator in research areas related to cardiovascular, pulmonary, hematologic, and sleep disorders of interest to NHLBI. They must identify and complete arrangements with a mentor (at the same institution or at a collaborating research center) who is recognized as an accomplished investigator in the research area proposed and who will provide guidance for their development and research plans. They must also be U.S. citizens, nationals, or permanent residents.

Financial data The awardee receives salary support of up to $75,000 per year plus fringe benefits. In addition, up to $36,000 per year may be provided for research project requirements and related support (e.g., technical personnel costs, supplies, equipment, candidate travel, telephone charges, publication costs, and tuition for necessary courses). Facilities and administrative costs may be reimbursed at the rate of 8% of total direct costs.

Duration 3 to 5 years.

Additional information Awardees must commit 75% of their effort to the proposed project.

Number awarded 2 to 3 each year; a total of approximately $300,000 is available for this program annually.

Deadline Letters of intent must be submitted by January of each year; final applications are due in February.

[1250]
NINR MENTORED RESEARCH SCIENTIST DEVELOPMENT AWARD FOR UNDERREPRESENTED OR DISADVANTAGED INVESTIGATORS

National Institute of Nursing Research
Attn: Office of Extramural Programs
6701 Democracy Boulevard, Suite 710
Bethesda, MD 20892-4870
(301) 496-9558 Fax: (301) 480-8260
TDD: (301) 451-0088 E-mail: banksd@mail.nih.gov
Web: grants.nih.gov/grants/guide/pa-files/PAR-09-074.html

Summary To provide funding for research career development to African American and other underrepresented or disadvantaged postdoctoral nursing investigators.

Eligibility This program is open to nurses who have a research or health-professional doctoral degree and are employed full time at an institution that conducts research. Applicants must qualify as an individual whose participation in scientific research will increase diversity, including 1) individuals from racial and ethnic groups that have been shown to be underrepresented in health-related science on a national basis; 2) individuals with disabilities; and 3) individuals from disadvantaged backgrounds, including those from a family with an annual income below established levels and those from a social, cultural, or educational environment that has demonstrably and recently directly inhibited the individual from obtaining the knowledge, skills, and abilities necessary to develop and participate in a research career. They must secured the commitment of an appropriate research mentor actively involved in research relevant to the mission of the National Institute of Nursing Research (NINR). Only U.S. citizens, nationals, and permanent residents are eligible.

Financial data The grant provides up to $50,000 per year for salary and fringe benefits plus an additional $20,000 per year for research development support. Facilities and administrative costs are allowed at 8% of total direct costs.

Duration Up to 3 years.

Additional information These grants have been awarded annually since 1998. Grantees are expected to spend at least 75% of their professional effort time to the program and the other 25% to other research-related and/or teaching or clinical pursuits consistent with the objectives of the award.

Number awarded 3 to 4 new grants are awarded each year.

Deadline February, June, or October of each year.

[1251]
NLM EXPRESS RESEARCH GRANTS IN BIOMEDICAL INFORMATICS

National Library of Medicine
Attn: Extramural Programs
6705 Rockledge Drive, Suite 301
Bethesda, MD 20892-7968
(301) 496-4221 Fax: (301) 402-0421
TDD: (301) 451-0088 E-mail: moweryd@mail.nih.gov
Web: grants.nih.gov/grants/guide/pa-files/PAR-13-300.html

Summary To provide funding to scholars (particularly African Americans, other underrepresented minorities, and individuals with disabilities) who are interested in conducting research related to biomedical informatics.

Eligibility This program is open to investigators affiliated with institutions of higher education, nonprofit organizations, small businesses, for-profit organizations, state and local governments, and other organizations authorized to conduct research. Applicants must be interested in conducting a research project in the field of biomedical informatics. Relevant topics include, but are not limited to, health care; public health and health services; disaster information management; basic biological, social, and behavioral research; multi-level computational models of biological and clinical processes; translational research that supports uses of data in electronic health records to support biomedical research and translation of biomedical research outcomes through application to problems in clinical care; and information sciences, simulation, user customization, virtual environments, and innovative information techniques. Members of underrepresented racial and ethnic groups and individuals with disabilities are especially encouraged to apply. Applications are also welcome from engineers, computer scientists, information scientists, social and behavioral scientists, and others not traditionally involved in biomedical research.

Financial data Grants may range up to $250,000 per year.

Duration Up to 4 years.

Number awarded Varies each year.

Deadline February, June, or October of each year.

[1252]
NOAA SMALL BUSINESS INNOVATION RESEARCH GRANTS

National Oceanic and Atmospheric Administration
Office of Research and Technology Applications
Attn: SBIR Program Manager
1335 East-West Highway, SSMC1, Room 106
Silver Spring, MD 20910-3284
(301) 713-3565 Fax: (301) 713-4100
E-mail: Kelly.Wright@noaa.gov
Web: www.oar.noaa.gov/orta

Summary To support small businesses (especially those owned by African Americans, other minorities, or women) that have the technological experience to contribute to the research and development mission of the National Oceanic and Atmospheric Administration (NOAA).

Eligibility For the purposes of this program, a "small business" is defined as a firm that is organized for profit with a location in the United States; is in the legal form of an individual proprietorship, partnership, limited liability company, corporation, joint venture, association, trust, or cooperative; is at least 51% owned and controlled by 1 or more individuals who are citizens or permanent residents of the United States; and has (including its affiliates) fewer than 500 employees. The primary employment of the principal investigator must be with the firm at the time of award and during the conduct of the proposed project. Applications are encouraged rom 1) women-owned small business concerns, defined as those that are at least 51% owned by a woman or women who also control and operate them; and 2) socially and economically disadvantaged small business concerns that are at least 51% owned by an Indian tribe, a Native Hawaiian organization, or 1 or more socially and economically disadvantaged individuals (African Americans, Hispanic Americans, Native Americans, Asian Pacific Americans, or subcontinent Asian Americans). Current priority areas of research include: 1) resilient coastal communities and economics; 2) healthy oceans; 3) climate adaptation and mitigation; or 4) weather-ready nation. Selection is based on the technical approach and anticipated agency and commercial benefits that may be derived from the research (25 points); the adequacy of the proposed effort and its relationship to the fulfillment of the requirements of the research topic (20 points); the soundness and technical merit of the proposed approach and its incremental progress towards topic solution (20 points); qualifications of the principal investigators, supporting staff, and consultants (15 points); and the proposal's commercial potential (20 points).

Financial data Grants are offered in 2 phases. In phase 1, awards normally do not exceed $95,000 (for both direct and indirect costs); in phase 2, awards normally do not exceed $400,000 (including both direct and indirect costs).

Duration Phase 1 awards may extend up to 6 months; phase 2 awards may extend up to 2 years.

Number awarded Varies each year; recently, NOAA planned to award 15 Phase 1 contracts. Approximately half of Phase 1 awardees receive Phase 2 awards.

Deadline January of each year.

[1253]
NOTRE DAME INSTITUTE FOR ADVANCED STUDY RESIDENTIAL FELLOWSHIPS

University of Notre Dame
Institute for Advanced Study
Attn: Programs Administrator
1124 Flanner Hall
Notre Dame, IN 46556
(574) 631-6240 E-mail: csherman@nd.edu
Web: ndias.nd.edu/fellowships/residential

Summary To provide funding to scholars (particularly African Americans and members of other traditionally underrepresented groups) who are interested in conducting research on topics of interest to the Notre Dame Institute for Advanced Study (NDIAS) while in residence at the institute.

Eligibility This program is open to faculty, scholars, public intellectuals, fellows from other institutes, and professional researchers in all disciplines, including the arts, engineering, the humanities, law, and the natural, social, and physical sciences. Applicants must be interested in conducting research that aligns with the intellectual orientation of the NDIAS, which asks scholars "to include questions of values in their analyses, to integrate diverse disciplines, and to ask how their findings advance civilization." They must be able to demonstrate excellent records of scholarly, artistic, or research accomplishment in their field; ability to interact with other fellows and to engage in collegial discussions of research presentations; a willingness to contribute to a cooperative community of scholars; and projects that touch on normative, integrative, or ultimate questions, especially as the involve the Catholic intellectual tradition. Applications are especially encouraged from traditionally underrepresented groups. There are no citizenship requirements; non-U.S. nationals are welcome to apply.

Financial data The grant is $60,000 for a full academic year or pro-rated amounts for shorter periods. Other benefits include subsidized visiting faculty housing, research support up to $1,000, a private office at the institute, a computer and printer, access to university libraries and other facilities, and weekly institute seminars and events.

Duration Up to 1 academic year.

Number awarded 1 or more each year.

Deadline October of each year.

[1254]
NSF SMALL BUSINESS INNOVATION RESEARCH GRANTS

National Science Foundation
Directorate for Engineering
Attn: Division of Industrial Innovation and Partnerships
4201 Wilson Boulevard, Room 590 N
Arlington, VA 22230
(703) 292-8050 Fax: (703) 292-9057
TDD: (800) 281-8749
Web: www.nsf.gov/eng/iip/spir

Summary To provide funding to small and creative engineering, science, education, and technology-related firms (particularly those owned by African Americans, other minorities, or women) to conduct innovative, high-risk research on scientific and technical problems.

Eligibility For the purposes of this program, a "small business" is defined as a firm that is organized for profit with a location in the United States; is in the legal form of an individual proprietorship, partnership, limited liability company, corporation, joint venture, association, trust, or cooperative; is at least 51% owned and controlled by 1 or more individuals who are citizens or permanent residents of the United States; and has (including its affiliates) fewer than 500 employees. The primary employment of the principal investigator must be with the firm at the time of award and during the conduct of the proposed project. Applications are encouraged from 1) women-owned small business concerns, defined as those that are at least 51% owned by a woman or women who also control and operate them; and 2) socially and economically disadvantaged small business concerns that are at least 51% owned by an Indian tribe, a Native Hawaiian organization, or 1 or more socially and economically disadvantaged individuals (African Americans, Hispanic Americans, Native Americans, Asian Pacific Americans, or subcontinent Asian Americans). Current priorities for critical technology areas of national importance include 1) biological and chemical technologies; 2) education applications; 3) electronics, information and communication technologies; and 4) nanotechnology, advanced materials, and manufacturing. Selection is based on the intellectual merit and the broader impacts of the proposed activity.

Financial data Support is offered in 2 phases. In phase 1, awards normally may not exceed $150,000 (for both direct and indirect costs); in phase 2, awards normally may not exceed $500,000 (including both direct and indirect costs).

Duration Phase 1 awards may extend up to 6 months; phase 2 awards may extend up to 2 years.

Number awarded Depends on the availability of funds; the National Science Foundation (NSF) plans to award approximately 100 phase 1 grants each year; recently, $15 million was budgeted for this program.

Deadline June of each year.

[1255]
NSF SMALL BUSINESS TECHNOLOGY TRANSFER GRANTS

National Science Foundation
Directorate for Engineering
Attn: Division of Industrial Innovation and Partnerships
4201 Wilson Boulevard, Room 590 N
Arlington, VA 22230
(703) 292-8050 Fax: (703) 292-9057
TDD: (800) 281-8749
Web: www.nsf.gov/eng/iip/spir

Summary To provide financial support for cooperative research and development projects carried out between small business concerns and research institutions ((particularly those owned by African Americans, other minorities, or women) in areas of concern to the National Science Foundation (NSF).

Eligibility For the purposes of this program, a "small business" is defined as a firm that is organized for profit with a location in the United States; is in the legal form of an individual proprietorship, partnership, limited liability company, corporation, joint venture, association, trust, or cooperative; is at least 51% owned and controlled by 1 or more individuals who are citizens or permanent residents of the United States; and has (including its affiliates) fewer than 500 employees. Unlike the NSF Small Business Innovation Research Grants, the primary employment of the principal investigator does not need to be with the business concern. This program, however, requires that the small business apply in collaboration with a nonprofit research institution for conduct of a project that has potential for commercialization. Principal investigators from the nonprofit research institution must commit at least 10% of their effort to the project. At least 40% of the work must be performed by the small business and at least 30% of the work must be performed by the research institution. Applications are encouraged from 1) women-owned small business concerns, defined as those that are at least 51% owned by a woman or women who also control and operate them; and 2) socially and economically disadvantaged small business concerns that are at least 51% owned by an Indian tribe, a Native Hawaiian organization, or 1 or more socially and economically disadvantaged individuals (African Americans, Hispanic Americans, Native Americans, Asian Pacific Americans, or subcontinent Asian Americans). Recently, the program was accepting applications only for the topic area of enhancing access to the radio spectrum; previous topics have included 1) advanced materials, chemical technology and manufacturing; 2) biotechnology; 3) electronics; 4) information technology; and 5) emerging opportunities (projects with a focus on near-term commercialization). Selection is based on the intellectual merit and the broader impacts of the proposed activity.

Financial data In the first phase, annual awards may not exceed $150,000 for direct costs, indirect costs, and negotiated fixed fees. In the second phase, awards up to $500,000 are available.

Duration Normally, 12 months for phase 1 and 2 years for phase 2.

Additional information Grants in the first phase are to determine the scientific, technical, and commercial merit and feasibility of the proposed cooperative effort and the quality of performance of the small business concern. In the second phase, the research and development efforts continue, depending on the results of the first phase.

Number awarded 35 phase 1 grants are awarded each year. Approximately one-third of phase 1 awardees receive phase 2 grants. Approximately $5,250,000 is budgeted for this program each year.

Deadline December of each year.

[1256]
NSF STANDARD AND CONTINUING GRANTS

National Science Foundation
4201 Wilson Boulevard
Arlington, VA 22230
(703) 292-5111 TDD: (800) 281-8749
E-mail: info@nsf.gov
Web: www.nsf.gov

Summary To provide financial support to engineers and educators (particularly African Americans, other underrepresented minorities, and women) for research in broad areas of science and engineering.

Eligibility The National Science Foundation (NSF) supports research through its Directorates of Biological Sciences; Computer and Information Science and Engineering; Education and Human Resources; Engineering; Geosciences; Mathematical and Physical Sciences; and Social, Behavioral, and Economic Sciences. Within those general areas of science and engineering, NSF awards 2 types of grants: 1) standard grants, in which NSF agrees to provide a specific level of support for a specified period of time with no statement of NSF intent to provide additional future support without submission of another proposal; and 2) continuing grants, in which NSF agrees to provide a specific level of support for an initial specified period of time with a statement of intent to provide additional support of the project for additional periods, provided funds are available and the results achieved warrant further support. Although NSF often solicits proposals for support of targeted areas through issuance of specific program solicitations, it also accepts unsolicited proposals. Scientists, engineers, and educators usually act as the principal investigator and initiate proposals that are officially submitted by their employing organization. Most employing organizations are universities, colleges, and nonprofit non-academic organizations (such as museums, observatories, research laboratories, and professional societies). Certain programs are open to for-profit organizations, state and local governments, or unaffiliated individuals. Principal investigators usually must be U.S. citizens, nationals, or permanent residents. In the selection process, consideration is given to the achievement of societally relevant outcomes, including full participation of women, persons with disabilities, and underrepresented minorities.

Financial data Funding levels vary, depending on the nature of the project and the availability of funds. Awards resulting from unsolicited research proposals are subject to statutory cost-sharing.

Duration Standard grants specify the period of time, usually up to 1 year; continuing grants normally specify 1 year as the initial period of time, with support to continue for additional periods.

Additional information Researchers interested in support from NSF should contact the address above to obtain further information on areas of support and programs operating within the respective directorates. They should consult with a program officer before submitting an application. Information on programs is available on the NSF home page. NSF does not normally support technical assistance, pilot plant efforts, research requiring security classification, the development of products for commercial marketing, or market research for a particular project or invention. Bioscience research with disease-related goals, including work on the etiology, diagnosis, or treatment of physical or mental disease, abnormality, or malfunction in human beings or animals, is normally not supported.

Number awarded Approximately 11,000 new grants are awarded each year.

Deadline Many programs accept proposals at any time. Other programs establish target dates or deadlines; those target dates and deadlines are published in the *NSF Bulletin* and in specific program announcements/solicitations.

[1257] NUCLEAR REGULATORY COMMISSION HISTORICALLY BLACK COLLEGES AND UNIVERSITIES FACULTY RESEARCH PARTICIPATION PROGRAM

Oak Ridge Institute for Science and Education
Attn: Science and Engineering Education
P.O. Box 117
Oak Ridge, TN 37831-0117
(865) 576-3937 Fax: (865) 241-5220
E-mail: michael.hubbard@orau.gov
Web: see.orau.org

Summary To provide funding to full-time faculty members at Historically Black Colleges and Universities (HBCUs) who wish to participate in science and engineering research at various facilities of the U.S. Nuclear Regulatory Commission (NRC).

Eligibility This program is open to full-time faculty members at HBCUs who are U.S. citizens or permanent residents. Applicants must be interested in conducting research either at NRC laboratories or at host universities under the guidance of principal investigators who have NRC research grants. Eligible fields of specialization include computer science, engineering, geosciences, health physics, materials science, mathematics, molecular/radiation biology, physical sciences, and statistics-related nuclear material control and accounting.

Financial data Faculty members receive a stipend equal to $3,800 per month or their regular salary, whichever is greater. Also provided is limited travel reimbursement for round-trip transportation between the facility and home or campus.

Duration Appointments are normally 10 to 12 weeks during the summer; some 9 to 12-month on-campus appointments are also available.

Additional information This program is funded by the NRC and administered by Oak Ridge Institute for Science and Education (ORISE).

Number awarded Varies each year.

Deadline January of each year.

[1258] OAK RIDGE NATIONAL LABORATORY/OAK RIDGE ASSOCIATED UNIVERSITIES HBCU/MEI FACULTY SUMMER RESEARCH PROGRAM

Oak Ridge Institute for Science and Education
Attn: Science and Engineering Education
P.O. Box 117
Oak Ridge, TN 37831-0117
(865) 574-4550 Fax: (865) 241-5219
E-mail: Michael.Ickowitz@orau.gov
Web: see.orau.org

Summary To provide funding to faculty at Minority-serving Educational Institutions (MEIs) who wish to engage in ongoing research at Oak Ridge National Laboratory (ORNL) in Tennessee.

Eligibility This program is open to full-time faculty members at Hispanic Serving Institutions (HSIs), Historically Black Colleges and Universities (HBCUs), Tribal Colleges and Universities TCUs), Alaska Native Serving Institutions (ANSIs), and Native Hawaiian Serving Institutions (NHSIs). Applicants must be interested in collaborating on specific research projects at ORNL in computer science; earth, environmental, or marine sciences; engineering; life, health, or medical sciences; mathematics; or physical sciences. Research projects are currently available in quantum imaging by compressive sampling, quantum lightwave circuits, decadal-scale hydroclimatic predictions and impact assessments, novel neutron detector for scattering applications, timely discovery and situational understanding of cyber attacks, lignin as a precursor for high performance energy storage applications, intelligent advanced propulsion systems, incorporating molecular-scale mechanisms stabilizing soil organic carbon into terrestrial carbon cycle models, citizen engagement for energy efficient communities, ultrascale algorithms for verification of security properties, data-driven threat radar for local-to-regional energy grid stability, and unraveling the molecular and biochemical basis of crassulacean acid metabolism in agave for sustainable biofuel production. Selection is based on the strength of the applicant's capabilities and experience; the match between the applicant's qualifications and the research needs of the selected project; and the potential for establishing an ongoing research partnership.

Financial data The stipend is based on the recipient's regular university salary, at least $4,500 per month. Participants also receive limited reimbursement for inbound and outbound transportation and a monthly dislocation allowance of $1,000.

Duration 10 weeks during the summer.

Additional information This program is funded by ORNL and Oak Ridge Associated Universities (ORAU) and administered by Oak Ridge Institute for Science and Education (ORISE).

Number awarded Varies each year.

Deadline January of each year.

[1259]
OCEAN SCIENCES POSTDOCTORAL RESEARCH FELLOWSHIPS

National Science Foundation
Directorate for Geosciences
Attn: Division of Ocean Sciences
4201 Wilson Boulevard, Room 725N
Arlington, VA 22230
(703) 292-7240 Fax: (703) 292-9085
TDD: (800) 281-8749 E-mail: lweber@nsf.gov
Web: www.nsf.gov

Summary To provide funding to African Americans and members of other underrepresented groups who are interested in conducting postdoctoral research training in the ocean sciences.

Eligibility This program is open to U.S. citizens, nationals, or permanent residents who are members of groups underrepresented in the ocean sciences (women, persons with disabilities, African Americans, Hispanics, Native Americans, Alaska Natives, and Pacific Islanders). Applicants must have earned within the past 24 months a doctoral degree in the ocean sciences, including biological oceanography, chemical oceanography, physical oceanography, marine geology and geophysics, ocean drilling, ocean science and technology, or ocean education. They must be interested in conducting research training at a U.S. or foreign host institution under the mentorship of a sponsoring scientist who will provide guidance for the research.

Financial data Grants are $85,000 per year, including an annual stipend of $60,000 and an annual fellowship allowance of $25,000 that is intended to cover direct research expenses, facilities and other institutional resources, and fringe benefits.

Duration Up to 2 years.

Number awarded 10 each year.

Deadline January of each year.

[1260]
OCEAN SCIENCES RESEARCH INITIATION GRANTS

National Science Foundation
Directorate for Geosciences
Attn: Division of Ocean Sciences
4201 Wilson Boulevard, Room 725N
Arlington, VA 22230
(703) 292-7240 Fax: (703) 292-9085
TDD: (800) 281-8749 E-mail: lweber@nsf.gov
Web: www.nsf.gov

Summary To provide funding to African Americans and members of other underrepresented groups who are junior faculty members interested in conducting research in the ocean sciences.

Eligibility This program is open to U.S. citizens, nationals, or permanent residents who are members of groups underrepresented in the ocean sciences: women, persons with disabilities, African Americans, Hispanics, Native Americans, Alaska Natives, and Pacific Islanders. Applicants must have held a tenure-track assistant professor level faculty position or equivalent research appointment for no more than 3 years. They must be interested in conducting research in the ocean sciences, including biological oceanography, chemical oceanography, physical oceanography, marine geology and geophysics, ocean drilling, ocean science and technology, or ocean education.

Financial data The maximum grant is $100,000 in direct and indirect costs for 12 to 24 months.

Duration Up to 2 years.

Number awarded 6 each year.

Deadline January of each year.

[1261]
OFFICE OF NAVAL RESEARCH SABBATICAL LEAVE PROGRAM

American Society for Engineering Education
Attn: ONR Summer Programs
1818 N Street, N.W., Suite 600
Washington, DC 20036-2479
(202) 331-3558 Fax: (202) 265-8504
E-mail: onrsummer@asee.org
Web: onr.asee.org/about_the_sabbatical_leave_program

Summary To provide support to faculty members in engineering and science (particularly those at Minority Serving Institutions) who wish to conduct research at selected Navy facilities while on sabbatical leave.

Eligibility This program is open to U.S. citizens with teaching or research appointments in engineering and science at U.S. universities or colleges. Applicants must intend to conduct research while in residence at selected facilities of the U.S. Navy. Faculty from Historically Black Colleges and Universities, Hispanic Serving Institutions, and Tribal Colleges and Universities are especially encouraged to apply.

Financial data Fellows receive a stipend equivalent to the difference between their regular salary and the sabbatical leave pay from their home institution. Fellows who must relocate their residence receive a relocation allowance and all fellows receive a travel allowance.

Duration Appointments are for a minimum of 1 semester and a maximum of 1 year.

Additional information Participating facilities include the Naval Air Warfare Center, Aircraft Division (Patuxent River, Maryland); Naval Air Warfare Center, Naval Training Systems Division (Orlando, Florida); Naval Air Warfare Center, Weapons Division (China Lake, California); Space and Naval Warfare Systems Center (San Diego, California and Charleston, South Carolina); Naval Facilities Engineering Service Center (Port Hueneme, California); Naval Research Laboratories (Washington, D.C.; Stennis Space Center, Mississippi; and Monterey, California); Naval Surface Warfare Centers (Bethesda, Maryland; Indian Head, Maryland; Dahlgren, Virginia; and Panama City, Florida); Naval Undersea Warfare Center (Newport, Rhode Island; New London, Connecticut; and Keyport, Washington); Defense Equal Opportunity Management Institute (Cocoa Beach, Florida); Navy Personnel Research, Studies & Technology Department (Millington, Tennessee); Naval Medical Research Unit (Dayton, Ohio); Naval Health Research Center (San Diego, California); Naval Medical Research Center (Silver Spring, Maryland); and Naval Submarine Medical Research Laboratory (Groton, Connecticut). This program is funded by the U.S. Navy's Office of Naval Research and administered by the American Society for Engineering Education.

Number awarded Varies each year.

Deadline Applications may be submitted at any time, but they must be received at least 6 months prior to the proposed sabbatical leave starting date.

[1262]
OFFICE OF NAVAL RESEARCH SUMMER FACULTY RESEARCH PROGRAM

American Society for Engineering Education
Attn: ONR Summer Programs
1818 N Street, N.W., Suite 600
Washington, DC 20036-2479
(202) 331-3558 Fax: (202) 265-8504
E-mail: onrsummer@asee.org
Web: onr.asee.org/about_the_summer_faculty_program

Summary To provide support to faculty members in engineering and science (particularly those at Minority Serving Institutions) who wish to conduct summer research at selected Navy facilities.

Eligibility This program is open to U.S. citizens and permanent residents who have teaching or research appointments in engineering and science at U.S. universities or colleges. In addition to appointments as Summer Faculty Fellows, positions as Senior Summer Faculty Fellows are available to applicants who have at least 6 years of research experience in their field of expertise since earning a Ph.D. or equivalent degree and a substantial, significant record of research accomplishments and publications. A limited number of appointments are also available as Distinguished Summer Faculty Fellows to faculty members who are preeminent in their field of research, have a senior appointment at a leading research university, and are internationally recognized for their research accomplishments. Faculty from Historically Black Colleges and Universities, Hispanic Serving Institutions, and Tribal Colleges and Universities are especially encouraged to apply.

Financial data The weekly stipend is $1,400 at the Summer Faculty Fellow level, $1,650 at the Senior Summer Faculty Fellow level, and $1,900 at the Distinguished Summer Faculty Fellow level. Fellows who must relocate their residence receive a relocation allowance and all fellows receive a travel allowance.

Duration 10 weeks during the summer; fellows may reapply in subsequent years.

Additional information Participating facilities include the Naval Air Warfare Center, Aircraft Division (Patuxent River, Maryland); Naval Air Warfare Center, Naval Training Systems Division (Orlando, Florida); Naval Air Warfare Center, Weapons Division (China Lake, California); Space and Naval Warfare Systems Center (San Diego, California and Charleston, South Carolina); Naval Facilities Engineering Service Center (Port Hueneme, California); Naval Research Laboratories (Washington, D.C.; Stennis Space Center, Mississippi; and Monterey, California); Naval Surface Warfare Centers (Bethesda, Maryland; Indian Head, Maryland; Dahlgren, Virginia; and Panama City, Florida); Naval Undersea Warfare Center (Newport, Rhode Island; New London, Connecticut; and Keyport, Washington); Defense Equal Opportunity Management Institute (Cocoa Beach, Florida); Navy Personnel Research, Studies & Technology Department (Millington, Tennessee); Naval Medical Research Unit (Dayton, Ohio); Naval Health Research Center (San Diego, California); Naval Medical Research Center (Silver Spring, Maryland); and Naval Submarine Medical Research Laboratory (Groton, Connecticut). This program is funded by the U.S. Navy's Office of Naval Research and administered by the American Society for Engineering Education.

Number awarded Varies each year.

Deadline December of each year.

[1263]
OFFICE OF NAVAL RESEARCH YOUNG INVESTIGATOR PROGRAM

Office of Naval Research
One Liberty Center
875 North Randolph Street, Suite 1425
Arlington, VA 22203-1995
(703) 696-4111 E-mail: paula.barden.ctr@navy.mil
Web: www.onr.navy.mil

Summary To provide funding to academic scientists and engineers (particularly African Americans and other minorities) who are interested in conducting research on topics of interest to the U.S. Navy.

Eligibility This program is open to U.S. citizens, nationals, and permanent residents who received their first tenure-track faculty positions at a U.S. university within the preceding 5 years. Applicants must be proposing to conduct research relevant to 1 of the divisions within the Office of Naval Research: expeditionary maneuver warfare and combating terrorism; command, control communications, computers, intelligence, surveillance, and reconnaissance; ocean battlespace sensing; sea warfare and weapons; warfighter performance; and naval air warfare and weapons. Selection is based on 1) past performance, demonstrated by the significance and impact of previous research, publications, professional activities, awards, and other recognition; 2) a creative proposal, demonstrating the potential for making progress in a listed priority research area; and 3) a long-term commitment by the university to the applicant and the research. Researchers at Historically Black Colleges and Universities (HBCUs) and Minority Institutions (MIs) are encouraged to submit proposals and join others in submitting proposals, but no portion of funds is set aside for HBCU and MI participation.

Financial data Awards up to $170,000 per year are available.

Duration 3 years.

Additional information Approximately 2 recipients of these awards are also nominated to receive Presidential Early Career Awards for Scientists and Engineers to provide an additional 2 years of funding.

Number awarded Approximately 16 each year.

Deadline December of each year.

[1264]
ONLINE BIBLIOGRAPHIC SERVICES/TS JOINT RESEARCH GRANT

American Association of Law Libraries
Attn: Online Bibliographic Services Special Interest Section
105 West Adams Street, Suite 3300
Chicago, IL 60603
(312) 939-4764 Fax: (312) 431-1097
E-mail: aallhq@aall.org
Web: www.aallnet.org

Summary To provide funding to members of the American Association of Law Libraries (AALL), particularly minorities and women, who are interested in conducting a research project related to technical services.

Eligibility This program is open to AALL members who are technical services law librarians. Preference is given to members of the Online Bibliographic Services and Technical Services Special Interest Sections, although members of other special interest sections are eligible if their work relates to technical services law librarianship. Applicants must be interested in conducting research that will enhance technical services law librarianship. Women and minorities are especially encouraged to apply. Preference is given to projects that can be completed in the United States or Canada, although foreign research projects are given consideration.

Financial data Grants range up to $1,000.

Duration 1 year.

Number awarded 1 or more each year.

Deadline March or September of each year.

[1265]
OPEN BOOK AWARD

PEN American Center
Attn: Literary Awards Associate
588 Broadway, Suite 303
New York, NY 10012
(212) 334-1660, ext. 126 Fax: (212) 334-2181
E-mail: awards@pen.org
Web: www.pen.org/content/pen-open-book-award-5000

Summary To recognize and reward African Americans and other outstanding authors of color from any country.

Eligibility This award is presented to an author of color (African, Arab, Asian, Caribbean, Latino, and Native American) whose book-length writings were published in the United States during the current calendar year. Works of fiction, literary nonfiction, biography/memoir, poetry, and other works of literary character are strongly preferred. U.S. citizenship or residency is not required. Nominations must be submitted by publishers or agents.

Financial data The prize is $5,000.

Duration The prizes are awarded annually.

Additional information This prize was formerly known as the Beyond Margins Award. The entry fee is $50.

Number awarded 5 each year.

Deadline December of each year.

[1266]
PAUL HOCH DISTINGUISHED SERVICE AWARD

American College of Neuropsychopharmacology
Attn: Executive Office
5034-A Thoroughbred Lane
Brentwood, TN 37027
(615) 324-2360 Fax: (615) 523-1715
E-mail: acnp@acnp.org
Web: www.acnp.org/programs/awards.aspx

Summary To recognize and reward members (particularly African Americans, other minorities, and women) who belong to the American College of Neuropsychopharmacology (ACNP) and have contributed outstanding service to the organization.

Eligibility This award is available to ACNP members who have made unusually significant contributions to the College. The emphasis of the award is on service to the organization, not on teaching, clinical, or research accomplishments. Any member or fellow of ACNP may nominate another member. Nomination of women and minorities is highly encouraged.

Financial data The award consists of a monetary honorarium, an expense-paid trip to the ACNP annual meeting, and a plaque.

Duration The award is presented annually.

Additional information This award was first presented in 1965.

Number awarded 1 each year.

Deadline Nominations must be submitted by June of each year.

[1267]
PAUL TOBENKIN MEMORIAL AWARD

Columbia University
Attn: Graduate School of Journalism
Mail Code 3809
2950 Broadway
New York, NY 10027-7004
(212) 854-7696 Fax: (212) 854-3939
E-mail: lt2026@columbia.edu
Web: www.journalism.columbia.edu

Summary To recognize and reward outstanding newspaper writing that reflects the spirit of Paul Tobenkin, who fought all his life against racial and religious hatred, bigotry, bias, intolerance, and discrimination.

Eligibility Materials reflecting the spirit of Paul Tobenkin may be submitted by newspaper reporters in the United States, editors of their publications, or interested third parties. The items submitted must have been published during the previous calendar year in a weekly or daily newspaper.

Financial data The award is $1,500 plus a plaque.

Duration The award is presented annually.

Additional information This award was first presented in 1961.

Number awarded 1 or more each year.

Deadline March of each year.

[1268]
PAULA DE MERIEUX RHEUMATOLOGY FELLOWSHIP AWARD

American College of Rheumatology
Attn: Research and Education Foundation
2200 Lake Boulevard N.E.
Atlanta, GA 30319
(404) 633-3777 Fax: (404) 633-1870
E-mail: ref@rheumatology.org
Web: www.rheumatology.org/ref/awards/index.asp

Summary To provide funding to African Americans, other underrepresented minorities, and women who are interested in a program of training for a career providing clinical care to people affected by rheumatic diseases.

Eligibility This program is open to trainees at ACGME-accredited institutions. Applications must be submitted by the training program director at the institution who is responsible for selection and appointment of trainees. The program must train and prepare fellows to provide clinical care to those affected by rheumatic diseases. Trainees must be women or members of underrepresented minority groups, defined as Black Americans, Hispanics, and Native Americans (Native Hawaiians, Alaska Natives, and American Indians). They must be U.S. citizens, nationals, or permanent residents. Selection is based on the institution's pass rate of rheumatology fellows, publication history of staff and previous fellows, current positions of previous fellows, and status of clinical faculty.

Financial data The grant is $25,000 per year, to be used as salary for the trainee. Other trainee costs (e.g., fees, health insurance, travel, attendance at scientific meetings) are to be incurred by the recipient's institutional program. Supplemental or additional support to offset the cost of living may be provided by the grantee institution.

Duration Up to 1 year.

Additional information This fellowship was first awarded in 2005.

Number awarded 1 each year.

Deadline July of each year.

[1269]
PEARSON EARLY CAREER GRANT

American Psychological Foundation
750 First Street, N.E.
Washington, DC 20002-4242
(202) 336-5843 Fax: (202) 336-5812
E-mail: foundation@apa.org
Web: www.apa.org/apf/funding/pearson.aspx

Summary To provide funding to early career psychologists (particularly African Americans, other minorities, and individuals with disabilities) who are interested in conducting a project in an area of critical society need.

Eligibility This program is open to psychologists who have an Ed.D., Psy.D., or Ph.D. from an accredited experience and no more than 7 years of postdoctoral experience. Applicants must be interested in conducting a project to improve areas of critical need in society, including (but not limited to) innovative scientifically-based clinical work with serious mental illness, serious emotional disturbance, incarcerated or homeless individuals, children with serious emotional disturbance (SED), or adults with serious mental illness (SMI). The sponsor encourages applications from individuals who represent diversity in race, ethnicity, gender, age, disability, and sexual orientation.

Financial data The grant is $12,000.

Duration 1 year.

Additional information This grant was first awarded in 2010.

Number awarded 1 each year.

Deadline December of each year.

[1270]
PEMBROKE CENTER POSTDOCTORAL FELLOWSHIPS

Brown University
Attn: Pembroke Center for Teaching and Research on Women
172 Meeting Street
Box 1958
Providence, RI 02912
(401) 863-2643 Fax: (401) 863-1298
E-mail: Pembroke_Center@brown.edu
Web: www.brown.edu

Summary To provide funding to postdoctoral scholars (particularly African Americans and other underrepresented minorities) who are interested in conducting research at Brown University's Pembroke Center for Teaching and Research on Women on the cross-cultural study of gender.

Eligibility Fellowships are open to scholars in relevant fields who have completed their Ph.D. but do not have a tenured position at an American college or university. Applicants must be willing to spend a year in residence at the Pembroke Center for Teaching and Research on Women and participate in a research project related to gender and/or sexuality. The project focuses on a theme that changes annually (recently: "Aesthetics and the Question of Beauty"). The center encourages underrepresented minority and international scholars to apply.

Financial data The stipend is $50,000. Health insurance is also provided.

Duration 1 academic year.

Additional information Postdoctoral fellows in residence participate in weekly seminars and present at least 2 public papers during the year, as well as conduct an individual research project. Supplementary funds are available for assistance with travel expenses from abroad. This program includes the following named fellowships: the Nancy L. Buc Postdoctoral Fellowship, the Artemis A.W. and Martha Joukowsky Postdoctoral Fellowship, and the Carol G. Lederer Postdoctoral Fellowship.

Number awarded 3 or 4 each year.

Deadline December of each year.

[1271] POSTDOCTORAL FELLOWSHIP IN MENTAL HEALTH AND SUBSTANCE ABUSE SERVICES

American Psychological Association
Attn: Minority Fellowship Program
750 First Street, N.E.
Washington, DC 20002-4242
(202) 336-6127 Fax: (202) 336-6012
TDD: (202) 336-6123 E-mail: mfp@apa.org
Web: www.apa.org/pi/mfp/psychology/postdoc/index.aspx

Summary To provide financial assistance to postdoctoral scholars (particularly African Americans and members of other ethnic minority groups) who are interested in a program of research training related to providing mental health and substance abuse services to ethnic minority populations.

Eligibility This program is open to U.S. citizens, nationals, and permanent residents who received a doctoral degree in psychology in the last 5 years. Applicants must be interested in participating in a program of training under a qualified sponsor for research and have a strong commitment to a career in ethnic minority behavioral health services or policy. Members of ethnic minority groups (African Americans, Hispanics/Latinos, American Indians, Alaskan Natives, Asian Americans, Native Hawaiians, and other Pacific Islanders) are especially encouraged to apply. Selection is based on commitment to a career in ethnic minority mental health service delivery or public policy; qualifications of the sponsor; the fit between career goals and training environment selected; merit of the training proposal; potential as a future leader in ethnic minority psychology, demonstrated through accomplishments and goals; consistency between the applicant's work and the goals of the program; and letters of recommendation.

Financial data The stipend depends on the number of years of research experience and is equivalent to the standard postdoctoral stipend level of the National Institutes of Health (recently ranging from $39,264 for no years of experience to $54,180 for 7 or more years of experience).

Duration 1 academic or calendar year; may be renewed for 1 additional year.

Additional information Funding is provided by the U.S. Substance Abuse and Mental Health Services Administration.

Number awarded Varies each year.

Deadline January of each year.

[1272] POSTDOCTORAL FELLOWSHIP IN THE HISTORY OF MODERN SCIENCE AND TECHNOLOGY IN EAST ASIA

Harvard University
Attn: Department of East Asian Languages and Civilizations
2 Divinity Avenue
Cambridge, MA 02138
(617) 495-2754 Fax: (617) 496-6040
E-mail: ealc@fas.harvard.edu
Web: harvardealc.org/postdoc.html

Summary To provide funding to postdoctoral scholars (particularly African Americans, other minorities, and women) who wish to conduct research at Harvard University on a topic related to the history of science and technology in east Asia.

Eligibility This program is open to junior scholars who completed a Ph.D. within the past 5 years. Applicants must be interested in conducting research in residence at Harvard University to revise their dissertation and prepare it for publication. Preference is given to research projects exploring the understudied histories of modern science and technology in Korea and Japan, but all proposals concerning the development of science and technology in post-19th century east Asia are eligible. Applicants from women and minority candidates are strongly encouraged.

Financial data The stipend is $43,000.

Duration 1 academic year.

Additional information Fellows are provided with office space and access to the libraries and resources of Harvard University. They are invited to participate in the academic life of the Departments of East Asian Languages and Civilizations and the History of Science. Fellows are expected to reside in the Cambridge/Boston area during the term of the fellowship; work on revising their dissertation for publication; teach or collaborate on a course related to the history of modern science and/or technology in east Asia; and give at least 1 presentation of research to faculty and graduate students in East Asian Languages and Civilizations and the History of Science.

Number awarded 1 each year.

Deadline February of each year.

[1273] POSTDOCTORAL FELLOWSHIPS AT FDA

National Science Foundation
Directorate for Engineering
Attn: Division of Chemical, Bioengineering, Environmental, and Transport Systems
4201 Wilson Boulevard, Room 565S
Arlington, VA 22230
(703) 292-7942 Fax: (703) 292-9098
TDD: (800) 281-8749 E-mail: lesterow@nsf.gov
Web: www.nsf.gov/funding/pgm_summ.jsp?pims_id=5605

Summary To provide an opportunity for recent postdoctorates (particularly African Americans, underrepresented minorities, women, and individuals with disabilities) to conduct research at an intramural laboratory of the U.S. Food and Drug Administration (FDA).

Eligibility Applicants for these fellowships must have held a Ph.D. degree in a science, engineering, or mathematics field of interest to NSF for no more than 3 years. They must be U.S. citizens, nationals, or permanent residents. Along with their application, they must submit a plan for full-time work at an FDA laboratory under the guidance of an FDA mentor. The program encourages applications from all citizens, including women and men, underrepresented minorities, and persons with disabilities.

Financial data Grants range up to $80,000 per year. Funding includes 85% of the fellow's stipend and fringe benefits, transportation and moving expenses (up to $3,000), up to 10% of the total as allowance to the faculty adviser for research-related expenses, and an allowance of up to 15% of the total direct costs as an administrative allowance for a sponsoring academic institution. FDA provides office space, research facilities, research costs in the form of expendable and minor equipment purchases in the host laboratory, and the time of its research staff.

Duration 1 to 2 years.

Additional information This program is also offered by the NSF Directorate for Computer and Information Science and Engineering.

Number awarded A total of 3 to 10 grants for all FDA programs is awarded each year; total funding is approximately $500,000.

Deadline March of each year.

[1274]
POSTDOCTORAL FELLOWSHIPS IN DIABETES RESEARCH

Juvenile Diabetes Research Foundation International
Attn: Grant Administrator
26 Broadway, 14th Floor
New York, NY 10004
(212) 479-7572 Toll Free: (800) 533-CURE
Fax: (212) 785-9595 E-mail: info@jdrf.org
Web: jdrf.org

Summary To provide research training to scientists (particularly African Americans, other underrepresented minorities, women, and individuals with disabilities) who are beginning their professional careers and are interested in participating in research training on the causes, treatment, prevention, or cure of diabetes or its complications.

Eligibility This program is open to postdoctorates who are interested in a career in Type 1 diabetes-relevant research. Applicants must have received their first doctoral degree (M.D., Ph.D., D.M.D., or D.V.M.) within the past 5 years and may not have a faculty appointment. There are no citizenship requirements. Applications are encouraged from women, members of minority groups underrepresented in the sciences, and people with disabilities. The proposed research training may be conducted at foreign or domestic, for-profit or nonprofit, or public or private institutions, including universities, colleges, hospitals, laboratories, units of state or local government, or eligible agencies of the federal government. Applicants must be sponsored by an investigator who is affiliated full time with an accredited institution and who agrees to supervise the applicant's training. Selection is based on the applicant's previous experience and academic record; the caliber of the proposed research; and the quality of the mentor, training program, and environment.

Financial data Stipends range from $44,764 to $59,680 per year (depending upon years of experience). In any case, the award may not exceed the salary the recipient is currently earning. Fellows also receive a research allowance of $5,500 per year.

Duration 3 years.

Additional information Fellows must devote 100% of their effort to the fellowship project.

Number awarded Varies each year.

Deadline August of each year.

[1275]
POSTDOCTORAL FELLOWSHIPS OF THE CONSORTIUM FOR FACULTY DIVERSITY

Consortium for Faculty Diversity at Liberal Arts Colleges
c/o Gettysburg College
Provost's Office
300 North Washington Street
Campus Box 410
Gettysburg, PA 17325
(717) 337-6796 E-mail: sgockows@gettysburg.edu
Web: www.gettysburg.edu/about/offices/provost/cfd

Summary To make available the facilities of liberal arts colleges to scholars, particularly African Americans and others who will enhance diversity at their college and who recently received their doctoral/advanced degree.

Eligibility This program is open to scholars in the liberal arts and engineering who are U.S. citizens or permanent residents and received the Ph.D. or M.F.A. degree within the past 5 years. Applicants must be interested in a residency at a participating institution that is part of the Consortium for a Strong Minority Presence at Liberal Arts Colleges. They must be able to enhance diversity at the institution.

Financial data Fellows receive a stipend equivalent to the average salary paid by the host college to beginning assistant professors. Modest funds are made available to finance the fellow's proposed research, subject to the usual institutional procedures.

Duration 1 year.

Additional information The following schools are participating in the program: Allegheny College, Bard College, Bowdoin College, Bryn Mawr College, Carleton College, Centenary College of Louisiana, Centre College, College of Wooster, Colorado College, Denison University, DePauw University, Dickinson College, Gettysburg College, Goucher College, Grinnell College, Gustavus Adolphus College, Hamilton College, Haverford College, Hobart and William Smith Colleges, Lafayette College, Lawrence University, Luther College, Macalester College, Mount Holyoke College, Muhlenberg College, New College of Florida, Oberlin College, Pitzer College, Pomona College, Reed College, Rhodes College, University of Richmond, Ripon College, Scripps College, St. Olaf College, Skidmore College, Smith College, Southwestern University, Swarthmore College, Transylvania University, Trinity College, Vassar College, and Wellesley College. Fellows are expected to teach at least 1 course in each academic term of residency, participate in departmental seminars, and interact with students.

Number awarded Varies each year.

Deadline October of each year.

[1276]
POSTDOCTORAL FELLOWSHIPS OF THE FORD FOUNDATION DIVERSITY FELLOWSHIP PROGRAM

National Research Council
Attn: Fellowships Office, Keck 576
500 Fifth Street, N.W.
Washington, DC 20001
(202) 334-2872 Fax: (202) 334-3419
E-mail: infofell@nas.edu
Web: sites.nationalacademies.org

Summary To provide funding for postdoctoral research to African American scholars and others whose success will increase the racial and ethnic diversity of U.S. colleges and universities.

Eligibility This program is open to U.S. citizens, permanent residents, and nationals who earned a Ph.D. or Sc.D. degree within the past 7 years and are committed to a career in teaching and research at the college or university level. The following are considered as positive factors in the selection process: evidence of superior academic achievement; promise of continuing achievement as scholars and teachers; membership in a group whose underrepresentation in the American professoriate has been severe and longstanding, including Black/African Americans, Puerto Ricans, Mexican Americans/Chicanos/Chicanas, Native American Indians, Alaska Natives (Eskimos, Aleuts, and other indigenous people of Alaska), and Native Pacific Islanders (Hawaiians, Micronesians, or Polynesians); capacity to respond in pedagogically productive ways to the learning needs of students from diverse backgrounds; sustained personal engagement with communities that are underrepresented in the academy and an ability to bring this asset to learning, teaching, and scholarship at the college and university level; and likelihood of using the diversity of human experience as an educational resource in teaching and scholarship. Eligible areas of study include most fields of the arts, sciences, humanities, or social sciences or many interdisciplinary ethnic or area studies, but not for most practice-oriented areas. Research may be conducted at an appropriate institution of higher education in the United States (normally) or abroad, including universities, museums, libraries, government or national laboratories, privately sponsored nonprofit institutes, government chartered nonprofit research organizations, or centers for advanced study. Applicants should designate a faculty member or other scholar to serve as host at the proposed fellowship institution. They are encouraged to choose a host institution other than that where they are affiliated at the time of application.

Financial data The stipend is $40,000. Funds may be supplemented by sabbatical leave pay or other sources of support that do not carry with them teaching or other responsibilities. The employing institution receives an allowance of $1,500, paid after fellowship tenure is completed; the employing institution is expected to match the grant and to use the allowance and the match to assist with the fellow's continuing research expenditures.

Duration 9 to 12 months.

Additional information Fellows may not accept another major fellowship while they are being supported by this program.

Number awarded Approximately 24 each year.

Deadline November of each year.

[1277] POSTDOCTORAL RESEARCH FELLOWSHIPS IN BIOLOGY

National Science Foundation
Directorate for Biological Sciences
Attn: Division of Biological Infrastructure
4201 Wilson Boulevard, Room 615N
Arlington, VA 22230
(703) 292-8470 Fax: (703) 292-9063
TDD: (800) 281-8749 E-mail: bio-dbi-prfb@nsf.gov
Web: www.nsf.gov

Summary To provide funding for research and training in specified areas related to biology to junior doctoral-level scientists (particularly African Americans, other underrepresented minorities, and individuals with disabilities) at sites in the United States or abroad.

Eligibility This program is open to citizens, nationals, and permanent residents of the United States who are graduate students completing a Ph.D. or who have earned the degree no earlier than 12 months preceding the deadline date. Applicants must be interested in a program of research and training in any of 4 competitive areas: 1) Broadening Participation in Biology, designed to increase the diversity of scientists by providing support for research and training to biologists with disabilities and underrepresented minority (Native American, Native Pacific Islander, Alaskan Native, African American, and Hispanic) biologists; 2) Intersections of Biology and Mathematical and Physical Sciences, for junior researchers who have conducted doctoral research in biology or physical and mathematical sciences and who present a research and training plan at the intersection of biology with mathematical and physical sciences; 3) National Plant Genome Initiative Postdoctoral Research Fellowships, for postdoctoral training in plant improvement and associated sciences such as physiology and pathology, quantitative genetics, or computational biology; or 4) International Postdoctoral Research Fellowships in Biology, for junior biologists who wish to obtain training at a foreign institution. They must identify a sponsor at a host institution who will serve as a mentor for their training program.

Financial data Grants are $69,000 per year, including $54,000 as a stipend for the fellow and $15,000 as a fellowship allowance that is intended to cover direct research expenses, facilities and other institutional resources, and fringe benefits.

Duration Fellowships in the area of Intersections of Biology and Mathematical and Physical Sciences are normally for 24 months; fellowships in other areas are normally for 36 months.

Number awarded Approximately 15 fellowships are awarded each year in each competitive area.

Deadline October of each year.

[1278]
POSTDOCTORAL RESEARCH TRAINING FELLOWSHIPS IN EPILEPSY

Epilepsy Foundation
Attn: Research Department
8301 Professional Place
Landover, MD 20785-2353
(301) 459-3700 Toll Free: (800) EFA-1000
Fax: (301) 577-2684 TDD: (800) 332-2070
E-mail: grants@efa.org
Web: www.epilepsyfoundation.org

Summary To provide funding for a program of postdoctoral training to academic physicians and scientists (particularly African Americans, other minorities, women, and individuals with disabilities) who are committed to epilepsy research.

Eligibility Applicants must have a doctoral degree (M.D., Sc.D., Ph.D., or equivalent) and be a clinical or postdoctoral fellow at a university, medical school, research institution, or medical center. They must be interested in participating in a training experience and research project that has potential significance for understanding the causes, treatment, or consequences of epilepsy. The program is geared toward applicants who will be trained in research in epilepsy rather than those who use epilepsy as a tool for research in other fields. Equal consideration is given to applicants interested in acquiring experience either in basic laboratory research or in the conduct of human clinical studies. Academic faculty holding the rank of instructor or higher are not eligible, nor are graduate or medical students, medical residents, permanent government employees, or employees of private industry. Applications from women, members of minority groups, and people with disabilities are especially encouraged. U.S. citizenship is not required, but the project must be conducted in the United States. Selection is based on scientific quality of the proposed research, a statement regarding its relevance to epilepsy, the applicant's qualifications, the preceptor's qualifications, and the adequacy of facility and related epilepsy programs at the institution.

Financial data The grant is $45,000. No indirect costs are covered.

Duration 1 year.

Additional information Support for this program is provided by many individuals, families, and corporations, especially the American Epilepsy Society, Abbott Laboratories, Ortho-McNeil Pharmaceutical, and Pfizer Inc. The fellowship must be carried out at a facility in the United States where there is an ongoing epilepsy research program.

Number awarded Varies each year.

Deadline August of each year.

[1279]
PRIZE FOR A FACULTY MEMBER FOR RESEARCH IN AN UNDERGRADUATE INSTITUTION

American Physical Society
Attn: Honors Program
One Physics Ellipse
College Park, MD 20740-3844
(301) 209-3268 Fax: (301) 209-0865
E-mail: honors@aps.org
Web: www.aps.org

Summary To recognize and reward physics faculty members (particularly African Americans, other underrepresented minorities, and women) who are at undergraduate institutions.

Eligibility Nominees for this prize must be members of the physics faculty at undergraduate institutions. They must have contributed substantially to physics research and provided inspirational guidance and encouragement to undergraduate students participating in that research. Nominations of qualified women and members of underrepresented minority groups are especially encouraged.

Financial data The prize consists of a stipend of $5,000 to the recipient, a grant of $5,000 to the recipient's institution for research, a certificate citing the accomplishments of the recipient, and an allowance for travel expenses to the meeting of the American Physical Society (APS) at which the prize is presented.

Duration The prize is presented annually.

Additional information This prize was established in 1984 by a grant from the Research Corporation.

Number awarded 1 each year.

Deadline June of each year.

[1280]
PUBLIC HEALTH SERVICE SMALL BUSINESS INNOVATION RESEARCH PROGRAM

Public Health Service
c/o National Institutes of Health
Attn: SBIR/STTR Program Coordinator
6705 Rockledge Drive, Room 3534
Bethesda, MD 20892-7911
(301) 435-2688 Fax: (301) 480-0146
TDD: (301) 451-0088 E-mail: sbir@od.nih.gov
Web: grants.nih.gov/grants/funding/sbir.html

Summary To support small businesses (especially those owned by African Americans, other minorities, and persons with disabilities) that have the technological experience to contribute to the research and development mission of components of the U.S. Public Health Service.

Eligibility For the purposes of this program, a "small business" is defined as a firm that is that is independently owned and operated for profit, not dominant in the field in which it is operating, and meets the size standard of 500 employees or less. The primary employment of the principal investigator must be with the firm at the time of award and during the conduct of the proposed project. Individuals from underrepresented racial and ethnic groups as well as individuals with disabilities are encouraged to apply. Research is supported in all areas of biomedical and behavioral science that fall within the mission of the agency. Selection is based on scientific and technical merit of the proposed project, availability of funds, and relevance of the proposed project to program priorities.

Financial data Support is offered in 2 phases. In phase 1, awards normally do not exceed $150,000 (for both direct and indirect costs); in phase 2, awards normally do not exceed $1,000,000 (including both direct and indirect costs).

Duration Phase 1 awards may extend up to 6 months; phase 2 awards may extend up to 2 years.

Additional information Grants are offered by 4 components of the Public Health Service (PHS): National Institutes of Health (NIH), Centers for Disease Control and Prevention

(CDC), Food and Drug Administration (FDA), and Administration for Children and Families (ACF). For information on the research interests of each of those components and their various agencies, contact the sponsor. Actual solicitations are available only from that address.

Number awarded Varies each year.

Deadline April, August, or December of each year.

[1281]
PUBLIC HEALTH SERVICE SMALL BUSINESS TECHNOLOGY TRANSFER GRANTS

Public Health Service
c/o National Institutes of Health
Attn: SBIR/STTR Program Coordinator
6705 Rockledge Drive, Room 3534
Bethesda, MD 20892-7911
(301) 435-2688 Fax: (301) 480-0146
TDD: (301) 451-0088 E-mail: sbir@od.nih.gov
Web: grants.nih.gov/grants/funding/sbir.html

Summary To provide financial support to cooperative research and development projects carried out between small business concerns (especially those owned by African Americans, other minorities, and persons with disabilities) and research institutions in areas of concern to the research and development mission of components of the U.S. Public Health Service.

Eligibility For the purposes of this program, a "small business" is defined as a firm that is organized for profit with a location in the United States; is in the legal form of an individual proprietorship, partnership, limited liability company, corporation, joint venture, association, trust, or cooperative; is at least 51% owned and controlled by 1 or more individuals who are citizens or permanent residents of the United States; and has (including its affiliates) fewer than 500 employees. Unlike the Public Health Service Small Business Innovation Research Grants, the primary employment of the principal investigator does not need to be with the business concern. This program, however, requires that the small business apply in collaboration with a nonprofit research institution for conduct of a project that has potential for commercialization. Principal investigators from the nonprofit research institution must commit at least 10% of their effort to the project. At least 40% of the work must be performed by the small business and at least 30% of the work must be performed by the research institution. Individuals from underrepresented racial and ethnic groups as well as individuals with disabilities are encouraged to apply. Research is supported in all areas of biomedical and behavioral science that fall within the mission of the agency. Selection is based on scientific and technical merit of the proposed project, availability of funds, and relevance of the proposed project to program priorities.

Financial data Support is offered in 2 phases. In phase 1, awards normally do not exceed $150,000 (for both direct and indirect costs); in phase 2, awards normally do not exceed $1,000,000 (including both direct and indirect costs).

Duration Phase 1 awards may extend up to 6 months; phase 2 awards may extend up to 2 years.

Additional information Grants are offered by 4 components of the Public Health Service (PHS): National Institutes of Health (NIH), Centers for Disease Control and Prevention (CDC), Food and Drug Administration (FDA), and Administration for Children and Families (ACF). For information on the research interests of each of those components and their various agencies, contact the sponsor. Actual solicitations are available only from that address.

Number awarded Varies each year.

Deadline April, August, or December of each year.

[1282]
R. ROBERT & SALLY D. FUNDERBURG RESEARCH AWARD IN GASTRIC CANCER

American Gastroenterological Association
Attn: AGA Research Foundation
Research Awards Manager
4930 Del Ray Avenue
Bethesda, MD 20814-2512
(301) 222-4012 Fax: (301) 654-5920
E-mail: awards@gastro.org
Web: www.gastro.org/aga-foundation/grants

Summary To provide funding to established investigators (particularly African Americans, other minorities, and women) who are working on research that enhances fundamental understanding of gastric cancer pathobiology.

Eligibility This program is open to faculty at accredited North American institutions who have established themselves as independent investigators in the field of gastric biology, pursuing novel approaches to gastric mucosal cell biology, including the fields of gastric mucosal cell biology, regeneration and regulation of cell growth, inflammation as precancerous lesions, genetics of gastric carcinoma, oncogenes in gastric epithelial malignancies, epidemiology of gastric cancer, etiology of gastric epithelial malignancies, or clinical research in diagnosis or treatment of gastric carcinoma. Applicants must be individual members of the American Gastroenterological Association (AGA). Women and minority investigators are strongly encouraged to apply. Selection is based on the novelty, feasibility, and significance of the proposal. Preference is given to novel approaches.

Financial data The grant is $50,000 per year. Funds are to be used for the salary of the investigator. Indirect costs are not allowed.

Duration 2 years.

Number awarded 1 each year.

Deadline August of each year.

[1283]
RALPH J. BUNCHE AWARD

American Political Science Association
1527 New Hampshire Avenue, N.W.
Washington, DC 20036-1206
(202) 483-2512 Fax: (202) 483-2657
E-mail: apsa@apsanet.org
Web: www.apsanet.org/content_4129.cfm?navID=756

Summary To recognize and reward outstanding scholarly books on ethnic/cultural pluralism.

Eligibility Eligible to be nominated (by publishers or individuals) are scholarly political science books issued the previous year that explore issues of ethnic and/or cultural pluralism.

Financial data The award is $1,000.

Duration The award is presented annually.

Additional information This award was first presented in 1978.

Number awarded 1 each year.

Deadline January of each year for nominations from individuals; February of each year for nominations from publishers.

[1284]
REGINALD F. LEWIS FELLOWSHIP FOR LAW TEACHING

Harvard Law School
Attn: Lewis Committee
Griswold Two South
1525 Massachusetts Avenue
Cambridge, MA 02138
(617) 495-3109 E-mail: oaa@law.harvard.edu
Web: www.law.harvard.edu

Summary To provide funding to law school graduates, especially those of color, who are preparing for a career in law teaching and are interested in a program of research and training at Harvard Law School.

Eligibility This program is open to recent graduates of law school who have demonstrated an interest in law scholarship and teaching. Applicants must be interested in spending time in residence at Harvard Law School where they will audit courses, attend workshops, and follow a schedule of research under the sponsorship of the committee. The program encourages the training of prospective law teachers who will enhance the diversity of the profession and especially encourages applications from candidates of color.

Financial data The stipend is $50,000 per year.

Duration 2 years.

Number awarded 1 each year.

Deadline February of each year.

[1285]
RESEARCH AND EDUCATION PROGRAM FOR HISTORICALLY BLACK COLLEGES AND UNIVERSITIES AND MINORITY-SERVING INSTITUTIONS

Army Research Office
Attn: Army Contracting Command-Aberdeen Proving Ground
4300 South Miami Boulevard
P.O. Box 12211
Research Triangle Park, NC 27709-2211
(919) 549-4385 Fax: (919) 549-4388
E-mail: lanelle.t.shanks.civ@mail.mil
Web: www.arl.army.mil/www/default.cfm?Page=362

Summary To provide funding to researchers at Historically Black Colleges and Universities (HBCUs) and other Minority-Serving Institutions (MIs) for the purchase of equipment.

Eligibility This program is open to researchers at HBCUs and MIs that have degree-granting programs in science, mathematics, and/or engineering. Applicants must be seeking funding for the acquisition of major equipment to augment current or to develop new research capabilities to support research in technical areas of interest to the Department of Defense. That includes basic equipment for use in research and education, as well as more sophisticated equipment and instrumentation (including software).

Financial data Grants range from $50,000 to $500,000.

Duration Grants are typically 1 year in length.

Additional information This program is also offered by the Air Force Office of Scientific Research and the Office of Naval Research.

Number awarded Varies each year; recently, $25 million was available for this program.

Deadline August of each year.

[1286]
RESEARCH AND TRAINING FELLOWSHIPS IN EPILEPSY FOR CLINICIANS

Epilepsy Foundation
Attn: Research Department
8301 Professional Place
Landover, MD 20785-2353
(301) 459-3700 Toll Free: (800) EFA-1000
Fax: (301) 577-2684 TDD: (800) 332-2070
E-mail: grants@efa.org
Web: www.epilepsyfoundation.org

Summary To provide funding to clinically-trained professionals (particularly African Americans, other minorities, women, and individuals with disabilities) who are interested in gaining additional training in order to develop an epilepsy research program.

Eligibility Applicants must have an M.D., D.O., Ph.D., D.Sc., or equivalent degree and be a clinical or postdoctoral fellow at a university, medical school, or other appropriate research institution. Holders of other doctoral-level degrees (e.g., Pharm.D., D.S.N.) may also be eligible. Candidates must be interested in a program of research training that may include mechanisms of epilepsy, novel therapeutic approaches, clinical trials, development of new technologies, or behavioral and psychosocial impact of epilepsy. The training program may consist of both didactic training and a supervised research experience that is designed to develop the necessary knowledge and skills in the chosen area of research and foster the career goals of the candidate. Academic faculty holding the rank of instructor or higher are not eligible, nor are graduate or medical students, medical residents, permanent government employees, or employees of private industry. Applications from women, members of minority groups, and people with disabilities are especially encouraged. U.S. citizenship is not required, but the project must be conducted in the United States. Selection is based on the quality of the proposed research training program, the applicant's qualifications, the preceptor's qualifications, and the adequacy of clinical training, research facilities, and other epilepsy-related programs at the institution.

Financial data The grant is $50,000 per year. No indirect costs are provided.

Duration Up to 2 years.

Additional information Support for this program is provided by many individuals, families, and corporations, especially the American Epilepsy Society, Abbott Laboratories, Ortho-McNeil Pharmaceutical, and Pfizer Inc. Grantees are expected to dedicate at least 50% of their time to research training and conducting research.

Number awarded Varies each year.

Deadline September of each year.

[1287]
RESIDENT RESEARCH GRANTS

J. Robert Gladden Orthopaedic Society
Attn: Scientific Committee
6300 North River Road, Suite 727
Rosemont, IL 60018-4226
(847) 698-1633 Fax: (847) 823-4921
E-mail: jrgos@aaos.org
Web: www.gladdensociety.org

Summary To provide funding to members of the J. Robert Gladden Orthopaedic Society (JRGOS) who medical residents, African Americans or from another underrepresented minority group, and interested in conducting a research project.

Eligibility This program is open to members of underrepresented minority groups who are medical residents and JRGOS members. Applicants must be seeking funding to conduct a research project with a measurable outcome that can be achieved at the end of the grant cycle. They must be able to demonstrate that their proposed project correlates with the mission and goals of the society. Preference is given to applicants planning to work with a senior JRGOS member.

Financial data The grant is $10,000.

Duration 1 year.

Additional information This program is sponsored by DePuy/Johnson & Johnson.

Number awarded 1 or more each year.

Deadline September of each year.

[1288]
ROBERT L. FANTZ MEMORIAL AWARD

American Psychological Foundation
750 First Street, N.E.
Washington, DC 20002-4242
(202) 336-5843 Fax: (202) 336-5812
E-mail: foundation@apa.org
Web: www.apa.org/apf/funding/fantz.aspx

Summary To provide funding to promising young investigators in psychology (particularly African Americans and individuals from other diverse groups).

Eligibility This program is open to young investigators in psychology or related disciplines. Candidates must show 1) evidence of basic scientific research or scholarly writing in perceptual-cognitive development and the development of selection attention; and 2) research and writing on the development of individuality, creativity, and free-choice of behavior. The sponsor encourages applications from individuals who represent diversity in race, ethnicity, gender, age, disability, and sexual orientation.

Financial data The award is $2,000. Funds are paid directly to the recipient's institution for equipment purchases, travel, computer resources, or other expenses related to the work recognized by the award.

Duration The award is presented annually.

Additional information This award was first presented in 1992.

Number awarded 1 each year.

Deadline Deadline not specified.

[1289]
ROBERT WOOD JOHNSON CLINICAL SCHOLARS PROGRAM

Robert Wood Johnson Foundation
c/o University of North Carolina at Chapel Hill
Department of Social Medicine
333 MacNider Hall
Chapel Hill, NC 27599-7105
(919) 843-1351 Fax: (919) 843-2666
E-mail: rwjcsp_admin@med.unc.edu
Web: rwjcsp.unc.edu

Summary To provide financial support to young physicians (particularly African Americans, other minorities, and women) who wish to conduct additional research and training in areas of importance to health care policy.

Eligibility This program is open to U.S. citizens and permanent residents who have completed residency requirements for an M.D. or D.O. degree. Applicants must be committed to a career in academic medicine, public health, health policy, or other career related to developing physician leaders and skilled researchers. They must be interested in participating in a research and training program at 1 of 4 designated universities. The program embraces racial, ethnic, and gender diversity and encourages applications from candidates with diverse backgrounds and clinical disciplines.

Financial data The stipend is $67,000 for the first year and greater for the second year. Additional support is provided for research projects and professional travel.

Duration 2 years. Interested scholars may be considered for a third year.

Additional information Currently, the participating institutions are schools of medicine at the University of California at Los Angeles, the University of Michigan, the University of Pennsylvania, and Yale University. Each institution offers a program of study with generous protected time for research.

Number awarded Up to 20 each year, including 10 supported by the Robert Wood Johnson Foundation and 10 by the U.S. Department of Veterans Affairs through VA medical centers affiliated with the participating universities.

Deadline February of each year.

[1290]
ROBERT WOOD JOHNSON FOUNDATION HEALTH AND SOCIETY SCHOLARS PROGRAM

Robert Wood Johnson Foundation
c/o New York Academy of Medicine
1216 Fifth Avenue
New York, NY 10029-5202
(212) 419-3566 Fax: (212) 419-3569
E-mail: hss@nyam.org
Web: www.healthandsocietyscholars.org

Summary To provide support to scholars (particularly African Americans and other scholars from diverse backgrounds) who from a variety of disciplines and wish to become leaders in health policy.

Eligibility This program is open to scholars who have a doctoral degree in fields that include (but are not limited to) behavioral and social sciences, biological and natural sciences, health professions, public policy, public health, history, demography, environmental sciences, urban planning, or engineering. Applicants must be U.S. citizens or permanent residents who have significant research experience. They must be interested in participating in a program at 1 of 4 universities that includes intensive seminars, mentored research, and focused training in the skills necessary for effective leadership, program implementation, and policy change. The sponsor is committed to a program that embraces diversity and inclusion across multiple dimensions of race, ethnicity, gender, age, socioeconomic background, and academic discipline; it encourages applications from candidates who will help it include diverse perspectives and experiences.

Financial data The stipend is $80,000 per year. Additional support is available for research-related expenses, training workshops, and travel to professional meetings.

Duration 2 years.

Additional information Fellows train at 1 of 4 nationally prominent universities: University of California at Berkeley (in collaboration with the University of California at San Francisco), Harvard University, Columbia University, or University of Wisconsin at Madison.

Number awarded Up to 12 each year.

Deadline September of each year.

[1291]
ROBERT WOOD JOHNSON HEALTH POLICY FELLOWSHIPS

Institute of Medicine
Attn: Health Policy Fellowships Program
500 Fifth Street, N.W.
Washington, DC 20001
(202) 334-1506 Fax: (202) 334-3862
E-mail: info@healthpolicyfellows.org
Web: www.healthpolicyfellows.org/fellowship.php

Summary To provide an opportunity for health professionals or behavioral and social scientists (particularly minorities and others with diverse backgrounds) who have an interest in health to participate in the formulation of national health policies while in residence at the Institute of Medicine (IOM) in Washington, D.C.

Eligibility This program is open to mid-career professionals from academic faculties and nonprofit health care organizations who are interested in experiencing health policy processes at the federal level. Applicants must have a background in allied health professions, biomedical sciences, dentistry, economics or other social sciences, health services organization and administration, medicine, nursing, public health, or social and behavioral health or health law. They must be sponsored by the chief executive officer of an eligible nonprofit health care organization or academic institution. Selection is based on potential for leadership in health policy, potential for future growth and career advancement, professional achievements, interpersonal and communication skills, and individual plans for incorporating the fellowship experience into specific career goals. U.S. citizenship or permanent resident status is required. Applications are especially encouraged from candidates with diverse backgrounds of race, ethnicity, gender, age, disadvantaged socioeconomic status, and discipline.

Financial data Total support for the Washington stay and continuing activities may not exceed $165,000. Grant funds may cover salary support at a level of up to $94,000 plus fringe benefits. Fellows are reimbursed for relocation expenses to and from Washington, D.C. No indirect costs are paid.

Duration The program lasts 1 year and includes an orientation in September and October; meetings in November and December with members of Congress, journalists, policy analysts, and other experts on the national political and governmental process; and working assignments from January through August. Fellows then return to their home institutions, but they receive up to 2 years of continued support for further development of health policy leadership skills.

Additional information This program, initiated in 1973, is funded by the Robert Wood Johnson Foundation.

Number awarded Up to 6 each year.

Deadline November of each year.

[1292]
RUTH L. KIRSCHSTEIN NATIONAL RESEARCH SERVICE AWARDS FOR INDIVIDUAL POSTDOCTORAL FELLOWS

National Institutes of Health
Office of Extramural Research
Attn: Grants Information
6705 Rockledge Drive, Suite 4090
Bethesda, MD 20892-7983
(301) 435-0714 Fax: (301) 480-0525
TDD: (301) 451-5936 E-mail: grantsinfo@od.nih.gov
Web: grants.nih.gov/grants/guide/pa-files/PA-11-113.html

Summary To provide funding to postdoctoral scholars (particularly African Americans, other underrepresented minorities, and individuals with disabilities) who are interested in pursuing research training in the biomedical or behavioral sciences.

Eligibility Applicants must 1) be U.S. citizens, nationals, or permanent residents; 2) have received a Ph.D., M.D., D.O., D.D.S., D.V.M., or equivalent doctoral degree from an accredited domestic or foreign institution; 3) be interested in conducting biomedical or behavioral research; and 4) have arranged for appointment to an appropriate institution and acceptance by a sponsor who will supervise the training and research experience. The institution may be a 1) public or private institution of higher education (especially a Hispanic Serving Institution, Historically Black College or University, Tribal College or University, or Alaska Native or Native Hawaiian Serving Institution); 2) nonprofit institution; 3) for profit organization; 4) eligible agency of the federal government; or 6) foreign organization. If a foreign institution is selected as the research training site, applicants must demonstrate that it presents special opportunities for furthering research programs through the use of unusual talent, resources, populations, or environmental conditions that exist in other countries and either are not available in the United States or augment existing U.S. resources. Members of underrepresented racial and ethnic groups and individuals with disabilities are especially encouraged to apply.

Financial data The award provides an annual stipend based on the number of years of postdoctoral experience, ranging from $39,264 for less than 1 year to $54,180 for 7 or more years. For fellows sponsored by domestic nonfederal institutions, the stipend is paid through the sponsoring institution; for fellows sponsored by federal or foreign institutions, the monthly stipend is paid directly to the fellow. Institutions also receive an allowance to help defray such awardee expenses as self-only health insurance, research supplies, equipment, travel to scientific meetings, and related items; the allowance is $7,850 per 12-month period for fellows at nonfederal, nonprofit, and foreign institutions and $6,750 per 12-month period at federal laboratories and for-profit institutions. In addition, tuition and fees are reimbursed at a rate of 60%, up to $4,500; if the fellow's program supports postdoctoral individuals in formal degree-granting training, tuition is supported at the rate of 60%, up to $16,000 for an additional degree. Awards for training at a foreign site include economy or coach round-trip airfare for the fellow only; no allowance is provided for dependents.

Duration Up to 3 years.

Additional information This award is offered by all funding Institutes and Centers of the National Institutes of Health (NIH) as part of the National Research Service Award (NRSA) program, originally established in 1974.

Number awarded Varies each year; recently, 603 awards were made through this program.

Deadline April, August, or December of each year.

[1293] RUTH L. KIRSCHSTEIN NATIONAL RESEARCH SERVICE AWARDS FOR INDIVIDUAL SENIOR FELLOWS

National Institutes of Health
Office of Extramural Research
Attn: Grants Information
6705 Rockledge Drive, Suite 4090
Bethesda, MD 20892-7983
(301) 435-0714 Fax: (301) 480-0525
TDD: (301) 451-5936 E-mail: grantsinfo@od.nih.gov
Web: grants.nih.gov/grants/guide/pa-files/PA-11-114.html

Summary To provide funding for mentored research training to experienced scientists (particularly African Americans, other underrepresented minorities, and individuals with disabilities) who wish to make major changes in the direction of their research careers.

Eligibility This program is open to U.S. citizens, nationals, and permanent residents who have a doctoral or equivalent degree from an accredited domestic or foreign institution and at least 7 subsequent years of relevant research or professional experience. Applications may be submitted on behalf of the candidates by a sponsoring institution, which may be a 1) public or private institution of higher education (especially a Hispanic Serving Institution, Historically Black College or University, Tribal College or University, or Alaska Native or Native Hawaiian Serving Institutions); 2) nonprofit institution; 3) for profit organization; 4) eligible agency of the federal government; or 6) foreign organization. If a foreign institution is selected as the research training site, applicants must demonstrate that it presents special opportunities for furthering research programs through the use of unusual talent, resources, populations, or environmental conditions that exist in other countries and either are not available in the United States or augment existing U.S. resources. Members of diverse racial and ethnic groups, individuals with disabilities, and individuals from disadvantaged backgrounds are especially encouraged to apply.

Financial data The award provides an annual stipend based on the number of years of postdoctoral experience, ranging from $39,264 for less than 1 year to $54,180 for 7 or more years. For fellows sponsored by domestic non-federal institutions, the stipend is paid through the sponsoring institution; for fellows sponsored by federal or foreign institutions, the monthly stipend is paid directly to the fellow. Institutions also receive an allowance to help defray such awardee expenses as self-only health insurance, research supplies, equipment, travel to scientific meetings, and related items; the allowance is $7,850 per 12-month period for fellows at non-federal, nonprofit, and foreign institutions and $6,750 per 12-month period at federal laboratories and for-profit institutions. In addition, tuition and fees are reimbursed at a rate of 60%, up to $4,500; if the fellow's program supports postdoctoral individuals in formal degree-granting training, tuition is supported at the rate of 60%, up to $16,000 for an additional degree. The initial 12 months of National Research Service Award postdoctoral support carries a service payback requirement, which can be fulfilled by continued training under the award or by engaging in other health-related research training, health-related research, or health-related teaching. Fellows who fail to fulfill the payback requirement of 1 month of acceptable service for each month of the initial 12 months of support received must repay all funds received with interest.

Duration Up to 2 years.

Additional information This program is offered by 11 components of the National Institutes of Health: the National Institute on Aging, the National Institute on Alcohol Abuse and Alcoholism, the National Institute of Arthritis and Musculoskeletal and Skin Diseases, the National Cancer Institute, the National Institute of Dental and Craniofacial Research, the National Institute of Environmental Health Sciences, the National Heart, Lung, and Blood Institute, the National Institute of General Medical Sciences, the National Human Genome Research Institute, the National Institute of Neurological Disorders and Stroke, and the National Institute of Nursing Research.

Number awarded Varies each year.

Deadline April, August, or December of each year.

[1294] SAN FRANCISCO INTERNATIONAL LGBT FILM FESTIVAL PRIZES

Frameline
Attn: Festival
145 Ninth Street, Suite 300
San Francisco, CA 94103
(415) 703-8650 Fax: (415) 861-1404
E-mail: info@frameline.org
Web: www.frameline.org

Summary To recognize and reward outstanding films of interest to the lesbian, gay, bisexual, and transgender (LGBT) audience, particularly those produced by people of color or women.

Eligibility This competition is open to directors of films by, about, and of interest to LGBT people. Applicants must submit previews of their work on DVD or VHS in the following categories: narrative feature films (40 minutes and longer), documentary feature films (40 minutes and longer), and shorts (all films less than 40 minutes in length). The program actively seeks out work by women and people of color. Recently, awards have been presented for best feature film, best documentary film, and best short film.

Financial data Awards are $2,000 for best feature and best documentary and $1,000 for best short film.

Duration The awards are presented annually.

Additional information No fees are charged for the early deadline. Standard fees are $35 for the regular deadline, $50 for the late deadline, or $55 for the extended deadline. Student fees are $15 for regular, late, and extended deadlines. Fees are waived for youth up to 18 years of age.

Number awarded 3 each year.

Deadline December of each year for the early deadline; January of each year for the regular deadline; mid-February for the late deadline; and the end of February for the extended deadline.

[1295]
SARA WHALEY BOOK PRIZE

National Women's Studies Association
Attn: Book Prizes
11 East Mount Royal Avenue, Suite 100
Baltimore, MD 21202
(410) 528-0355 Fax: (410) 528-0357
E-mail: awards@nwsa.org
Web: www.nwsa.org/content.asp?pl=16&contentid=16

Summary To recognize and reward members of the National Women's Studies Association (NWSA), particularly African Americans and other women of color, who have written outstanding books on topics related to women and labor.

Eligibility This award is available to NWSA members who submit a book manuscript that relates to women and labor, including migration and women's paid jobs, illegal immigration and women's work, impact of AIDS on women's employment, trafficking of women and women's employment, women and domestic work, or impact of race on women's work. Both senior scholars (who have issued at least 2 books and published the entry within the past year) and junior scholars (who have a publication contract or a book in production) are eligible. Women of color of U.S. or international origin are encouraged to apply.

Financial data The award is $2,000.

Duration The awards are presented annually.

Additional information This award was first presented in 2008.

Number awarded 2 each year: 1 to a senior scholar and 1 to a junior scholar.

Deadline April of each year.

[1296]
SBE POSTDOCTORAL RESEARCH FELLOWSHIPS

National Science Foundation
Directorate for Social, Behavioral, and Economic Sciences
Attn: Office of Multidisciplinary Activities
4201 Wilson Boulevard, Room 907.09
Arlington, VA 22230
(703) 292-4672 Fax: (703) 292-9083
TDD: (800) 281-8749 E-mail: fchowdhu@nsf.gov
Web: www.nsf.gov

Summary To provide financial assistance for postdoctoral research training to African American and other underrepresented minority scientists in fields of interest to the Directorate for Social, Behavioral, and Economic Sciences (SBE) of the National Science Foundation (NSF).

Eligibility This program is open to U.S. citizens, nationals, and permanent residents who completed a doctorate within the past 24 months but are not already in a full-time tenure-track faculty position. Applicants may be interested in either of 2 tracks offered by this program: 1) Broadening Participation, to increase involvement in social, behavioral, and economic research by members of ethnic groups that are currently underrepresented, including Native Americans (Alaska Natives and American Indians), African Americans, Hispanics, and Native Pacific Islanders; and/or 2) Interdisciplinary Research in which at least 1 of the disciplines is an SBE science. Proposals must involve research training to be conducted at any appropriate U.S. or foreign nonprofit institution (government laboratory, institution of higher education, national laboratory, or public or private research institute), but not at the same institution where the doctorate was obtained. For the first track, applications must include a statement on how the fellowship will help broaden the participation of scientists from currently underrepresented groups in the United States. For the second track, applications must include a statement on why the project requires interdisciplinary training beyond the core doctoral experiences.

Financial data Grants include an annual stipend of $45,000, a research and travel allowance of $10,000 per year, an institutional allowance at the awardees current federal negotiated indirect cost rate, and additional travel expenses up to $10,000 if the project includes an international component.

Duration 2 years.

Number awarded Up to 15 each year.

Deadline October of each year.

[1297]
SCHOLARLY EDITIONS AND TRANSLATIONS GRANTS

National Endowment for the Humanities
Attn: Division of Research Programs
1100 Pennsylvania Avenue, N.W., Room 318
Washington, DC 20506
(202) 606-8200 Toll Free: (800) NEH-1121
Fax: (202) 606-8204 TDD: (866) 372-2930
E-mail: editions@neh.gov
Web: www.neh.gov

Summary To provide funding to scholars (particularly those at Minority Serving Institutions) and organizations interested in preparing texts and documents in the humanities.

Eligibility This program is open to 1) U.S. citizens and foreign nationals who have been living in the United States or its jurisdictions for at least 3 years; 2) state and local governmental agencies; and 3) nonprofit, tax-exempt institutions and organizations in the United States. It supports the preparation of editions and translations of pre-existing texts and documents of value to the humanities that are currently inaccessible or available in inadequate editions. Projects must be undertaken by a team of at least 1 editor or translator and 1 other staff member. Grants typically support editions and translations of significant literary, philosophical, and historical materials, but other types of work, such as the editing of musical notation, are also eligible. Selection is based on 1) the intellectual significance of the project, including its potential contribution to scholarship in the humanities, the likelihood that it will stimulate new research, its relationship to larger themes in the humanities, and the significance of the material on which the project is based; 2) the appropriateness of the research methods, critical apparatus, and editorial policies; the appropriateness of selection criteria; the thoroughness and feasibility of the work plan; and the quality of the samples; 3) the qualifications, expertise, and levels of commitment of the project director and key project staff or contributors, and the appropriateness of the staff to the goals of the project; 4) the promise of quality, usefulness, and impact on scholarship of any resulting publication or other product; and 5) the potential for success, including the likelihood that the project will be successfully completed within the projected time frame. The program encourages submission of applications from faculty at Historically Black Colleges and Universities, Hispanic Serving Institutions, and Tribal Colleges and Universities.

Financial data Grants range from $50,000 to $100,000 per year. The use of federal matching funds in encouraged. Normally, support does not exceed 80% of total costs.

Duration 1 to 3 years.

Number awarded Approximately 26 each year.

Deadline December of each year.

[1298]
SCHOLARS IN HEALTH POLICY RESEARCH PROGRAM

Robert Wood Johnson Foundation
c/o Boston University Health Policy Institute
53 Bay State Road
Boston, MA 02215-2197
(617) 353-9220 Fax: (617) 353-9227
E-mail: rwjf@bu.edu
Web: www.healthpolicyscholars.org

Summary To provide support for postdoctoral training in health policy to scholars (particularly African Americans, other underrepresented minorities, and women) in economics, political science, and sociology.

Eligibility This program is open to scholars who have a doctoral degree in economics, political science, or sociology. Applicants must have earned their degree during the past 5 years and be U.S. citizens or permanent residents. Preference is given to applicants who have not worked previously in the areas of health or health policy research. Selection is based on the applicant's commitment to a health policy career, quality of the past research, capability to undertake this challenging program, recommendations, and potential to contribute creatively to future U.S. health policies. The program embraces racial, ethnic, and gender diversity and encourages applications from candidates from groups that historically have been underrepresented in the 3 disciplines of interest.

Financial data The stipend is $89,000 per year.

Duration 2 years.

Additional information Fellows train at 1 of 3 nationally prominent academic institutions: University of California at Berkeley (in collaboration with the University of California at San Francisco), Harvard University, or the University of Michigan. There, they have the opportunity to work closely with faculty from the social sciences, as well as from medicine, public health, and public policy. Specific activities vary by institution but generally include seminars, workshops, tutorials, independent research projects, and policy placements in local or state government.

Number awarded Up to 9 each year.

Deadline October of each year.

[1299]
SCHOMBURG CENTER SCHOLARS-IN-RESIDENCE PROGRAM

New York Public Library
Attn: Schomburg Center for Research in Black Culture
515 Malcolm X Boulevard
New York, NY 10037-1801
(212) 491-2218 Fax: (212) 491-6760
Web: www.nypl.org/locations/tid/64/node/131

Summary To provide financial support for research and writing on the history, literature, and cultures of the peoples of Africa and the African Diaspora at the Schomburg Center of the New York Public Library.

Eligibility This program is open to 1) scholars studying the history, literature, and culture of the peoples of African descent from a humanistic perspective; and 2) professionals in fields related to the sponsor's collections and program activities. Projects in the social sciences, psychology, science and technology, education, and religion are eligible if they utilize a humanistic approach and contribute to humanistic knowledge. Applicants must be U.S. citizens or foreign nationals who have resided in the United States for at least 3 years. Selection is based on qualifications of the applicant, quality and feasibility of the project plan, importance of the proposed project to the applicant's field and to the humanities, relationship of the project to the humanities, relationship of the project to the resources of the Schomburg Center, likelihood that the project will be completed successfully, and provisions for making the results of the project available to scholars and to the public at large.

Financial data The stipend is $30,000.

Duration 6 months.

Additional information This program is made possible by grants from the National Endowment for the Humanities, the Andrew W. Mellon Foundation, the Ford Foundation, and the Samuel I. Newhouse Foundation. Participants in the program must be in residence at the Schomburg Center of the New York Public Library on a full-time basis. They may not hold other major fellowships/grants or be employed during the residency. No support is available to students conducting research leading to a degree.

Number awarded Up to 6 each year.

Deadline October of each year.

[1300]
SHORT-TERM RESEARCH EDUCATION PROGRAM TO INCREASE DIVERSITY IN HEALTH-RELATED RESEARCH

National Heart, Lung, and Blood Institute
Attn: Division of Cardiovascular Diseases
6701 Rockledge Drive
Bethesda, MD 20892-7940
(301) 435-0535 Fax: (301) 480-1454
TDD: (301) 451-0088 E-mail: carlsonde@nhlbi.nih.gov
Web: grants.nih.gov

Summary To provide funding to African Americans and members of other underrepresented groups who are interested in conducting a research education program relevant to the mission of the National Heart, Lung, and Blood Institute (NHLBI).

Eligibility This program is open to principal investigators at U.S. domestic institutions (universities, colleges, hospitals, laboratories, units of state and local governments, and eligible agencies of the federal government) who are interested in conducting a research education program related to activities of NHLBI. Applications are especially encouraged from principal investigators who qualify as underrepresented: 1) a member of an ethnic or racial group shown to be underrepresented in health-related sciences on a national basis; 2) an individual with a disability; or 3) an individual from a disadvantaged background, including those from a low-income family and those from a social, cultural, and/or educational environment that has inhibited them from preparation for a research career. The proposed education program must encourage the participation of undergraduate and health professional students who are also currently underrepresented in the biomedical, clinical, and behavioral sciences. Students participating in the program are not required to be enrolled at the sponsoring institution.

Financial data Grants depend on the nature of the project and the number of student participants. Maximum total direct costs should not exceed $319,000. Compensation to participating students must conform to the established salary and wage policies of the institution. Facilities and administrative costs may be reimbursed at the rate of 8% of total direct costs.

Duration Up to 5 years.

Number awarded 3 to 5 each year; a total of $900,000 is available for this program annually.

Deadline Letters of intent must be submitted by January of each year; final applications are due in February.

[1301] SMALL GRANTS FOR NEW INVESTIGATORS TO PROMOTE DIVERSITY IN HEALTH-RELATED RESEARCH

National Institute of Diabetes and Digestive and Kidney Diseases
Attn: Office of Minority Health Research Coordination
6707 Democracy Boulevard, Room 906-B
Bethesda, MD 20892-5454
(301) 594-9652 Fax: (301) 594-9358
TDD: (301) 451-0088 E-mail: mcbrydekd@mailnih.gov
Web: grants.nih.gov/grants/guide/pa-files/PAR-13-074

Summary To provide funding to new investigators from underrepresented groups (e.g., African Americans) who are interested in conducting a research project in fields of interest to designated components of the National Institutes of Health (NIH).

Eligibility This program is open to U.S. citizens, nationals, and permanent residents who 1) have a health professional doctoral degree (e.g., M.D., D.D.S., D.O., D.V.M., O.D., Psy.D., Dr.P.H.); 2) have at least 2 to 4 years of postdoctoral research experience; 3) qualify as new investigators; and 4) belong to a population group nationally underrepresented in biomedical or behavioral research, including members of designated racial and ethnic groups (e.g., African Americans, Hispanics, Native Americans, Alaska Natives, Hawaiian Natives, and non-Asian Pacific Islanders), individual with disabilities, or individuals from a disadvantaged background (defined to include those who come from a low-income family and those who come from a social, cultural, and/or educational environment that has inhibited them from obtaining the knowledge, skills, and abilities necessary to develop and participate in a research career). Applicants must be interested in conducting a research project in areas of interest to the NIH National Institute of Diabetes and Digestive and Kidney Diseases (NIDDK), National Institute of Mental Health (NIMH), or Office of Dietary Supplements (ODS). Those include, for NIKKD, diabetes, endocrinology, metabolism, digestive diseases, hepatology, obesity, nutrition, kidney, urology, or hematology; for NIMH, mental disorders; or ODS, dietary supplements and/or their ingredients.

Financial data Direct costs are limited to $125,000 per year. Facilities and administrative costs are reimbursed at 8% of modified total direct costs.

Duration 3 years; nonrenewable.

Number awarded Varies each year.

Deadline Letters of intent are due in May of each year; completed applications may be submitted in June.

[1302] SOCIETY OF PEDIATRIC PSYCHOLOGY DIVERSITY RESEARCH GRANT

American Psychological Association
Attn: Division 54 (Society of Pediatric Psychology)
c/o Anna Maria Patino-Fernandez
University of Miami School of Medicine
Mailman Center for Child Development
Division of Clinical Psychology
1601 N.W. 12th Avenue, 4018B
Miami, FL 33136-1005
(305) 243-6837 Fax: (305) 243-8470
E-mail: Apatino-fernandez@med.miami.edu
Web: www.apadivisions.org

Summary To provide funding to graduate student and postdoctoral members of the Society of Pediatric Psychology (particularly African Americans and others who come from diverse backgrounds) who are interested in conducting research on diversity aspects of pediatric psychology.

Eligibility This program is open to current members of the society who are graduate students, fellows, or early-career (within 3 years of appointment) faculty. Applicants must be interested in conducting pediatric psychology research that features diversity-related variables, such as race or ethnicity, gender, culture, sexual orientation, language differences, socioeconomic status, and/or religiosity. Along with their application, they must submit a 2,000-word description of the project, including its purpose, methodology, predictions, and implications; a detailed budget; a current curriculum vitae, and (for students) a curriculum vitae of the faculty research mentor and a letter of support from that mentor. Selection is based on relevance to diversity in child health (5 points), significance of the study (5 points), study methods and procedures (10 points), and investigator qualifications (10 points).

Financial data Grants up to $1,000 are available. Funds may not be used for convention or meeting travel, indirect costs, stipends of principal investigators, or costs associated with manuscript preparation.

Duration The grant is presented annually.

Additional information The Society of Pediatric Psychology is Division 54 of the American Psychological Association (APA). This grant was first presented in 2008.

Number awarded 1 each year.

Deadline September of each year.

[1303]
SONIA KOVALEVSKY HIGH SCHOOL MATHEMATICS DAYS GRANTS

Association for Women in Mathematics
11240 Waples Mill Road, Suite 200
Fairfax, VA 22030
(703) 934-0163 Fax: (703) 359-7562
E-mail: awm@awm-math.org
Web: sites.google.com

Summary To provide funding to faculty at colleges and universities (particularly Historically Black Colleges and Universities) who wish to conduct Sonia Kovalevsky High School and Middle School Mathematics Days.

Eligibility Faculty and staff at universities and colleges may apply for these grants to support Sonia Kovalevsky High School and Middle School Mathematics Days; staff at Historically Black Colleges and Universities are particularly encouraged to apply. Programs targeted towards inner-city or rural high schools are especially welcomed. The proposed activity should consist of workshops, talks, and problem-solving competitions for female high school or middle school students and their teachers (both women and men).

Financial data The maximum grant is $3,000; most range from $1,500 to $2,200. Funds must be used for direct costs for the activity. Stipends and personnel costs are not permitted for organizers. Reimbursement for indirect costs or fringe benefits is not allowed.

Duration The grants are awarded annually.

Additional information This program is supported by grants from the National Science Foundation.

Number awarded 12 to 20 each year.

Deadline August or February of each year.

[1304]
STANFORD HUMANITIES CENTER EXTERNAL FACULTY FELLOWSHIPS

Stanford Humanities Center
Attn: Fellowship Administrator
424 Santa Teresa Street
Stanford, CA 94305-4015
(650) 723-3054 Fax: (650) 723-1895
E-mail: rbarrick@stanford.edu
Web: shc.stanford.edu/fellowships/non-stanford-faculty

Summary To offer scholars in the humanities (particularly African Americans and other underrepresented minorities) an opportunity to conduct research and teach at Stanford University.

Eligibility External fellowships at Stanford University fall into 2 categories: 1) senior fellowships for scholars who are more than 10 years beyond receipt of the Ph.D.; and 2) junior fellowships for scholars who at the time of application are at least 3 but normally no more than 10 years beyond receipt of the Ph.D. The fields of study should be the humanities as defined in the act that established the National Foundation for the Arts and Humanities. There are no citizenship requirements; non-U.S. nationals are eligible. Scholars who are members of traditionally underrepresented groups are encouraged to apply. Applications are judged on 1) the promise of the specific research project being proposed; 2) the originality and intellectual distinction of the candidate's previous work; 3) the research project's potential interest to scholars in different fields of the humanities; and 4) the applicant's ability to engage in collegial interaction and to contribute to the discussion of presentations.

Financial data The annual stipend is up to $70,000. In addition, a housing/travel subsidy of up to $30,000, depending on size of family, is offered.

Duration 1 academic year.

Additional information Fellows are expected to make an intellectual contribution not only within the center but to humanistic studies in general at Stanford. Normally, this requirement is fulfilled by teaching an undergraduate or graduate course or seminar for 1 quarter within a particular department or program. Fellows should live within 10 miles of Stanford University. Regular attendance at center events is expected and fellows are expected to be present during the fall, winter, and spring quarters and to attend weekday lunches on a regular basis.

Number awarded 6 to 8 each year.

Deadline October of each year.

[1305]
STUDIO MUSEUM IN HARLEM ARTIST-IN-RESIDENCE PROGRAM

Studio Museum in Harlem
Attn: Education and Public Programs Department
144 West 125th Street
New York, NY 10027
(212) 864-4500, ext. 230 Fax: (212) 864-4800
Web: www.studiomuseum.org/learn/artist-in-residence

Summary To support visual artists of African and Latino descent who are interested in a residency at the Studio Museum in Harlem.

Eligibility This program is open to artists of African and Latino descent locally, nationally, or internationally. Applicants may be working in sculpture, painting, photography, printmaking, film and video, digital art, or mixed media. They must be professional artists with at least 3 years of professional commitment and currently engaged in studio work; high school, college, and graduate students are not considered. Selection is based on quality of the work, a record of exhibition and critical review, demonstration of a serious and consistent dedication to the professional practice of fine arts, evidence that the applicant is at a critical juncture in development that will be advanced by a residency, and letters of recommendation.

Financial data This fellowship provides non-living studio space, a stipend of $20,000, and a $1,000 material grant.

Duration 11 months.

Additional information Artists must spend at least 20 hours per week in their studios, exhibit their works in the museum, and conduct 2 public presentations/workshops.

Number awarded 3 each year.

Deadline March of each year.

[1306]
SYLVIA TAYLOR JOHNSON MINORITY FELLOWSHIP IN EDUCATIONAL MEASUREMENT

Educational Testing Service
Attn: Fellowships
660 Rosedale Road
MS 19-T
Princeton, NJ 08541-0001
(609) 734-5543 Fax: (609) 734-5410
E-mail: internfellowships@ets.org
Web: www.ets.org/research/fellowships

Summary To provide funding to African American and other minority scholars who are interested in conducting independent research under the mentorship of senior researchers at the Educational Testing Service (ETS).

Eligibility This program is open to scholars from diverse backgrounds (especially members of traditionally underrepresented groups such as African Americans, Hispanic/Latino Americans, and American Indians) who have earned a doctorate within the past 10 years and are U.S. citizens or permanent residents. Applicants must be prepared to conduct independent research at ETS under the mentorship of a senior researcher. They should have a commitment to education and an independent body of scholarship that signals the promise of continuing contributions to educational measurement. Projects should relate to issues involved in measurement theory, validity, natural language processing and computational linguistics, cognitive psychology, learning theory, linguistics, speech recognition and processing, teaching and classroom research, or statistics. Studies focused on issues concerning the education of minority students are especially encouraged. Selection is based on the scholar's record of accomplishment, proposed topic of research, commitment to education, and promise of continuing contributions to educational measurement.

Financial data The stipend is set in relation to compensation at the home institution. Scholars and their families also receive reimbursement for relocation expenses.

Duration Up to 2 years.

Number awarded 1 each year.

Deadline Preliminary application materials must be submitted by December of each year; final application materials are due by the end of February.

[1307]
THEODORE BLAU EARLY CAREER AWARD FOR OUTSTANDING CONTRIBUTION TO PROFESSIONAL CLINICAL PSYCHOLOGY

American Psychological Foundation
750 First Street, N.E.
Washington, DC 20002-4242
(202) 336-5843 Fax: (202) 336-5812
E-mail: foundation@apa.org
Web: www.apa.org/apf/funding/blau.aspx

Summary To recognize and reward young clinical psychologists (particularly African Americans, other minorities, women, and individuals with disabilities) who have a record of outstanding professional accomplishments.

Eligibility This award is available to clinical psychologists who are no more than 7 years past completion of their doctoral degree. Nominees must have a record of accomplishments that may include promoting the practice of clinical psychology through professional service; innovation in service delivery; novel application of applied research methodologies to professional practice; positive impact on health delivery systems; development of creative educational programs for practice; or other novel or creative activities advancing the service of the profession. Self-nominations are accepted. The sponsor encourages nominations of individuals who represent diversity in race, ethnicity, gender, age, disability, and sexual orientation.

Financial data The award is $4,000.

Duration The award is presented annually.

Additional information This award, first presented in 1998, is sponsored by Division 12 (Society of Clinical Psychology) of the American Psychological Association.

Number awarded 1 each year.

Deadline Nominations must be submitted by October of each year.

[1308]
THEODORE MILLON AWARD IN PERSONALITY PSYCHOLOGY

American Psychological Foundation
750 First Street, N.E.
Washington, DC 20002-4242
(202) 336-5843 Fax: (202) 336-5812
E-mail: foundation@apa.org
Web: www.apa.org/apf/funding/millon.aspx

Summary To recognize and reward psychologists (particularly African Americans, other minorities, women, and individuals with disabilities) who have a record of outstanding contributions to the science of personality psychology.

Eligibility This award is available to psychologists engaged in advancing the science of personality psychology, including the areas of personology, personality theory, personality disorders, and personality measurement. Nominees should be between 8 and 20 years past completion of their doctoral degree. The sponsor encourages nominations of individuals who represent diversity in race, ethnicity, gender, age, disability, and sexual orientation.

Financial data The award is $1,000.

Duration The award is presented annually.

Additional information This award, established in 2004, is sponsored by Division 12 (Society of Clinical Psychology) of the American Psychological Association.

Number awarded 1 each year.

Deadline Nominations must be submitted by October of each year.

[1309]
TIMOTHY JEFFREY MEMORIAL AWARD IN CLINICAL HEALTH PSYCHOLOGY

American Psychological Foundation
750 First Street, N.E.
Washington, DC 20002-4242
(202) 336-5843 Fax: (202) 336-5812
E-mail: foundation@apa.org
Web: www.apa.org/apf/funding/jeffrey.aspx

Summary To recognize and reward psychologists (particularly African Americans, other minorities, women, and individuals with disabilities) who have made outstanding contributions to clinical health psychology.

Eligibility This award is available to full-time providers of direct clinical services who demonstrate an outstanding commitment to clinical health psychology. Nominees must be members of Division 38 (Health Psychology) of the American Psychological Association. They must have a full and unrestricted license to practice psychology and typically spend 15 to 20 hours per week in direct patient care. Letters of nomination should be accompanied by a curriculum vitae, at least 1 letter of support from a non-psychologist professional colleague, and another letter of support from a psychologist colleague. The sponsor encourages nominations of individuals who represent diversity in race, ethnicity, gender, age, disability, and sexual orientation.

Financial data The award is $3,000.

Duration The award is presented annually.

Additional information This award is sponsored by Division 38.

Number awarded 1 each year.

Deadline April of each year.

[1310]
TRAINEESHIPS IN AIDS PREVENTION STUDIES (TAPS)

University of California at San Francisco
Attn: Center for AIDS Prevention Studies
50 Beale Street, Suite 1300
San Francisco, CA 94105
(415) 597-9260 Fax: (415) 597-9213
E-mail: Rochelle.Blanco@ucsf.edu
Web: www.caps.ucsf.edu/training/taps

Summary To provide funding to scientists (particularly African American and other minority scientists) who are interested in conducting HIV prevention research at the Center for AIDS Prevention Studies (CAPS) of the University of California at San Francisco (UCSF).

Eligibility This program is open to U.S. citizens, nationals, and permanent residents who have a Ph.D., M.D., or equivalent degree. Applicants must be interested in a program of research training at CAPS in the following areas of special emphasis in AIDS research: epidemiological research, studies of AIDS risk behaviors, substance abuse and HIV, primary prevention interventions, research addressing minority populations, studies of HIV-positive individuals, policy and ethics, international research, and other public health and clinical aspects of AIDS. Recent postdoctorates who have just completed their training as well as those who are already faculty members in academic or clinical departments are eligible. Members of minority ethnic groups are strongly encouraged to apply.

Financial data Stipends depend on years of relevant postdoctoral experience, based on the NIH stipend scale for Institutional Research Training Grants (currently ranging from $39,264 for fellows with no relevant postdoctoral experience to $54,180 for those with 7 or more years of experience). Other benefits include a computer, travel to at least 1 annual professional meeting, health insurance, and other required support. The costs of the M.P.H. degree, if required, are covered.

Duration 2 or 3 years.

Additional information The TAPS program is designed to ensure that at the end of the training each fellow will have: 1) completed the M.P.H. degree or its equivalent; 2) taken advanced courses in research methods, statistics, and other topics relevant to a major field of interest; 3) participated in and led numerous seminars on research topics within CAPS, as well as in the formal teaching programs of the university; 4) designed several research protocols and completed at least 1 significant research project under the direction of a faculty mentor; and 5) made presentations at national or international meetings and submitted several papers for publication.

Number awarded Varies each year.

Deadline November of each year.

[1311]
TRAINING PROGRAM FOR SCIENTISTS CONDUCTING RESEARCH TO REDUCE HIV/STI HEALTH DISPARITIES

University of California at San Francisco
Attn: Center for AIDS Prevention Studies
50 Beale Street, Suite 1300
San Francisco, CA 94105
(415) 597-9139 Fax: (415) 597-9213
E-mail: dale.danley@ucsf.edu
Web: www.caps.ucsf.edu

Summary To provide funding to scientists (particularly African Americans and other minorities) who are interested in obtaining additional training at the University of California at San Francisco (UCSF) Center for AIDS Prevention Studies (CAPS) for HIV prevention research in minority communities.

Eligibility This program is open to scientists in tenure-track positions or investigators in research institutes who have not yet obtained research funding from the U.S. National Institutes of Health (NIH) or equivalent. Applicants must be interested in a program of activity at CAPS to improve their programs of HIV-prevention research targeting vulnerable ethnic minority populations. They must be eligible to serve as principal investigators at their home institutions. Selection is based on commitment to HIV social and behavioral research, prior HIV prevention research with communities and community-based organizations targeting communities with high levels of health disparities (e.g., communities with a high proportion of disadvantaged or disabled persons, racial and ethnic minority communities), creativity and innovativeness for a pilot research project to serve as a preliminary study for a subsequent larger R01 grant proposal to NIH or other suitable funding agency, past experience conducting research and writing papers, quality of letters of recommendation from colleagues and mentors, and support from the home institution (e.g., time off for research, seed money). A goal of the program is to increase the number of minority group members among principal investigators funded by NIH and other agencies. U.S. citizenship or permanent resident status is required.

Financial data Participants receive 1) a monthly stipend for living expenses and round-trip airfare to San Francisco for each summer; and 2) a grant of $25,000 to conduct preliminary research before the second summer to strengthen their R01 application.

Duration 6 weeks during each of 3 consecutive summers.

Additional information This program is funded by the NIH National Institute of Child Health and Human Development (NICHHD) and National Institute on Drug Abuse (NIDA).

Number awarded Approximately 4 each year.
Deadline January of each year.

[1312]
UC BERKELEY'S CHANCELLOR'S POSTDOCTORAL FELLOWSHIPS FOR ACADEMIC DIVERSITY

University of California at Berkeley
Attn: Division of Equity and Inclusion
104 California Hall
Berkeley, CA 94720-1508
(510) 643-8235 E-mail: ppfpinfo@berkeley.edu
Web: diversity.berkeley.edu/ChancPostdocFellowship

Summary To provide an opportunity for African Americans and other recent postdoctorates who will increase diversity at the University of California at Berkeley to conduct research on the campus.

Eligibility This program is open to U.S. citizens and permanent residents who received a doctorate within 3 years of the start of the fellowship. The program particularly solicits applications from individuals who are members of groups that are underrepresented in American universities (e.g., women, ethnic minorities, religious minorities, differently-abled, lesbian/gay/bisexual/transgender). Special consideration is given to applicants committed to careers in university research and teaching and whose life experience, research, or employment background will contribute significantly to academic diversity and excellence at the Berkeley campus.

Financial data The stipend is $41,496 per year (11 months, plus 1 month vacation). The award also includes health insurance, vision and dental benefits, and up to $4,000 for research-related and program travel expenses.

Duration 1 year; may be renewed 1 additional year.

Additional information This program operates in addition to the University of California President's Postdoctoral Fellowship Program for Academic Diversity. Interested candidates may apply to either program.

Number awarded Varies each year; recently, 4 of these fellowships were awarded.

Deadline October of each year.

[1313]
UC DAVIS CHANCELLOR'S POSTDOCTORAL FELLOWSHIP PROGRAM

University of California at Davis
Attn: Office of the Vice Provost for Academic Affairs
Mrak Hall, Fifth Floor
One Shields Avenue
Davis, CA 95616
(530) 752-0963 Fax: (530) 752-6359
E-mail: binsingh@berkeley.edu
Web: academicpersonnel.ucdavis.edu/cpf.html

Summary To provide an opportunity for African Americans and other recent postdoctorates who will increase diversity at the University of California at Davis to conduct research at the university or its School of Medicine.

Eligibility This program is open to U.S. citizens and permanent residents who received a doctorate within 3 years of the start of the fellowship. Applicants must be interested in conducting research at UC Davis, either on the main campus or at the School of Medicine. The program particularly solicits applications from scholars whose research, teaching, and service will contribute to the diversity and equal opportunity at the university. Those contributions may include public service addressing the needs of our increasingly diverse society, efforts to improve equitable access to higher education, or research focusing on underserved populations or understanding inequities related to race, gender, disability, or LGBT status.

Financial data The stipend ranges from $41,000 to $50,000 per year (11 months, plus 1 month vacation). The award also includes health insurance, vision and dental benefits, and up to $4,000 for research-related and program travel expenses.

Duration 1 year; may be renewed 1 additional year.

Additional information This program, which began in 2012, operates in addition to the University of California President's Postdoctoral Fellowship Program for Academic Diversity. Interested candidates may apply to either program.

Number awarded 2 each year: 1 supported by the Chancellor's office and 1 by the School of Medicine.

Deadline October of each year.

[1314]
UC SAN DIEGO CHANCELLOR'S POSTDOCTORAL FELLOWSHIP PROGRAM FOR ACADEMIC DIVERSITY

University of California at San Diego
Attn: Office of the Vice Chancellor for Equity, Diversity and Inclusion
302 University Center, Room 102
La Jolla, CA 92093-0029
(858) 822-3542 Fax: (858) 822-3013
E-mail: diversity@ucsd.edu
Web: www.diversity.ucsd.edu/fellowship

Summary To provide an opportunity for African Americans and other recent postdoctorates who will increase diversity at the University of California at San Diego to conduct research at the university.

Eligibility This program is open to U.S. citizens and permanent residents who received a doctorate within 3 years of the start of the fellowship. Applicants must be interested in conducting research at UCSD. The program particularly solicits applications from scholars whose research, teaching, and service will contribute to the diversity and equal opportunity at the university. Those contributions may include public service addressing the needs of our increasingly diverse society, efforts to improve equitable access to higher education for women and minorities, or research focusing on underserved populations or understanding issues of racial or gender inequalities.

Financial data The stipend is $40,000 per year (11 months, plus 1 month vacation). The award also includes health insurance, vision and dental benefits, and up to $4,000 for research-related and program travel expenses.

Duration 1 year; may be renewed 1 additional year.

Additional information This program operates in addition to the University of California President's Postdoctoral Fellowship Program for Academic Diversity. Interested candidates may apply to either program.

Number awarded 2 each year: 1 supported by the Chancellor's office and 1 supported by a department expressing interest in hosting a fellow.

Deadline October of each year.

[1315]
UCLA AFRICAN AMERICAN STUDIES VISITING SCHOLAR AND VISITING RESEARCHER PROGRAM

University of California at Los Angeles
Institute of American Cultures
Attn: Bunche Center for African American Studies
160 Haines Hall
P.O. Box 951545
Los Angeles, CA 90095-1545
(310) 825-7403 Fax: (310) 206-3421
E-mail: acramon@bunche.ucla.edu
Web: www.iac.ucla.edu/fellowships_visitingscholar.html

Summary To provide funding to scholars interested in conducting research in African American studies at UCLA's Bunche Center for African American Studies.

Eligibility Applicants must have completed a doctoral degree in African American or related studies. They must be interested in teaching or conducting research at UCLA's Bunche Center for African American Studies. Visiting Scholar appointments are available to people who currently hold permanent academic appointments; Visiting Researcher appointments are available to postdoctorates who recently received their degree. UCLA faculty, students, and staff are not eligible. U.S. citizenship or permanent resident status is required.

Financial data Fellows receive a stipend of $32,000 to $35,000 (depending on rank, experience, and date of completion of the Ph.D.), health benefits, and up to $4,000 in research support. Visiting Scholars are paid through their home institution; Visiting Researchers receive their funds directly from UCLA.

Duration 9 months, beginning in October.

Additional information Fellows must teach or do research in the programs of the center. The award is offered in conjunction with UCLA's Institute of American Cultures (IAC).

Number awarded 1 each year.

Deadline February of each year.

[1316]
UCLA CHANCELLOR'S POSTDOCTORAL FELLOWSHIP PROGRAM

University of California at Los Angeles
Attn: Office for Diversity and Faculty Development
3109 Murphy Hall
P.O. Box 951407
Los Angeles, CA 90095-1407
(310) 206-7411 Fax: (310) 206-8427
E-mail: facdiversity@conet.ucla.edu
Web: faculty.diversity.ucla.edu

Summary To provide an opportunity for African Americans and other recent postdoctorates who will increase diversity at the University of California at Los Angeles to conduct research at the university.

Eligibility This program is open to U.S. citizens and permanent residents who received a doctorate within 3 years of the start of the fellowship. Applicants must be interested in conducting research at UCLA. The program particularly solicits applications from scholars whose research, teaching, and service will contribute to the diversity and equal opportunity at the university. Those contributions may include public service addressing the needs of our increasingly diverse society, efforts to improve equitable access to higher education, or research focusing on underserved populations or understanding inequities related to race, gender, disability, or LGBT status.

Financial data The stipend ranges from $41,000 to $50,000 per year (11 months, plus 1 month vacation). The award also includes health insurance, vision and dental benefits, and up to $4,000 for research-related and program travel expenses.

Duration 1 year; may be renewed 1 additional year.

Additional information This program operates in addition to the University of California President's Postdoctoral Fellowship Program for Academic Diversity. Interested candidates may apply to either program.

Number awarded 2 each year.

Deadline October of each year.

[1317]
UNDERSTANDING THE DEVELOPMENT AND DEVISING TREATMENTS FOR ALZHEIMER'S DISEASE IN INDIVIDUALS WITH DOWN SYNDROME

Alzheimer's Association
Attn: Medical and Scientific Affairs
225 North Michigan Avenue, 17th Floor
Chicago, IL 60601-7633
(312) 335-5747 Toll Free: (800) 272-3900
Fax: (866) 699-1246 TDD: (312) 335-5886
E-mail: grantsapp@alz.org
Web: www.alz.org

Summary To provide funding investigators (particularly African Americans and others from diverse groups) who are interested in conducting research on the development of Alzheimer's Disease in individuals with Down Syndrome.

Eligibility This program is open to investigators who have full-time staff or faculty appointments at research laboratories, medical centers, hospitals, or universities. Investigator-initiated grants are available to those at the level of assistant professor or higher; new investigator grants are available to those who have less than 10 years of research experience. Applicants must be interested in conducting research on understanding the mechanisms that lead to the initiation of Alzheimer's Disease in persons with Down Syndrome. Scientists from underrepresented groups are especially encouraged to apply.

Financial data Investigator-initiated grants up to $125,000 per year and new investigator grants up to $60,000 per year are available; both types of grants cover direct expenses and up to 10% for overhead costs. The total award for the life of the grant may not exceed $300,000 for investigator-initiated grants or $150,000 for new investigator grants.

Duration 2 to 3 years.

Additional information This program began in 2013 with support from the Linda Crnic Institute for Down Syndrome and the Global Down Syndrome Foundation.

Number awarded Up to 2 investigator-initiated grants and up to 4 new investigator grants are awarded each year.

Deadline Letters of intent must be submitted by the end of January of each year. Final applications are due in March.

[1318]
UNIVERSITY OF CALIFORNIA PRESIDENT'S POSTDOCTORAL FELLOWSHIP PROGRAM FOR ACADEMIC DIVERSITY

University of California at Berkeley
Attn: Office of Equity and Inclusion
102 California Hall
Berkeley, CA 94720-1508
(510) 643-6566 E-mail: ppfpinfo@berkeley.edu
Web: ppfp.ucop.edu/info/uc_ppfp.html

Summary To provide an opportunity to conduct research at campuses of the University of California to recent postdoctorates (particularly African Americans and other groups historically underrepresented in higher education) who are committed to careers in university teaching and research and who will contribute to diversity.

Eligibility This program is open to U.S. citizens or permanent residents who have a Ph.D. from an accredited university. Applicants must be proposing to conduct research at a branch of the university under the mentorship of a faculty or laboratory sponsor. Preference is given to applicants 1) with the potential to bring to their academic careers the critical perspective that comes from their nontraditional educational background or their understanding of the experiences of groups historically underrepresented in higher education; 2) who have the communications skill and cross-cultural abilities to maximize effective collaboration with a diverse cross-section of the academic community; 3) who have demonstrated significant academic achievement by overcoming barriers such as economic, social, or educational disadvantage; and 4) who have the potential to contribute to higher education through their understanding of the barriers facing women, domestic minorities, students with disabilities, and other members of groups underrepresented in higher education careers, as evidenced by life experiences and educational background.

Financial data The stipend ranges from $41,000 to $50,000, depending on the field and level of experience. The program also offers health benefits and up to $4,000 for supplemental and research-related expenses.

Duration Appointments are for 1 academic year, with possible renewal for a second year.

Additional information Research may be conducted at any of the University of California's 10 campuses (Berkeley, Davis, Irvine, Los Angeles, Merced, Riverside, San Diego, San Francisco, Santa Barbara, or Santa Cruz). The program provides mentoring and guidance in preparing for an academic career. This program was established in 1984 to encourage applications from minority and women scholars in fields where they were severely underrepresented; it is now open to all qualified candidates whose research, teaching, and service will contribute to diversity and equal opportunity at the University of California. In addition to this program for UC campuses in general, the Universities of California at Berkeley, Davis, Los Angeles, and San Diego offer separate Chancellor's Postdoctoral Fellowship programs for their institutions. Interested candidates may apply to those programs and/or this system-wide program.

Number awarded Varies each year; recently, 30 of these fellows were selected.

Deadline October of each year.

[1319]
UNIVERSITY OF HOUSTON AFRICAN AMERICAN STUDIES PROGRAM VISITING SCHOLARS

University of Houston
African American Studies Program
Attn: Visiting Scholars Program
629 Agnes Arnold Hall
Houston, TX 77204-3047
(713) 743-2811 Fax: (713) 743-2818
E-mail: jconyers@uh.edu
Web: www.uh.edu

Summary To provide support to junior scholars who are interested in conducting research on the African American community while affiliated with the University of Houston's African American Studies Program.

Eligibility Applications are sought from junior scholars in social sciences, humanities, or African American studies who completed their Ph.D. within the past 6 years. They must be interested in conducting research on the African American community while affiliated with the University of Houston's African American Studies Program and in assuming a tenured or tenure-track position there after their residency as a Visiting Scholar is completed. They must be available for consultation with students and professional colleagues, make at least 2 formal presentations based on their research project, and contribute generally to the intellectual discourse in the discipline of African Studies/Africology. Along with their application, they must submit a current curriculum vitae, a 2-page description of the proposed research, 3 letters of recommendation, and a syllabus of the undergraduate course to be taught. Minorities, women, veterans, and persons with disabilities are specifically encouraged to apply.

Financial data Visiting Scholars receive a salary appropriate to their rank.

Duration 1 academic year.

Additional information Visiting Scholars are assigned a research assistant, if needed, and are provided administrative support. Recipients must teach 1 class related to African American studies. They are required to be in residence at the university for the entire academic year and must make 2 presentations on their research. In addition, they must acknowledge the sponsor's support in any publication that results from their tenure at the university.

Number awarded At least 2 each year.

Deadline March of each year.

[1320]
UNIVERSITY OF ILLINOIS AT CHICAGO ACADEMIC RESIDENT LIBRARIAN PROGRAM

University of Illinois at Chicago
Attn: Library Human Resources
801 South Morgan
MC 234
Chicago, IL 60607
(312) 996-7353
Web: library.uic.edu

Summary To provide a residency at the University of Illinois at Chicago (UIC) to librarians (particularly African Americans, other underrepresented minorities, and individuals with disabilities) who are interested in preparing for a career in academic librarianship.

Eligibility This program is open to librarians who graduated within the past year with a master's degree from an ALA-accredited program. Applicants must be interested in preparing for a career as an academic librarian through a residency at (UIC). Preference is given to applicants who can demonstrate an interest in 1 or more of the following areas: 1) technical services, with an emphasis on development and assessment of library discovery tools; 2) outreach, with an emphasis on initiatives to rural and underserved users; 3) reference and instruction, with an emphasis on instructional technical design and the development of multimedia learning objects; 4) E-science, with an emphasis on data curation in support of university-wide data management and preservation initiatives; 5) digital preservation, with an emphasis on preservation architectures, standards, and workflows; or 7) digital image collections, with an emphasis on mapping using GIS technologies. A goal of the program is to increase diversity within the profession of academic librarianship; applications are especially welcome from women, underrepresented minority group members, persons with disabilities, members of sexual minority groups, and others whose background, education, experience, and academic interests would enrich the diversity of the profession.

Financial data The stipend is at least $42,000.

Duration 1 year; may be renewed 1 additional year.

Number awarded 2 or more each year.

Deadline June of each year.

[1321]
UNIVERSITY OF NORTH CAROLINA POSTDOCTORAL PROGRAM FOR FACULTY DIVERSITY

University of North Carolina at Chapel Hill
Attn: Office of Postdoctoral Affairs
301 Bynum Hall, CB #4100
Chapel Hill, NC 27599-4100
(919) 843-4793 Fax: (919) 962-6769
E-mail: jhfraley@email.unc.edu
Web: www.research.unc.edu/carolina-postdocs/applicants

Summary To support African American and other minority scholars who are interested in teaching and conducting research at the University of North Carolina (UNC).

Eligibility This program is open to scholars from underrepresented groups (African Americans, Native Americans, and Hispanics) who have completed their doctoral degree within the past 4 years. Applicants must be interested in teaching and conducting research at UNC. Preference is given to U.S. citizens and permanent residents. Selection is based on the evidence of scholarship potential and ability to compete for tenure-track appointments at UNC and other research universities.

Financial data Fellows receive $39,874 per year, plus an allowance for research and travel. Health benefits are also available.

Duration Up to 2 years.

Additional information Fellows must be in residence at the Chapel Hill campus for the duration of the program. They teach 1 course per year and spend the rest of the time in research. This program began in 1983.

Number awarded 5 or 6 each year.

Deadline November of each year.

[1322]
UNIVERSITY RESEARCH INSTRUMENTATION PROGRAM

Army Research Office
Attn: Army DURIP Program Manager
4300 South Miami Boulevard
P.O. Box 12211
Research Triangle Park, NC 27709-2211
(919) 549-4251 Fax: (919) 549-4248
E-mail: aro.durip@us.army.mil
Web: www.arl.army.mil/www/default.cfm?Page=8

Summary To provide funding to researchers at colleges and universities, especially those at Historically Black Colleges and Universities (HBCUs) and other Minority Institutions (MIs), for the purchase of equipment.

Eligibility This program is open to researchers at colleges and universities in the United States with degree-granting programs in science, mathematics, and/or engineering. Applicants must be seeking funding for the acquisition of major equipment to augment current or to develop new research capabilities to support research in technical areas of interest to the Department of Defense. Proposals are encouraged from researchers at HBCUs and MIs.

Financial data Grants range from $50,000 to $1,100,000; recently, they averaged $305,000.

Duration Grants are typically 1 year in length.

Additional information This program is also offered by the Air Force Office of Scientific Research and the Office of Naval Research.

Number awarded Varies each year; recently, 169 of these grants, worth $51.4 million, were awarded.

Deadline October of each year.

[1323]
USDA SMALL BUSINESS INNOVATION RESEARCH PROGRAM

Department of Agriculture
National Institute of Food and Agriculture
Attn: Director, SBIR Program
1400 Independence Avenue, S.W.
Stop 2201
Washington, DC 20250-2201
(202) 401-4002 Fax: (202) 401-6070
E-mail: sbir@nifa.usda.gov
Web: www.csrees.usda.gov/funding/sbir/sbir.html

Summary To stimulate technological innovation related to agriculture in the private sector by small business firms, especially those owned by African Americans, members of other socially and economically disadvantaged groups, and women.

Eligibility For the purposes of this program, a "small business" is defined as a firm that is organized for profit with a location in the United States; is in the legal form of an individual proprietorship, partnership, limited liability company, corporation, joint venture, association, trust, or cooperative; is at least 51% owned and controlled by 1 or more individuals who are citizens or permanent residents of the United States; and has (including its affiliates) fewer than 500 employees. The primary employment of the principal investigator must be with the firm at the time of award and during the conduct of the proposed project. Applications are encouraged from 1) women-owned small business concerns, defined as those that are at least 51% owned by a woman or women who also control and operate them; and 2) socially and economically disadvantaged small business concerns that are at least 51% owned by an Indian tribe, a Native Hawaiian organization, or 1 or more socially and economically disadvantaged individuals (African Americans, Hispanic Americans, Native Americans, Asian Pacific Americans, or subcontinent Asian Americans). Proposals are accepted in 10 topic areas: forests and related resources; plant production and protection (biology); animal production and protection; air, water, and soils; food science and nutrition; rural development; aquaculture; biofuels and biobased products; small and mid-sized farms; and plant production and protection (engineering). Selection is based on scientific and technical feasibility of the project, importance of the problem, qualifications of the investigator and research facilities, appropriateness of the budget, and extent of duplication of the project with other ongoing or previous research.

Financial data Support is offered in 2 phases. In phase 1, awards normally do not exceed $100,000 (for both direct and indirect costs); in phase 2, awards normally do not exceed $450,000 (including both direct and indirect costs).

Duration Phase 1 awards may extend up to 8 months; phase 2 awards may extend up to 2 years.

Additional information Phase 1 is to determine the scientific or technical feasibility of ideas submitted by the applicants on research topic areas. Phase 2 awards are made to firms with approaches that appear sufficiently promising as a result of phase 1 studies.

Number awarded Recently, the department granted 80 phase 1 awards and 32 phase 2 awards. Total program funding was approximately $19 million.

Deadline September of each year for phase 1 awards; February of each year for phase 2 awards.

[1324]
VIRGINIA HAMILTON AWARD FOR LIFETIME ACHIEVEMENT/AUTHOR-ILLUSTRATOR CATEGORY

American Library Association
Attn: Ethnic and Multicultural Material Information Exchange Round Table
c/o Office for Literacy and Outreach Services
50 East Huron Street
Chicago, IL 60611-2795
(312) 280-4294 Toll Free: (800) 545-2433, ext. 4294
Fax: (312) 280-3256 TDD: (888) 814-7692
E-mail: olos@ala.org
Web: www.ala.org

Summary To recognize and reward African American authors and illustrators who have made outstanding contributions to literature for children and/or young adults.

Eligibility This award is available to African American authors and illustrators whose published books for children and/or young adults has made a significant and lasting contribution. Nominees' work must represent distinguished writing and/or illustrations by and about the African American experience. In the selection process, special consideration is given to bodies of work 1) whose interpretation consistently motivates youth readers to stretch their imagination and thinking; 2) which denote exceptional examples of specific types of literature; and 3) represent trend-setters, innovations, or fresh explorations of themes, topics, or perspectives in African American literature for children and/or young adults.

Financial data The award includes an honorarium of $1,500 and a plaque.

Duration The award is presented biennially, in even-numbered years.

Additional information This award was first presented in 2010.

Number awarded 1 each year.

Deadline June of each even-numbered year.

[1325]
VISIONARY GRANTS

American Psychological Foundation
750 First Street, N.E.
Washington, DC 20002-4242
(202) 336-5843 Fax: (202) 336-5812
E-mail: foundation@apa.org
Web: www.apa.org/apf/funding/vision-weiss.aspx

Summary To provide funding to professionals (particularly African Americans and those from other diverse backgrounds) who are interested in conducting projects that use psychology to solve social problems related to the priorities of the American Psychological Foundation (APF).

Eligibility This program is open to professionals at nonprofit organizations engaged in research, education, and intervention projects and programs. Applicants must be interested in conducting an activity that uses psychology to solve social problems in the following priority areas: understanding and fostering the connection between mental and physical health; reducing stigma and prejudice; understanding and preventing all forms of violence; or addressing the long-term psychological needs of individuals and communities in the aftermath of disaster. Selection is based on the criticality of the proposed funding for the proposed work; conformance with stated program goals and requirements; innovative and potential impact qualities; quality, viability, and promise of proposed work, and competence and capability of project leaders. The sponsor encourages applications from individuals who represent diversity in race, ethnicity, gender, age, disability, and sexual orientation.

Financial data Grants range from $2,500 to $20,000.

Duration 1 year; nonrenewable.

Additional information This program began in 2003.

Number awarded 1 or more each year.

Deadline March of each year.

[1326]
WAYNE F. PLACEK GRANTS

American Psychological Foundation
750 First Street, N.E.
Washington, DC 20002-4242
(202) 336-5843 Fax: (202) 336-5812
E-mail: foundation@apa.org
Web: www.apa.org/apf/funding/placek.aspx

Summary To provide funding to pre- and postdoctoral scholars (particularly African Americans, other minorities, women, and individuals with disabilities) who are interested in conducting research that will increase the general public's understanding of homosexuality and alleviate the stress experienced by gay men and lesbians.

Eligibility This program is open to scholars who have a doctoral degree (e.g., Ph.D., Psy.D., M.D.) and to graduate students in all fields of the behavioral and social sciences. Applicants must be interested in conducting empirical studies that address the following topics: prejudice, discrimination, and violence based on sexual orientation, including heterosexuals' attitudes and behaviors toward lesbian, gay, bisexual, and transgender (LGBT) people; family and workplace issues relevant to LGBT people; and subgroups of the LGBT population that have been historically underrepresented in scientific research. Selection is based on conformance with stated program goals, magnitude of incremental contribution, quality of proposed work, and applicant's demonstrated scholarship and research competence. The sponsor encourages applications from individuals who represent diversity in race, ethnicity, gender, age, disability, and sexual orientation.

Financial data The grant is $15,000.

Duration 1 year.

Additional information This program began in 1995.

Number awarded 1 or 2 each year.

Deadline February of each year.

[1327]
W.E.B. DUBOIS FELLOWSHIP PROGRAM

Department of Justice
National Institute of Justice
Attn: W.E.B. DuBois Fellowship Program
810 Seventh Street, N.W.
Washington, DC 20531
(202) 514-6205 E-mail: Marilyn.Moses@usdoj.gov
Web: www.nij.gov

Summary To provide funding to junior investigators (particularly African Americans and other minorities) who are interested in conducting research on "crime, violence and the administration of justice in diverse cultural contexts."

Eligibility This program is open to investigators who have a Ph.D. or other doctoral-level degree (including a legal degree of J.D. or higher). Applicants should be early in their careers and not have been awarded tenure. They must be interested in conducting research that relates to specific areas that change annually but relate to criminal justice policy and practice in the United States. The sponsor strongly encourages applications from diverse racial and ethnic backgrounds. Selection is based on quality and technical merit; impact of the proposed project; capabilities, demonstrated productivity, and experience of the applicant; budget; dissemination strategy; and relevance of the project for policy and practice.

Financial data Grants range up to $100,000. Funds may be used for salary, fringe benefits, reasonable costs of relocation, travel essential to the project, and office expenses not provided by the sponsor. Indirect costs are limited to 20%.

Duration 6 to 12 months; fellows are required to be in residence at the National Institute of Justice (NIJ) for the first 2 months and may elect to spend all or part of the remainder of the fellowship period either in residence at NIJ or at their home institution.

Number awarded 1 each year.

Deadline January of each year.

[1328]
WESLEY-LOGAN PRIZE IN AFRICAN DIASPORA HISTORY

American Historical Association
Attn: Book Prize Administrator
400 A Street, S.E.
Washington, DC 20003-3889
(202) 544-2422 Fax: (202) 544-8307
E-mail: info@historians.org
Web: www.historians.org

Summary To recognize and reward outstanding books published on African Diaspora history.

Eligibility The prize is awarded to the best book on some aspect of the history of the dispersion, settlement, adjustment, or return of peoples originally from Africa. Books in any chronological period and any geographical location are eligible. Only works of high scholarly and literary merit are considered.

Financial data The prize is $1,000.

Duration The award is granted annually.

Additional information This prize was established in 1992 to honor 2 early pioneers in the field, Charles H. Wesley and Rayford W. Logan. It is jointly sponsored by the American Historical Association and the Association for the Study of African American Life and History.

Number awarded 1 each year.

Deadline May of each year.

[1329]
WILLIAM L. FISHER CONGRESSIONAL GEOSCIENCE FELLOWSHIP

American Geological Institute
Attn: Government Affairs Program
4220 King Street
Alexandria, VA 22302-1502
(703) 379-2480, ext. 212 Fax: (703) 379-7563
E-mail: govt@agiweb.org
Web: www.agiweb.org/gap/csf/index.html

Summary To provide members of an American Geological Institute (AGI) component society (particularly African Americans, other minorities, and women) with an opportunity to gain professional experience in the office of a member of Congress or a Congressional committee.

Eligibility This program is open to members of 1 of AGI's 49 member societies who have a master's degree and at least 3 years of post-degree work experience or a Ph.D. Applicants should have a broad geoscience background and excellent written and oral communications skills. They must be interested in working with Congress. Although prior experience in public policy is not required, a demonstrated interest in applying science to the solution of public problems is desirable. Applications from women and minorities are especially encouraged. U.S. citizenship or permanent resident status is required.

Financial data Fellows receive a stipend of up to $65,000 plus allowances for health insurance, relocation, and travel.

Duration 12 months, beginning in September.

Additional information This program is 1 of more than 20 Congressional Science Fellowships operating in affiliation with the American Association for the Advancement of Science (AAAS), which provides a 2-week orientation on Congressional and executive branch operations.

Number awarded 1 each year.

Deadline January of each year.

[1330]
WILLIAM SANDERS SCARBOROUGH PRIZE

Modern Language Association of America
Attn: Committee on Honors and Awards
26 Broadway, Third Floor
New York, NY 10004-1789
(646) 576-5141 Fax: (646) 458-0030
E-mail: awards@mla.org
Web: www.mla.org

Summary To recognize and reward authors of outstanding books on African American literature.

Eligibility This award is presented to authors of outstanding scholarly studies of African American literature or culture published the previous year. Books that are primarily translations are not eligible. Authors need not be members of the Modern Language Association.

Financial data The prize is $1,000 and a certificate.

Duration The prize is awarded annually.

Additional information This prize was first awarded in 2001.

Number awarded 1 each year.

Deadline April of each year.

[1331]
WILLIAM TOWNSEND PORTER FELLOWSHIP FOR MINORITY INVESTIGATORS

Marine Biological Laboratory
Attn: Chief Academic and Scientific Officer
7 MBL Street
Woods Hole, MA 02543-1015
(508) 289-7173 Fax: (508) 457-1924
E-mail: casoofice@mbl.edu
Web: hermes.mbl.edu

Summary To support African Americans and other underrepresented minorities who wish to conduct research during the summer at the Marine Biological Laboratory (MBL) in Woods Hole, Massachusetts.

Eligibility This program is open to young scientists (undergraduates, senior graduate students, and postdoctoral trainees) who are from an underrepresented minority group (African American, Hispanic American, or Native American), are U.S. citizens or permanent residents, and are interested in conducting research with senior investigators at MBL. Applicants must submit a statement of the potential impact of this award on their career development. Fields of study include, but are not limited to, cell biology, developmental biology, ecology, evolution, microbiology, neurobiology, physiology, regenerative biology, and tissue engineering.

Financial data Grants range from $5,000 to $25,000, typically to cover laboratory rental and/or housing costs. Awardees are responsible for other costs, such as supplies, shared resource usage, affiliated staff who accompany them, or travel.

Duration 8 to 10 weeks during the summer.

Additional information This fellowship was first awarded in 1921. Funding is provided by the Harvard Apparatus Foundation.

Number awarded 1 or more each year.

Deadline December of each year.

[1332]
WILLIAM W. GRIMES AWARD FOR EXCELLENCE IN CHEMICAL ENGINEERING

American Institute of Chemical Engineers
Attn: Minority Affairs Committee
Three Park Avenue
New York, NY 10016-5991
(646) 495-1348 Fax: (646) 495-1504
E-mail: awards@aiche.org
Web: www.aiche.org

Summary To recognize and reward chemical engineers who serve as a role model for African American students.

Eligibility Members of the American Institute of Chemical Engineers (AIChE) may nominate any individual who serves as a role model for African Americans in chemical engineering. Nominees must be chemical engineers who have demonstrated outstanding technical, business, or related achievements and have voluntarily given time and effort to help increase the interest and/or performance of members of underrepresented minority groups in science, mathematics, engineering, and related areas in either an educational or business environment.

Financial data The award consists of a plaque and $1,000, plus a $500 travel allowance to attend the AIChE annual meeting where the award is presented.

Duration The award is presented annually.

Additional information The Minority Affairs Committee has presented this award in honor of William W. Grimes, the first African American Fellow of AIChE, since 1995.

Number awarded 1 each year.

Deadline Nominations must be submitted by June of each year.

[1333]
YERBY POSTDOCTORAL FELLOWSHIP PROGRAM

Harvard School of Public Health
Attn: Office of Faculty Affairs
90 Smith Street, First Floor
Boston, MA 02120
(617) 432-1047 Fax: (617) 432-4711
E-mail: cburkot@hsph.harvard.edu
Web: www.hsph.harvard.edu

Summary To provide African Americans and other postdoctorates who will contribute to diversity with an opportunity to pursue a program of research training at Harvard School of Public Health.

Eligibility This program is open to postdoctorates who are interested in preparing for a career in public health. The program emphasizes applicants who will contribute to academic diversity, meaning 1) members of minority groups underrepresented in public health (American Indians or Alaska Natives, Blacks or African Americans, Hispanics or Latinos, and Native Hawaiians or other Pacific Islanders); and 2) individuals with disabilities.

Financial data Fellows receive a competitive salary.

Duration 1 year; may be renewed 1 additional year.

Number awarded Up to 5 each year.

Deadline October of each year.

[1334]
ZENITH FELLOWS AWARD PROGRAM

Alzheimer's Association
Attn: Medical and Scientific Affairs
225 North Michigan Avenue, 17th Floor
Chicago, IL 60601-7633
(312) 335-5747 Toll Free: (800) 272-3900
Fax: (866) 699-1246 TDD: (312) 335-5886
E-mail: grantsapp@alz.org
Web: www.alz.org

Summary To provide funding to established investigators (particularly African Americans and members of other underrepresented groups) who are interested in conducting advanced research on Alzheimer's Disease.

Eligibility Eligible are scientists who have already contributed significantly to the field of Alzheimer's Disease research and are likely to continue to make significant contributions for many years to come. The proposed research must be "on the cutting edge" of basic, biomedical research and may not fit current conventional scientific wisdom or may challenge the prevailing orthodoxy. It should address fundamental problems related to early detection, etiology, pathogenesis, treatment, and/or prevention of Alzheimer's Disease. Scientists from underrepresented groups are especially encouraged to apply.

Financial data Grants up to $250,000 per year, including direct expenses and up to 10% for overhead costs, are available. The total award for the life of the grant may not exceed $450,000.

Duration 2 or 3 years.

Additional information This program began in 1991.

Number awarded Up to 4 each year.

Deadline Letters of intent must be submitted by the end of January of each year. Final applications are due in March.

Indexes

Program Title Index

If you know the name of a particular funding program open to African Americans and want to find out where it is covered in the directory, use the Program Title Index. Here, program titles are arranged alphabetically, word by word. To assist you in your search, every program is listed by all its known names or abbreviations. In addition, we've used an alphabetical code (within parentheses) to help you determine if the program is aimed at you: U = Undergraduates; G = Graduate Students; P = Professionals/Postdoctorates. Here's how the code works: if a program is followed by (U) 241, the program is described in the Undergraduates chapter, in entry 241. If the same program title is followed by another entry number—for example, (P) 1101—the program is also described in the Professionals/Postdoctorates chapter, in entry 1101. Remember: the numbers cited here refer to program entry numbers, not to page numbers in the book.

A

B

U–Undergraduates G–Graduate Students P–Professionals/Postdoctorates

C

D

E

F

G

H

I

J

M

U–Undergraduates **G–Graduate Students** **P–Professionals/Postdoctorates**

O

P

R

S

T

U

V

W

X

Y

Sponsoring Organization Index

The Sponsoring Organization Index makes it easy to identify agencies that offer financial aid to African Americans. In this index, the sponsoring organizations are listed alphabetically, word by word. In addition, we've used an alphabetical code (within parentheses) to help you identify the intended recipients of the funding offered by the organizations: U = Undergraduates; G = Graduate Students; P = Professionals/Postdoctorates. For example, if the name of a sponsoring organization is followed by (U) 241, a program sponsored by that organization is described in the Undergraduate chapter, in entry 241. If that sponsoring organization's name is followed by another entry number—for example, (P) 1101—the same or a different program sponsored by that organization is described in the Professionals/Postdoctorates chapter, in entry 1101. Remember: the numbers cited here refer to program entry numbers, not to page numbers in the book.

U–Undergraduates **G–Graduate Students** **P–Professionals/Postdoctorates**

B

C

D

E

F

O

P

R

S

V

Residency Index

Some programs listed in this book are set aside for African Americans who are residents of a particular state or region. Others are open to applicants wherever they may live. The Residency Index will help you pinpoint programs available in your area as well as programs that have no residency restrictions at all (these are listed under the term "United States"). To use this index, look up the geographic areas that apply to you (always check the listings under "United States"), jot down the entry numbers listed for the educational level that applies to you (Undergraduates, Graduate Students, or Professionals/Postdoctorates), and use those numbers to find the program descriptions in the directory. To help you in your search, we've provided some "see" and "see also" references in the index entries. Remember: the numbers cited here refer to program entry numbers, not to page numbers in the book.

Tenability Index

Some programs listed in this book can be used only in specific cities, counties, states, or regions. Others may be used anywhere in the United States (or even abroad). The Tenability Index will help you locate funding that is restricted to a specific area as well as funding that has no tenability restrictions (these are listed under the term "United States"). To use this index, look up the geographic areas where you'd like to go (always check the listings under "United States"), jot down the entry numbers listed for the recipient group that represents you (Undergraduates, Graduate Students, Professionals/Postdoctorates), and use those numbers to find the program descriptions in the directory. To help you in your search, we've provided some "see" and "see also" references in the index entries. Remember: the numbers cited here refer to program entry numbers, not to page numbers in the book.

C

D

E

F

G

H

I

J

K

Subject Index

There are hundreds of specific subject fields covered in this directory. Use the Subject Index to identify this focus, as well as the recipient level supported (Undergraduates, Graduate Students, or Professionals/Postdoctorates) by the available funding programs. To help you pinpoint your search, we've included many "see" and "see also" references. Since a large number of programs are not restricted by subject, be sure to check the references listed under the "General programs" heading in the subject index (in addition to the specific terms that directly relate to your interest areas); hundreds of funding opportunities are listed there that can be used to support activities in any subject area—although the programs may be restricted in other ways. Remember: the numbers cited in this index refer to program entry numbers, not to page numbers in the book.

A

B

H

I

T

U

V

W

Calendar Index

Since most funding programs have specific deadline dates, some may have already closed by the time you begin to look for money. You can use the Calendar Index to identify which programs are still open. To do that, go to the recipient category (Undergraduates, Graduate Students, or Professionals/Postdoctorates) that interests you, think about when you'll be able to complete your application forms, go to the appropriate months, jot down the entry numbers listed there, and use those numbers to find the program descriptions in the directory. Keep in mind that the numbers cited here refer to program entry numbers, not to page numbers in the book.